ABNORMAL PSYCHOLOGY

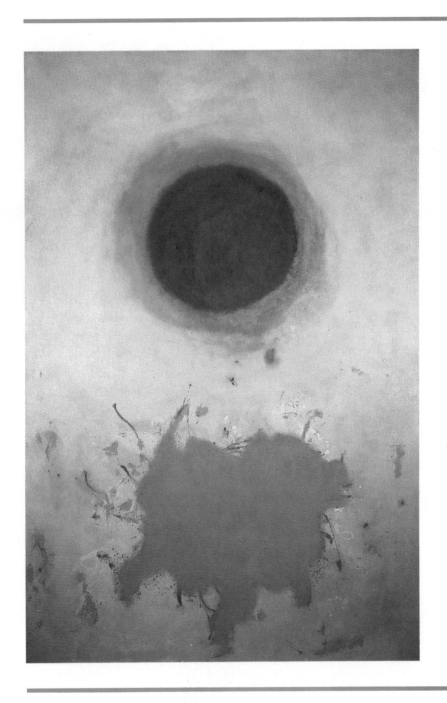

FOURTH EDITION

ABNORMAL PSYCHOLOGY
AN EXPERIMENTAL CLINICAL APPROACH

GERALD C. DAVISON
University of Southern California

JOHN M. NEALE
State University of New York at Stony Brook

JOHN WILEY & SONS
New York   Chichester   Brisbane   Toronto   Singapore

Cover Art: Adolph Gottlieb, *Deep Over Pale*, 1964.
Private Collection.

Production Supervisor: Beth Meder
Development Editor: Priscilla Todd
Interior and cover design: Dawn L. Stanley
Photo research: Ilene Cherna and Inge King
Fine art opener research: Joelle Burrows
Photo Editor: Stella Kupferberg

Library of Congress Cataloging in Publication Data

Davison, Gerald C.
    Abnormal psychology.

    Bibliography: p.
    Includes index.
    1. Psychology, Pathological. I. Neale, John M.,
1943–   . II. Title. [DNLM: 1. Psychopathology.
WM 100 D265a]
RC454. D3   1986   616.89   85-26408

Printed in the United States of America

10 9 8 7 6 5 4

To Carol, Eve, and Asher
GCD

To Gail and Sean
JMN

GERALD C. DAVISON is Chair and Professor of Psychology at the University of Southern California, where he was also Director of Clinical Training from 1979 to 1984. Previously he was on the psychology faculty at the State University of New York at Stony Brook (1966–1979). In 1969–70 he was visiting associate professor at Stanford University (where he received his Ph.D. in 1965), and in 1975–76, a National Institute of Mental Health Special Fellow at Harvard (where he obtained his B.A. in 1961). Davison has published widely in the general area of behavior therapy and personality, particularly on theoretical and philosophical issues, and is coauthor of *Clinical Behavior Therapy* (1976) and *Case Studies in Abnormal Psychology* (1986, second edition). He is a Fellow of the American Psychological Association and has served on the Executive Committee of the Division of Clinical Psychology, on the Board of Scientific Affairs, on the Committee on Scientific Awards, and on the Council of Representatives. He is presently serving on a National Academy of Sciences Committee on the Study of Techniques for Enhancing Human Performance and is also a past-president of the Association for Advancement of Behavior Therapy. He has been on the editorial board of several professional journals, including the *Journal of Consulting and Clinical Psychology*, *Behavior Therapy*, and *Cognitive Therapy and Research*. His current research program focuses on the relationship between cognition and a variety of behavioral and emotional states. In addition to his teaching and research, he is a practicing clinical psychologist.

JOHN M. NEALE, a Canadian, received his B.A. from the University
of Toronto in 1965 and his Ph.D. from Vanderbilt University in 1969.
Thereafter he spent a year as Fellow in Medical Psychology at Langley Porter
Neuropsychiatric Institute and since then has been at the State University of
New York at Stony Brook, where he is Professor of Psychology. His major
research interests are psychopathology and the effects of life stress on
health and the immune system. In 1974 he won the American Psychological
Association's Early Career Award for his research in schizophrenia.
In addition to being on the editorial boards of several professional journals and
an active contributor to the psychological literature, he has coauthored five
books, *Science and Behavior: An Introduction to Methods of Research*, *The
Early Window*: *Effects of Television on Children and Youth, Psychology, Case
Studies in Abnormal Psychology* (1986, second edition), and *Schizophrenia*.
He has just finished a term as associate editor of the *Journal of Abnormal
Psychology* and is currently directing a new health psychology program at
Stony Brook.

Contemporary abnormal psychology is a field in which there are few hard and fast answers. Indeed, the very way the field should be conceptualized and the kinds of questions that should be asked are hotly debated issues. In this book we have tried to present what glimpses there are of answers to two primary questions: what causes psychopathology and which treatments are most effective in preventing or reducing psychological suffering.

It has become commonplace in psychology to recognize the selective nature of perception. Certainly the writing of a textbook is guided by biases on the part of the authors, and our effort is no exception. We share a strong commitment to a scientific approach but at the same time appreciate the often uncontrollable nature of the subject matter and the importance of clinical findings. Rather than pretend that we are unbiased and objective, we have tried to alert readers to our assumptions. Forewarned in this manner, they may consider on their own the merits of our point of view. At the same time, we attempt as best we can to represent fairly and comprehensively the major alternative conceptualizations in contemporary psychopathology. A recurrent theme in the book is the importance of points of view or, to use Kuhn's (1962) phrase, paradigms. Our experience in teaching undergraduates has made us very much aware of the importance of making explicit the unspoken assumptions underlying any quest for knowledge. In our handling of the paradigms, we have tried to make their premises clear. Long after specific facts are forgotten, the student should retain a grasp of the basic problems in the field of psychopathology.

A related issue is the use of more than one paradigm in studying abnormal psychology. Rather than force an entire field into, for example, a social-learning paradigm, we argue, from the available information, that different problems in psychopathology are amenable to analyses within different frameworks. For instance, physiological processes must be considered when examining mental retardation and schizophrenia, but for other disorders a cognitive behavioral theory seems the most helpful. Over the course of our several revisions the importance of a diathesis-stress approach has become more and more evident. Emerging data indicate that many, perhaps most, disorders arise from subtle interactions between organic or psychological predispositions and stressful life events. Our coverage continues to reflect these hypotheses and findings, strengthening our basic position that a diathesis-stress paradigm is useful in understanding most psychopathologies.

Preparing this fourth edition has given us an opportunity to strengthen many parts of the book and to include significant new material that has appeared since completion of the third edition. Those familiar with our earlier efforts will find that our basic orientation has not changed. Our intent is to communicate to students our own excitement about our discipline, particularly the puzzles that challenge researchers in their search for the causes of psychopathology and for ways to prevent and ameliorate it. We try to encourage readers to participate with us in a process of discovery as we sift through the evidence on the origins of psychopathology and the effectiveness of specific interventions.

Any abnormal psychology textbook written in the 1980s must attend to the third edition of the *Diagnostic and Statistical Manual of Mental Disorders*, and ours is no exception. It has been gratifying to note that many of the changes introduced into DSM-III—recategorizing affective disorders, better operational definitions of each category, omission of homosexuality from the list of mental disorders, a narrower definition of schizophrenia—were anticipated and advocated in our first two editions. To help readers find their way through DSM-III, a summary table on the back endpapers of the book compares DSM-III with DSM-II.

We do not, however, accept DSM-III uncritically; those responsible for its compilation are themselves aware of our incomplete and evolving understanding of human suffering. Many times throughout the book we comment critically on this diagnostic scheme. We have every expectation that there will be a DSM-IV one day, and we hope to make some contribution, along with other colleagues, to the continuing refinement of the manual.

As in the third edition, treatments of specific disorders are discussed in the chapters reviewing them. The final section on intervention is also retained, for we continue to believe that only a separate and extended consideration allows us to explore with the reader the many perplexing and intriguing problems encountered by health professionals who try to prevent or treat mental disorders. Chapter 2, the pivotal chapter devoted to paradigms, lays the foundation for Chapters 5 through 17, which describe the various disorders and give what is known about their etiologies and about treating and preventing them.

It is a pleasure to acknowledge the contributions of a number of colleagues and students to this revision. Ian Evans, State University of New York at Binghamton; Stephen A. Lisman, State University of New York at Binghamton; Martha Storandt, Washington University; and Paul Wachtel, New York University, provided thoughtful recommendations for the fourth edition. Helpful library research was done at the University of Southern California by Sharon Dolezal, Max Fuentes, David Haaga, Kathie Hilterbrand, Elizabeth Kandel, and Linda Louie; and at the State University of New York at Stony Brook by Alexandra Gaughan, Jill Hooley, Kevin Leach, Sally Thomason, and Heiddis Valdimarsdottir. Special thanks go to Keri Weed and Wendy Weicker for drafting and rewriting major portions of the revisions of Chapters 16 and 17, respectively, and to Stephen J. Morse, for consultation on Chapter 21.

We continued to enjoy and benefit from the skills and dedication of our "Wiley family," Carol Luitjens, Mark Mochary, Stella Kupferberg, Elizabeth Meder, Dawn Stanley, Ed Burke, and Barbara Heaney. As before, our deepest appreciation goes to Priscilla Todd, who lent her writing talents to what we have striven mightily to make a readable and engaging text, without sacrificing scientific accuracy or professional responsibility. We wish to thank Fran McCleod and Barbara Conklin at Stony Brook and Gertrude Langerud at USC, for their secretarial work, as well as Eve Davison and Asher Davison for their clerical assistance. Our loving thanks to our respective families, who once again put up with "lost weekends" and occasional grumpiness: Gail and Sean Neale, and Carol, Eve, and Asher Davison. Finally, we have maintained the order of authorship as it was for the first edition, decided by the toss of a coin.

GERALD C. DAVISON
JOHN M. NEALE
September 1985

A NOTE
TO THE STUDENT

There are several features of this book that we hope will make it easier for you to master and enjoy the material. Some are common to all textbooks, others particular to our book.

1. *Chapter Summaries*. Though a summary appears at the end of each chapter, we recommend that you read it first. Even if you do not understand all of it, you will get some idea of what the chapter is about. Then, when you read it after completing the chapter itself, your enhanced understanding of it will give you an immediate sense of what you have learned in just one reading of the chapter; if something remains unclear in the Summary, you have some indication of what you would do well to reread then and there.

2. *Heads and Subheads*. We have employed four orders of heads. The first level heads are listed at the beginning of the chapter to provide a general idea of how the chapter is organized. You might also want to flip through the chapter and note the subheads; this will give you a better idea of how the chapter as a whole is organized. Another way to take note of the organization of each chapter is to flip backwards to the detailed Table of Contents at the beginning of the book, where we have listed both first and second level heads, with the pages on which they appear.

3. *Key Terms*. When an important term is introduced, it is italicized and underlined. Usually a discussion of that term immediately follows. Of course, the term will probably appear again later in the book, in which case it will not be highlighted in this way. If its meaning eludes you on this second or third meeting, then the next feature will help.

4. *Glossary*. We have provided at the end of the book a detailed dictionary of sorts that includes all key terms, as well as some other words and phrases that may not have been so highlighted. Unlike an ordinary dictionary, a glossary is a very specialized listing of terms and definitions tied to a particular area of study—in the present instance, of course, to abnormal psychology.

5. *Subject and Name Indices*. Also in the back of the book is an index of terms and ideas, the subject index, and a listing of names cited as bibliographic sources, the name index. Sometimes you may wish to know where in the book a certain topic, such as malnutrition, has been discussed. You will find in the subject index that malnutrition is mentioned in more than one context, and the page numbers enable you to look up quickly these several discussions, perhaps to compare how malnutrition was dealt with in the different contexts. The name index can help you find a particular reference, though sometimes we think that a principal purpose is to enable colleagues to look themselves up quickly to see if they have been cited in someone else's book! (We've certainly been guilty of this "sin.")

6. *DSM-III and DSM-II Tables*. On the endpapers of the book are listings of the new psychiatric nomenclature, DSM-III, and its predecessor DSM-II, along with a method for comparing the two. This provides a handy guide to where particular

disorders appear in the currently and formerly used listings. You will see, as you read our book, that we make considerable use of DSM-III, yet in a selective vein. Sometimes we find it better to discuss theory and research on a particular problem in a way that is different from DSM's conceptualization.

7. *Study Guide.* A *Student Study Guide*, written by Douglas Hindman, is available to help you read and study the textbook. For each chapter there is a summary of the chapter, a list of key concepts, important study questions, and practice tests to encourage active reading and learning. We think that it is a very helpful study aid.

8. *Supplemental Text.* Finally, with Thomas Oltmanns we have developed a supplemental paperback text, *Case Studies in Abnormal Psychology*, second edition, based on our own clinical experience with real clients. We hope that it will give you an appreciation of the range and nature of abnormal behavior. The response from students who have used the first edition has been overwhelmingly positive.

One of the things previous users have liked about the book is the way it reads. We hope you, too, will find it engaging and interesting. From time to time students have written us their comments on the book. Should the spirit move you to do so, you can glean our addresses from the brief biographies that appear next to our pictures at the beginning of the book.

GCD AND JMN

CONTENTS IN BRIEF

CONTENTS

PART TWO EMOTIONAL DISORDERS AND REACTIONS TO STRESS 111

PART THREE SOCIAL PROBLEMS 227

ABNORMAL PSYCHOLOGY

Ernest Trova, *Study/Falling Man #25*, 1963

INTRODUCTION
AND BASIC ISSUES

Giorgio de Chirico, *The Disquieting Muses*, 1925 Art Resource

INTRODUCTION: HISTORICAL AND SCIENTIFIC CONSIDERATIONS

The Mental Health Professions
History of Psychopathology
Science: A Human Enterprise

Slumping in a comfortable leather chair, Ernest H., a thirty-five-year-old city policeman, looked skeptically at his therapist as he struggled to relate a series of problems. His recent inability to maintain an erection when making love to his wife was the immediate reason for his seeking therapy, but after gentle prodding from the therapist, Ernest recounted a host of other difficulties, some of them dating from his childhood but most of them originating during the previous several years.

Ernest's childhood had not been a happy one. His mother, whom he loved dearly, died suddenly when he was only six, and for the next ten years he lived either with his father or with a maternal aunt. His father drank so heavily that he seldom managed to get through any day without some alcohol. Moreover, the man's moods were extremely variable; he had even spent several months in a state hospital with a diagnosis of "manic-depressive psychosis." The father's income was irregular and never enough to pay bills on time or to allow his son and himself to live in any but the most run-down neighborhoods. At times the father was totally incapable of caring for himself, let alone his son. Ernest would then spend weeks, sometimes months, with his aunt in a nearby suburb.

Despite these apparent handicaps, Ernest completed high school and entered the tuition-free city university. He earned his miscellaneous living expenses by waiting table at a small restaurant. During these college years his psychological problems began to concern him. He often became profoundly depressed, for no apparent reason, and these bouts of sadness were sometimes followed by periods of manic elation. His lack of control over these mood swings troubled him greatly, for he had observed this same pattern in his alcoholic father. He also felt an acute self-consciousness with people who he felt had authority over him—his boss, his professors, and even some of his classmates, with whom he compared himself unfavorably. He was especially sensitive about his clothes, which were old and worn compared to those of his peers; their families had more money than his.

It was on the opening day of classes in his junior year that he first saw his future wife. When the tall, slender young woman moved to her seat with grace and self-assurance, his were not the only eyes that followed her. He spent the rest of that semester watching her from afar, taking care to sit where he could glance over at her without being conspicuous. Then one day, as they and the other students were leaving class, they bumped into each other quite by accident, and her warmth and charm emboldened him to ask her to join him for some coffee. When she said yes, he almost wished she had not.

Amazingly enough, as he saw it, they soon fell in love, and before the end of his senior year they were married. Ernest could never quite believe that his wife, as intelligent a woman as she was beautiful, really cared for him. As the years wore on, his doubts about himself, and about her feelings toward him, would continue to grow.

He hoped to enter law school, and both his grades and law school boards made these plans a possibility, but he decided instead to enter the police academy. His reasons, as he related them to his therapist, had to do with doubts about his intellectual abilities, as well as his increasing uneasiness in situations in which he felt himself being evaluated. Seminars had become unbearable for him in his last year in college, and he had hopes that the badge and uniform of a police officer would give him the instant recognition and respect that he seemed incapable of earning on his own.

To help him get through the academy, his wife quit college at the end of her junior year, against Ernest's pleas, and sought a secretarial job. He felt she was far brighter than he and saw no reason why she should sacrifice her potential to help him make his way in life. But at the same time he recognized the fiscal realities and grudgingly accepted her financial support.

The police academy proved to be even more stressful than college. Ernest's mood swings, although less frequent, still troubled him. And like his father, who was now confined to a state mental hospital, he drank to ease his psychological pain. He felt that his instructors considered him a fool when he had difficulty standing up in front of the class to give an answer that he himself knew was correct. But he made it through the physical, intellectual, and social rigors of the academy, and he was assigned to foot patrol in one of the wealthier sections of the city.

Several years later, when it seemed that life should be getting easier, he found himself in ever-greater turmoil. Now thirty-two years of age, with a fairly secure job which paid reasonably well, he began to think of starting a family. His wife wanted this as well, and it was at this time that his problems with impotence began. He thought at first it was the alcohol—he was drinking at least six ounces of bourbon every night, except when on the swing shift. Soon, though, he began to wonder whether he was actually avoiding the responsibility of having a child, and later he began to doubt that his wife really found him attractive and desirable. The more understanding and patient she was about his sometimes frantic efforts to consummate sex with her, the less "manly" he felt himself to be. He was unable to accept help from his wife, for he did not believe that this was the "right" way to maintain a sexual relationship. The problems in bed spread to other areas of their lives. The less often they made love, the more suspicious he was of his wife, for she had become even more beautiful and vibrant as she entered her thirties. In addition, she had been promoted to the position of administrative assistant at the law firm where she worked. She would mention—perhaps to taunt him—long, martini-filled lunches with her boss at a posh uptown restaurant.

The impetus for his contacting the therapist was an ugly argument with his wife one evening when she came home from work after ten. Ernest had been elated and agitated for several days. To combat his fear that he was losing control, he had consumed almost a full bottle of bourbon each night. By the time that his wife walked in the door on that final evening, Ernest was already very drunk, and he attacked her both verbally and physically about her alleged infidelity. In her own anger and fear, she questioned his masculinity in striking a woman and taunted him with the disappointments of their love-making. Ernest stormed out of the house, spent the night at a local bar, and the next day somehow pulled himself together enough to seek professional help.

Every day of our lives we try to understand other people. Determining why another person does or feels something is a difficult task. Indeed, we do not always understand why we ourselves feel and behave as we do. Acquiring insight into what we consider the normal range of expected behavior is arduous enough, but human behavior beyond the normal range, such as that of the policeman just described, is even more perplexing.

When we refer to strange behavior or ideas, we frequently use phrases such as "He's out of his mind," "He's all screwed up," "He's a maniac," "She's a hysteric," or "She's really paranoid." Such terms indicate that as observers we have found a person's behavior inexplicable and can attribute it only to an unbalanced mind. These minds, however, are very often much sounder than such phrases and adjectives imply. Terrifying instances of unusual behavior although not personally observed by most of us, are very much in the public eye. Hardly a week passes without a violent act, such as an ugly axe murder or multiple slayings, being reported. The assailant is diagnosed by a police officer or mental health authority as a "mental case" and is found to have had a history of mental instability. Sometimes we learn that the person has previously been confined in a mental hospital.

This book is concerned with the whole range of abnormality and with the various explanations for it, both past and present. There are, however, numerous pitfalls in seeking valid explanations. To study abnormal psychology, we must have what might be called "great tolerance for ambiguity," an ability to be comfortable with very tentative, often conflicting pieces of information. Much less is known with certainty about the field than we might hope, presenting problems both for the professional and for the beginning student. Indeed, as already indicated, precious little is known of why human beings behave in a normal fashion, to say nothing of their abnormal behavior. In approaching the study of psychopathology, we do well to keep in mind that the subject offers few hard and fast answers. Although we shall report such findings as there are, many of the facts that will be introduced will undoubtedly be outdated in a matter of years. And yet, as will become evident when we discuss our orientation to scientific inquiry, the study of psychopathology is no less worthwhile because of its ambiguities. The kinds of questions asked rather than the specific answers available at any particular time constitute the very essence of the field.

Another problem that professionals share with laypeople is the closeness of any human being to the subject matter of behavior. Physicists, for example, would seem better able to detach themselves emotionally from their subject matter than psychologists, particularly those who specialize in the study of abnormal behavior. The pervasiveness and disturbing effects of abnormal behavior intrude on our lives. Who, for example, has not experienced irrational thoughts and feelings? Or who has not known someone, a friend or perhaps a relative, whose behavior was impossible to fathom? If you have, you realize how frustrating and frightening it is to try to understand and help a person suffering psychological difficulties.

Our closeness to the subject matter, of course, adds to its intrinsic fascination; no wonder that undergraduate courses in abnormal psychology are among the most popular in psychology departments and indeed in the entire college curriculum. Familiarity with the subject matter encourages people to study abnormal psychology, but it has one distinct disadvantage. All of us have already developed certain ways of thinking and talking about behavior, certain words and concepts that somehow seem to *fit*. For example, some may assert that the study of fear should concentrate on the immediate experience of fear; this is technically known as a *phenomenological* approach and is one formal way of setting about the study of human behavior. As behavioral scientists, we ourselves have had to grapple with the difference between what we may *feel* is the appropriate way to talk about human behavior and experience, and what we have learned to be more fruitful means of discussing them. Where most people would speak of a "feeling of terror," for example, we might be more inclined to use a phrase such as "fear-response of great magnitude." In doing so we would not be merely playing verbal games. The word "games" does indeed apply in the sense that our procedures have rules, but it does not apply in the sense that we are engaging in activities that do not mean very much or that could just as well be carried out in another fashion. The crucial point is that the concepts and verbal labels we use in the serious study of abnormal behavior must be free of the subjective feelings of appropriateness ordinarily attached to certain human phenomena. We may be asking you, then, to adopt frames of reference different from those you are accustomed to, and indeed different from those we ourselves employ when we are not wearing our professional hats.

The case study with which this chapter began is open to a wide range of interpretations. No doubt you have some ideas about how Ernest's problems developed, what his primary difficulties are, and perhaps even how you might try to help him. We know of no greater intellectual or emotional challenge than deciding both how to conceptualize the life of a person with psychological problems and how best to treat him or her. At the end of the next chapter we refer back to the case of Ernest H. to illustrate how workers from different theoretical orientations might describe him and seek to help.

THE MENTAL HEALTH PROFESSIONS

The training of clinicians, the various professionals who are regarded as legitimate providers of psychological services, takes different forms. A *psychiatrist* holds an M.D. degree and has taken postgraduate training, called a residency, wherein he or she has received supervision in psychotherapy. By virtue of the medical degree, the psychiatrist can also continue functioning as a physician—giving physical examinations, diagnosing medical problems, and the like. In actuality, however, the only aspect of medical practice that most psychiatrists engage in is prescribing *psychoactive drugs*, chemical compounds which are able to change how people feel and think.

The term *psychoanalyst* is reserved for those individuals who have received specialized training at a psychoanalytic institute; the program usually involves several years of clinical training as well as an in-depth psychoanalysis of the trainee. Although Sigmund Freud held that psychoanalysts do not need medical training, until recently most psychoanalytic institutes required of their graduates an M.D. and a psychiatric residency. After the B.A., then, it can take up to ten years to become a psychoanalyst. Psychoanalysts are usually in private practice, and their fees are extremely high.

To practice *clinical psychology* (the profession of the authors of this textbook) usually requires a Ph.D. degree, which entails four to five years of graduate study. Training for the Ph.D. in clinical psychology is much like that for the other special fields of psychology—experimental, physiological, social, developmental, aging—with a heavy emphasis on laboratory work, research design, statistics, and the empirically based study of human and animal behavior. As with these other fields of psychology, the degree is basically a research one, and candidates are required to write a lengthy dissertation on a specialized topic. In addition, however, Ph.D. clinical psychologists learn how to diagnose mental disorders and practice psychotherapy, much as a psychiatrist in training does. They take courses in which they master specific techniques under close professional supervision; then, during an intensive internship or postdoctoral training, they gradually assume increasing responsibility for the care of patients.

Other graduate programs prepare people for clinical practice. Some schools have initiated Psy.D. (Doctor of Psychology) programs for training in clinical psychology. The curriculum offered candidates for this new degree is generally the same as that available to Ph.D. students, but there is less emphasis on research and more on clinical training. The assumption is that clinical psychology has advanced to a level of knowledge that justifies—and even requires—intensive training in specific techniques of assessment and therapeutic intervention. A *psychiatric social worker* obtains a Master of Social Work degree. There are also master's and doctoral-level programs in *counseling psychology*, somewhat similar to graduate training in clinical psychology but usually with less emphasis on research. Recent years have seen a movement to *paraprofessional training*, in which workers without advanced degrees learn to conduct various forms of therapy under the close supervision of professionals.

The actual clinical work conducted by any of these individuals depends for the most part on the orientation of the school attended. By and large, except for the administration of drugs, specific therapies relate very little to the therapist's academic degree.

In addition to professionals who offer therapeutic services to the public, there is a highly diverse group who can be called *psychopathologists*. These people conduct research into the nature and development of the various disorders that their therapist colleagues try to treat. Psychopathologists may come from any number of disciplines; some are clinicians, but the educational backgrounds of others may range from biochemistry to developmental psychology, and their academic degrees are at virtually any level. What unites them is their commitment to the study of how abnormal behavior develops. Since relatively little is known about psychopathology, the diversity of backgrounds and interests is an advantage, for it is too soon to be certain where major advances will be made. The work of both psychopathologists and clinicians provides the subject matter of this book.

HISTORY OF PSYCHOPATHOLOGY

As psychopathologists, our interest is in the causes of deviant behavior. The search for these causes has gone on for a considerable period of time. Before the age of scientific inquiry, all good and bad manifestations of power beyond the control of humankind—eclipses, earthquakes, storms, lightning and thunder, fire, serious and disabling disease, darkness and light, the passing of the seasons—were regarded as supernatural. Any behavior seemingly beyond the control of the individual was subject to similar interpretation. The earliest writings of the philosophers, theologians, and physicians who studied the troubled mind found its deviancy to reflect the displeasure of the gods or possession by demons.

Early Demonology

The doctrine that a semiautonomous or completely autonomous evil being, such as the devil, may dwell within a person and control his or her mind and body is called *demonology*. The ancient Babylonians had in their religion a specific demon for each disease. Idta was the demon who caused insanity. Similar examples of demonological thinking can be found in the records of early Chinese, Egyptians, and Greeks. Among the Hebrews as well, deviancy was attributed to possession of the person by bad spirits, after God in his wrath had withdrawn protection. Christ is reported to have cured a man with an "unclean spirit" by casting out the devils from within him and hurling them onto a herd of swine. The animals were then said to have become possessed and to have run "violently down a steep place into the sea" (Mark 5: 8–13).

Treatment to combat and exorcise demons typically took the form of elaborate prayer rites, noise making, forcing the afflicted to drink terrible-tasting brews, and on occasion more extreme measures such as flogging and starvation in order to render the body uninhabitable to the devils.

Even in these early times, however, priests learned to temper their incantations with kindness. In Memphis, Egypt, the temple of Imhotep, the deity of healing, became a hospital and medical school. Sleeping in the temple was a principal means of therapy. Patients were also urged to engage in artistic endeavors, to take excursions on the Nile, and to attend concerts and dances. The temples to Asclepius, the Greek god of medicine, were erected near healing springs or on high mountains. The priests of this sect too relied on sleep within the sanctuaries; in their dreams patients were supposedly visited and advised by Asclepius or one of his priests. In the morning they departed cured or began the regimens revealed to them in their dreams. Baths, diet, and walking, riding, and other exercise all played a part in treatment. But those whose erratic behavior lay beyond these healing measures might be chased from the temples by stoning.

Somatogenesis

In the fifth century B.C. Hippocrates (460?–?377 B.C.) received his early medical training at the famous temple of Asclepius at Cos. Often regarded as the father of modern medicine and operating outside the *Zeitgeist* or intellectual and emotional orientation of the times, he separated medicine from religion, magic, and superstition and rejected the prevailing Greek belief that the gods sent serious physical diseases and mental disturbances as punishment. He insisted instead that such illnesses had natural causes and hence should be treated like other more common maladies such as colds and constipation. Hippocrates regarded the brain as the organ of consciousness, of intellectual life and emotion, and it followed that if someone's thinking and behavior were deviant, there was some kind of brain pathology. He is often considered one of the very earliest proponents of a *somatogenic* hypothesis to explain disordered behavior—that something wrong with the *soma* or physical body disturbs thought and action. He also recognized that environmental and emotional stress can damage the body and mind. Hippocrates classified mental disorders into three categories, mania, melancholia, and phrenitis or brain fever. Through his teachings the phenomena of abnormal behavior became more clearly the province of physicians than of priests.

The Greek physician Hippocrates held a somatogenic view of abnormal behavior, considering insanity a disease of the brain.

In treating patients, Hippocrates tried to find natural remedies for what he regarded as natural phenomena. For melancholia he prescribed tranquility, sobriety, care in choosing food and drink, and abstinence from sexual activity. Such a regimen was assumed to have a healthful effect on the brain and the body. Because Hippocrates believed in natural causes rather than supernatural, he depended on his own keen observations and made a valuable contribution as a clinician. Remarkably detailed records describing many of the symptoms now recognized in epilepsy, alcoholic delusion, stroke, and paranoia have come down to us from him.

Hippocrates' physiology was rather crude, however, for he conceived of normal brain functioning, and therefore of mental health, as dependent on a delicate balance among four "humors" or fluids of the body, namely blood, black bile, yellow bile, and phlegm. An imbalance produced disorders. If a person was sluggish and dull, for example, the body supposedly contained a preponderance of phlegm. A preponderance of black bile was the explanation for melancholia, too much yellow bile explained irascibility and anxiousness, and too much blood changeable temperament. Hippocrates' humoral pathology has not withstood later scientific scrutiny. His basic premise, however, that human behavior is directly determined by bodily structures or substances, and that abnormal behavior is produced by some kind of imbalance or even damage, foreshadowed aspects of contemporary thought. In the next seven centuries, before and after the birth of Christ, Hippocrates' naturalistic approach to disorder was generally accepted by other Greeks, such as Plato, Aristotle, and Galen, as well as by the Romans, who adopted the medicine of the Greeks after their city became the seat of power in the ancient world.

Galen, the last major physician of the classical era (A.D. 130–200), was a prolific writer who codified the medicine of antiquity, from Hippocrates to his own time. He accepted and elaborated on the doctrine of the humors, although he was also the first experimental physiologist. The dissection of the human body was illegal in his day, but Galen was an avid explorer of the anatomy of the Barbary ape and pigs. Through his scientific examination of the nervous system, he was able to draw attention to the role of the brain in mental functioning.

The Dark Ages and Demonology

In a massive generalization, historians have often suggested that the death of Galen in the third century A.D. marked the beginning of the Dark Ages for all medicine and for the treatment and investigation of abnormal behavior in particular.

Medieval woodcuts of the four temperaments thought by the followers of Galen to result from excesses of the four humors. From left to right: the man with changeable temperament, who has plenty of blood; the melancholy man, full of dark bile; the hot-tempered man, who has a surplus of choler or yellow bile; and the sluggish man with too much phlegm.

Indeed, during the third century the imperial power of Rome became invested in the military as it wholly absorbed civilian administration. The one aim of the military was to preserve the frontiers of the overextended empire. The economy collapsed, and intellectual life was greatly diminished. Toward the end of the fifth century (476), the last Roman emperor was deposed. After several centuries of decay, Greek and Roman civilization had finally ceased to be. During these same centuries the churches had gained in influence. The papacy was soon declared independent of the state and became the important element of unity. Christian monasticism, through its missionary and educational work, replaced classical culture. Nature was regarded as a reflection of divine will and beyond the reach of human reason. The principles of systematic observation established by the Greeks were not applicable in such a scheme.

The monasteries provided care and nursing of the sick, and a few were repositories for the classic Greek medical manuscripts, even though the knowledge within them might not be applied. When monks cared for the mentally disordered, they prayed over them and touched them with relics, or they concocted fantastic potions for them to drink in the waning phase of the moon. The families of the deranged might take them to shrines, or they sometimes disavowed them out of fear and superstition. Many of the mentally ill roamed the countryside, becoming more and more bedraggled and losing more and more of their faculties.

The early church was always both skeptical about witchcraft and disapproving of any effort to practice it. God alone was viewed as all powerful. In 1140 a paragraph of canon law urged the clergy to renounce as fantasies any claims made by wicked women that Satan had empowered them to ride great distances by night on the backs of beasts. But in the next thirty years the dualistic heresy, which ascribed real power to the devil as an equal opponent to God, grew with catastrophic rapidity in western Germany, Flanders, France, and northern Italy. Both the church and the state felt enormously threatened. By 1252 they had put in place all the machinery of the Inquisition. Heretics were tried in an ecclesiastical court and the unrepentant turned over to civil authorities for their punishment, which was usually burning. Papal inquisitors, who were authorized to use torture to obtain confessions and the names of other heretics, were sent to oversee the inquiries into heresy in the threatened bishoprics.

In this century and the next few a populace already suffering from social unrest and recurrent famines and plagues became obsessed with the devil. Witchcraft, now viewed as instigated by the powerful Satan of the heretics, was itself a heresy and denial of God. The reputed practices of witches—attending sabbats, having intercourse with the devil, turning themselves into animals, rendering men impotent, causing a neighbor's wheat to rot, his cattle to sicken, and making people die by melting wax images of them—were no longer regarded as fantasies but believed to take place in fact. Such evil was clearly within the scope of the Inquisition, and so witches began to be hunted and burned throughout Europe, especially in Germany. Faced with inexplicable and frightening occurrences, people tend to seize on whatever explanation is available. The times conspired to heap enormous blame on those regarded as witches.

In 1484 Pope Innocent VIII, in a papal bull, exhorted the clergy of Europe to leave no stone unturned in the search for witches. He sent two Dominicans, Jakob Sprenger and Henricus Institoris, to northern Germany as inquisitors. Two years later they issued a comprehensive and explicit manual, *Malleus Maleficarum* ("the witches' hammer"), to guide the witch hunts. It was a legal and theological document which came to be regarded by Catholics and Protestants alike as a textbook on witchcraft. "Carnal lust," insatiable in some women, was the reason they consorted "even with devils" and became witches. Various signs by which witches could be detected, such as red spots or areas of insensitivity on the skin, supposedly made by the claw of the devil when touching the person to seal a pact, were described. And the manual confirmed that the rules the Inquisition followed for heretics applied to the witches. Those accused of witchcraft should be tortured if they did not confess, those convicted and penitent were to be imprisoned for life, those convicted and unrepentant were to be handed over to the law for execution. The manual specified that a person's sudden loss of reason was a symptom of demonic possession, and that burning was the usual method of driving out the supposed demon. A number of witchcraft trials were mass trials, and eventually many were before secular tribunals. Over the next several centuries hundreds of thousands of women, men and children are said to have been accused, tortured, and put to death, but records of the period are not reliable.

The first abatement in witch hunting came in Spain, in 1610, when the inquisitor Alonso Salazar y Frías concluded that most of the accusations in Logroño, Navarre, had been false. He ordained that accusations must be accompanied by independent evidence, that torture could not be used, and that the property of the convicted would not be confiscated. Thereafter accusations of witchcraft dropped sharply in Spain. Although there

Tortures by which confessions were extracted from accused witches.

was to be an episode of witch hunting twenty years later, during a succeeding reign, Queen Christina of Sweden wrote a letter to one of her ministers on February 16, 1649, ordering him to free all prisoners accused of witchcraft except those clearly guilty of murder. In France witchcraft trials declined after an edict was issued by Louis XIV in 1682. The last execution of a witch was in Switzerland, in the year 1782.

The Mentally Ill as Witches

For some time the prevailing interpretation has been that all the mentally ill of the later Middle Ages were considered witches (Zilboorg and Henry, 1941). In their confessions the accused sometimes reported having had intercourse with the devil and having flown to sabbats, the secret meetings of their cults. These reports have

Witch burning.

The dunking test. If the woman did not drown, she was thought to be in league with the devil.

In this painting a priest is conducting an exorcism, trying to get the evil spirit to leave the woman's body.

THE COMMONWEALTH OF MASSACHUSETTS

In the Year One Thousand Nine Hundred and Fifty-seven

RESOLVE RELATIVE TO THE INDICTMENT, TRIAL, CONVICTION AND EXECUTION OF ANN PUDEATOR AND CERTAIN OTHER PERSONS FOR "WITCHCRAFT" IN THE YEAR SIXTEEN HUNDRED AND NINETY-TWO.

Whereas, One Ann Pudeator and certain other persons were indicted, tried, found guilty, sentenced to death and executed in the year sixteen hundred and ninety-two for "Witchcraft"; and

Whereas, Said persons may have been illegally tried, convicted and sentenced by a possibly illegal court of oyer and terminer created by the then governor of the Province without authority under the Province Charter of Massachusetts Bay; and

Whereas, Although there was a public repentance by Judge Sewall, one of the judges of the so-called "Witchcraft Court", and by all the members of the "Witchcraft" jury, and a public Fast Day proclaimed and observed in repentance for the proceedings, but no other action taken in regard to them; and

Whereas, The General Court of Massachusetts is informed that certain descendants of said Ann Pudeator and said other persons are still distressed by the record of said proceedings; therefore be it

Resolved, That in order to alleviate such distress and although the facts of such proceedings cannot be obliterated, the General Court of Massachusetts declares its belief that such proceedings, even if lawful under the Province Charter and the law of Massachusetts as it then was, were and are shocking, and the result of a wave of popular hysterical fear of the Devil in the community, and further declares that, as all the laws under which said proceedings, even if then legally conducted, have been long since abandoned and superseded by our more civilized laws no disgrace or cause for distress attaches to the said descendants or any of them by reason of said proceedings; and be it further

Resolved, That the passage of this resolve shall not bestow on the commonwealth or any of its subdivisions, or on any person any right which did not exist prior to said passage, shall not authorize any suit or other proceeding nor deprive any party to a suit or other proceeding of any defense which he hitherto had, shall not affect in any way whatever the title to or rights in any real or personal property, nor shall it require or permit the remission of any penalty, fine or forfeiture hitherto imposed or incurred.

House of Representatives, August 26, 1957.

Passed, *[signature]* Speaker

A bill passed in 1957 by the Massachusetts legislature exonerating a woman who had been executed for witchcraft in 1692.

been interpreted by contemporary writers as delusions or hallucinations and thus are taken to indicate that some witches were psychotic. Moreover, to identify people with the "Devil's mark," areas of insensitivity to pain, professional witch prickers went from town to town sticking pins into the bodies of the accused. Because anesthesia is regarded as a symptom of hysteria, the fact that some "witches" did not respond to the prickings is considered evidence of their madness.

More careful analyses of the witch hunts, however, reveal that although some accused witches were mentally disturbed, many more sane than insane people were tried. The delusionlike confessions were typically obtained during brutal torture; words were put on the lips of the tortured by their accusers and by the beliefs of the times. Indeed, in England, where torture was not allowed, the confessions did not usually contain descriptions indicative of delusions or hallucinations. Similarly, insensitivity to pain has many causes, including organic dysfunctions. More important, there are documented cases of deliberate trickery. Oftentimes a needle was attached to a hollow shaft so that it did not actually puncture the skin, although to observers it appeared to be penetrating deeply (Schoeneman, 1977; Spanos, 1978).

Evaluations of other sources of information indicate that witchcraft was not the prevailing interpretation of mental illness. From the thirteenth century onward, as the cities of Europe grew larger, hospitals began to come under secular jurisdiction. Municipal authorities, when they grew powerful, tended to supplement or take over some of the activities of the church, one of these of course being the care of the ill. The foundation deed for the Holy Trinity Hospital in Salisbury, England, dating from the mid-fourteenth century, specified the purposes of the hospital. Among them was that "the mad are kept safe until they are restored of reason." British laws during this period allowed both the dangerously insane and the incompetent to be confined in a hospital. Notably, the people to be confined were not described as being possessed (Allderidge, 1979).

Neugebauer (1979) has examined the records from lunacy trials in Britain during the Middle Ages. Beginning in the thirteenth century, these trials were held to determine a person's sanity. The trials were conducted under the Crown's right to protect the mentally impaired, and a judgment of insanity allowed the Crown to become guardian of the lunatic's estate. The defendant's orientation, memory, intellect, daily life, and habits were at issue in the trial. Explanations for strange behavior typically linked it to physical illness or injury or to some emotional shock. Of all the cases that Neugebauer examined, in only *one* was demonological possession referred to. The preponderance of evidence, then, indicates that this explanation of mental disturbance was not as dominant during the Middle Ages as had once been thought (see Box 1.1).

Development of Asylums

Until the end of the Crusades, in the fifteenth century, there were virtually no mental hospitals in Europe. Earlier than this, however, there were thousands of hospitals for lepers. In the twelfth century, for example, England and Scotland had 220 for a population of a million and a half. After the principal Crusades had been waged, leprosy gradually disappeared from Europe, probably because of the break with the eastern sources of the infection. With leprosy no longer of such great social concern, attention seems to have focused on the mad.

Confinement of the mentally ill began in earnest in the fifteenth and sixteenth centuries, sometimes in what had been leprosariums. Some of these *asylums* took in a mixed lot, beggars as well as disturbed people. Beggars were regarded as a great social problem at the time. Indeed, in the sixteenth century, Paris had 30,000 beggars in its population of fewer than 100,000. These institutions had no specific regimen for their inmates other than to get them to work. But during the same period hospitals geared more specifically for the confinement of the mentally ill also appeared. The Priory of St. Mary of Bethlehem was founded in 1243. By 1403 it housed six insane men, and in 1547 Henry VIII handed it over to the city of London, thereafter to be a hospital devoted solely to the confinement of the mentally ill. The conditions in Bethlehem were deplorable. Over the years the word "bedlam," a contraction and popular name for this hospital, became a descriptive term for a place or scene of wild uproar and confusion. Bethlehem eventually became one of London's great tourist attractions, by the eighteenth century rivaling both Westminster Abbey and the Tower of London. Even as late as the nineteenth century, viewing the violent patients and their antics was considered entertainment, and tickets of admission to Bedlam were sold. In the Lunatics' Tower, constructed in Vienna in 1784, patients were confined in the spaces between inner square rooms and the outer walls. There they could be looked at from below by pass-

A tour of St. Mary's of Bethlehem (Bedlam) provides amusement for these two upper-class women. Hogarth captures the poignancy of the scene in this well-known eighteenth-century painting.

BOX 1.1

THE SALEM INCIDENT: WITCHCRAFT OR POISONING?

In December 1691 eight girls who lived in or near Salem Village were afflicted with "distempers," which called for medical attention. Physicians, however, could find no cause for their disorderly speech, strange postures and gestures, and their convulsive fits. One of the girls was the daughter of the minister, Samuel Parris, another his niece. A neighbor soon took it upon herself to have Parris's Barbados slave, Tituba, concoct a "witch cake" of rye meal and the urine of the afflicted, and to feed it to a dog to determine whether witchcraft was indicated. Shortly thereafter, in February 1692, the girls accused Tituba and two elderly women of witchcraft, and the three were taken into custody. In his church records Parris denounced his neighbor's action and stated that until a community member had gone "to the Devil for help against the Devil," there had been no suspicion of witchcraft and no reports of torture by apparitions.

But now the accusations began to spew from the young girls and from other residents of the village. The jails of Salem, of surrounding towns, and even of faraway Boston filled with prisoners awaiting trial. By the end of September, nineteen people had been sent to the gallows, and one man had been pressed to death. The convictions were all obtained on the bases of "spectral evidence"—an apparition of the accused had appeared to the accuser; and the test of touch—an accuser's fit ceased after he or she was touched by the accused. The afflicted girls were present at the trials and often disturbed the proceedings with their violent fits, convulsions, and apparent hallucinations of spec-

Residence patterns in Salem, 1692. The names in parenthesis indicate the homes where the "possessed" girls lived. Residents are labeled as follows: X, afflicted girl; W, accused witch; D, defender of an accused witch; and A, accuser. Thirty of the thirty-two adult accusers lived in the western section of the village, and twelve of the fourteen accused witches in the eastern section.

ters and "familiars." (Familiars are spirits, often in animal form, who are believed to act as servants to a witch.)

Even before the last execution the witchcraft trials were adjourned until November. But the special court appointed earlier by Governor Phips never met again for this purpose. In January 1693 a superior court convened and received the fifty indictments for witchcraft that had already been made by a grand jury. It tried twenty persons, acquitted seven-

ersby. The first mental hospital in the United States was founded in Williamsburg, Virginia, in 1773.

It should not be assumed, however, that the inclusion of abnormal behavior within the domain of hospitals and medicine necessarily led to more humane and effective treatment. Benjamin Rush (1745–1813), who began practicing medicine in Philadelphia in 1769 and was also deeply involved in his country's struggle for independence, is considered the father of American psychiatry. He believed that mental disorder was caused by an excess of blood in the brain. Consequently, his favored treatment was to draw from "the insane" great quanti-

ties of blood, as much as six quarts over a period of a few months. Little wonder that patients so treated became less agitated (Farina, 1976)! Rush entertained another hypothesis, namely that many "lunatics" could be cured by frightening them. In one such recommended procedure the physician was to convince the patient of his impending death. A New England doctor of the nineteenth century implemented this prescription in an ingenious manner. "On his premises stood a tank of water, into which a patient, packed into a coffin-like box pierced with holes, was lowered. . . . He was kept under water until the bubbles of air ceased to rise, after which teen, and condemned three, although they were never executed. In May of 1693 Governor Phips ordered a general reprieve; about 150 persons still being held on charges of witchcraft were released, ending the strange episode.

These happenings in Salem are usually discussed as an illustration of how the hapless mentally ill of the era were mistreated through the widespread belief in possession, although the accused witches were for the most part persons of good reputation in the community. The accusers are sometimes proposed to have been schizophrenic, on the basis of their hallucinations. But schizophrenia is not likely to occur simultaneously in a group of young women. Or the episode is sometimes seen as an instance of "mass hysteria"; the witchcraft accusation, once made, mushroomed for some reason. Earlier accusations of witchcraft in Puritan communities of New England had never had such an outcome, however. Linnda Caporael (1976) has recently proposed a new theory, that the accusers were suffering from ergot poisoning.

Ergot, a parasitic fungus, grows on cereal grains, principally rye, and its development is fostered by warm, rainy growing seasons. Several of the alkaloids* of ergot contain as their basis lysergic acid, from which LSD is synthesized. Ingestion of food made from flour contaminated with ergot can cause crawling sensations on the skin, tingling in the fingers, vertigo, headache, hallucinations, vomiting, diarrhea, and convulsions. The alkaloids of ergot can also induce delirium and mood changes such as mania and depression.

Could ergot poisoning account for the events in question? First, the behavior of the initial accusers is indeed similar to the known effects of ergot poisoning. The girls did report having hallucinations; they also vomited, had convulsions, and said that they felt as though they were being choked and pricked with pins. Second, rye was a well-established crop in Salem, and there had been heavy rains in 1691, which would promote the growth of the fungus. Rye was usually harvested in August and threshed in the late autumn. The onset of the girls' strange behavior occurred at about the time they would be beginning to eat food made from the new grain. The accumulating accusations of witchcraft apparently came to an abrupt halt in the following autumn, when a new supply of grain, grown during a dry 1692, became available. After that time the afflictions of the girls and those of others in Salem were not mentioned in accounts of the period.

Why then did only some people feel that their bodies had been possessed? Caporael argues that the western portion of Salem Village, where the ground is lower and the meadows are swampy, would be the most likely source of contaminated grain. The pattern of residence of the young girls and of the other accusers fits this hypothesis; they were more likely to reside in or to eat grain grown in the western fields. Most of the accused witches and their defenders lived in the eastern section of the village.

Caporael has presented a compelling set of arguments for her ergot poisoning theory. Of course, it remains a theory, but it is interesting to speculate how many witchcraft persecutions throughout the later Middle Ages may have had ergotism as a root cause.

*Alkaloids are organic substances that are found for the most part in seed plants, usually not singly but as mixtures of similar alkaloids. They all contain nitrogen and are the active agents that give a number of natural drugs their medicinal and also their toxic properties.

he was taken out, rubbed, and revived—if he had not already passed beyond reviving!'' (Deutsch, 1949, p. 82).

Moral Treatment

A primary figure in the movement for humanitarian treatment of those in asylums was Philippe Pinel (1745-1826). In 1793, while the French Revolution raged, he was put in charge of a large asylum in Paris known as La Bicêtre. A historian has written of the conditions at this particular hospital.

[The patients were] shackled to the walls of their cells, by iron collars which held them flat against the wall and permitted little movement. . . . They could not lie down at night, as a rule. . . . Oftentimes there was a hoop of iron around the waist of the patient and in addition . . . chains on both the hands and the feet. . . . These chains [were] sufficiently long so that the patient could feed himself out of a bowl, the food usually being a mushy gruel—bread soaked in a weak soup. Since little was known about dietetics, [no attention] was paid to the type of diet given the patients. They were presumed to be animals . . . and not to care whether the food was good or bad (Selling, 1940, p. 54).

At the Lunatics' Tower (e, center) in Vienna, a remarkable collection of strange instruments and fetters were employed in the treatment of the insane. (a) A lunatic in hood and straitjacket, padlocked to a cell wall. (b) The machine in which lunatics were swung until they were in a state of stupefaction and therefore remained quiet. (c) A maniac strapped in a chair in a position sometimes held for weeks. (d) The "English coffin," in which the lunatic was kept, his face at the hole, for discipline. The face and the box together resembled a standing clock. (f) A cell door with its iron "spy-hole." (g) An enormous wheel, which turned each time the lunatic inside it moved. (h) A maniac's hands in padlocked handcuffs, and (i) another straitjacketed lunatic.

Pinel was reluctantly allowed to remove the chains of the people imprisoned in La Bicêtre and to treat them as sick human beings rather than as beasts. Many who had been excited and completely unmanageable became calm and much easier to handle. Formerly considered dangerous, they strolled through the hospital and grounds with no inclination to create disturbances or to harm anyone. Light and airy rooms replaced their dungeons. Some who had been incarcerated for years were soon restored to health and were eventually discharged from the hospital.

Freeing the patients of their restraints was not the only humanitarian reform advocated by Pinel.[1] Consistent with the egalitarianism of the new French Republic, he believed that the mental patients in his care were essentially normal people who should be approached with compassion and understanding and treated as individual human beings with dignity. Their reason supposedly having left them because of severe personal and social problems, it might be restored to them through comforting counsel and purposeful activity.

About the time Pinel began reforming La Bicêtre, a prominent merchant and Quaker, William Tuke (1732–

[1]Not all scholars agree that Pinel deserves as much adulation as he enjoys. Thomas Szasz (1974), whose influential writings on involuntary hospitalization are reviewed in Chapter 21, points to sections of Pinel's famous *A Treatise on Insanity* (1801). They indicate that he relied on terror and coercion in dealing with patients of the lower classes.

Pinel releasing the patients at La Bicêtre.

1822), had occasion to be shocked by the conditions at York Asylum in England. He proposed to the Society of Friends that they found their own institution. In 1796 York Retreat was established on a country estate. It provided the mentally ill with a quiet and religious atmosphere in which to live, work, and rest. They discussed their difficulties with attendants, worked in the garden, and took walks through the countryside. In the United States the Friends' Asylum, founded in 1817 in Pennsylvania, and the Hartford Retreat, established in 1824 in Connecticut, were patterned after the York Retreat. A number of other American hospitals were influenced by the sympathetic and attentive treatment provided by Pinel and Tuke. Of course not all asylums adopted their so-called *moral practices*, but the smaller ones that did achieved remarkable successes. Unfortunately, this personal attention to the patients was no longer possible when the large mental hospitals that are prevalent today began to be built (Bockhoven, 1963).

The "tranquilizing chair," used by Benjamin Rush as a means of treating mental disorders.

Some early mental hospitals were pleasant sanctuaries located in the country. Pictured here is the retreat founded by William Tuke.

The Beginning of Contemporary Thought

Somatogenesis

Hippocrates was earlier described as the first to enunciate a somatogenic hypothesis of mental illness. His view was revived in Europe in the middle of the nineteenth century by a German physician, Wilhelm Griesinger, who insisted that any diagnosis of mental disorder specify a physiological cause. A textbook of psychiatry, written by his well-known follower, Emil Kraepelin (1856–1926), and first published in 1883, furnished a classification system to help establish the organic nature of mental illnesses. Kraepelin discerned among mental disorders a tendency for a certain group of *symptoms*, called a *syndrome*, to appear together regularly enough to be regarded as having an underlying physical cause, much as a particular medical disease and its syndrome may be attributed to a physiological dysfunction. He regarded each mental illness as distinct from all others, having its own genesis, symptoms, course, and outcome. Even though cures had not been worked out, at least the course of the disease could be predicted. Kraepelin proposed that there were two major groups of severe mental diseases: dementia praecox, an early term for schizophrenia, and manic-depressive psychosis. He postulated a chemical imbalance as the cause of schizophrenia and an irregularity in metabolism as the explanation of manic-depressive psychosis. Kraepelin's scheme for classifying these and other mental illnesses became the basis for the present diagnostic categories, which will be described more fully in Chapter 3.

Much was being learned about the nervous system in the second half of the nineteenth century but not enough yet to reveal all the expected abnormalities in structure that might underlie mental disorders. Degenerative changes in the brain cells associated with senile and presenile psychoses and some structural pathologies that accompany mental retardation were identified, however. Pellagra and the serious disorientation brought on by it were traced to a vitamin deficiency. Perhaps the most striking medical success was the discovery of the full nature and origin of *syphilis*. The venereal disease syphilis had been recognized for several centuries, and since 1798 it had been known that a number of mental patients manifested a similar and steady deterioration of both physical and mental abilities. These patients were observed to suffer multiple impairments, including delusions of grandeur and progressive paralysis. Soon after these symptoms were recognized, it was realized that these patients never recovered. In 1825 this deterioration in mental and physical health was designated a disease, *general paresis*. Although in 1857 it was established that some patients with paresis had earlier had syphilis, there were many competing theories of the origin of paresis. For example, in attempting to account for the high rate of the disorder among sailors, some supposed that seawater might be the cause. And Griesinger, in trying to explain the higher incidence among men, speculated whether liquor, tobacco, and coffee were implicated. Then in the 1860s and 1870s Louis Pasteur established the *germ theory of disease*. It thus became possible to demonstrate the relation between syphilis and general paresis. In 1897 Richard von Krafft-Ebing inoculated paretic patients with matter from syphilitic sores. The patients did not develop syphilis, indicating that they had been infected earlier. Finally, in 1905, the specific microorganism causing syphilis was discovered. Fortunately, measures that can detect the presence of syphilis and prevent its spread were developed soon after the discovery of the spirochete that causes it.

Psychogenesis

The search for somatogenic causes dominated psychiatry until well into the twentieth century, no doubt partly because of the stunning discoveries made about general paresis. But in other parts of western Europe, in the late eighteenth century and throughout the nineteenth, mental illnesses were considered to have an entirely different genesis. Various *psychogenic* points of view, attributing mental disorders to psychic malfunctions, were fashionable in France and Austria. For reasons that are not clear to us even today, many people in western Europe were at that time subject to hysterical states (in contemporary terms, conversion disorders): they suffered from physical incapacities that made absolutely no anatomical sense (see page 146). For example, in "glove anesthesia" the person had no feeling in his or her hand, but sensation was present just beyond the wrist and on up into the arm. Since the nerves run continuously from the shoulder down to the fingertips, there is no known physiological explanation for such an anesthesia.

Franz Anton Mesmer (1734–1815), an Austrian physician practicing in Vienna and Paris in the late eighteenth century, believed that hysterical disorders were caused by a particular distribution of a universal magnetic fluid in the body. Moreover, he felt that one person could influence the fluid of another to bring about a change in the person's behavior. He conducted meetings cloaked in mystery and mysticism, during which afflicted patients sat around a covered *baquet* or tub with iron rods protruding through the cover from the bottles of various chemicals that were beneath. Mesmer would enter a room, clothed in rather outlandish lilac garments, and take various rods from the tub and touch afflicted parts of his patients' bodies. The rods were believed to transmit "animal magnetism" and adjust the distribution of the universal magnetic fluid, thereby removing the hysterical anesthesias and paralyses. What-

Two portrayals of Franz Anton Mesmer's procedure for transmitting animal magnetism from the *baquet* to his patients. The caricature shows the process as a form of exorcism. Ordered to leave Austria, Mesmer took up practice in Paris. Benjamin Franklin was a member of the French commission that investigated his activities in 1784.

BOX 1.2

HYPNOSIS

A discussion of hypnosis could appear in several chapters of this book; inasmuch as it played a central role in the development of psychogenic theories of psychopathology, we include it here.

An initial question to be asked is what exactly is hypnosis. In view of how often psychologists and psychiatrists employ the term, it is sobering to realize how much heated controversy there is about its very nature. Hilgard (1979) suggests the following characteristics.

1. *Increased suggestibility*. Hypnotized subjects seem much more open to suggestions from the hypnotist than they would be in a waking state.

2. *Enhanced imagery and imagination*. Hypnotized subjects are able to imagine vividly the sensory experiences suggested to them and also report that they are able to retrieve images, sometimes from childhood, with great clarity.

3. *Disinclination to plan*. The hypnotized subject loses initiative and instead looks to the hypnotist as a source of direction. Indeed, many hypnotized subjects become annoyed when asked to do some planning on their own.

4. *Reduction in reality testing*. Many hypnotized subjects readily accept all kinds of perceptual distortions that they would not tolerate when awake. Thus hypnotized subjects may accept suggestions that an animal is talking to them or that someone is present in the room when no one is actually there. The logic that operates during a hypnotic trance, allowing a person to perceive the world in a way remarkably different from how he or she regards it when awake, has been called "trance logic" (Orne, 1959).

These, then, are what many workers regard as characteristics of hypnotized subjects. As in all aspects of human behavior, not all people manifest all these characteristics in the same way, and it is indeed possible for subjects who otherwise appear to be deeply hypnotized not to give all these noticeable indications at any one time.

Our historical review mentions Mesmer's therapy for hysterical disabilities and subsequent work by Charcot, Janet, and Breuer. During the same period of time, surgeons were "mesmerizing" patients to block pain. For example, in 1842 a British physician, W.S. Ward, amputated the leg of a patient after hypnotizing him. Apparently the patient felt nothing during what would otherwise have been an excruciatingly painful operation. And in 1849 a mesmeric infirmary was opened in London. Hundreds of apparently painless operations were performed while the patients were in hypnotic trances. In the same decade, however, ether was proved to produce insensibility to pain. The term anesthesia had heretofore been applied to the numbness felt in hysterical states and paralysis. Oliver Wendell Holmes is credited with suggesting that it be applied to the effects of this new agent and others like it, and that the agents be called anesthetics. The availability of these chemicals for surgical operations forestalled the continuing use of hypnosis as an alleviator of pain.

The person who coined the modern term hypnotism is usually considered to be James Braid (1795–1860), a British physician who was also hypnotizing people to reduce pain. Unlike Mesmer, however, Braid did not break with his profession, describing what happened in terms that were more consistent with the *Zeitgeist*. He characterized the trance as a "nervous sleep," from which came the name "neurohypnology," later shortened to hypnotism. Braid rejected the

---

ever we may think of what seems today to be a questionable theoretical explanation and procedure, the fact remains that Mesmer seemingly helped quite a number of people overcome their hysterical problems. Our discussion of Mesmer's work under the rubric of psychogenic causes is rather arbitrary, since Mesmer regarded the hysterical disorders as strictly physical. Because of the setting in which Mesmer worked with his patients, however, he is generally considered one of the earlier practitioners of our modern-day *hypnosis* (see Box 1.2). The familiar word mesmerize is the older term for hypnotize. The phenomenon itself, however, was known to the ancients of probably every culture, belonging to the armamentaria of sorcery and magic, of conjurers, fakirs, and faith healers.

Although Mesmer was regarded as a quack by his contemporaries, the study of hypnosis gradually became respectable. A great Parisian neurologist, Jean Martin Charcot (1825–1893), also studied hysterical states, not only anesthesia and paralysis, but blindness, deafness, convulsive attacks, and gaps in memory brought about by hysteria. Charcot initially espoused a somatogenic point of view. One day, however, some of his enterprising students hypnotized a normal woman and suggested to her certain hysterical symptoms. Charcot was deceived into believing that she was an actual hysterical patient. When the students showed him how readily they could remove the symptoms by waking the woman, Charcot changed his mind about hysteria and became interested in nonphysiological interpretations of these mystical orientation of Mesmer and yet continued to experiment with the phenomenon as he saw it. He sought a physiological cause and felt he had found one in his discovery that trances could be readily induced by having people stare at a bright object located somewhat above the line of vision. The object was placed in front of a person in such a way that the levator muscles of the eyelids had to be strained in order to keep it in view. Braid suggested that the muscles were markedly affected by having them remain fixed in this position for a given period of time and that somehow this led to nervous sleep or hypnosis. He therefore placed the cause of the sleep inside the subject rather than external to him, as Mesmer had suggested with his concept of animal magnetism. In this way he was able to perform many public demonstrations without incurring the disapproval of his medical colleagues.

As already indicated, the discovery of drugs for anesthesia discouraged the use of hypnosis in medicine, for drugs are clearly more reliable, although more dangerous as well, than hypnotic inductions. In clinical work many practitioners have employed hypnotic procedures for psychotherapeutic purposes, especially during World War II. To relieve the combat exhaustion of frightened and sleepless soldiers, doctors hypnotized them and encouraged them to relive traumatic events in the imagination.

The scientific study of hypnosis had to await the development of relatively objective measures in the 1950s. Perhaps the principal device is that developed at Stanford University by Weitzenhoffer and Hilgard (1959), the Stanford Hypnotic Susceptibility Scale. In the application of this scale, or, more properly, scales, since there are number of them, the subject is hypnotized and then asked to undertake a series of tasks. For example, the hypnotist may suggest to a subject that his right hand is so heavy that it is doubtful whether he can raise it. Then the hypnotist will ask the subject to try to lift the heavy hand, even though he

probably will not be able to do so. The hypnotist observes the degree to which the subject can or cannot raise the hand and gives a plus or minus score. After the subject has been observed at a number of tasks, he is given a score ranging from zero to twelve, and this score is regarded as a measure of how deeply hypnotized he is.

Most of these scales, however, do not measure the more subjective aspects of hypnosis. For example, many hypnotized subjects, even though they have not been specifically told that it may happen, experience sensations such as floating or spinning. Many hypnotists consider such subjective experiences at least as important as the more observable performances tapped by the various scales. As we might expect, this divergence of interests contributes to the controversy within the field, with the more clinically oriented hypnotists rejecting the validity of such scales as the Stanford. They instead content themselves with what subjects report of their subjective reactions.

Stanford psychologist Ernest Hilgard, who pioneered the development of a reliable method of assessing hypnotic susceptibility.

very puzzling phenomena. Further psychological theorizing and research was done by Pierre Janet (1859–1947), one of Charcot's pupils. He believed that in hysteria part of the organized system of thoughts, emotions, and sensations broke loose from the rest through a weakness of the nervous system.

In Vienna, toward the end of the century, a physician named Josef Breuer (1842–1925) treated a young woman who had become bedridden with a number of hysterical symptoms. Her legs and right arm and side were paralyzed, her sight and hearing impaired, and she often had difficulty speaking. She also sometimes went into a dreamlike state or "absence," during which she mumbled to herself, seemingly preoccupied with troubling thoughts. Perhaps not knowing what else to do, Breuer

hypnotized Anna O. and repeated some of her mumbled words. He succeeded in getting her to talk more freely and ultimately with considerable emotion about some very disquieting past events. Upon awakening from these hypnotic sessions, she would frequently feel much better. With Anna O. and other hysterical patients Breuer found that the relief and cure of their symptoms seemed to last longer if, under hypnosis, they were able to recall the original precipitating event for the symptom and if, furthermore, their original emotion was expressed. This reliving of an earlier emotional catastrophe and the release of the emotional tension produced by previously forgotten thoughts about the event were called abreaction or catharsis. Breuer's method became known as the *cathartic method*. In 1895 one of his col-

Josef Breuer, the Austrian physician and physiologist whose collaboration with Freud was important in the early development of psychoanalysis. He treated only Anna O. by the cathartic method he originated. Becoming alarmed by what would later be called her transference and his own countertransference, he described his procedures to a colleague and turned her treatment over to him.

leagues joined him in the publication of *Studies in Hysteria*, a book considered to be a milestone in abnormal psychology. To be examined in the next chapter is the thinking of Breuer's collaborator, Sigmund Freud.[2]

SCIENCE: A HUMAN ENTERPRISE

In space exploration highly sophisticated satellites are sent aloft to make observations. Astronauts have also been catapulted to the moon, where they use their human senses as well as man-made machines to carry out still more observations. It is possible, however, that certain phenomena are being missed because our instruments do not have sensing devices capable of recording the presence or absence of such phenomena, and because people are not trained to look for them. When the Viking 1 and Viking 2 Mars landers began to forage for life in July and September of 1976, space scientists repeatedly cautioned against concluding that there was no life on Mars just because instruments failed to detect

any. Scientists are sophisticated enough by training to know that they are in a bind. Life on another planet can be looked for only with the instruments they themselves have developed, but these devices are limited by their own preconceptions. The tests run on Mars make assumptions about the nature of living matter that may not match what has evolved on this distant planet. Carl Sagan, renowned Cornell space scientist, has cautioned that we may simply be asking the wrong questions. The Viking experiments can determine only whether the Martian soil samples contain earthlike life, but life on Mars could be based on an entirely different chemistry (*Time*, August 2, 1976, p. 23).

This discursion on outer-space exploration is one way of pointing out that scientific observation is a human endeavor, reflecting both the strengths of human ingenuity and scholarship as well as our intrinsic incapacity to be fully knowledgeable about the nature of our universe. Scientists are able to design instruments to make only the kinds of observations about which they have some initial idea. They realize that certain observations are not being made because our knowledge about the general nature of the universe is limited. Thomas Kuhn, a well-known philosopher of science, has put the problem this way: "The decision to employ a particular piece of apparatus and to use it in a particular way carries an assumption that only certain sorts of circumstances will arise" (1962, p. 59). Robert Pirsig, in *Zen and the Art of Motorcycle Maintenance* (1974), expressed the issue somewhat more poetically: "We take a handful of sand from the endless landscape of awareness around us and call that handful of sand the world" (p. 75).

Subjectivity in Science: The Role of Paradigms

We believe that every effort should be made to study abnormal behavior according to scientific principles. It should be clear at this point, however, that science is *not* a completely objective and certain enterprise. Rather, as

---

[2]Anna O., the young woman treated by Breuer with the cathartic method or *"talking cure,"* has become one of the best-known clinical cases in all psychotherapy literature, and as indicated above, the report of this case and four others in 1895 formed the basis of Freud's important later contributions. But historical investigations by Ellenberger (1972) cast serious doubt on how accurate Breuer's reporting was. Indeed, Anna O.—in reality Bertha Pappenheim, member of a well-to-do Viennese family—was apparently helped only temporarily by Breuer's talking cure! Carl Jung, Freud's renowned colleague, is

quoted as saying that, during a conference in 1925, Freud told him that Anna O. had never been cured. Hospital records discovered by Ellenberger confirmed that she continued to rely on morphine to ease the "hysterical" problems that Breuer is reputed to have removed by catharsis. In fact, evidence suggests that some of her problems were organic, not psychological. It is fascinating and ironic to consider that psychoanalysis traces its roots back to an improperly reported clinical case.

we can infer from the comment by Kuhn, subjective factors, as well as limitations in our perspective on the universe, enter into the conduct of scientific inquiry. Central to any application of scientific principles, in Kuhn's view, is the concept of *paradigm*, which may be defined as a conceptual framework within which a scientist works. A paradigm, according to Kuhn, is a set of basic assumptions that outline the particular universe of scientific inquiry, specifying both the kinds of concepts that will be regarded as legitimate as well as methods that may be used to collect and interpret data. Indeed, every decision about what constitutes a datum, or scientific observation, is made within a paradigm. A paradigm has profound implications for how scientists operate at any given time, for "[People] whose research is based on shared paradigms are committed to the same rules and standards for scientific practice" (Kuhn, 1962, p. 11). Paradigms specify what problems scientists will investigate and how they will go about the investigation.

Although made explicit only when scientists address themselves to philosophy, paradigms are nonetheless an intrinsic part of a science, serving the vital function of indicating how the game is to be played. In perceptual terms a paradigm may be likened to a general *set*, a tendency to see certain factors and not to see others.

In addition to injecting inevitable biases into the definition and collection of data, a paradigm may also affect the interpretation of facts. In other words, the meaning or import attributed to data may depend to a considerable extent on a paradigm (see Box 1.3).

An Example of Paradigms in Abnormal Psychology

A striking demonstration of this "I'll see it when I believe it" feature of science is provided in an experiment by Langer and Abelson (1974). They were interested in how different theoretical orientations might affect the ways in which trained clinicians view the "adjustment" of a person.

Behavior therapy stems from the behaviorism-learning branch of psychology, which sees its purpose to be the objective observation of overt behavior and which has formulated laws describing learning. Behavior therapists believe that abnormal behavior is acquired according to the same learning principles as normal behavior and that the very designation of a person as mentally ill reflects a social judgment. More traditionally trained clinicians look for the inner conflict supposedly causing disturbed behavior and tend more than behavior therapists to think in terms of mental illness. Langer and Abelson reasoned that behavior therapists might be less swayed by being told that a person was ill than would traditionally trained clinicians. To test this supposition, they conceived the following experiment. A group of behavior therapists and another of therapists trained in *psychoanalysis* were shown a videotape of an interview in progress between two men. Before viewing this videotape, half the subjects in each group were told that the interviewee was a job applicant, the other half that he was a patient. The traditional clinicians who were told that the interviewee was a patient were expected to rate him as more disturbed than those who considered him a job applicant. It was also predicted that the ratings of the two groups of behavior therapists would be less affected by the labels and would thus be rather similar.

The videotape shown to all subjects depicted a bearded professor interviewing a young man in his mid-twenties. The interviewee had been recruited through a newspaper advertisement that offered ten dollars to someone who had recently applied for a new job and was willing to be interviewed and videotaped. The fifteen-minute segment chosen from the original interview contained a rambling, autobiographical monologue by the young man in which he described a number of past jobs and dwelt on his conflicts with bureaucrats. His manner was considered by Langer and Abelson to be intense but uncertain; they felt that he could be regarded either as sincere and struggling or as confused and troubled.

A questionnaire measured the clinicians' impressions about the mental health of the interviewee. When the young interviewee was identified as a job applicant, there were no significant differences in the adjustment ratings given by the traditional clinicians and the behavior therapists. But the patient label, as expected, produced sharp differences (Figure 1.2). When the interviewee was identified as a patient, the traditional clinicians rated him relatively disturbed—significantly more so than did the traditional clinicians who viewed the man as a job applicant. In contrast, the behavior therapists rated the "ill" interviewee as relatively well adjusted, in fact, no less adjusted than the other behavior therapists rated the man they considered a job applicant.

Qualitative evaluations obtained from the clinicians supported their ratings. Whereas the behavior therapists described the man as "realistic," "sincere," and "responsible," regardless of label, the traditional clinicians

BOX 1.3

PARADIGM CLASH IN THE STUDY OF HYPNOSIS

Box 1.2 reviewed some of the history of hypnosis and its generally accepted characteristics. There is a continuing clash of paradigms in the study of hypnosis, for the very idea that we should talk about hypnosis as a state in which special psychological processes take over has been challenged (for example, Barber, 1969; Spanos, 1982).

To illustrate the controversy, we shall examine some recent findings concerning hypnotic analgesia, the reduction of pain by hypnosis. Hilgard, Morgan, and MacDonald (1975) studied subjects who were easily hypnotized and already known to be able to reduce pain substantially when hypnotized. Subjects were required to keep a hand in circulating ice water, called the cold pressor test, and report pain while awake and while hypnotized. As can be seen in Figure 1.1, while in the normal waking condition subjects report that pain becomes rapidly more severe during the 45-second period in which the hand is immersed in ice water. Then the subjects were hypnotized, given a suggestion of anesthesia, and asked to report their pain in two ways, verbally as before and also by pressing a key. The two responses were meant to tap two different levels of experience. Subjects were told that through hypnosis it is possible to reach a "hidden part" of the self that is normally inaccessible. The conscious part of the hypnotized subject will verbally report the level of pain experienced. The hidden part, however, will be aware of things going on in the body outside of conscious awareness and will automatically press the key to indicate the pain experienced on this level.

As can be seen in Figure 1.1, the two reports yielded very different results. As expected, the verbal reports indicated little pain during the 45 seconds. The "hidden observer" key presses, however, signaled substantial pain. Hilgard (1979) interprets these data in a way that clearly ascribes special psychological processes to the hypnotic state. He believes that in hypnotic analgesia the experience of pain is dissociated or separated from conscious awareness. It is experienced unconsciously, behind an "amnesialike barrier." The hidden-observer technique is thought to allow access to this normally unconscious experience.

Hilgard's theory has elicited considerable interest and critical comment, particularly from those who do not believe that hypnosis involves special processes. A study by Spanos, Gwynn, and Stam (1983), for example, attributed the hidden-observer effect to playing a social role. In brief, Spanos and his colleagues believe that the instructions to subjects in Hilgard's studies clearly convey the information that the hypnotized, conscious self will experience little pain and that the hidden part will experience more pain. The experimental situation, then, *demands* a specific pattern of response from subjects, and they provide reports consistent with these demands.

In their experiment Spanos, Gwynn, and Stam examined the responses of easily hypnotized subjects given the cold pressor test in four different situations. The first report was made in a waking state, and the other responses were obtained during hypnotic analgesia but with varying instructions about the hidden observer. In one of these conditions, the uncued, subjects were told that hypnosis would allow a hidden part of them to be reached, but they were given no expectations concerning what their hidden part would experience. In the remaining two conditions subjects were told that the hidden observer would be either more aware—"The hidden part of you can continue to remain aware of everything going on around it, and everything going on in your body . . ."; or less aware—" . . . less aware of everything going on in your body. . . ."

Results indicated that ratings of overt pain after each suggestion of analgesia were lower than those given in the waking state, as Hilgard and his co-workers (1975) had found. More important, however, the types of cues subjects were given had an effect on the hidden-observer reports. In

FIGURE 1.1 The highest curve indicates the pain that awake subjects felt in one of their hands as they held it in circulating ice water. The small amount of overt pain that they reported verbally when in the same situation but hypnotized and given a suggestion of analgesia is indicated by the lowest curve. The middle curve shows the pain that the hidden parts of their hypnotized selves reported by key pressing. After Hilgard, Morgan, and MacDonald, 1975.

the uncued condition, key-pressed reports of pain from the hidden observer did not differ from subjects' verbal reports of overt pain. Subjects who expected their hidden observer to be more aware did in fact report more hidden pain than overt. Those who expected their hidden observer to be less aware reported less hidden pain than overt. Clearly, these results suggest that hidden-observer reports can be substantially affected by the information provided by the experimenter. Furthermore, the fact that the level of hidden pain varied with the instructions is contradictory to Hilgard's theory that a high level of unconscious pain is present during hypnotic analgesia.

But the results of the Spanos study have by no means resolved the controversy. For example, Nogrady, McConkey, Laurence, and Perry (1983) performed a study that yielded results more favorable to Hilgard's theory. Subjects were first divided into three groups according to their susceptibility to hypnosis. The subjects of high and medium susceptibility were hypnotized and given several tests. The subjects with little susceptibility were not hypnotized before the tests but rather were instructed to *simulate* the behavior of a hypnotized person. The purpose of the simulation group was to assess the extent to which subjects can determine what is wanted from the cues provided by the experimenter. If the subjects simulating hypnosis behave similarly to those who are actually hypnotized, it can be concluded that the experimenter gave sufficient information to elicit the expected response. Such a result does not prove that hypnotized subjects respond as they do because of the cues given, but it does indicate that either hypnosis or the cues could be operating. On the other hand, if the hypnotized subjects behave differently from the simulators, we can conclude that their behavior is not simply a response to the cues.

In one of the tests administered in the Nogrady study, subjects received electric shocks both to the right hand, which had been suggested to be analgesic, and to the left hand, which had not been the subject of any suggestions. This pain test was administered twice, the first time after the hypnotic induction or instructions to simulate hypnosis, the second after hidden-observer instructions were given. In the second test subjects were to report the pain level felt by the hidden observer. Subjects were also asked whether they had experienced different levels of awareness, that is, a hidden observer. An important feature of the Nogrady study was to modify somewhat the hidden-observer instructions in order to give the subjects more leeway. For example, subjects were told that there *may* be another part of them rather than that there *is* another part.

The groups differed significantly in making the hidden-observer response—42 percent of the highly susceptible subjects experienced a hidden observer, but no subject in the other two groups did so! To analyze the pain ratings, the experimenters divided the highly susceptible subjects into two groups according to whether they did or did not have a hidden observer. As can be seen from Table 1.1, only the pain ratings reported by the hidden observers of highly susceptible subjects increased for the analgesic hand following the hidden-observer instructions. Thus on both measures the simulating subjects were not able to mimic the behavior of the highly susceptible subjects.

The conflicting findings of the Spanos and Nogrady studies illustrate well the unresolved argument between investigators who believe that hypnosis does involve some special psychological processes and those who believe that it does not. The effects of paradigm can be clearly seen in the publications of each camp. A pro-Hilgard finding will soon elicit a critical commentary or new experiment from the social-role camp. And findings favoring the social-role interpretation usually elicit rebuttals from researchers favoring the view that in hypnosis special psychological processes do take over. The debate is likely to continue to be a lively one for years to come, and it is doubtful whether either camp will ever be convinced that it is wrong.

TABLE 1.1 Pain Ratings of Subjects of Varying Levels of Hypnotic Susceptibility   *(from Nogrady et al., 1983)*

Group	Analgesic Hand Before Hidden-Observer Instructions	After Hidden-Observer Instructions	Control Hand
High susceptibility			
Hidden observer	3.4	6.2	6.2
No hidden observer	3.6	2.4	8.7
Medium susceptibility	3.9	4.0	8.1
Low susceptibility and simulation	2.8	2.6	6.8

who viewed him as a patient used phrases such as "tight, defensive person," "conflict over homosexuality," and "impulsivity shows through his rigidity."

Why, in this particular experiment, did the behavior therapists appear to be unbiased? Langer and Abelson explain it this way. The behavioral approach encourages clinicians to concentrate on overt or manifest behavior and to be skeptical about illness that is not readily apparent. Those with such an orientation had the advantage in this particular study because, however the interviewee rambled, his behavior on balance was not overtly disturbed. The traditional therapists, on the other hand, had presumably been trained to look beyond what is most obvious in a client. Therefore, when the traditional therapists heard the negative ramblings about bureaucrats, they probably paid too much attention to them and inferred that something was basically wrong with the young man.

Langer and Abelson properly alert readers to the limitations of their experiment, reminding them that a different study—perhaps using an interviewee who is obviously disturbed—might put behavior therapists at a disadvantage. The purpose of the experiment, and this discussion of it, is not to pit one orientation against another but rather to illustrate how a theoretical persuasion can affect perception. Indeed, psychopathology can be in the eye of the beholder.

Thus subjective factors in the guise of theoretical persuasions pervade psychology and very much affect our conception of the nature of abnormal behavior. Scientists, whatever their field, do not resign from the family of human beings when they formulate hypotheses and conduct investigations and controlled research. Perhaps it is especially appropriate for the psychologist-as-scientist to remain aware of this simple, although frequently overlooked, point.

SUMMARY

The study of psychopathology is a search for why people behave, think, and feel in unexpected, sometimes bizarre, and typically self-defeating ways. Much less is known than we would like; this book will focus on the ways in which psychopathologists have been trying to learn the causes of abnormal behavior and what they know about preventing and alleviating it.

A history of the field was provided, indicating its origins in ancient demonology and crude medical theorizing. Since the beginning of scientific inquiry into abnormal behavior, two major points of view have vied for attention: the somatogenic, which assumes that every mental aberration is caused by a physical malfunction; and the psychogenic, which assumes that the sufferer's body is intact and that difficulties are to be explained in psychological terms.

Scientific inquiry was presented as a special way in which human beings acquire knowledge about their world. In a very important sense people see only what they are prepared to see, and certain phenomena may go undetected because scientists can discover only the things about which they already have some general idea. There is subjectivity in science as there is in everyday perception and problem solving.

Hypnosis was reviewed in some detail, both because it occupies an important position in the historical development of the field and because the controversies about hypnosis provide a good example of how the paradigms of science—the sets of basic assumptions that determine the kinds of scientific questions to be asked and the procedures to be used in collecting data—can vary and thus affect the conclusions drawn.

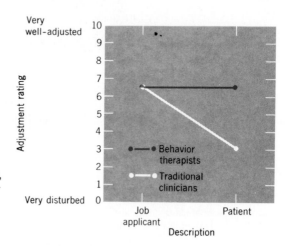

FIGURE 1.2 The mean adjustment ratings given the interviewee, depending on the investigators' description of him and the diagnosticians' training. Adapted from Langer and Abelson, 1974.

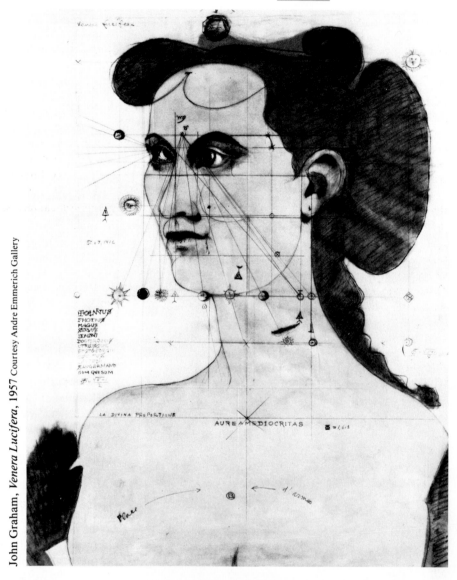

John Graham, *Venera Lucifera*, 1957 Courtesy Andre Emmerich Gallery

CURRENT PARADIGMS
IN PSYCHOPATHOLOGY
AND THERAPY

This chapter is concerned with the principal paradigms or perspectives that have been used to conceptualize abnormal behavior, how it develops, and how best to treat it. Some authors have applied the term model rather than paradigm to these points of view. The term model implies that concepts from one domain, for example, learning theory, are applied to another, such as abnormal psychology, with the expectation that understanding of the second will be increased. Or, as another example, the brain can be thought of as a computer. Adopting a computer model of the brain does not mean that we believe the brain to be a computer, constructed of electronic circuitry, tape decks, and typewriter terminals. Rather, we assume that the *functioning* of the brain might be better understood by likening it to the operation of a computer (Maher, 1966; Price, 1972).

Models are used in various sciences. They are concepts from one domain applied to another.

The term model, however, implies a degree of precision that does not seem to fit the way people have thought about abnormal behavior and its treatment. Instead of formulating models, different investigators have adopted various perspectives, loose sets of general *assumptions* about what should be studied, how to gather data, and how to think about behavior. We shall discuss five major paradigms of contemporary abnormal psychology: the *physiological paradigm*, the *psychoanalytic*, the *learning*, the *cognitive*, and the *humanistic*. The particular postulates of each paradigm cannot be listed item by item. Instead, we shall try to convey the flavor of the five general points of view.

Many people go about the study of abnormal psychology without explicitly considering the nature of the paradigm that they have adopted. But, as this chapter will indicate, the choice of a paradigm has some very important consequences for the way abnormal behavior is defined, investigated, and treated. In fact, our discussion of paradigms will lay the groundwork for the in-depth examination of the major categories of disorder and of intervention that makes up the rest of the book.

THE PHYSIOLOGICAL PARADIGM

What we designate as the physiological paradigm of abnormal behavior is often referred to as the *medical* or *disease model*. We prefer our term for two reasons. First, it has proved difficult to define exactly what is meant by medical model. Second, and more important, arguments about the so-called medical model most often reduce to whether or not behavior is abnormal because of physiological defects.

The Choice of Terms

Let us first examine the prevalent definition of the medical model. As indicated in Chapter 1, the study of abnormal behavior is historically linked to medicine. Many early workers and many contemporaries as well have used the model of physical illness as the basis for defining deviant behavior. Clearly, within the field of abnormal behavior the terminology of medicine is pervasive. As Maher (1966) has noted, "[deviant] behavior is termed *pathological* and is classified on the basis of *symptoms*, classification being called *diagnosis*. Processes designed to change behavior are called *therapies* and are applied to patients in mental *hospitals*. If the deviant behavior ceases, the patient is described as *cured*" (p. 22).

The critical assumption of the medical model is that abnormal behavior may be likened to a disease. To determine how a disease model can be applied to abnormal behavior, we must first examine the concept of disease as it is employed in medicine. During the Dark Ages a disease was thought to consist simply of observable signs and symptoms, such as a rash and high temperature. As medical science, particularly autopsy studies, increased in sophistication, the observable symptoms were attributed to internal malfunctions. Then, when Louis Pasteur discovered the relation between bacteria and disease, and soon thereafter postulated viruses, the *germ theory* of disease provided a new explanation of pathology. External symptoms were assumed to be produced through infection of the body by minute organisms and viruses. For a time this germ theory was the paradigm of medicine. But it soon became apparent that not all diseases could be explained by the germ theory. Diabetes, for example, a malfunction of the insulin-secreting cells of the pancreas, cannot be attributed to infection. Nor does it even have a single cause. As another example, consider heart disease. A multitude of factors—genetic makeup, stress produced by smoking and obesity, type A behavior (see page 180)—are all related to the frequency of heart disease. Is there a single paradigm here?

We think not. Because medical diseases themselves vary in their causes and symptoms, asserting that abnormal behavior can be considered a disease clarifies little (see Box 2.1). But all diseases are disturbances of the body's physiological processes. This is why we have chosen the term physiological paradigm. It is meaningful to say that a behavioral abnormality may be attributed, at least in part, to a disruption in one or more physiological processes.

There is now a considerable literature, both research and theory, dealing with physiological factors relevant to psychopathology. For example, heredity probably predisposes a person, through physiological malfunction, to develop schizophrenia (see Chapter 14). Depression may result from a failure of the usual processes of neural transmission (Chapter 9). Anxiety disorders have been considered to stem from a defect within the autonomic nervous system that causes a person to be too easily aroused (Chapter 6). Other so-called organic brain syndromes can be traced to impairments in structures of the brain (Appendix). In each case a type of psychopathology is viewed as caused by the disturbance of some physiological process. Those working with this paradigm assume that answers to puzzles of psychopathology will be found by concentrating on somatic, that is, bodily, causes.

Physiological Approaches to Treatment

An important implication of the physiological paradigm is that surgery or a drug able to alter bodily functioning may well be effective in treating or even preventing certain abnormalities. Certainly if a deficiency in a particular biochemical substance is found to underlie or contribute to some problem, it makes sense to attempt to correct the imbalance by providing appropriate doses of the deficient chemical. Here there is a clear connection between viewing disorder as physiological defect and attempting to correct the fault through a physiological intervention.

As an example, phenylketonuria (PKU) is a form of mental retardation caused by a genetically determined enzyme deficiency that makes the body unable to metabolize phenylalanine into tyrosine. The prevention of some of these ravages is a successful example of physiological intervention to correct a physiological anomaly. State laws require routine testing of an infant's blood for excess phenylalanine; if the test is positive, a specific diet low in the amino acid is prescribed. Children otherwise doomed to profound mental deficiency can thereby be brought closer to the normal range of intelligence (Chapter 16).

Other physiological interventions in widespread use do not necessarily derive from knowledge of what causes a given disorder in the first place. Again, we are notably short on information about etiology. But the minor tranquilizers, like Valium, can be effective in reducing the tension associated with anxiety disorders. The controversial electroconvulsive shock treatment (ECT) seems to be useful in alleviating severe depression. Neither of these somatic therapies is as yet known to be related meaningfully to possible causes of these disorders, but both are to be regarded as physiological treatments (Chapter 20).

THE PSYCHOANALYTIC PARADIGM

Probably the most widespread paradigm in psychopathology and therapy is the psychodynamic or psychoanalytic, originally developed by Sigmund Freud (1856–1939).

Structure of the Mind

Freud came to divide the mind or the psyche into three principal parts, the *id*, *ego*, and *superego*; each of these are metaphors for specific functions or energies. The id is present at birth and is the part of the personality that

BOX 2.1

CRITICISMS OF THE MEDICAL OR DISEASE MODEL OF ABNORMAL BEHAVIOR

Although we have argued that the term medical model is not very valuable, it is so widely discussed by psychopathologists and clinicians that an overview of some of its problems may be useful. A common criticism of the medical model is that in examining the abnormal behavior of an individual, the clinician has no independent means of verifying the existence of a disease. In medicine both the symptoms and the factors producing them, that is, the disease process, can often be assessed. It is possible, for example, to determine that an individual has a temperature of 104 degrees. Moreover, the particular germ or microorganism that has initiated the processes raising temperature can also be independently determined, say by taking a throat culture and analyzing the foreign organisms present. When a disease model is applied to abnormal behavior, however, it is often not possible to assess independently both the symptoms and the supposed cause of the symptoms. Certain behavior or symptoms are categorized as mental illnesses and given names, but then the name of the illness itself is often cited as an explanation for or cause of these same symptoms. For example, a patient who is withdrawn and hallucinating is diagnosed as schizophrenic; however, when we ask why the patient is withdrawn and hallucinating, we are often told that it is because the patient is schizophrenic. Thus the label schizophrenia is applied to certain behavior and then in addition is specified as a cause of this same behavior. This is a clear example of circular reasoning, something to be avoided in scientific inquiry.

This criticism of the way mental illnesses are assessed is reasonable, but it is not always entirely applicable. Someone holding a medical or disease model point of view could take a somewhat more sophisticated position. He or she could assert that we may make a diagnosis of schizophrenia on the basis of symptoms without claiming that these symptoms are produced by the presence of schizophrenia. This diagnostician would propose that although we do not now know the cause of the symptoms, such knowledge will eventually be forthcoming. Some deviant chemical may eventually be located within schizophrenics and be identified as the cause of the disorder. In sum, the more sophisticated disease modeler may acknowledge that we currently have little information about causes, but that when such information becomes available, it will, in principle, be possible to assess independently both the symptoms and the *etiology* as is the case in medicine.

A second common criticism of applying medical models to abnormal behavior involves an alleged difference between the symptoms of physical illness and the symptoms of mental illness. This argument, most often associated with Thomas Szasz (1960), holds that so-called mental symptoms are a patient's communications about himself and others. When we call such statements symptoms, Szasz

---

accounts for all the energy to run the psyche. It consists of the basic urges for food, water, elimination, warmth, affection, and sex. Freud, trained as a neurologist, regarded the source of all energy of the id as physiological; it is later converted by some means into psychic energy, all of it unconscious, below the level of awareness.

Within the id Freud postulated two basic instincts, Eros and Thanatos. The more important is Eros, which Freud saw as a life-integrating force, principally sexual. The energy of the instinct Eros is called *libido*. Eros, libido, and sexual energy are sometimes indiscriminately equated, but libido and Eros are also occasionally expanded to include all integrative, life-furthering forces, some of which may not be strictly sexual. Thanatos, the death instinct, plays a relatively small role in Freudian thinking, and indeed its energy never received a name.[1]

The id seeks immediate gratification and operates on

what Freud called the *pleasure principle*. When the id is not satisfied, tension is produced, and the id strives to eliminate this tension as quickly as possible. For example, the infant feels hunger, an aversive drive, and is impelled to move about, sucking, in order to reduce the tension arising from the unsatisfied drive. This behavior, called reflex activity, is one means by which the id obtains gratification; it represents the organisms's first commerce with the environment. The other means is *primary process*, generating images of what is desired. The infant who wants its mother's milk imagines the mother's breast and thereby obtains some short-term satisfaction of the hunger drive through its wish-fulfilling fantasy. Even in adult life id impulses remain relatively dissociated from the reality-oriented, adaptational processes of the ego. The id, with its need to reduce and eliminate tension, seeks a state of quiescence, which, perhaps ironically, can be achieved only in death.

The second part of the personality, primarily conscious and called the ego, begins to develop out of the id

[1]One analyst (Wachtel, personal communication, 1983) doubts that Freud ever even used the term. Nowadays people simply refer to an aggressive instinct.

asserts, we are making a judgment within a particular social and cultural context. For example, a patient's belief that he is Christ might be enough for an observer to make a diagnosis of paranoid schizophrenia. Even in this extreme case, however, the diagnosis depends on the observer's disbelieving the patient's assertion. If the observer gives credence to the patient's statement, the behavior will clearly not be judged a symptom of mental illness.

Szasz and his followers also say that the symptoms of mental illness are *subjective*, whereas those of physical illness are *objective*. This assertion has some merit, but the distinction is not as clear-cut as Szasz would have it (Ausubel, 1961b). For example, a patient who has entered a physician's office may complain that he is suffering pain. But because tolerance of pain differs widely among individuals, how can the physician determine the actual amount of pain the patient is experiencing? Although the importance of subjective factors as they enter into the definition of so-called mental illness should not be minimized, distinguishing between mental and physical illnesses on this basis alone is a questionable procedure. Subjective factors appear to be implicated in determining the presence of physical diseases as well, although the exact nature of a medical disorder is likely to be assessed further by objective laboratory tests.

Finally, many people have alleged that so-called mental illnesses have neither a specific etiology nor a specific set of symptoms and thus do not qualify as diseases (for example, Milton and Wahler, 1969). Our knowledge of the etiologies of psychopathologies is indeed extremely limited. As we have indicated, however, the fact that these etiologies have not been uncovered as yet does not mean that we should stop looking for them.

Our failure to define specific sets of symptoms for many categories of deviant behavior may be a more damning criticism. Specific syndromes have simply not been discerned for all psychopathologies. Again, however, a person wishing to maintain a medical model for mental illness may counter this criticism with the following line of reasoning. Many medical diseases do *not* have a set of specific symptoms. Paresis is a good example. Before it was discovered to be infectious, there was considerable debate whether the symptoms had a physical cause or whether paresis should be considered a psychological disturbance. Proponents of the psychological view argued that the symptoms were not entirely consistent from one person to another, for some patients suffer depression rather than delusions of grandeur. Therefore they did not consider paresis a medical disease. Although paresis was indeed found to have a *single* causal agent, the manifestations of its *later* stage may *differ markedly from patient to patient*. Thus even an infectious disease may not necessarily have a homogeneous set of symptoms.

The information just presented indicates that the decision to view abnormal behavior as a medical disease is determined partly by subjective factors. The medical model is subject to many potential criticisms. For each of these, however, there is a possible rejoinder.

in the second six months of life. The ego is the part of the id that is modified by the direct influence of the environment. It must deal with reality and hence often attempts to delay the immediate gratification desired by the id. The ego frowns upon primary process, for fantasy will not keep the organism alive. Through its planning and decision-making functions, called *secondary process*, the ego realizes that operating on the pleasure principle at all times, as the id would like to do, may not be the most effective way of maintaining life. The ego then operates on the *reality principle* as it mediates between the demands of reality and those of the id.

The ego, however, derives all its energy from the id and may be likened to a horseback rider who receives energy from riding the horse. But a real horseback rider directs the horse with his or her own energy, not depending on that of the horse for thinking, planning, and moving. The ego, on the other hand, derives *all* its energies from the id and yet must direct what it is entirely dependent on for energy.

The superego is the third part of the personality, being essentially the carrier of society's moral standards as interpreted by the child's parents. The superego develops through the resolution of the oedipal conflict, to be discussed shortly, and is generally equivalent to what we call conscience. When the id pressures the ego to satisfy its needs, the ego must cope not only with reality constraints but also with the "right-wrong" moral judgments of the superego. The behavior of the human being, as conceptualized by Freud, is thus a complex interplay of three psychic systems, all vying for the achievement of goals that cannot always be reconciled. This interplay of active forces is referred to as the *psychodynamics* of the personality.

Freud was drawn into studying the mind by his work with Breuer on hypnosis and hysteria (see page 21). The apparently powerful role played by factors of which patients seemed unaware led Freud to postulate that much of our behavior is determined by forces that are inaccessible to awareness. Both the id instincts and many of the

(Left) A portrait of Freud at twenty with his fiancée, Martha Bernays. (Below) The room in which Freud saw many of the patients written about in his famous psychoanalytic cases. (Top right page) The ailing Freud sits and works at his desk. (Bottom right page) The Freud family in Vienna, 1896. Standing, left to right: Paula (sister), Anna (sister), unidentified girl, Sigmund, Emmauel (half brother), Rosa (sister), Marie (sister), and Simon Nathanson (cousin). Seated, left to right: Adolfine (sister), Amalie (mother), and Jacob (father). Seated in front: Alexander (brother) and an unidentified boy.

superego's activities are not known to the conscious mind. The ego is primarily conscious, for it is the metaphor for the psychic systems that have to do with thinking and planning. But the ego too has important unconscious aspects, the *defense mechanisms*, which protect it from anxiety; these will also be discussed shortly. Basically, Freud considered most of the important determinants of behavior to be *unconscious*.

Freud saw the human personality as a closed energy system; at any one time there is a fixed amount of energy in the id to run the psychic apparatus. The three parts of the personality therefore battle for a share of a specific amount of energy. Moreover, Freud's theorizing was totally deterministic. Natural scientist that he was, Freud saw every bit of behavior, even seemingly trivial slips of the tongue, as having specific causes, some of them unconscious.

Stages of Psychosexual Development

Freud conceived of the personality apparatus as developing through a series of four separate psychosexual stages. At each stage a different part of the body is the most sensitive to sexual excitation and therefore the most capable of providing libidinal satisfaction to the id. The first is the *oral* stage, during which the infant derives maximum gratification of id impulses from excitation of the sensory endings around the mouth. Sucking and feeding are the principal pleasures. In the second year of life the child enters the *anal* stage as enjoyment shifts to the anus and the elimination and retention of feces. In the *phallic* stage, which extends from age three to age five or six, maximum gratification comes from stimulation of the genitalia. Between ages six to twelve the child is in a *latency* period, which is not considered a psychosexual stage. During these years the id impulses are less intense and do not play a direct role in motivating behavior. The child behaves asexually, although according to Freud's theoretical scheme all behavior is *basically* driven by id impulses. The final and adult stage is the *genital*, during which heterosexual interests predominate.

The manner in which the growing person at each stage resolves the conflicts between what the id wants and what the environment will provide determines basic personality traits which will last throughout the person's life. For example, a person who in the anal stage experiences either excessive or deficient amounts of gratification, depending on his or her toilet-training regimen, and thus does not progress beyond this stage, is called

an *anal personality*. One type, the anal retentive, is considered stingy and sometimes obsessively clean. These traits, appearing throughout life but receiving the greatest attention in adulthood, when people typically consult psychoanalysts, are traced back to early events and to the manner in which gratification was provided or denied the child. Freud referred to this "freezing" of development at an earlier psychosexual stage as *fixation*.

Perhaps the most important crisis of development occurs during the phallic stage, around age four, for then, Freud asserted, the child is overcome with sexual desire for the parent of the opposite sex. Through the threat of dire punishment from the parent of the same sex, he or she may repress the entire conflict, unconsciously pushing it into the unconscious. This desire and repression are referred to as the *Oedipus complex* for the male and the *Electra complex* for the female. The dilemma is usually resolved through increased identification with the parent of the same sex and through the adoption of society's mores, which forbid the child to desire its parent. Through this learning of moral values the superego is developed.

Anxiety and Defense

Freud proposed two different theories of anxiety. In the first formulation, published in 1895, *neurotic anxiety* was regarded as stemming from the blockage of unconscious impulses. Such impulses are blocked, for example, under conditions of extreme sexual deprivation. When repressed they become susceptible to transformation into neurotic anxiety. The first theory did not pay much attention to the circumstances surrounding the repression of an unconscious impulse. In his second theory, proposed in 1926, Freud made more explicit the situations that may cause the individual to repress an unconscious impulse, and he reversed the relationship between neurotic anxiety and repression. According to the first theory, neurotic anxiety develops through repression of impulses. In the second, anxiety about impulses signals the need for their repression. In a sense, according to the first theory we become anxious because we want things that we do not get; according to the second we are anxious because we fear our wants (Wachtel, 1977).

The second theory viewed birth as the prototypic anxiety situation, for the infant is flooded with excitation over which it can exert no control. After the development of the ego in the first year of life, anxiety becomes a signal of impending overstimulation. The person is warned that he or she is in danger of being reduced to an infantile state of helplessness through overstimulation by id impulses and other forces. Anxiety thus plays a functional role, signaling the ego to take action before being overwhelmed.

Three kinds of anxiety were differentiated by Freud, depending on their source. *Objective anxiety* refers to the ego's reaction to danger in the external world, as for example the anxiety felt when life is in real jeopardy. This kind of anxiety is the same as realistic fear. *Moral anxiety*, experienced by the ego as guilt or shame, is really fear of the punishment that the superego imposes for failure to adhere to standards of moral conduct. *Neurotic anxiety* is the fear of the disastrous consequences that are expected to follow if a previously punished id impulse is allowed expression. Neurotic anxiety has its roots in reality anxiety. As Hall (1954) has noted,

Neurotic anxiety is based upon reality anxiety in the sense that a person has to associate an instinctual demand with an external danger before he learns to fear his instincts. As long as instinctual discharge does not result in punishment, one has nothing to fear from [the instincts]. . . . However, when impulsive behavior gets the person into trouble, as it usually does, he learns how dangerous the instincts are. Slaps and spankings and other forms of punishment show the child that impulsive instinctual gratification leads to a state of discomfort. The child acquires neurotic anxiety when he is punished for being impulsive (p. 67).

What must be added is that this conflict between desiring something and fearing that desire *has to be repressed*, or driven out of conscious awareness, before we can properly speak of neurotic anxiety. It is this type of anxiety that will concern us throughout the book, whenever we discuss psychoanalytic theories of disorder and treatment.

Perhaps because Freud's earlier views held that repression of id impulses would create neurotic anxiety, we often hear that Freudians preach as much gratification of impulses as possible, lest a person become neurotic. But this is not the case. For Freudians the essence of neurotic anxiety is repression. Being unaware of conflicts lies at the core of neurotic anxiety, rather than simply being reluctant, unwilling, or unable to reduce the demands of the id. A celibate Catholic priest and a nun, for example, are not considered candidates for neurosis provided they consciously acknowledge their sexual or aggressive tendencies. Such individuals do not have to act on these felt needs in order to avoid neurotic anxiety. They must only remain aware of these needs whenever they vie for expression.

Initially, Freud postulated that traumatic childhood sexual experiences lay behind the neurotic problems of his patients. But by 1897 he came to realize that perverted acts against children would have to be far more prevalent than he was willing or able to assume. He then coupled his patients' reports of such trauma with his own supposition that the unconscious does not distinguish between fact and fantasy. Performing what one commentator has termed a stunning intellectual tour de force (Wachtel, 1977), he proposed that his patients were reporting to him not actual events of their childhood but rather their fantasies. Young children, he assumed, have to deal with intense feelings and longings. Ill-equipped to do so, they are prone to *invent* gratifications. Scientists, wishing to retain certain tenets of their theorizing, can be remarkably creative in adjusting particular aspects of their thinking in order to accommodate newly emerging evidence. By switching from actual events to fantasies, Freud was able to retain early childhood trauma as the central cause of neurotic anxiety.[2]

Forms of Neurotic Anxiety

Neurotic anxiety can be expressed in several ways: as *free-floating anxiety*, as *phobia*, and as *panic reaction*. The stimuli triggering all these expressions of neurotic anxiety are actually internal, stemming from previously punished id impulses. In free-floating anxiety the person appears to be apprehensive nearly all the time, in the absence of reasonable danger. The theory assumes that the person is actually afraid of his own id—which, of course, is always with him. A phobia is an intense irrational fear and avoidance of specific objects and situations, such as kittens, open spaces, closed spaces, and nonpoisonous snakes. The feared objects and situations are hypothesized to be symbolic representations of the object or situation chosen earlier for gratification of the id impulse. That choice and thus the impulse were subsequently punished, and then the whole conflict was repressed. "Behind every neurotic fear there is a primitive wish of the id for the object of which one is afraid" (Hall, 1954, p. 65). Finally, neurotic anxiety may become manifest as a panic reaction, a sudden and inexplicable outburst of severe and prolonged fear.

[2]In recent years investigators have become aware of a greater prevalence of child molestation within families than we perhaps had wanted to consider. It is possible, then, that Freud seriously underestimated incest and may therefore not have needed to alter his theorizing about traumatic childhood sexual experiences to the extent that he did.

Agoraphobia, a fear of crowds, open spaces, and public places, is among the most debilitating of the phobias. Fear of heights is among the most common of the simple phobias.

Defense Mechanisms

According to Freud, the discomfort experienced by the anxious ego can be reduced by several maneuvers. Objective anxiety, rooted in reality, can often be handled by removing or avoiding the danger in the external world, or by dealing with it in a rational way. Neurotic anxiety, and sometimes moral anxiety, may be handled through an unconscious distortion of reality by means of one of the defense mechanisms. A defense mechanism is a strategy, unconsciously utilized, which serves to protect the ego from anxiety. Perhaps the most important is _repression_, whereby impulses and thoughts unacceptable to the ego are pushed into the unconscious. Repression not only prevents awareness but also keeps buried desires from growing up (Wachtel, 1977). By remaining repressed, these infantile memories cannot be corrected by adult experience and therefore retain their original intensity. Another defense mechanism, important in paranoid disorders (see Chapter 14), is _projection_, attributing to external agents characteristics or desires that are possessed by an individual and yet are unacceptable to conscious awareness. For example, a hostile woman may unconsciously find it aversive to regard herself as angry at others and may project her angry feelings onto them; thus she sees others as angry with her. Other defense mechanisms are _displacement_, redirecting emotional responses from a perhaps dangerous object to a substitute, for instance, kicking the cat instead of the boss; _reaction formation_, converting one feeling such as hate into its opposite, love; _regression_, retreating to the behavioral patterns of an earlier age; and _rationalization_, inventing a reason for an action or attitude.[3] All these defense mechanisms allow the ego to discharge some id energy while at the same time not facing frankly the true nature of the motivation. Because defense mechanisms are more readily observed than other symptoms of a disordered personality, they very often make people aware of their troubled natures and persuade them to consult a therapist.

Psychoanalytic Therapy

Since Freud's time the body of psychoanalytic thinking has changed in important ways, but all treatments purporting to be psychoanalytic have some basic tenets in common. Classical psychoanalysis is based on Freud's second theory of neurotic anxiety, that it is the reaction of the ego when a previously punished and repressed id impulse presses for expression (Freud, 1949). The unconscious part of the ego, encountering a situation that reminds it of a repressed conflict from childhood—one usually having to do with sexual or aggressive im-

[3] A psychoanalytic quip defines a rationalization as a _good_ reason for an action—but not the _real_ reason.

pulses—is overcome by debilitating tension. Psychoanalytic therapy attempts to remove the earlier repression and to help the patient face the childhood conflict and resolve it in the light of adult reality. The repression, occurring so long ago, has prevented the ego from growing in an adult fashion; the lifting of the repression is supposed to enable this relearning to take place.

The essence of psychoanalysis has been captured by Paul Wachtel (1977) in the metaphor of the _woolly mammoth_. Some of these gigantic creatures, frozen alive eons ago, have been recovered so perfectly preserved that their meat can actually be eaten. Neurotic problems were considered by Freud to be the encapsulated residue of conflicts from long ago. Present adult problems are merely reflections or expressions of these "frozen" intrapsychic conflicts.

The patient's neurosis is seen as deriving most essentially from his continuing and unsuccessful efforts to deal with internalized residues of his past [the "woolly mammoth"] which, by virtue of being isolated from his adaptive and integrated ego, continue to make primitive demands wholly unresponsive to reality. It is therefore maintained that a fully successful treatment must create conditions whereby these anachronistic inclinations can be experienced consciously and integrated into the ego, so that they can be controlled and modified (Wachtel, 1977, p. 36.)

A number of techniques are employed by analysts in their efforts to lift repressions. Perhaps the best known is _free association_. The patient, reclining on a couch, is encouraged to give free rein to his or her thoughts, verbalizing whatever comes to mind, without the censoring ordinarily done in everyday life. It is assumed that the analysand can gradually learn this skill, and that defenses built up over many years can eventually be bypassed. _Dream analysis_ is another classic analytic technique. Psychoanalytic theory holds that, in sleep, ego defenses are relaxed, allowing normally repressed material to enter the sleeper's consciousness. But since this material is extremely threatening, it usually cannot be allowed into consciousness in its actual form. Rather, the repressed material is disguised, dreams taking on heavily symbolic content. For example, a woman concerned about aggressive sexual advances from men may dream of being attacked by savages who throw spears at her; the spears are considered phallic symbols, substituting for an explicit sexual advance.

"I will, however, say this for Freud—he got a lot of people thinking."

(Drawing by Donald Reilly; © 1983 The New Yorker Magazine, Inc.)

Analysis of defenses, long a focus of psychoanalysis, is emphasized even more by contemporary psychoanalysts, who are sometimes referred to as *ego analysts*. They dispute the relatively weak role that Freud assigned the ego. Defense mechanisms, as we have seen, are the ego's unconscious tools for warding off a confrontation with anxiety. For instance, a man who appears to have trouble with intimacy may look out the window and change the subject whenever anything touches on closeness during the course of a session. The analyst will attempt at some point to offer an *interpretation* of the patient's behavior, pointing out its defensive nature, in hopes of stimulating the patient to acknowledge that he is, in fact, avoiding the topic.

Psychoanalytic treatment has in the past extended over several years, with as many as five sessions a week.[4] Often a distinction is made between psychoanalysis and psychoanalytic psychotherapy, the more contemporary mode of treatment. Sessions of this therapy are not as frequent, nor does the patient as regularly lie down on the proverbial couch. To our mind, however, these procedural changes do not reflect important theoretical differences. Session frequency and body position do not matter. What does is that the patient, with support from the therapist, slowly examines the true sources of tension and unhappiness by a lifting of repression. Psychoanalysis and related therapies are discussed in depth in Chapter 18.

LEARNING PARADIGMS

The Rise of Behaviorism

Before we discuss learning paradigms, it will be helpful to trace briefly the rise of behaviorism. Early twentieth-century psychology was dominated by structuralism, which held that the proper subject of study was mental functioning and structure. The goal of psychology, then a very new discipline, was to learn more about what goes on in the mind by analyzing the elementary constituents making up its contents. To do this, experimental psychologists Wilhelm Wundt (1882–1920), who in Leipzig in 1879 had founded the first formal psychological laboratory and the discipline itself, and Edward Titchener (1867–1927), whose laboratory was at Cornell University, devised elaborate training procedures to teach subjects to report on the most basic aspects to elements of their experiences while being exposed to stimuli. Through painstaking *introspection* subjects would un-

---

[4]It is interesting to note that Freud's psychoanalyses seldom lasted longer than six months.

BOX 2.2

METHODOLOGICAL AND CONCEPTUAL PROBLEMS IN FREUD

Perhaps no investigator of the vagaries of human life has been honored and criticized as much as Freud. During the last years of the nineteenth century and the first years of this, when he was first espousing his views of infantile sexuality, he was personally vilified. At that time sexuality was little discussed among adults. How scandalous, then, to assert that infants and children were also motivated by sexual drives! In the history of science few have shown greater intellectual integrity and personal bravery than Freud.

Because of his very great importance in the field, some current criticisms of his methodology and concepts will be reviewed. Although we attach considerable importance to case reports compiled by clinicians who are "on the front line," clinical reporting by its very nature presents problems that are extremely difficult to avoid. Freud's theorizing, as well as the thinking of the "*Neo-Freudians*," those who have adapted and changed his basic framework, rests primarily on case studies. Like many clinicians, Freud did not take careful notes during his sessions and had to rely almost completely on recollection. The reliability of his perceptions and recollections is impossible to evaluate. Furthermore, the behavior of a listener affects what a speaker has to say. It is possible that Freud's patients were influenced, at least to some degree, to talk about the childhood events that he was most interested in.

The inferential leaps that are made by Freud and other psychoanalysts may be difficult to accept unless one has a prior commitment to the point of view. The distinction between observation and interpretation is sometimes blurred. Consider an example from the analyst Main (1958). "The little boy who babbles tenderly to himself as he soaps himself in his bath does so because he has taken into himself his tender soaping mother." What, in fact, is readily observed by the average onlooker is the child bathing himself. To see his mother incorporated in the soapy bath play is to operate at a very high level of inference. The paradigm problem is once again evident. What we perceive is strongly colored by the paradigm we adopt.

There is considerable disagreement whether Freud's theorizing should be considered scientific, for it is difficult to disprove or prove. Few of the statements are very explicit. If our view of science requires concepts to be measurable, and theories testable, psychoanalytic thinking cannot be regarded as scientific.

Freud's findings do not have general applicability because his sample of patients was very selective and small. Nearly all his patients were from the upper middle class of early twentieth-century Vienna, hardly a representative sampling of human beings. Nonetheless, Freud was prepared to apply his findings to all humankind. In a related vein, after making limited observations, Freud held that a repressed homosexual inclination was the basis for all paranoid disorders. But he never considered, nor for that matter have others who have accepted his point of view, how many paranoids have not had homosexual desires in the past and, indeed, how many people with repressed homosexuality do not develop into paranoids.

Although Freud insisted that he used concepts like id, ego, superego, and the unconscious as metaphors to describe psychic functions, they seem reified, that is, they are made into independent, behavior-determining agents whose own actions must still be explained. For example, Freud spoke of ". . . immediate and unheeding satisfaction of the instincts, such as the id demands. . . . The id knows no solicitude about ensuring survival . . ." (1937). Thus the id "demands" immediate satisfaction and "knows" certain things. In spite of occasional reminders in psychoanalytic writings that these concepts are meant as metaphors, or as summary statements of functions, they are typically written about as though they had an existence of their own and had a power to push things around, to think, and to act.

It should be obvious by now that the authors of this book view the validity and usefulness of Freud's work with some skepticism. On the other hand, it would be a serious mistake to minimize his importance in psychopathology or, for that matter, in the intellectual history of Western civilization. Freud was an astute observer of human nature. Moreover, his work has elicited the kind of critical reaction that helps to advance knowledge. He was instrumental in getting people to consider nonphysiological explanations for disordered behavior. It is impossible to acquire a good grasp of the field of abnormal psychology without some familiarity with his writings.

---

cover the building blocks of experience and the structure of consciousness. For example, Wundt's subjects listened to a metronome, set to click slowly and sometimes to click fast, sometimes sounding only a few times and then many. They decided that a fast series of clicks made them excited, a slow series relaxed. Just before each click they were conscious of a slight feeling of tension and afterward slight relief. After some years many in the field began to lose faith in the ability of this kind of introspection to gather useful knowledge about people.

John B. Watson, American psychologist, who was the major figure in making psychology the study of observable behavior rather than an investigation of subjective experience.

Pavlov's laboratory assistants became aware that the dog began salivating when it saw the person who fed it and then even earlier, when it heard the footsteps of its feeder. Pavlov was intrigued and excited by what his laboratory had happened upon and decided to study the dog's reactions systematically. In the first of many experiments, a bell was rung behind the dog, and then the meat powder was placed in its mouth. After this procedure had been repeated a number of times, the dog began salivating as soon as it heard the bell ring and before meat powder was given.

Since the meat powder automatically elicits salivation, with no prior learning, the powder is termed an *unconditioned stimulus* (UCS) and the response of salivation an *unconditioned response* (UCR). Then when the offering of meat powder is preceded several times by a neutral stimulus, the ringing of a bell (Figure 2.1), the sound of the bell itself (the *conditioned stimulus*, CS) is able to elicit the salivary response (the *conditioned response*, CR). Figure 2.2a is a typical *learning curve*. As the number of paired presentations of the bell and the meat powder increases, the number of salivations elicited by the bell increases. The *extinction curve* in Figure 2.2b indicates what happens to the established CR when the repeated soundings of the bell are later not followed by meat powder: fewer and fewer salivations are elicited, and the CR is extinguished.

Another famous experiment, questionable from an ethical point of view, was conducted by John Watson and Rosalie Rayner (1920). They introduced a white rat to an eleven-month-old boy, Little Albert, who indi-

This dissatisfaction was brought to a head by John B. Watson (1878–1958), who in 1913 revolutionized psychology with statements such as the following:

Psychology as the behaviorist views it is a purely objective experimental branch of natural science. Its theoretical goal is the prediction and control of behavior. Introspection forms no essential part of its methods, nor is the scientific value of its data dependent upon the readiness with which they lend themselves to interpretation in terms of consciousness (p. 158).

To replace introspection, Watson looked to the experimental procedures of the psychologists who were investigating learning in animals. In this way learning rather than thinking became the dominant focus of psychology in the post-Watsonian period. Finding out which stimuli would elicit which directly observable responses was now considered the task of psychology. With such objective S–R information it was hoped that human behavior could be both predicted and controlled.

Classical Conditioning

With the focus of psychology now on learning, a vast amount of research and theorizing was generated. Two types of learning attracted the research efforts of psychologists. The first type, *classical conditioning*, had originally been discovered quite by accident by the Russian physiologist Ivan Pavlov (1849–1936) at the turn of the century. In his studies of the digestive system, a dog was given meat powder to make it salivate. Before long

Ivan P. Pavlov, Russian physiologist and Nobel Laureate, responsible for extensive research and theory in classical conditioning. His influence is still very strong in Soviet psychology.

FIGURE 2.1 The process of classical conditioning. (a) Before learning the meat powder (UCS) elicits salivation (UCR), but the bell (CS) does not. (b) A training or learning trial consists of presentations of the CS, followed closely by the UCS. (c) Classical conditioning has been accomplished when the previously neutral bell elicits salivation (CR).

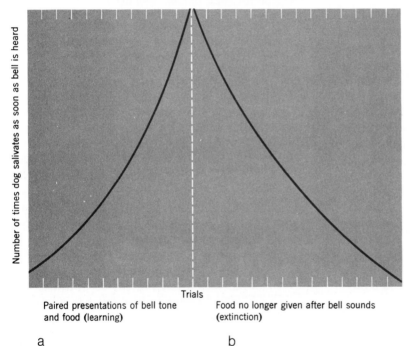

FIGURE 2.2 Classical conditioning: (a) typical learning curve; (b) typical extinction curve.

cated no fear of the animal and appeared to want to play with it. But whenever he reached for the rat, the experimenter made a loud noise (the UCS) by striking a steel bar behind Albert's head, causing him great fright (the UCR). After five such experiences Albert became very disturbed (the CR) by the sight of the white rat, even when the steel bar was not struck. The fear initially associated with the loud noise had come to be elicited by the previously neutral stimulus, the white rat (now the CS). This study suggests the possible relation between classical conditioning and the development of certain emotional disorders, in this instance a phobia.

Operant Conditioning

The second principal type of learning drew primarily on the work of Edward Thorndike (1874–1949), begun in the 1890s. Rather than investigating the association between stimuli as Pavlov was to do, Thorndike was interested in the effect that consequences have on behavior. He had observed that alley cats, angered by being caged and making furious efforts to escape, would eventually and accidentally hit the latch that freed them. Recaged again and again, they would soon immediately and purposely touch the latch. Thorndike formulated what was to become an extremely important principle, the *law of effect*: behavior that is followed by consequences satisfying to the organism will be repeated, and behavior that is followed by noxious or unpleasant consequences will be discouraged. Thus the behavior or response that has consequences serves as an instrument, encouraging or discouraging its own repetition. For this reason learning that focuses on consequences was first called instrumental learning.

B. F. Skinner, perhaps the most influential living psychologist. He is responsible both for the in-depth study of operant behavior and for the extension of experimental findings to American education and society as a whole.

Over fifty years ago Burrhus Frederick Skinner began applying the law of effect to many different aspects of human behavior. He renamed it the principle of *reinforcement*, the word he prefers to consequences. He argues that freedom of choice is a myth and that all behavior is determined by the positive and negative reinforcers provided by the social environment. The goal of Skinner (1953) and the Skinnerians, like that of Watson,

their mentor, is the prediction and control of behavior. These experimenters hope that by analyzing behavior in terms of stimuli, observable responses, and reinforcement, they will be able to determine when certain behavior will occur. The information gathered should then help to indicate how behavior is acquired, maintained, changed, and eliminated. In the Skinnerian approach, often called *operant* because it studies behavior that operates on the environment, abstract terms and concepts are avoided. For example, references to needs, motivation, and wants are conspiciously absent in Skinnerian writings. To provide an entirely satisfactory account of human behavior, Skinner believes that psychology must restrict its attention to directly observable stimuli and responses and to the effects of reinforcement. Psychologists who hold this view do not, as human beings, deny the existence of inner states of mind and emotion. Rather, they urge that investigators not employ such *mediators* in trying to develop a science of behavior.

In a prototypical *operant conditioning* experiment a hungry rat might be placed in a box that has a bar located at one end (the well-known "Skinner box"). Initially the rat will explore its new environment and, by chance, come close to the bar. At this time the experimenter may drop a food pellet into the receptacle located near the bar. After a few such rewards the animal will come to spend more and more time in the area around the bar. But now the experimenter may drop a pellet into the receptacle only when the rat happens to touch the bar. After capitalizing on a few chance touches, the rat begins to touch the bar frequently. With bar touching well established, the experimenter can make the criterion for reward more stringent: the animal must now actually press the bar. Thus the desired operant behavior, bar pressing, is gradually *shaped* by rewarding a series of responses that are *successive approximations*. The number of bar presses increases as soon as they become the criterion for the release of pellets and decreases as soon as the pellet is no longer dropped into the receptacle after a bar press (Figure 2.3).

Modeling

There is a good deal of current interest in yet a third type of learning, *modeling*. We all realize that we learn by watching and imitating others. Experimental work has proved that witnessing someone perform certain activities can increase or decrease diverse kinds of behavior, such as sharing, aggression, and fear. For example, Bandura and Menlove (1968) used a modeling treatment

FIGURE 2.3 (a) Operant conditioning, or instrumental learning, is concerned with the development and maintenance of behavior as a function of its consequences. (b) A typical learning curve, showing increases in responding when the operant behavior is reinforced. (c) A typical extinction curve, showing decreases in responding when the accustomed reward is withheld.

a

Animal produces a motor response ➝ food (reinforcement)

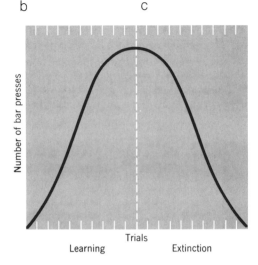

to reduce fear of dogs in children. After witnessing a fearless model engage in various activities with a dog, initially fearful children showed a decided increase in their willingness to approach and handle a dog (see Box 2.3).

Applying Learning Points of View to Deviant Behavior

We are now ready to examine, in general, the application of learning principles to the study of deviant behavior. The crucial assumption of behavioral and learning approaches is that abnormal behavior is learned in the same manner as most other human behavior. This view minimizes the importance of physiological factors. It focuses instead on elucidating the learning processes that supposedly make behavior maladaptive. The gap between normal and abnormal behavior is reduced, since both are viewed within the same general framework; thus a bridge is forged between general experimental psychology and the field of abnormal psychology. Moreover, according to many who have adopted a learning paradigm, abnormality is a *relativistic* concept. Labeling someone or some behavior as abnormal is inextricably linked to a particular social or cultural context. For example, in the United States hallucinating may be one of the grounds for commitment to a mental institution. In some African tribes, however, witch doctors and shamans rely on their trances and visions to help them cure the sick and predict events affecting the welfare of their people.

One very important advantage of applying a learning view in psychopathology is the increased precision of observation. Stimuli must be accurately observed and controlled; the magnitude and rate of responses, and their latency, the rapidity with which they are made, are measured and recorded; and relationships among stimuli, responses, and outcomes are carefully noted. What will be taken to indicate unobservable processes such as fear and thought must be stated explicitly; all such unobservables must be described in terms of their measurable outcomes. Although we judge these and other features of learning approaches to deviant behavior to be extremely advantageous, it is difficult to persuade those not already committed to the paradigm that it is adequate. The learning paradigm of abnormal behavior is in much the same position as the physiological. Just as pertinent physiological malfunctions have not been uncovered, abnormality has not yet been convincingly traced to particular learning experiences, as will be documented in later chapters. Although adopting a learning explanation of abnormal behavior has clearly led to many treatment innovations (see the following section on behavior therapy), the effectiveness of these treatments does not mean that the particular deviant behavior was learned in the first place. The fact that a treatment based on learning principles is effective in changing behavior does not show that the behavior was itself learned in a similar way. For example, if the mood of depressed persons is elevated by providing them with rewards for increased activity, this fact cannot be considered evidence that the depression and apathy were initially produced by an absence of rewards (Rimland, 1964).

Behavior Therapy

In recent years a number of therapeutic techniques have been developed that are an outgrowth of the learning

BOX 2.3

MEDIATIONAL LEARNING PARADIGMS: LITTLE r

By now it should be apparent that there are a number of learning paradigms. Modeling illustrates clearly an important issue, namely the role of mediators in learning and behavior. Consider what happens in the typical modeling experiment. A person watches another do something and immediately shows a change in behavior. No overt responding is necessary for the learning to take place, nor for that matter need the observer be reinforced. Something is learned before the person makes any observable response. Outcomes similar to this one had led learning theorists of the 1930s and 1940s to infer mediators of various kinds in order to explain overt behavior.

In the most general terms, a _mediational_ theory of learning holds that an environmental stimulus does not initiate an overt response directly; rather it does so through some intervening process. This process is conceptualized as an internal response, known affectionately as the little r. Without divorcing themselves from behaviorism, mediational learning theorists adopt the paradigmatic position that, under certain conditions, it is both legitimate and important to go beyond observables. Psychologists, who fondly aspire to the status accorded physicists and chemists, will point out that in these natural sciences ample and effective use is made of supposed entities, like the gluon, which are not directly observed but whose existence is guessed at or inferred in order to make sense of existing data and to encourage the search for new data (see page 95).

Consider the mediational learning analysis of anxiety, as developed by O. Hobart Mowrer and Neal Miller in the late 1930s. In the years after John Watson and Rosalie Rayner had provoked fear in Little Albert, American learning theorists, working mostly with rats, had shown little concern with behavior commonly thought to reflect anxiety. The study of anxiety was at the time more actively pursued by clinicians, particularly Freudians, who of course construed it as the threat of or the flooding of the ego by excessive and worrisome stimulation from impulses. Mowrer (1939) is credited with bringing the study of anxiety into the mainstream of experimental psychology. He suggested that anxiety be considered an internal response which can be learned by means of classical conditioning.

In a typical experiment rats were shocked repeatedly in the presence of a neutral stimulus such as the sound of a buzzer. The shock (UCS) produced a UCR of pain, fear, and flight. After several pairings the fear that was naturally produced by the shock came to be produced by the buzzer, fear being assumed the learnable component of the pain-fear response. It was observed that shock could eventually be omitted, and yet the animal would continue to react fearfully to the previously neutral stimulus (CS). In addition, it was shown (for example, Miller, 1948) that the rat could learn new responses to avoid the CS. The question became how to conceptualize the finding that animals would learn to _avoid_ a harmless event. Mowrer (1947) and others suggested that in this, a typical _avoidance conditioning_ ex-

paradigms. The terms "behavior therapy" and "behavior modification" are applied to them because they were at least initially asserted to be based on the experimentally tested laws of learning formulated by the behaviorists.

Since in mediation theory anxiety is assumed to be classically conditioned, an effective way to eliminate fear is to associate the conditioned stimulus with a nonfearful response. Referred to as _counterconditioning_, this principle of behavior change holds that (see Figure 2.5) a response (R_1) to a given stimulus (S) can be eliminated by eliciting a new response (R_2) in the presence of that stimulus. For example, if a child is afraid of a harmless animal (S), the therapist might attempt to elicit a playful reaction (R_2) in the presence of the animal. Clinical and experimental evidence suggests that this counterconditioning, or substitution of a response, can eliminate R_1.

The counterconditioning principle has played a central role in the innovative thinking of Joseph Wolpe

(1958), who devised a set of behavior therapy techniques which he asserts are effective for the reasons just stated. The most widely used technique is _systematic desensitization_. A person who suffers from anxiety works with

FIGURE 2.5 Schematic diagram of counterconditioning, whereby an original resonse (R_1) to a given stimulus (S) is eliminated by evoking a new response (R_2) to the same stimulus.

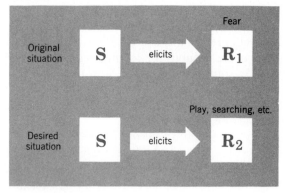

periment, two bits of learning were taking place (Figure 2.4): (1) the animal, by means of classical conditioning, learned to fear the CS, that is, acquired a fear-drive; and (2) the animal, by means of operant conditioning, learned an overt behavior to remove itself from the CS and thus to reduce the fear-drive.

The essential features of this theorizing are that fear or anxiety can be conceived of both as an internal response, which can be learned as observable responses are learned, and as a drive, which can mediate avoidance behavior. Anxiety, then, becomes amenable to the same kind of experimental analysis employed in the investigation of observable behavior. Mowrer and Miller speak of "mediating fear-responses" to point up their assumption that such responses, although inferred, are much the same as overt responses. The knowledge gleaned about overt behavior can therefore, it is hoped, be transferred to the study of mental and emotional life. For instance, if we know that repetition of an overt response without reinforcement leads to the extinction of the response, we can predict that repeated evocation of a fear-response while withholding the expected pain or punishment will reduce the fear. This is no trivial possibility, and indeed, as will be indicated (see page 44), treatments based on such reasoning have helped people become less fearful of animals and of objects and situations that do not merit such reactions.

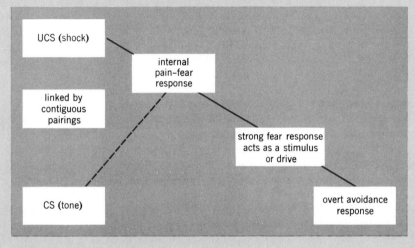

FIGURE 2.4 Schematic representation of Mowrer's account of avoidance learning. The dotted line indicates that the subject is learning to fear the buzzer tone, the solid line that the subject is learning to avoid the shock.

UCS (shock)

linked by contiguous pairings

CS (tone)

internal pain–fear response

strong fear response acts as a stimulus or drive

overt avoidance response

the therapist to compile a list of feared situations, starting with those that arouse minimal anxiety and progressing onward to those that are the most frightening. He or she is also taught to relax deeply. Then step by step, while relaxed, the person imagines the graded series of anxiety-provoking situations. The relaxation tends to inhibit any anxiety that might otherwise be elicited by the imagined scenes. The fearful person becomes able to tolerate increasingly more difficult imagined situations, as he or she climbs the hierarchy over a number of therapy sessions. Clinical and experimental evidence has confirmed that this technique is useful in reducing a wide variety of fears.

The thirty-five-year-old substitute mail carrier who consulted us had dropped out of college sixteen years ago because of crippling fears of being criticized. Earlier, his disability had taken the form of extreme tension when faced with tests and speaking up in class. When we saw him, he was debilitated by fears of criticism in general and of evaluations of his mail sorting in particular. As a consequence, his everyday activities were severely constricted and, though highly intelligent, he had apparently settled for an occupation that did not promise self-fulfillment.

After the client agreed that a reduction in his unrealistic fears would be beneficial, he was taught over several sessions to relax all the muscles of his body while in a reclining chair. We also helped him draw up a list of anxiety-provoking scenes.

You are saying "Good morning" to your boss.

You are standing in front of your sorting bin in the post office, and your supervisor asks why you are so slow.

You are halfway through your route, and it is already 2:00 P.M.

As you are delivering Mrs. Mackenzie's mail, she opens her screen door and complains about how late you are.

Your wife criticizes you for bringing home the wrong kind of bread.

The officer at the bridge toll gate appears impatient as you fumble in your pocket for the correct change.

These and other scenes were arranged in an *anxiety hierarchy*, from least to most fear-evoking. Desensitization proper began with the client being instructed first to relax deeply as he had been taught. Then he was to imagine the easiest item, remaining as relaxed as possible. When he had learned to confront this image without becoming anxious, he went on to the next scene, and so on. After ten sessions the man was able to imagine the most distressing scene in the hierarchy without feeling anxious, and gradually his tension in real life became markedly less.[5]

Another behavioral approach is *assertion training*, which encourages people to speak up and react openly when with others, expressing both their positive and negative feelings. In *aversive "conditioning"* an attractive stimulus is paired with an unpleasant event, such as shock to the fingertips, in hopes of endowing it with negative properties. Aversive techniques, somewhat controversial as might be imagined, have been employed to reduce the socially inappropriate attraction that objects have for some people, such as the irresistible appeal a woman's boots may have for a fetishist.

Several behavioral procedures derive from operant conditioning. For example, children who misbehave in classrooms can be systematically rewarded by the teacher for their socially acceptable behavior while their undesirable behavior is ignored and thus eventually extinguished. The *token economy*, a program established in many mental hospitals to encourage severely disturbed patients to behave more appropriately, is an operant treatment. Explicit rules are set up for obtaining rewards in the form of tokens or other moneylike scrip. At predetermined intervals patients can trade in their tokens for specific reinforcers, such as a visit to the canteen or a more desirable sleeping arrangement.

Modeling has enjoyed increasing attention as a therapeutic intervention. Bandura, Blanchard, and Ritter (1969) were able to help people reduce their phobias of nonpoisonous snakes by having them view both live and filmed close and successful confrontations between people and snakes. In an analogous fashion, some behavior therapists use *role playing* in the consulting room. They demonstrate to a patient patterns of behaving that might prove more effective than those he or she usually engages in and then have the patient practice them. Lazarus (1971), in his *behavior rehearsal* procedures, demonstrates exemplary ways of handling a situation and then encourages the patient to imitate them during the therapy session. For example, a student who does not know how to ask a professor for an extension on a term paper would watch the therapist portray an effective way of making the request. The clinician would then help the student practice the new skill in a similar contrived role-playing situation.

THE COGNITIVE PARADIGM

Cognition is a term that groups together the mental processes of perceiving, recognizing, conceiving, judging, and reasoning. The focus of cognitive psychology is on how people (and animals as well!) *structure* their experiences, how they make sense of them, transforming environmental stimuli into information that is usable. At any given moment we are bombarded by far more stimuli than we can possibly respond to. How do we filter this overwhelming input, put it into words or images, form hypotheses, and arrive at a perception of what is out there? Cognitive psychologists consider the learning process to be much more complex than passively forming new stimulus-response associations. They regard the learner as aware and actively interpreting a situation in the light of what has been acquired in the past, as imposing a perceptual funnel on experience, so to speak. The learner fits new information into an organized network of already accumulated knowledge, often referred to as a *schema* (Neisser, 1976). New information may fit or, if not, the learner reorganizes the schema to the necessary extent.

Contemporary experimental psychology is very much concerned with cognition. The following illus-

---

[5]Unreferenced case reports such as this one have been drawn from our own clinical files. Identifying features are changed to protect the confidentiality of the individual.

trates how a schema or *cognitive set* may alter the way information is processed and remembered.

The man stood before the mirror and combed his hair. He checked his face carefully for any places he might have missed shaving and then put on the conservative tie he had decided to wear. At breakfast, he studied the newspaper carefully and, over coffee, discussed the possibility of buying a new washing machine with his wife. Then he made several phone calls. As he was leaving the house he thought about the fact that his children would probably want to go to that private camp again this summer. When the car didn't start, he got out, slammed the door and walked down to the bus stop in a very angry mood. Now he would be late (Bransford and Johnson, 1973, p. 415.)

Now read the excerpt again, but add the word "unemployed" before the word "man." Now read it a third time, substituting "stockbroker" for "man." Notice how differently you understand the passage. Ask yourself what parts of the newspaper these men read. If this query had been posed on a questionnaire, you might have answered "the want ads" for the unemployed man, "the financial pages" for the stockbroker. In actual fact, the passage does not specify which part of the paper was read. Your answers would have been erroneous, but in each instance the error would have been a meaningful, predictable one.

Cognitive psychologists study how we acquire, store, and use information. Strict behaviorists, those who follow Skinner in describing behavior in terms of openly observable events, cannot accept cognitive explanations. Cognitive psychologists have until recently paid little systematic attention to how their research findings bear on psychopathology or how they might help generate effective therapies. Now cognitive explanations come up more and more often in the search for the causes of abnormality and for new methods of intervention. A widely held view of depression, for example, places the blame on a cognitive set, the individual's overriding sense of helplessness (see page 201). Many who are depressed supposedly believe themselves to have no important effect on their surroundings, regardless of what they do. Their destiny seems to them out of their hands. If depression does develop through a sense of helplessness, this fact would have implications for how clinicians might treat the disorder.

Some clinicians assert that cognitive theorizing is nothing more than a mediational stimulus-response analysis of behavior (for example, Wolpe, 1980), similar

to the historically important contributions of Mowrer and Miller. We would disagree. A cognitive explanation of behavior is *fundamentally different* from a "little r" analysis. The mediational researcher asserts than an environmental stimulus automatically evokes an internal mediational response, which is subject to the same reinforcement principles as are overt responses. The cognitive researcher, in contrast, does not conceptualize perception or thinking as a little response. Rather, this worker focuses on how people actively interpret environmental stimuli, and how these transformed stimuli affect behavior. Reinforcement plays a minor role in the theorizing of cognitive psychologists (Davison, 1980).

Cognitive Behavior Therapy

The cognitive point of view has recently gained widespread attention in behavior therapy. Generally speaking, cognitively oriented behavior therapists attempt to change the thinking processes of their patients in order to influence their emotions and behavior. The following is an early example of *cognitive restructuring* (Davison, 1966).

A man had been diagnosed as paranoid schizophrenic, primarily because of his complaints of "pressure points" on his forehead and other parts of his body. He believed that these pressure points were signals from outside forces helping him to make decisions. These paranoid delusions had been resistant to drug treatment and other psychotherapeutic approaches. The behavior therapist, in examining the man's case history, hypothesized that the patient became very anxious and tense when he had to make a decision, that his anxiety took the form of muscular tension in certain bodily parts, and that the patient misconstrued the tension as "pressure points," signals from helpful spirits. Both patient and therapist agreed to explore the possibility that the pressure points were in fact part of a tension reaction to specific situations. For this purpose the therapist decided to teach the man deep-muscle relaxation, with the hope that relaxation would enable him to control his tensions, including the pressure points.

But it was also important to have the man question his delusional system. So in the first session the therapist asked the patient to extend his right arm, clench his fist, and bend his wrist downward so as to bring the fist toward the inside of the forearm. The intent was to produce a feeling of tension in his forearm; this is precisely what happened, and the man noted that the feeling was quite similar to his pressure points.

Extensive relaxation training enabled the client to begin to control his anxiety in various situations within the hospital and at the same time to reduce the intensity of the pressure points. As he gained control over his feelings, he gradually came to refer to his pressure points as "sensations," and his conversation in general began to lose its earlier paranoid flavor.

The relaxation training apparently allowed the patient to test a nonparanoid hypothesis about his pressure points, to see it confirmed, and thereby to shake off a belief about these sensations that had contributed to a diagnosis of paranoia.

A prominent cognitive therapist, Albert Ellis (1962), holds that maladaptive feelings and activity are caused by "*irrational beliefs.*" Through mistaken assumptions people place excessive demands on themselves. A man who believes that he must always be perfect in everything he does feels terrible whenever he makes a mistake. A woman may think "I should be able to win the love and approval of everyone" and then exhaust herself trying to please others. Ellis and his followers, the so-called "*rational-emotive* therapists," help their patients to challenge such assumptions and teach them to substitute ideas like "Although it would be terrific never to make a mistake, that doesn't mean I *have* to be without fault."

Learning Paradigms and Cognitive Paradigms

It is a matter of great controversy whether to regard cognitive points of view as basically different and separate from the learning paradigms. Much of what we have just said suggests that we should. But the growing field of "cognitive behavior therapy" gives us pause, for here workers study the complex interplay of beliefs, expectations, perceptions, and attitudes on the one hand and overt behavior on the other. For example, Albert Bandura (1977), a leading advocate of changing behavior through cognitive means, argues that a parsimonious way of explaining how different therapies work their im-

provement is that they increase people's sense of self-efficacy, a belief that they can achieve desired goals (see page 517). *But* at the same time he argues that changing behavior, through behavioral techniques, is the most powerful way to enhance self-efficacy. People like Ellis, by way of contrast, emphasize direct alteration of cognitions through argument, persuasion, Socratic dialogues, and the like, in order to bring about improvements in emotion and behavior. Complicating matters still further, Ellis and his followers also place considerable importance on homework assignments requiring clients to behave in ways that they, presumably blocked by negative thoughts, have been unable to heretofore. Indeed, therapists identified with cognitive behavior therapy work at both the cognitive and behavioral levels, and most of those who employ cognitive concepts and try to change beliefs with verbal means also employ behavioral procedures to alter behavior directly.

Whatever their differences in theory and practice, behavior therapists and cognitive therapists are alike in allying themselves philosophically with their colleagues in experimental psychology. For this reason these approaches are regarded by some (for example, Davison and Goldfried, 1973; Goldfried and Davison, 1976) not as a set of techniques but rather as a particular epistemological stance, one which demands rigorous standards of proof. Specific techniques, it is assumed, will be revised as new research uncovers better ways of altering and preventing abnormality. The implications of this emphasis on experimental research and methodology will become clearer when behavior therapy and its cognitive variations are discussed in depth in Chapter 19.

THE HUMANISTIC PARADIGM

Reacting against the dominance of psychology and psychiatry by psychoanalytic and behavioristic views, Abraham Maslow (1908–1970) began exhorting his colleagues of the 1950s to work toward the development of a "third force" in the study of human behavior (Maslow, 1968). Maslow had a much more positive opinion of human nature and potential. He held that the individual is basically sound, whole, healthy, and unique, with an innate drive for growth and *self-actualization*; that humankind is by nature active, resourceful, purposive, and good; that human suffering comes from denial of this basic goodness.

Consider what the paradigm—known variously as

humanistic psychology, existential analysis,[6] the human potential movement, and the personal growth movement—says in contrast to the psychoanalytic and behavioral views already examined. The psychodynamic paradigm assumes that human nature, the id, is something in need of restraint, that effective socialization requires the ego to mediate between the environment and the basically antisocial, or at best asocial, impulses stemming from physiological urges. The behavioral point of view, in considering environmental contingencies of activity—reward and punishment—to be the major determinants of effective and normal behavior, stresses the social consequences of beliefs and actions. In contrast, Carl Rogers (1951), a leading figure in humanistic psychology, asserts that the developing personality goes astray when it concerns itself with the evaluations and expectations of others instead of following its own innate drive for self-fulfillment.

The phenomenological world of individuals is of utmost importance to the humanists. They regard each of us as having an internal frame of reference which is the product of the totality of earlier experiences. This subjective universe renders each of us unique and gives each of us our own truth. To contact one another, each human being must attempt to view the world through the perspective of the other person. As for immediate behavior, it is guided by the experienced stimulus rather than the external stimulus. A person's actions—in fact entire existence—are decided by the way he or she experiences the world at any given moment.

Finally, the humanistic view reflects an abiding belief in free will. Human beings possess freedom of choice; they initiate action instead of being passively influenced by the environment or driven by internal id impulses. The freedom-determinism issue is an exceedingly complex one, running through philosophy, literature, psychology, and politics.

Existential Neurosis

Although the disorder is not formally recognized in the current diagnostic classification scheme (DSM-III, to be presented in Chapter 3), clinicians have noticed what they call an *existential neurosis*. They attribute it to an inability to exert free will and to seek fulfillment. The essence of existential philosophy, as of humanistic psychology, is that people are responsible for their lives and realize their existence the most fully by making choices. Maddi (1967) has described the neurosis.

The cognitive component of the existential neurosis is meaninglessness or chronic inability to believe in the truth, importance, usefulness, or interest value of any of the things one is engaged in or can imagine doing. The most characteristic [emotional] features . . . are blandness and boredom, punctuated by periods of depression which become less frequent as the disorder is prolonged. As to the realm of action, activity level may be low to moderate, but more important than the amount of activity is the introspective and objectively observable fact that activities are not chosen. There is little selectivity, it being immaterial to the person what if any activities he pursues. If there is any selectivity shown, it is in the direction of ensuring minimal expenditures of effort and decision making (p. 313).

Maddi suggests that even before the individual suffers from existential neurosis, he or she has developed a *premorbid personality*, a way of behaving that predisposes the individual to the disorder. Such a person satisfies the physiological needs of the body quite adequately—eating, drinking, keeping warm, and avoiding physical danger—and plays social roles, perhaps very well indeed. These talents are important, as Maddi hastens to point out. People whose lives consist *only* of these acquired skills, however, are candidates for existential neurosis, for they have merely "gone along with" society instead of creating a personal destiny. Such people will feel a great sense of emptiness and lack of fulfillment, *in spite of the fact that they may be extremely effective in satisfying society's demands in every possible way.* Conditions of stress—for example, the imminence of death or a gross disruption in the social order, such as war or an economic depression—can trigger the onset of the neurosis itself.

Maddi suggests further that children can be "taught" to become premorbid existential neurotics if they are valued and rewarded only for their ability to satisfy their physiological needs and to assume society's social roles. For a healthier development they should be encouraged to make independent decisions based on some system of values, which may be shared by other people, and to have an active internal life, which they can maintain whatever happens in the external world.

Humanistic Therapy

The humanistic paradigm holds that therapists should help people to get in touch with their inner selves, with

---

[6]Although often grouped together, humanistic and existential approaches are in fact different in some respects. The subtleties are spelled out in Chapter 18 (page 489).

their true feelings, and to learn to express them without undue concern for what others think. The most prevalent and best-developed form of humanistic therapy is the *client-centered* approach of Carl Rogers. The person seeking therapy is regarded as client rather than patient and becomes responsible for much of his or her own treatment. Consistent with the view that a mature and well-adjusted person chooses what is innately satisfying and actualizing, therapists do not impose goals on their clients. Rather they create conditions during the therapy hour, conditions which enable clients to discover their own basic natures and make their own judgments about what they need, what they want, and how they might maintain and enhance themselves. True to the humanist's positive view of people, the decisions reached by clients are assumed to be good ones.

Pathology supposedly results from undue sensitivity to the judgments of others and a denial of the individual's own nature. People come to adopt negative, limiting attitudes toward themselves and do not remain open to experiences. The basic tool of the client-centered therapist is therefore *unconditional positive regard*, that is, complete and unqualified acceptance and respect for the client's feelings and actions. Through skillful inquiry and attentive listening, the therapist helps clients uncover, clarify, and express their deepest concerns and conflicts. Gradually clients learn to talk in a more honest and emotional way about themselves and thereby gain access to their basically healthy inner natures.

Rogers and other humanistic therapists believe that people must take responsibility for themselves, even when they are troubled. It is often difficult for a therapist to refrain from giving advice, from taking charge of a client's life, especially when the client appears incapable of making his or her own decisions. But workers like Rogers hold steadfastly to the rule that an individual's innate capacity for growth and self-direction will assert itself provided the therapeutic atmosphere is warm, attentive, and receptive. Indeed, if the therapist steps in, the process of growth and self-actualization will only be thwarted. Whatever short-term relief might come from the therapist's intervening will sacrifice long-term growth. The therapist must not become yet another person whose wishes the client strives to satisfy.

Humanistic therapists tend to de-emphasize techniques, but most of them utilize *empathy*. In the following excerpt a Rogerian therapist tries to enter the phenomenological universe of the client and view her complaint from her own frame of reference. He then restates what she has expressed in order to help her clarify her thoughts and feelings—and also to be perceived as someone who understands and cares.

Client: I just can't stand not knowing what Fred's feelings are. Is he really involved with me, or is he just stringing me along?

Therapist: I can see how frustrating it is for you not to know how Fred feels about you, how he views the relationship.

This reflection of feeling is not a simple parroting of the client's words. Rather, the therapist attempts to extract the essence of what she is trying to express—sometimes a feeling only hinted at—and then communicates her concerns back to her, in hopes that she will better understand and acknowledge what is truly at issue. Gradually, encouraged by the empathic acceptance of the therapist, she should gain the self-confidence to listen to feelings from within, which she has shut off as not part of herself.

CONSEQUENCES OF ADOPTING A PARADIGM

The student of abnormal behavior who adopts a particular paradigm necessarily makes a prior decision concerning what kinds of data will be collected and how they will be interpreted. Thus he or she may very well ig-

Carl Rogers (second from right), developer of client-centered therapy, leading a group therapy session.

nore possibilities and overlook other information in advancing what seems to be the most probable explanation. A behaviorist is prone to attribute the prevalence of schizophrenia in lower-class groups to the paucity of social rewards that these people have received, the assumption being that normal development requires a certain amount and patterning of reinforcement. A physiologically oriented theorist will be quick to remind the behaviorist of the many deprived people who do *not* become schizophrenic. The behaviorist will undoubtedly counter with the argument that those who do not become schizophrenic had different reinforcement histories. The physiologically oriented theorist will reply that such *post hoc* or after-the-fact statements can always be made.[7]

Our physiological theorist may suggest that certain biochemical factors that predispose both to schizophrenia and to deficiencies in the intellectual skills necessary to maintain occupational status account for the observed correlation between social class and schizophrenia. The behaviorist will be entirely justified in reminding the physiological theorist that these alleged factors have yet to be found, to which the physiological theorist might rightfully answer, "Yes, but I'm placing my bets that they are there, and if I adopt *your* behavioral paradigm, I may not look for them." To which the learning theorist may with justification reply, "Yes, but *your* assumption regarding biochemical factors makes it less likely that you will look for and uncover the subtle reinforcement factors that in all likelihood account for both the presence and the absence of what you call schizophrenia."

The fact that our two colleagues are in a sense correct and in another sense incorrect is at the same time both exasperating and exciting. They are both correct in asserting that certain data are more likely to be found through work done within a particular paradigm. But they are incorrect to become unduly agitated because each and every social scientist is not assuming that one and the same factor will ultimately be found crucial in the development of all mental disorders. Abnormal behavior is much too diverse to be explained or treated adequately by any of the current paradigms (see Box 2.4). As we subsequently examine various categories of psychopathology, we will find substantial differences in the extent to which physiological and learning paradigms are applicable. As for future discoveries, it is well that psychologists do *not* agree on which paradigm is the *best*. We know far too little to make hard-and-fast decisions on the exclusive superiority of any one paradigm, and there is enough important work to go around. And we will often see that a plausible way of looking at the data is to assume multiple causation. A particular disorder may very well develop through an interaction of physiological defects and environmental factors, a view we turn to next.

Diathesis-Stress: A Proposed Paradigm

A general point of view, one which meaningfully links both physiological and environmental factors, does in fact guide our own search for answers. Termed the *diathesis-stress* approach, it considers the often subtle interaction between a *predisposition* toward disease—the diathesis—and environmental, or life, events disturbing people—the stress. Diathesis refers most precisely to a constitutional predisposition toward illness, but the term may be extended to any tendency or inclination a person may have to respond in a particular way to an environmental stress. The cognitive set already mentioned, the chronic feeling of helplessness sometimes found in the depressed, may be considered a diathesis for depression.

It is a fact that some break down in certain ways when exposed to certain stressors, whereas others come through even more terrible trauma apparently unscathed. Certain people have, for example, inherited a physiological predisposition that places them at high risk for schizophrenia (see Chapter 14). Given a certain amount of stress, they are so physiologically constituted that they stand a good chance of becoming schizophrenic. Other people, those at low risk, are not likely to develop schizophrenia, regardless of how difficult their lives are.

[7]The behavioral concept of *reinforcement history* poses an interesting dilemma for those sympathetic to any of the learning paradigms. It is invariably invoked whenever a given individual's development is to be explained or when differences between people raised in apparently the same environment are to be accounted for. For example, if identical twins reared by their natural parents become schizophrenic later in life, the clinician holding a learning view will usually assert that they had similar reinforcement histories. When fraternal twins—they do not develop from the same egg and can be so physically unlike that they are of different genders—are raised at home and only one becomes schizophrenic, the learning "explanation" is that their reinforcement histories were different. Such explanations are as circular and as unsatisfactory as the psychoanalyst's inference of unconscious processes, a practice deplored by behaviorists. And with good reason. Neither hypothesis explains anything, nor does either encourage the search for new data.

BOX 2.4

ECLECTICISM IN PSYCHOTHERAPY: PRACTICE MAKES IMPERFECT

A word is in order about paradigms and the activities of therapists. The several types of treatment have been presented as though they were practices of separate, nonoverlapping schools of therapy. The impression may have been conveyed that a behavior therapist would never listen to a client's report of a dream, nor would a psychoanalyst be caught dead prescribing assertion training to a patient. Such suppositions could not be farther from the truth. Most therapists describe themselves as *eclectics*, workers who employ ideas and techniques from a variety of schools (Garfield and Kurtz, 1974). Therapists often behave in ways that are not entirely consistent with the theories they might hold. For years practicing behavior therapists have listened empathically to clients, trying to make out their perspectives on events, on the assumption that this understanding would help them plan a better program for changing troublesome behavior. Behavioral theories do not prescribe such a procedure, but on the basis of clinical experience, and perhaps through their own humanity, be-

havior therapists have realized that empathic listening helps them in establishing rapport, in determining what is really bothering the client, and in planning a sensible therapy program. By the same token, Freud himself is said to have been far more directive and done far more to change immediate behavior than would be concluded from his writings alone. And today especially, psychoanalysts are paying more attention to overt behavior and the relieving of symptoms than analytic theory would lead them to do. Some contemporary writers, like Paul Wachtel (see page 524), even propose that analysts employ behavior therapy techniques, openly acknowledging that behavior therapy has something to offer in the alleviation of behavior pathology.

These are weighty issues; the final section of this textbook will give them the attention they need and deserve. The reader should be aware of this complexity at the beginning, however, and be spared misconceptions about the intricacies and realities of psychotherapy.

Different Perspectives on a Clinical Problem

It will be useful to recall now the case of the policeman with which this book began. The material provided is open to a number of interpretations, depending on the paradigm adopted. For instance, if you hold a physiological point of view, you will be attentive to the similarity between the man's alternately manic and depressed states and the cyclical swings of mood suffered by his father. For you are mindful of the research (to be reviewed in Chapter 9) that suggests a genetic factor in bipolar affective disorder. You do not, however, discount environmental contributions to his problems, but you hypothesize that some inherited, probably biochemical, defect predisposes him to break down under stress. After all, not everyone who experiences a difficult childhood and adolescence develops the kinds of problems Ernest H. has. For treatment you may prescribe lithium carbonate, a drug which many consider helpful in reducing the magnitude of mood swings in manic-depression.

Now suppose that you are committed to a cognitive-behavioral perspective, which encourages you to analyze human behavior in terns of reinforcement patterns as well as cognitive variables. You may focus on Ernest's self-consciousness at college, which seems related to the fact that, compared to his fellow students, he had grown

up with few advantages. Economic insecurity and hardship may have made him unduly sensitive to criticism and rejection. Moreover, he regards his wife as warm and charming, pointing up his own perceived lack of social skills. Alcohol has been his escape from such tensions. But heavy drinking, coupled with persistent doubt about his own worth as a human being, has interfered with sexual functioning, worsening an already deteriorating marital relationship. As a behavior therapist, you may employ systematic desensitization. You teach Ernest to relax deeply as he imagines a hierarchy of situations in which he is being evaluated by others. Or you may decide on rational-emotive therapy, to convince Ernest that he need not obtain universal approval for every undertaking. Or, given Ernest's deficiency in social skills, you may choose behavior rehearsal in order to teach him how to function effectively in social situations in which he has had little experience. His sexual problems might be breached via a Masters and Johnson therapy program of undemanding but increasingly more intimate sexual encounters with his wife.

A psychoanalytic point of view will cast Ernest H. in yet another light. Believing that events in early childhood are of great importance in later patterns of adjustment, you may hypothesize that Ernest has blamed his father for his mother's early death. Such strong anger at the father has been repressed, but Ernest has not been

BOX 2.5

WHAT IS ABNORMAL?

The various paradigms that we have discussed all make some guiding assumption about the nature of abnormal behavior. They do not, however, explicitly define it. The physiological paradigm, for example, asserts that physiological processes make people behave abnormally, and the learning paradigms blame unfortunate experiences. But these paradigms do not tell us exactly what abnormal behavior is. Can we draw a clear-cut distinction between normal and abnormal? Can we offer a satisfactory definition of abnormality?

To address these questions, let us consider some definitions that have been proposed. We will see that no single one is adequate. Each has merit and captures some part of what might be the full definition. But each by itself has too many exceptions to be considered acceptable.

One definition of abnormal behavior is that it is statistically infrequent. Those who adopt the statistical approach measure specific characteristics of people, such as personality traits and ways of behaving, and the distribution of these characteristics in the population. One type of population distribution, the *normal curve* (Figure 2.6), depicts the majority of people as being in the middle as far as any particular characteristic is concerned: that is, very few people fall at either extreme. An assertion that a person is normal implies that he or she does not deviate much from the average in a particular trait or behavior pattern. For example, if we take anxiety as one dimension of abnormality, persons who are ''average'' in anxiety level will be considered normal. In contrast, people who are extremely anxious and people who suffer little or no anxiety will be considered abnormal. Statistical infrequency is used explicitly in diagnosing mental retardation. Figure 2.6 gives the normal distribution of intelligence in the population. When an individual's intelligence quotient is below 70,* intelligence functioning is considered sufficiently subnormal to be designated as mental retardation.

Although much infrequent behavior indeed strikes us as abnormal, in some instances the relationship breaks down. Having great athletic ability is infrequent but not abnormal in the sense implied here. Only certain infrequent behavior, such as being subject to hallucinations or deep depression, falls into the domain considered in this book. Unfortunately, the statistical definition gives us no guidance in determining what infrequent behavior psychopathologists should study.

Another definition of abnormality invokes the notion of personal suffering: people are to be judged abnormal if their behavior creates great distress and torment in themselves. As with the statistical approach, this definition fits many of the forms of abnormality we consider in this book.

People with anxiety disorders and depression truly suffer greatly. But some disorders clearly do not cause acute distress. The sociopath, for example, treats others callously and may continually violate the law without experiencing any guilt, remorse, or anxiety whatsoever. Another difficulty personal discomfort has as a defining characteristic is that it is inherently subjective. People decide and report on how much they are suffering. The degrees of their distress are difficult to compare, since their standards for defining their own psychological states can vary greatly.

Finally, some writers have proposed that abnormal behavior is whatever violates social norms and threatens or makes anxious those observing it. Again, this definition rings true, at least partially. Now the sociopath's callousness fits the definition, as do the sometimes wild behavior of a manic and the strange antics of a schizophrenic. The definition also has the advantage of explicitly making abnormality a relative concept; various forms of unusual behavior can be tolerated, depending on the prevailing cultural norms. But the definition is also at once too broad and too narrow. Criminals and prostitutes, who violate social norms, are usually not studied within the domain of abnormal psychology. The highly anxious person, who is generally regarded as a central character in the field, would not be noticed by many lay observers.

Our position is that no current definition of abnormal behavior is fully satisfactory. Over the years a number of the categories of abnormal behavior that appear in official diagnostic manuals have changed, but not because any particular definition of abnormal behavior was adopted. Rather, norms and values have shifted. Over the last century, for example, more and more people have decided that their psychological problems warranted professional help. With this increased flow of patients, therapists and researchers saw problems that were new to them, and new diagnoses emerged. What we present in a text such as this is a list of conditions that are currently thought to be abnormal. The disorders in the list will undoubtedly change with time.

FIGURE 2.6 The distribution of intelligence among adults, illustrating a normal or bell-shaped curve.

*Although low intelligence is a principal criterion for defining mental retardation, other diagnostic features must also be considered.

able to regard him as a competent, worthwhile adult and to identify with him. Fixation at the oedipal stage of psychosexual development may have made Ernest anxious about authority and kept him from functioning as an adult male. For treatment you may choose dream analysis and free association to help Ernest lift his repressions and deal openly and consciously with his hitherto buried anger toward his father.

If you are a humanist, you will say that Ernest H. has consistently chosen not to follow his inner feelings, his basic nature, and that his pattern of seeking security rather than self-expression has caused his current difficulties and frustrations. He did not follow his inclination to attend law school, but rather became a policeman in order to obtain the instant respect accorded a uniform. He thought about having a child as something he *should* do at the age of thirty-two and thus transformed his sexual relationship into one of duty rather than self-expression. These failures to follow his authentic feelings ended in accusations, frustration, and an explosive outburst. In your sessions with Ernest, you will try to help him trust his innermost feelings and take chances in pursuing his own life goals rather than acting only to counter fear and social pressures. Your empathic listening will help Ernest to uncover his own needs and to decide for himself what he wants out of life.

SUMMARY

This chapter has reviewed the major paradigms, or points of view, that are current in the study of psychopathology and therapy. The *physiological* paradigm assumes that psychopathology is caused by an organic defect. Previous discussions of this point of view have taken the form of arguments, pro and con, about a "medical" or "disease" model. But an examination of the meaning of the term medical model reveals that it is actually too vague about etiology to enjoy the status of a formal model of psychopathology. The medical model does have one implication—that psychopathology may be attributed to physiological malfunctions and defects. Therefore we have proposed instead the physiological paradigm. Physiological therapies attempt to rectify the specific organic defects underlying disorders or to alleviate symptoms of disorders that have not been traced to such defects.

Another paradigm derives from the work of

Sigmund Freud. The *psychoanalytic* point of view directs our attention to repressions and other unconscious processes that are traced to early childhood conflicts. Whereas present-day ego analysts who are part of this tradition place greater emphasis on conscious ego functions, the psychoanalytic paradigm has generally searched the unconscious and early life of the patient for the causes of abnormality. Therapeutic interventions based on psychoanalytic theory usually attempt to lift repressions so that the analysand can examine the infantile and unfounded nature of his or her fears.

Behavioral, or *learning*, paradigms suggest that aberrant behavior has developed through classical conditioning, operant conditioning, or modeling. More recently, *cognitive* points of view that blame schemata and interpretations for abnormality have been espoused and often blended with the behavioral. Investigators who believe that abnormal behavior may have been learned share a commitment to examine carefully all situations affecting behavior, as well as to define concepts carefully. Behavior therapists try to apply learning and cognitive principles to the direct alteration of overt behavior, thought, and emotion. Less attention is paid to the historical causes of abnormal behavior than to what maintains it, such as the reward and punishment contingencies encouraging problematic response patterns. Finally, the *humanistic* paradigm assumes that humankind is by nature good and that psychopathology develops from a blockage or denial of this innate worthiness. Therapists encourage clients to discover and trust their inner true selves and to express their needs and impulses.

The *diathesis-stress* paradigm is one that may integrate the most applicable feature of several points of view. People are assumed disposed to react inadequately to particular environment stresses. The diathesis may be constitutional, as appears to be the case in schizophrenia, or it may be extended to the psychological, for example, the chronic sense of helplessness considered a factor contributing to depression.

The most important implication of paradigms is that they determine where and how investigators look for answers. Paradigms necessarily limit their perceptions of the world, for investigators will interpret data differently according to their points of view. In our opinion it is fortunate that workers are not all operating within the same paradigm, for at this point too little is known about psychopathology and its treatment to settle on any one of them.

Joseph Cornell, *Medici Slot Machine*, 1942 Private Collection

CLASSIFICATION AND DIAGNOSIS

DSM-III—The Diagnostic System
   of the American Psychiatric Association
Issues in the Classification of Abnormal Behavior

By the end of the nineteenth century, medicine had progressed far beyond the stage it had been in during the Middle Ages, when a common technique, bloodletting, was at least part of the treatment of virtually all physical problems. It was gradually recognized that different illnesses required different treatments. Diagnostic procedures were improved, diseases classified, and applicable remedies administered. Impressed by the successes that new diagnostic procedures had achieved in the field of medicine, investigators of abnormal behavior also sought to develop classification schemes that grouped disorders according to symptoms. Moreover, advances in other sciences such as botany and chemistry had followed the development of classification systems, reinforcing hope that similar efforts in the field of abnormal behavior might bring progress.

But during the nineteenth century, and indeed into the twentieth as well, there had been great inconsistency in the way abnormal behavior was classified. By the end of the nineteenth century, the diversity of classifications in use was recognized as a serious problem, greatly impeding communication among people in the field. In 1889 in Paris, the Congress of Mental Science adopted a single classification system, but it was never widely used. Earlier, in Britain in 1882, the Statistical Committee of the Royal Medico-Psychological Association had produced a classification scheme which, even though going through several revisions, was never adopted by the members. In the United States, in 1886, the Association of Medical Superintendents of American Institutions for the Insane, a forerunner of the American Psychiatric Association, adopted a somewhat revised version of the British system. Then in 1913 this group accepted a new classification incorporating some of Kraepelin's ideas. But again, consistency did not emerge. The New York State Commission on Lunacy, for example, insisted on retaining its own system (Kendell, 1975).

More contemporary efforts at achieving uniformity of classification have not been totally successful either. In 1939 the World Health Organization added mental disorders to the *International List of Causes of Death*. In 1948 WHO expanded the previous list, and it became the *International Statistical Classification of Diseases, Injuries, and Causes of Death*, a comprehensive listing of all diseases, including a classification of abnormal behavior. Although this nomenclature was unanimously adopted at a WHO conference, the mental disorders section failed to be widely accepted. In the United States, for example, even though American psychiatrists had a prominent role in the WHO effort, the American Psychiatric Association published its own *Diagnostic and Statistical Manual* (DSM-I) in 1952.

In 1969 the WHO published a new classification system, and it was more widely accepted. A second version of the American Psychiatric Association's DSM (DSM-II, 1968) was similar to it, and in Britain a glossary of definitions was produced to accompany it (General Register Office, 1968). But whether a true consensus had been reached was doubtful. The WHO classifications are simply a listing of diagnostic categories; the actual behavior or symptoms that are the basis for the diagnoses are not specified. DSM-II and the British Glossary provided this crucial information, but the symptoms listed by each were not always similar. Therefore actual diagnostic practices still varied widely. At present, a newer version of the WHO system is in use, and the latest edition (1980) of the American Psychiatric Association's *Diagnostic and Statistical Manual*—DSM-III—is closely linked to it.

In this chapter the major DSM-III categories are given in brief summary. We then examine criticisms of classification in general and of the DSM in particular. In the next chapter we consider the assessment procedures that provide the data on which diagnostic decisions are based.

DSM-III—THE DIAGNOSTIC SYSTEM OF THE AMERICAN PSYCHIATRIC ASSOCIATION

The Axes

A number of major innovations distinguish the third edition of the American Psychiatric Association's *Diagnostic and Statistical Manual*. Perhaps the most sweeping is that classification has become *multiaxial*; each individual is to be rated on five separate dimensions or axes (Table 3.1). The multiaxial system, by requiring judgments to be made on each of the five axes, forces the diagnostician to consider a broad range of information. Axis I includes all categories except for the personality and specific developmental disorders, which make up axis II. Thus axes I and II comprise the classification of abnormal behavior. Axes I and II were separated to ensure that the possible presence of long-term disturbances is considered when attention is directed to the current one. For example, a person who is now a heroin addict would be diagnosed on axis I as having a substance use disorder; he might also have a long-standing

TABLE 3.1 DSM-III Multiaxial Classification System*

Axis I	Axis II	Axis III
Disorders Usually First Evident in Infancy, Childhood, or Adolescence Organic Mental Disorders Substance Use Disorders Schizophrenic Disorders Paranoid Disorders Affective Disorders Anxiety Disorders Somatoform Disorders Dissociative Disorders Psychosexual Disorders Psychological Factors Affecting Physical Condition	Personality Disorders: paranoid, schizoid, schizotypal, histrionic, narcissistic, antisocial, borderline, avoidant, dependent, compulsive, passive-aggressive Specific Developmental Disorders: reading, arithmetic, language, articulation	Physical Disorders and Conditions

Axis IV	Axis V
Severity of Psychosocial Stressors 1 none 2 minimal (e.g., small loan) 3 mild (e.g., argument with neighbor) 4 moderate (e.g., pregnancy) 5 severe (e.g., serious illness) 6 extreme (e.g., death of close relative) 7 catastrophic (e.g., natural disaster)	Highest Level of Adaptive Functioning Past Year 1 superior: unusually effective in social relations, occupation, and use of leisure time (e.g., single parent in reduced circumstances takes excellent care of children, has warm friendships and a hobby) 2 very good: better than average in job, leisure time, and social functioning (e.g., retired person does volunteer work, sees old friends) 3 good: no more than slight impairment in either occupational or social functioning (e.g., individual with many friends does a difficult job extremely well but finds it a strain) 4 fair: moderate impairment in either social or occupational functioning or some impairment in both (e.g., lawyer has trouble carrying through assignments, has almost no close friends) 5 poor: marked impairment in either social or occupational functioning or moderate impairment in both (e.g., man with one or two friends has trouble holding a job for more than a few weeks) 6 very poor: marked impairment in social and occupational functioning (e.g., woman is unable to do any housework and has violent outbursts) 7 grossly impaired: gross impairment in virtually all areas of functioning (e.g., elderly man needs supervision in maintaining personal hygiene, is usually incoherent)

*This listing is generally selective rather than complete. A more comprehensive listing of DSM-III categories is given on the back endpapers of this book.

antisocial personality disorder, which should be listed for axis II.

Although the remaining three axes are not needed to make the actual diagnosis, their inclusion in DSM-III indicates recognition that factors other than a person's symptoms should be considered in an assessment. On axis III the clinician indicates any current physical dis-

orders believed to be relevant to the mental disorder in question. In some individuals a physical disorder, a neurological dysfunction, for example, may be the cause of the abnormal behavior, whereas in others it may be an important factor in their overall condition, for example, diabetes in a child with a conduct disorder. Axis IV codes the level of psychosocial stress that the person has

TABLE 3.2 Example of a DSM-III Multiaxial Diagnosis

Axis I: Alcohol Dependence.

Axis II: Antisocial Personality.

Axis III: Cirrhosis.

Axis IV: Psychosocial stressors: Death of only child, marital stress.
Severity: 6, extreme.

Axis V: Highest level of adaptive functioning past year: 6, very poor.

been experiencing and that may be contributing to the disorder. A rating scale of 1 (none) to 7 (catastrophic, for example, multiple family deaths) is to be used. Finally, on axis V, the clinician indicates the person's highest level of adaptive functioning during the past year. Life areas to be considered are social relationships, occupational functioning, and use of leisure time. Axis V ratings, from 1 to 7 (superior to grossly impaired), are included because the better the person has been functioning, regardless of what problems they have for axes I and II, the better the outlook for the future. Table 3.2 shows how a psychiatric diagnosis à la DSM-III would look.

Diagnostic Categories

The following major *diagnostic categories* are to be considered when determining how the patient should be described for axes I and II.

Disorders usually first evident in infancy, childhood, or adolescence   Within this broad-ranging category are the intellectual, emotional, physical, and developmental disorders that usually begin in infancy, childhood, or adolescence. Some of the problems covered are mental retardation; conduct disorders; eating disorders, such as anorexia nervosa, in which considerable weight is lost through an intense fear of becoming fat; and infantile autism, an aloofness from others and a disinclination to learn any means of communicating with them. These disorders are discussed in Chapters 15 and 16.

Organic mental disorders   In organic mental disorders the functioning of the brain is known to be impaired, either permanently or transiently. The primary symptoms, which vary with the location and extent of the dysfunction, are delirium—clouding of consciousness, wandering attention, incoherent stream of thought, misperceptions; dementia—deterioration of intellectual capabilities, of memory, abstract thinking, judgment, and control over impulses; persistent and recurrent hallucinations; and disturbed emotions. These disorders are studied in Chapter 17 and in the Appendix.

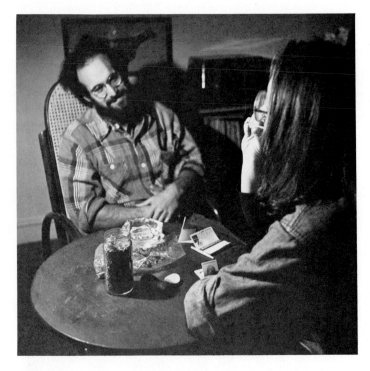

Marijuana remains among the most widely used of illegal drugs.

Substance use disorders   In substance use disorders the ingestion of various substances—alcohol, opiates, cocaine, amphetamines, and so on—has changed behavior enough to impair social or occupational functioning. The individual may become unable to control ingestion of the substance, or to discontinue it, and may develop withdrawal symptoms if he or she stops using it. Substance use disorders are examined in Chapter 11.

Schizophrenic disorders   The self-care, social relations, and work of patients with schizophrenic disorders have deteriorated from a previous level. Their language and communication are disordered, and they may shift from one subject to another only obliquely related or even completely unrelated. Delusions, such as believing that thoughts not their own have been placed in their heads, are common. Hallucinations, in particular hearing voices that come from outside themselves, plague them. Their emotions are blunted, flattened, or inappropriate, and they have lost contact with the world and with others. These serious mental disorders are discussed in Chapter 14.

Paranoid disorders   The most obvious symptoms of people with paranoid disorders are their delusions of being persecuted. The diagnosis can also be applied to extreme and unjustified jealousy, as when a spouse becomes convinced, without reasonable cause, that his or her partner is unfaithful. DSM-III indicates the difficulty in distinguishing paranoid disorders from *schizophrenia, paranoid type*, noting that in schizophrenia, the more serious disorder, delusions tend to be more bizarre and fragmented and the person also has hallucinations. Paranoid disorders are discussed in Chapter 14.

Affective disorders   Affective disorders are primarily disturbances of mood. In *major depression* the person is deeply sad and discouraged and is also likely to lose weight and energy, to have suicidal thoughts and feelings of self-reproach. The person suffering mania may be described as euphoric, more active than usual, distractable, and possessed of unrealistically great self-esteem. *Bipolar disorder* is diagnosed if the person experiences episodes of mania or of both mania and depression. The disorders of mood are surveyed in Chapter 9.

Anxiety disorders   Anxiety disorders are those that have some form of anxiety as the central disturbance. Individuals with a *phobia* fear an object or situation so intensely that they must avoid it, even though they know that their fear is unwarranted and unreasonable and disrupts their lives. In *panic disorder*, the first of three so-

Alcohol, one of the most dangerous of drugs, is also one of the most common substances of potential abuse. Problem drinking cuts across all social strata and ages.

called anxiety states, the person is subject to sudden but brief attacks of intense apprehension, so upsetting that he or she is likely to tremble and shake, feel dizzy, and have trouble breathing. The anxiety of *generalized anxiety disorder* is pervasive and persistent. Individuals are jumpy and may have a lump in the throat and a pounding heart. They ruminate and feel generally on edge. The person with *obsessive-compulsive disorder* is subject to persistent obsessions or compulsions. Obsessions are recurrent thoughts, ideas, and images which, uncontrollably, dominate a person's consciousness. A compulsion is an urge to perform a stereotyped act with the

Depression frequently reduces the individual to solitary crying.

seeming but usually impossible purpose of warding off an impending feared situation. Attempts to resist a compulsion create so much tension that the individual usually yields.

The anxiety and numbness suffered in the aftermath of a traumatic event outside the usual range of human experience is called *posttraumatic stress disorder*. Individuals have painful, intrusive recollections by day and bad dreams at night. They find it difficult to concentrate and feel detached from others and ongoing affairs. The anxiety disorders are reviewed in Chapter 6.

Somatoform disorders The physical symptoms of somatoform disorders have no known physiological cause but seem to serve a psychological purpose. Persons with *somatization disorder*, or Briquet's syndrome, have a long history of multiple physical complaints for which they have taken medicine or consulted doctors. In *conversion disorder* the person reports the loss of motor or sensory function, such as a paralysis, an anesthesia, or blindness. Individuals with *psychogenic pain disorder* suffer from severe and prolonged pain. *Hypochondriasis* is the misinterpretation of minor physical sensations as serious illness.

Dissociative disorders Psychological dissociation is a sudden alteration in consciousness affecting memory and identity. Persons with *psychogenic amnesia* may forget their whole past or more selectively lose memory for a particular time period. With *psychogenic fugue* the individual suddenly and unexpectedly travels to a new locale, starts a new life, and is amnesic for his or her previous identity. The person with *multiple personality* possesses two or more distinct ones, each complex and dominant one at a time. *Depersonalization disorder* is a severe and disruptive feeling of self-estrangement or unreality. Somatoform and dissociative disorders are examined in Chapter 7.

Psychosexual disorders The psychosexual disorders section of DSM-III lists three principal subcategories. People with *gender identity disorders* have feelings of discomfort and inappropriateness concerning their anatomical sex. Transsexuals, for example, want to alter their genitals and live as someone of the opposite sex. In *paraphilias* the sources of sexual gratification—as in sadism and masochism—are unconventional. Finally, persons with *psychosexual dysfunctions* are unable to complete the usual sexual response cycle. Inability to maintain an erection, premature ejaculation, and inhibition of orgasm are examples of their problems. A separate diagnosis, *ego-dystonic homosexuality*, is applied to distressed homosexuals who deeply yearn to be heterosexual. These sexual disorders are studied in Chapters 12 and 13.

Psychological factors affecting physical condition If an illness appears to be caused, in part, or exacerbated by a psychological condition, the diagnosis for axis I is *psychological factors affecting physical condition*. Referred to previously as psychophysiological or psychosomatic disorders, these conditions are reviewed in detail in Chapter 8.

Personality disorders Personality disorders are defined as "inflexible and maladaptive" patterns of behavior. They are listed on axis II. Eleven distinct personality disorders make up the category. In *schizoid personality disorder*, for example, the person is aloof, has few friends, and is indifferent to praise and criticism. The individual with a *narcissistic personality* has an overblown sense of self-importance, fantasizes about great successes, requires constant attention, and is likely to exploit others. The *antisocial personality* has surfaced before the age of fifteen, through truancy, running away from home, delinquency, and general belligerency. Now, in adulthood, he or she is indifferent about holding a job, being a responsible mate or parent, planning ahead for the future and even for tomorrow, and staying on the right side of the law. Chapter 10 covers the personality disorders and examines sociopathy in particular.

Specific developmental disorders Specific developmental disorders, which are listed on axis II, cover delays in the development of language, reading skills, articulation, and arithmetic competence. They are studied in Chapter 15.[1]

ISSUES IN THE CLASSIFICATION OF ABNORMAL BEHAVIOR

This review of the major categories of abnormal behavior was brief, for they will be examined in more detail throughout this volume. On the basis of this overview, however, let us scrutinize the usefulness of the system as

---

[1]The organization of diagnostic categories in DSM-III differs substantially from the system that appeared in DSM-II. Furthermore, some diagnoses are given for the first time in DSM-III, and some of the categories of DSM-II are no longer listed. The most important of these changes will be discussed in chapters on individual disorders. The back endpapers of the book contain a comprehensive comparison of DSM-III listings with those of DSM-II.

it exists today. Two major lines of criticism can be distinguished. One group of critics assert that classification per se is irrelevant to the field of abnormal behavior. These critics hold that there is a *continuum* ranging from adjustment to maladjustment and consider discrete judgments inappropriate. The second group of critics find specific deficiencies in the way diagnoses are made.

The Relevance of Classification Per Se

Those opposed to any attempt to classify argue that whenever we do so we lose information and hence overlook some of the uniqueness of the person being studied.[2] The simple example of casting dice will help to explain this argument. Any of the numbers one through six may come up on a given toss of a single die. Let us suppose, however, that we classify each outcome as odd or even. Whenever a one, three, or five comes up on a roll, we call out "odd," and whenever a two, four, or six appears, we say "even." A person listening to our calls will not know whether the call "odd" refers to a one, three, or five, or whether a two, four, or six has turned up when he or she hears "even." In classification some information must inevitably be lost.

What matters, however, is whether the information lost is *relevant*, which in turn depends on the *purposes* of the classification system. Any classification is designed to group together objects having a common property and to ignore differences in the objects that are not relevant to the purposes at hand. If our intention is merely to count odd and even rolls, it is irrelevant whether a die comes up one, three, or five or two, four, or six. In judging abnormal behavior, however, we cannot so easily decide what is wheat and what is chaff, for the relevant and irrelevant dimensions of abnormal behavior are uncertain. Thus when we do classify, we may indeed be grouping people together on rather trivial bases while ignoring their extremely important differences.

It may also be argued that classification, because it postulates discrete entities, does not allow the continuity between normal and abnormal behavior to be taken

into consideration. Those who advance this argument, for example psychopathologists operating within a learning paradigm, hold that abnormal and normal behavior differ only in intensity or degree, not in kind. Therefore discrete diagnostic categories foster a false impression of discontinuity. Rimland (1969) has summarized this position and, in our opinion, effectively criticized it.

. . . The idea is that if it is difficult to make a distinction between two neighboring points on a hypothetical continuum, no valid distinctions can thereafter be made even at the extremes of the continuum. There are thus persons who would argue that the existence of several variations of gray precludes a distinction between black and white. Hokum. While I will agree that some patients in mental hospitals are saner than nonpatients, and that it is sometimes hard to distinguish between deep unhappiness and psychotic depression, I do not agree that the difficulty sometimes encountered in making the distinction between normal and abnormal necessarily invalidates all such distinctions (pp. 716–717).

In other words, the fact that some distinctions are difficult to make, such as deciding whether sundown is night or day, does not mean it is impossible to distinguish between noon and midnight.

Classification may stigmatize a person. Consider how you might be affected by being told, for example, that you are a schizophrenic. You might become guarded and suspicious lest someone recognize your disorder. Or you might be chronically on edge, fearing the onset of another "attack." Furthermore, the fact that you are a "former mental patient" could have a great impact on your life. Friends and loved ones now treat you differently, and employment may be difficult to obtain.

There is little doubt that diagnosis can have such negative consequences, but social stigmatization does not appear to be as extensive as once believed. Gove and Fain (1973), for example, followed up a large sample of patients one year after discharge from a hospital. The former patients were interviewed about jobs, social relationships, and outside activities. The patients' descriptions of how they were functioning now and had in the past were not very different. Thus, although we must recognize and be on guard against the possible social stigma of a diagnosis, the problem may not be as serious as generally believed.

Assuming that various types of abnormal behavior do differ one from another, however, it is essential to classify them, for these differences may constitute keys

---

[2]The reader is invited to recall our discussions in Chapters 1 and 2 of paradigms and their effect on how we glean information about our world. It appears to be in the nature of humankind that we categorize whenever we perceive and think about anything. Those who argue against classification per se therefore overlook the inevitability of classification or categorization in human thought.

to the causes and treatments of the various deviant behaviors. For example, the form of mental retardation already mentioned, phenylketonuria, is attributed to a deficiency in the metabolism of the protein phenylalanine, resulting in the release of incomplete metabolites which injure the brain (see page 409). A diet drastically reduced in phenylalanine prevents some of this injury. As Mendels (1970) has noted, however,

> . . . . had we taken 100, or even 1000, people with mental deficiency and placed them all on the phenylalanine-free diet, the response would have been insignificant and the diet would have been discarded as a treatment. It was first necessary to recognize a subtype of mental deficiency [retardation], phenylketonuria, and then subject the value of a phenylalanine-free diet to investigation in this specific population, for whom it has been shown to have value in preventing the development of mental deficiency (p. 35).

Forming classes may thus further knowledge, for once a class is formed, additional information may be ascertained about it. Even though the class is only an asserted and not a proven entity, it may still be heuristically[3] useful in that it facilitates the acquisition of new information. Only after a diagnostic class has been formed can people who fit its definition be studied in hopes of uncovering factors that were responsible for the development of their problems and of devising treatments that may help them.

Criticisms of Actual Diagnostic Practice

More specific criticisms are commonly made of psychiatric classification, the principal ones being that diagnostic classes are neither reliable nor valid. These criticisms were frequently leveled at DSM-II and its predecessor. At the close of this section, we see how DSM-III has come to grips with them.

Lack of Reliability
Whether or not different diagnosticians will agree that a given diagnostic label should be applied to a particular person is the test of its *reliability*. Clearly, for a classification system to be useful, those applying it must be able to agree on what is and what is not an instance of a particular class. Thus reliability becomes the primary requisite for judging any classification system.

Before the evidence is discussed, a problem in assessing the reliability of diagnosis should be addressed. In medicine a diagnosis made by a physician can usually be checked by some sort of laboratory test. That is, an objective measurement is available by which the reliability of a physician's diagnosis can be determined. For diagnosing abnormal behavior no such infallible measurement exists; the only means of assessing reliability is whether or not diagnosticians agree.

The reliability of psychiatric diagnosis has been well researched. One exemplary investigation, illustrating the unreliability of older diagnostic systems, was reported by Aaron T. Beck and his colleagues (1962). Beck and three other highly experienced psychiatrists diagnosed 153 patients within one week of their admission to a psychiatric facility. Each patient was interviewed twice in succession by two different psychiatrists. Before beginning their study, the four psychiatrists had met to discuss the current diagnostic manual so that they could agree on its application. No attempt was made to ensure that the four interviewers would employ the same techniques in gathering the information necessary to make their diagnoses, however.

The overall agreement among the psychiatrists, calculated as the number of diagnoses on which they agreed divided by the total number of diagnoses made, was a disappointingly low 54 percent. The data were later reexamined by the same four psychiatrists (Ward et al., 1962), in an attempt to determine why diagnosticians might disagree. Meeting again after they had completed the interviews and made their diagnoses, the psychiatrists found three major reasons why they had not always reached the same determination. First, accounting for 5 percent of the disagreements, were *inconsistencies in the information presented by the patients*. The second major group of diagnostic disagreements, 32.5 percent of them, were attributed to *inconsistencies on the part of the diagnostician*. Differences in interview techniques, in judging the importance of particular symptoms, and in interpreting the same pathology constituted most of these inconsistencies.

The third and largest group of disagreements, comprising 62.5 percent of them, were considered to stem from *inadequacies of the diagnostic system*. The diagnosticians found the criteria unclear. Either too fine distinctions were required, or the classification system

---

[3]Heuristic is a central word and concept in science. It comes from the Greek *heuriskein*, to discover, find, and is defined in *Webster's* as serving to guide, discover, or reveal, and more specifically as valuable for stimulating or conducting empirical research. The frequent use of this word and its derivatives underlines the importance scientists place on ideas in generating new knowledge.

A medical diagnosis is typically checked against results of well-validated laboratory tests. Such objective criteria are not available in the realm of abnormal psychology.

seemingly forced the diagnostician to choose a major category that was not specific enough.

. . . A twenty-one-year-old single white female . . . was seen whose chief complaints were nervous tension and self-consciousness since she was three years old. In recent years, she had been unable to

hold down a job, although she had some secretarial training. . . . She had received various forms of psychiatric treatment over the past four years and had seen twelve psychiatrists in all, remaining with only one for a period as long as seven months and leaving all of them with open hostility. . . . It was open knowledge in the family that the patient was supposed to have been a boy; and her parents, especially the somewhat alcoholic father, had told her that she was no good because she was a girl and had approved of her only when she was successfully competitive with boys. The patient finished high school with difficulty, having to leave one school because of her marked discomfort in efforts to make speeches before mixed groups, and also because of much daydreaming, which still continued. She now felt frustrated, bitter, and had long felt that life was not worthwhile. She had never had a serious interpersonal involvement of a positive nature, and to the extent that she let herself react with others, the pattern was that of hostile anticipation, poorly modulated aggression, and suspiciousness. She often wished she were dead and had frequent thoughts of turning on the gas or jumping in front of a car, but at the same time she was aware of an excessively strong fear of death. She was compelled to wash her hands after touching certain articles of furniture; she had phobias of eating with other people. She had many physical symptoms of . . . anxiety and autonomic tension. . . . She had a sleep pattern which was a mixture of anxiety and depression, was not rarely awakened by nightmares in which she saw herself dead or bad things happening to her family. She had on several occasions [experienced] . . . visual images upon awakening from these dreams and had remained anxious and unable to sleep long afterwards. However, she definitely had had no auditory or visual hallucinations in the waking state and had had no clear delusions. There was a peculiar quality to her affect which suggested flatness or a manifestation of depression, though it was hard to distinguish between the two, and neither observer felt that she was making any substantial attempt to be melodramatic or impressive.

Both observers were impressed with the borderline nature of her problem. One was reminded of a previous patient who became "overtly psychotic"; the resemblance was less in specific, recognizable details and more in terms of a vague general feeling of the examiner's. He was also impressed with the chronicity, quantity, and multiplicity of her symptoms. The other examiner volunteered that on another day he might well agree, but as the patient struck him now, after an hour's interview, he felt she had a certain integration and inner consistency; he had seen similar patients who consolidated themselves and improved their adjustment without any

clearly psychotic episode. In view of the absence of any clear break with reality; because of the reactive elements in the picture; because the patient was intelligent and did well on routine tests of similarities, differences, and proverb interpretation; because of the potential damage to the patient of being labeled with a psychotic diagnosis; and because of personal antipathy to the poorly conceived phrase "chronic undifferentiated schizophrenic," he gave the patient the benefit of a very sizable doubt as to where schizoid personality left off and schizophrenia began. Diagnostic conflict: chronic undifferentiated schizophrenic reaction vs. chronic anxiety reaction in a severely schizoid personality (pp. 203–204).

The Issue of Validity

Whether or not accurate statements and predictions can be made about a class once it has been formed is the test of its *validity*. We should state at the outset that validity bears a particular relation to reliability; the less reliable a category is, the more difficult it is to make valid statements about the category. If the reliability of diagnosis is not entirely adequate, we can expect that its validity will not be either.

A diagnosis can have three kinds of validity: etiological, concurrent, and predictive. It has *etiological validity* if the same historical antecedents have caused the disorder in the patients diagnosed. In other words, for a diagnosis to be considered etiologically valid, the same factors must be found to have caused the disorder in the people who comprise the diagnostic group. Consider, for example, the supposition that bipolar disorder is, in part, genetically determined. According to this theory, people with episodes of both depression and mania must have a "family tree" that contains other bipolars. As we shall see in Chapter 9, evidence that supports this theory has been collected, giving this diagnostic category some etiological validity.

A diagnosis has *concurrent validity* if other symptoms or disordered processes not part of the diagnosis itself are discovered to be characteristic of those diagnosed. Finding that most people with schizophrenia have difficulty in personal relationships is an example. *Predictive validity* refers to similar future behavior on the part of the disorder or patients suffering from it. The disorder may have a particular "natural history," that is, take a certain course. Or members of the diagnostic group may be expected to respond in a similar way to a particular treatment. Bipolar patients, for example, tend to respond well to a new drug called lithium carbonate. The fact that this drug does not work well for people in other diagnostic classes supports the predictive validity of the bipolar diagnosis. Clearly, because we have organized this book around the major diagnostic categories, we believe that they indeed possess some validity. Certain categories have greater validity than others, however; these differences will become apparent as we discuss each diagnostic classification.

DSM-III and Criticisms of Diagnosis

DSM-III was devised to be more diagnostically reliable and valid than its predecessors. In DSM-III each diagnostic category in axes I and II is described much more extensively than was the case in DSM-II. First there is a description of "essential features," then of "associated features." Given next are statements, drawn from the research literature, about age of onset, course, degree of impairment and complications, predisposing factors, prevalence and sex ratio, familial pattern, and differential diagnosis. Finally, specific _diagnostic criteria_ for the category are spelled out in a more precise fashion. These are the symptoms and other facts that must be present to justify the diagnosis. Table 3.3 compares the descriptions of a manic episode given in DSM-II to the diagnostic criteria given in DSM-III. Clearly the bases for making diagnoses are decidedly more detailed and concrete in DSM-III.

The explicitness of the DSM-III criteria can be expected to reduce the descriptive inadequacies found by Beck and his colleagues to be the major source of diagnostic unreliability. Results of field testing of DSM-III were reported in the manual itself and are shown in Table 3.4. As can be seen, the reliabilities vary but are quite acceptable for most of the major categories.[4]

Thus far the description of DSM-III has been in positive terms. The attainment of adequate diagnostic reliability is a considerable achievement. But problems remain. It is unclear, for example, whether the rules for making diagnostic decisions are ideal. Examining Table 3.3, we see that for patients to be diagnosed as suffering from mania, they must have three symptoms from a list of seven, or four if their mood is irritable. But the reason why three symptoms rather than two or five were selected is unknown (see Finn, 1982). Furthermore, the reliability of axes I and II may not always be as high in everyday usage, for diagnosticians may not adhere as precisely to the criteria as have those whose work was being scrutinized in formal studies. And although the improved reliability of DSM-III _may_ lead to more validity, there is no guarantee that it will. The diagnoses made according to it may not reveal anything useful about the patients. Moreover, subjective factors still play a role in evaluations made according to DSM-III. For example, on axis V the clinician must judge the patient's highest level of adaptive functioning in the preceding year. The clinician determines what, for the patient, is adaptive and how his or her behavior compares

---

[4]Progress has also been made in dealing with the second largest source of diagnostic unreliability, inconsistency on the part of the diagnostician. The use of standardized, reliably scored interviews, discussed in the following chapter, greatly reduces this problem.

TABLE 3.3 Description of Manic Disorder in DSM-II Versus DSM-III

DSM-II (APA, 1968, p. 36)

Manic-depressive illness, manic type. This disorder consists exclusively of manic episodes. These episodes are characterized by excessive elation, irritability, talkativeness, flight of ideas, and accelerated speech and motor activity. Brief periods of depression sometimes occur, but they are never true depressive episodes.

DSM-III Diagnostic Criteria for a Manic Episode (APA, 1980, p. 208)

A. One or more distinct periods with a predominantly elevated, expansive, or irritable mood. The elevated or irritable mood must be a prominent part of the illness and relatively persistent, although it may alternate or intermingle with depressive mood.

B. Duration of at least one week (or any duration if hospitalization is necessary), during which, for most of the time, at least three of the following symptoms have persisted (four if the mood is only irritable) and have been present to a significant degree:

(1) increase in activity (either socially, at work, or sexually) or physical restlessness,

(2) more talkative than usual or pressure to keep talking,

(3) flight of ideas or subjective experience that thoughts are racing,

(4) inflated self-esteem (grandiosity, which may be delusional),

(5) decreased need for sleep,

(6) distractability, i.e., attention is too easily drawn to unimportant or irrelevant external stimuli,

(7) excessive involvement in activities that have a high potential for painful consequences which is not recognized, e.g., buying sprees, sexual indiscretions, foolish business investments, reckless driving.

TABLE 3.4 Reliabilities for Major Diagnostic Categories Achieved in Field Trials with DSM-III*

Diagnostic Category	Reliability†
Disorders Usually First Evident in Infancy, Childhood, or Adolescence	.65
Organic Mental Disorders	.79
Substance Use Disorders	.86
Schizophrenic Disorders	.81
Paranoid Disorders	.66
Affective Disorders	.69
Anxiety Disorders	.63
Somatoform Disorders	.54
Dissociative Disorders	.80
Psychosexual Disorders	.92
Psychological Factors Affecting Physical Condition	.62
Personality Disorders	.56

*The data shown are from phase I of the field trial. The number of patients was 339.

†These reliabilities use a statistic called kappa, which reflects the percent agreement corrected for chance agreements.

with that of an average person. As Taylor (1983) cautions, such a judgment sets the stage for cultural biases to creep in, as well as the clinician's own personal ideas of what the average person *should* be doing at a given stage of life and in particular circumstances. Additional problems of this nature are detailed later, when we examine the way DSM-III describes homosexuality (see page 309). Finally, not all DSM-III's classification changes seem positive. The developmental disorders of childhood—of reading, arithmetic, language, and articulation—and oppositional disorder really cover the waterfront! Should a specific problem like difficulty in learning arithmetic be considered a "psychiatric disorder"? By expanding its coverage, DSM-III seems to

have made too many childhood problems into psychiatric disorders, without good justification for doing so.

In sum, although we regard DSM-III as promising, it is far from perfect. Throughout this book, as we present the literature on various disorders, there will be further opportunities to describe both the strengths and weaknesses of this most recent effort of health professionals to categorize mental disorders.

SUMMARY

The third edition of the *Diagnostic and Statistical Manual of Mental Disorders* (DSM-III), published in 1980 by the American Psychiatric Association, is the latest in a series of efforts by mental health professionals to categorize the various psychopathologies. A novel feature of DSM-III is its multiaxial organization: every time a diagnosis is made, the clinician must describe the patient's condition according to each of five axes, or dimensions. Axes I and II make up the mental disorders per se; on axis III are listed any physical disorders believed to bear on the mental disorder in question; axis IV is used to indicate the degree of psychological stress the person has been experiencing; and axis V rates the person's highest level of adaptive functioning during the preceding year. A multiaxial diagnosis made on the basis of DSM-III is believed to provide a more adequate and useful description of the patient's mental disorder.

Both general and specific issues in the classification of abnormality were discussed. Because DSM-III is far more concrete and descriptive than its predecessor, diagnoses based on it are more reliable. Validity, however, remains an open question. It is too soon to know whether more useful knowledge about psychopathology, its prevention, and treatment will be gained through widespread use of DSM-III.

Ernest Trova, *Study/Falling Man #25*, 1963 Abrams Family Collection

CLINICAL ASSESSMENT PROCEDURES

The account with which this book began, that of the policeman with drinking and marital problems, allowed no opportunity to find out why he was behaving as he was. We had no possibility of learning more about him by any of the means commonly available to clinicians—interviews, tests, and a variety of other procedures for assessing behavior. These modes of assessment may occasionally be given different, perhaps more impressive-sounding names. An interview may be called "the psychiatric interview," "the diagnostic interview," or "a depth interview"; tests "psychologicals" or "projectives." All clinical *assessment procedures* are more or less formal ways of finding out what is wrong with a person, what may have caused a problem or problems, and what steps may be taken to improve the individual's condition.

PERSONALITY ASSESSMENT

Clinical Interviews

Most of us have probably been interviewed at one time or another, although the conversation may have been so informal that it was not regarded as an interview. To the layperson the word interview connotes a formal, highly structured conversation, but we find it useful to construe the term as any interpersonal encounter, conversational in style, in which one person, the interviewer, uses language as the principal means of finding out about another, the interviewee. Thus a Gallup pollster who asks a college student whom she will vote for in an upcoming presidential election is interviewing with the restricted goal of learning which candidate she prefers. And a clinical psychologist who asks a patient about the circumstances of his most recent hospitalization is similarly conducting an interview.

One way in which a *clinical interview* is perhaps different from a casual conversation and from a poll is the attention the interviewer pays to *how* the respondent answers questions—or does not answer them. For example, if a client is recounting her marital conflicts with her husband, the clinician will generally be attentive to any emotion accompanying her comments. If the woman does not seem upset about a difficult situation, her answers will probably be interpreted differently than if she were to cry while relating her story.

The paradigm within which an interviewer operates determines the type of information sought and obtained. A psychoanalytically trained clinician can be expected to inquire about the person's childhood history. He or she is also likely to remain skeptical of the verbal reports because the analytic paradigm holds that the most significant aspects of a disturbed or normal person's developmental history are repressed into the unconscious. By the same token, the behaviorally oriented clinician is likely to focus on current environmental conditions that can be related to changes in the person's behavior, trying to determine, for example, the circumstances under which the person may become anxious. Thus the clinical interview does not follow a prescribed course, varying rather with the paradigm adopted by the interviewer. Like scientists, clinical interviewers in some measure find only the information that they look for.

Great skill is necessary to carry out good clinical interviews, for they are conducted with people who are often under considerable personal stress. Clinicians, regardless of their theoretical orientations, recognize the importance of establishing *rapport* with the client. The interviewer must obtain the trust of the person; it is naive to assume that a client will easily reveal information to another, even to an authority figure with the title "Dr." Furthermore, even a client who sincerely, perhaps desperately, wants to recount intensely personal problems to a professional may not be able to do so without assistance. Indeed, psychodynamic and humanistic clinicians assume that people entering therapy usually are not even aware of what is truly bothering them. And behavioral clinicians, although concentrating more on observables, also appreciate the difficulties people have in sorting out the factors responsible for their distress.

Most clinicians employ the kinds of empathy statements discussed in connection with humanistic therapy (see page 50) in order to draw clients out, to encourage them to elaborate on their concerns, and to examine different facets of a problem. A simple summary statement of what the client has been saying can help sustain the momentum of talk about painful and possibly embarrassing events and feelings. And an accepting attitude toward personal disclosures dispels the fear that revealing terrible secrets to another human being will have disastrous consequences.

Vast amounts of information can be obtained by means of the interview; its importance in abnormal psychology and psychiatry is unquestioned. Whether the information gleaned can always be depended on is not so clear, however. Clinicians often tend to overlook *situational* factors of the interview that may exert strong influences on what the patient says or does. Consider, for a moment, how a teenager is likely to respond to the question "How often have you used illegal drugs?" when it is asked by a young, informally dressed psychologist and again when it is asked by a sixty-year-old psychologist in a three-piece suit.

Interviews may vary in the degree to which they are structured. In practice, most clinicians operate from only the vaguest outlines. Exactly *how* such information is collected is left largely up to the particular interviewer. Through years of clinical experience and of both teaching and learning from students and colleagues, each clinician has developed ways of asking questions with which he or she is comfortable and which seem to extract the information that will be of maximum benefit to the client. Thus, to the extent that an interview is unstructured, the interviewer must rely on intuition and general experience, which may be either good or bad, for obvious reasons.

In response to the need in research to collect standardized information, investigators have developed structured interviews, such as the Schedule for Affective Disorders and Schizophrenia. The SADS has one section covering current problems, the other past history. Many symptoms are rated on a six-point scale of severity, others on a three-point scale indicating absence or presence.

The sample item given in Table 4.1 indicates the questions that are asked to probe in depth the content of hallucinatory experiences. A section called Research Diagnostic Criteria gives criteria for most diagnoses and definitions of many key terms. Reliability in using the SADS is impressive (Endicott and Spitzer, 1978). It has proved to be a very useful interview schedule with which to collect information about the patient's current and past mental status.

Psychological Tests

Psychological tests structure still further the process of assessment. The same test is administered to many people at different times, and the responses collected are analyzed to indicate how certain kinds of people tend to respond. Statistical norms for the test can thereby be established as soon as the data collected are extensive enough. This process is called *standardization*. The responses of a particular patient can then be compared to the statistical norms. The three basic types are projec-

Picture from the Thematic Apperception Test, introduced in 1935 by Henry Murray and his associates at the Harvard Psychological Clinic. Like the Rorschach, this projective test is designed to reveal unconscious conflicts and concerns.

tive personality tests, self-report personality inventories, and tests of intelligence.

Projective Personality Tests

The *Rorschach inkblot test* and the *Thematic Apperception Test* are perhaps the best-known *projective techniques*. In both of these tests a set of standard stimuli, vague enough to allow variation in responses, is presented to an individual. In an inkblot test the subject is shown ten blots, one at a time, and asked to tell what figures or objects he or she sees in each of them. Half of the inkblots are in black, white, and shades of gray, two add red splotches, and three are in pastel colors. Similarly, in the Thematic Apperception Test (TAT) the examinee is shown a series of pictures one by one and asked to tell a story related to each. In both these tests it

TABLE 4.1 Sample Item from the SADS Interview   *(from Spitzer and Endicott, 1978)*

HALLUCINATIONS

If there is no evidence from the case record, informants, or from your interview to suggest hallucinations, ask the following questions and any others from the section on hallucinations which you think are appropriate.

Has there been anything unusual about the way things looked, or sounded, or smelled?

Have you heard voices or other things that weren't there or that other people couldn't hear, or seen things that were not there?

☐ If there is still no evidence to suggest hallucinations, check here and skip to Bizarre Behavior.

Experienced auditory hallucinations of voices, noises, music, etc. (Do not include if limited to hearing name being called.)*	0 No information 1 Absent 2 Suspected or likely 3 Definite

The (sounds, voices) that you said you heard, did you hear them outside your head, through your ears, or did they come from inside your head?

Could you hear what the voice was saying?

(Did it talk about you or repeat your thoughts?)

Did you hear anything else? What about noises?

Auditory hallucinations in which a voice keeps up a running commentary on the subject's behaviors or thoughts as they occur.	0 No information 1 Absent 2 Suspected or likely 3 Definite

Did the voice describe or comment upon what you were doing or thinking?

Auditory hallucinations in which 2 or more voices converse with each other.	0 No information 1 Absent 2 Suspected or likely 3 Definite

Did you hear 2 or more voices talking with each other?

Non-affective Verbal Hallucinations Spoken to the Subject. A voice or voices are heard by the subject speaking directly to him, the content of which is unrelated to depressed or elated mood (although he may be depressed or elated at the time). Rate absent if limited to voices saying only 1 or 2 words. Examples: A woman heard voices telling her that she was having a baby and should go to the hospital. A man heard a voice telling him he was being watched by his neighbors for signs of perversion.	0 No information 1 Absent 2 Suspected or likely 3 Definite

Visual hallucinations.*	0 No information 1 Absent 2 Suspected or likely 3 Definite

Have you had visions, or seen things that are invisible to other people?

Olfactory hallucinations. (Do not include delusion that subject himself smells.*)	0 No information 1 Absent 2 Suspected or likely 3 Definite

Have you noticed strange or unusual smells that other people didn't notice?

Somatic or tactile hallucinations (e.g., electricity, things creeping, snake in his body).*	0 No information 1 Absent 2 Suspected or likely 3 Definite

What about strange feelings in your body?

Hallucinations of any type with a grandiose or persecutory content. Examples: Voices insult him. Voices praise him. Electrical rays torture him.	0 No information 1 Absent 2 Suspected or likely 3 Definite

*If the subject reports only unformed visual (spots, flashes, etc.) or auditory (roaring, ringing, rumbling, etc.) hallucinations, or only somatic or tactile hallucinations, the rater should be extremely cautious about scoring the symptom as definitely present. Such phenomena may be a drug reaction or an illusion rather than a hallucination. The item should be rated as "suspected" unless the rater is certain that it is a real hallucination.

is assumed that because the stimulus materials are unstructured, the patient's responses will be determined primarily by unconscious processes and will reveal his or her own attitudes, motivations, and modes of behavior. This is referred to as the *projective hypothesis*. For example, reporting eyes on the Rorschach has been said to indicate paranoia. Those of the psychoanalytic bent tend to favor such tests. A preference for ambiguous stimuli is entirely consistent with the psychoanalytic assumption that people defend against unpleasant thoughts and feelings by repressing them into the unconscious. In order to bypass the defense mechanism of repression (see page 37) and get to the basic causes of distress, the real purposes of a test are best left unclear. Indeed, this has to be the case, for psychoanalytic theory asserts that the factors of greatest importance are unconscious.

As might be imagined, the interpretation of the responses to projective tests poses a severe problem, for the examinee is not merely answering yes or no to a series of questions or indicating which of a series of statements are true and which are false. Rather, the person is providing a complex response to a complex stimulus,

Hermann Rorschach (1884–1922), Swiss psychiatrist who during a ride in the country with his two children noticed that what they saw in clouds reflected their personalities. From this observation came his famous inkblot test.

Inkblots resembling those used by Rorschach.

which is, by design, open to an immense range of interpretations. In many instances the reliability of the scoring of the Rorschach and Thematic Apperception tests is quite low. With extensive training in a particular scoring system, however, examiners can achieve satisfactory levels of agreement (Goldfried, Stricker, and Weiner, 1971). A more serious problem is the often woefully low validities of responses in projective tests. We assume that these responses tell us something important and useful about the person. But as Nunnally (1967) has written,

. . . Most projective techniques do a rather poor job of measuring personality traits. . . . In applied settings, the evidence is clear that projective techniques have, at most, only a low level of validity. . . . They do a poor job of differentiating normal people from people who are diagnosed as neurotic and they do a poor job of differentiating various types of mentally ill persons (p. 497).

Certain responses to projective tests are nevertheless viewed as diagnostic signs, and some clinicians may rely to a considerable extent on them in making their diagnoses. In other words, and as noted by Chapman and Chapman (1969), clinicians often show considerable consensus in assigning meanings to various responses, even though there is little evidence to back up their interpretations. Let us examine this issue of consensus. If a patient is asserted to be homosexual on the basis of certain responses to the Rorschach test, the validity of this assertion can be determined.

Chapman and Chapman conducted a study that you may participate in right now. Imagine yourself part of a psychological experiment in which you are asked to rate the amount of association between homosexuality and particular Rorschach responses. Specifically, you are to rate the degree to which each of the responses signifies homosexuality, using the following six-point scale: 6, very strong; 5, strong; 4, moderate; 3, slight; 2, very slight; and 1, no tendency at all. The eight Rorschach responses to be rated are presented in Table 4.2.

Now you may compare your ratings to those actually obtained from a sample of undergraduate students. In Table 4.3 the responses are divided into three different classes. The popular, invalid signs are those that clinicians tend to *believe* reflect homosexuality, although they have *not* been validated by research evidence. The unpopular but valid signs are infrequently listed by clinicians, but they do have some modest research support as being indicators. The filler items are unrelated to ho-

TABLE 4.2 Rorschach Responses To Be Rated as Signs of Homosexuality

Response	Rating
Feminine clothing	
Food	
Rectum and buttocks	
Maps	
Figure, part man—part woman	
Sexual organs	
Monsters	
Figure, part animal—part human	

mosexuality and to how clinicians assess it. The students in the Chapmans' study gave much higher ratings to the *popular but invalid signs* than to the other responses.

Professional clinicians may rely on particular signs in making a diagnosis because they *assume* such responses to be valid indicators of homosexuality. But as Chapman and Chapman themselves noted, "The popular meanings of many test signs, as reported by clinicians, are *illusory correlations* [italics added] based on verbal associative connection of the test sign to the symptom" (p. 272). Chapman and Chapman are saying that, in our culture, we all seem to have developed similar ideas of what homosexuals say, think, or do. In this study of how students rated Rorschach responses, the students *assumed*, as clinicians have, that homosexuals would be inclined to see such things as buttocks in the inkblots, and they accepted such responses as indicators. But these accepted popular signs are *not* valid. No empirical research has established their connection to homosexuality. There is no evidence to indicate that such responses differentiate between homosexuals and heterosexuals.

More promising, and of much greater interest to many clinicians, is analyzing the *formal* properties of a person's responses to the Rorschach cards (Exner, 1978). The examiner pays little attention to the content of the responses and instead analyzes such things as whether the whole card is incorporated in what is seen or only large or small details, how often white spaces are the figure rather than background, whether color affects responses, and whether the figures seen are moving or static. Rorschach himself suggested this approach in his original manual, *Psychodiagnostics: A Diagnostic Test Based on Perception* (1921), but he died only eight months after publishing his ten inkblots, and his immediate followers devised other methods of interpreting the test.

Personality Inventories

In *personality inventories* examinees are asked to indicate whether a large number of statements do or do not apply to them. The investigators who have been involved in the construction of such *self-report* instruments have usually been well schooled in the general principles of test construction and standardization. It is therefore rare for a personality inventory to lack reliability. Validity, however, still presents a problem, especially if the personality inventory has been designed to reveal unconscious conflicts and the like. Some personality inventories have been constructed with more specific purposes in mind. Perhaps the best-known of these is the Minnesota Multiphasic Personality Inventory (MMPI), which was developed in the early 1940s as an inexpensive device to simplify the differential diagnosis of mental patients. The inventory is called multiphasic because it was designed to detect a number of psychiatric problems.

In developing the test, the investigators relied on factual information. First, many clinicians provided large numbers of statements that they considered indicative of various mental problems. Second, these items were rated as self-descriptive or not by people already diagnosed as having particular disorders. Items that served to discriminate among the patients were retained: that is, items were selected if patients in one clinical group responded to them more often in a certain way than did those in other groups. With additional refinements, sets of these items were established as scales for determining whether or not a respondent should be diagnosed in a particular way. If the individual answered a large number of the items in a scale in the same way as had a certain diagnostic group, his or her behavior was expected to resemble that of the particular diagnostic group. The scales of the instrument do, in fact, relate well to psychiatric diagnoses. Thus the MMPI has been widely used to screen large groups of people for whom clinical interviews are not feasible. Items similar to those on the various scales are presented in Table. 4.4.[1]

We may well wonder whether answers that would designate the subject as normal might not be easy to fake. A superficial knowledge of contemporary abnormal psychology would alert even a seriously disturbed

TABLE 4.3 Mean Rated Strength of Association Between Particular Rorschach Responses and Homosexuality
(from Chapman and Chapman, 1969)

Response	Rated Strength
Popular, invalid signs	
Rectum and buttocks	4.38
Figure, part man—part woman	3.53
Feminine clothing	3.12
Sexual organs	4.47
Unpopular, valid signs	
Figure, part animal—part human	1.93
Monsters	1.68
Filler items	
Food	1.09
Maps	1.09

person to the fact that, if he wants to be regarded as normal, he must not admit to worrying a great deal about germs on doorknobs. In fact, there is evidence that these tests *can* be "psyched out." In many testing circumstances, however, people do not *want* to falsify their responses, for they want to be helped. Moreover, the test designers have included as part of the MMPI several scales designed to detect deliberately faked responses (see Table 4.4). In one of these, the lie scale, a series of statements sets a trap for the person who is trying to "look too good." One such item from the lie scale declares "I read the newspaper editorials every night." The assumption is that few people would be able to endorse such a statement honestly. Thus persons who do endorse a large number of the statements in the lie scale

[1]The manner in which the MMPI was constructed is referred to as *empirical*, that is, relying on data or experience rather than speculation. It is also worth noting that the MMPI's diagnostic scheme for the most part incorporated symptoms later listed in the DSM. Not surprisingly, clinicians who disliked the DSM were unenthusiastic about the MMPI. Moreover, because the MMPI was devised using an older diagnostic system, it may not predict DSM-III diagnoses well. Winters, Weintraub, and Neale (1981), for example, found that the MMPI did very poorly in predicting the DSM-III diagnosis of schizophrenia. The publisher of the MMPI is now collecting new information on diagnosed groups and updating and broadening its items.

TABLE 4.4 Typical Clinical Interpretations of Items Similar to Those on the MMPI
(adapted from Kleinmuntz, 1967)

Scale	Sample Item	Interpretation
Cannot say	This is merely the number of items marked in the "cannot say" category.	A high score indicates evasiveness.
Lie	I have never had a bad night's sleep (false).*	Persons trying to look good (i.e., wholesome, honest) obtain high scores.
Frequency	Everything tastes salty (true).	High scores on this scale suggest lack of interest or a wish to appear abnormal.
Correction	I am more satisfied with my life than most of my friends (true).	High scores on this scale suggest a guarded test-taking attitude.
Hypochondriasis	I wake up tired most mornings (true).	High scorers have been described as cynical and dissatisfied.
Depression	I rarely see the bright side of things (true).	High scorers are usually withdrawn, sad, and troubled.
Hysteria	My fingers sometimes feel numb (true).	High scorers have multiple bodily complaints.
Psychopathic deviate	I did not like school (true).	High scorers tend to be adventurous and antisocial.
Masculinity-femininity	I do not like sports (true).	Men with high scores tend to be artistic and sensitive. High-scoring women have been described as rebellious and assertive.
Paranoia	I am envied by many people (true).	High scorers on this scale tend to be suspicious and jealous.
Psychasthenia	I have a great deal of self-confidence (false).	High scorers are described as anxious, self-doubting, and rigid.
Schizophrenia	I sometimes smell strange odors (true).	Adjectives such as seclusive and bizarre describe high scorers.
Hypomania	I never have any difficulty making decisions (true).	High scorers tend to be outgoing and impulsive.
Social introversion—extroversion	I avoid getting together with people (true).	High scorers are modest and shy; low scorers are sociable and exhibitionistic.

*The true or false responses in parentheses indicate the answer expected if the respondent is to accumulate a high score on this scale.

might well be attempting to present themselves in a particularly good light. Their scores on other scales are usually viewed with more than the usual skepticism.

Tests such as the MMPI are subject to certain other difficulties. It has been found that many people tend to answer test questions on bases other than the specific content of the question. For example, suppose that a test statement reads, "I attend a party at least once a week." If the individual answers "Yes," or "True," can we conclude without reservation that he or she really attends social gatherings frequently? Research suggests that such answers cannot be accepted as necessarily true, for a certain test-taking or questionnaire "set" may have determined the response. In this instance the subject may have a *social desirability* response set and, believing that attending parties frequently is the "right" thing to do, says "Yes" on this basis. Fortunately, psychologists have developed ways to reduce the influence of such response sets (see Edwards, 1957).

Intelligence Tests

Psychological measures of intelligence play a central role in diagnoses of mental retardation. Alfred Binet, a French psychologist, originally constructed mental tests to help the Parisian school board predict which children were in need of special schooling. *Intelligence testing* has since developed into one of the largest psychological industries. The word aptitude is frequently applied to these widely used standardized procedures. The Scholastic Aptitude Test, The Graduate Record Examination, and the individually administered tests, such as the Wechsler Adult Intelligence Scale and the Stanford-Binet, are all based on the assumption that one sample from an individual's current intellectual functioning can predict how well he or she will perform in school.

When such tests are evaluated, it is important to keep in mind two points that are only infrequently made explicit by those who have a heavy professional commitment to intelligence testing. First, strictly speaking, the tests measure only what a psychologist considers intelligence to be. The tasks and items on an IQ test are, after all, invented by psychologists—they did not come down to us inscribed on stone tablets. Second, the tests are widely used because they do indeed accomplish what they were designed for, that is, predict who will succeed in our educational system. If and when there are major changes in our school systems, we can expect analogous changes in our definition and assessment of intelligence. Further discussion of IQ tests can be found in Chapter 16.

ASSESSMENT OF BRAIN ABNORMALITIES

CAT Scan and PET Scan

As indicated in Chapter 3, one major section of DSM-III, Organic Mental Disorders, refers to behavioral problems brought on by brain abnormalities. Neurological tests such as checking the patellar reflex, examining the retina for any indication of blood vessel damage, and evaluating motor coordination and perception are useful procedures in diagnosing brain dysfunction. The X-ray can sometimes detect tumors, and the electroencephalograph (EEG) abnormalities in the brain's electrical activity.

Computerized axial tomography, the CAT scan, has increased enormously our ability to investigate structural abnormalities in a living person.

Computerized axial tomography, the *CAT scan*, and positron emission tomography, the *PET scan*, are recent advances in assessing brain abnormalities. In the CAT scanner a moving beam of X-rays passes into a horizontal cross section of the patient's brain, scanning it throughout 360 degrees. The moving X-ray detector on the other side measures the amount of radioactivity that gets through; thus it detects subtle differences in tissue density. The computer takes the information and constructs a two-dimensional, detailed image of the cross section, giving it optimal contrasts. Then the patient's head is moved, and the machine scans another cross section of his or her brain. The images can show the locations of tumors and blood clots and the enlargement of ventricles (see Box A.1, page 600), which signals degeneration of tissue.

In PET scanning a substance used by the brain is labeled with a short-lived radioactive isotope and injected into the bloodstream of the patient. The radioactive molecules of the substance emit a particle called a positron, which quickly collides with an electron. A pair of high-energy light particles shoot out from the skull in opposite directions and are detected by the scanner. The computer analyzes millions of such recordings and converts them into a motion picture of the functioning brain in horizontal cross section, projected onto a television screen. The images are in color; fuzzy spots of lighter and warmer colors are areas in which metabolic rates for the substance are higher. These PET scans, moving visual images of the working brain, can indicate sites of epileptic seizures, brain cancers, strokes, and trauma from head injuries, a well as the distribution in the brain of psychoactive drugs. The PET scanner is also being used to study possible abnormal physiological processes underlying disorders.

We might reasonably assume that neurologists and physicians, with the help of such procedures and technological devices, can observe the brain and its functions more or less directly and thus assess brain abnormalities. Many brain abnormalities and injuries, however, involve alterations in structure so subtle or slight in extent that they have thus far eluded direct physical examination.

Neuropsychological Assessment

Since the way the person functions is the problem—what he or she does, says, thinks, or feels—a number of tests assessing behavioral disturbances that are caused by organic brain dysfunctions have been developed by psychologists. The literature on these tests is extensive and, as with most areas of psychology, so too is disagreement about them. The weight of the evidence, however, does seem to indicate that psychological tests have some validity in the assessment of brain damage. They are accordingly called *neuropsychological tests*. One of them is Reitan's modification of a battery or group of tests previously developed by Halstead. The concept of using a battery of tests, each tapping different functions, is critical, for only by studying a person's pattern of performance can an investigator judge accurately whether the person is indeed brain-damaged. But the Halstead-Reitan battery can do even more than this, locating the area of the brain that has been affected. Some of the tests in the battery are the following.

1. **Tactual Performance Test.** While blindfolded, the subject tries to fit variously shaped blocks into spaces in a board, using each hand in turn. After finishing this part of the test, the subject tries to draw the board from memory, showing the spaces and the blocks filling them in their proper locations.

2. **Trail-Making Test**—see Figure 4.1.

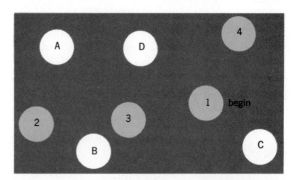

FIGURE 4.1 Sample item from the Trail-Making Test. The subject is instructed to alternate numbers and letters, for example, by drawing a line from 1 to A, A to 2, 2 to B, and so on.

3. **Finger Oscillation Task.** In this procedure the subject depresses a key with the index finger as fast as he or she can for five trials of ten seconds each. The index finger of each hand is tested.

4. **Category Test.** The subject, seeing an image on a screen that suggests one of the numbers between one and four, presses a button to show which number he or she thinks it is. A bell indicates that the choice is correct, a buzzer that it is wrong. The subject must

keep track of these images and signals in order to figure out the rules for making the correct choices.

5. **Aphasia Screening Test.** A number of language abilities are studied by asking the subject to name objects, to identify letters and numbers, to spell, read, write, and pronounce words, to do arithmetic calculations, to identify body parts and pantomime simple actions, to follow directions.

Performance on the tests is interpreted by drawing on knowledge of the relation between certain brain structures and behavior. Finger tapping, for example, is thought to be controlled by a brain area just in front of the central sulcus (see Box A.1). And control of speech and language tends to be localized in the left cerebral hemisphere. Thus particular deficits suggest that a problem exists in a specific brain area and in one or the other hemisphere.

The newly developed Luria-Nebraska battery (Golden, Hammeke, and Purisch, 1978), based on the work of the Russian psychologist Aleksandr Luria (1902–1977), is currently being both widely promoted as an effective neuropsychological test and subjected to much critical scrutiny (Adams, 1980; Spiers, 1982). A battery of 269 items makes up 11 sections to determine basic and complex motor skills, rhythm and pitch abilities, tactile and kinesthetic skills, verbal and spatial skills, receptive speech ability, expressive speech ability, writing, reading, arithmetical skills, memory, and intellectual processes. The pattern of scores on these sections, as well as on the pathognomic scale, the thirty-two items found to be the most discriminating and indicative of overall impairment, reveals damage to the frontal, temporal, sensorimotor, or parietal-occipital area (see Box A.1) of the right or left hemisphere.

For example, patients with lesions in the frontal lobe of the left hemisphere have very high scores—with this battery a zero is given for no errors—on the pathognomonic scale. Expressive speech is more extensively disrupted than receptive ability, and motor impairment is greater than tactile. As for motor impairment, patients do better on items testing fine coordination than on those testing complex, sequential movements. High scores on the arithmetic, memory, and intelligence sections indicate severe injuries to the left frontal lobe. Patients with damage in the right parietal-occipital area have generally equal motor and tactile scores. Their motor loss is of spatial analysis and drawing skills. Their worst, or highest, scores will be tactile, motor, arith-

metic, and pathognomonic. They make better scores on memory and writing, and the writing score is generally better than the reading (Golden, 1981). The Luria-Nebraska battery can be administered in two and a half hours. The Halstead-Reitan takes six.

BEHAVIORAL ASSESSMENT

The Rorschach inkblot test, the TAT, and the MMPI, three of the assessment devices in most common use today, are intimately related to psychoanalytic theory or to an old diagnostic system. As already mentioned, within a psychodynamic framework it makes sense to use a projective test because truly important material is assumed repressed in the unconscious, and ambiguous stimuli rather than direct questions are viewed as the best means to bypass defense mechanisms. The MMPI, a more direct, self-report measurement, was developed to make some diagnoses not listed in DSM-III.

In recent years, as part of the continuing development of behavioral approaches to the study of psychopathology and treatment, interest has been growing in assessment procedures that are different from those examined so far. In Chapter 2 learning researchers and behaviorists are described as being interested in *situational determinants* of behavior, that is, in the environmental conditions that precede and follow certain responses. In addition, with the growing interest in cognitive explanations, we can expect the assessments made by behaviorists to include self-reports as well; but, as we shall see, interpretations of self-reports within a behavioral framework differ from those in more traditional assessment.

Traditional assessment concentrates on measuring underlying personality structures and *traits*, such as "anal personality," "obsessive personality," "paranoid personality," coldness, aggressiveness, and so on. "A chief aim of the trait approach is to infer the underlying personality structure of individuals and to compare persons and groups on trait dimensions" (Mischel, 1968, pp. 5–6). Behavioral clinicians, on the other hand, focus on specifying conditions under which behavior does or does not occur. Clients typically consult a therapist with vague, generalized compliants such as "I'm all messed up," or "I'm depressed all the time." It is a considerable challenge to the behavior therapist to obtain from clients information that can prove useful in analyzing the problem in learning terms and, more importantly, in planning various therapy programs.

Behavioral clinicians are concerned with four sets of variables, sometimes referred to by the acronym *SORC* (Kanfer and Phillips, 1970). The S stands for stimuli, the environmental situations that precede the problem. For instance, the clinician will try to ascertain which situations tend to elicit an especially high degree of anxiety. The O stands for organismic, referring to both physiological and psychological factors assumed to be operating "under the skin." Perhaps the client's fatigue is caused in part by excessive use of alcohol, or by a tendency to deprecate the self with such statements as "I never do anything right, so what's the point in trying?" The R refers to overt responses, which probably demand the most attention from behavioral clinicians. They must determine what behavior is problematic, its frequency, intensity, and form. For example, a client might

Assessment of behavior by direct observation through a one-way mirror. Subjects cannot see the experimenters making observations, although they are aware of and have consented to being observed.

say that she is forgetful and procrastinates. Does she mean that she does not return phone calls, comes late for appointments, or both? Finally, C or consequent variables are events that appear to be reinforcing the behavior in question. When the client avoids a feared situation, does his spouse offer sympathy and excuses, thereby unwittingly keeping the person from facing up to his fears?

SORC factors are those that a behavioral clinician attempts to specify for a particular client. It might be mentioned in passing that O variables are understandably underplayed by Skinnerians; similarly, C variables receive less attention from cognitively oriented behavior therapists than do O variables.

The information necessary for a *behavioral assessment* is gathered by several methods. These include direct observation of the behavior in real life as well as in contrived settings, interviews and self-report measures, cognitive assessment, and physiological measurement.

Direct Observation of Behavior

It is not surprising that behavior therapists have paid considerable attention to careful observation of behavior in a variety of settings. But it should not be assumed that they simply go out and *observe*. Like other scientists, they try to fit physical events into a framework consistent with their point of view. This excerpt from a case report by Gerald Patterson and his colleagues (1969), describing an interaction between a boy named Kevin and his mother, father, and sister Freida, serves as the first part of an example.

Kevin goes up to father's chair and stands alongside it. Father puts his arms around Kevin's shoulders. Kevin says to mother as Freida looks at Kevin, "Can I go out and play after supper?" Mother does not reply. Kevin raises his voice and repeats the question. Mother says "You don't have to yell; I can hear you." Father says "How many times have I told you not to yell at your mother?" Kevin scratches a bruise on his arm while mother tells Freida to get started on the dishes, which Freida does. Kevin continues to rub and scratch his arm while mother and daughter are working at the kitchen sink (p. 21).

This informal description could probably be provided by any observer. But a behavioral observer would divide the uninterrupted sequence of behavior into various parts and apply terms that make sense within a learning framework. "Kevin begins the exchange by asking a routine question in a normal tone of voice. This ordinary behavior, however, is not reinforced by the mother's attention; for she does not reply. Because she does not reply, the normal behavior of Kevin ceases and he yells his question. The mother expresses disapproval—punishing her son—by telling him that he does not have to yell. And this punishment is supported by the father's reminding Kevin that he should not yell at his mother." This behavioral rendition acknowledges the consequences of ignoring a child's question. At some point the behavior therapist will undoubtedly advise the parents to attend to Kevin's requests when expressed in an ordinary tone of voice, lest he begin yelling. This example indicates an important aspect of behavioral assessment, namely its link to *intervention*. The clinician's way of conceptualizing a situation often implies a way to try to change it.

It is difficult to observe most behavior as it actually takes place, and little control can be exercised over where and when it may occur. For this reason many therapists contrive artificial situations in their consulting rooms or in a laboratory so that they can observe how a client or a family acts under certain conditions. The sequence just described might well have happened in such a contrived setting.

The foregoing operant interpretation of a family scene employs no inferential concepts; the observations are interpreted in a fairly straightforward way. Behavioral assessment techniques can also be applied within a framework that does make use of mediators. For instance, Gordon Paul (1966) was interested in assessing the "anxiety" of public speakers. He decided to count the frequency of behavior that is deemed indicative of this emotional state. One of his principal measures, the Timed Behavorial Checklist for Performance Anxiety, is shown in Table 4.5. Subjects were asked to deliver a speech in front of a group, some members of which were raters trained to consider each subject's behavior every thirty seconds and to record the presence or absence of twenty specific behaviors. By summing the scores, Paul arrived at a behavioral index of anxiety. This study is one example of how observations of overt behavior have been used to infer an internal state.

In Paul's study people other than the speaker whose behavior was being described made the observations. For several years behavior therapists and researchers have also asked individuals to observe their *own* behavior, to keep track of various categories of response. The general approach is called *self-monitoring*. An early application of self-monitoring was in research to reduce

smoking. Subjects were provided with booklets in which they recorded the time each cigarette was lighted at baseline, before treatment had been introduced, during treatment, and after.

Although some research indicates that self-monitoring can provide accurate measurement of such behavior as smoking and the eating of certain foods, many report that the information collected is unreliable (Nelson, 1977). And yet there are ways to improve the accuracy of self-monitoring: by rewarding people for accuracy (Lipinski et al., 1975), by taking care to motivate subjects to be honest and conscientious (Bornstein et al., 1977), by training them in the demands of the particular self-monitoring task (Nelson, Lipinski, and Boykin, 1978), and by informing people that their self-monitoring is in turn being watched by other observers (Nelson, Lipinski, and Black, 1975). At the same time, however, considerable research indicates that behavior may be altered by the very fact that it is being self-monitored (Haynes and Horn, 1982). *Reactivity* of behavior is the phenomenon of its changing because it is being observed. Generally speaking, desirable behavior, such as engaging in social conversation, often increases in frequency when self-monitored (Nelson, Lipinski, and Black, 1976), whereas behavior the subject wishes to reduce, like cigarette smoking, diminishes (McFall and Hammen, 1971). Such findings suggest that the reactivity which is an outcome of self-monitoring can be taken advantage of in therapeutic interventions.

Interviews and Self-Report Measures

For all their interest in direct observation of behavior, behavioral clinicians still rely very heavily on the interview to assess the needs of their clients. Like other clinicians, they make every effort to establish good rapport, creating an atmosphere of trust and caring which encourages clients to reveal aspects of their lives that they may not have shown any other person—what London (1964) has poetically called "secrets of the heart." Within this trusting relationship the behavior therapist's job is to determine, via skillful questioning and careful observation of the client's emotional reactions during the interview, the SORC factors already mentioned—the situations in which the problematic behavior occurs, the internal conditions mediating the influence of the environment, the particular patterns of behavior causing distress, and the events that may help to maintain the problem. The authors of this textbook, in their behav-

TABLE 4.5 Timed Behavioral Checklist for Performance Anxiety   *(from Paul, 1966)*

Behavior Observed	Time Period								
	1	2	3	4	5	6	7	8	Σ
1. Paces									
2. Sways									
3. Shuffles feet									
4. Knees tremble									
5. Extraneous arm and hand movement (swings, scratches, toys, etc.)									
6. Arms rigid									
7. Hands restrained (in pockets, behind back, clasped)									
8. Hand tremors									
9. No eye contact									
10. Face muscles tense (drawn, tics, grimaces)									
11. Face "deadpan"									
12. Face pale									
13. Face flushed (blushes)									
14. Moistens lips									
15. Swallows									
16. Clears throat									
17. Breathes heavily									
18. Perspires (face, hands, armpits)									
19. Voice quivers									
20. Speech blocks or stammers									

iorally oriented clinical work, conduct an initial interview with the goal of writing an intake report like the one shown in Table 4.6.

The self-report inventories that behavior therapists develop are a great deal more specific and detailed than those typically used by nonbehavioral clinicians. For example, McFall and Lillesand (1971) employed a Conflict Resolution Inventory, containing thirty-five items which focus on the ability of the respondent to refuse unrea-sonable requests. Each item describes a specific situation in which a person is asked for something unreasonable. For example, "You are in the thick of studying for exams when a person you know slightly comes into your room and says, 'I'm tired of studying, mind if I come in and take a break for a while?'" Subjects are asked to indicate the likelihood that they would refuse such a request and how comfortable they would be in doing so. This and similar inventories are used by the practicing clinician and have helped behavioral researchers measure the outcome of clinical interventions as well.

Cognitive Assessment

The thoughts of patients may be probed both in interviews and by self-report inventories, as we have just seen. Patients reflect backward in time and provide a retrospective and rather general report of their thoughts in certain situations. "When someone criticizes you in class, what thoughts go through your mind?" is a question a client might be asked in an interview or on a paper-and-pencil inventory. The methods by which cognitions of clinical interest are assessed have been reviewed by Kendall and Hollon (1981). Perhaps the most widely employed has patients fill out several self-report questionnaires, one ascertaining, for example, their fear of negative evaluation, another their tendency to think irrationally.

Replies of subjects to questions asked by interviewers and inventories about their thoughts in certain situations may well be different from what they would report were they able to do so in the immediate circumstance. Moreover, cognitive-behavioral clinicians like Albert Ellis and Aaron Beck make predictions about the kinds of thoughts troubled people will have under very specific conditions. Behavioral researchers have been working on ways to enable subjects to tap into their immediate and ongoing thought processes when confronted with particular circumstances. Can we show, for example, that a socially anxious person does in fact, as Ellis would predict, think it a catastrophe when companions look askance at him or her, whereas someone who is not socially insecure does not?

The Articulated Thoughts During Simulated Situations method of Davison and his associates (Davison, Robins, and Johnson, 1983; Davison, Feldman, and Osborn, 1984) is an example of research allowing the immediate thoughts of individuals to be expressed. In this procedure a subject pretends that he or she is a participant in a situation, such as listening to a teaching assistant criticize a term paper, one which the subject hopes will receive a good grade. Presented on audiotape, the scene pauses every ten or fifteen seconds. During the following thirty seconds of silence, the subject talks aloud about whatever is going through his or her mind in reaction to the words just heard. Then the audiotaped scene continues, stopping after a few moments so that the subject can articulate his or her thoughts another time. One taped scene in which the subject overhears two pretend acquaintances criticizing him or her includes the following segments.

First acquaintance: He certainly did make a fool of himself over what he said about religion. I just find that kind of opinion very closed-minded and unaware. You have to be blind to the facts of the universe to believe that. [Thirty-second pause for subject's response.]

Second acquaintance: What really bugs me is the way he expresses himself. He never seems to stop and think, but just blurts out the first thing that comes into his head. [Thirty-second pause.]

Subjects readily become involved in the pretend situations, regarding them as credible and realistic. The following findings have emerged from several of the studies conducted thus far.

1. More of the articulated thoughts of subjects hearing a tape of two pretend acquaintances criticizing them were coded as "critical evaluation of the speaker" and "desire to harm the speaker" than were their thoughts in response to a neutral tape (Davison, Robins, and Johnson, 1983).

2. The articulated thoughts of subjects hearing the taped criticisms of two pretend acquaintances or the taped disparaging remarks of a pretend teaching assistant about their term paper were more irrational than was their thinking aloud to a neutral tape (Davison, Feldman, and Osborn, 1984).

3. Depressed patients from a psychiatric clinic and fellow outpatients with other psychological disorders listened to a tape describing an outdoor barbecue, one which they had supposedly planned and on which it had rained. The articulated thoughts of the depressed patients were more illogical, as Beck predicts (see page 200), than those of the other outpatients (White, Davison, and White, 1985).

4. Subjects referred by a campus counseling center as being excessively shy, withdrawn, and sensitive to criticism articulated thoughts of greater irrationality than did subjects recruited from an introductory psychology course (Davison and Zighelboim, 1985).

This pattern of results indicates that the method does indeed ferret out people's thinking about both inherently bothersome and "objectively" innocuous situations.

The interest in cognitive assessment has recently brought cognitive-behavioral clinicians into contact with literature in experimental cognitive psychology, the

TABLE 4.6 A Behaviorally Oriented Intake Report   *(after Goldfried and Davison, 1976)*

Name: BRIAN, James (fictitious name)   Age: 22 Sex: Male

Class: Senior
                                                Date of interview: March 26, 1984
                                                         Therapist: John Doe

1. Behavior during interview and physical description:
   James is a clean-shaven, long-haired young man who appeared for the intake interview in well-coordinated college garb: jeans, wide belt, open shirt, and sandals. He came across as shy and soft-spoken, with occasional minor speech blocks. Although uneasy during most of the session, he nonetheless spoke freely and candidly.

2. Presenting problem:
   (a) Nature of problem: Anxiety in public-speaking situations and in other situations in which he is being evaluated by others.

   (b) Historical setting events: James was born in France and arrived in this country seven years ago, at which time he experienced both social and language problems. His social contacts had been minimal until he entered college; there a socially aggressive friend helped him to break out of his shell. James describes his father as an overly critical perfectionist who would, on occasion, rip up his son's homework if it fell short of the mark. His mother he pictures as a controlling, overly affectionate person who always shows concern about his welfare. His younger brother, who has always been a good student, is continually thrown up to James by his parents as being far better than he.

   (c) Current situational determinants: Interaction with his parents, examinations, family gatherings, participation in classes, initial social contacts.

   (d) Relevant organismic variables: The client appears to be approaching a number of situations with certain irrational expectations, primarily unrealistic strivings for perfection and an overwhelming desire to receive approval from others. He is not taking any medication at this time except as indicated under 10 below.

   (e) Dimensions of problem: The client's anxiety about social relationships and evaluations of himself is long standing and occurs in a wide variety of day-to-day situations.

   (f) Consequences of problem: His chronic level of anxiety resulted in an ulcer operation at the age of 15. In addition, he has developed a skin rash on his hands and arms, apparently from excessive perspiration. He reports that his nervousness at one time caused him to stutter, but this problem appears to have diminished in recent years. His anxiety when taking examinations has typically interfered with his ability to perform well.

3. Other problems:

   (a) Assertiveness: Although obviously a shy and timid individual, James says that lack of assertiveness is no longer a problem with him. At one time in the past, his friends would take advantage of him, but he

branch of empirical psychological research concerned with the ways people transform environmental input into usable information, how they think and plan, remember and anticipate. In addition to self-talk research, workers have developed assessment tools for inferring the existence of a number of cognitive structures, particularly schemata. The term schema, introduced by the British psychologist Frederick Bartlett in 1932, has been defined as ". . . that portion of the entire perceptual cycle which is internal to the perceiver, modifiable by experience, and somehow specific to what

is being perceived'' (Neisser, 1976, p. 54). A simple example of a schema would be the idea we carry around in our heads of what a face is—a configuration having two eyes, a nose and mouth, and two ears. We are able to identify an object as a face, even when its configuration has much that is unusual about it.

More germane to our clinical concerns is the concept of *script*, a term introduced by Schank and Abelson (1977) to describe sequences of actions that are internalized in our minds and guide our progress to a goal. For example, we all have a "restaurant script," according to claims that this is no longer the case. His statements should be followed up, for it is unclear what he means by assertiveness.

(b) Forgetfulness: The client reports that he frequently misses appointments, misplaces items, locks himself out of his room, and is generally absentminded.

4. Personal assets:

The client is fairly bright and comes across as a warm, friendly, and sensitive individual.

5. Targets for modification:

Unrealistic self-statements about how he should fare in social evaluative situations; possible behavioral deficits associated with unassertiveness; and forgetfulness.

6. Recommended treatment:

It appears that relaxation training would be a good way to begin, especially in light of the client's high level of anxiety. Treatment should then undertake the restructuring of his unrealistic expectations. Behavior rehearsal is a possibility. The best strategy for dealing with forgetfulness is unclear as yet.

7. Motivation for treatment:

High.

8. Prognosis:

Good.

9. Priority for treatment:

High.

10. Expectancies:

On occasion, especially when going out on a date, James takes a tranquilizer (Valium, 10 mg) to calm himself down. He wants to get away from this and feels that he needs to learn to cope with his anxieties by himself. It would appear that he will be receptive to whatever treatment plan we finally decide on, especially if the emphasis is on self-control of anxiety.

11. Other comments:

Considering the brief time available between now and the end of the semester, between-session homework assignments should be given.

which we know and anticipate a series of fairly predictable events and actions that take place from the time we enter a restaurant to the time we leave it with our appetites satisfied. We sit down, look at a menu, order, eat, pay the bill, and leave (Bower, Black, and Turner, 1979). The cognitive internalization of this general plan enables us to cope with a wide variety of situations without having to pay close attention to them while they are happening.

Many methods of isolating people's scripts are based not on direct self-report but on inferences made from

behavior. Thus we can observe people eating in a restaurant, see regularities in their behavior—even see emotional upset when irregularities occur, such as when food does not come after being ordered—and then infer that a restaurant script is operating. Research indicates that memory as well is affected by the script. Subjects faced with recalling a story about an accident in a restaurant distort happenings so that they conform to a prevalent script. For example, they recall that the characters in the story paid the bill, even though the story omitted this detail.

A common script is the ritual trip to the bank during lunch hour on payday.

Here a psychologist monitors the output of several channels of a polygraph, a device for measuring a number of physiological responses such as heart rate, blood pressure, respiration, and electrodermal activity.

Physiological Measurement

Experimentally minded behavioral clinicians and therapy researchers often employ sophisticated procedures for measuring physiological aspects of behavior. The discipline of _psychophysiology_ is concerned with the bodily changes that accompany psychological events (Grings and Dawson, 1978; see Box 4.1). For example, we know that the heart rate of most people will increase markedly under conditions of psychological, as well as physical, stress.

Experimenters have studied such changes, as well as alterations in the conductivity of the skin, tension in the muscles, blood flow in various parts of the body, and even brain waves (see page 239), while subjects are afraid, depressed, asleep, imagining, solving problems, and so on. Special attention has been paid to the _patterning_ of such responses, as when heart rate increases while skin conductivity remains constant.

Behavioral clinicians have come to realize that a more complete picture of the human being is obtained by assessing physiological functioning along with overt behavior and cognitive activity. If experimenters wonder whether showing schizophrenic patients pictures of their mothers is stressful, they can, in addition to asking the patients how they feel about looking at the pictures, measure their heart rate and electrical skin activity. Psychophysiological measuring procedures, which are constantly being improved and added to, are relatively unobtrusive. Once the person has adapted to having electrodes pasted on his or her arm, for example, measurement of heart rate does not interfere with many ex-

perimental tasks, such as listening to a story or solving a mathematical problem.

Inasmuch as psychophysiology employs highly sophisticated electronic machinery, and inasmuch as many psychologists aspire to be as scientific as possible, it sometimes happens that they believe uncritically in these apparently objective assessment devices without appreciating their real limitations and complications. Many of the measurements do not differentiate clearly among emotional states. Heart rate, for example, increases with a variety of emotions, not just with anxiety. Special care must be taken to ensure a proper setting for taking measurements so that the data collected are meaningful.

Behavioral Assessment for Behavioral Change

We have already mentioned that a principal aspect of behavioral assessment is its close ties to procedures for changing behavior. Behavior therapists always search thoroughly for the situational determinants of behavior because they believe it can be altered by manipulating

BOX 4.1

MEASUREMENT OF AUTONOMIC NERVOUS SYSTEM ACTIVITY

The mammalian nervous system can be considered to have two relatively separate functional divisions: the *somatic* or voluntary, and the *autonomic* or involuntary. Because the autonomic nervous system is especially important in the study of emotional behavior, it will be useful to review its principal characteristic and the ways in which its activity can be monitored.

Skeletal muscles, such as those that move our limbs, are innervated by the voluntary nervous system. Much of our behavior, however, is dependent on a nervous system that

operates generally without our awareness and has traditionally been viewed as beyond voluntary control. Hence the term autonomic. The autonomic nervous system (ANS) innervates the endocrine glands, the heart, and the smooth muscles which are found in the walls of the blood vessels, stomach, intestines, kidneys, and other organs. This nervous system is itself divided into two parts, the *sympathetic* and *parasympathetic* nervous systems (Figure 4.2), which sometimes work against each other, sometimes in unison. The sympathetic portion of the ANS, when energized, ac-

Sympathetic ——
Parasympathetic ——

Eye
Lacrimal gland
Mucous membrane of
nose and palate
Submaxillary gland
Sublingual gland
Mucous membrane of mouth
Parotid gland
Heart
Larynx
Trachea
Lungs
Esophagus
Stomach
Abdominal
blood vessels
Liver and ducts
Pancreas
Small
intestine
Large
intestine
Adrenal gland
Rectum
Kidney
Bladder
Sexual organ
External genitalia

Thoracic
Lumbar
Sacral
Spinal cord

FIGURE 4.2 The autonomic nervous system.

celerates the heartbeat, dilates the pupils, inhibits intestinal activity, and initiates other smooth muscle and glandular responses that prepare the organism for sudden activity and stress. Indeed, some physiologists view the sympathetic nervous system as primarily excitatory, whereas the other division, the parasympathetic, is viewed as responsible for maintenance functions and more quiescent behavior, such as deceleration of the heartbeat, constriction of the pupils, and speeding up contractions of the intestines. Division of activities is not quite so clear-cut, however, for the parasympathetic system may be active during situations of stress. Animals, and human beings to their consternation, may urinate and defecate involuntarily when extremely frightened.

The activities of the ANS are frequently assessed by electronic and chemical measurements and analyses in attempts to understand the nature of emotion. One important measure is heart rate. Each heartbeat generates spreading changes in electric potential, which can be recorded by an electrocardiograph or on a suitably tuned polygraph. Electrodes are usually placed on both arms and lead to a galvanometer, an instrument for measuring electric currents. The deflections of this instrument may be seen as waves on an oscilloscope, or a pen recorder may register the waves on a continuously moving roll of graph paper. Both types of recordings are called electrocardiograms. More recently available is the cardiotachometer, a device which measures the precise elapsed time between two heartbeats and then instantaneously provides heart rate on

a beat-to-beat basis. This technological advance is especially important for experimental psychologists, who are typically interested in bodily changes that occur over short periods of time in response to rapidly shifting circumstances. Generally a fast heart rate is taken to indicate increased arousal.

A second measure is *electrodermal responding*, sometimes referred to as the *galvanic skin response* (GSR). Anxiety, fear, anger, and other emotions increase sweat gland activity. The electrophysiological processes in the cells of these glands change the electric conductance of the skin as well as producing sweat. There are two methods of measuring the electrodermal response. Skin potential may be measured by recording with surface electrodes the very small differences in electric potential that always exist between any two points on the skin. This voltage shows a pronounced rise after the sweat glands have been stimulated to activity. Or we may determine the current that flows through the skin when a known small voltage derived from an external source is passed between two electrodes pasted to the palm and back of the hand. This current also shows a pronounced increase after activation of the sweat glands. The percentage of change from the normal or baseline reading is for either method the measure of reactivity. High conductance, or alternatively low resistance, is thought to reflect increased autonomic activity. Since the sweat glands are innervated only by the sympathetic nervous system, increased sweat gland activity indicates sympathetic autonomic excitation and is often taken as a measure of anxiety.

the environment. One behavior therapy procedure, systematic desensitization, seems to be effective in reducing a variety of fears. This technique requires that the therapist know the particular situations that make the patient fearful. Rather than make a general diagnosis, such as phobic reaction, and then begin to search for underlying personality dynamics, behavior therapists believe that quicker and greater progress can be made by ascertaining the specific situations in which people are phobic and then lessening their fears of them. To take another example, an aggressive youngster might be directly observed to see whether teachers and parents reinforce his abrasive behavior with their attention. If this is the case, they can be cautioned to ignore the outbursts as much as possible. These steps contrast with diagnosing the boy as having a conduct disorder and then seeking the reasons for his general problem. The range of behavior therapies for different disorders, to be described in later chapters, will reveal again and again this direct link between assessment and intervention.

Reliability of Behavioral Assessment

We have now surveyed the major approaches to behavioral assessment. The reader has probably become aware of how much more *direct* this type of assessment is than the traditional techniques, such as the Rorschach described earlier in this chapter. If the behavioral researcher wants to determine how anxious a person is, he or she decides what will be taken to indicate anxiety, such as hand tremors or a particular pattern of psychophysiological response recorded on a polygraph, and then measures the person's responses under controlled conditions, as when taking a test.

Are things really so simple? Because a behavioral researcher directly observes a bit of behavior, are better data necessarily being collected? The answer is maybe. Let us examine the problem in terms first of reliability and then of validity.[2]

[2]Reliability and validity issues in behavioral assessment are very complex. A sophisticated discussion can be found in Kanfer and Nay (1982).

The reliability of diagnoses depends on whether various diagnosticians agree on how to categorize patients' problems. That of behavioral assessment procedures too depends on whether outcomes are similar. Do two raters using a particular coding system make similar observations of the same event, and does a respondent, when taking two versions of a test judged to be roughly equivalent, make similar scores? For example, Paul (1966), in employing the behavioral checklist shown in Table 4.5, trained his research assistants extensively until two of them, while watching the same subject give a speech, could reach similar judgments of the frequency of the several signs of anxiety.

Over the years the reliability of behavioral assessment has been shown to be affected by several factors. The complexity or difficulty of the assessment task can lower reliability. If an investigator is using a time-sampling procedure as Paul did, whereby raters watch for certain indicators at fixed time intervals, reliability can be enhanced if the interval between observations is long enough to allow raters time to make careful judgments—every minute rather than every ten seconds, for instance; and if the behaviors to be watched for are few rather than many—five, for example, rather than twenty.

Another consideration is the way observers are monitored. At the earliest stages of a research project, the people with overall responsibility, the investigators, usually work very closely with the experimenters, those who actually have contact with the subjects. Before running a study, the investigators spend many hours with their assistants, ensuring that instructions are being followed and that any behavioral assessments are being done reliably. It has been shown that once the experimenters are left unsupervised—or, more precisely, once they *believe* themselves to be on their own—they tend to become slipshod and hence less reliable as observers (Romanczyk et al., 1973). An effective and ethical way to increase reliability is to inform the experimenters that their work will be checked now and again, without telling them exactly when. This unscheduled observing of the observers seems to keep them on their toes and thus increases reliability (Bernstein and Nietzel, 1980).

Validity of Behavioral Assessment

Behavioral researchers have only recently attended to the validity of their measures. As implied in Chapter 3, the validity of any measure is the extent to which it reflects what it is supposed to reflect. For example, if an investigator asserts that frequent lateness is an indicator of hostility, he or she is making a statement about the validity of lateness as a measure of hostility. Is this researcher justified in making such an assertion? Or, put differently, are we prepared to agree that hostility can be assessed by taking note of lateness?

Because behavioral assessment is so much more direct than traditional personality assessment, we can be seduced into assuming validity uncritically and perhaps prematurely. Common sense and the already discussed reactivity of self-monitored behavior, however, suggest that people behave or think differently when they are aware of being watched. For example, Zeigob, Arnold, and Forehand (1975) found that mothers acted more positively toward their children when they knew that they were being observed than when observations were made surreptitiously. Therefore the behavior of the mothers aware of being watched may not provide a valid assessment of their typical level of positive mothering.

Not all behavior, however, is reactive to being measured, and much remains to be learned about this possible source of invalidity (see Haynes and Horn, 1982). We do know that clients and subjects must become accustomed to being observed before the information being collected can be taken seriously. For example, a recorder might run for half an hour before the taped

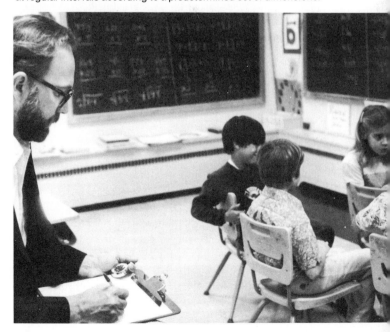

Daniel O'Leary, Stony Brook psychologist, observing and recording the behavior of children in a classroom. He is coding their behavior at regular intervals according to a predetermined set of dimensions.

BOX 4.2

THE ASSESSMENT OF ANXIETY: IN PURSUIT OF AN ELUSIVE CONSTRUCT

Many issues in assessment can be appreciated by considering efforts to measure anxiety, one of the most prevalent emotions and one of great concern to psychopathologists and therapists. They have generally relied on three modes of measurement: self-report questionnaires, observations of overt behavior, and physiological measurements.

Allowing people to describe the phenomena of their emotions in their own terms, as is done in clinical interviews, provides useful information about the one individual interviewed; but this strategy alone makes it difficult to compare the experiences of a number of people and, even more important, to quantify what they say. Researchers have therefore devised various self-report questionnaires which attempt to direct the individual's impressions into standardized terms. The following are some sample items from the Taylor Manifest Anxiety Scale (Taylor, 1953), which consists of fifty items drawn from the MMPI.

I work under a great deal of strain.	True	False
I am usually calm and not easily upset.	True	False
I sweat very easily even on cool days.	True	False
I always have enough energy when faced with difficulty.	True	False
My sleep is restless and disturbed.	True	False

An anxious person would underline the true and false responses as indicated. The test is scored by simply summing the number of "anxious" responses made by the subject. This score is then assumed to represent the person's general level of anxiety.

The second means of assessing anxiety is to observe overt behavior for reactions and movements that are believed to reflect the internal emotional state—trembling, perspiring, nail biting, fleeing from a situation. Observers trained to administer Paul's (1966) Timed Behavioral Checklist for Performance Anxiety time-sampled the overt behavior of subjects in a stressful situation, recording in-

stances of twenty indices of anxiety whenever they were observed.

Physiological measurements of activities of the autonomic nervous system and the output of certain endocrine glands also indicate levels of anxiety. The availability of these measurements has encouraged researchers to define anxiety in physiological terms. The situation in which physiological measurements are taken is very important, however. What would be revealed, for example, if recording electrodes were attached to a woman who is about to have sexual relations? Both before and during sexual activity the heartbeat is very likely to be faster, blood pressure higher, perspiration greater, and breathing more rapid, all physiological responses that are generally regarded as indicators of sexual excitement as well as of anxiety. But why would we not conclude that our female subject is, indeed, anxious as she contemplates sexual intercourse? As we shall see in Chapter 13, many people are debilitated by fear in sexual situations. How can an investigator distinguish rapid breathing that reflects sexual excitement from rapid breathing that reflects anxiety? Part of the answer necessarily lies in other observations being made concurrently. If at the time physiological measures are being taken the female subject convincingly reports that she is looking forward to what is to come, and if she ultimately derives great enjoyment from her sexual partner, we would almost certainly choose to interpret her rapid breathing and other physiological responses as indicating sexual arousal. The situation and her self-report of it must be taken into consideration.

Not only are the physiological indicators of anxiety evident in other emotional states, but the many measures of anxiety have been found time and again *not* to correlate well with one another (see Martin, 1961; Lang, 1969). In a stressful situation such as being threatened with painful electric shock, many people report being very nervous, but their heart rates may be lower rather than elevated. An indi-

---

conversation of a group becomes a source of data on group interaction.

Another problem is the *external* or *ecological validity* of an assessment, whether it applies to the actual situations of interest to the researcher or clinician. Imagine that a therapist has a client role-play in the office to determine whether the young woman asserts herself to her mother, the therapist taking the part of the parent. If she proves to be assertive, can the therapist conclude that she has no assertion problems with her mother? It

would be hasty to do so. The most obvious consideration is that the therapist is not the client's mother! Moreover, the particular situation selected for role playing, such as asking the mother not to telephone so often, might not touch on other problems requiring more assertion. The client might be able to ask her mother for a loan but not for some baby-sitting help. Any observation made of behavior is necessarily limited. We can *never* observe all conceivable situations; assessment, like any other knowledge-gathering enterprise, always vidual taking an important examination for which he or she is ill-prepared may deny feeling anxious and yet be observed trembling. Moreover, if people are asked to report on their awareness of various signs of anxiety, such as a feeling of tightness in the neck, their avoidance of social gatherings, and worrying, their self-reports tend to cluster into one of three fairly independent groups—somatic, behavioral, and cognitive (Lehrer and Woolfolk, 1982). Thus the anxiety reported by people appears to be made up of one of three relatively separate components. One person may have bodily indicators, such as muscle tension and acid stomach, and yet not experience cognitive signs, such as ruminating about an alarming event.

On a more general level many workers regard the concept of anxiety as a useful one for organizing and interrelating data from numerous sources. Maher (1966) and Lang (1969), for example, consider anxiety to be a hypothetical _construct_, a convenient fiction or inferred state that mediates between a threatening situation and the observed behavior of an organism. They also assume that the construct is multifaceted or multidimensional, and that each facet is not necessarily evoked by a given stressful situation or always expressed to the same degree, another explanation of the low intercorrelations for the measures of anxiety.

As a scientific construct, anxiety must be tied to observables, the conditions that produce it and the effects that follow its induction. For this very reason Skinner (1953), as we indicated earlier (see page 42), argues that mediators are not essential in accounting for behavior. Since the construct of anxiety is linked to stimuli and responses, why not dispense with it and talk only of observables? Furthermore, might not the inference of an internal state lead us to believe that an adequate explanation has been found and thereby discourage the continuing search for ways to predict and control behavior?

These are cogent objections, and they have forced workers to exercise great care in their use of the anxiety construct. As will be noted in Chapter 5, investigators who employ mediators such as anxiety do so in hopes of better

organizing their data and of generating hypotheses. We seldom find experimental psychologists speaking about anxiety without being able at any time to explain how and why they infer that the emotional state exists.

Finally, certain experiments would not be undertaken or could not be explained without inferring the mediating state. To illustrate, let us consider an experiment reviewed by Rescorla and Solomon (1967). Dogs were taught to avoid a stimulus (CS) by pairing it repeatedly with a painful shock (UCS). Then they were totally paralyzed with injections of curare, a drug which prevents movement of the skeletal muscles. One group of animals, while paralyzed, were repeatedly presented with the CS, but shock did not accompany it. In Pavlovian, classical conditioning terms, these would be considered attempts to extinguish the conditioned response. Did these animals learn, while paralyzed and unable to move, that the CS was in fact no longer followed by shock? Phrased another way, did the previously learned fear of the CS undergo any extinction? The answer was obtained on a subsequent day when the dogs in this group had completely recovered from the curare and were confronted with the CS. The unshocked presentations of the CS a day or two earlier had indeed reduced avoidance behavior, even though no overt response could have occurred during the curare paralysis. The control animals, who had not been confronted with the CS while paralyzed, did not show a reduction in avoidance behavior.

How do we account for such remarkable findings? Rescorla and Solomon deem it necessary, and legitimate, to infer a mediating fear which was lessened when the dogs were presented with the CS while paralyzed with curare. Clearly something was being unlearned during the time that the dogs could not respond by avoiding the CS. By positing a mediating fear, we can make sense of these findings and relate them to a wealth of other theory and research. The experiment just described does indicate that anxiety, or fear, can be useful as an explanatory device. Nonetheless, the anxiety construct poses continual difficulties for those who employ it.

touches on less than exists or could exist. Behavioral assessors must be mindful how restricted their observations are and maintain a modest and cautious attitude about the external validity of their assessments.

Yet another issue are the many distortions that can creep into any observation made by a human being. We have discussed in Chapters 1 and 2 the important roles that paradigms play in science. Any assessor has a point of view and is subject to the effects of this bias. Most importantly, assessors may have expectations and com-

municate them to subjects. Some years ago Robert Rosenthal (1966) reported on a series of experiments that shocked experimental psychologists and clinicians alike. He demonstrated through review of others' work and by his own ingenious techniques that experimenters can often unwittingly influence the outcome of a study by virtue of having certain expectations about the results. This difficulty of experimenter bias has come to be called the _Rosenthal effect_. But in an interesting demonstration by Kent, O'Leary, and their colleagues (1974), experimenter bias was shown to affect overall conclusions rather than specific behavioral observations. In this study observers used a behavioral coding system as they watched videotapes of children who were being treated for disruptive behavior. One group of observers was told that the treatment would decrease disruptive behavior, the other that no change was expected. As Rosenthal's studies would suggest, observers afterward made the judgment that disruptive behavior had decreased if they had been told it was expected to. More importantly, however, their *specific behavior recordings* did not show bias. These results indicate the usefulness of relatively objective coding schemes in observing behavior.

Finally, the indicators we choose for measuring what interests us are the most basic issue in the validity of behavioral assessment. Consider the example mentioned earlier, measuring hostility by counting instances of lateness. Is this the best measure of hostility we can select? People might be late frequently for reasons other than hostility. Any person who has had to fight traffic at rush hour can surely come up with at least one example! We would have to take care, then, that a person whose hostility we wish to assess will not be late for non-emotional reasons.

There are many ways to evaluate how meaningful our measures are, and the validity of a wide range of behavioral assessment methods is actively being investigated (see Hersen and Bellack, 1981). Weiss, Hops, and Patterson (1973), for example, have developed an inventory that each member of a married couple fills out at the end of a day. The items of the inventory tap into such aspects of marriage as the frequency of pleasing behavior on the part of the spouse. In evaluating the validity of this Spouse Observation Checklist, Margolin (1978) determined that fewer "pleases" were reported by couples complaining of a distressed marriage than by couples reporting marital satisfaction. In another study Margolin and Weiss (1978) found that the frequency of displeasing behavior decreased markedly during a month in which couples underwent therapy to improve their communication. Such relationships strongly suggest that this instrument is valid as a measure of marital satisfaction.

These, then, are some of the problems in determining the validity of behavioral assessment and some of the strategies employed to handle them. Behavioral assessment has emerged as one of the liveliest and most important areas of work in clinical psychology and psychiatry.

THE CONSISTENCY AND VARIABILITY OF BEHAVIOR

Walter Mischel, in *Personality and Assessment* (1968), has argued that the environment is a more important determinant of behavior than are personality traits. Trait theorists, as stated earlier, believe that human beings can be described as having a certain "amount" of a characteristic, such as "stinginess," or "obsessiveness," and that their behavior in a variety of situations can be predicted by the degree to which they possess this

Walter Mischel, the prominent psychologist whose work stimulated the current debate concerning whether traits or situations are the most powerful determinants of behavior.

characteristic. This position implies that people will behave consistently in a variety of situations—for example, an aggressive person will be aggressive at home, at work, and at play. Mischel's analysis of the evidence bearing on this question, however, indicates that the behavior of people is often not very consistent from situation to situation.

Not surprisingly, Mischel's attack on trait theory elicited a heated debate in the literature. For example, the psychodynamic theorist Paul Wachtel (1977) argues that social-learning theorists like Mischel ignore current psychoanalytic thinking, which does not entirely overlook the way behavior varies in different situations. Moreover, Wachtel argues, the behavior of individuals whom clinicians tend to encounter may indeed be predictable on the basis of some underlying trait or disposition. Clinical problems may, in fact, be associated with a rigidity or inflexibility to changing conditions.[3]

Wachtel also suggests that people tend to perceive certain kinds of situations in a particular fashion; the perception in effect renders situations that look different to an experimenter equivalent in their own eyes. For example, a person who might be described as paranoid sees threats in seemingly innocuous situations. Insensitivity to circumstances is not his or her problem; rather this person perceives a great many situations as threatening events. In addition, people can *elicit* certain kinds of reactions from their surroundings. The paranoid individual may not only perceive people as threatening but make them so by attacking them first. In effect, he transforms different situations into similar and dangerous ones. As a result his own behavior varies little.

Wachtel goes on to argue that the experiments Mischel attends to are generally done with normal college undergraduates, whose behavior is probably more flexible than that of patients. As just mentioned, one of the hallmarks of mental disorder may be rigidity and inflexibility, which is another way of saying that behavior is consistent in a variety of situations. Therefore, by studying basically normal people, social-learning theorists have concluded that people are more variable than they might had they studied patients.

Thus, contrary to what some behavioral critics contend, contemporary psychodynamic thinkers do not dispute the important role that environmental events play in determining behavior. They argue instead that people perceive situations in certain ways, even transforming them, and then respond in a rather consistent manner.

Mischel, in an important paper published in 1973, replied to some of his critics by suggesting that social-learning theory can indeed incorporate certain personality variables in a more systematic fashion than was made clear in his original pronouncements in 1968. He suggested a set of primarily cognitive "person variables." The expectancy of affecting or not affecting the environment may, for example, be a major factor determining behavior and allowing its prediction. This and other person variables, argues Mischel, should be derived from experimental research and not from speculation, as tends to be the case in psychodynamic theorizing.

In the course of the debate touched off by Mischel's important book, a number of psychologists have suggested that his original position was too extreme. Jack Block challenged Mischel's conclusions regarding the inconsistency of behavior. In examining the studies Mischel used to support his claim, Block finds that most of them have serious flaws. For example, Mischel cites a single study (Burwen and Campbell, 1957) to support his contention that attitudes toward authority figures are not consistent. In this study, Block notes, reliability is not reported for some of the assessments made, and for others the reliability figures were quite low. Low reliability precludes finding strong relationships in measurements and thus of course any degree of consistency in the attitudes assessed. Block also presents information that does show consistency of behavior and was not considered by Mischel. A notable example is Block's own longitudinal study (1971), which indicated considerable consistency of personality as it was assessed in young people when they were attending junior high school, then senior high school, and later when they were adults.

Additional evidence of consistency and stability of behavior comes from Epstein (1979), who also criticized the studies used by Mischel to buttress the situationist position. These studies, noted Epstein, looked only at small bits of behavior, a strategy as inappropriate as it would be to measure IQ by looking at a person's score on a single item. More appropriate is an *averaging* of behavior from a range of situations. In the experiments he conducted, Epstein collected data on a number of occa-

---

[3]It has been suggested that people at the other extreme, those who "shift with the wind," so to speak, may also be subject to emotional disorder. That is, some forms of disorder may be connected to overdependence on the environment as a guide to behavior. To be totally at the mercy of one's surroundings, like a rudderless ship, would seem to pose as many problems as being insensitive to varying environmental demands (Phares, 1979).

sions and was indeed able to demonstrate marked consistency in behavior.

Mischel and Peake (1982), however, have countered these criticisms, pointing out that major assessment studies have all employed multiple measures and observations and yet have still failed to find significant behavioral consistencies. In their view Epstein confused stability of behavior over time for cross-situational consistency. That is, people can indeed be shown to behave consistently if their behavior is sampled more than once in the same kinds of situations, for example, being punctual for a lecture on day 1 as well as for one on day 2. Finding behavior to be similar in similar situations, however, is different from demonstrating that a person is, for example, anxious in situations Y and Z as well as in situation X.

SUMMARY

Clinicians rely on several modes of assessment in trying to find out how best to describe a patient, in their search for the reasons he or she is troubled, and in designing effective treatments. Described in some detail were clinical interviews, projective tests such as the Rorschach, standardized personality inventories such as the MMPI, intelligence tests, and tomographic and neuropsychological tests for organic brain dysfunction.

In their assessment, behavior therapists gather information on four sets of factors: situational determinants, organismic variables, responses, and the consequences of behavior. Whereas traditional diagnosis, of which DSM-III is an example, seeks to understand people in terms of general traits or personality structure, behavioral assessment is concerned more with how people act, feel, and think in particular kinds of situations. Specificity is the hallmark of behavioral assessment, the assumption of behavioral clinicians and researchers being that by operating within this framework they will gather more useful information about people. Some of the procedures adopted by behavior therapists, such as direct observation of behavior and behaviorally oriented interviews, were also described. Problems of reliability and validity in behavioral assessment were examined.

No concept is at the same time more important and more difficult to define and to measure than anxiety. This elusive concept was discussed separately.

Finally, the lively controversy about how stable human behavior is in varying situations was reviewed. The issue has for years been of both theoretical and practical interest to psychologists. Now, with the development of behavioral models of psychopathology and treatment, it has assumed special importance. The answers are far from in, but it appears prudent to say that behavior is probably more variable than was once thought by traditional personality theorists and also more stable in different situations than those working in the learning paradigm believe.

Victor Vasarely, *Gotha*, 1959 From a portfolio of 12 serigraphs, printed in color, 19-3/4" × 13-3/16". Collection, The Museum of Modern Art, New York. Transferred from the Museum Library.

RESEARCH METHODS
IN THE STUDY
OF ABNORMAL BEHAVIOR

Science and Scientific Methods
The Research Methods of Abnormal Psychology

From our discussion of different ways of conceptualizing and treating abnormal behavior and of problems in its classification and assessment, it should be clear that there is less than total agreement on how abnormal behavior ought to be studied. Our approach to the field is based on the belief that more progress will be made through scientific research than armchair speculation. Abnormal behavior, as we have already noted, has been the subject of theorizing for centuries. We are studying a field that has a high ratio of speculation to data. Because facts are hard to come by, it is important to discuss in some detail the contemporary research methods that are applied in psychopathology.

SCIENCE AND SCIENTIFIC METHODS

In Chapter 1 we indicated the important role that subjective factors play in the collection and interpretation of data, indeed, in the very definition of what constitutes an observation. Thus there is actually no one science or scientific method, although we often read in college textbooks of "the scientific method." The phrase "as currently practiced" should really be added.

Let us consider science from the point of view of Baruch Spinoza, a famous Dutch philosopher of the seventeenth century. He believed that the scientist's role was to discover God's law. Today we say that Spinoza did not hold a "constructive" view of science. We do not necessarily imply that Spinoza's views were not useful, rather that they can be differentiated from perspectives that emphasize the active role people play in constructing laws and principles. Contemporary scientists tend to regard the laws and theories in existence as constructions or inventions made by scientists. And the rules to be followed in formulating and evaluating these hypotheses and laws are also constructed by people and might very well be changed at any time. Science, as currently practiced, is the pursuit of systematized knowledge[1] through observation. Thus the term refers to a method, the systematic acquisition and evaluation of information. It also refers to a goal, the development of principles that explain the information. Contemporary science strives for explanations that are an outgrowth of, and can be modified by, publicly observed evidence. Both observations and explanations must meet certain criteria.

[1]The word science comes from the Latin *scire*, to know.

Testability and Falsifiability

A scientific approach requires first that propositions and ideas be stated in a clear and precise way. Only then can scientific claims be exposed to systematic probes and tests, any one of which could negate the scientist's expectations about what will be found. Statements, theories, and assertions, regardless of how plausible they may seem, must be testable in the public arena and be subject to being disproved. The attitude of science is an extremely doubting one. It is not enough to assert, for example, that particular traumatic experiences during childhood may cause psychological maladjustment in adulthood. This is no more than a possibility or proposition. According to a scientific point of view, such a hypothesis must be amenable to testing and to being found false.

Reliability

Closely related to testability is the demand that each observation forming a scientific body of knowledge be reliable. Whatever is observed must occur under prescribed circumstances not once but repeatedly. The event cannot be seen or detected only by a single individual or individuals in a given laboratory, community, or country. Instead, it must be reproducible under the circumstances stated, anywhere, anytime. If the event cannot be reproduced, scientists become wary of the legitimacy of the original observation.

The Role of Theory

A *theory* is a set of propositions meant to explain a class of phenomena. A primary goal of science is to advance theories to illuminate, often by proposing cause-effect relationships, the information with which it deals. The results of empirical research allow the adequacy of theories to be evaluated. Theories themselves can also play an important role in guiding research by suggesting that certain additional data be collected. The generation of a theory is perhaps the most challenging part of the scientific enterprise—and one of the least understood. It is sometimes asserted, for example, that a scientist formulates a theory simply by considering data that have been previously collected and then deciding, in a rather straightforward fashion, that a given way of talking about them is the most economical and useful and suggests still further experimentation for testing its own adequacy.

Although some theory building follows this course, not all does. Aspects too seldom mentioned are the *creativity* of the act and the *excitement* of finding a novel way to conceptualize things. A theory sometimes seems to leap from the scientist's head in a wonderful moment of insight. New ideas suddenly occur to the scientist, and connections hitherto overlooked are suddenly grasped. What seemed obscure or meaningless just a moment before now makes a new kind of sense within the framework that the new theory provides.

In formulating a theory, scientists must often make use of theoretical concepts, of unobservable states or processes that are inferred from observable data. Although theoretical concepts are inferred from observable data, they go beyond what can actually be seen or measured. Several advantages may thus be gained. First, theoretical concepts often bridge spatiotemporal relations. For example, in early physics it was noted that a magnet placed close to some iron filings would cause some of the filings to move toward it. How does one piece of metal influence another over the spatial distance? The inferred concept of magnetic fields proved to be very useful in accounting for this phenomenon. Similarly, in abnormal psychology we may often want to bridge temporal gaps with theoretical concepts. If a child has had a particularly frightening experience and his or her behavior is changed for a lengthy period of time, we need to explain how the earlier event is able to exert an influence over subsequent behavior. The unobservable and inferred concept of *acquired fear* has been very helpful in this regard.

Theoretical concepts may also be used to account for already observed relationships. Let us take a classic example proposed by a philosopher of science, Carl Hempel (1958). An early observer of nature has been studying what happens to various objects as they are placed in water. He or she formulates some lawlike generalizations, such as "Wood floats in water, iron sinks." In addition to the fact that a large number of such generalizations would be needed to describe exhaustively the behavior of all objects placed in liquids, exceptions to the generalizations are likely. Iron in a particular shape (boatlike) will float on water, and a water-logged piece of wood will sink. The solution is to propose a theoretical term, in this case specific gravity, which can both simplify descriptions of what will and will not float and allow errorless statements to be made. Specific gravity is the ratio of the weight of an object to its volume. And with this theoretical term we can now readily specify what will happen to *any* body placed in *any* liquid. If the specific gravity of the object is less than that of the liquid displaced, the object will float.

Let us now examine a similar and familiar instance, closer to the field of psychopathology. We may observe that people who are taking an examination, who expect a momentary electric shock, or who are fighting with a companion all have sweaty palms, trembling hands, and a fast heartbeat. If we ask them how they feel, they all report that they are agitated. The relationships can be depicted as shown in Figure 5.1a. Or we could say that all the situations have made these individuals anxious, and that anxiety has in turn caused the reported agitation, the sweaty palms, the faster heartbeat, and the trembling hands. Figure 5.1b shows anxiety as a theoretical concept explaining what has been observed. The first part of the figure is much more complex than the second, where the term anxiety becomes a mediator of the relationships.

With these advantages in mind, we must consider the criteria to be applied in judging the legitimacy of a theoretical concept. One earlier school of thought, the *operationist*, proposed that each such concept take as its meaning a single observable and measurable operation. In this way each theoretical concept would be nothing more than one particular measurable effect. For example, anxiety might be identified as *nothing more* than scoring 50 on an anxiety questionnaire. It was soon realized, however, that this approach would take away from theoretical concepts their greatest advantage. If each theoretical concept is *operationalized* in only one way, its generality is lost. If the theoretical concept of learning, for instance, is identified as a *single* operation or effect that can be measured, such as how often a rat presses a bar, other behavior such as a child performing arithmetic problems or a college student studying this book cannot also be called learning, and attempts to relate the different phenomena to one another might be discouraged. The early operationist point of view quickly gave way to the more flexible position that a theoretical concept can be defined by *sets* of operations or effects. In this way the concept may be linked to several different measurements, each of which taps a different facet of the concept (see Figure 5.1b).

THE RESEARCH METHODS
OF ABNORMAL PSYCHOLOGY

All empirical research entails the collection of observable data. Sometimes research will stay at a purely descriptive level, but more often researchers will observe several events and try to determine how they are associ-

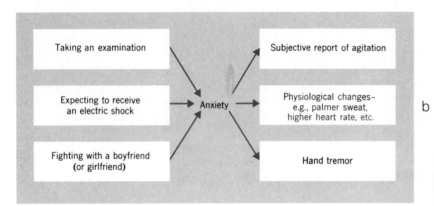

FIGURE 5.1 An illustration of the advantages of using anxiety as a theoretical concept. The arrows in part b are fewer and more readily understood. After Miller, 1959.

ated or related. In the field of abnormal psychology, for example, there is a large literature concerning the typical symptoms of people who have been diagnosed as having particular disorders. The association or relationship is between a particular diagnostic category and a set of characteristic symptoms. But science demands more than describing relationships. We often want to understand the *causes* of the relationships we have observed. For example, we want to know not only that phobics tend actively to avoid a feared situation but also why they do so.

In this section we describe the most commonly used research methods in the study of abnormal behavior: the *case study*; the *correlation*; the *experiment*, both with *groups* and *single subjects*; and the *mixed design*. Each of the methods varies in the degree to which it permits the collection of adequate descriptive data and the extent to which it allows causal relationships to be inferred.

The Case Study

The most familiar method of observing others is to study them one at a time and to record their behavior. In making a case study, the clinician collects historical and biographical information from the individual and other sources. A comprehensive case study would cover family history and background, medical history, educational background, jobs held, marital history, and details concerning development, adjustment, personality, the life course, and the current situation. Clinicians may also carefully describe all efforts to treat the individual. Case reports from practicing clinicians may lack the degree of control and objectivity of research done by other methods, but these descriptive histories have played some important roles in the study of abnormal behavior. Specifically, the case history has been used in each of the following ways: (1) to provide a detailed description of a rare or unusual phenomenon and of important, often novel, methods or procedures of interviewing, diagnosis, and treatment; (2) to disconfirm allegedly universal aspects of a particular theoretical proposition; and (3) to generate hypotheses that can be tested through controlled research (Lazarus and Davison, 1971).

Descriptive Uses

In a famous case history of multiple personality reported in 1954, Thigpen and Cleckley described a patient, "Eve White," who assumed at various times three very distinct personalities. Their description of the case required an entire book, *The Three Faces of Eve*. The following very brief summary emphasizes the moments in which new personalities emerged and what the separate selves knew of one another.

Eve White had been seen in psychotherapy for several months because she was experiencing severe headaches accompanied by blackouts. Her therapist described her as a retiring and gently conventional figure. One day during the course of an interview, however, she changed abruptly and in a surprising way.

As if seized by sudden pain, she put both hands to her head. After a tense moment of silence, both hands dropped. There was a quick, reckless smile, and, in a bright voice that sparkled, she said, "Hi there, Doc!" The demure and constrained posture of Eve White had melted into buoyant repose. . . . This new and apparently carefree girl spoke casually of Eve White and her problems, always using she or her in every reference, always respecting the strict bounds of a separate identity. . . . When asked her name, she immediately replied, "Oh, I'm Eve Black" (p. 137).

After this rather startling revelation, Eve was observed over a period of fourteen months in a series of interviews that ran to almost a hundred hours. A very important part of Eve White's therapy was to help her learn about Eve Black, her other infectiously exuberant self, who added seductive and expensive clothing to her wardrobe and lived unremembered episodes of her life. During this period still a third personality, Jane, emerged while Eve White was recollecting an early incident in which she had been painfully scalded by water from a washpot.

Jane, who from then on knew all that happened to the two Eves, although they did not share in her existence, was "far more mature, more vivid, more boldly capable, and more interesting than Eve White." She also developed a deep and revering affection for the first Eve, who was considered somewhat of a ninny by Eve Black. Jane, however, knew nothing of Eve White's earlier life, except as she learned of it through Eve's memories.

Some eleven months later, in a calamitous session, with all three personalities present at different times, Eve Black emerged and reminisced for a moment about the many good times she had had in the past but then remarked that she did not seem to have real fun anymore. She began to sob, the only time Dr. Thigpen had seen her in tears. She told him that she wanted him to have her red dress to remember her by. All expression left her face and her eyes closed. Eve White opened them. When Jane was summoned a few minutes later, she soon realized that there was no longer any Eve White either and began to experience a terrifying lost event. "No, no . . .! Oh no, Mother. . . . I can't. . . . Don't make me do it," she cried. Jane, who earlier had known nothing of Eve's childhood, was five years old and at her grandmother's funeral. Her mother was holding her high off the floor and above the coffin and say-

In this scene from *The Three Faces of Eve*, Eve Black (played by Joanne Woodward) is in a therapy session with her psychiatrist (Lee J. Cobb).

ing that she must touch her grandmother's face. As she felt her hand leave the clammy cheek, the young woman screamed so piercingly that Dr. Cleckley came running from his office across the hall.

The two physicians were not certain who confronted them. In the searing intensity of the remembered moment, a new personality had been welded. Their transformed patient did not at first feel herself as apart, and as sharply distinct a person, as had the two Eves and Jane, although she knew a great deal about all of them. When her initial bewilderment lessened, she tended to identify herself with Jane. But the identification was not sure or complete, and she mourned the absence of the two Eves, as though they were lost sisters. This new person decided to call herself Mrs. Evelyn White.

The case of Eve White, Eve Black, Jane, and eventually Evelyn constitutes a valuable classic in the literature because it is one of only a few detailed accounts of a rare phenomenon, multiple personality. Moreover, in addition to illustrating the phenomenon itself, the original report of Thigpen and Cleckley provides valuable details about the interview procedures that they followed; and it sheds light on the way in which the woman's behavior may have developed and how the treatment progressed in this one case of multiple personality.

The Case History as Disconfirming Evidence

Case histories can provide especially telling instances that negate an assumed universal relationship or law. Freud, for example, initially believed that his female patients' reports of sexual assaults by their fathers or uncles were accurate descriptions of events and, moreover, that these events had a bearing on the problems being treated. Later, on the basis of a chance finding that the supposed sexual assailant of one of his patients could not have been physically present at the time indicated, he came to recognize that some of these sexual assaults were fantasies. This single case provided a negative instance and led Freud to reject his previously held belief that his patients' recollections of early sexual assaults were necessarily true.[2]

But the case history fares less well in providing evidence *in favor of* a particular theory or proposition. In the presentation of a case history, the means for confirming one hypothesis and ruling out alternative hypotheses are usually absent. To illustrate this lack of validity, let us consider another case that received a great deal of public attention in the 1950s, the case of "Bridey Murphy."

When hypnotized, a sedate New England woman "regressed," apparently beyond her early childhood and back into a previous life in which she claimed to be Bridey Murphy, an Irish lass. Under hypnosis the woman was able to report, in a distinct Gaelic brogue, many remarkable details of a town in Ireland which she had never visited. Her case history supposedly demonstrated a true instance of reincarnation. Later, however, it was learned that the woman had been reared, in part, by an Irish maid who had described to her most of the long-ago happenings later reported under hypnosis. The maid had also provided an excellent model for the brogue that the hypnotized subject used so convincingly. In this instance the reincarnation hypothesis presented by the case history was indeed discounted.

Similarly, Chris Sizemore's book *I'm Eve* (Sizemore and Pittillo, 1977) indicates the incompleteness of Thigpen and Cleckley's case study just discussed. This woman—the real Eve White—claims that following her period of therapy with them her personality continued

---

[2]But recall the footnote on page 35. Freud may well have been in error in changing his mind.

to fragment. In all, twenty-one separate and distinct "strangers" have come to inhabit her body at one time or another. Contrary to Thigpen and Cleckley's report, Sizemore maintains that nine of them existed before Eve Black ever appeared. One set of personalities—they usually came in threes—would weaken and fade, to be replaced by others. Eventually her personality changes were so constant and numerous that she might become her three persons in rapid switches resembling the flipping of television channels. The debilitating round robin of transformations and the fierce battle for dominance among her selves filled her entire life. After resolving what she hopes is her last trio, by realizing finally that her alternate personalities were true aspects of herself rather than strangers from without, Chris Sizemore decided to reveal her story as a means of minimizing the past.

Generating Hypotheses

Finally, the case study plays a unique and important role because it is very often of great heuristic value. Through exposure to the life histories of a great number of patients, clinicians gain experience in understanding and interpreting them. Eventually they may notice similarities of circumstances and outcomes and formulate important hypotheses that could not have been uncovered in a more controlled investigation.

. . . It is a serious mistake to discount the importance of clinical experience per se. There is nothing mysterious about the fact that repeated exposure to any given set of conditions makes the recipient aware of subtle cues and contingencies which elude the scrutiny of those less familiar with the situation. Clinical experience enables a therapist to recognize problems and identify trends that are usually beyond the perception of novices, regardless of their general expertise. It is at this level that new ideas will come to the practitioner and often constitute breakthroughs that could not be derived from animal analogues or tightly controlled investigations. Different kinds of data and different levels of information are obtained in the laboratory and the clinic. Each is necessary, useful, and desirable (Lazarus and Davison, 1971, p. 197).

In summary, the case study is an excellent way of examining the behavior of a single individual in great detail and in generating hypotheses that can later be evaluated by controlled research. Thus it is useful in clinical settings, where the focus is on just one person. In the fields of clinical and personality psychology, some investigators argue that the essence of psychological studies always lies in the unique characteristics of an individual (for example, Allport, 1961). The case history is an ideal method in an individualistic of *idiographic* context. But in a *nomothetic* context, when only general, universal laws apply, the case study is of limited usefulness. Information collected on a single person may *not* reveal principles that are characteristic of people in general. Furthermore, the case history is unable to provide satisfactory evidence concerning cause-effect relationships.

The Correlational Method

In contrast to the case study, which is a rather informal gathering of information about a single individual, the correlational method requires a more systematic collection of data on particular aspects of a group of research participants. Correlational techniques address questions of the form "Are variable X and variable Y associated in some way so that they vary together (correlate)?" In other words, questions are asked concerning relationships; for example, "Is schizophrenia related to social class?" or "Are scores obtained on college examinations related to anxiety?" Thus the correlational method establishes whether there is a relationship between or among two or more variables. Numerous examples can be drawn from everyday life. Income correlates positively with the number of luxuries purchased: the higher the income, the more luxuries purchased. Height tends to be positively correlated with weight: taller people are usually heavier. This second relationship, that between height and weight, is by no means perfect, for many individuals are "overweight" or too fat for their height and "underweight" or too thin for their height. The relationship, however, is a strong and positive one.

Measuring Correlation

The first step in determining a correlation is to obtain pairs of observations of the variables in question, such as height and weight, on each member in a group of subjects (Table 5.1). Once such pairs of observations are obtained, we can determine how strong the relationship is between the two sets of observations. The most prevalent means of measuring such a relationship was devised by Karl Pearson and is referred to as the Pearson product-moment *correlation coefficient*, denoted by the symbol r. This statistic may take any value between

−1.00 and +1.00 and measures both the magnitude and the direction of a relationship. The higher the absolute value of r, the larger or stronger the relationship between the two variables. An r of either +1.00 or −1.00 indicates a perfect relationship, whereas an r of .00 indicates that the variables are unrelated. If the sign of r is positive, the two variables are said to be *positively related*. As the values for variable X increase, those for variable Y also tend to increase. Conversely, when the sign of r is negative, variables are said to be *negatively related*; in this instance as values for one variable increase, those for the other tend to decrease. The correlation between height and weight, based on the data in Table 5.1, is +.97, indicating a very strong positive relationship; as height increases so does weight.

TABLE 5.1 Data for Determining a Correlation*

Individuals	Height	Weight, pounds
John	5'10"	170
Asher	4'7"	70
Eve	5'4"	112
Carol	5'8"	130
Gail	5'3"	105
Jerry	5'10"	170
Bob	6'1"	175
Gayla	5'2"	100
Steve	5'8"	145
Margy	5'5"	128
Gert	5'6"	143
Don	6'0"	170
Sean	4'7"	75

*For these figures $r = +.97$.

Plotting a relationship graphically will often impart a better feel for it. Figure 5.2 presents diagrams of several of the correlations just discussed. In the diagrams each entry point corresponds to two values determined for the given subject, the value of variable X and that for variable Y. In perfect relationships all the points fall on a straight line: if we know the value of only one of the variables for an individual, we can state with certainty the value of the other variable. Similarly, when the correlation is relatively large, there is only a small degree of scatter about the line of perfect correlation. The values tend to scatter increasingly and become dispersed as the correlations become lower. When the correlation reaches .00, knowledge of a person's score on one variable tells us nothing about his or her score on the other.

Thus far we have established that the magnitude of a correlation coefficient tells us the strength of a relationship between two variables. But scientists demand a more rigorous evaluation of the importance of correlations and use the concept of *statistical significance* for this purpose. Essentially, statistical significance has to do with the likelihood that the obtained relationship happened by chance and thus would be very unlikely to occur again were the research conducted a second time. A statistically significant correlation is one that is *not* likely to have occurred by chance. Traditionally, in psychological research, a correlation is considered statistically significant if the likelihood is five or less in one hundred that it is a chance finding. This level of significance is called the .05 level, commonly written as $p < .05$. In general, as the size of the correlation coefficient increases, the result is more and more likely to be statistically significant.[3]

Statistical significance should not be confused with the social or real-life significance of research results. Research can yield findings that are statistically significant yet devoid of practical importance. Moreover, the level of statistical significance considered acceptable is determined by *social convention*, that is, the rules by which contemporary scientists agree to play the game. Thus if the results of a correlational study have a probability of .10 or less that they occurred by chance rather than a probability of .05 or less, it is nowhere mandated that these are chance events and that the study is therefore totally worthless. Investigators may decide that, given the nature of a particular study, these results are quite encouraging and should not be disregarded. Then they must convince their colleagues that these findings are indeed valid. In a sense, science is a game of *persuasion*.

[3]Whether a correlation attains statistical significance also depends on the number of observations that were made. The greater the number of observations, the smaller r needs to be in order to reach statistical significance. Thus a correlation of $r = .30$ is statistically significant when the number of observations is large, for example, 300, although it would not be significant if only 20 observations have been made.

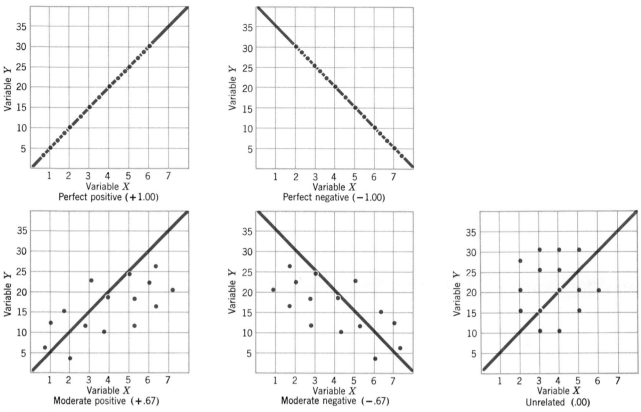

FIGURE 5.2 Scatter diagrams showing various degrees of correlational relationship.

Applications to Psychopathology

The correlational method is widely used in the field of abnormal psychology. Whenever we compare people given one diagnosis with those given another or with normal people, the study is correlational. For example, two diagnostic groups may be compared to see how much stress members of each experienced before the onset of their disorders. Many investigators have also compared the performances of schizophrenics and normal people on laboratory tasks such as proverb interpretation or size estimation and on tests of reaction time (for example, Kopfstein and Neale, 1972). Often such investigations are not recognized as correlational, perhaps because—as is often so in experiments—subjects come to a laboratory for testing, or data are analyzed by comparing the average scores of the groups on each test or measure. But the logic of such studies is correlational: the correlation between two variables—being schizophrenic or nonschizophrenic and the average scores of each group on the laboratory test—is what is being examined. Variables such as being schizophrenic or nonschizophrenic are called *classificatory variables*. Schizo-

phrenics have already been so diagnosed before they perform the laboratory task. Other examples of classificatory variables are age, sex, social class, and body build. These variables are naturally occurring patterns and are not manipulated by the researcher, an important requirement for the experimental variables to be discussed shortly. Thus classificatory variables fall into the domain of correlational research.

Nor should a classificatory variable such as a psychopathology be manipulated, for both practical and moral reasons. Although inflicting mild pain or discomfort might be (or might not be) ethically acceptable, inducing in an experiment extremely painful but psychologically significant experiences—of the kind people are only too often subjected to in their everyday lives—would be without question highly unethical. Inducing enough distress to cause psychopathology would be indefensible. Thus the correlational technique is the major strategy in studying the vagaries of psychopathology. By this technique the psychopathologist can determine whether the responses and characteristics of patients correlate with their abnormality.

Directionality and Third-Variable Problems

The correlational method, although often employed in abnormal psychology, has a serious flaw. It does not allow us to determine cause-effect relationships because of two major problems of interpretation, the *directionality problem* and the *third-variable problem*. With respect to directionality, a sizable correlation between two variables tell us only that they are related or tend to covary with each other, but we do not really know which is cause and which effect. For example, correlations have been found between the diagnosis of schizophrenia and social class; lower-class people are more frequently diagnosed as schizophrenic than are middle- and upper-class people. One possible explanation is that the stresses of living in the lower social classes produce the behavior that is subsequently labeled schizophrenic. But a second and perhaps equally plausible hypothesis has been advanced: it may be that the disorganized behavior patterns of schizophrenic individuals cause them to lose their jobs and thus to become impoverished. The problem of directionality is present in many correlational research designs; hence the often-cited dictum "Correlation does not imply causation."

People from the lower socioeconomic classes are more likely to develop schizophrenia. This impoverished man may well be suffering from the disorder.

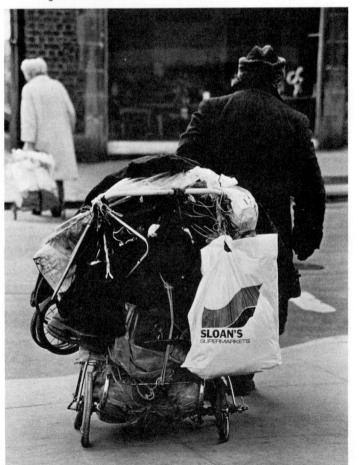

Although correlation does not imply causation, determining whether or not two variables correlate may allow for the *disconfirmation* of certain causal hypotheses. That is, *causation does imply correlation*. For example, if an investigator has asserted that cigarette smoking causes lung cancer, he or she implies that lung cancer and cigarette smoking will be positively correlated. Studies of the two variables must show this positive correlation, or the theory will be disproved.

As for the third-variable problem, it may be that neither of the two variables studied in the correlation produces the other. Rather, some as yet unspecified variable or process may be responsible for the correlation. Consider the following example, which points out an obvious third variable.

. . . One regularly finds a high positive correlation between the number of churches in a city and the number of crimes committed in that city. That is, the more churches a city has, the more crimes are committed in it. Does this mean that religion fosters crime or does it mean that crime fosters religion? It means neither. The relationship is due to a particular third variable— population. The higher the population of a particular community the greater . . . the number of churches and . . . the frequency of criminal activity (Neale and Liebert, 1980, p. 109).

Are there any solutions to the directionality and third-variable problems? In general, the answer is yes, although the solutions are only partially satisfactory and do not permit unambiguous causal inferences to be made from correlational data. A discussion of these techniques, however, is beyond the scope of this book.[4]

The Experiment

The factors causing the associations and relationships revealed by correlational research cannot, as we have seen, be determined with absolute certainty. The experiment is generally considered to be the most powerful tool for determining causal relationships between events. As an introduction to the basic components of experimental research, let us consider a study of how violence seen on television influences the aggressive behavior of children (Liebert and Baron, 1972). A group of 136 children participated in the research. Each child

[4]A readable presentation of the techniques to handle directionality and third variables can be found in Neale and Liebert's *Science and Behavior* (1980).

was first taken to a room containing a television monitor and was told he could watch it for a few minutes until the experimenter was ready for him. For all the children the first two minutes of film consisted of two commercials. After that, *half* the children viewed a sequence from "The Untouchables" which contained a chase, two fistfights, two shootings, and a knifing. The remaining children saw an exciting but nonviolent sports sequence. For all subjects the last minute of the film was another commercial.

Each child was then escorted to a nearby room and seated in front of a large box which had wires leading to another room. On the box was a white light, below which were a green button labeled HELP and a red button labeled HURT. The experimenter explained that the wires were connected to a game a child in the other room was going to play. The game involved turning a handle, and each time the other child did this the white light would come on. The experimenter explained that by pushing the buttons the subject could either help the other child by making the handle easier to turn or hurt him by making the handle hot. Each time the white light came on, the subject was to push one of the buttons; the longer he pushed it, the more he would help or hurt the other child. After making certain that the instructions were understood, the experimenter left the room. Each subject was given twenty trials; that is, the white light came on twenty times.

Table 5.2 shows the average length of time that a subject in each of the two groups—the children who had seen the violent episodes on television and those who had seen the sports sequence—pushed the HURT button. Children who had viewed the violent television sequences were more aggressive than those who had not.

Experimental investigations have shown that seeing violence on television increases the likelihood that children will behave aggressively.

TABLE 5.2 Effect of Television Viewing on the Aggressiveness of Children
(from Leibert and Baron, 1972)

Television Program Viewed	Average Duration of Each Aggressive Response, seconds
Aggressive—"The Untouchables"	9.92
Nonaggressive—sports sequence	7.03

Basic Features of Experimental Design

The foregoing example illustrates many of the basic features of an experiment. The researcher typically begins with an *experimental hypothesis*. Liebert and Baron hypothesized that viewing violence would stimulate aggressive behavior. Second, the investigator chooses an *independent variable* that can be manipulated, that is, some factor that will be under the control of the experimenter. Liebert and Baron exposed some children to an aggressive sequence on television and others to a nonaggressive sequence. Finally, the researcher arranges for the measurement of a *dependent variable*, which is expected to depend on or vary with manipulations of the independent variable. The dependent variable in this study was the duration of the HURT response, an operational definition of aggression. When in such an investigation differences between groups are indeed found to be a function of variations in the independent variable, the researcher is said to have produced an *experimental effect*.

Internal Validity

An additional feature of any experimental design is the inclusion of at least one *control group*. A control group is necessary if the effects in any experiment are to be attributed to the manipulation of the independent variable. In the Liebert and Baron study the control group saw the nonviolent sports sequence.

To illustrate this point with another example, consider a study of the effectiveness of a particular therapy in modifying some form of abnormal behavior. Let us assume that persons with initially poor self-concepts have asked for treatment and that they undergo therapy designed to remedy their condition. At the end of six months the patients are reassessed, and it is found that their self-concepts have improved compared to what they were at the beginning of the study. Unfortunately, such an investigation would not produce valid data. The improvement in self-concept from the beginning of the treatment to the end could have been brought about by several factors in addition to or instead of the particular treatment employed. For example, it may be that certain environmental events occurred within the six months and produced the improvement. Or it may be that people with a poor self-concept acquire better feelings about themselves with the mere passage of time. Variables such as these are often called *confounds*; they, like the third variables in correlational studies, confound the results, making them impossible to interpret.[5] Studies in which the effect obtained cannot be attributed with confidence to the independent variable are called *internally invalid* studies. The design of *internally valid* research, that is, research in which the effect obtained can be confidently attributed to the manipulation of the independent variable, is a primary goal in social sciences.

In the example just outlined, *internal validity* could have been secured by the inclusion of a control group. Such a group might have consisted of individuals with poor self-concepts who did *not* receive the therapeutic treatment. Changes in the self-concepts of these control subjects would constitute a *baseline* or standard against which the effects of the independent variable can be assessed. If a change in self-concept is brought about by particular environmental events, quite beyond any therapeutic intervention, the experimental group receiving the treatment and the control group receiving no treatment are equally likely to be affected. On the other

hand, if after six months the self-concepts of the treated group have improved more than those of the untreated control group, we can be relatively confident that this difference is, in fact, attributable to the treatment.

The mere inclusion of a control group, however, does not ensure internal validity. To illustrate, let us consider another study of therapy, this time the treatment of two hospital wards of psychiatric patients. An investigator may decide to select one ward to receive an experimental treatment and then select another ward as a control. When the researcher later compares the frequencies of deviant behavior in these two groups, he or she will want to attribute any differences between them to the fact that patients in one ward received treatment and those in the other did not. But the researcher cannot legitimately draw this inference, for a competing hypothesis cannot be disproved—that even before treatment the patients who happened to receive therapy might have had a lower level of deviant behavior than the patients who became the control group. The principle of experimental design disregarded in this defective study is that of *random assignment*.

Random assignment is achieved by ensuring that every subject in the research has an equal chance of being assigned to any of the groups. For example, in a two-group experiment a coin can be tossed for each subject. If the coin turns up heads, the subject is assigned to one group; if tails, he or she is assigned to another. This procedure minimizes the likelihood that differences between or among the groups after treatment will reflect pretreatment differences in the samples rather than true experimental effects.

Even with both a control group and random assignment, the results of the research may still be invalid. An additional source of error is the potential biasing influence of the experimenter or observers. This is the "Rosenthal effect" already mentioned in Chapter 4. As Rosenthal (1966) has suggested, the expectancies of an experimenter about the outcome of a study may conspire to produce results favorable to the initial hypothesis. He or she may subtly manipulate the subject to give expected and desired responses. Although the pervasiveness of these effects has been questioned (Barber and Silver, 1968; Kent et al., 1974), experimenters must remain on guard lest their results be influenced by their own expectations. To avoid biases of this type, many studies apply the so-called *double-blind* procedure. For example, in an investigation comparing the psychological effects of two drugs, the person dispensing the pills is kept ignorant (that is, blind) about their actual content,

[5]These confounds, and others described in this chapter, are unfortunately widespread in research on the effects of psychotherapy, as will be documented often throughout this book, especially in Part 6.

and the subject is also not informed about the treatment he or she is receiving. With such controls the behavior observed during the course of the treatment is probably not influenced by biasing.

Earlier, we briefly defined the term experimental effect, but we have yet to learn how it can be decided that an effect is important. To evaluate the importance of experimental results, as with correlations, researchers determine their statistical significance. A significant difference between groups is one that has little probability of occurring by chance alone. Thus this difference can be expected to be found again whenever the same experiment is repeated. And a difference between groups in an experiment, like a correlation, is typically considered statistically significant and therefore admissible as evidence if the likelihood is five or less in one hundred that it is a chance finding.

External Validity

The extent to which the results of any particular piece of research can be generalized beyond the immediate experiment is the measure of their *external validity*. For example, if investigators have demonstrated that a particular treatment helps a group of patients they have tried it on, they will undoubtedly want to determine whether this treatment will be effective in ministering to other patients, at other times, and in other places. Liebert and Baron would hope that the findings of their television experiment apply to violence of many kinds, shown on home television sets to children other than those who served as subjects in the contrived experimental setting.

The external validity of the results of a psychological experiment is extremely difficult to determine. For example, there is the reactivity of observed behavior: merely knowing that one is a subject in a psychological experiment often alters behavior, and thus results are produced in the laboratory that may not automatically be produced in the natural environment. In many instances results obtained from investigations with laboratory animals such as rats have been generalized to human beings. Such generalizations are hazardous, since there are enormous differences between *Homo sapiens* and *Rattus norvegicus*. Researchers must be continually alert to the extent to which they claim generalization for findings, for there are, in fact, no entirely adequate ways of dealing with the questions of external validity. The best that can be done is to perform similar studies in new settings with new participants so that the limitations, or the generality, of a finding can be determined.

Analogue Experiments

The experimental method is judged to be the most telling way to determine cause-effect relationships. As you may well have surmised, however, the method has in fact been little used by those seeking the causes of abnormal behavior. Suppose that a researcher has hypothesized that a child's emotionally charged, overdependent relationship with his or her mother causes schizophrenia. An experimental test of this hypothesis would require assigning infants randomly to either of two groups of mothers! The mothers in one group will have undergone an extensive training program to ensure that they are able to create a highly emotional atmosphere and foster overdependence in children. The mothers in the second group will have been trained not to create such a relationship with the children they care for. The researcher then waits until the subjects in each group reach adulthood and determines how many of them become schizophrenic. Obviously, such an experimental design already contains insurmountable practical problems. But practical issues are hardly the principal ones that must concern us. Consider the ethics of such an experiment. Would the potential scientific gain of proving that an overdependent relationship with a person's mother brings on schizophrenia outweigh the suffering that would surely be imposed on some of the participants? In almost any person's view it would not.

Experiments are used, though, in some areas of abnormal psychology. The effectiveness of treatments for psychopathology is usually evaluated by the experimental method, for it has proved a powerful tool for determining whether a therapy reduces suffering. Experimental research on the causes of abnormal behavior, however, has taken the *analogue* approach. Investigators have attempted to bring a *related* phenomenon, that is, an analogue, into the laboratory for more intensive study. In this way internally valid results may be obtained, although the problem of external validity may be accentuated. In one type of analogue study, behavior is rendered temporarily "abnormal" through experimental manipulations such as the administration of drugs, hypnotic suggestions, sensory deprivation, or operant shaping. If "pathology" can be experimentally induced by any one of these manipulations, the same variable, existing in the natural environment, might well be a cause of the disorder. The key to interpreting such studies lies in the validity of the dependent variable as an analogue of a true clinical state. Are transient increases in anxiety or depression, for example, reasonable analogues of their clinical counterparts? Results of such ex-

Early in their development monkeys need a mother, even if only a cloth surrogate like this one. Monkeys reared in isolation later show signs of both emotional distress and depression. When we generalize these findings about monkeys to human beings, we have used the monkey studies as analogues.

periments must be interpreted with great caution, but they do provide valuable hypotheses about the origins of psychopathology.

In another type of analogue study, subjects are selected because they are considered similar to patients given certain diagnoses. A large amount of research, for example, has been conducted with college students who were selected for study because they have scored high on a paper-and-pencil measure of anxiety or depression. The question here is whether these anxious or depressed students are adequate analogues for those with an anxiety disorder or major depression. Some research bearing on this issue will be discussed in Chapter 9.

Whether experiments are regarded as analogues depends not on the experiment itself but rather on the use to which it is put. We can very readily study avoidance behavior in a white rat by running experiments with rats. The data collected from such studies are not analogue data if we limit our discussion to the behavior of rats. They become analogue data only when we draw implications from them and apply them to other domains, such as anxiety in human beings.

Some of the animal experiments we examine in later chapters are analogue in nature, with their results being generalized to human beings. It will be important to keep in mind that we are arguing by analogy when, for example, we attempt to relate reactions to stress of white rats to anxiety in people. At the same time, however, we do not agree with those who regard such analogue research as totally and intrinsically worthless for the study of human behavior. Although human beings

and other mammals differ on many important dimensions, it does not follow that principles of behavior derived from animal research are necessarily irrelevant to human behavior.

Single-Subject Experimental Research

Experiments do not always have to be conducted on *groups* of people. In this section we shall consider experimental designs for studying a single subject.

The strategy of relying on a single subject appears to violate many of the principles of research design that we have discussed. As with the case study, no control group can act as a check on a single subject. Moreover, generalization will be difficult because the findings may relate to a unique aspect of the one individual whose behavior we have explored. Hence the study of a single individual would appear unlikely to yield any findings that could possess the slightest degree of internal or external validity. But, as we shall see, the experimental study of a single subject *can* be an effective research technique for certain purposes.

A method developed by Tate and Baroff (1966) for reducing the self-injurious behavior of a nine-year-old boy, Sam, serves as an example. The child, who had been diagnosed as psychotic, engaged in a wide range of self-injurious behavior, such as banging his head against the floors and walls, slapping his face with his hands, punching his face and head with his fists, hitting his shoulder with his chin, and kicking himself. Despite his self-injurious behavior, Sam was not entirely antisocial. In fact, he obviously enjoyed contact with other people and would cling to them, wrap his arms around them, and sit in their laps. This affectionate behavior gave the investigators the idea for an experimental treatment.[6]

The study ran for twenty days. For a period of time on each of the first five days, the frequency of Sam's self-injurious actions was observed and recorded. Then on each of the next five days the two adult experimenters accompanied Sam on a short walk around the campus, during which they talked to him and held his

---

[6]The use of the adjective experimental in this context prompts us to distinguish between two different meanings of the word. As applied to the research methods that have been discussed, the adjective refers to the manipulation of a variable that allows conclusions of a cause-effect relationship to be drawn. But here the word refers to a treatment whose effects are unknown or only poorly understood. Thus an "experimental drug" is one about which we know relatively little; however, such a drug might well be used in a correlational design or reported in a case study.

hands continuously. The adults responded to each of Sam's self-injurious actions by immediately jerking their hands away from him and not touching him again until three seconds after such activity had ceased. The frequency of the self-injurious acts was again recorded. As part of the experiment, the schedule was then systematically reversed. For the next five days there were no walks, and Sam's self-afflicting behavior was again merely observed. Then for the last five days the experimenters reinstated their experimental procedure. The dramatic reduction in undesirable behavior induced by the treatment is shown in Figure 5.3. The design of such experiments, usually referred to as a *reversal*, or ABAB, *design* requires that some aspect of the subject's behavior be carefully measured during a given time period, the baseline (A), during a period when a treatment is introduced (B), during a reinstatement of the conditions that prevailed in the baseline period (A), and finally during a reintroduction of the experimental manipulation (B). If behavior in the experimental period is different from that in the baseline period, reverses when the experimentally manipulated conditions are reversed, and "re-reverses" when the treatment is again introduced, there is little doubt that the manipulation, rather

than chance or uncontrolled factors, has produced the change.

The reversal technique cannot always be employed, however, for the initial state of a subject may not be recoverable, as when treatment produces an irreversible change. Moreover, in studies of therapeutic procedures, reinstating the original condition of the subject or patient would generally be considered an unethical practice. Most therapists would be extremely unwilling to act in any way that might bring back the very behavior for which a client has sought help, merely to prove that a particular treatment was indeed the effective agent in changing the behavior.

When the reversal technique does not apply, the method of choice is the *multiple-baseline* procedure, in which two or more behaviors are selected for study. For example, if a child has "learning problems," both mathematical and reading performances might be picked as the two areas for treatment. When observing the child, the experimenter may notice that he or she is inattentive during lessons and proceed to collect baseline data on the degree of attentiveness during *both* mathematics *and* reading sessions. Rewards are then given the child for attention paid to the mathematics les-

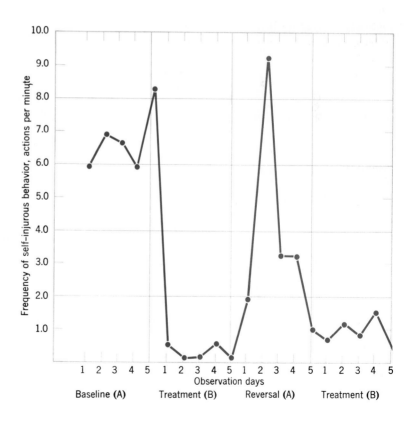

FIGURE 5.3 Effects of a treatment for injurious behavior in an experiment with an ABAB single-subject design. Note the rapid shifts in frequency of problem behavior as treatment is introduced (B), withdrawn (A), and finally reinstated (B). Adapted from Tate and Baroff, 1966.

sons but not for attention paid during reading sessions. Again, the attentiveness of the child during both kinds of lessons is measured. Finally, in a third phase of the experiment, the child is rewarded for attention paid during reading as well as mathematics lessons.

A hypothetical pattern of the attentiveness of the child during the course of the experiment is shown in Figure 5.4. If such a pattern were indeed obtained, it would provide convincing evidence that the introduction of reward, and not other factors, was responsible for modifying the child's behavior. Had some uncontrolled environmental influence improved the child's attention, it presumably would have worked equally well during both mathematics and reading classes. Moreover, if reward were not the agent responsible for change, attentiveness during mathematics lessons would not have markedly improved as compared to attentiveness during reading sessions. Thus, by choosing two baselines of behavior to be modified (hence the term multiple baselines), the investigator was able to eliminate certain possible sources of invalidity.

FIGURE 5.4. Outcome of a multiple-baseline, single-subject experiment that rewarded attention, initially during lessons in mathematics, ultimately during both mathematics and reading instruction.

As indicated earlier, even though an experiment with a single subject demonstrates an experimental effect, no generalization may be possible. The fact that a particular treatment works for a single subject does not necessarily imply that the treatment will be universally effective. If the search for more widely applicable treatment is the major focus of an investigation, the single-subject design has a serious drawback. It may well help investigators to decide whether large-scale research with groups is warranted, however.

Mixed Designs

The experimental and correlational research techniques that we have just discussed can be combined in what is called a mixed design. In a mixed design subjects who can be divided into two or more discrete and typically nonoverlapping populations are assigned as groups to each experimental condition. The two different types of populations, for example, schizophrenics and phobics, constitute classificatory variables. That is, the variables schizophrenia and phobia were not manipulated, nor were they created by the investigator, and they can only be correlated with the manipulated conditions, which are true experimental variables.

To illustrate how a mixed design is applied, we shall consider an investigation of the effectiveness of three types of therapy (the experimental variable) on psychiatric patients who were able to be divided into two groups on the basis of the severity of their illnesses (the classificatory variable). The question was whether the effectiveness of the treatments varied with the severity of illness. The hypothetical outcome of such a study is presented in Figure 5.5. The b part of the figure shows the results obtained when the patients were divided into two groups, on the basis of the severity of their problems. The a part of the figure illustrates the unfortunate conclusions that would be drawn were the patients not able to be divided into those with severe and those with less severe illnesses. When all patients were grouped together, treatment 3 produced the greatest amount of improvement. Therefore, when no information about differential characteristics of the patients is available, treatment 3 would be preferred. When the severity of the patients' difficulties is considered, however, treatment 3 would no longer be the therapy of choice for *any* of the patients. Rather, as seen in Figure 5.5b, for those with less severe illness treatment 1 would be selected and for patients with more severe illness treatment 2 would be preferred. Thus a mixed design can identify which particular treatment applies best to which group of subjects.

In interpreting the results of mixed designs, we must be continually aware of the fact that one of the variables (severity of illness in our example) is not manipulated. Therefore the problems we have previously noted in interpreting correlations are to be found in interpreting the results of mixed designs as well.

And yet the inclusion of a manipulated variable, particularly one with multiple levels, does offer some advantages. Consider a study (Neale, 1971) in which schizophrenic and control subjects were administered an information-processing task of four different levels of

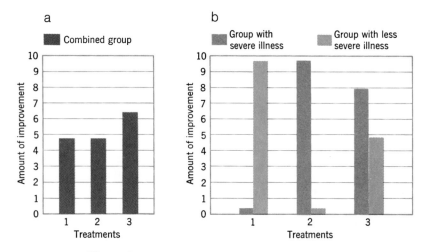

FIGURE 5.5 Effects of three treatments on patients whose symptoms are severe and less severe. The amount of improvement brought about by each treatment varies, depending on to whom it is administered. (a) When the severity of the illness is not known, the patients are treated together. (b) When the severity is known, they are divided into two groups and treated separately.

complexity. The subjects were briefly presented with visual displays containing one, four, eight, or twelve alphabetic characters. Their task was to search the display and tell the experimenter whether it contained a *T* or an *F*. The results of this investigation showed that schizophrenics differed from control subjects whenever the two groups saw more than one letter. This pattern is referred to as a *differential deficit*. The schizophrenics' performance was poorer than the control subjects' in one but not all the conditions. A differential deficit is more informative than a simple deficit on a single task. Maher (1974) explains why.

With the hypothesis that bulls are characterized by a desire to break Royal Worcester China, we stock a shop exclusively with that item, turn the bulls loose, and watch the ensuing destruction. Our hypothesis is duly confirmed—especially if our control group is composed of mice (p. 2).

Maher goes on to point out, "Just as bulls tend to break any kind of china, patient populations tend to do poorly at many tasks." In other words, the demonstration of a simple deficit provides little specific information, because the poor performance could be caused by any number of factors. A differential deficit, however, allows certain plausible rival hypotheses to be ruled out. The equality of performance of schizophrenics and control subjects when only a single letter was presented makes it unlikely that the schizophrenics' difficulties

with larger displays could be attributed to a general failure to comprehend the task. If the schizophrenic subjects had been unable to understand the task or comply with the experimenter's instructions, they would not have done as well as control subjects in determining whether a single letter was a *T* or an *F*.

SUMMARY

Science represents an agreed-upon problem-solving enterprise, with specific procedures for gathering and interpreting data in order to build a systematic body of knowledge. Scientific statements must have the following characteristics: they must be testable in the public arena, they must be subject to falsification, they must derive from reliable observations, and although they may contain references to unobservable processes, the concepts inferred must be linked to observable and measurable events or outcomes.

It is important to consider the various methods that scientists employ to collect data and arrive at conclusions. Clinical case studies serve unique and important functions in psychopathology, such as allowing rare phenomena to be studied intensively in all their complexity. Case studies also encourage the formulation of hypotheses which can be tested later through controlled research.

Correlational methods are the important means of conducting research in abnormal psychology, for diagnoses are classificatory and not experimentally manipulated variables. In correlational studies statistical procedures allow us to determine the extent to which two or more variables correlate or co-vary. Conclusions drawn from nearly all correlational studies cannot legitimately be interpreted in cause-effect terms, however, although there is great temptation to do so.

The experimental method entails the manipulation of independent variables and the careful measurement of their effects on dependent variables. An experiment usually begins with a hypothesis to be tested, that manipulation of one variable will cause another to change in a specific way. Subjects are generally assigned to one of at least two groups: an experimental group, which experiences the manipulation of the independent variable, and a control group, which does not. If differences between the experimental and control groups are observed on the dependent variable, we can conclude that the independent variable did have an effect. Since it is important to ensure that experimental and control subjects do not differ from one another before the introduction of the independent variable, they are usually assigned randomly to groups. Experimenters must guard against bias by keeping themselves unaware of what group a given subject is in, experimental or control. If these conditions are met, the experiment has internal validity. The external validity of the findings, whether they can be generalized to situations and people not studied within the experiment, can be assessed only by performing similar experiments in the external domain with new subjects.

Single-subject experimental designs that expose one subject to different treatments over a period of time can provide internally valid results, although the generality of conclusions may be limited. Mixed designs are combinations of experimental and correlational methods. For example, two different kinds of patients (the classificatory variable) may be exposed to various treatments (the experimental variable).

A science is only as good as its methodology. Thus students of abnormal psychology must appreciate the rules that social scientists currently abide by if they are to be able to evaluate the research and theories that form the subject matter of the remainder of this book.

PART TWO

James Strombotne, *The Group,* 1960

EMOTIONAL DISORDERS
AND
REACTIONS TO STRESS

George Tooker, *The Subway*, 1950 Collection of the Whitney Museum of American Art, New York. Juliana Force Purchase

ANXIETY DISORDERS

How would you like to be a tame, somewhat shy and unaggressive little boy of nine, somewhat shorter and thinner than average, and find yourself put three times a week, every Monday, Wednesday, and Friday, as regularly and inexorably as the sun sets and the sky darkens and the globe turns black and dead and spooky with no warm promise that anyone anywhere ever will waken again, into the somber, iron custody of someone named Forgione, older, broader, and much larger than yourself, a dreadful, powerful, broad-shouldered man who is hairy, hard-muscled, and barrel-chested and wears immaculate tight white or navy-blue T-shirts that seem as firm and unpitying as the figure of flesh and bone they encase like a mold, whose ferocious, dark eyes you never had courage enough to meet and whose assistant's name you did not ask or were not able to remember, and who did not seem to like you or approve of you? He could do whatever he wanted to you. He could do whatever he wanted to me (Heller, 1966, p. 236).

This excerpt from Joseph Heller's second novel, *Something Happened*, portrays the terrified helplessness of a nine-year-old boy who has to interact every other school day with a burly gym teacher. As described by his equally fearful father, the youngster has an overwhelming anxiety about his gym class, a situation into which he is forced and from which he cannot escape, a situation which makes demands on him that he feels utterly unable to meet. Once again a gifted novelist captures the phenomenology—the direct experience—of an important human emotion in a way that speaks vividly to each of us.

There is, perhaps, no other single topic in abnormal psychology that is as important and controversial as anxiety. This emotional state can occur in many psychopathologies and is a principal aspect of the disorders to be considered in this chapter. Furthermore, anxiety plays an important role in the study of the psychology of normal people as well, for very few of us go through even a week of our lives without experiencing in at least some measure what we would all agree is the emotion anxiety or fear. But the briefer periods of anxiety that beset the normal individual are hardly comparable in intensity or duration, nor are they as debilitating, as those suffered by someone with an anxiety disorder.

The specific disorders considered in this chapter and the next were for a considerable period all regarded as forms of *neuroses*. The conceptualization of them became established through Freud's clinical work with his patients, and thus the diagnostic category of neuroses was inextricably bound up with psychoanalytic theory. DSM-II offered the following definition:

Anxiety is the chief characteristic of the neuroses. It may be felt and expressed directly, or it may be controlled unconsciously and automatically by conversion, displacement and various other psychological mechanisms. Generally, these mechanisms produce symptoms experienced as subjective distress from which the patient desires relief (p. 39).

The behavior encompassed by the forms of neuroses varied greatly—the fear and avoidance of the phobic, the irresistible urge to perform certain acts over and over again found in compulsives, the paralyses and other "neurological" symptoms of conversion hysterics. How could such diverse problems be grouped into a single category? Although the observed symptoms differ, all neurotic conditions were *assumed*, according to the psychoanalytic theory of neuroses, to reflect an underlying problem with repressed anxiety. Over the years many psychopathologists questioned this assumption, however, and their doubts are reflected in the manner in which DSM-III progressed through several drafts on the way to its final form. At one point the category of neuroses was dropped entirely. But in the introduction to the final version it is noted that "the omission of the DSM-II diagnostic class of Neuroses has been a matter of great concern to many clinicians," and the category has been restored, at least partially. In DSM-III the old categories of neuroses are distributed in several new diagnostic classes which form new sections: anxiety disorders, the topic of this chapter; and somatoform disorders and dissociative disorders, both of which are covered in Chapter 7. When a DSM-II neurosis category appears in one of the new sections, the new diagnosis, for example, phobic disorder, is followed by the old, phobic neurosis, given in parentheses. Thus DSM-III has tried for a middle-of-the-road approach, which is not likely to please anyone. In our view neurosis is an undesirable diagnostic category because no data support the assumption that all such patients share some common problem or set of symptoms. In all likelihood many people will continue to use the term—indeed it is part of our everyday vocabulary and appears throughout the book—but in this chapter and the next the presentation is organized according to the newer diagnostic categories.

Psychosis is another term that is part of our everyday vocabulary and that was prominent in DSM-II. Certain diagnoses in DSM-III—pervasive developmental disorders, some organic mental disorders, schizophrenic and paranoid disorders, and some affective disorders—are recognized as psychoses, although they are not generally grouped as such. Individuals with a psychosis generally suffer extreme mental unrest and have lost contact with reality. Their hallucinations and delusions—false perceptions and misguided beliefs, which are a jumble of distortions and impossibilities but are firmly accepted by them—so take them over that they are often unable to meet even the most ordinary demands of life. Psychotic persons are more likely to need confinement. At the end of the last century Charcot identified neuroses as clinical problems that could be dealt with outside the walls of a mental hospital.

This chapter covers the *anxiety disorders*, those in which a subjectively experienced feeling of anxiety is clearly present. DSM-III proposes three principal categories: *phobic disorders*; the *anxiety states*, which are *panic disorder*, *generalized anxiety disorder*, and *obsessive-compulsive disorder*; and *posttraumatic stress disorder* (Table 6.1).

TABLE 6.1 Anxiety Disorders

Phobic disorders
Anxiety states: panic disorder, generalized anxiety disorder, obsessive-compulsive disorder
Posttraumatic stress disorder

PHOBIAS

Psychopathologists define a phobia as a disrupting, fear-mediated avoidance, out of proportion to the danger posed by a particular object or situation, and indeed recognized by the sufferer as groundless. For example, when people are extremely fearful of heights, closed spaces, snakes, or spiders, provided there is no objective danger and their distress is sufficient to disrupt their lives, the label phobia is likely to be applied to their avoidance and fear.

Over the years complex terms have been formulated as names for such unwarranted avoidance patterns. In each instance the suffix -phobia is preceded by a Greek word for the feared object or situation. The suffix is derived from the name of the Greek god Phobos, who frightened his enemies. Some of the more familiar terms are claustrophobia, fear of closed spaces; agoraphobia, fear of public places; and acrophobia, fear of heights.

More exotic fears have also been given Greek-derived names, for example, ergasiophobia, fear of writing; pnigophobia, fear of choking; and taphephobia, fear of being buried alive. All too often the impression is conveyed that we understand how a particular problem originated or even how to treat it merely because we have an authoritative-sounding name for it. Nothing could be farther from the truth, however. As with so much else in the field of abnormal psychology, there are more theories and jargon pertaining to phobias than there are firm findings.

In comparison to other diagnostic categories, phobias are relatively common in the general population. For example, Agras, Sylvester, and Oliveau (1969) found a rate of 7.7 per 100 in a population study done in New England. A more recent and more extensive survey found a rate of 5.9 per 100, with women having a substantially higher rate, 8.0, than men, 3.4 (Myers et al., 1984). The Agras study, however, revealed that most of the phobias recorded were relatively mild, only 2.2 per 1000 being rated as severely disabling. Indeed, many specific fears do not cause enough hardship to compel an individual to seek treatment. If a person with an intense fear or phobia of nonpoisonous snakes lives in a metropolitan area, he or she will probably have little direct contact with the feared object and may therefore not believe that anything is seriously wrong.

Subclassification of Phobias

Up to now we have been discussing phobias as though they are alike in every respect except the object or situation that is fearfully avoided. Behaviorists have been remiss in not considering whether the differences between fearing a small animal and fearing the prospect of leaving the house are important. This neglect of the content of the phobia is consistent with the fact that the behaviorists take a functional stance rather than a topographical one (Wilson and Davison, 1969). *Topography* here means specification of the actual physical behavior. Thus avoidance of a snake is topographically different from avoidance of heights, for the simple reason that a snake is not a height. According to the *functional* approach adopted by most behaviorists, however, the two responses may be treated as equivalent because both perform the same function, removing the individual from a fear-eliciting situation. Within a functional framework fear of snakes and fear of heights are viewed as equivalent in the means by which they are acquired, in how they might be changed, and so on.

BOX 6.1

LITTLE HANS

A classic case of phobia, reported by Freud in 1909, was that of a five-year-old boy, Little Hans, who was afraid of horses and thus would not venture out of his home. The importance of this case is attested to by many psychoanalytic scholars. Ernest Jones, Freud's famous biographer, calls it "the brilliant success of child analysis" (1955, p. 289); and Glover, a respected scholar, terms it "a remarkable achievement . . . [constituting] one of the most valued records in psychoanalytic archives" (1956, p. 76).

Freud's analysis of Little Hans was based on information reported in letters written to Freud by the boy's father; Freud actually saw the child only once. Two years before the development of his phobia, when he was three, Hans was reported to have "a quite peculiarly lively interest in the part of his body which he used to describe as his widdler." When he was three and a half his mother caught him with his hand on his penis and threatened to arrange for his penis to be cut off if he continued "doing that." At age four and a half, while on summer vacation, Hans is described as having tried to "seduce" his mother. As his mother was powdering around his penis one day, taking care not to touch it, Hans said, "Why don't you put your

"Why can't you be more like Oedipus?"

Drawing by Charles Addams; © 1972, The New Yorker Magazine, Inc.

finger there?" His mother answered "Because that would be piggish." Hans replied "What's that? Piggish? Why?" Mother: "Because it's not proper." Hans, laughing: "But it's great fun." These events were taken by Freud as proof that Hans had strong sexual urges, that they were directed toward his mother, and that they were repressed for fear of castration. According to Freud's first theory of anxiety (see page 34), this sexual privation would ultimately be transformed into neurotic anxiety.

The first signs of the phobia appeared about six months later while Hans was out for a walk with his nursemaid. After a horse-drawn van had tipped over, he began crying, saying that he wanted to return home to "coax" (caress) with his mother. Later he indicated that he was afraid to go out because a horse might bite him, and he soon elaborated on his fears by referring to "black things around horses' mouths and the things in front of their eyes."

Freud considered this series of events to reflect Hans's oedipal desires to have his father out of the way so that he could possess his mother. His sexual excitement for his mother was converted into anxiety because he feared that he would be punished. Hans's father was considered the initial source of his son's fear, but the fear was then transposed to a symbol for his father—horses. The black muzzles and blinders on horses were viewed as symbolic representations of the father's moustache and eyeglasses. Thus, by fearing horses, Hans was said to have succeeded unconsciously in avoiding the fear of castration by his father—even though it was the *mother* who had threatened this punishment—while at the same time arranging to spend more time at home with his principal love-object, his mother.

There are many other details in the case study, which occupies 140 pages in Freud's *Collected Papers*. In our brief account we have attempted to convey the flavor of the theorizing. We agree with Wolpe and Rachman (1960) that Freud made large inferential leaps from the data of the case. First, the evidence for Hans's wanting sexual contact with his mother is minimal, making it debatable that Hans wanted to possess his mother sexually and replace his father. Second, there is little evidence that Hans hated or feared his father, and in the original case report it is stated that Hans directly denied any symbolic connection between horses and his father. This denial was interpreted as evidence for the connection, however. Third, there is no evidence, or any reason to believe, that intense sexual excitement was somehow translated into anxiety. Indeed, the fact that Hans became afraid of horses after being frightened by an accident involving a horse may be more parsimoniously explained by the classical conditioning model, although this interpretation has its own problems (see page 119).

If behaviorists underplay the content of phobias, analysts go to the other extreme, seeing great significance in the phobic object as a symbol of an important unconscious fear. In a celebrated case reported by Freud, Little Hans was afraid of encountering horses if he went outside (see Box 6.1). Freud paid particular attention to Hans's reference to the "black things around horses' mouths and the things in front of their eyes." The horse was regarded as "standing for the father," who had a moustache and wore eyeglasses. Freud theorized that fear of the father had become transformed into fear of horses, which were then avoided by Hans. Countless other such examples might be cited; the principal point is that psychoanalysts believe that the content of phobias has important symbolic value.

Marks (1969) proposed an extensive scheme for classifying various phobias (Table 6.2). He noted many potentially important differences, which behaviorists have paid little if any attention to, and which analytically oriented workers have also ignored, but for other reasons. The variables examined by Marks are frequency, sex distribution, age of onset, whether or not additional symptoms are present, psychophysiological responses, and the course of the problem.

Agoraphobia

A complicated syndrome, _agoraphobia_ (from the Greek _agora_, place of assembly, marketplace) is a cluster of fears centering around public places and being unable to escape or find help should the individual suddenly become incapacitated. Fears of shopping, encountering crowds, traveling, and of being alone are often a part of agoraphobia. From a patient's point of view, agoraphobia is surely very distressing. Consider how limiting it must be to be afraid of leaving the house. Perhaps for this reason agoraphobia is the most common phobia seen in the clinic, constituting roughly 60 percent of all phobias examined.[1] Most agoraphobics are women (see Box 6.2), and the majority develop their problems in adolescence and early adulthood. The disorder often begins with recurrent panic attacks. Numerous other symptoms are also evident, including tension, dizziness, minor checking compulsions—seeing that the screen door is latched, no intruder is under the bed, the iron is off—rumination, depression, and fear of going mad. One study found that 93 percent of a sample of agoraphobics also reported fears of heights and enclosed spaces such as subways and elevators (Buglass et al., 1977). But many agoraphobics have "good days," when they can move about with relative ease. Being with a trusted companion can also help them leave the house. Psychophysiological responses confirm the clinical impression that agoraphobics are subject to a rather diffuse, nonspecific anxiety. Recordings taken of their autonomic activity usually show high levels of arousal, even when they are supposedly relaxing (Marks, 1969).

Social Phobias

A _social phobia_, sometimes referred to in its milder forms as social anxiety, is a persistent, irrational fear generally linked to the presence of other people. The individual tries to avoid a particular situation in which he or she might be scrutinized and reveal signs of anxiousness or behave in an embarrassing way. Speaking or performing in public, eating in public, using public lavatories, or virtually any other activity that might be carried out in the presence of others, can elicit extreme anxiety. Although this phobia is not uncommon, social phobics seek help much less frequently than do agoraphobics. Women are seen in therapy for these difficulties slightly more often than are men. As might be expected, onset is generally during adolescence, when social awareness and interaction with others are assuming much more importance in the person's life. Few additional symptoms are generally present, although recordings of psychophysiological responses indicate rather high levels of arousal.

Severe fear of public speaking is one form of social phobia.

[1]An irony about the prevalence of agoraphobia is that it is probably underestimated, for those with the more severe cases are unable to leave their homes to go to a clinic or private office for therapy.

BOX 6.2

SEX ROLES AND AGORAPHOBIA

In numerous surveys more women than men are found to be agoraphobic (Brehony and Geller, 1981). Even allowing for the possibility that women may admit to such problems more readily than men, the numbers still indicate that most agoraphobics are women. Why?

In recent years, as part of women's liberation and appreciation of how women have been and are still being stereotyped, agoraphobia has been explained in terms of traditional sex roles. Consider the following. Clinical descriptions of agoraphobics employ such words as passive, shy, and dependent, descriptors traditionally applied to women (Bem, 1974; Broverman et al., 1970). It may be, as Fodor (1978) suggests, that being agoraphobic is in part a logical, although exaggerated, extension of the stereotyped female role. Until recently, and still in many segments of

American and other societies, it has been more acceptable for a woman than for a man to be housebound. Any indications that men might be housebound would be more readily criticized, hence encouraging their continuing forays into the outside world and giving them opportunities to extinguish fears of leaving their homes.

Sex-role models in some media still support the female stereotype. A task force of the National Organization for Women determined from a study of children's readers that female characters in them are usually portrayed as helpless, home-oriented, passive, dependent, fearful, and incompetent compared to males (Brehony and Geller, 1981). As these stereotypes change, there should be corresponding shifts in the male-female sex ratio of agoraphobics.

TABLE 6.2 Summary of Classification of Phobias   *(adapted from Marks, 1969)*

Variables	Agoraphobia	Social Phobias	Animal Phobias	Simple Phobias
Frequency	Common	Not uncommon	Rare	Not uncommon
Sex incidence	75 to 90% women	60% women	95% women	50% women
Onset age	After puberty	After puberty	Childhood	Anytime
Associated symptoms	Multiple—general anxiety, depression, panic, other phobias	Few	Few	Not determined
Psychophysiology	High arousal	High arousal	Normal	Not determined

Animal and Other Simple Phobias

Although easy to define, phobias of animals are the rarest seen in clinical practice. Only 3 percent of all phobics have them. The majority of *animal phobias* occur in women, and they begin very often in early childhood (Marks and Gelder, 1966). It is likely that among both boys and girls animal phobias are quite common, but that some boys extinguish their phobias because of social pressures to approach and confront what they dread. Recordings of autonomic activity while the subject is at rest indicate that arousal levels are within the normal range. At the sight of the feared animal, however, arousal does increase.

Also included in the catch-all category of simple phobias are those of heights, thunder, darkness, travel, closed spaces, driving, infections, running water, and the like. Few other symptoms are generally present. Further evaluation of this category is not possible because few data have been collected.[2]

The Psychoanalytic Theory of Phobias

As is true of many of the anxiety disorders, Freud was the first to attempt to account systematically for the de-

[2]Phobias of childhood will be discussed in Chapter 15.

velopment of phobic behavior. According to Freud, phobias are a defense against the anxiety that is produced by repressed id impulses. This anxiety is displaced from the id impulse that is feared to an object or situation that has some symbolic connection to it. These objects or situations—for example, elevators or closed spaces—then become the phobic stimuli. By avoiding them, the person is able to avoid dealing with repressed conflicts. As discussed in Chapter 2 (page 35), the phobia is the ego's way of warding off a confrontation with the real problem, a repressed childhood conflict.

More recently, another psychoanalytic theory of phobias has been proposed by Arieti (1979). According to him, repression is of a particular interpersonal problem of childhood rather than of an id impulse. Arieti theorizes that, as children, phobics first lived through a period of innocence during which they trusted the people around them to protect them from danger. But then these children came to fear that adults, usually the parents, were not reliable. This mistrust, or generalized fear of others, was something they could not live with; in order to be able to trust people again, they unconsciously transformed this fear of others into a fear of impersonal objects or situations. The phobia supposedly surfaces when, in adulthood, the person undergoes some sort of stress. As is true of most psychoanalytic theorizing, evidence in support of these views is restricted to conclusions drawn from uncontrolled clinical case reports.

Behavioral Theories of Phobias

As in psychoanalytic theory, the primary assumption of all behavioral accounts of phobias is that such reactions are learned. But the exact learning mechanisms and what is actually learned in the development of a phobia are specified differently in the various behavioral theories.

The Avoidance Conditioning Model

Historically, Watson and Rayner's (1920) demonstration of the apparent conditioning of a fear or phobia in Little Albert (see page 40) is considered the model of how a phobia may be acquired. Learning theorists have elaborated on the case by asserting that the classically conditioned fear of an objectively harmless stimulus forms the basis of an operant avoidance response. This formulation, based on the two-factor theory originally proposed by Mowrer (1947), holds that phobias develop from two related sets of learning (see page 44). (1) Via classical conditioning a person can learn to fear a neu-

tral stimulus (the CS) if it is paired with an intrinsically painful or frightening event (the UCS). (2) Then the person can learn to reduce this conditioned fear by escaping from or avoiding the CS. This second kind of learning is assumed to be operant conditioning; the response is maintained by its reinforcing consequences.

Certain clinically reported phobias seem to fit such a model rather well. For example, a phobia of a specific object has sometimes been reported to have developed after a particularly painful experience with that object. Some people become intensely afraid of driving an automobile after a serious accident, or of descending stairs after a bad fall. Other phobias apparently originate in similar fashion.

> A young boy would often pass a grocery store on errands and when passing would steal a handful of peanuts from the stand in front. One day the owner saw him coming and hid behind a barrel. Just as the boy put his hand in the pile of peanuts the owner jumped out and grabbed him from behind. The boy screamed and fell fainting on the sidewalk.
>
> The boy developed a phobia of being grasped from behind. In social gatherings he arranged to have his chair against the wall. It was impossible for him to enter crowded places or to attend the theater. When walking on the street he would have to look back over his shoulder at intervals to see if he was closely followed (Bagby, 1922).

A major problem exists in the application of this model, however. The fact that Little Albert's fear and certain clinically reported phobias were acquired through conditioning can *not* be taken as evidence that *all* fears and phobias are acquired by this means. Rather, the evidence demonstrates only the *possibility* that some fears *may* be acquired in this particular way. Indeed, other clinical reports suggest that phobias may develop *without* prior frightening experience. Many individuals with severe fears of snakes, germs, airplanes, and heights tell clinicians that they have had no particularly unpleasant experiences with any of these objects or situations.[3] In a systematic study Keuthen (1980) found

---

[3]Such accounts are called *retrospective* reports, that is, reports made by people looking back into their past, sometimes for many, many years. Since memory of long-ago events is often distorted, such reports must be viewed with some skepticism. The fact that many phobics cannot recall traumatic experiences with their now-feared objects may indeed be distortions of memory. Accounts of traumatic episodes may be questioned on the same grounds. Retrospective reports are discussed again on page 237.

that half of a sample of phobics could recall no upsetting experience in the feared situation. Similarly, many people who have had a harrowing automobile accident or a bad fall down stairs do *not* become phobic to automobiles or stairs. Thus the avoidance conditioning model cannot account for the acquisition of all phobias.

Furthermore, attempts to replicate Watson and Rayner's experiment and demonstrate again the acquisition of fear via classical conditioning have for the most part *not* been successful. For example, English (1929) attempted to condition fear in a fourteen-month-old girl by pairing the presentation of a duck with a loud noise. Despite fifty trials, no conditioned response to the duck was established. In a more extensive investigation Bregman (see Thorndike, 1935) tried to condition fear in fifteen infants of about the same age as Little Albert, using various CSs and a loud bell as the UCS. Again, relatively few fears were acquired by the subjects. (From an ethical point of view, it is fortunate that these workers failed to produce phobias in their young subjects.)

There is actually very little experimental evidence to support the contention that human beings can be classically conditioned to fear neutral stimuli even when such stimuli are paired repeatedly with primary aversive stimuli, such as electric shock (for example, Davison, 1968b). Ethical considerations have of course restrained most researchers from employing highly aversive stimuli with human beings, but considerable evidence indicates that fear is extinguished rather quickly when the CS is presented a few times without the reinforcement of moderate levels of shock (Bridger and Mandel, 1965; Wickens, Allen, and Hill, 1963).

In sum, the data we have reviewed suggest that not all phobias are learned through avoidance conditioning. Such a process *may* be involved in the etiology of some phobias, but other processes must also be implicated in their development (see Box 6.3).

Modeling

Phobic responses may also be learned through imitating the reactions of others. As we have previously noted (see page 42), a wide range of behavior, including emotional responses, may be learned by witnessing a model. The learning of phobic reactions by observing others is generally referred to as *vicarious conditioning*. In one study Bandura and Rosenthal (1966) arranged for subjects to watch another person, the model, in an aversive conditioning situation. The model was hooked up to an impressive-looking array of electrical apparatus. Upon hearing a buzzer, the model withdrew his hand rapidly from the arm of the chair and feigned pain. The physiological responses of the subjects witnessing this behavior were recorded. After the subjects had watched the model "suffer" a number of times, they showed an increased frequency of emotional responses when the buzzer sounded. The subjects began to react emotionally to a harmless stimulus even though they had had no direct contact with a noxious event.

Vicarious learning may also be accomplished through verbal instructions. That is, phobic reactions can be learned through another's description of what might happen as well as by observing another's fear. As an example from everyday life, a mother may repeatedly warn her child not to engage in some activity lest dire consequences ensue. Vicarious examples can apparently be provided through words. (We should not assume, however, that such learning is necessarily a product of conditioning.)

As with classical conditioning, however, vicarious learning experiments fail to provide an adequate model for all phobias. In the first place, the vicarious fear extinguishes quickly. Second, phobics who seek treatment do not often report that they became frightened after witnessing someone else's distress. And third, many people have been exposed to the bad experiences of others but have not themselves developed phobias.

Operant Conditioning

Phobic reactions may also be learned by virtue of the positive consequences that follow. Avoidance responses may be directly rewarded and thereby learned. For example, a daughter who wants to stay close to a parent may invent excuses so that she does not have to attend school. If the mother or father gives in to these excuses, the child is directly rewarded by being allowed to stay home with the adult. In this instance fear is not mentioned as a mediator. The child avoids school simply because it produces favorable results.

Although some phobias may develop because of the payoff provided by the environment, the fact that the lives of many phobics become severely limited through their compelling need to avoid harmless situations strains the general applicability of the theory.

Research on Social Anxiety

Phobias of small animals, elevators, and heights can disrupt people's lives, to be sure, but not to the extent that social phobias can. To be excessively sensitive to the opinions of others, to be constantly embarrassed about how one acts—these concerns interfere markedly in meaningful activities, for the simple reason that human beings are social creatures, spending much of their time with others or, when alone, reflecting about how others might regard their actions. Accordingly, a great deal of research has been conducted on social phobias.

Experimental psychopathologists have relied on three theoretical models to explain social anxiety (Curran, 1977). The first conceives of social anxiety as stemming from an unfortunate episode that classically conditioned the individual in the manner already described. Presumably a socially sensitive person lived through very unpleasant events in the presence of other people, thereby learning to associate fear with others. The second model considers a lack of social skills or inappropriate behavior as the cause of social anxiety. According to this view, the individual has not learned how to behave with others so that he or she feels comfortable with them, or the person repeatedly commits faux pas, is awkward and socially inept, and is often criticized by social companions.

More recently, the ways people think in social situations have been stressed (Glass and Merluzzi, 1981). The rational-emotive theory of Ellis (1962) is a good example. Ellis holds that socially anxious people harbor the irrational belief that they must be approved of by everyone and that they must never make a mistake. Because it is impossible to win the approval of all and to be perfect in each and every endeavor, such people become very fearful and anxious about the reactions of others to their behavior. They make a catastrophe of the situation—"This is awful"—whenever someone criticizes them or whenever they make a mistake.

There is evidence to support Ellis's views. Newmark and his co-workers administered a questionnaire that had been designed to assess a person's various irrational beliefs. Their three groups of subjects were people who had been previously diagnosed as having an anxiety disorder—they were called "neurotics"; as having a personality disorder; and as being basically normal. Many more of the anxious subjects than the others admitted to a number of Ellis's traditional beliefs (Table 6.3). In another study women who considered the social approval of their peers very important reacted with greater self-reported anxiety when they imagined themselves being rejected in a social situation than did women for whom social approval was less important (Goldfried and Sobocinski, 1975).

Similar but more direct evidence comes from the recent study by Davison and Zighelboim (1985) mentioned in Chapter 4 . The thoughts of two groups of subjects were compared — by the Articulated

Feelings of personal inadequacy are likely to cause social anxiety and keep an individual from joining others.

Thoughts During Simulated Situations method—as they role-played participation in a neutral situation and one in which they were being sharply criticized. One group of subjects were volunteers from an introductory psychology course, the second undergraduates referred from the student-counseling center and identified as shy, withdrawn, and socially anxious. The thoughts articulated by the socially anxious subjects in both the stressful and neutral situations were more irrational than those of the control subjects.

Here are examples of some of the thoughts expressed by socially anxious subjects as they imagined themselves being criticized:

I've been rejected by these people. I have this very depressed feeling, a feeling of rejection. There is no place to turn to now. There is no way to eliminate that feeling I have inside. [These thoughts reflect the belief that one must be loved and approved of by everyone.]

I think I am boring when I talk to people. I often think I should not talk at all. [These thoughts reflect the

BOX 6.3

AVOIDANCE CONDITIONING AND PREPAREDNESS

Perhaps the avoidance conditioning view of phobias would be more valid if modified enough to take into account the fact that certain neutral stimuli may be more likely to become classically conditioned stimuli than others. Pavlov (1928) did not address this question, stating that "... every imaginable phenomenon of the outer world affecting a specific receptive surface of the body may be converted into a CS" (p. 88).

Seligman (1971) has suggested that phobias may well reflect classical conditioning to stimuli that an organism is physiologically predisposed to be sensitive to. Accordingly, classical conditioning experiments that show quick extinction of fear may have employed CSs that the organism was really not "prepared" to learn to associate with UCSs.

An example from the research that has given rise to this *preparedness* notion may make this hypothesis clearer. Garcia and his associates (Garcia, McGowan, and Green, 1972) found that rats could learn to avoid the taste of a given food if nauseated following its ingestion—even if the nausea did not begin for many hours. In contrast, they could not be aversively conditioned to the *sight* of food if they were nauseated in its presence but had not actually tasted it. Similarly, rats could readily learn to avoid a light paired with shock (a common experimental finding), but they could not learn to avoid taste paired with shock. Thus, as seen in Figure 6.1, gustatory sensations and illness (taste-nausea) are readily associated, as are visual and tactile modalities (light-shock). But visual stimuli and illness (sight of food-nausea) and gustatory and tactile sensations (taste-shock) are not.

Seligman has provided a personal illustration of the operation of this process.

Sauce Béarnaise is an egg-thickened, tarragon-flavored concoction, and it used to be my favorite sauce. It now tastes awful to me. This happened several years ago. . . . After eating filet mignon with Sauce Béarnaise, I became violently ill and spent most of the night vomiting. The next time I had Sauce Béarnaise, I couldn't bear the taste of it. At the time I had no ready way to account for the change,

FIGURE 6.1 The organism may be prepared through innate sensitivity to learn certain associations but not be prepared to learn others. Solid lines indicate easily made associations; dotted lines connect classes of stimuli that are difficult to associate.

belief that one should excel and be perfect in everything.]

I should maybe not be so argumentative and maybe let things drop even if I don't like the way they are . . . like if I am not happy with the situation. Just for the sake of everybody else, to keep everybody else happy, I should let things go at times. [These thoughts reflect the belief that one must be loved and approved of by everyone.]

Physiological Factors Predisposing to the Development of Phobias

Both psychoanalytic and learning theories look to the environment for the cause and maintenance of phobias. Indeed, as already indicated, the primary assumption of both theories is that phobias are learned. But why do some people acquire unrealistic fears whereas others do not, given similar opportunities for learning? Perhaps those who are adversely affected by stress have a physiological malfunction (the diathesis) that somehow predisposes them to develop a phobia following a particular stressful event.

Autonomic Nervous System

What characteristic may be important in determining the susceptibility of individuals to particular environment experiences? One way people may react differently to certain environmental situations is the ease with which their autonomic nervous systems become aroused. Lacey (1967) has referred to a dimension of autonomic activity which he calls stability-lability. Labile or "jumpy" individuals are those whose autonomic systems are readily aroused by a wide range of stimuli.

although it seemed to fit a classical conditioning paradigm: CS (sauce) paired with US (illness) and UR (vomiting) yields CR (nauseating taste). [Although I learned that flu had caused the nausea and others with me did not get sick . . .], I could not later inhibit my aversion (Seligman and Hager, 1972, p. 8).

This and related research prompted Seligman to hypothesize that some associations, and thereby phobias, are easily learned by human beings and thus are not readily extinguished. Marks (1969), in a related observation, points to the fact that human beings tend to be afraid of certain types of objects and events. People may have phobias of dogs, cats, and snakes—but few lamb phobics have been encountered. It is even more remarkable how few people phobically avoid electric outlets, which do present certain dangers under specified circumstances.

Some more direct evidence that certain fears are easily learned comes from a conditioning study in which different types of stimuli were used as the CS (Öhman, Erixon, and Löfberg, 1975). All subjects viewed three sets of pictures varying in content—snakes, houses, and faces. Half the participants received a shock (UCS) immediately after viewing each slide of snakes. The remainder received shocks after viewing slides either of houses or of faces. The GSR served as the CR and was analyzed for both the conditioning trials and for a subsequent extinction series. During the conditioning part of the study, the GSRs of the groups of participants receiving shocks after viewing slides of any of the three classes of stimuli were about the same. During extinction, however, the CR to the slides of houses or faces quickly diminished, whereas the CR to slides of snakes re-

mained strong. Thus the CR was more durably associated with the sight of snakes, which are a fairly common elicitor of clinical phobias.

In a later study (Hugdahl, Fredrikson, and Öhman, 1977) the subjects' level of physiological arousal (see page 85) was also found to be related to the extent to which fears can be conditioned. People with high levels of arousal were more readily made fearful of stimuli easily associated with the emotion than were those with lower levels. These findings suggest that people are "prepared" to fear certain stimuli, particularly people with high levels of arousal.

Seligman has also linked his preparedness theory to psychoanalytic concepts. He proposed that the kind of symbolism mentioned in psychoanalytic theory may one day be found to have a basis in the sensitivities of people and what they are prepared to associate and to learn. Hans, after all, came to fear horses after he saw one of them fall down in the street in a rather memorable incident. But he did not become afraid of the van which tipped over, and he must have observed other dramatic incidents and been struck by particularly vivid aspects of them during his walks with the nursemaid. Although the symbolic connection with the father is still unclear unless Freud's hypothesis is accepted, it does seem significant that the particular incident mentioned in the case report loomed larger than others, and that in its aftermath Hans came to be afraid of horses. Even though not all investigators are convinced that people are prepared to acquire conditioned responses to certain stimuli (see Bitterman, 1975; Evans, 1976; McNally and Reiss, 1982), the preparedness hypothesis nevertheless appears worth exploring.

TABLE 6.3 Responses to Ellis's Set of Irrational Beliefs by Neurotics, Patients with Personality Disorders, and Normal Controls *(from Newmark et al., 1973)*

Irrational Belief	Neurotic, percent	Personality Disorder, percent	Normal, percent
It is essential that one be loved or approved of by virtually everyone in his community.	65*	5	2
One must be perfectly competent, adequate, and achieving to consider oneself worthwhile.	80	30	25
It is easier to avoid than to face certain life difficulties and responsibilities.	75	34	29
Past experiences and events are the determinants of present behavior; the influence of the past cannot be eradicated.	89	45	38
Some people are bad, wicked, or villainous and therefore should be blamed or punished.	70	48	40

*Entries are percentages of subjects in each group who endorsed the statement. The table shows only the items on which the groups differed substantially.

BOX 6.4

BEHAVIOR GENETICS

When the ovum, the female reproductive cell, is joined by the male's spermatozoan, a zygote or fertilized egg is produced. It has forty-six chromosomes, the number characteristic of the human being. Each chromosome is made up of thousands of *genes*. The genes are the carriers of the genetic information that is passed on from parents to child. Each cell of the human body will contain a full complement of chromosomes and genes in its nucleus.

Behavior genetics is the study of individual differences in behavior that are attributable in part to differences in ge-

netic makeup. The total genetic makeup of an individual, consisting of the inherited genes, is referred to as the *genotype*. An individual's genotype is the unobservable, physiological genetic constitution, in contrast to the totality of observable characteristics, which is referred to as the *phenotype*. The genotype is fixed at birth, whereas the phenotype changes and is generally viewed as the product of an interaction between the genotype and experience. For example, an individual may be born with the capacity for high intellectual achievement. Whether he or she develops

In family studies the investigator capitalizes on the degree of genetic similarity in family members. Shown here is a marked similarity in physical appearance.

Clearly, because of the extent to which the autonomic nervous system is involved in fear and hence in phobic behavior, a dimension such as *autonomic lability* would assume considerable importance. Since there is reason to believe that autonomic lability is to some degree genetically determined (Eysenck, 1957; Lacey, 1967), the heredity (see Box 6.4) of individuals may very well have a significant role in the development of phobias.

Genetic Studies

Several studies have questioned whether a genetic or innate factor is involved in anxiety disorders, although

most have not been directly concerned with whether such a factor is implicated in the formation of phobias per se. Brown (1942) investigated the incidence of neuroses in relatives of people who had already been diagnosed as neurotic. Consistent with the view that a predisposition for a disorder can be genetically transmitted, he found the incidence of neurosis in first-degree relatives—siblings, mothers, and fathers—to be 16.8 percent. In contrast, for a control group made up of nonneurotic individuals, the incidence of neurosis in first-degree relatives was only 1.1 percent. Similarly, Noyes and his associates (1978) found that 15 percent of the first-degree relatives of individuals diagnosed as this genetically given potential depends on such environmental factors as rearing and education. Any measure of intelligence (IQ) is therefore best viewed as an index of the phenotype.

On the basis of the distinction made between phenotype and genotype, we realize that various clinical syndromes are disorders of the phenotype. Thus it is not proper to speak of the direct inheritance of schizophrenia or anxiety disorders. At most, only the genotypes for these disorders can be inherited. Whether these genotypes will eventually engender the phenotypic behavioral disorder will depend on environment and experience; a predisposition (diathesis) may be inherited but not the disorder itself.

The two major methods of study in behavior genetics are to compare members of a family and pairs of twins. Members of a family are compared because we can determine, on the average, how many genes are shared by two blood relatives. For example, children receive half their genes from one parent and half from the other. Siblings will, on the average, be identical in 50 percent of their genetic background. In contrast, relatives not as closely related share fewer genes. For example, nephews and nieces share 25 percent of the genetic makeup of an uncle. If a predisposition for a mental disorder can be inherited, a study of the family should reveal a correlation between the number of shared genes and the incidence of the disorder in relatives. The starting point in such investigations is to collect a sample of individuals who bear the diagnosis in question; these are referred to as *index cases* or *probands*. Then relatives are studied to determine the frequency with which the same diagnosis might be applied to them.

In the twin method *monozygotic* and *dizygotic* (DZ) pairs of twins are compared. MZ twins develop from a single fertilized egg and are genetically identical. DZ pairs develop from separate eggs and on the average are only 50 percent alike genetically, actually no more alike than two siblings. MZ twins are always the same sex, but DZs or fraternal twins can be either the same sex or opposite in sex. Again, such studies begin with diagnosed cases and then search for the presence of the disorder in the other twin. When the twins are similar diagnostically, they are said to be *concordant*. To the extent that a predisposition for a mental disorder can be inherited, concordance for the disorder should be greater in MZ pairs than in DZ pairs.

Although the methodology of the *family* and *twin studies* is clear, the data they yield are not always easy to interpret. Let us assume that neurotic parents have been found to produce more than the average number of neurotic offspring. Does this mean that anxiety disorders are genetically transmitted? Not necessarily. The greater number of anxiety disorders could as well reflect child-rearing practices and exposure of the children to neurotic adult models. Consider also a finding of greater concordance for schizophrenia among MZ than among DZ twins. Again, such data do not necessarily implicate heredity, since MZ twins, perhaps because they look so much alike, may be raised in a more similar fashion than are DZs, thus accounting for the greater concordance for schizophrenia among them. There are, however, special but infrequent circumstances that are not subject to the aforementioned problems: children reared completely apart from their abnormal parents and MZ twins reared separately from very early infancy. A high frequency of anxiety disorders in children reared apart from their anxious parents would offer convincing support for the theory that genetic factors figure in these disorders. Similarly, greater concordance of separately reared MZ twins than of DZ twins would offer compelling evidence that a predisposition for a disorder can be inherited.

having anxiety neurosis[4] also suffered from the disorder. The corresponding figure for the first-degree relatives of the controls, a group of surgical patients, was only 3 percent. Rosenthal (1970) summarized the earlier studies of the incidence of neurosis in the co-twins of neurotic probands. Again, consistent with the theory of genetic transmission, among monozygotic or identical pairs of twins there was a 53 percent concordance or similarity in diagnosis. Among dizygotic or fraternal pairs of twins there was only a 40 percent concordance. More recent

studies have generally corroborated the pattern of findings from the older work. In a family study of anxiety disorders, Harris and her fellow workers (1983) found that the first-degree relatives of individuals with agoraphobia were at greater risk for it or one of the other anxiety disorders than were the first-degree relatives of unanxious control subjects. First-degree relatives of patients with panic disorder were at greater risk primarily for it. Similarly, Torgersen (1983) found more concordance for agoraphobia in identical twins than in fraternal.

These data do not unequivocally implicate innate factors, however. Although close relatives share genes,

---

[4]Anxiety neurosis is a DSM-II diagnosis that covered both panic attacks and generalized anxiety disorder.

Identical or monozygotic twins are genetically identical. Fraternal or dizygotic twins are no more alike genetically than siblings and can be either the same or opposite in sex. The identical twins in the two photos were separated when very young and reared apart from one another. Even so, they are amazingly alike as adults. In their homes both have workshops in which they build furniture.

they also have considerable opportunity to observe and influence one another. The fact that a son and his father are both afraid of heights may indicate not a genetic component but rather direct modeling of the son's behavior after that of his father. In sum, although there is some reason to believe that genetic factors are involved in the etiology of phobias, there has yet been no clear-cut demonstration of the extent to which they may be important.

Therapies for Phobias

Throughout the book, after reviewing theories about the causes of the various disorders, we will briefly describe the principal therapies for them. The treatment sections of Chapter 2 were meant to furnish the reader with a context for understanding these discussions of therapy. An in-depth study and evaluation of therapy is reserved for the final section of the book.

Psychoanalytic Approaches

Psychoanalytic treatments of phobias generally attempt to uncover the repressed conflicts that are assumed to underlie the extreme fear and avoidance characteristic of these disorders. Because the phobia itself is regarded as *symptomatic* of underlying conflicts, it is not dealt with directly. Indeed, direct attempts to reduce phobic avoidance are contraindicated because the phobia is assumed to protect the person from repressed conflicts that are too painful to confront. The various techniques that have been developed within the psychoanalytic tradition are used in various combinations to help lift the repression. During free association (see page 475) the analyst listens carefully to what the patient mentions in connection with any references to the phobia. The analyst also attempts to discover in the manifest content of dreams clues to the repressed origins of the phobia. Exactly what the therapist believes these repressed origins to be depends, of course, on the particular psychoanalytic theory held. An orthodox analyst will look for sexual conflicts, whereas an analyst holding to Arieti's interpersonal theory will encourage patients to examine their generalized fear of other people.

The contemporary ego analysts, however, focus less on historical insights and encourage the patient to confront the phobia, even though they continue to view it as an outgrowth of an earlier problem. Alexander and French in their classic book, *Psychoanalytic Therapy* (1946), spoke of the "corrective emotional experience" in therapy, by which they meant the patient's confrontation of what is so desperately feared. They observed that "Freud himself came to the conclusion that in the treatment of some cases, phobias for example, a time arrives when the analyst must encourage the patient to engage in those activities he avoided in the past" (p. 39). Wachtel (1977) has even more boldly recommended that analysts employ the fear reduction techniques of behavior therapists, such as systematic desensitization.

Behavioral Approaches

The principal behavioral treatment for phobias is systematic desensitization (Wolpe, 1958). The phobic individual imagines a series of increasingly frightening scenes while in a state of deep relaxation. Both clinical and experimental evidence indicates that this technique is effective in eliminating or at least reducing phobias (Wilson and O'Leary, 1980). Some behavior therapists have, over the years, come to recognize the importance of exposure to real-life phobic situations, sometimes during the period in which a patient is being desensitized in imagination, sometimes instead of the imagery-based procedure. Indeed, evidence is beginning to accumulate on the long-term effectiveness of treating agoraphobics by graded exposures to real-life crowds and public places (Munby and Johnston, 1980).

Fearful clients who are treated through modeling are exposed to either filmed or live demonstrations of other people interacting fearlessly with the phobic object. _Flooding_ therapy forces exposure to the source of the phobia at full intensity. The extreme discomfort that is an inevitable part of this procedure has tended to discourage therapists from employing it, except perhaps as a last resort.

Behavior therapists who favor operant techniques ignore the fear assumed to underlie phobias and attend instead to the overt avoidance of phobic objects and to the approach behavior that must replace it. They treat approach like any other operant and shape it according to the principle of successive approximation. The real-life exposures to the phobic object are graded, and the client is rewarded for even minimal successes in moving closer to it.

Many behavior therapists attend both to fear and to avoidance, using techniques like desensitization to reduce fear and operant shaping to encourage approach. Lazarus, Davison, and Polefka (1965) first proposed this two-pronged strategy. At the initial stages of treatment, when fear and avoidance are both very great, the therapist concentrates on reducing the fear through relaxation training and graded exposures to the phobic situation. As therapy progresses, however, fear becomes less of an issue and avoidance more. A phobic individual has often over time settled into an existence in which other people cater to his or her incapacities and thus in a way reinforce the person for having a phobia. As the person's anxieties diminish, he or she is able to approach what used to be terrifying; this overt behavior should be positively reinforced by relatives and friends as well as by the therapist.

Especially for agoraphobics, the spouse, who will usually be the husband, should be involved in treatment. Clinical reports suggest that, by being overly solicitous and supportive—perhaps out of his own understandable concern of his wife's plight, perhaps to satisfy some inner need of his own to be dominant—he may have unwittingly "conspired" to perpetuate his wife's agoraphobia (Brehony and Geller, 1981). Indeed, Milton and Hafner (1979) found that as the wife improves, an already distressed marital relationship can worsen.[5]

Agoraphobics, indeed, may present a unique set of problems for therapists in planning effective treatment strategies. The clinical literature notes in particular the "fear of fear" that most agoraphobics complain about. Theirs seems to be a "portable phobia" (Brehony and Geller, 1981). They are greatly concerned about becoming the slightest bit nervous, for fear that their nervousness will escalate into a panic attack, in which they may lose control and suffer possible harm and social embarrassment.

Cognitive treatments for phobias have been viewed with skepticism because of a central defining characteristic. As stated in DSM-III, the phobic fear ". . . is recognized by the individual as excessive or unreasonable in proportion to the actual dangerousness of the object, activity, or situation" (p. 225). Thus if an otherwise well-functioning person is intensely afraid of something that, intellectually, he or she acknowledges to be relatively harmless, of what use can it be to alter the person's thoughts about it? One proposal comes from Ellis; he suggests that a phobia is maintained by irrational beliefs such as "If something seems dangerous or fearsome, you must be terribly occupied with and upset about it" or "It is easier to avoid than to face certain life difficulties." The client is taught to dispute the irrational belief whenever encountering the phobic object or situation. But even Ellis, with his strong cognitive bias, encourages clients to approach and confront what they fear. His intellectual debates with clients may very well help goad them into real-life exposures, which will ex-

---

[5]This phenomenon is one of several lying at the core of the _family therapy_ movement, described in detail in Chapter 20 (page 534). It should be mentioned, however, that this family systems view of agoraphobia has not gone unchallenged. Bland and Hallam (1981) argue that data do _not_ support the contention that improvement in the wife's agoraphobia worsens the marital relationship. Rather, they suggest, "Dissatisfied spouses remained dissatisfied; satisfied spouses tended to become more satisfied as the patient's phobia improved" (p. 338).

tinguish the fear. Indeed, there is no evidence that eliminating irrational beliefs alone, without exposures to the fearsome situations, reduces phobic avoidance (Williams and Rappoport, 1983).

All these various therapies for phobias have a recurrent theme, namely the need for the phobic to desist from customary avoidance of the phobic object or situation and to begin facing what has been deemed too fearsome, too terrifying. To be sure, analysts consider the fear to reside in the buried past and therefore delay direct confrontation, but eventually they too encourage it. Thus all these therapies reflect a time-honored bit of folk wisdom, one which tells us that we must face up to what we fear. As an ancient Chinese proverb puts it, "Go straight to the heart of danger, for there you will find safety."

Somatic Approaches

Psychoactive drugs, principally *tranquilizers* like Valium and Librium, are widely used with phobics. Physicians, whether they be general practitioners or psychiatrists, prescribe them in hopes of enabling their patients to deal more calmly with their fears. Physicians, or psychologists working cooperatively with physicians, may also combine drug treatment with a program of graduated exposure. Tranquilizers are relied on to quiet the patient in much the same way that deep relaxation does in systematic desensitization. Some studies also suggest that antidepressants like imipramine are useful in treating agoraphobia (Zitrin, Klein, and Woerner, 1980).

The problem in treating phobias and other anxiety disorders with drugs, however, is that they may be difficult to discontinue. All too often people calmed down by tranquilizers find themselves still fearful when weaned from the drugs (Marks, 1981a); consequently, they tend to become dependent on them for long periods of time. In fact, in their efforts to reduce their anxiety, many phobics and other anxious people use tranquilizers and alcohol on their own. The use and abuse of drugs and alcohol are not uncommon among anxiety-ridden people.

ANXIETY STATES

The anxiety states consist of panic disorder, generalized anxiety disorder, and obsessive-compulsive disorder.

Panic Disorder

In panic disorder there is a sudden and inexplicable attack of a host of jarring symptoms—labored breathing, heart palpitations, chest pain, feelings of choking and smothering; dizziness, sweating, and trembling; and intense apprehension, terror, and feelings of impending doom. *Depersonalization* and *derealization*, feelings of being outside one's body and of the world's not being real; and fears of losing control, of going crazy, or even of dying may beset and overwhelm the patient. Panic attacks occur frequently, perhaps once weekly or more often; usually last minutes, rarely hours; and are sometimes linked to specific situations, such as driving a car. The rate of panic disorder is about 0.7 percent for men and slightly over 1 percent for women (Myers et al., 1984). There is some evidence, however, that many more people have occasional panic attacks but not as often as the DSM-III criterion stipulates, three attacks in a three-week period. Norton and his colleagues (1985), for example, surveyed a group of college students and found that over 30 percent of them had experienced a panic attack in the past year. Furthermore, over 80 percent of patients diagnosed as having one of the other anxiety disorders experience panic attacks, although not with the frequency that they would also be diagnosed as having panic disorder (Barlow et al., 1985).

Little is known about panic disorder, although in recent years some studies have been done. The disorder does appear to run in families (Crowe et al., 1983) and has greater concordance in identical twin pairs than in fraternal (Torgersen, 1983).

Some evidence suggests a physiological cause for a substantial proportion of diagnosed cases. Specifically, a cardiac malfunction, mitral valve prolapse (MVP) syndrome, can produce symptoms very similar to those of a panic attack. It has been hypothesized that some individuals with MVP syndrome become alarmed at their sensations of heart palpitations and thereby contribute to their escalation. They consider the palpitations a panic attack (Kantor, Zitrin, and Zeldis, 1980). Indeed, this physical problem is very frequent in patients diagnosed as having panic disorder (Crowe et al., 1980). The therapy implied by their reactions would be to explain to such MVP sufferers exactly what is happening to them, that the palpitations are rarely harmful, and that they are not in themselves signals of anxiety. Perhaps this reattribution could forestall the rapid buildup of anxiety in people with MVP syndrome.

Another line of physiological inquiry has linked panic disorder to overactivity in the β-adrenergic nervous system. The β-adrenergic system controls the activity of many of the organ systems affected in a panic attack, and therefore heart palpitations, sweating, and choking become evidence of β-adrenergic overactivity. Drugs that block the activity of this division of the nervous system, β-blockers, do reduce anxiety. More recently, however, the benzodiazepines have been found more effective than β-blockers in treating panic disorder (Noyes et al., 1984). Similarly, when persons with the disorder are infused with lactate in an attempt to induce a panic attack, β-blockers are ineffective in preventing the lactate-induced panic (Gorman et al., 1983), whereas antidepressants have been able to do so (Liebowitz et al., 1984). Therefore the β-adrenergic theory appears questionable at this time. What is tantalizing, however, is that lactate can induce a panic attack and that antidepressants are effective in blocking these induced attacks and, more generally, in treating people with the disorder. The physiological mechanisms bringing about these effects are not yet understood.

Less research has been done on psychological factors that may play a role in panic disorder. Retrospective reports of childhood reveal separation anxiety and generally disturbed backgrounds, although like all retrospections these must be accepted with great caution. More promising, perhaps, is the finding that panic disorder patients ruminate about serious illnesses, both physical and mental (Hibbert, 1984). In this overconcern they may amplify slight physical sensations into signs of impending disaster, which could then spiral into full-blown panic.

Generalized Anxiety Disorder

The individual with generalized anxiety disorder is chronically and persistently anxious in many life situations. So pervasive is this distress that it is sometimes referred to as "free-floating anxiety." Moreover, the person is upset in so many different situations and so much of the time that many psychopathologists have regarded as fruitless any systematic search for specific eliciting causes. Somatic complaints—sweating, flushing, pounding heart, upset stomach, diarrhea, frequent urination, cold, clammy hands, a dry mouth, a lump in the throat—are frequent and reflect hyperactivity of the autonomic nervous system. Pulse and respiration rates too may be high. The person may also report disturbances of the skeletal musculature: muscle tension and aches, especially of the neck and shoulders; eyelid and other twitches; trembling, becoming tired easily, and an inability to relax. He or she is easily startled, fidgety, restless, and sighs often. As for the state of mind, the person is generally apprehensive, often imagining and worrying about impending disasters, such as losing control, having a heart attack, or dying. Impatience, irritability, insomnia, and distractibility are also common, for the person is all "on edge." Easily discouraged, extremely sensitive to criticism, indecisive, and often mildly depressed, these individuals are a considerable trial to themselves and sometimes others, but they usually manage to struggle through their days.

The patient, a twenty-four-year-old mechanic, had been referred for psychotherapy by his physician, whom he had consulted because of dizziness and difficulties in falling asleep. He was quite visibly distressed during the entire initial interview, gulping before he spoke, sweating, and continually fidgeting in his chair. His repeated requests for water to slake a seemingly unquenchable thirst were another indication of this extreme nervousness. Although he first related his physical concerns, a more general picture of pervasive anxiety soon emerged. He reported that he nearly always felt tense. He was apprehensive of possible disasters that could befall him as he worked and interacted with other people. He reported a long history of difficulties in interpersonal relationships, which had led to his being fired from several jobs. As he put it, "I really like people and try to get along with them, but it seems like I fly off the handle too easily. Little things they do upset me too much. I just can't cope unless everything is going exactly right."

Psychoanalytic View

Psychoanalytic theory regards the source of generalized anxiety as an unconscious conflict between the ego and id impulses. The impulses, usually sexual or aggressive in nature, are struggling for expression, but the ego cannot allow this because it unconsciously fears that punishment will follow. Since the source of the anxiety is unconscious, the person experiences apprehension and distress without knowing why. The true source of anxiety, namely previously punished id impulses which are striving for expression, is ever present. In a sense there is no way to evade anxiety; if the person escapes the id, he is no longer alive. Anxiety is felt nearly all the time. The phobic may be regarded as more fortunate since, according to psychoanalytic theory, his or her anxiety is displaced onto a specific object or situation, which can then be avoided. The person with generalized anxiety disorder has not developed this type of defense and thus is constantly anxious.

Learning View

Learning theorists (for example, Wolpe, 1958) attempting to account for generalized anxiety would, by the very nature of their paradigm, reject a concept of "free-floating anxiety." Instead, they look with greater persistence for external causes. For example, a person anxious most of his or her waking hours might well be fearful of social contacts. If that individual spends a good deal of time with other people, it may be more useful to regard the anxiety as tied to these circumstances rather than to any internal factors. This behavioral model of generalized anxiety, then, is identical to one of the learning views of phobias. The anxiety is regarded as having been classically conditioned to external stimuli, although the range of conditioned stimuli is considerably broader.

Cognitive-Behavioral View

A cognitive-behavioral model of generalized anxiety focuses on control and helplessness. Mandler (1966) suggests that the feeling of not being in control is a central characteristic of all views of anxiety. According to psychoanalytic theory, the ego is anxious because it is threatened with overstimulation that it cannot control. Learning theory sees people as confronted with painful stimuli over which they have no control until they learn to avoid them. This concept of _helplessness_ had earlier been examined by workers in several disciplines.

Richter (1957), in an article entitled "On the Phenomenon of Sudden Death in Animals and Man," quoted the following anthropological observation from an earlier source.

A Brazilian Indian condemned and sentenced by a so-called medicine man is helpless against his own emotional response to this pronouncement—and dies within hours. In Africa a young Negro knowingly eats the inviolably banned wild hen. On discovery of his "crime" he trembles, is overcome by fear and dies in twenty-four hours. In New Zealand a Maori woman eats fruit that she only later learns has come from a taboo place. Her chief has been profaned. By noon the next day she is dead (Basedow, 1925, cited in Richter, 1957, p. 191).

That such seemingly supernatural events actually occur in primitive societies may be difficult for us to believe. Walter Cannon (1942), a well-known American physiologist of the earlier part of this century, studied reports of such "voodoo" deaths and concluded that they do take place and are worthy of serious scientific study. He drew on his own experimental work on the emotions of rage and fear in cats to propose that a person whose autonomic nervous system is maintained in a highly aroused state, with little opportunity for effective action to reduce the tension, may indeed die. Under such tension, Cannon suggested, certain vital bodily organs can be irreparably harmed, and death is actually brought about by severe fright.

Bruno Bettelheim's (1960) descriptions of the reactions of certain prisoners to conditions in the Nazi concentration camps indicate another instance in which a feeling of having lost control overcame people.

Prisoners who came to believe the repeated statements of the guards—that there was no hope for them, and that they would never leave the camp except as a corpse—who came to feel that their environment was one over which they could exercise no influence whatever [emphasis added], these prisoners were in a literal sense, walking corpses. . . . They were people who were so deprived of affect, self esteem, and every form of stimulation, so totally exhausted, physically and emotionally, that they had given the environment total power over them (pp. 151–152).

These people, typically well educated, reacted in a helpless and self-defeating manner because they believed that they had no control over their lives.

Experimental psychologists have also been interested in related phenomena. Mowrer and Viek (1948) trained rats to obtain food by making a particular operant response. Then they were all shocked at the feeding place. One group was able to terminate the shock by jumping. Each member of the second group was yoked to, that is paired with, a member of the first so that the amount and duration of shock received by the pair were identical. But the members of the second group were unable to jump in a way that would give them control. The group of rats who had control over shock exhibited less fear than did those animals who were yoked helplessly to a partner.

Thus far we have examined anecdotal accounts of human helplessness and a report of rats rendered helpless by experiment. But rats are not people, and uncontrolled variables make it impossible to know what may really cause voodoo deaths and extreme apathy in prisoners. Fortunately, much experimental work has been

Prisoners in Nazi concentration camps experienced an extreme sense of helplessness; many gave up all hope.

done with human beings. Early on, Haggard (1943) showed that human subjects who administered electric shocks to themselves were less anxious about the situation than those who received the same amount and intensity of shock but who had no control over its administration. Furthermore, Pervin (1963) found that electric shocks that could be controlled were preferred to those that could not be controlled. Another study has indicated that intellectual performance is superior when the subjects believe that they have control over the order in which they take a series of tests (Neale and Katahn, 1968). And in yet another study, in which human beings received aversive stimulation, Staub, Tursky, and Schwartz (1971) indicated that "The ability to predict and control events in the environment is important for the comfort and safety of organisms. Consequently . . . lack of control . . . may become intrinsically aversive" (p. 157). In all this experimental work with human beings, stressful events that the subjects could exert some control over were less anxiety-provoking than those over which no control could be exercised. Indeed, some research (for example, Geer, Davison, and Gatchel, 1970)

People who live through natural disasters such as tornados are often anxious for a very long time. The realization that they have no control over such events is probably a factor.

suggests that in certain circumstances the control need only be perceived by the subject and not actually be real.

Research on the effects of control has been extensive over the years, yielding a more complex array of results than we have presented thus far. Some of the complexity comes from the different ways in which control can be conceptualized. Thompson (1981) distinguishes four means of exercising control.

1. Individuals have *behavioral* control if they have means to halt an aversive event, to lessen its probability of happening, to shorten its duration, or to change the time that it happens.

2. They have *cognitive* control if they have a strategy to reduce their emotional reaction to an aversive event, for example, through self-distraction.

3. People have *informational* control when they know something useful about an impending aversive event, for example, a signal warning that it is about to begin or the sensations that they will experience.

4. Individuals exercise *retrospective* control when they decide what caused a past aversive event. For example, blaming the self may enhance efforts to cope with it (Bulman and Wortman, 1977).

In addition to studying these differences in how control is exercised, researchers may assess control by self-report and by behavioral and physiological measures. They may deal with stress manipulated in the laboratory, such as electric shock, or with a naturally occurring life stress, such as an unpleasant medical examination. Despite all this variability, research on behavioral control and cognitive control has generally yielded consistent findings: either means can reduce anticipatory anxiety and physiological arousal and lessen stress after the event. Whether cognitive or behavioral control reduces the impact of the stressful event itself, as indicated by physiological or self-reported reactions, is, however, less clear (Thompson, 1981; see Box 6.5).

Humanistic View

A statement on how humanistic workers explain phobias and generalized and other anxiety disorders has not been offered until now because their thinking about all of them is generally the same and not specific. As indicated in Chapter 2, humanists hold human nature to be basically good and beautiful, with psychological problems resulting from a denial of this innate worth. Thus the individual becomes anxious in various ways when his or her basic nature is not expressed. Humanistic psychologists believe that neurotic individuals are particularly preoccupied with two conflicting self-concepts. They have accepted the unfavorable opinion of themselves held by others, which interferes with their own more natural, self-enhancing image. Their energy is expended on this conflict rather than on self-actualization.

Genetic Studies

Genetic researchers have also examined generalized anxiety disorder. In one study (Slater and Shields, 1969) comparisons were made of seventeen identical pairs of twins and twenty-eight fraternal pairs; one twin of each pair had been diagnosed as having anxiety neurosis. Of the identical co-twins, 49 percent were also diagnosed as having anxiety neurosis. In contrast, only 4 percent of the fraternal co-twins were so diagnosed. Torgersen (1983), however, found the same concordance for generalized anxiety disorder in identical and fraternal twin pairs. Thus, at this time, the research data are equivocal.

Therapies for Generalized Anxiety Disorder

As might be expected from their view of generalized anxiety disorder, that it stems from repressed conflicts, most psychoanalysts work to help patients confront the true sources of their conflicts. Treatment is much the same as that for phobias.

Behavioral clinicians approach generalized anxiety in various ways. If they can *construe* the anxiety as a set of responses to identifiable situations, the free-floating anxiety can be reformulated into one or more phobias. For example, through situational assessment (see page 77) a behavior therapist may determine that the generally anxious client seems more specifically afraid of criticizing others and of being criticized by them. The anxiety only appears free-floating because the client spends so many hours with other human beings. Systematic desensitization becomes a possible treatment.

If a feeling of helplessness seems to underlie the pervasive anxiety, the therapist will help the client acquire whatever skills might engender a sense of competence, the vital "self-efficacy" that Bandura (1977) speaks of. The skills may be taught by verbal instructions, modeling, or operant shaping—and very likely some judicious combination of the three (Goldfried and Davison, 1976).

Humanistic treatment of generalized anxiety encourages the person to sense what he or she truly needs and wants at any given time and to develop the trust to ex-

BOX 6.5

CONTROL AND MEANING

The relations between control and stress are complex. As indicated in the text, research has established that having or believing that one has control often reduces the emotional reaction to an inherently unpleasant situation. If future research continues to support this finding, how are we to account for it?

Thompson (1981) has reviewed the experimental literature on control and stress in human beings and found several possible explanations that have the ring of truth about them. Perhaps, as deCharms (1968) theorizes, people by nature have a strong need to feel a sense of mastery and competence. This need becomes evident again and again in study of the various psychopathologies. Many depressed people, for example, may suffer from the belief that nothing they can do will reliably affect their situation (Seligman, 1975).

Miller (1979) proposes that people need to believe that any stress to which they are subjected will not exceed their ability to tolerate it. A useful way for individuals to strengthen this belief is to see themselves as exercising control in difficult situations that they are currently confronting. Thus, if they can reduce or at least tolerate the suffering that they are undergoing right now, chances are that they can handle future situations occasioning distress.

In an effort to synthesize the research and theorizing of others, Thompson focuses on the *meaning* that suffering has for individuals. If people can view a setback or an illness as part of a grand plan—their own or God's, for example—they can place it in some meaningful perspective and endure it. We probably all know of people whose serious, debilitating physical illness set the stage for an examination of their values, so that they emerged from the trauma stronger and better able to cope with their problem. An intriguing aspect of this proposal on meaning is that it emerged from a hard-nosed examination of tightly controlled experimental studies, most of them analogical in nature. Thompson's cognitive hypothesis should remind the reader of our earlier discussion of humanistic-existential views (see page 00), which center on humankind's search for meaning in life.

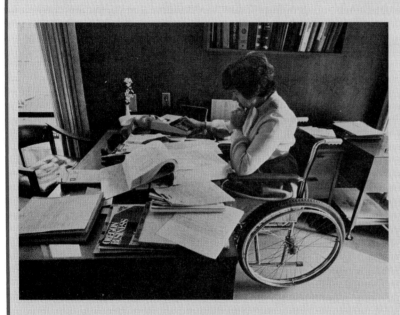

Some people are able to withstand and even become stronger after experiencing a severe stress, such as paralysis. One way of doing so is to place the stressful event in some meaningful perspective, to view it as part of an encompassing plan.

press those needs and satisfy those wants. For example, an aim of *Gestalt therapy*, one of the humanistic therapies, is to help the client become aware of moment-to-moment feelings and perceptions. Ingenious exercises are often used to achieve this goal. In the *empty-chair technique* the client is instructed to talk to an important person or to a feeling as though that individual or emotion were sitting in an empty chair nearby. Gestalt therapists believe that by this unusual procedure clients will confront their most basic wants and fears. The increased awareness and insight that follow are assumed to be both necessary and sufficient for the alleviation of a host of psychological problems, including anxiety.[6] Client-centered therapists, following the work of Carl Rogers, provide a warm, nonjudgmental atmosphere in which the client will be better able to come upon his or her innermost feelings.

Tranquilizers, such as those mentioned earlier for the treatment of phobias, are probably the most widespread treatment for generalized anxiety disorder. A psychoactive drug is viewed by medical practitioners as especially appropriate for disorder defined by its pervasiveness, for the simple reason that, once it takes effect, a drug will continue to work for several hours in whatever situation clients find themselves. Unfortunately, as will be seen in Chapter 20, many tranquilizing drugs have undesirable side effects, ranging from drowsiness and depression to physical addiction and damage to certain bodily organs.

Community psychologists or psychiatrists have yet another approach to generalized anxiety, and to most other psychological disorders. They view human suffering as a normal reaction to abnormal or untenable living conditions. Rather than help the individual cope with or adjust to an environment considered brutalizing, community workers strive for social change. Their work is very different indeed from any discussed so far; much of Chapter 20 is devoted to a close examination of *community psychology*.

Obsessive-Compulsive Disorder

Obsessive-compulsive disorder affects between 1 and 2 percent of the population (Myers et al., 1984). The disorder itself usually begins in early adulthood, often following some stressful event such as pregnancy, childbirth, family conflict, and difficulties at work (Kringlen, 1970). During an episode of depression, patients occasionally develop obsessive-compulsive disorder, and significant depression is often found in obsessive-compulsive patients (Rachman and Hodgson, 1980).

Obsessions are intrusive and recurring thoughts and images which come unbidden to the mind and appear irrational and uncontrollable to the individual experiencing them. Whereas many of us may have similar fleeting

[6]See page 491 for an in-depth examination of Gestalt therapy.

experiences, the obsessive has them with such force and frequency that they interfere with normal functioning. Cameron (1963) gives an example illustrating the onset of an obsessive thought in a forty-two-year-old mother.

> She was serving the family dinner one evening when she dropped a dish on the table and smashed it. The accident appalled her. While clearing up the fragments she was seized with an unreasonable fear that bits of glass might get into her husband's food and kill him. She would not allow the meal to proceed until she had removed everything and reset the table with fresh linen and clean dishes. After this her fears, instead of subsiding, reached out to include intense anxiety over the possibility that she herself and the children might be killed by bits of glass (p. 384).

Obsessions may also take the form of extreme doubting, procrastination, and indecision. The patient may be unable to come to a conclusion and cease reconsidering an issue (Salzman and Thaler, 1981).

A *compulsion* is an irresistible impulse to repeat some ritualistic act over and over again. The activity, however, is not realistically connected with its apparent purpose or is clearly excessive. Lady Macbeth washed her hands continually after the murder of King Duncan. Often an individual who continually repeats some action fears dire consequences if the act is not performed. The sheer frequency with which an act is repeated may often be staggering. One woman treated by the authors of this book washed her hands over 500 times per day, despite the painful sores that resulted. She reported that she had a very strong fear of contamination by germs and could temporarily alleviate this concern only by washing her hands. Frequently reported compulsions have to do with cleanliness and orderliness, sometimes achieved only by elaborate ceremonies which take hours and even most of the day; with avoiding particular objects, such as staying away from anything brown; with repetitive "magical" protective practices, such as counting, saying particular numbers, touching a talisman or a particular part of the body; and with checking, going back seven or eight times to make certain that already performed acts were actually carried out—lights, gas jets, faucets turned off, windows fastened, doors locked, the silver chest hidden away beneath the guest tablecloths.

Bernice was forty-six when she entered treatment. This was the fourth time she had been in outpatient therapy, and she had previously been hospitalized twice. Her obsessive-compulsive disorder had begun twelve years ago, shortly after the death of her father. Since then it had waxed and waned and currently was as severe as it had ever been.

Bernice was obsessed with a fear of contamination, a fear she vaguely linked to her father's death from pneumonia. Although she reported that she was afraid of nearly everything, because germs could be anywhere, she was particularly upset by touching wood, "scratchy objects," mail, canned goods, and "silver flecks." By silver flecks Bernice meant silver embossing on a greeting card, eyeglass frames, shiny appliances, and silverware. She was unable to state why these particular objects were special sources of possible contamination.

To try to reduce her discomfort, Bernice engaged in a variety of compulsive rituals which took up almost all her waking hours. In the morning she spent three to four hours in the bathroom, washing and rewashing herself. Between each bath she would have to scrape away the outside layer of her bar of soap so that it would be totally free of germs. Mealtimes also lasted for hours, as Bernice performed her rituals—eating three bites of food at a time, chewing each mouthful three hundred times. These were meant "magically" to decontaminate her food. Even Bernice's husband was sometimes involved in these mealtime ceremonies, and he would shake a teakettle and frozen vegetables over her head to remove the germs. Bernice's rituals and fear of contamination had reduced her life to doing almost nothing else. She would not leave the house, do housework, or even talk on the telephone.

The clinical definition of a compulsion differs somewhat from the way the term is used in common parlance. We hear people described as compulsive gamblers, compulsive eaters, and compulsive drinkers. But even though such individuals may report an irresistible urge to gamble, eat, and drink, such behavior is not clinically regarded as a compulsion because it is often engaged in with pleasure and is not "ego-alien." A true compulsion is viewed by the person as somehow foreign to his or her personality. Stern and Cobb (1978), for example, found that 78 percent of a sample of compulsives viewed their rituals as either "rather silly, or "absurd."

A frequent consequence of obsessive-compulsive disorder is the negative effect it can have on the individual's relations with other people, especially with members of the family. A person saddled with the irresistible need to wash his hands every ten minutes, or touch every doorknob he passes, or count every tile in a bathroom floor is likely to cause concern and even resentment in a spouse, children, friends, or coworkers. And the antagonistic feelings experienced by these significant others are likely to be tinged with guilt, for at some level they understand that the person cannot really help doing these senseless things. Finally, the undesirable effects on others can, in turn, be expected to have additional consequences, engendering feelings of depression and generalized anxiety in the obsessive-compulsive person and setting the stage for even further deterioration of personal relationships. For such reasons family therapists (Hafner, 1982; Hafner et al., 1981) have suggested that obsessive-compulsive disorder is sometimes embedded in marital distress and actually substitutes for overt marital conflict. This speculative hypothesis cautions therapists to consider marital treatment as well as therapies that focus on the individual.

The content of obsessions and compulsions has been investigated by Akhter and his colleagues (1975). After

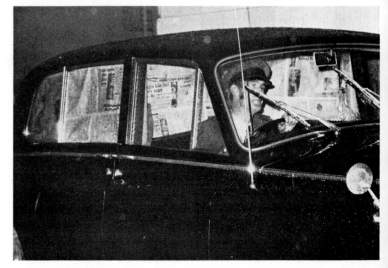

Howard Hughes, the famous industrialist, suffered from an obsessive fear of contamination. Here, on a trip to London, Hughes has lined the windows of his Rolls-Royce with newspaper to protect himself from unclean air.

interviews with eighty-two obsessive-compulsive patients, five distinguishable forms of obsession and two of compulsion were identified.

Obsessions

1. **Obsessive doubts.** Persistent thoughts that a completed task had not been adequately accomplished were found in 75 percent of the patients. "Each time he left his room a twenty-eight-year-old student began asking himself 'Did I lock the door? Am I sure?' in spite of a clear and accurate remembrance of having done so" (p. 343).

2. **Obsessive thinking.** Seemingly endless chains of thoughts, usually focusing on future events, were reported by 34 percent of those interviewed. A pregnant woman tormented herself with these thoughts: "If my baby is a boy he might aspire to a career that would necessitate his going away from me, but he might want to return to me and what would I do then, because if I . . ." (p. 343).

3. **Obsessive impulses.** Seventeen percent had powerful urges to perform certain actions, ranging from rather trivial whims to grave and assaultive acts. "A forty-one-year-old lawyer was obsessed by what he understood to be the 'nonsensical notion' of drinking from his inkpot but also the serious urge to strangle an apparently beloved only son" (p. 343).

4. **Obsessive fears.** Twenty-six percent were anxious about losing control and doing something that would be socially embarrassing. "A thirty-two-year-old teacher was afraid that in the classroom he would refer to his unsatisfactory sexual relations with his wife, although he had no wish to do so" (p. 344).

5. **Obsessive images.** Persisting images of some recently seen or imagined event plagued 7 percent of the sample. A patient " 'saw' her baby being flushed away in the toilet whenever she entered the bathroom" (p. 344).

Compulsions

1. **Yielding compulsions.** Compulsive urges seemingly forced actions on 61 percent of the patients. "A twenty-nine-year-old clerk had [a notion] that he had an important document in one of his pockets. He knew that this was not true, but found himself impelled to check his pocket, again and again" (p. 344).

2. **Controlling compulsions.** Diverting actions apparently allowed 6 percent of the patients to control a compulsive urge without giving in to it. "A sixteen-year-old boy with incestuous impulses controlled the anxiety these aroused by repeatedly and loudly counting to ten" (p. 344).

Additional information on the content of compulsions is provided by Rachman and Hodgson's (1980) analysis of the responses of obsessive-compulsive patients to a questionnaire. The two major compulsions centered around cleaning and checking. In addition, many patients complained of what Rachman and Hodgson call primary obsessional slowness. Dressing, personal hygiene, folding clothes, and the like can take up so much of the patients' days that they are unable to meet other obligations.

Theories of Obsessive-Compulsive Disorder

In **psychoanalytic theory** obsessions and compulsions are viewed as similar, resulting from instinctual forces,

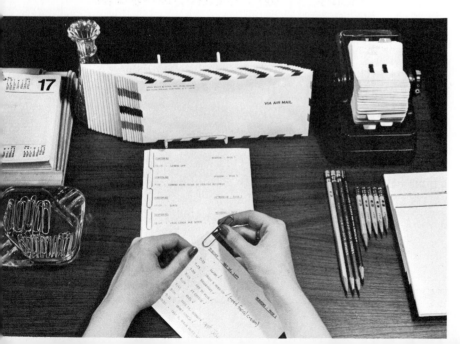

The orderly world of the obsessive-compulsive.

sexual or aggressive, which are not under control because of overly harsh toilet training. The person is thus fixated at the anal stage. The symptoms observed represent the outcome of the struggle between the id and the defense mechanisms; sometimes the id predominates, sometimes the defense mechanisms. For example, when obsessive thoughts of killing intrude, the forces of the id are dominant. More often, however, the observed symptoms reflect the partially successful operation of one of the defense mechanisms. An individual fixated at the anal stage may by reaction formation resist his urge to soil and become compulsively neat, clean, and orderly. Similarly, in undoing the individual engages in a ritualistic behavior which represents a magical attempt to cancel out the forbidden impulse. Or the ritual may serve as penance, erasing guilt for misdeeds.

Alfred Adler (1931), an early colleague of Freud who broke with the master because he did not agree with Freud's libido theory, viewed obsessive-compulsive disorders within the framework of his theory that pathology results when children are kept from developing a sense of competence by their doting or excessively dominating parents. Saddled with an inferiority complex, people may adopt compulsive rituals in order unconsciously to carve out for themselves a domain in which they exert control and can feel proficient. Adler proposed that the compulsive act allows a person mastery of *something*, even if only the positioning of writing implements on a desk.

Behavioral accounts of obsessions and compulsions (Meyer and Chesser, 1970) consider them learned behavior reinforced by their consequences. One set of consequences is the reduction of fear. For example, compulsive hand washing is viewed as an operant escape-response which reduces an obsessional preoccupation with contamination by dirt or germs. Similarly, compulsive checking may reduce anxiety about whatever disaster the patient anticipates were the checking ritual not completed. Anxiety as measured by self-report (Hodgson and Rachman, 1972) and psychophysiological responses (Carr, 1971) can indeed be reduced by such compulsive behavior. Research has also shown, however, that not all compulsive acts reduce anxiety to the same degree. Rachman and Hodgson (1980) report that patients with a cleaning compulsion are more often able to lessen their anxiety than patients with a checking compulsion. Furthermore, the reduction of anxiety cannot account for obsessions. Indeed, the obsessions of obsessive-compulsive patients make them anxious (Rabavilas and Boulougouris, 1974), much as do the some-

what similar intrusive thoughts of normal subjects about stressful stimuli, such as a scary movie (Horowitz, 1975).

Compulsive behavior may also be directly rewarded, as in Skinner's demonstration of the acquisition of so-called superstitious behavior in pigeons. The birds were reduced to 75 percent of their normal body weight and then presented with food at regular intervals, whatever their behavior happened to be. In this way and quite by chance, as Skinner described it,

One bird was conditioned to turn counterclockwise about the cage. . . . Another repeatedly thrust its head into one of the upper corners of the cage. A third developed a "tossing" response, as if placing its head beneath an invisible bar and lifting it repeatedly (1948, p. 168).

The implication is that compulsive behavior in human beings is similarly learned through chance reward. Perhaps, for example, obsessive-compulsive behavior elicits sympathy and support from the spouse, who may cater to all the patient's concerns.

In a related but more **cognitive view**, Carr (1974) proposes that obsessive-compulsives, when in a situation that has a potentially undesirable or harmful outcome, overestimate the likelihood that the harmful outcome will occur. In other words, the obsessive-compulsive has an "If anything can go wrong, it will" view of life. This cognitive set, according to Carr, necessitates avoiding the sources of threat and thus increases the likelihood of obsessive-compulsive behavior.

As plausible as these formulations appear, we still have much more to learn about the etiology of obsessive-compulsive disorder.

Therapies for Obsessive-Compulsive Disorder

Psychoanalytic treatment for obsessions and compulsions resembles that for phobias and generalized anxiety, namely lifting repression and allowing the patient to confront what he or she is truly afraid of, that a particular impulse will be gratified. The intrusive thoughts and irresistible behavior are not appropriate targets for therapeutic change, serving as they do to protect the ego from the repressed conflict.

The failure of psychoanalytic procedures has prompted some analytic workers to advocate taking a more action-oriented approach to these disorders. Salzman (1980), for example, warns that free association merely feeds into the patient's obsessionalism; hence he suggests that the analyst be more directive in guiding discussion. He suggests as well that the analyst encourage the patient to abandon the ego defense of acting compulsively. The patient's resolve can be strengthened by making him or her realize that anxiety is universal in life and therefore cannot be totally eliminated by anyone. The ultimate focus of the treatment, however, remains on insight into unconscious determinants.

Active interruption of the "symptoms," a trend in psychoanalytic treatment, is the core of behavioral approaches to obsessive-compulsive disorders. Generally speaking, behavioral treatment of obsessive thoughts has concentrated either on reducing the anxiety assumed to underlie them, in procedures such as desensitization, or on a technique called thought stopping. This straightforward procedure has the client signal to the therapist when an obsessive thought creeps into consciousness, at which time the therapist shouts "Stop!" Not surprisingly, the client is startled and realizes immediately that this interruption has driven out the unwanted cognition. The client is then trained to utter "Stop" subvocally whenever intrusive thoughts or images invade consciousness. Data on the efficacy of this technique are meager indeed, however (Marks, 1981b).

Behavior therapy for compulsive rituals usually entails what is called *response prevention*, dissuading the person from performing the act whenever the urge arises (Rachman and Hodgson, 1978).[7] Although in the short term such curtailment is very arduous and unpleasant for clients, the extreme discomfort is believed worth enduring in order to alleviate these disabling problems. Clearly, however, conditions must be such that the client can be persuaded to go along with the treatment. Sometimes control over rituals is possible only in a hospital. Victor Meyer (1966), a renowned behavioral expert in the treatment of compulsions, pioneered the development of a controlled environment at Middlesex Hospital in London, England. There staff members are specially trained to restrict the patient's opportunities for engaging in ritualistic acts. Generalization of the treatment to the home requires that family members become involved. Suffice it to say that preparing them for this work is no mean task, requiring as it does skills and care that go beyond whatever specific behavioral technique is being employed.

The monoamine oxidase inhibitors and the tricyclics, drugs which are more commonly used in treating depression (see Chapter 9), are sometimes given to obsessive-compulsives. The desperation of mental health workers, surpassed only by that of the sufferers, explains the occasional use of psychosurgery in treating obsessions and compulsions. Some improvement has been reported, but it may well be simply the general dulling of emotion and behavior often found in people who have been lobotomized.

Obsessive-compulsive disorder is overall one of the most difficult psychological problems to treat.

POSTTRAUMATIC STRESS DISORDER

The Symptoms and Diagnosis

In posttraumatic stress disorder a traumatic event or catastrophe of the worst order, such as rape,[8] combat, or a natural disaster, brings in its aftermath difficulties with concentration and memory, an inability to relax, impulsiveness, a tendency to be easily startled, disturbed sleep, anxiety, depression, and above all a psychic numbing. Previously enjoyed activities lose their interest. There is a feeling of estrangement from others and from "the passing parade" and, if the trauma was shared and took the lives of companions, a deadening sense of guilt for having survived. As for the experience itself, the person has great difficulty keeping it out of mind. "Flashbacks"—vivid and intrusive recollections of the painful event—and recurring nightmares and dreams of it are common. Posttraumatic stress disorder may be acute, chronic, or delayed. It is believed to be more severe and longer lasting after a trauma caused by human beings, as in war, physical assaults, torture, than after a catastrophe of nature, such as a flood or an earthquake. Symptoms often worsen when the individual is exposed to situations that resemble the original trauma: a thunderstorm may remind a soldier of the firings and rumbles of the past unendurable bloody battle.

The anxiety disorders discussed so far in this chapter, phobic disorders and anxiety states, seem to share an important characteristic: they cannot be adequately explained on environmental grounds alone. Although

---

[7]This modern treatment of compulsive rituals was anticipated by Janet, who discovered a number of unplanned cures of obsessive-compulsive disorder brought about through the institutional practices of the military and of religious orders. Their rules and strictures, which did not tolerate obsessive-compulsives' performing their "uncontrollable" actions, remedied their condition (Marks, 1981a).

[8]The aftermath of sexual assault is discussed in a separate section on rape in Chapter 12 (page 301).

the evidence is still sketchy, these anxiety problems probably become the lot of only a minority of people who are exposed to certain life situations. Indeed, the information that we have on the life histories of these individuals does not consistently point to a specific set of circumstances, such as having overly punitive parents.

In contrast, people diagnosed as having posttraumatic stress disorder, although surely different from one another in countless ways before trauma, do have in their lives a major, salient, and powerful happening—in the words of DSM-III "a psychologically traumatic event that is generally outside the range of usual human experience" (p. 236). DSM-III goes on to state, as the literature on trauma had for years, that "The stressor producing this syndrome would evoke significant symptoms of distress in most people" (p. 236).

Although clinicians had written about a disorder that they called traumatic neurosis, DSM-II itself lacked a specific category for stress disorders of some duration. The posttraumatic stress disorder listed in DSM-III represents no small change in overall point of view, for it constitutes a formal recognition that, regardless of premorbid history, many people may be adversely affected by overwhelming catastrophic stress, and that their reaction should be distinguished from other disorders. The newly listed disorder can be seen, then, as shifting the "blame" for the problem from the survivor to the event. Instead of implicitly concluding that the person would be all right were he or she made of sterner stuff, DSM-III acknowledges the onerousness of the traumatizing circumstances (Haley, 1978).[9]

The reader is invited to reflect on whether these reactions to trauma should even be considered abnormal. If most people are indeed significantly distressed by severe trauma, why should PTSD be of concern to psychopathologists any more than the tendency of most people to become dehydrated when deprived of liquids and exposed for hours to temperatures in excess of a hundred degrees? To be sure, PTSD can and should be studied and treated, but perhaps both activities can be conducted without considering the phenomenon as abnormal.

Posttraumatic Stress Disorder and the Vietnam War

Combat Stress in Earlier Wars
In the 1970s and early 1980s the psychological plight of Vietnam combat veterans received wide attention from the media. During and after war, military personnel must contend with devastating stress, and some of them break down. The American Civil War was the first one in which the psychological disintegration suffered under the rigors of battle was acknowledged as a clinical entity. William Hammond, Surgeon General of the Union Army, considered it to be "nostalgia," meaning a severe melancholia brought on by protracted absence from home. The incidence of nostalgia was reported to be 2.34 cases per 1000 troops in the first year of the Civil War, 3.3 in the second. In addition, 20.8 per 1000 troops were discharged for "paralysis" and 6 per 1000 for insanity (Bourne, 1970).

In World War I, the first global conflict, the term used was "shell shock," reflecting the somatogenic belief that the soldier's brain suffered chronic concussions through the sudden and severe atmospheric pressure changes from nearby explosions. Eventually, the soldier's dazed loss of self-command, his tremulousness and terror were recognized as the cumulative emotional and psychological reaction to the strain of war. But those who succumbed were also regarded as vulnerable to stress, as having a "breaking point." Some maladjustment extending back before their service in the war had presumably predisposed them to their breakdown. In World War II and the Korean War the great weariness of a soldier, his sleeplessness, startle at the slightest sounds, inability to speak, terror, and either stupor or agitated excitement were called "exhaustion" and then "combat fatigue" (Figley, 1978a), putting the blame clearly on the stressful circumstances of battle.

Combat Stress in the Vietnam War
What was unusual about the psychological breakdowns during and in the aftermath of the Vietnam War? As Figley (1978b) has noted, this war was believed at first to have caused far fewer psychological casualties than did World War I or II—1.5 percent in Vietnam[10] versus

---

[9]We must not overlook entirely the role of premorbid factors, however, for the simple reason that not all people subjected to the same kind of trauma develop PTSD. It is more a question of emphasis. The externally imposed trauma is a clear, powerful, and completely obvious circumstance in the lives of those who do suffer emotional wounds.

[10]Figley also notes, however, that stress-related difficulties may have been underreported, for the military resorted to administrative discharges to rid itself of those with "discipline problems." Rather than recognizing problems as produced by stress and taking responsibility for treating them, the military, asserts Figley, often shipped the troubled soldiers home with a dishonorable discharge, the cruel irony then being that these men would be denied necessary mental health services by the Veterans Administration (Figley and Leventman, 1980).

10 percent in World War II—perhaps because battle duty was more intermittent and limited in time. The Vietnam War was a moving war, with very few fixed "front lines" of defense subjecting soldiers to enemy bombardment for weeks at a time. Helicopters flew men to the field missions of guerrilla warfare, then evacuated them back to more secure bases. After a few months of combat, they were allowed a period of rest and recuperation at beach resorts in Vietnam or cities outside the country. A tour of duty was one year long. Each soldier had his DEROS, his date expected to return from overseas, and thus a day on which he would no longer have to go into combat (Bourne, 1970). His DEROS must have helped him to gird himself for this one year of duty and to concentrate his energies on staying alive.

After men had been home for a few months or years, however, signs of great distress began to appear. The public was made aware of their incidence in veterans who availed themselves of the free medical and psychological services offered by the Veterans Administration. Were these men malingering? Were they to be considered somehow weak or lazy, unable and unwilling to reenter civilian life? The times were indeed difficult during the 1970s, for the United States and the rest of the industrialized world were going through a severe economic recession. Many of these veterans had also returned with drug problems.

The upcoming listing of posttraumatic stress disorder in DSM-III eventually made it easier for Vietnam veterans to obtain help within the Veterans Administration system. They were acknowledged to have a recognized mental disorder. Their treatment centered on the combat stress itself and not on any emotional "weakness" presumed to have existed prior to the war, or on their efforts to deal with their stress, such as abusing drugs.

In the past few years efforts have been made to document the extent of PTSD among Vietnam veterans. Penk and his colleagues (1981) studied 87 combat veterans and 120 who had not seen combat. All had sought treatment for substance abuse at a Veterans Administration medical center. The veterans were compared on their answers to questions designed specifically by Figley to tap into their life problems since leaving military service. Overall, the combat veterans showed significantly more stress, which statistical techniques indicated was not likely to be explained by adjustment differences before the war experience. Moreover, those who saw heavy combat were more distressed than those who saw light. In particular, combat veterans reported significantly more problems identified as part of the PTSD syndrome than did controls, such as getting along poorly with others, finding it difficult to become emotionally close to someone, to trust others, to express feelings; having family or marriage problems; being unable to sleep and to control temper; being nervous much of the time. Taken together with other research, these findings confirm the claims made by veterans' groups since the end of the Vietnam War, that those who saw combat, especially heavy combat, have many stress-initiated psychological problems, even though in some cases their reactions have been delayed until well after their return to civilian life.

An Unpopular War

Several factors other than the abbreviated and time-limited periods of combat differentiated the Vietnam War from others in recent history. It was extremely unpopular and controversial, and it was a war that this country did not win in spite of the infusion of billions of dollars, fatalities exceeding 58,000 and many more seriously wounded and permanently maimed. The military men, after their one-year tour of duty, returned home alone and quickly by jet. There were no battalions of soldiers arriving stateside together at war's end, no parades, no homecomings, indeed, none of the grateful hoopla that all of us have seen in newsreels taken of the end of World War II. To make matters worse, the soldiers were subjected to criticism and sometimes abuse from those who regarded them as murderers for their participation in what many in the United States had come gradually to regard as an immoral war. Here is one example from many cited by Figley and Leventman (1980).

Walking across the Boston Commons his first day home, his service uniform and gear fully apparent, he was greeted by peace demonstrators with shouts of "Killer! How many babies did you burn over there?" Returning home, his brother offered, "You asshole! Why did you go to Vietnam anyway?" Seeking solace and companionship that night in the American Legion Hall, he was confronted with "Hey buddy! How come you guys lost the war over there?" (p. xxv).

The alienation and meaningless of the war that the soldiers had just left are summed up well in this excerpt.

Winning the hearts and minds of the Vietnamese was the goal. But hamlets were destroyed only to increase the number of Vietcong recruits. Containment policies and confusing restrictions often resulted in GIs taking and retaking the same hill or hamlet five or six times a year. . . . Faulty intelligence reports, fabricated body counts, an invisible enemy, high civilian involvement, an inability to measure positive military results, and awareness of divided political support at home all contributed to a sense of deep despair and anomie among combatants in Vietnam (Figley and Leventman, 1980, p. xxiii).

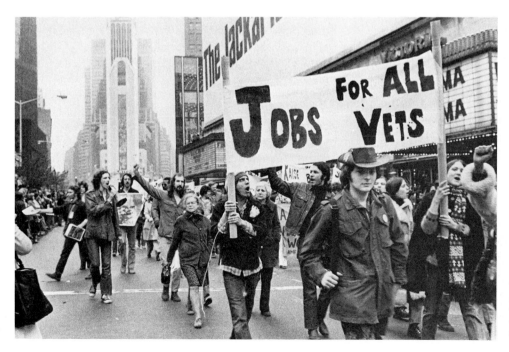

There was a great contrast between the ways America welcomed home its soldiers from World War II and from the Vietnam War.

Existential philosophy teaches us that people must find meaning and purpose in their lives. Sheer survival is important, but men and women suffer distress and depression if they cannot develop some sense of self-worth in what they do. It is terrible enough for soldiers to see a friend torn up by shrapnel, or to plunge a bayonet into the throat of a man designated as the enemy. How much worse are these experiences if soldiers know that back home people are protesting the morality of their being in the war in the first place? Many American soldiers in Vietnam began to harbor their own doubts about the value and legitimacy of their being there.

The Returned Soldier's Lot

The military have always suffered dearly after as well as during war. Their economic lot when peace is restored often lags behind that of the men who remained at home. Highly decorated soldiers have sometimes found themselves in miserable poverty upon return to civilian life. And yet for the most part the veterans of wars have been welcomed back as patriots and incorporated into the fabric of society, even if they were on the losing side, as the South was in the Civil War. This was not the case for those who served in Vietnam. Their continuing dislocation may have contributed to the long-term effects of the trauma of combat.

Moreover, men from the working class and minority groups were overrepresented in the military forces in Vietnam. Their cohorts of civilian society were those who do not fare well, which undoubtedly added to the estrangement that the veterans felt and to their job difficulties when they returned home (Figley and Leventman, 1980). As pointed out by the French sociologist Émile Durkheim (1897), group support can help people endure considerable stress. Many Vietnam veterans lacked this.

In addition, the most intimate aspects of the home-lives of veterans were sometimes disturbed by their battle experiences. Haley (1978), a social worker with extensive experience treating Vietnam veterans, provides a chilling and poignant account of how the particular nature of the war affected one soldier years afterward.

Because of the guerrilla nature of the Vietnam war, the "enemy" could be anyone, including women and children. Thus, some stress responses are activated by closeness to women and the responsibility of marriage, a wife's pregnancy and the birth of a child. Veterans who have fought and killed women and children during combat often find it impossible to make a smooth transition to the roles of husband, protector and father. One vet-eran had warned his close friend, the squad medic, not to go near a crying baby lying in a village road until they had checked the area. In his haste to help the child, the medic raced forward and "was blown to bits" along with the child, who had been booby-trapped. The veteran came into treatment three years later, after a period of good adjustment, because he was made fearful and anxious by his eight-month-old daughter's crying. He had been unable to pick her up or hold her since her birth despite his conscious wish to "be a good father" (p. 263).

Treatment of Posttraumatic Stress Disorder

The treatment of combat-related stress has for some time been guided by the three principles of immediacy, proximity, and expectancy (Lifton, 1976). When signs of stress, such as sleeplessness, are detected, the soldier is removed immediately to a quiet area as near as possible to his fighting unit and his comrades. There he is encouraged to talk things out and to rest. The soldier is also made aware that he is expected to return soon to his unit, for anxiety is regarded as an inevitable aspect of war, not sufficient cause to be excused from military responsibilities. Those severely affected are given more intensive therapy.

As stated earlier, during World War II combat-exhausted soldiers were hypnotized. They were also treated by narcosynthesis (Grinker and Spiegel, 1945), a procedure which might be considered a drug-assisted abreaction à la Breuer. The soldier was sedated with an intravenous injection of sodium Pentothal, enough to make him very drowsy. The therapist then told him in a matter-of-fact voice that he was on the battlefield, in the front lines, and if necessary and possible mentioned circumstances of the particular battle. The patient would usually begin recalling sometimes frightening events which he had perhaps forgotten, often with intense emotion. Many times the actual trauma was relived and even acted out by the patient. As he gradually returned to the waking state, the therapist would continue encouraging him to discuss the terrifying events, the hope being that he would realize that they were in the past, no longer a threat. In this fashion a synthesis, or coming together, of the past horror with the patient's present life was worked for (Cameron and Magaret, 1951).

The Veterans Administration, which had served veterans of World War II as well as those of the Korean

War, was not prepared at first to address the psychological plight of the Vietnam vet. First of all, many had left the service with ''bad paper,'' that is, with less than honorable discharges. Some of the offenses for which a soldier could receive undesirable discharges included ''character and behavior disorders,'' ''alcoholism,'' and ''drug addiction'' (Kidder, 1978). It seems likely that some of these men were suffering from the trauma of combat. Not until 1979—six years after the truce was signed with North Vietnam—was upgrading of dishonorable discharges effected through the assistance of the American Civil Liberties Union (Beck, 1979).

But in 1971, earlier than these governmental efforts which have helped bring more Vietnam veterans within the purview of the Veterans Administration hospital system, a Yale University psychiatrist, Robert Jay Lifton, was approached by antiwar veterans from the New York–New Haven area to work with them in forming ''rap groups.'' Initiated by the men themselves, these veterans' groups had a twofold purpose: a therapeutic one of healing themselves and a political one of forcing the American public to begin to understand the human costs of the war (Lifton, 1976). The rap groups spread outward from New York City until, in 1979, Congress approved a $25 million package establishing Operation Outreach, a network of ninety-one storefront counseling centers for psychologically distressed Vietnam veterans. In 1981 funding was extended for three additional years.

The rap groups have focused on the residual guilt and rage felt by the veterans: guilt over what their status as soldiers had called on them to do, in fighting a guerrilla war in which enemy and ally were often impossible to distinguish one from the other; and rage at being placed in the predicament of risking their lives in a cause to which their country was not fully committed. Discussion extends as well to present life concerns, such as relationships with women and feelings about masculinity, in particular, the ''macho'' view of physical violence.

The treatment of PTSD should also, argue Stanton and Figley (1978), encompass the complexities of the veteran's family life. Does he feel guilt over infidelities or rage at his wife's extramarital involvements while he was away? Is he having trouble with the increased independence of his wife, which she developed out of necessity in his absence and may be reluctant to give up on his return, especially in this era of raised feminist consciousness?

Group therapy is discussed in some detail in Chapter 20 (page 528). For now it suffices to say that in the rap groups—and in more conventional group therapy sessions in the 172 Veterans Administration hospitals across the country—at least two factors have probably helped the veterans. For perhaps the first time they could partake of the company of returned comrades-in-arms and feel the mutual support of others who had shared their war experiences. They were also able finally to begin confronting, in often emotional discussions, the combat events whose traumatic effects had been suppressed and thereby not looked at. As people have known for many, many years, in order for individuals to come to terms with fearsome happenings, to loose themselves from the hold that events can have over them, they must, in effect, return to the events and expose themselves fully.

Rap sessions, a form of group therapy for Vietnam veterans, played an important role in treating their posttraumatic stress disorder.

SUMMARY

People with anxiety disorders, alternately called anxiety neuroses, feel an overwhelming apprehension that seems unwarranted. DSM-III lists three principal diagnoses: phobic disorders; the anxiety states, which are panic disorder, generalized anxiety disorder, and obsessive-compulsive disorder; and posttraumatic stress disorder.

Phobias are intense, unreasonable fears that disrupt the life of an otherwise normal person. They are relatively common. Agoraphobia is fear of being outside one's home; social phobia is fear of social situations in which one may be scrutinized by other people. Other simple phobias are fears of animals, of closed-in spaces, and of heights. The psychoanalytic view of phobias is that they are a defense against repressed conflicts. Behavioral theorists have several ideas of how phobias are acquired—through classical conditioning, the pairing of an innocuous object or situation with an innately painful event; through operant conditioning, whereby a person is rewarded for continuing avoidance; through modeling, imitating the fear and avoidance of others; and through cognition, by making a catastrophe of a social mishap that could be construed in a less threatening fashion. But not all people who have such experiences develop a phobia. Perhaps a physiological diathesis, lability of the autonomic nervous system, predisposes certain people to acquire phobias.

A patient suffering from panic disorder has sudden inexplicable and periodic attacks of intense anxiety. Some people who have panic attacks also suffer from mitral valve prolapse syndrome. They may regard their heart palpitations as evidence of anxiety and escalate them into full-blown panics. Panic disorder patients, in general, ruminate about serious illnesses, physical and mental; they may magnify slight physical sensations until they are overwhelmed.

In generalized anxiety disorder, sometimes called "free-floating anxiety," the individual's life is beset with virtually constant tension and apprehension. Psychoanalytic theory regards the source as an unconscious conflict between the ego and id impulses. Behavioral theorists assume that, with adequate assessment, this pervasive anxiety can be pinned down to a finite set of anxiety-provoking circumstances, thereby likening it to a group of phobias. A sense of helplessness can also cause people to be anxious in a wide range of situations.

Humanistic theorists find that people go into anxiety states when they accept the unfavorable opinions others hold of them and do not express their basic self-worth.

People with obsessive-compulsive problems have intrusive, ego-alien thoughts and feel pressured to engage in stereotyped rituals lest they be overcome by frightening levels of anxiety. This disorder can become quite disabling, interfering not only with the life of the unfortunate who experiences the difficulties but also with the lives of those close to the person. Psychoanalytic theory posits strong id impulses that are under faulty and inadequate ego control. In behavioral accounts obsessions and compulsions are considered learned avoidance responses.

There are many therapies for phobias and anxiety states. Psychoanalytic treatment tries to lift repression so that childhood conflicts can be resolved; direct alleviation of the manifest problems is discouraged. In contrast, behavior therapists employ a range of procedures, such as systematic desensitization and modeling, designed to reduce the fear and avoidance. Dissuading compulsives from their rituals is an apparently effective although initially arduous technique. Rational-emotive therapy attempts to substitute more realistic self-statements for irrational beliefs. Humanistic therapies help the person discover his or her denied needs and wants and assume responsibility for satisfying them.

Perhaps the most widely employed treatments are tranquilizing drugs, dispensed by medical practitioners. Drugs, however, are subject to abuse, and their long-term use may have untoward and still inadequately understood side effects. Weaning a person from reliance on a chemical that reduces anxiety is also a problem.

Finally, posttraumatic stress disorder was examined, with particular attention given to the delayed reactions of many veterans of the Vietnam War. These anxiety reactions are often the fate of those who have suffered life-threatening trauma that would evoke extreme distress in most individuals. Treatment is by intense remembrances of the traumatic events. If we are to understand the veterans of Vietnam who suffer from this disorder and how best to render complete their return to and reintegration into society, we must grapple with the moral and political aspects of this conflict. The particular horrors of the war seem to lie at the core of the veterans' problems in adjusting to civilian life.

René Magritte, *He Doesn't Speak*, 1926 Photo G.D. Hackett, New York

SOMATOFORM AND DISSOCIATIVE DISORDERS

Complaints of bodily symptoms that suggest a physical defect or dysfunction, some rather dramatic in nature, but for which no physiological basis can be found, are diagnosed as *somatoform disorders*. *Dissociative disorders* are rarer, even more dramatic disruptions of consciousness, memory, and identity. The somatoform and dissociative disorders seem to serve some purpose or need of those who suffer them (Table 7.1). In DSM-II somatoform problems were called hysterical conversion neurosis and hypochondriacal neurosis. The DSM-II designation for dissociative disorders was hysterical dissociative neurosis.

TABLE 7.1 Somatoform and Dissociative Disorders

Somatoform Disorders
   Conversion disorder
   Somatization disorder (Briquet's syndrome)
   Psychogenic pain disorder
   Hypochondriasis
Dissociative Disorders
   Psychogenic amnesia
   Psychogenic fugue
   Multiple personality
   Depersonalization disorder

SOMATOFORM DISORDERS

The physical symptoms of somatoform disorders, which have no known physiological explanation and are not under voluntary control, are assumed to be linked to sometimes rather discernible psychological factors. Two major forms of somatoform disorders are distinguished, *conversion disorder* and *somatization disorder*, sometimes called *Briquet's syndrome*. DSM-III proposes two other somatoform disorders, about which little information is available. In *psychogenic pain disorder* the person reports severe, long-lasting pain that cannot be accounted for by organic pathology, even after extensive investigation. The pain may have a temporal relation to some conflict or stress, or it may allow the individual to avoid some hated activity and to secure attention and sympathy not otherwise available. In *hypochondriasis*, which was called hypochondriacal neurosis in DSM-II, the person is preoccupied with fears of having a serious disease. He or she overreacts to ordinary physical sensa-

tions and minor abnormalities—such as irregular heartbeat, sweating, occasional coughing, a sore spot, stomachache—as evidence for this belief and cannot be medically persuaded otherwise. Hypochondriasis is not very well differentiated from somatization disorder.

Conversion Disorder

Symptoms
In conversion disorders the operations of the musculature or sensory functions are impaired, although the bodily organs themselves and the neuromuscular apparatus are sound. The classic conversion symptoms suggest neurological disease. We find reports of partial or complete paralyses of arms or legs; seizures and coordination disturbances; paresthesia, a sensation of pricking, tingling, or creeping on the skin; anesthesias (Figure 7.1), the loss or impairment of sensations; analgesias, insensitivity to pain—all occurring in physiologically normal people. Vision may be seriously disturbed: the person may become partially or completely blind or have "tunnel vision," wherein the visual field is constricted as it would be were the observer peering through a tunnel. Aphonia, loss of the voice and all but whispered speech; anosmia, loss or impairment of the sense of smell; and false pregnancy are other conversion disorders.

Conversion symptoms by their very nature suggest that they, like psychogenic pain, are linked to psychological factors. They usually appear suddenly in stressful situations, allow patients to avoid some activity or responsibility, or secure them badly wanted attention. The term "conversion" originally derived from Freud, who thought that the energy of a repressed instinct is diverted into sensory-motor channels and blocks functioning. Thus anxiety and psychological conflict were believed to be *converted* into physical symptoms. Some of the people suffering conversion disorders may in fact seem complacent, even serene, and not particularly eager to part with their symptoms. Nor do they connect them with whatever straits they may be in.

Hysteria, the earlier term for such reactions, has of course a long history dating back to the earliest writings on abnormal behavior. Hippocrates considered it an affliction limited solely to women and brought on by the wandering of the uterus through the body. The Greek word *hystera* means womb. Presumably the wandering uterus symbolized the longing of the body for the production of a child. Freud considered the specific nature of the hysterical symptom to relate either to the repressed instinctual urge or to its repressing counterforce, representing them in disguised form. A hysterical convulsion might be the symbolic expression of a forbidden sexual wish, a hysterical paralysis the manifestation of self-punishment for a hidden aggressive urge. Conversion symptoms usually develop in adolescence or early adulthood. An episode may end abruptly, but sooner or later the disorder is likely to return, either in its original form or with a symptom of a different nature and site. The consensus among writers is that conversion disorders are found primarily in females. During both world wars, however, a large number of males developed conversionlike difficulties in combat (Ziegler, Imboden, and Meyer, 1960).

Diagnostic Problems

Diagnostically, it is important to distinguish a conversion paralysis or sensory dysfunction from similar problems that have a true neurological basis. Sometimes this is an easy task, as when the paralysis does not make anatomical sense. But in other cases the diagnostic decision is more difficult.

Since the majority of paralyses, analgesias, and sensory failures do have organic causes, true neurological problems may sometimes be misdiagnosed as conversion disorders. Slater and Glithero (1965) investigated this disturbing possibility in a follow-up of patients who nine years earlier had been diagnosed as suffering from conversion symptoms. An alarming number, in fact 60 percent, of these individuals had either died in the meantime or developed symptoms of physical disease! A high proportion had diseases of the central nervous system. Similarly, Whitlock (1967) compared the incidence of organic disorders in patients earlier diagnosed as having conversion disorders and in patients earlier diagnosed as having depressive reactions, anxiety reactions, or both. Organic disorders were found in 62.5 percent of the patients earlier diagnosed as having conversion disorders and in only 5.3 percent of the other groups. The most common organic problem was head injury, generally found to have occurred about six months before the onset of the conversion symptoms. Other common organic problems were stroke, encephalitis, and brain tumor. Finally, Watson and Buranen (1979) found that 25 percent of patients whose symptoms had been considered conversion reactions actually had physical disorders.

From these data we can see that some symptoms labeled as conversion reactions and thought to have psychological causes may, in fact, be physical disorders. We have already learned that the assessment of organic

FIGURE 7.1 Hysterical anesthesias can be distinguished from neurological dysfunctions. On the left are shown the patterns of neural innervation of the skin. On the right are superimposed typical areas of anesthesias in hysterical patients. The hysterical anesthesias do not make anatomical sense. (Adapted from an original painting by Frank H. Netter, M.D. From *The CIBA Collection of Medical Illustrations*, copyright by CIBA Pharmaceutical Company, Division of CIBA-GEIGY Corporation.)

problems is still rather crude. Therefore it is not always possible to distinguish between psychologically and organically produced symptoms. The diagnosis of conversion disorder may be applied too frequently; some individuals diagnosed in this way may have an organic problem that has gone undetected. The damage that such inappropriate diagnoses can do is sobering to contemplate.

A second diagnostic problem with conversion disorders is differentiating them from *malingering*, which is faking an incapacity in order to avoid a responsibility. In trying to discriminate conversion reactions from malingering, clinicians may attempt to decide whether the symptoms have been consciously or unconsciously adopted.[1] This means of resolving the issue is at best a dubious one, for it is difficult if not impossible to know with any degree of certainty whether behavior is consciously or unconsciously motivated. One aspect of behavior is sometimes revealing, however, *la belle indifférence*—a relative lack of concern, the adoption of a blasé attitude toward the symptoms out of keeping with their severity and supposedly long-term consequences. But these patients also appear willing and eager to talk endlessly and dramatically about them. In contrast, the malingerer is likely to be more guarded and cautious, perhaps because he or she considers interviews a challenge or threat to the success of the lie. But this distinction is not foolproof, for only about one-third of people with conversion disorders show *la belle indifférence* (Stephens and Kamp, 1962).

Somatization Disorder (Briquet's Syndrome)

In 1859 the French physician Pierre Briquet described a syndrome which has since borne his name and now in DSM-III is referred to as somatization disorder. Recurrent, multiple somatic complaints for which medical at-

tention is sought but which have no apparent physical cause are the basis of this diagnosis. Common complaints include headaches, fatigue, allergies, abdominal, back, and chest pains, genitourinary symptoms, and palpitations. Conversion symptoms may also be present. Visits to physicians, sometimes to a number of them simultaneously, are frequent, as is the use of medication. Hospitalization and even surgery are common (Guze, 1967). Patients are given to histrionics, presenting their complaints in a dramatic, exaggerated fashion or as part of a long and complicated medical history. Many believe that they have been ailing all their lives.

The colloquial term for these problems is hypochondria, but DSM-III draws a distinction between hypochondriasis and somatization disorder. In the first the patient is preoccupied with the fear of having a specific and serious physical disease, whereas in the second the patient's concern is with the many symptoms themselves. As noted at the beginning of this chapter, such a distinction appears to be of dubious value. Table 7.2 gives a picture of the pervasiveness of health problems reported by people with Briquet's syndrome.

Somatization disorder typically begins in late adolescence and is more common in women than in men (Kroll, Chamberlain, and Halpern, 1979). Anxiety and depression are frequently reported, as are a host of behavioral and interpersonal problems, such as truancy, poor work records, and marital difficulties. Somatization disorders also seem to run in families; they are found in about 20 percent of the first-degree relatives of index cases (Arkonac and Guze, 1963). The following case indicates one woman's complaints.

Alice was referred to the psychological clinic by her physician, Joyce Williams. Dr. Williams had been Alice's physician for about six months and in that time period had seen her twenty-three times. Alice had dwelt on a number of rather vague complaints—general aches and pains, bouts of nausea, tiredness, irregular menstruation, and dizziness. But various tests—complete blood workups, X-rays, spinal tap, and so on—had not revealed any pathology.

Upon meeting her therapist, Alice immediately let him know that she was a somewhat reluctant client: "I'm here only because I trust Dr. Williams and she urged me to come. I'm physically sick and don't see how a psychologist is going to help." But when Alice

---

[1]Two DSM-III diagnoses, *malingering* and *factitious disorders*, should also be mentioned. Both are applied to people whose conversionlike symptoms or psychological symptoms are under voluntary control. In malingering the symptoms are obviously linked to a recognizable goal, the altering of the individual's circumstances. An example would be a claim of physical illness to avoid standing trial. In a factitious disorder the motivation for adopting the physical or psychological symptoms is much less clear. Apparently the individual for some unknown reason wants to assume the role of "patient."

TABLE 7.2 Various Symptoms and Their Frequency as Reported by a Sample of Patients with Briquet's Syndrome *(after Perley and Guze, 1962)*

Symptom	Percent Reporting	Symptom	Percent Reporting	Symptom	Percent Reporting
Dyspnea (labored breathing)	72	Weight loss	28	Back pain	88
Palpitation	60	Sudden fluctuations in weight	16	Joint pain	84
Chest pain	72	Anorexia	60	Extremity pain	84
Dizziness	84	Nausea	80	Burning pains in rectum, vagina, mouth	28
Headache	80	Vomiting	32	Other bodily pain	36
Anxiety attacks	64	Abdominal pain	80	Depressed feelings	64
Fatigue	84	Abdominal bloating	68	Phobias	48
Blindness	20	Food intolerances	48	Vomiting all nine months of pregnancy	20
Paralysis	12	Diarrhea	20	Nervous	92
Anesthesia	32	Constipation	64		
Aphonia (loss of voice above a whisper)	44	Dysuria (painful urination)	44	Had to quit working because felt bad	44
Lump in throat	28	Urinary retention	8	Trouble doing anything because felt bad	72
Fits or convulsions	20	Dysmenorrhea (painful menstruation, premarital only)	4	Cried a lot	70
Faints	56	Dysmenorrhea (prepregnancy only	8	Felt life was hopeless	28
Unconsciousness	16	Dysmenorrhea (other)	48	Always sickly (most of life)	40
Amnesia	8	Menstrual irregularity	48	Thought of dying	48
Visual blurring	64	Excessive menstrual bleeding	48	Wanted to die	36
Visual hallucination	12	Sexual indifference	44	Thought of suicide	28
Deafness	4	Frigidity (absence of orgasm)	24	Attempted suicide	12
Olfactory hallucination	16	Dyspareunia (painful sexual intercourse)	52		
Weakness	84				

was asked to describe the history of her physical problems, she quickly warmed to the task. According to Alice, she had always been sick. As a child she had had episodes of high fever, frequent respiratory infections, convulsions, and her first two operations, appendectomy and tonsillectomy. As she continued her somewhat loosely organized chronological account of her medical history, Alice's descriptions of her problems became more and more colorful (and probably exaggerated as well): "Yes, when I was in my early twenties I had some problems with vomiting. For weeks at a time I'd vomit up everything I ate. I'd even vomit up liquids, even water. Just the sight of food would make me vomit. The smell of food cooking was absolutely unbear-

able. I must have been vomiting every ten minutes." During her twenties Alice had gone from one physician to another. She saw several gynecologists for her menstrual irregularity and dyspareunia (pain during intercourse) and had dilatation and curetage (scraping the lining of the uterus). She had been referred to neurologists for her headaches, dizziness, and fainting spells, and they had performed EEGs, spinal taps, and even a CAT scan. Other physicians had ordered X-rays to look for the possible causes of her abdominal pain and EKGs for her chest pains. Both rectal and gallbladder surgery had also been performed.

When the interview finally shifted away from Alice's medical history, it became apparent that she was a

The medicine chest of a patient with somatization disorder.

highly anxious person in many situations, particularly those in which she thought she might be evaluated by other people. Indeed, some of her physical complaints could be regarded as consequences of anxiety. Furthermore, her marriage was quite shaky, and she and her husband were considering divorce. Their marital problems seemed to be linked to sexual difficulties stemming from Alice's dyspareunia and her general indifference toward sex.

[2]Much of the theorizing in this area has been directed toward hysteria and thus assumes that conversion disorder and somatization disorder are similar etiologically. Although this assumption is unsupported, we have little choice but to present the theories as they exist.

Theories of Somatoform Disorders[2]

Conversion disorder occupies a central place in **psychoanalytic theory**, for in the course of treating such cases Freud was led to many of the major concepts of psychoanalysis. Conversion disorders offered him a clear opportunity to invoke the concept of the unconscious. Consider for a moment how you might try to make sense of a patient's report that she awakened one morning with a paralyzed left arm. Your first reaction might be to give her a series of neurological tests to assess possible physiological causes of the paralysis. Let us assume that these tests are negative. No evidence of neurological disorder is present. You are now faced with choosing whether to believe or to doubt the patient's communication. On the one hand, she might be lying; she may know that her arm is not paralyzed but has decided to "fake" paralysis in order to achieve some end. This would be an example of malingering. But what if you believe the patient? Now you are almost forced to consider that unconscious processes are operating. On a conscious level the patient is telling the truth; she believes and reports that her arm is paralyzed. Only on a level that is not conscious does she know that her arm is actually normal.

In their *Studies in Hysteria* (1895) Breuer and Freud proposed that a conversion disorder is caused by an experience that had created great emotional arousal. The affect, however, was not expressed, and the memory of the event was cut off from conscious experience. Two reasons were suggested to explain why the affect associated with the experience was not expressed. The experience may have been so distressing that the person could not allow it to enter consciousness and therefore repressed it. Or the experience may have occurred while the person was in an abnormal psychological state, such as semihypnosis. In both situations, Breuer and Freud proposed, the specific conversion symptoms are related to the traumatic event that caused them.

Anna O., for example, while watching at the bedside of her seriously ill father, had dropped off into a waking dream with her right arm over the back of her chair. She saw a black snake emerge from the wall and come toward her sick father to bite him. She tried to ward it away, but her right arm had gone to sleep. When she looked at her hand, her fingers turned into little snakes with death's heads. The next day a bent branch recalled her hallucination of the snake, and at once her right arm became rigidly extended. Thenceforward it acted the same way whenever some object revived her hallucination. Later, when Anna O. fell into her absences and took to her own bed, the contracture of her right arm became chronic and extended to paralysis and anesthesia of her right side.

In his later writings Freud formulated a theory of conversion disorder in which sexual impulses became primary. Specifically, he hypothesized that conversion disorders are rooted in an early, unresolved Electra complex. The young female child becomes incestuously attached to her father, but these early impulses are repressed, producing both a preoccupation with sex and, at the same time, an avoidance of it. At a later period of her life, sexual excitement or some happenstance reawakens these repressed impulses, at which time they are transformed or converted into physical symptoms that represent in distorted form the repressed libidinal urges or the repressing forces. Thus the *primary gain* from conversion disorder is the avoidance of previously repressed id impulses. Freud allowed, however, that there could also be a *secondary gain* from the symptoms. That is, they might allow the patient to avoid or escape from some currently unpleasant life situation. (In learning theory terms, the symptoms are reinforced by their consequences.) Modern psychoanalytic theorists, however, do not all agree that conversion disorders stem from the Electra complex. Some (for example, Sperling, 1973) see the problem originating much earlier, during the oral period, when the basic security system of the infant is taking form.

A contemporary psychodynamic interpretation of one form of conversion disorder, hysterical blindness, has been offered by Sackeim, Nordlie, and Gur (1979). The starting point of their analysis is experimental studies of hysterically blind people whose behavior on visual tests shows that they are being influenced by the stimuli, even though they explicitly deny seeing them.

A case in point was described by Theodor and Mandelcorn (1973). The patient, a sixteen-year-old, had experienced a sudden loss of peripheral vision, reporting that her visual field had become tubular and constricted. Although a number of neurological tests had proved negative, the authors wanted to be even more certain that they were not dealing with a neurological problem. So they arranged a special visual test in which a bright, oval target was presented either in the center or in the periphery of the patient's visual field. On each trial there were two time intervals, which were bounded by the sounding of a buzzer. The target was illuminated during one of the intervals, and the young woman's task was to report which one.

When the target was presented in the center of the visual field, the patient always correctly identified the time interval during which it was illuminated. This had been expected since she had not reported any loss of central vision. What happened when the oval was presented peripherally? The patient could be expected to be correct 50 percent of the time by chance alone; the authors reasoned that this would be the outcome if she were truly "blind" in peripheral vision. For the peripheral showings of the target, however, the young woman was correct only 30 percent of the time. She had performed significantly more poorly than would a person who was indeed blind! The clinicians reasoned that she must have been in some sense aware of the illuminated stimulus, and that she wanted, either consciously or unconsciously, to preserve her "blindness" by performing poorly on the test.

Grosz and Zimmerman (1970), on the other hand, observed almost perfect visual performance by a hysterically blind adolescent girl. Fifteen-year-old Celia's initial symptom was a sudden loss of sight in both eyes, followed thereafter by severe blurring of vision. Celia claimed not to be able to read small or large print. Celia had set high standards for herself and did very well at school. Her busy parents, continually rushing off on their own many activities, professed concern about their four children's education but often left Celia responsible for the three younger children. When Celia's vision blurred so severely, her parents became obliged to read her studies to her. Even so, testing revealed that Celia could with no difficulty identify objects of various sizes and shapes and count fingers at a distance of fifteen feet. When three triangles were projected on three display windows of a console, two of the triangles inverted, one of them upright, in 599 trials out of 600 she pressed the switch under the upright triangle, the correct response, which then turned off a buzzer for five seconds.

Sackeim and his colleagues argue that a two-stage defensive reaction can account for these conflicting findings. First, perceptual representations of visual stimuli are blocked from awareness, and on this basis people report themselves blind. Second, information is still extracted from the perceptual representations. If subjects feel that they must deny being privy to this information, they do more poorly than they would do by chance on perceptual tasks. If subjects do not need to deny to themselves having such information, they perform the task well but still maintain that they are blind. Whether hysterically blind people unconsciously need to deny receiving perceptual information is viewed as being

BOX 7.1

AWARENESS, THE UNCONSCIOUS, AND BEHAVIOR

The first experimental psychologists working in the last two decades of the nineteenth century realized very soon that we are unaware of much that goes on in our minds as we perceive and encode stimuli from our environment. Much of the workings of the mind proceeds out of our awareness. Consider a recent example. In studying selective attention, researchers often use a dichotic-listening task in which separate tapes are played to each ear; subjects are asked to attend to only one of them. Subjects usually report later on that they know little about the sounds that came into the unattended ear. *But these unattended stimuli can affect behavior.* For example, Wilson (1975) had people listen to a human voice while tone sequences were playing in the unattended ear. Subjects reported having heard no tones. Furthermore, in a memory task in which they listened to tone sequences played earlier and others that had not been played, the subjects were unable to distinguish between the two types. Despite this demonstration that the subjects did not recognize tone stimuli played previously, another measure had a startling result. It is known that familiarity affects judgments of tone stimuli similar to those Wilson used. Familiar sequences are liked better than novel ones. When subjects in Wilson's study were asked to rate how much they liked a series of tone sequences, the ones that had been presented earlier to the unattended ears were preferred to novel sequences. Some aspects of the tone sequences played during the dichotic-listening task must have

been absorbed, even though subjects said that they had not heard them and demonstrated that they did not recognize them. A similar phenomenon has been observed with vision (Kunst-Wilson and Zajonc, 1980). Subjects were presented with different shapes for one millisecond (one-thousandth of a second). Their ability to recognize later the shapes that they had seen was essentially nil. But when they rated how much they liked the shapes, they preferred the ones that they had "seen" to new ones that were presented for the first time.

A series of studies reported by Nisbett and Wilson (1977) also indicate that awareness, as measured by verbal report, is not always a very accurate indication of the effect stimuli have on behavior. In one of their studies, Nisbett and Wilson first had subjects memorize a list of word pairs. For some subjects the pairs of words were specially constructed so that they would be likely to have an effect on subjects' performances in a second part of the study. For example, one of the word pairs these subjects first memorized was "ocean-moon." This pair was expected to make them more likely to respond "Tide" when they were later asked to name a detergent. The results agreed with expectation: subjects who had memorized the special word pairs gave double the number of expected associations as subjects who had not memorized them. Right after the second part of the test, subjects were asked why they had given their particular responses. Even though they could still re-

---

dependent on personality factors and motivation.

Are the people who claim that they are blind and yet on another level respond to visual stimuli being truthful? Sackeim and his colleagues report that some patients with lesions in the visual cortex, rather than damage to the eye, say that they are blind and yet perform well on visual tasks. They have vision, but they do not *know* that they can see. So it is possible for people to claim truthfully that they cannot see and at the same time give evidence that they can. On a more general level, a dissociation between awareness and behavior has been reported in many perceptual and cognitive studies (see Box 7.1). To test in the laboratory their assumption that motivation has bearing, Sackeim and his colleagues hypnotized two susceptible subjects, gave each a suggestion of total blindness, and then tested them on a visual discrimination task. One was given instructions

designed to motivate her to maintain her blindness. She was expected to deny her perceptions and perform more poorly than chance on the visual task. The other subject was not so explicitly urged to maintain her blindness and was expected to do better than chance on the task. A third subject was asked to simulate the behavior of someone who had been hypnotized and given a suggestion of total blindness.

The results agreed with the predictions. The subject highly motivated to maintain blindness indeed performed more poorly than chance, and the less motivated subject performed perfectly, even though still reporting that she was blind. The simulator performed, for the most part, at a chance level. In a postexperimental interview she stated that she had deliberately tried to simulate chance performance. As Sackeim and his colleagues have proposed, verbal reports and behavior can

Subject being given a dichotic-listening task. Different tapes are played simultaneously to the left and right ears; the subject is instructed to attend only to what is coming in one ear.

call the word pairs, subjects almost never mentioned them as bringing their responses to mind. Instead they gave reasons such as "My mother uses Tide," or "Tide is the most popular detergent."

The studies just reviewed, which are but a small sampling of current research making a similar point, are closely related to the psychoanalytic concept of the unconscious. Contemporary investigators have begun to corroborate Freud's view that much of human behavior is determined by unconscious processes. But the unconscious processes are understood in a different way. Freud postulated the existence of "the" unconscious, a repository of instinctual energy and repressed conflicts and impulses. Contemporary researchers reject the energy reservoir and repression, holding more simply that we are not aware of everything going on around us and of some of our cognitive processes.* At the same time, these stimuli and processes of which we are unaware can affect behavior powerfully. This recent research suggests that understanding the causes of human behavior will be a difficult task. It will not be sufficient merely to ask someone "Why did you do that?"

*In a sense, the distinction resides in whether "unconscious" is a noun, as Freud used it, or an adjective, as contemporary researchers employ the term. As an adjective, "unconscious" can encourage further exploration into the factors that render something unavailable to awareness.

apparently be unconsciously separated from one another. Hysterically blind persons are able to say that they cannot see and yet at the same time be influenced by visual stimuli. And the way in which they show signs of being able to see may depend on how much they need to be considered blind.

Sociocultural theories are based on the supposed decrease in conversion disorders over the last century. Although Charcot and Freud seemed to have had an abundance of female patients with this sort of difficulty, contemporary clinicians rarely see anyone with such problems. A number of hypotheses have been proposed to explain this apparent decrease. For example, those of a psychoanalytic bent point out that in the second half of the nineteenth century, when the incidence of conversion reactions was apparently high in France and Austria, sexual attitudes were quite repressive and may have contributed to the increased incidence of the disorder.

The decline of the conversion reaction, then, is attributed to a general relaxing of sexual mores and also to the greater psychological and medical sophistication of twentieth-century culture, which is more tolerant of anxiety than it is of dysfunctions that do not make physiological sense.

A study by Proctor (1958) is often cited as providing evidence for this theory. The incidence of conversion reaction was found to be particularly high among children who were patients at the University of North Carolina Medical School Psychiatric Clinic. In interpreting this very high incidence, 13 percent, the author noted that most of the children came from rural areas where the socioeconomic status of the inhabitants was low and little education was provided for them. Moreover, the religious background of these people was generally strong and fundamentalist. The mid-twentieth-century conditions in this area of North Carolina may have approximated in some respects those prevailing in nineteenth-century France and Austria.

Ironically, *there is in fact little evidence that the incidence of conversion disorders is decreasing*. For example, Stephens and Kamp (1962) compared the outpatient diagnoses of two periods, the first from 1913 to 1919 and the second from 1945 to 1960. In both they found the incidence of conversion reaction to be 2 percent. We can also find reasons that explain away the seemingly high incidence of conversion disorders found in the nineteenth century. The large numbers seen by clinicians such as Charcot and Freud may have reflected a selective process. Patients with these particular difficulties may have come to these clinicians because they were known to be successful in treating hysterias. With regard to Proctor's data, the high incidence of conversion reactions in children at the North Carolina clinic may have reflected not a "true" high incidence but rather differences in diagnostic practices. In view of the difficulties in assessing incidence at different periods of time, it would seem ill-advised to use alleged changes in frequency of occurrence as validation for an etiological theory of a disorder.

A **behavioral account** of the development of conversion disorders has been proposed by Ullmann and Krasner (1975). In their opinion the person with a conversion reaction attempts to behave according to his or her own conception of how a person with a disease affecting the motor or sensory abilities would act. This theory raises two questions. Are people capable of such behavior? Under what conditions might such behavior be most likely to occur?

Considerable evidence supports an affirmative answer to the first question, that people can adopt patterns of behavior that match many of the classic conversion symptoms. For example, paralyses and analgesias, and blindness as we have seen, can be induced in people under hypnosis. Similarly, chemically inert drugs called placebos have reduced the pain of patients who had been considered truly ill. As a partial answer to the second question, Ullmann and Krasner specify two conditions that increase the likelihood that motor and sensory disabilities will be imitated. First, the individual must have some experience with the role to be adopted. He or she may have had similar physical problems or may have observed them in others. Second, Ullmann and Krasner note that the enactment of a role must be rewarded. An individual will assume a disability only if it can be expected either to reduce stress or to reap other positive consequences. For Ullmann and Krasner conversion disorders are the same as malingering in that the person adopts the symptom to gain some end.

The patient of Grosz and Zimmerman mentioned earlier did not act in accord with Ullmann and Krasner's theory, however. The very intelligent Celia performed perfectly in the visual discrimination task while still claiming severely blurred vision. Such a pattern of behavior seems a rather clumsy enactment of a role. If you wanted to convince someone that you could not see, would you always correctly identify the upright triangle? Again, Celia's actions seem more consistent with the theorizing offered by Sackeim and his co-workers. On the level of conscious awareness, Celia probably saw only blurred images, as she claimed. But during the test the triangles were distinguished on an unconscious level, and she could pick out the upright one, whichever console window it appeared in.[3]

Another behavioral view of somatoform disorders, at least of Briquet's syndrome, holds that the various aches and pains, discomforts and dysfunctions are unrealistic anxiety manifesting itself in particular bodily systems. Perhaps the extreme tension of an individual localizes in his stomach muscles, and he feels nauseous and even vomits. Once normal functioning is disrupted, the maladaptive pattern may strengthen because of the attention it receives or the excuses it provides.

Genetic and physiological factors have been suggested as playing some role in the development of conversion disorders. Slater (1961) investigated concordance rates in twelve identical and twelve fraternal pairs of twins. Probands of each pair had been diagnosed as having the disorder, but none of the co-twins in either of the two groups manifested a conversion reaction. Similarly, Gottesman (1962) found the reactions of identical twins to statements on the hysteria scale of the MMPI to be no more similar than those of fraternal twins. Genetic factors, then, from the studies done so far, seem to be of no importance.

Several studies have examined physiological reactions in patients with conversion symptoms. The ques-

[3]Celia's visual problems had gained her crucial attention and help from her parents, which is in the nature of conversion disorders as well as of malingering. Three years after the onset of her visual difficulties Celia suddenly and dramatically recovered clear sight while on a summer trip with her parents across the country to the West coast. In June she had graduated from high school with grades well above average.

tion asked is whether patients' verbal reports have physiological correlates. For example, are the areas of the body in which analgesia or anesthesia is reported less physiologically responsive? Unfortunately, results are contradictory (Hernández-Peón, Chávez-Ibarra, and Aguilar-Figueroa, 1963; Levy and Muskin, 1973).

A hint of a neurophysiological explanation of why emotions connected with conversion disorders remain unavailable to conscious awareness comes from studies showing that conversion symptoms are more likely to occur on the left side of the body than on the right (Galin, Diamond, and Braff, 1977; Stern, 1977). In most instances these left-side body functions are controlled by the right hemisphere of the brain. Thus the majority of conversion symptoms may be related to the functioning of the right hemisphere. Research on patients who have had the hemispheres of their brains surgically disconnected to prevent the spread of epileptic seizures has shown that the right hemisphere can separately generate emotions, and indeed it is suspected of generating more of them than does the left hemisphere. Conversion symptoms would in this way be neurophysiologically linked to emotional arousal. Furthermore, this same research indicates that the right hemisphere depends on the neural passageways of the corpus callosum (see Box A.1, page 600) for connection with the left hemisphere's verbal capacity to describe and explain emotions and by these means to gain awareness of them. In conversion disorders it may be that the left hemisphere somehow blocks impulses carrying painful emotional content from the right hemisphere. Thus individuals with a conversion disorder make no connection between it and their troubling circumstances or their emotional needs. This is an intriguing bit of speculation.

Therapy for Somatoform Disorders

Not surprisingly, people with hypochondriacal complaints, and those too with conversion disorders and psychogenic pain, go far more often to physicians than to psychiatrists and nonmedical clinicians like psychologists, for they define their problems in somatic terms. They are not open to psychological explanations of their predicaments and therefore resent referrals to "shrinks." Many such patients try the patience of their physicians, who often find themselves prescribing one drug or medical treatment after another in hopes of remedying the somatic complaint.

Psychoanalysis of course has a special connection to conversion disorders, inasmuch as many of Freud's patients were women who suffered from these phenomena. The "talking cure" that psychoanalysis developed into was based on the assumption that a massive repression had forced psychic energy to be transformed or converted into puzzling anesthesias or paralyses. The catharsis of the patient as she faced up to the infantile origins of the repression was assumed to help, and even today free association and other efforts to lift repression are a common approach. Psychoanalysis and psychoanalytically oriented psychotherapy have not been demonstrated to be particularly useful with conversion disorders, however, except perhaps to reduce the patient's concern about her disabling problems (Ochitil, 1982).

Behavioral clinicians consider the high levels of anxiety associated with somatization disorder, or Briquet's syndrome, to be linked to certain situations. Alice, the woman described earlier, revealed herself to be extremely anxious about her shaky marriage and about situations in which other people might judge her. Techniques like systematic desensitization or any of the cognitive therapies could be addressed to her fears, the reduction of which would help to lessen somatic complaints. But it is likely that more treatment would be needed, for a person who has been "sick" for a period of time has grown accustomed to weakness and dependency, to avoiding everyday challenges rather than facing them as an adult. Chances are that people who live with Alice have adjusted to her "infirmity" and are even unwittingly reinforcing her for her avoidance of normal adult responsibilities. Family therapy, then, would be called for to help Alice and the members of her family change the web of relationships in order to support her movements toward greater autonomy. Assertion training and *social-skills training*—coaching Alice in effective ways to approach and talk to people, to keep eye contact, give compliments, accept criticism, make requests—could be useful in helping her acquire, or reacquire, means of relating to others and meeting her needs that do not begin with the premise "I am a poor, weak, sick person."

Behavior therapists have applied to somatoform disorders a wide range of techniques intended to make it worthwhile for the patient to give up the symptoms. A case reported by Liebson (1967) is an example of this tack. A man had relinquished his job because of pain and weakness in the legs and attacks of giddiness. Liebson helped the patient return to full-time work by persuading his family to refrain from reinforcing him for his idleness and by arranging for the man to receive a pay increase if he succeeded in getting himself to work. A reinforcement approach, then, attempts to provide the patient with greater incentives to get better than to remain incapacitated. An important consideration with any such operant tactic, as noted by Walen, Hauserman, and Lavin (1977), is to make it possible for the patient not to lose face when parting with the disorder. That is, the therapist should appreciate the possibility that the patient will feel humiliated at becoming better through treatment that does not deal with the "medical" problem.

Because somatoform disorders are rarer than other problems people take to mental health professionals, no true research has been done on the relative efficacy of different treatments. Case reports and clinical specula-

tion are, for now, the only sources of information on how to help people with these puzzling disruptions in bodily functioning.

DISSOCIATIVE DISORDERS

DSM-III distinguishes among three major dissociative disorders—*psychogenic amnesia*, *psychogenic fugue*, and *multiple personality*—in all of which there is "a sudden, temporary alteration in the normally integrative functions of consciousness, identity, or motor behavior" (p. 253). Important personal events cannot be recalled, or customary identity is temporarily lost. The individual may even wander far from his or her usual surroundings. *Depersonalization disorder*, in which the person's perception or experience of the self is discon-

Dissociative disorders are usually preceded by a severe stress, such as a death in the family or service in a war.

certingly and disruptively altered,[4] is also described as a dissociative disorder. But its inclusion is recognized as controversial because there is no disturbance of memory.

In **psychogenic amnesia** the person suddenly becomes unable to recall important personal information, usually after some stressful episode. The holes in memory are too extensive to be explained by ordinary forgetfulness. Most often the memory loss is for all events during a limited period of time following some traumatic experience, such as witnessing the death of a loved one. More rarely the amnesia is for only selected events during a circumscribed period of distress, is continuous from a traumatic event to the present, or is total, covering the person's entire life. During the period of amnesia, the person's behavior is otherwise unremarkable, except that the memory loss may bring some disorientation and purposeless wandering. With total amnesia the patient will not recognize relatives and friends, but he or she will retain the ability to talk, read, and reason and perhaps his or her talents and whatever knowledge of the world and how to function in it had previously been acquired. The amnesic episode may last several hours or as long as several years. Then it usually disappears as suddenly as it came on, with complete recovery and only a small chance of recurrence.

Memory loss is common in many organic brain disorders as well. But psychogenic amnesia and memory loss caused by a brain disease can be fairly easily distinguished. In organic disorders memory fails slowly over time and is not linked to life stress. Furthermore, recovery is rare or incomplete, and other symptoms, such as inattention and emotional upset, are also present.

If a person not only becomes totally amnesic but also moves away from home and work and assumes a new identity, the diagnosis of **psychogenic fugue** is made. Sometimes the assumption of the new identity can be quite elaborate, with the person taking on a new name, new home, new job, and even a new set of personality characteristics. He or she may succeed in establishing a fairly complex social life, all without questioning the inability to remember the past. More often, however, the new life does not crystallize to this extent and the fugue is of briefer duration. It consists for the most part of limited, but apparently purposeful, travel, during which social contacts are minimal or even avoided. Fugues typically occur after the person has experienced some severe stress, such as marital quarrels, personal rejections, war service, or a natural disaster. Recovery, although varying in the time it takes, is usually complete; the individual does not recollect what took place during the flight from his or her usual haunts.

Consider what it would be like to have a **multiple personality**, as did Chris Sizemore, the woman with the famous "three faces of Eve" (see pages 97 to 99). People have told you about things you have done that seem out of character, events that you have no memory of. You yourself have been waking up each morning with the remains of a cup of tea by your bedside—and you do not like to drink tea. How can you explain these happenings? If you were to seek treatment, might you not worry whether the psychiatrist or psychologist will believe you? Perhaps the clinician will think you psychotic.

Each of us has days when we are not "quite ourselves." This is assumed to be quite normal and is not what is meant by multiple personality. According to

---

[4]In a depersonalization episode individuals rather suddenly lose the sense of self. Their limbs may seem drastically changed in size, or they may have the impression that they are outside their bodies, viewing themselves from a distance. Sometimes they feel mechanical, that they and others too are robots, or they move as though in a dream, in a world that has lost its reality. Similar, but much more intense, episodes sometimes occur in schizophrenia. The schizophrenic's experience, however, does not have the "as if" quality that the person in depersonalization reports. The schizophrenic's estrangement from the self is real and complete.

"Don't be silly. If you were afflicted with a multiple personality, I'd have noticed something."

Drawing by Francino; © 1981, The New Yorker Magazine, Inc.

DSM-III, a proper diagnosis of multiple personality requires that a person have at least two separate "ego states," two different modes of being and feeling and acting that exist independently of each other, coming forth and being in control at different times.[5] At least one ego state usually has no contact with the other, that is, the person in ego state A has no memory for what state B is like, or even any knowledge of having an alternate state of being. The existence of different states must furthermore be chronic and severe, not attributable to the ingestion of some drug, for example.

Each personality is fully integrated and complex, with its own behavior patterns, memories, and relationships; they determine the nature and acts of the individual when the particular personality is in command. Usually the personalities are quite different, even opposites of one another. The original and subordinate personalities are all aware of lost periods of time, and the voices of the others may sometimes echo into their consciousness, even though they do not know to whom these voices belong. When an individual has more than two subpersonalities, each of these is to some extent aware of the others. In fact, they may talk to each other and be constant companions. The disorder may begin in early childhood or later, but it is rarely diagnosed until adolescence. Multiple personality is more chronic and serious than other dissociative disorders, and recovery may be less complete.

The case of Eve White was at one time the most carefully documented report of multiple personality in the clinical literature. But now a number of other cases have been described. One such account appeared in 1976 in the *Journal of Abnormal Psychology*. "The Three Faces of Evelyn" is a detailed history by Robert F. Jeans, the psychiatrist who treated the woman.

> Jeans provides the following background on his patient. He was consulted in December 1965 by a Gina Rinaldi, referred to him by her friends. Gina, single and thirty-one years old, lived with another single woman and was at the time working successfully as a writer at a large educational publishing firm. She was considered an efficient, businesslike, and productive person, but her friends had observed that she was becoming forgetful and sometimes acted out of character. The youngest of nine siblings, Gina reported that she had been sleepwalking since her early teens; her present roommate had told her that now she would sometimes scream in her sleep.
>
> Gina described her mother, then age seventy-four, as the most domineering woman she had ever known. She reported that as a child she had been

[5]Cases of multiple personality are frequently mislabeled in the popular press as schizophrenic reactions. This diagnostic category, discussed in greater detail in Chapter 14, derives part of its name from the Greek root *schizo*, which means "splitting away from." Hence the confusion. A split in the personality, wherein two or more fairly separate and coherent systems of being exist alternately in the same person, is different from the split between cognition and affect that is said to produce the schizophrenic's bizarre behavior. Bliss (1980) and Rosen-

baum (1980) both believe that multiple personality has indeed often been misdiagnosed as schizophrenia by clinicians. The number of cases of multiple personality fell off shortly after the term schizophrenia was introduced. A diagnostician may also inadvertently suggest to a patient a particular way of interpreting his or her symptoms. A schizophrenic patient who hears voices may, for example, be led to *interpret* them as evidence that he or she has multiple personality.

quite a fearful and obedient daughter. At age twenty-six Gina got braces for her teeth, and at age twenty-eight she had had an "affair," her first, with a former Jesuit priest, although it was apparently not sexual in nature. Then she became involved with "T.C.," a married man who assured her he would get a divorce and marry her. She indicated that she had been faithful to him since the start of their relationship. Partly on the basis of Jeans's analysis of one of Gina's dreams, the psychiatrist concluded that she was quite uncomfortable about being a woman, particularly when a close, sexual relationship with a man might be expected of her. But T.C. did not come through with his promised divorce, stopped seeing Gina regularly, and generally fell out of her favor.

After several sessions with Gina, Jeans began to notice a second personality emerging. "Mary Sunshine," as she came to be referred to by Jeans and Gina, was quite different from Gina. She seemed to be more childlike, more traditionally feminine, ebullient, and seductive. Gina felt that she herself walked like a coal miner, but Mary certainly did not. Some quite concrete incidents indicated Mary's existence. Sometimes Gina found in the sink cups that had had hot chocolate in them—neither Gina nor her roommate liked this beverage. There were large withdrawals from Gina's bank account that she could not remember making. One evening while watching television, Gina realized that she was crying and remarked to herself that it was stupid to feel sad about the particular program she was viewing. She even discovered herself ordering a sewing machine on the telephone, although she disliked sewing; some weeks later she showed up for her therapy session wearing a new dress that Mary had sewn. At work, Gina reported, people were finding her more pleasant to be with, and her colleagues took to consulting her on how to encourage people to work better with one another. All these phenomena were entirely alien to Gina. Jeans and Gina came to realize that sometimes Gina was transformed into Mary.

Then one day T.C. showed up again. Gina was filled with scorn and derision for him, yet she heard herself greeting him warmly with the words "Gee, I missed you so much! It's good to see you!" (Apparently the psychoanalytically oriented therapy was softening the hitherto impermeable boundaries

between the separate ego states of Gina and Mary.) Gina was also surprised to hear T.C. reply on this occasion, "All you ever wanted was to please me. You've done nothing but cater to my every whim, nothing but make me happy." Mary must have been active in the earlier relationship that Gina had had with this man.

Now more and more often Jeans witnessed Gina turning into Mary right before his eyes in the consulting room. T.C. accompanied Gina to a session during which her posture and demeanor became more relaxed, her tone of voice warmer. When T.C. explained that he really cared for her, Gina, or rather Mary, said warmly, "Of course, T., I know you do."

At another session Mary was upset and, as Jeans put it, chewed off Gina's fingernails. Then the two of them started having conversations with each other in front of Jeans.

A year after the start of therapy, an apparent synthesis of Gina and Mary began to emerge. At first it seemed that Gina had taken over entirely, but then Jeans noticed that Gina was not as serious as before, particularly about "getting the job done," that is, working extremely hard on the therapy. Jeans, probably believing that Mary wanted to converse with him, encouraged Gina to have a conversation with Mary. The following is what was said by the patient: "I was lying in bed trying to go to sleep. Someone started to cry about T.C. I was sure that it was Mary. I started to talk to her. The person told me that she didn't have a name. Later she said that Mary called her Evelyn. . . . I was suspicious at first that it was Mary pretending to be Evelyn. I changed my mind, however, because the person I talked to had too much sense to be Mary. She said that she realized that T.C. was unreliable but she still loved him and was very lonely. She agreed that it would be best to find a reliable man. She told me that she comes out once a day for a very short time to get used to the world. She promised that she will come out to see you [Jeans] sometime when she is stronger" (Jeans, 1976, pp. 254–255).

Throughout January Evelyn appeared more and more often, and Jeans felt that the patient was improving rapidly. Within a few months the patient seemed to be Evelyn all the time, and this woman soon married a physician. Now, years later, she still has had no recurrences of the other personalities.

As with conversion disorder, the possibility exists that the symptoms of the various dissociative disorders are deliberately adopted to avoid or escape from some alarming situation. One clinician has gone so far as to suggest that all cases of fugue are nothing more than malingering. When Symonds (reported in Merskey, 1979) sees a case of fugue, he says, "I know from experience that your pretended loss of memory is the result of some intolerable emotional situation. If you tell me the whole story I promise absolutely to respect your confidence, will give you all the help I can, and will say to your doctor and relatives that I have cured you by hypnotism." According to Symonds, such words have never failed to elicit an admission from the patient that the fugue was contrived. This is an extreme view, however.

Theories of Dissociative Disorders

According to the **psychoanalytic view** of dissociative disorders, one part of the mind or consciousness splits off or becomes dissociated from another part. The types of dissociative disorder are tied together etiologically in psychoanalytic theory, being viewed as instances of a massive repression, usually relating back to the unacceptable infantile sexual wishes of the oedipal stage. In adulthood these oedipal yearnings increase in strength until they are finally expressed, often as an impulsive sexual act. The ordinary form of repression is obviously no longer sufficient; the whole event must be obliterated from consciousness. The person succeeds in this by splitting off an entire part of the personality from awareness (Buss, 1966) or by acquiring a new identity for the dissociated portion of the self. In similar reasoning, Bliss (1980) believes that multiple personality is established in childhood by self-hypnosis. The new personalities are thought to be a way of coping with extremely disturbing events and sometimes with the individual's own unacceptable reactions to them.

Learning theorists have generally construed these rare phenomena as avoidance responses that serve to protect the individual from highly stressful events. Although not employing the concept of repression and not emphasizing the overriding importance of infantile sexual conflicts, the behavioral view of dissociative disorders is not dissimilar to psychoanalytic speculations about them. A recent study by Spanos, Weekes, and Bertrand (1985) supports the possibility that a person may adopt another personality in order to avoid punishment. The experimental manipulations were derived from an actual interview which had been conducted with Kenneth Bianchi, the Hillside strangler, while he was supposedly under hypnosis. The interviewer (I) asked for a second personality to come forward.

I. . . . I've talked a bit to Ken but I think that perhaps there might be another part of Ken that I haven't talked to. And I would like to communicate with that other part. And I would like that other part to come to talk with me. . . . And when you're here, lift the left hand off the chair to signal to me that you are here. Would you please come, Part, so I can talk to you? . . ., Part, would you come and lift Ken's hand to indicate to me that you are here? . . . Would you talk to me, Part, by saying "I'm here"? (Schwarz, 1981, pp. 142-143).

Bianchi (B) answered "Yes" to the last question, and then he and the interviewer had the following conversation.

I. Part, are you the same as Ken or are you different in any way. . . .

B. I'm not him.

I. You're not him. Who are you? Do you have a name?

B. I'm not Ken.

I. You're not him? Okay. Who are you? Tell me about yourself. Do you have a name I can call you by?

B. Steve. You can call me Steve (pp. 139-140).

While speaking as Steve, Bianchi stated that he hated Ken because Ken was nice, and that he, Steve, with the help of his cousin, had murdered a number of women. Bianchi's plea in the case became not guilty by reason of insanity; he claimed that he suffered from multiple personality.[6]

Subjects in the Spanos study were all told that they would play the role of an accused murderer and that, despite much evidence of guilt, a plea of not guilty had been entered. They were also told that they were to participate in a simulated psychiatric interview which might involve hypnosis. Then the subjects were taken to another room and introduced to the "psychiatrist," actually, of course, an experimental assistant. After a num-

---

[6]Bianchi was found guilty. His insanity plea did not hold up because evidence indicated that his role enactment differed in important ways from how true multiple personalities and deeply hypnotized subjects act (Orne, Dinges, and Orne, 1984).

ber of standard questions, the interview diverged for subjects assigned to one of three experimental conditions. Subjects in the *Bianchi condition* were hypnotized and were then instructed to let a second personality come forward, just as Bianchi's interviewer had done. Subjects in the *Hidden Part condition* were also hypnotized and given information suggesting that we may have "walled off" parts of ourselves. These instructions, however, were less explicit than those for the first condition. Subjects in a final condition were not hypnotized and were given even less explicit information about the possible existence of a hidden part.

After the experimental manipulations, the possible existence of a second personality was probed directly by the "psychiatrist." In addition, subjects were asked questions about the facts of the murders. Finally, in a second session, subjects who had acknowledged the presence of another personality were asked to take two personality tests twice—once each for their two personalities.

Eighty-one percent of subjects in the Bianchi condition adopted a new name, and many of these admitted guilt for the murders. Even the personality test scores of the two "personalities" differed considerably. Clearly, when the situation demands, people can adopt a second personality. We should remember, however, that this demonstration illustrates only that such role playing is possible and in no way claims that all cases of multiple personality have such origins.

If dissociative disorders are regarded as problems in memory, experimental research on memory might be brought to bear in trying to understand them. A recent area of investigation, *state-dependent memory*, offers some promise. In this phenomenon people are better able to recall an event if they are in the same psychic state as when it happened. If they are in a greatly different state when they try to remember, for example, sad now and happy then, memory of the earlier event is poor. Experimental research on state-dependent memory has manipulated mood by hypnosis and confirmed that recall is much better if mood at the time of learning matches mood at the time of recall. One of Bower's (1981) studies demonstrating this finding is outlined in Table 7.3. Two groups of subjects were first hypnotized and asked to get themselves into a happy or a sad mood. All subjects then learned a list of sixteen words. Next, subjects learned a second list of words in order to create interference with their initial learning. Subjects learned this second list in the affective state opposite that in which they had learned the original list. Finally, subjects were tested for their recall of the first list. During this

recall test, mood for some subjects was the same as during initial learning, and for some subjects it was not. As can be seen from the results given in Figure 7.2, mood had a strong effect on memory. Recall was much better if mood during recall matched mood during learning.

TABLE 7.3 Moods Created by Hypnosis in the Three Parts of a Study To Demonstrate State-Dependent Learning *(from Bower, 1981)*

Learn First Word List	Learn Second (Interference) Word List	Recall Test
Happy	Sad	Happy Sad
Sad	Happy	Sad Happy

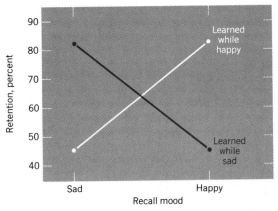

FIGURE 7.2 Results of the study of state-dependent learning outlined in Table 7.3, showing the effects of mood on memory. After Bower, 1981.

In applying the concept of state-dependent memory to dissociative disorders, Bower notes that there are often major mood differences in the several ego states of a person with multiple personality. Similarly, in fugue a person escapes from an emotionally charged situation into a calmer existence. The different emotional states may, in part, account for the selective memory loss.

We are unfortunately able to go little beyond these rather vague theories and analogue data. Information is scant, principally because of the rarity of these disorders. Dissociative disorders remain among the most poorly understood clinical syndromes.

Therapies for Dissociative Disorders

Dissociative disorders suggest, perhaps better than any other, the plausibility of Freud's concept of repression. For in all three—amnesia, fugue, and multiple personality—people behave in ways that very assuredly indicate they have forgotten earlier parts of their lives. And since these people may at the same time be unaware even of having forgotten something, the hypothesis that they have repressed massive portions of their lives is a compelling one.

Consequently, for dissociative disorders psychoanalytic treatment is perhaps administered with more élan than for other psychological problems. The goal of lifting repressions is the order of the day, pursued in ways with which we are already familiar.

Combs and Ludwig (1982) suggest that some patients with acute amnesia can regain lost memories if the therapist patiently encourages them to tell their life stories as completely as possible, without skipping over difficult-to-remember parts. This recounting of their lives can be combined with a modified free-association technique focusing on remembered events that took place just before the hole in memory. Thus, if the patient seems to be jumping forward in time, the therapist encourages him or her to free-associate to the event just preceding the memory gap (Parfitt and Gall, 1944). The therapist should all along suggest strongly that memory will be regained and should not imply that the patient is deliberately lying or malingering. In some cases, Combs and Ludwig propose, all that is necessary is the "tincture of time": a period during which the patient is separated from his or her stressful surroundings and given quietness, general support, and encouragement will diminish the vividness of earlier trauma and allow it to be remembered.

As discussed in Chapter 1, psychological theorizing about mental disorders began with the work on hypnosis of Mesmer in Vienna and Paris in the late eighteenth century and of Charcot in Paris in the second part of the nineteenth century. They apparently succeeded in removing various hysterical symptoms[7] by rather direct suggestion. Then Breuer and Freud encouraged patients to talk, while hypnotized, about their problems and especially about the earlier origins of them. Therefore psychoanalysis had its beginnings in hypnosis. But Freud eventually abandoned the practice in favor of techniques like free association, for he came to believe, mistakenly though it may be, that enduring cures are not possible by means of hypnosis.

Through the years practitioners have continued to hypnotize patients suffering from dissociative disorders, supposing that something special about the hypnotic state would permit the person access to hidden portions of the personality—to his or her lost identity or to a set of events precipitating or flowing from a trauma. Implicit in the choice of hypnosis for dissociative disorders are the assumptions that the problem, such as amnesia, is caused by a massive repression which protects the ego from intolerable anxiety, and that hypnosis can help lift the repression.

Some physicians have used sodium Amytal, the "truth serum," to induce a hypnoticlike state, again assuming that painful repressed memories will be brought forth and remove the "need" for the dissociative disorder. A number of dramatic case studies in the clinical literature attest to the efficacy of both hypnosis and barbiturates like sodium Amytal, but little of certainty can be said about their actual effectiveness because almost nothing approximating controlled research has been done.[8] When Dysken (1979) did compare the effects on

---

[7]Hysteria is of course the familiar vernacular diagnosis of several millenniums' standing. Hysterical neurosis was one of the neurotic diagnoses in both DSM-II and DSM-I, covering both conversion disorder and the dissociative disorders. In DSM-III conversion disorder is one of the somatoform disorders, and dissociative disorders make up a separate major section. Thus contemporary psychiatric thinking regards as fundamentally different two sets of problems formerly considered closely related. But hypnotism was and still is employed in treatment for hysteria, meaning both conversion disorder and the several dissociative disorders.

[8]To illustrate the problem inherent to case studies, we offer this personal observation. While working in a mental hospital some years ago, one of the authors encountered on the ward a man suffering from partial amnesia. He did not recognize members of his family when they came to visit him but could still recall most other events in his life. Many efforts were made to restore his memory, ranging from hypnotic suggestions to drug therapy. Both sodium Amytal and Methedrine, a powerful stimulant, were administered, Methedrine intravenously. It was hoped that Methedrine would energize his nervous system and "dislodge" the blocks to memory, much as Drano is used to open a clogged drain. In all these attempts the patient was cooperative and even eager for a positive outcome, but none of them worked. The unsuccessful treatment was never written up for publication. There is a strong editorial bias against publishing reports of failed clinical treatments, as indeed there is against publishing inconclusive results of experiments. This, a general problem for psychology and psychiatry, is a special detriment when, as for dissociative disorders, there is little in the way of controlled research.

amnesic patients of sodium amobarbital and normal saline, acting as a placebo, he failed to find significant differences in the amount of new information remembered.

Perhaps because of the rarity of dissociative disorders, the behavioral treatment of them has been little discussed in the published literature. Walton (1961) reported on the successful therapy he devised for a sleepwalker who tried to harm his wife nearly every night for six months during somnambulistic episodes. (Somnambulism was listed as a hysterical dissociative disorder in DSM-II.) Analyzing the case much as a psychoanalyst would, Walton determined that the thirty-five-year-old man, an architectural assistant, was very shy and inhibited, especially in relation to his authoritarian and rigid mother. His wife was at the time trying to force him to do things he objected to and reminded him of his domineering mother. Assertion training helped the man to treat his mother with firmness and to express his negative feelings directly. The sleepwalking incidents were soon eliminated. In general, behavioral clinicians might encourage the person to imagine and discuss aspects of the trauma being avoided in memory and might even desensitize him or her to situations related to the onset of the disorder. Recovering memory of the stressful event of course signals that it is no longer avoided.

SUMMARY

In somatoform disorders physical symptoms for which no physiological basis can be found are the problem. The sensory and motor dysfunctions of conversion disorders, one of the two principal types of somatoform disorders, suggest neurological impairments, but ones that do not make anatomical sense; the symptoms do, however, seem to serve some psychological purpose. In somatization disorder, or Briquet's syndrome, multiple physical complaints, which are not adequately explained by physical disorder or injury, eventuate in frequent visits to physicians, hospitalization, and even unnecessary surgery.

Hypnotist checking on the depth of a hypnotic trance by suggesting that a gas-filled balloon has been tied to the woman's arm.

Theory concerning the etiology of these disorders is very speculative and focuses primarily on conversion disorders. Psychoanalytic theory proposed that in conversion disorders repressed impulses are converted into physical symptoms. Behavioral theories focus on the more or less conscious and deliberate adoption of the symptoms as a means of obtaining a desired goal. As for therapies, analysts try to help the client face up to the repressed impulses, and behavioral treatments attempt to reduce anxiety and to reinforce behavior that will allow relinquishment of the symptoms.

Dissociative disorders are disruptions of consciousness, memory, and identity. An inability to recall important personal information, usually after some traumatic experience, is diagnosed as psychogenic amnesia. In psychogenic fugue the person moves away, assumes a new identity, and is amnesic for his or her previous life. The person with multiple personality has two or more distinct and fully developed ones, each with unique memories, behavior patterns, and relationships which determine the individual's nature and acts when it comes forth. Psychoanalytic theory regards dissociative disorders as instances of massive repression of some undesirable event or aspect of the self. Behavioral theories similarly consider dissociative reactions to be avoidance responses motivated by high levels of anxiety. Both analytic and behavioral clinicians focus their treatment efforts on the anxiety associated with the forgotten memories, since it is viewed as etiologically significant.

Edvard Munch, *By the Deathbed, Fever,* 1895 Private Collection, Courtesy Munch Museet, Oslo

PSYCHOPHYSIOLOGICAL
DISORDERS

In Chapter 6 we discussed voodoo deaths, a seemingly supernatural phenomenon whereby a curse from a witch doctor dooms his victim to extreme physical suffering and death. To explain such events, Cannon (1942) proposed that vital bodily organs are irreparably harmed if the autonomic nervous system is maintained in a highly aroused state through prolonged psychological stress, during which time there is no opportunity to take effective action. Inasmuch as the arousal of the autonomic nervous system is also regarded as one of the bodily indications of emotion, it is not surprising that psychopathologists have concerned themselves with physical diseases involving this system, in the belief that psychological factors may be implicated. In the expression of emotion, the bodily changes of autonomic arousal are viewed as transient; in psychophysiological disorders the usually reversible autonomic and hormonal responses to stress can cause irreversible tissue damage.

Psychophysiological disorders, such as asthma and ulcers, are characterized by genuine physical symptoms that are caused or can be worsened by emotional factors. The present term, psychophysiological disorders, is now preferred to one that is perhaps better known,

psychosomatic disorders. *Psychosomatic* connotes quite well the principal feature of these disorders, that the psyche or mind is having an untoward effect on the soma or body. The structure of both these terms, in fact, implies that mind and body are separate and independent, although they may, at times, influence each other (see Box 8.1). Dualism is a deeply ingrained paradigm of human thought. And yet the hope was that these terms would foster a monistic rather than dualistic view of the human being, since "... all functioning and all diseases are both mental and physical, because both mental and physiological processes are going on continuously" (Sternbach, 1966, p. 139). Instead of speaking of the emotions as causing body dysfunctions, we could instead, as Graham (1967) has noted, regard the psyche and soma as one and the same. Psychological and physical explanations of disease are then simply two different ways of describing the same events.

At the outset, two important points must be firmly established. First, a psychophysiological disorder is a real disease involving damage to the body. The fact that such disorders are viewed as being caused by emotional factors does not make the affliction imaginary. People

BOX 8.1

DESCARTES AND THE MIND-BODY PROBLEM

One of the most influential statements about the "mind-body" problem is found in the writings of the brilliant French philosopher of the seventeenth century, René Descartes (1596–1650). Being a deeply religious Catholic, he assumed that human beings differed from other animals by virtue of having a soul and thus being partly divine. But like the other animals, human beings had a body as well. Although the body was said to work on mechanical principles—Descartes was fascinated by the mechanical models of the body's workings that were prevalent at the time—these mechanics were seen to be under the control of the soul, or mind. But how could the body, operating like a machine, be affected by the soul, which is spiritual and nonphysical? How could two such basically different substances, in fact, "touch" each other? If the mind was to affect the body, there must be some point of *contact*. The pineal gland, located in the midbrain, was postulated by Descartes as the locus of this critical interaction, the point at which the mind could direct the mechanics of the body. By dualizing human beings in this way, with this vital connection between the mind and the body, Descartes felt that he could retain his religious view of people as being partly divine and yet an integral part of the rest of the animal world.

René Descartes, the French philosopher who proposed a dualistic view of mind and body.

can just as readily die from "psychologically produced" high blood pressure or ulcers as from similar diseases produced by infection or physical injury. Second, psychophysiological disorders should be distinguished from conversion disorders, which were discussed in Chapter 7. Conversion disorders do not involve actual organic damage to the body, and they are generally considered to affect function of the voluntary musculature. In contrast, in psychophysiological disorders bodily tissues *are* damaged.

Psychophysiological disorders as such do not appear in DSM-III as they did in DSM-II. Because virtually all physical diseases are now viewed as potentially related to psychological stress, a psychophysiological disorders category would become a complete listing of all diseases. Instead of such a cumbersome, overlapping system, DSM-III requires that a diagnostic judgment be made on axis I, to indicate the presence of a psychological factor influencing a physical condition, and also on axis III, to specify that physical condition.

The classic psychophysiological disorders are generally grouped together according to the organ system affected. Some of the major ones are given in the following list.

1. Psychophysiological skin disorders. Skin reactions such as neurodermatitis (inflammation), pruritis (itching), and hyperhydrosis (dry skin).

2. Psychophysiological respiratory disorders. Bronchial asthma, hyperventilation (breathing very rapidly), sighing, and hiccups.

3. Psychophysiological cardiovascular disorders. Tachycardia (heart racing), hypertension (high blood pressure), and migraine headache.

4. Psychophysiological gastrointestinal disorders. Peptic ulcers, chronic gastritis, ulcerative or mucous colitis, constipation, hyperacidity, and heartburn.

5. Psychophysiological genitourinary disorders. Disturbances in menstruation and urination, dyspareunia (painful sexual intercourse), and impotence (difficulty obtaining or maintaining an erection, or both).[1]

6. Psychophysiological musculoskeletal disorders. Backache, muscle cramps, and tension headaches.

Psychophysiological symptoms and disorders are quite common in industrialized societies, although they

[1]In DSM-III sexual dysfunctions, including dyspareunia and impotence, are now in their own section, Psychosexual Dysfunctions (see Chapter 13).

are apparently rare among nonindustrialized groups, such as the Australian aborigines and the American Indians. Schwab, Fennell, and Warheit (1974), for example, interviewed a randomly selected sample of close to 1700 Americans (Table 8.1). Over 40 percent of the respondents reported having had headaches during the previous year, and 50 percent reported a range of gastrointestinal symptoms. Actual disorders such as hypertension, however, were not as common as the less serious symptoms they were questioned about.

TABLE 8.1 Percentages of People* Reporting Psychophysiological Symptoms and Conditions for the Previous Year (from Schwab, Fennell, and Warheit, 1974)

Symptoms and Conditions	Yes— Regularly, percent	Yes— Occasionally, percent	No, percent
Symptoms			
Headaches	8.7	38.0	53.4
Indigestion	6.4	27.5	66.1
Constipation	6.9	19.6	73.5
Nervous stomach	5.2	17.5	77.3
Stomachaches	3.7	18.8	77.5
Diarrhea	0.9	14.4	84.8
Conditions			
Hypertension	6.2	8.0	85.8
Asthma	1.9	2.9	95.2
Ulcers	0.9	1.4	97.6
Colitis	0.4	0.9	98.7

*$N = 1647$.

STRESS AND ILLNESS

What is the evidence for the view that illness is, in part, stress-related? For years it had been known that various physical diseases could be produced in laboratory animals who were exposed to severe stress. Usually the diseases studied in this fashion were the classic psychophysiological disorders, such as ulcer and hypertension. More recent evidence has broadened the range of diseases that appear to be stress-related. Sklar and Anisman (1979), for example, first induced tumors in mice with a transplant of cancerous tissue and then studied

Major life events bring stress which can in turn cause medical and psychological problems.

the impact of stress on growth of the tumors. In animals exposed to electric shock, the tumors grew more rapidly and the animals died earlier.

Measuring Life Stress

Research with human beings poses an ethical problem: the experimental method cannot be used. Instead, re-searchers have sought to measure the amount of life stress a person has experienced and then correlate this with illness. A number of instruments have been devel-oped to measure life stress. One such test, whose items appear in Table 8.2, is the Social Readjustment Rating Scale (SRRS). In using the SRRS, the respondent simply checks off the life events that have been experienced during the time period in question. But merely summing the *number* of events would not work, for different *amounts* of stressfulness are inherent in different events. To solve this problem, Holmes and Rahe (1967) gave a list of life events to a large group of subjects and asked them to rate each item according to its "intensity and [the] length of time necessary to accommodate . . . *regardless of the desirability of the event.*" Marriage was arbitrarily assigned a stress value of 500; all other items were then evaluated using this reference point. For example, an event twice as stressful as marriage would be assigned a value of 1000, and an event one-fifth as stressful as marriage would be assigned a value of 100. The average ratings assigned to the events by the respondents in Holmes and Rahe's study are also shown in Table 8.2.

The ratings that indicate differential stressfulness of events are totaled for all the events actually experienced to produce a Life Change Unit (LCU) score, a weighted sum of events. The LCU score is then related to illness.

Rahe and Holmes (unpublished), for example, studied a sample of 200 physicians. Health problems (infectious diseases, allergies, musculoskeletal problems, and psychophysiological disorders) were strongly related to LCU scores. With an LCU score of less than 200, 37 percent of the life crises were associated with deterioration of health. But with an LCU score greater than 300, 79 percent of the life crises were accompanied by health problems. Other studies have shown that LCU scores are related to heart attacks (Rahe and Lind, 1971), fractures (Tollefson, 1972), leukemia onset (Wold, 1968), and colds and fevers (Holmes and Holmes, 1970).

We have, then, some promising information on the relationship between psychological stress and physical illness. But caution is in order before we assert that the relationship is a causal one. Illness, for example, could cause a high life change score, as when chronic absenteeism brings dismissal from a job. And the reports of stressful events in such studies could also be contami-

TABLE 8.2 Social Readjustment Rating Scale
(from Holmes and Rahe, 1967)

Rank	Life Event	Mean Value
1	Death of spouse	100
2	Divorce	73
3	Marital separation	65
4	Jail term	63
5	Death of close family member	63
6	Personal injury or illness	53
7	Marriage	50*
8	Fired at work	47
9	Marital reconciliation	45
10	Retirement	45
11	Change in health of family member	44
12	Pregnancy	40
13	Sex difficulties	39
14	Gain of new family member	39
15	Business readjustment	39
16	Change in financial state	38
17	Death of close friend	37
18	Change to different line of work	36
19	Change in number of arguments with spouse	35
20	Mortgage over $10,000	31
21	Foreclosure of mortgage or loan	30

Rank	Life Event	Mean Value
22	Change in responsibilities at work	29
23	Son or daughter leaving home	29
24	Trouble with in-laws	29
25	Outstanding personal achievement	28
26	Wife begins or stops work	26
27	Begin or end school	26
28	Change in living conditions	25
29	Revision of personal habits	24
30	Trouble with boss	23
31	Change in work hours or conditions	20
32	Change in residence	20
33	Change in schools	20
34	Change in recreation	19
35	Change in church activities	19
36	Change in social activities	18
37	Mortgage or loan less than $10,000	17
38	Change in sleeping habits	16
39	Change in number of family get-togethers	15
40	Change in eating habits	15
41	Vacation	13
42	Christmas	12
43	Minor violations of the law	11

*Marriage was arbitrarily assigned a stress value of 500; no event was found to be any more than twice as stressful. Here the values are reduced proportionally and range up to 100.

nated by knowledge of subsequently occurring illnesses. Furthermore, many of the studies have used a retrospective method; participants were asked to recall both the illnesses and the stressful life events that they had experienced over the previous two years. As mentioned previously (see page 119*n*), retrospective reports are subject to considerable distortion and forgetting.

The SRRS can also be criticized for *assuming* a particular definition of stress, namely that any change is stressful, whether it is a change usually regarded as negative, such as being fired from a job, or as positive, such as marrying. The available evidence is, in fact, contradictory, but it would seem to indicate that the undesirable aspects of events are as important as the fact that they change lives (Redfield and Stone, 1979). Another problem is that items on the SRRS were not selected to sample systematically all major stresses. In perusing Table 8.2, you can probably identify stressful events that you have experienced but that are not on the list.

In response to criticisms like these, new life event inventories have been created. Among the best of these is the Psychiatric Epidemiology Research Instrument (PERI). The investigators (Dohrenwend et al., 1978) began by having a large sample of respondents nominate stressful events. These were then reliably rated on several dimensions related to stressfulness and were also sorted into three categories: events which are possible indicators of physical illness, such as an injury; events which are possible consequences of the psychological state of the respondent, for example, made new friends; and events which are independent of either illness or psychological state, for example, the death of a close friend. This categorization is particularly important because it allows investigators to study the independent contribution of events to illness.

Methods of Studying the Stress-Illness Link

The Immune System

With improved instruments in hand, researchers have continued their search for links between stress and illness. Some have asked what physiological mechanism might translate life stress into illness. One mechanism of great interest is the immune system, which recognizes and then defends the body against disease-causing microorganisms. The immune system has two components, one secretory and the other cell-mediated. The secretory part of the system synthesizes and then releases antibodies, or immunoglobulins, into the blood and other bodily fluids such as saliva. The immunity conferred through the action of cells is acquired more slowly and does not rely on antibodies. Immune system cells can defend the body, but they can also reject transplanted organs.

If stress can interfere with the normal functioning of the immune system, we would expect first to find that stress makes the body more susceptible to infection. Research generally supports a relation between stress and susceptibility for a wide range of infections—those of the respiratory tract, tuberculosis, herpes simplex, and mononucleosis (Jammott and Locke, 1984). In addition, various possible measures of the functioning of the immune system indicate that stress affects it. For example, Jammott and his co-workers (1983) studied levels of immunoglobin A (lg A), the major immunoglobulin secretion defending against respiratory tract infections. Immunoglobin A was collected during three periods of great stress and two of little stress. As expected, lg A levels were lower during periods of considerable stress. What remains to be shown conclusively is the link between stress, impaired functioning of the immune system, and illness. Such research will need to use a longitudinal design and a large number of subjects. The research must be longitudinal so that increases in stress can be shown to precede disruptions of the immune system and the subsequent development of illness. A large number of subjects will be necessary because the immune systems of individuals vary. Only the immunological competence of some people who are exposed to stress will decline. And only some of these people who have become susceptible will then encounter a disease-causing pathogen.

Hardiness

The correlation between stressful life events and illness is indeed recognized as modest, about .30, at best. In other words, the stresses of life increase rates of illness only in some people. Can any of the characteristics of stress-responsive and stress-resistant individuals be identified? To illustrate this second general way to study the stress-illness relation, let us examine briefly hardiness, one variable which is receiving much attention from researchers.

Hardiness is defined as a constellation of three clinical personality characteristics—commitment, control, and challenge. . . . Persons high in hardiness easily commit themselves to what they are doing (rather than feeling alienated), generally believe that they can at least partially control events (rather than feeling powerless), and regard change to be a normal challenge or impetus to development (rather than a threat) (Kobasa and Puccetti, 1983, p. 840).

In her first study of hardiness, Kobasa (1979) examined executives under high levels of stress and divided them into groups with either high or low rates of illness. Hardiness scores, derived from scores on several personality questionnaires, differentiated between the groups in the expected manner. The executives with low rates of illness had higher hardiness scores than those with high rates of illness. In a subsequent study using a more powerful prospective methodology, executives' hardiness scores predicted whether they would later contract fewer or more illnesses (Kobasa, Maddi, and Kahn, 1982). Thus hardiness seems able to moderate the stress-illness relation. Similar research is currently proceeding with other potential moderators, such as the social support that an individual receives from the community; instrumental aid, for example, the information and technical help supplied by others; the sympathy and affection of family and friends (Thoits, 1982); and coping, a person's ability to handle problems and their emotional consequences (Stone and Neale, 1984).

In sum, the life stress and illness field is both active and promising. As yet, however, detailed prospective studies covering both stressful life events and illnesses have not been carried out.

THEORIES OF PSYCHOPHYSIOLOGICAL DISORDERS: AN OVERVIEW

In the remainder of the chapter we consider theory and research on the interaction of psychological and physiological factors in causing and alleviating particular psychophysiological disorders. Our primary concerns are how psychological stress affects physiological functioning and causes or exacerbates an illness and, at the end of the chapter, how psychological therapies can prevent or ameliorate physical illnesses.

In considering the etiology of psychophysiological disorders, we are confronted with three questions. (1) Why does stress produce difficulties in only some people who are exposed to it? (2) Why does stress sometimes cause an illness and not a psychological disorder? (3) Given that stress produces a psychophysiological disorder, what determines which one of the many disorders it will be? We have already discussed the concept of stress as it is related to various anxiety disorders, and we shall discuss it further in the chapter on schizophrenia.

How is it that this general concept can be used to "account for" such a wide range of disorders?

Answers to these questions have been sought by both physiologically and psychologically oriented theorists. Physiological approaches attribute particular psychophysiological disorders to specific weaknesses or overactivity of an individual's organ systems in responding to stress. Psychological theories account for specificity by positing particular emotional states for particular disorders.

Physiological Theories

Somatic-Weakness Theory
Genetic factors, earlier illnesses, diet, and the like may disrupt a particular organ system, which may then become weak and vulnerable to stress. According to the *somatic-weakness theory*, the connection between stress and a particular psychophysiological disorder is the weakness in a specific bodily organ. Like a tire that blows out at its weakest or thinnest portion, in the human body a congenitally weak respiratory system might predispose the individual to asthma.

Specific-Reaction Theory
Some investigators argue that there are differences, probably genetically determined, in the ways individuals respond to stress. People have been found to have their own particular patterns of autonomic response to stress. The heart rate of one individual may increase, whereas another person may react with increased respiration rate but no change in frequency of heartbeats (Lacey, 1967). Thus individuals respond to stress in their own idiosyncratic way, and the body system that is the most responsive may be a likely candidate for the locus of a subsequent psychophysiological disorder. Someone reacting to stress with considerable secretion of stomach acid may be more vulnerable to ulcers, and someone reacting to stress with blood pressure elevation may be more susceptible to essential hypertension. Later in this chapter, when we consider particular psychophysiological disorders, substantial evidence in support of both somatic-weakness and *specific-reaction* theories will be given.

Evolution Theory
A psychophysiological disorder usually affects a single organ system that is controlled by the autonomic nervous system. In a healthy body the actions of the two branches of this system, the sympathetic and the parasympathetic—which work sometimes in unison,

sometimes against each other to manage the body's internal affairs—must always be kept in a complex and delicate balance. The two systems act in concert. A burst of sympathetic activity must soon be redressed by increased activity of the parasympathetic. The healthy body can sustain prolonged overactivity of one or the other system on occasion, but for the viscera, blood vessels, and glands to act effectively and to remain unharmed, neither system can overexpend energy for protracted periods of time.

External, physical danger stimulates the sympathetic system to prepare the body for fight or flight. It increases heart rate, blood pressure, and rate of breathing. The liver releases into the bloodstream a large supply of sugar. The blood vessels of the limb muscles and other skeletal muscles dilate to ready them for strenuous activity. At the same time blood vessels of the stomach, intestines, skin, and brain constrict. But actual physical danger is usually transient. After the body has either fled or fought, its muscles relax, heart rate slows down again to normal, blood flow to the brain increases, and digestion resumes, all under the direction of the parasympathetic system.

Imagined and social dangers bring about the same preparations by the sympathetic system. Our brains have evolved to the point that they perceive other than physical threats (Simeons, 1961), and people can continually torment themselves even when real dangers are absent. Anger provoked by an annoying present situation, regrets about the past, and worries about the future all stimulate sympathetic activity. But resentment and regret and worry cannot as readily be fought or escaped from as external threats, nor do they easily pass. They may keep the sympathetic system aroused and the body in a continual state of emergency, sometimes for far longer than it can bear. Under these circumstances, moreover, the necessary balancing of sympathetic and parasympathetic actions is made that much more difficult and can go awry. Thus the distressed thoughts that evolution has made possible bring about bodily changes that both persist longer than they were meant to and that contribute to an imbalance between sympathetic and parasympathetic activity. Our higher mental capacities, it is theorized, subject our bodies to physical "storms" that they are not built to withstand.

Psychological Theories

Psychoanalytical Theory

Franz Alexander (1950) has perhaps been the most prominent of the psychoanalytic theorists who have concerned themselves with psychophysiological reactions. In his view the various psychophysiological disorders are products of unconscious emotional states specific to each disorder. For example,

It would appear that the crucial factor in the pathogenesis of ulcer is the frustration of the dependent, help-seeking and love-demanding desires. When these desires cannot find gratification in human relationships, a chronic emotional stimulus is created which has a specific effect on the functions of the stomach (p. 103).

Alexander assumed that ulcer patients have repressed their longing for parental love in childhood, and that this repressed impulse causes the overactivity of the autonomic nervous system and of the stomach, leading to ulcers. Physiologically, the stomach is continuously preparing to receive food, which the person has symbolically equated with parental love.

Undischarged hostile impulses are viewed as creating the chronic emotional state responsible for essential hypertension.

The damming up of his hostile impulses will continue and will consequently increase in intensity. This will induce the development of stronger defensive measures in order to keep pent-up aggressions in check. . . . Because of the marked degree of their inhibitions, these patients are less effective in their occupational activities and for that reason tend to fail in competition with others, . . . envy is stimulated and . . . hostile feelings toward more successful, less inhibited competitors are further intensified (p. 150).

Alexander formulated this unexpressed-anger or "anger-in" theory on the basis of his observations of patients undergoing psychoanalysis. Although some subsequent research appeared to substantiate the theory—for example, finding that hypertensives score high on measures of anger or hostility—such data were collected *after* the onset of the disease and thus cannot support the assertion that anger or hostility was a cause. Other research has not always confirmed Alexander's anger-in hypothesis, but it continues to be pursued in present-day studies of the psychological factors in essential hypertension (see page 178).

Conditioning Theories

Both classical and operant conditioning have been suggested as having a role in psychophysiological disorders, although conditioning is probably best viewed as a factor that can exacerbate an already existing illness rather than cause it. Consider a person who is allergic to pollen and thus subject to asthma attacks. It has been theorized that through classical conditioning neutral stimuli paired with pollen could also come to elicit asthma, thus broadening the range of stimuli that can bring on an attack (Bandura, 1969). The asthmatic attacks might also be viewed as operant responses producing rewards. For example, a child could "use" asthma as an excuse for not participating in unpleasant activities. Dworkin and his colleagues (1979) have proposed that hypertension too may be reinforcing. Their hypothesis begins with the assumption that many people live in surroundings that stimulate their aggressive tendencies but also discourage overt aggression. Animal research has shown that rage reactions can be inhibited by stimulation of the baroreceptors, which are pressure-sensitive neural cells located, among other places in the cardiovascular system, within the walls of the arch of the aorta and of the nearby carotid sinuses.[2] Perhaps, then, a similar mechanism operates in human beings. High blood pressure may stimulate the baroreceptors and thus help inhibit maladaptive aggressive responses.

None of these accounts excludes the importance of physiological factors in psychophysiological disorders. Classical and operant conditioning hypotheses typically assume that the physical symptoms already exist. Thus any learning model of a psychophysiological disorder requires a physiological predisposition, a diathesis of some kind.

Multifactorial Theory

When the germ theory of disease was established by Louis Pasteur, the hope was that a single cause would be found for every medical disorder. It is now known, however, that most diseases have multiple causes. Heart disease, for example, is attributed to a complex intertwining of genetic factors, a high-cholesterol diet, cigarette smoking, lack of exercise, and stress. The *multifactorial* point of view has found its way into current theorizing about the stress and the physiological and emotional reactions associated with psychophysiological disorders.

The somatic-weakness and the specific-reaction hypotheses both state that these physiological predispositions to illness are activated by stress. But what kind of

stress? Are we dealing with events or situations that are almost universally stressful, such as loss of job, death of a family member? Probably not, at least not entirely. The evidence seems to indicate that more idiosyncratic stressors, such as spilling a glass of water at a dinner party, can have a powerful impact on illness (for example, Lazarus, 1974). So can the hassles of daily living, which may be constant or at least chronic. The ongoing stresses of poverty, of excessive urban noise and pollution, of commuting, of an underload or an overload of work on the assembly line, of struggles to come to important family decisions, of disparity in status of spouses, of dealing with children and aged parents all strain patience and deplete reserves of energy (Lazarus and Cohn, 1977). The specific emotional states pointed out by Alexander could be expected to play the important role of "sensitizing" a person to overrespond to trying but not necessarily catastrophic life experiences. Thus a complete diathesis-stress theory of psychophysiological disorders requires an integration of several of the theories already considered.

Daily hassles, such as a crowded highway during the rush-hour commute, can drain reserves and increase a person's risk for disease.

[2]The carotid sinus is a slight enlargement of the carotid artery at the point where it bifurcates into an external branch supplying the face, scalp, tongue, teeth, and other external parts of the head and an internal branch supplying the brain, eye, and other internal structures. The rich supply of sensory nerve endings in its walls constitutes a major mechanism regulating heart rate and blood pressure.

Our general overview of theories concerning the etiology of psychophysiological disorders is complete. We turn now to a detailed review of the disorders that have attracted the most attention from researchers—*ulcer*, *hypertension*, *coronary heart disease*, *asthma*, and *migraine headache*.

ULCER

Ulcers are craterlike lesions or holes in the lining of the stomach or duodenum. In the digestive process gastric juice, made up of dilute hydrochloric acid and pepsin, acts on ingested food to break it down into components that the body can use. Ordinarily, the inner walls of the stomach and duodenum are protected from these gastric secretions by a layer of mucus. A reduction in the normal blood supply to the mucosa, excessive gastric secretions, or both may allow gastric juice to erode the mucous lining and then to digest the wall (Weiss, 1977).[3] Autonomic overactivity can reduce blood supply to the mucosa and increase the secretion of stomach acid. Thus a physiological process is linked to possible psychological factors through the relation between autonomic activity and emotions. The following case history illustrates the development of an ulcer.

Background. As a child, Mr. A was quiet and obedient, whereas his brother who was three years older was aggressive and independent. Socially, Mr. A was very close to his brother and his brother's companions and was always under the protection of his brother. Mr. A also spent much time with his parents, who provided him with much attention.

Emotion-arousing situations. When Mr. A was thirteen his brother died; about two years later his father also died. Both of those events were of major significance in Mr. A's young life. Following the death of his father, his mother became psychologically dependent on him, consulting him about important problems and requiring him generally to substitute for both his older brother and his father, a situation for which Mr. A was completely unprepared intellectually and otherwise. While maintaining a secure outer appearance, Mr. A was aroused emotionally, and his emotional reactions were repeatedly intensified by the excessive expectations of his mother. . . . At age eighteen, Mr. A experienced a short period of stomach discomfort that was followed by the initial hemorrhaging of a duodenal ulcer. When psychotherapy began about five years later, X-ray findings and general symptoms indicated an active ulcer.

Scanning electron micrographs of (a) a normal stomach and (b) a stomach with ulcers.

a

b

[3]Studies reported in the psychological literature have often been conducted on *peptic ulcers*, a category which includes ulcers of both the stomach and the duodenum. This practice is unfortunate because the etiology of each type of ulcer may well vary. For example, duodenal ulcers are usually associated with increased secretions of hydrochloric acid and are more common in men, but stomach ulcers do not follow this pattern (Weiner, 1977).

Follow-up. Follow-up study during a three-year period after conclusion of this initial psychotherapy disclosed the following facts. Mr. A had a mild relapse shortly after his marriage when he accepted a very strenuous assignment abroad and had an unsuitable diet; a second mild relapse occurred immediately prior to the birth of his first child, which corresponded in time with his mother's considering remarriage. A few psychotherapeutic consultations at that time involved examination of the existing emotion-provoking problems and apparently resulted in the resumption of more stable functioning. At the end of the three-year period (following conclusion of initial psychotherapy), Mr. A was on a normal diet with minimal daily medication (Lachman, 1972, pp. 1–2).

Stress and Ulcers

Many stressors have been implicated in the formation of ulcers. Among the first identified was *immobilization* (Selye, 1936). Wrapping rats in towels or tying their legs together reliably produced lesions in their stomachs. Approach-avoidance conflicts have also been extensively researched. Sawrey devised several illustrative experiments with rats to investigate whether prolonged approach-avoidance conflicts could produce ulcers. The animals lived in an environment in which shock was administered whenever they approached food or water. Thus they were in conflict over whether to approach the food or avoid the shock. At the end of approximately two weeks many had developed ulcers, and some had even died from hemorrhages (Sawrey and Weisz, 1956; Conger, Sawrey, and Turrell, 1958).

"THE FUNNY THING IS, I GOT MY ULCER AFTER I BECAME A BUM."

Several qualities of stressful stimuli have also been found to be related to the production of ulcers. Unpredictable shock, for example, is more likely to cause lesions than shock that is preceded by a signal and is thus predictable (Weiss, 1970). Similarly, the ability to control a stressor reduces the severity of ulcers that are produced in experimental situations (Weiss, 1968).

Various stressors may operate similarly in human beings. Cobb and Rose (1973), for example, found that ulcers were twice as frequent among air traffic controllers

Air traffic controllers are at high risk for ulcers, perhaps because their job is chronically stressful.

as among pilots. The stress pilots are under may be less because they have more control over their planes than do the air traffic controllers. There are alternative explanations, however, that do not involve the concept of control. Today's commercial jet planes are so automated that, except for takeoff and landing, pilots actually have little to do compared to the constant vigilance that a traffic controller must maintain for hours on end. Moreover, at any given moment the decisions of an air traffic controller can affect the survival of many more human beings than can those of the pilot of a single passenger plane. There would seem to be a marked difference, then, in the extent of personal responsibility shouldered by people in these two emotionally demanding occupations.

Physiological Predisposition

In the studies using various stressors to produce ulcers, only *some* of the animals actually develop a lesion. Thus stress, as we would expect, is not the whole story in causing ulcers. Some predisposing factor or factors are also necessary. Rats, for example, have been bred to be ulcer-sensitive. Sines (1963) established a strain of animals, every one of which developed an ulcer when restrained. These rats appeared to be very "emotional." When placed in an open field they defecated more often than other animals.

Another possible candidate for a physiological predisposition is the amount of pepsinogen secreted by the peptic cells of the gastric glands in the stomach. Pepsinogen is converted into pepsin, the stomach enzyme which digests proteins and which in combination with hydrochloric acid is the principal active agent in gastric juice. Pepsinogen levels are therefore implicated in the formation of ulcers. By taking measurements through the umbilical cord, Mirsky (1958) was able to detect marked individual differences in pepsinogen levels in newborns. Furthermore, young infants with high levels of pepsinogen were found to be members of families with a high incidence of excessive pepsinogen levels. That only some people secrete large amounts of pepsinogen, depending on their genetic inheritance, does demonstrate that this variable has a possible causal role in the development of ulcers. Much stronger evidence would come from a prospective study showing that individuals who do not yet have ulcers but do have high levels of pepsinogen secretion are more likely to develop ulcers than another group, also without ulcers but with lower pepsinogen levels.

Such an investigation has in fact been conducted by Weiner and his co-workers (1957). These researchers measured the level of pepsinogen in 2073 newly inducted draftees. From this large number two smaller groups were selected, the 63 with the highest levels of pepsinogen and the 57 with the lowest levels. A complete gastrointestinal examination, given before basic training, showed that none had ulcers at that time. The majority of these men were then reexamined during the eighth and sixteenth weeks of their basic training. Nine cases of ulcers had developed, all of them in the group with high pepsinogen levels. Another study (Mirsky, 1958) of a population of children and civilian adults who had earlier been classified as high and low pepsinogen secreters revealed a similar tendency for ulcers to develop among those with high levels of pepsinogen.

In sum, the data available on ulcers are consistent with a diathesis-stress theory implicating in their development both stress and the physiological predisposition to secrete excessive amounts of pepsinogen. Consistent with the specific-reaction theory, individuals who develop ulcers appear to be predisposed to react to stress with excessive gastric secretions, which then produce lesions.

CARDIOVASCULAR DISORDERS

Cardiovascular diseases are the leading cause of death in the United States, accounting for more than half of all deaths (*American Heart Association Heart Facts 1982*, 1981). The two forms to be discussed are hypertension and coronary heart disease (CHD). Coronary heart disease is of major significance because, of the cardiovascular diseases, it is the single greatest cause of death. Hypertension is a factor not only in CHD but in stroke. It is generally agreed that many of the deaths from cardiovascular diseases are premature and can be prevented by dealing with one or more of the known risk factors (Price, 1982).

Essential Hypertension

The pressure produced in the arteries as the heart pumps blood through them is referred to as blood pressure. Blood pressure may be elevated by increased cardiac output, the amount of blood leaving the left ventricle of the heart per minute; by increased resistance to the passage of blood through the arteries, that is, by vasoconstriction; and by an increase in the body's volume of fluids. Without question, one of the most serious psychophysiological disorders is hypertension, commonly called high blood pressure. This disease disposes people to atherosclerosis (clogging of the arteries), heart attacks, and strokes (see Chapter 17), and it can also cause death through kidney failure. Recent estimates are that varying degrees of hypertension are found in 15 to 33 percent of the adult population of the United States; as many as 10 percent of American college students have hypertension, most of them remaining unaware of their illness. No more than 10 percent of all these cases are attributable to an identifiable physical cause, which is usually kidney dysfunction. Hypertension without an evident organic cause is called *essential hypertension*.

Lyght (1966) has offered the following description of the course of hypertension and the symptoms associated with the disorder.

. . . Hypertension frequently is present for many years without symptoms or signs other than an elevated blood pressure. In the majority of cases, increased blood pressure first appears during early adult life (mean age of onset, the early thirties). These patients may complain of fatigue, nervousness, dizziness, palpitation, insomnia, weakness and headaches at some time in the course of the disorder. . . . The mean age of death for untreated patients is in the fifties, and their average life expectancy probably is close to twenty years from the onset, with extremes of from several years to many decades (pp. 218 ff).

Unless people have their blood pressure checked, they may go for years without knowing that they are hypertensive. The disease, then, is known as "the silent killer."

Essential hypertension is currently viewed as a heterogeneous condition brought on by many possible disturbances in the various systems of the body that are responsible for regulating blood pressure. The combination of physiological mechanisms that contribute to regulation of blood pressure is extremely complex. The sympathetic nervous system, hormones, salt and water metabolism, as well as central nervous system mechanisms, can all heighten stimulation of the heart, which in turn increases cardiac output and then blood pressure (Weiner, 1977). Many of these controlling physiological mechanisms can be affected by psychological stress.

Stress and Blood Pressure Increase

Various stressful conditions have been examined to determine their role in the etiology of essential hyperten-

Because hypertension produces no obvious effects in someone with the disease, blood pressure levels should be routinely tested.

sion. Stressful interviews, natural disasters, anger, and anxiety have been found to produce short-term elevations in blood pressure (Innes, Millar, and Valentine, 1959; Ruskin, Board, and Schaffer, 1948; Ax, 1953). Kasl and Cobb (1970) have examined the effects of the loss of employment. They studied a group of workers beginning two months before their jobs were to be terminated and for two years subsequent to loss of employment. A control group, consisting of men in similar occupations who did not lose their jobs, was examined for the same twenty-six-month period. Each participant in the study was visited at home several times by a nurse during six separate periods so that blood pressure could be measured. For the control subjects there were no overall changes in blood pressure. In the men who lost their jobs, however, elevated blood pressure was found with anticipation of job loss, after termination of employment, and during the initial probationary period of a new job. Those who had great difficulty finding stable employment suffered the longest periods of high blood pressure.

In another group of studies (Hokanson and Burgess, 1962; Hokanson, Burgess, and Cohen, 1963; Hokanson, Willers, and Koropsak, 1968; Stone and Hokanson, 1969), based in part on psychoanalytic theory, Jack Hokanson and his colleagues attempted to determine whether blood pressure elevation is associated with the inhibition of aggression. Subjects were given a task but were angered almost immediately by the interruptions of a supposed fellow subject, actually a confederate of the experimenter. Later on, half of the subjects were given the opportunity to retaliate against their harasser.

The results of this classic series of investigations indicate that harassment of course causes blood pressure to rise but that, for males, aggressing against a source of frustration then helps blood pressure to decrease. With no opportunity to aggress against the frustrater, blood pressure is significantly slower to decrease after frustration. Only aggression directed at a low-status frustrater (college student) proved helpful in decreasing blood pressure, however, not that directed toward a high-status frustrater (visiting professor). These findings did not hold for female subjects.

Hokanson favors the following interpretation of his data: "*Any* social response can be viewed as having arousal-reducing concomitants, if that response has been previously instrumental in terminating or avoiding aggression in others" (Stone and Hokanson, 1969, p. 72).

Hokanson's interpretation explains why aggression directed toward a high-status frustrater was not effective. Presumably, subjects have learned that it does not pay to retaliate against a high-status aggressor. Thus an aggressive response will *not* help to reduce arousal since such responses have not previously been rewarding. Similarly, Hokanson's position accounts for the fact that aggressive responses do not seem to reduce arousal for females. Social and cultural conditions prevailing for them when these studies were conducted dictated that the response to frustration not be aggression. This sex difference may disappear with growing social support for greater assertiveness in women.

A study by Harburg and others (1973) extends Hokanson's ideas to the natural environment and to the high incidence of hypertension among black Americans. Harburg and his colleagues chose two areas of Detroit in which to conduct their investigation. In one area, the high-stress location, the crime rate was substantial, population density, mortality rates, and frequency of marital breakups were all high, and the socioeconomic status of residents was generally low. Conditions in the low-stress area were more favorable.

In each area groups of married black and white men were selected for study. During a visit to the participants' homes, a nurse took blood pressure readings, the respondents were interviewed, and a specially designed test was administered. The test presented hypothetical situations and asked the participants how they would respond. An example follows.

Now imagine that you were searching to find another place to live in, and finally found one for sale or rent which you liked, but the owner told you he would not sell or rent to you because of your religion, national origin or race. How would you feel about that? The response categories . . . were as follows: (1) "I'd get angry or mad and show it, (2) I'd get annoyed and show it, (3) I'd get annoyed, but would keep it in, (4) I'd get angry or mad but would keep it in, (5) I wouldn't feel angry or annoyed" (p. 280).

Participants were also asked how they would feel if they had become angry and showed it. The dimension assessed here was guilt, and the possible responses ranged from very guilty to no feelings of guilt at all.

Blood pressure was higher among the black males than among the whites; and blacks living in the high-stress area had higher blood pressure than blacks living

Harburg and his co-workers found that blacks living in high-stress areas were likely to have high blood pressure, particularly if they felt guilty about expressing anger.

in the middle-class neighborhoods. Thus previous statistics revealing racial differences in blood pressure were substantiated, but with the important reservation that environmental stress is also a major factor. When responses on the test were related to blood pressure, the following pattern emerged: for all subjects except blacks in the middle-class neighborhood, holding anger in and guilt were related to higher blood pressure levels.

Harburg's findings, and a reanalysis of them (Gentry et al., 1981, 1982), have pointed out the role of "anger-in" in the development and maintenance of high blood pressure. Ongoing research (for example, Spielberger et al., 1984) is correlating blood pressure in normal subjects with their scores on the Anger Expression Scale, a twenty-item self-report inventory asking subjects the various ways in which they react when they are angry or furious. Do they control their temper? Do they keep things in? Do they slam doors or argue with others? A recent study of adolescents (Johnson, 1984, reported in Spielberger et al., 1984) found strong and positive correlations between elevated blood pressure and the tendency to suppress anger. Suppressed anger, through its continual activation of the autonomic nervous system, may in time cause elevations in blood pressure to become fixed, that is, it may cause essential hypertension.

The mechanism inducing long-term essential hypertension would necessarily involve some structural changes in the organism. For ethical reasons no experimental work has been done with human beings to determine whether short-term increases in blood pressure will develop into prolonged hypertension, but some research has been done on animals.

In general, true hypertension has proved elusive in the laboratory. In many studies using electric shock as a stressor, blood pressure increased during the period when the animal was stressed but returned to normal when the stress was removed. Somewhat more successful in producing long-term blood pressure elevations are studies that have used more naturalistic stress, such as competing with other animals for food (Peters, 1977). But the overall picture indicates that some predisposing factor or factors are required if stress, such as the activation of the autonomic nervous system by suppressed anger, is to bring on essential hypertension.

Predisposing Factors
In research with animals, several powerful diatheses have been identified—rearing in social isolation (Henry, Ely, and Stephens, 1972), a high level of emotionality (Farris, Yeakel and Medoff, 1945), and sensitivity to salt

(Friedman and Dahl, 1975). In the study having to do with salt, the researchers worked with two strains of rats who had been bred to be either sensitive or insensitive to the impact of their diet. The sensitive rats reliably developed hypertension and died on a high-salt diet. These salt-sensitive rats were also likely to show sustained blood pressure elevations when placed in an experimentally created conflict situation.

Unfortunately, the information on physiological predispositions for hypertension in human beings is not very clear. Several studies have, however, demonstrated that hypertensives show greater blood pressure reactivity, reacting to stress and other novel situations with blood pressure increases that are larger than those of normal people (Engel and Bickford, 1961; Shapiro, 1961). In the Engel and Bickford study twenty female hypertensive patients and twenty control subjects were exposed to various stressors. Fifteen of the twenty hypertensives showed an increase in blood pressure, but only five of the controls did. In a similar vein Hodapp, Weyer, and Becker (1975) studied the blood pressure of hypertensive patients and normal controls while they rested, while they attended to colored slides of landscapes, and while they performed a demanding cognitive task (the stressor). The blood pressure of all subjects increased during the stress task. But in the hypertensives blood pressure was elevated, in relation to that recorded during the rest period, even when they were simply viewing the slides.

The research on blood pressure reactivity as a possible physiological predisposition cannot be regarded as conclusive, however, for the individuals being studied were *already* hypertensive. Their reactivity might have been a *result* rather than a *cause* of their hypertension. To be conclusive, studies must begin with individuals who have the predisposition but have not yet developed essential hypertension. In one such longitudinal study (Rose, Jenkins, and Hurst, 1978) air traffic controllers were followed over a three-year period. Consistent with the other research we have discussed, men who initially showed greater blood pressure reactivity to their work were more likely to develop hypertension later on. There is little doubt that essential hypertension is caused by an interplay between a diathesis and a stress.

Coronary Heart Disease

A Characterization of the Disease
Coronary heart disease (CHD) takes two principal forms, angina pectoris and myocardial infarction or

heart attack. The symptoms of *angina pectoris* are periodic chest pains, usually located behind the sternum and frequently radiating into the left shoulder and arm. The principal cause of these paroxysms of pain is an insufficient supply of oxygen to the heart, which, in turn, is traced to coronary atherosclerosis, a narrowing or plugging of the coronary arteries by deposits of fatty material. Angina is generally precipitated by physical or emotional exertion and is commonly relieved by rest or medication. Serious physical damage to heart muscle rarely results from an angina attack, for blood flow is reduced but not cut off. *Myocardial infarction* (MI) is a much more serious disorder and is one of the leading causes of death in the United States today. Like angina pectoris, myocardial infarction is caused by an insufficient oxygen supply to the heart. The oxygen insufficiency, more extreme than in angina pectoris, results either from a general curtailment of the heart's blood supply through atherosclerosis or from coronary occlu-

During a heart stress test the individual exercises at an increasing expenditure of energy under controlled conditions. His heartbeat is monitored throughout and during the following rest period, and blood pressure is taken periodically.

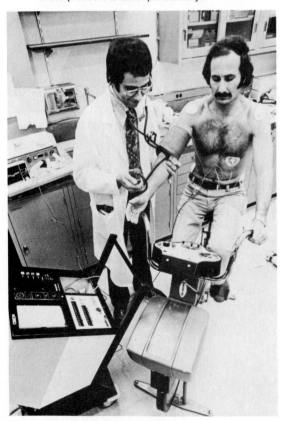

sion, a sudden obstruction of a large coronary artery by deposits or by a blood clot. In both instances parts of the heart muscle die. In addition to this greater severity and possibility of death, myocardial infarction differs from angina in that it is not necessarily precipitated by exertion, and the pain is longer and more severe (Friedberg, 1966).

The American Heart Association lists seven factors related to increased risk for CHD: age, sex (males are at a greater risk), cigarette smoking, elevated blood pressure, elevated serum cholesterol, an increase in the size of the left ventricle of the heart, as revealed by electrocardiogram, and diabetes (Insull, 1973). The risk for heart disease generally increases with the number and severity of these factors. Still, Jenkins (1976) has concluded that these traditional risk factors leave at least half of the etiology of CHD unexplained. Indeed, less attention was paid to contributing causes such as overweight, poor exercise habits, consumption of fatty foods, and smoking in the 1930s than is now, and yet in earlier decades the incidence of CHD and related cardiovascular diseases was much less. It has also been pointed out that in the Midwest, where people's diets are highest in saturated fats—from eating considerable amounts of red meat, for example—and where smoking rates are especially high, the incidence of CHD is low compared to that in more industrialized parts of the United States. And anyone who has visited Paris is aware of the intemperate smoking and the fat-rich diets of the French population—and yet CHD is relatively low there. *Why?*

Type A and Type B Behavior Patterns
The search for other causes of CHD has begun to focus on psychological factors such as stress and personality. Such considerations actually go back more than half a century. In 1910 the Canadian physician Sir William Osler (1849–1919) described the typical angina patient as ". . . vigorous in mind and body, and the keen and ambitious man, the indicator of whose engines is always set at full speed ahead" (Chesney, Eagleston, and Rosenman, 1980, p. 256). More recent evidence indicates a relationship between CHD and such stressors as an overload of work, chronic conflict, and the life stressors tapped by the SRRS (Jenkins, 1971, 1976; Rahe and Lind, 1971). The most promising evidence linking CHD to psychological variables, however, comes from investigations pioneered by two cardiologists, Meyer Friedman and Ray Rosenman (Friedman, 1969; Rosenman et al., 1975). In 1958 they identified a coronary-prone behavior pattern, called *type A*. Glass (1977) describes the

type A individual as having an intense and competitive drive for achievement and advancement; an exaggerated sense of the urgency of passing time, of the need to hurry; and considerable aggressiveness and hostility toward others. Type A persons are overcommitted to their work, often attempt to carry on two activities at once, and believe that to get something done well, they must do it themselves. They cannot abide waiting in lines and they play every game to win, even when their opponents are children. Fast-thinking, fast-talking, and abrupt in gesture, they often jiggle their knees, tap their fingers, and blink rapidly. Too busy to notice their surroundings or to be interested in things of beauty, they tabulate success in life in numbers of articles written, projects underway, and material goods acquired. The type B individual, on the other hand, is relaxed and relatively free of such pressures.

Type A and B individuals have been reliably identified by means of the Structured Interview (Rosenman et al., 1964) in which questions are asked about the intensity of ambitions, competitiveness, the urgency of deadlines, and hostility (see Box 8.2). A self-report inventory, the Jenkins Activity Survey (Jenkins, Rosenman, and Zyzanski, 1974), covers similar topics. Much research has documented differences between identified type A and B persons that support the validity of these behavior patterns. In one study, for example, students were asked to walk continuously on a treadmill. Measurements of expired air indicated that the uncompromising type A individuals had worked closer to their physical limits yet reported less fatigue (Glass, 1977).

Evidence supporting the predictive validity of the type A pattern comes from the Western Collaborative Group Study (WCGS) (Rosenman et al., 1975). In a double-blind prospective investigation, 3524 men aged thirty-nine to fifty-nine were to be followed over a period of eight and a half years. Some 3154 men completed their participation in the study. Individuals who had been identified as type A by the Structured Interview were more than twice as likely to develop CHD than were type B men. In addition, type A men with

"TYPICAL 'TYPE A' BEHAVIOR."

CHD were more than five times as likely to have a second myocardial infarction than were other individuals with CHD. Traditional risk factors—parental history of heart attacks; high blood levels of cholesterol, triglycerides, and lipids; diabetes; elevated blood pressure; cigarette smoking; lack of education; and lack of exercise—were also found to be related to CHD, but even when these factors were controlled for, type A individuals were still twice as likely to develop CHD. These findings from the WCGS have provided strong evidence that type A behavior contributes to the development of CHD, a conclusion affirmed by a panel of distinguished scientists meeting under the auspices of the National Heart, Lung, and Blood Institute (Review Panel on Coronary-Prone Behavior, 1981).[4]

Further research has been spurred by the success of the WCGS, such as the identification and study of type A women (Waldron, 1978) and attempts to identify subsets of type A behavior that may be related to specific manifestations of coronary disease (Jenkins, Zyzanski, and Rosenman, 1978). Evidence collected by this second line of investigation suggests that "future angina" individuals may be even more in a hurry, irritable, and competitive than "future MI" individuals.

[4]These findings are sometimes misinterpreted as meaning that type As are highly likely to develop CHD. The WCGS did not show this, nor did its report intend such an implication. What the findings do reveal is *relative* risk: 7 percent of the initially well subjects had developed coronary disease at the eight-and-a-half-year point; of this small percentage two-thirds were type A, one-third type B. Since half the subjects were rated as type A, the other half as type B, the risk was twice as high for the type As as for the Bs (Chesney, Eagleston, and Rosenman, 1980). The overwhelming majority of type As do *not* develop CHD; rather, type A personality is *one* of the significant risk factors in CHD. By the same token, many type Bs *do* develop CHD.

BOX 8.2

THE STRUCTURED INTERVIEW AND THE ASSESSMENT OF TYPE A

The interview used in the Western Collaborative Group Study for detecting the type A behavior pattern contained twenty-six questions—some of them are groups of questions—designed to set the occasion for it to reveal itself. For example,

Interviewer: When you are in your automobile, and there is a car in your lane going *far too slowly* for you, what do you do about it? Would you *mutter* and *complain* to yourself? Honk your horn? Flash your lights? Would anyone riding with you know that you were *annoyed*?

Interviewer: If you make a date with someone for, oh, two o'clock in the afternoon, would you *be there* on *time*? Always? Never? If you are kept waiting, do you *resent* it? Would you *say* anything about it? Why or why not?

Seldom taking more than fifteen minutes, the interviewer asks the questions in a manner that is abrupt and fast-paced, rather than warm and empathic. Although the interview is highly structured, its protocol requires the interviewer to push the respondent with challenging, probing follow-up questions delivered in a pressured fashion. For example, if the respondent says that he played games with his children to win when they were six, the interviewer might well ponder aloud, almost in disbelief, "Even with a six-year-old?" The interviewer also interrupts the subject now and then in the middle of an answer in order to keep things moving. The originators of this novel assessment device believe that only by nudging and goading the interviewees can reliable discriminations be made between type A and type B individuals.

At the end of the interview, the interviewer makes his or her own judgment whether the person is type A or B, but the more critical assessment is made later on when highly skilled raters listen to and view tapes of the interview and watch very closely for two sets of information: the content of what the person says and how he or she said it. Indeed, the tenor is deemed more important. For example, question 13 is delivered in a hesitant, halting manner, almost as though the interviewer has lost his or her place or wandered off in thought to something else.

Interviewer: Most people who work have to get up fairly early in the morning. In your particular case, uh-what-time-uh-do-you-uh, ordinarily uh-uh-uh-get up?

By the time the interviewer begins to uh-uh, it is obvious what the rest of the question is going to be. Note is taken whether the subject provides the answer before the question is completed, and whether he or she does so in an impatient, even hostile way, as if to say, "Hell, let's get on with this damned interview!" Answers to other questions also allow the raters to determine the subject's hostility, impatience, and sense of time urgency. Rosenman, in fact, believes that the interviewer should be a type A person!

There are several other techniques for detecting type A personality (see Chesney, Eagleston, and Rosenman, 1980; Matthews, 1982), one of them the Jenkins Activity Survey mentioned in the text. Each of them demonstrates a degree of validity in predicting CHD, and the results of each correlates significantly with those of the Structured Interview. But none predicts as well as the Structured Interview (Brand et al., in press), perhaps because, in addition to revealing the person's typical reactions to situations, it allows the interviewer and the raters to observe directly *how* he or she responds to a challenging question.

Indeed, the Structured Interview and the Jenkins Activity Survey, the two common ways of assessing type A behavior, are far from identical. When people are classified as type A or type B using both the Structured Interview and the Jenkins Activity Survey, the agreement rate is only 60 to 70 percent. Fifty percent agreement would be expected by chance alone (Matthews et al., 1982). Therefore, when considering the type A–type B distinction, we must be careful always to consider how it has been assessed in a particular study.

But how does a set of *psychological* characteristics mediate a *physiological* disease of the heart? In response to stress, type As have higher levels of norepinephrine in the blood than do type Bs (Simpson et al., 1974).[5] High levels of norepinephrine can lead to arterial damage and lesions in the heart. Furthermore, high levels of norepinephrine can increase the extent to which blood plate-

---

[5]Norepinephrine is a hormone released by the adrenal medulla. It and epinephrine, a somewhat similar hormone released with it, are called into play by the sympathetic nervous system. Norepinephrine raises diastolic pressure. And it is a very powerful vasoconstrictor, narrowing even the blood vessels of the skeletal muscles. Norepinephrine is also a neurotransmitter, a substance by which information is passed from one neuron to the next (see page 212). As well as working in some of the nerve tracts of the brain, norepinephrine is the principal neurotransmitter secreted by the sympathetic nerve fiber endings.

lets aggregate and thus make blockage in the arteries more likely. Patients who have undergone angiography and been found to have extensive atherosclerosis tend to be type A personalities (for example, Blumenthal et al., 1978). In this procedure a catheter is inserted into the heart so that a photosensitive dye can be introduced to permit filming of the coronary arteries.

On a more psychological level, we can ask what there is about type As that puts them at risk. One way of addressing this question is to examine individual items from the Structured Interview to see which ones are the best predictors of CHD. In the analysis of the interview data from the WCGS done by Matthews and her colleagues (1977), only seven of the whole set of items discriminated between type A individuals who developed CHD and those who did not. Three of these items were related to self-reports of impatience and hostility, one was self-reported competitiveness, and the remainder were aspects of voice style, such as explosiveness. Recent findings (for example, Williams et al., 1980) also suggest that hostility in particular is a major factor within the type A complex. The rate of occlusion of coronary arteries was especially high in type As who had earlier endorsed MMPI items reflecting a view of other people as inconsiderate, immoral, selfish, and deserving to be hurt or punished. These prospective data have been confirmed by Barefoot, Dahlstrom, and Williams (1983). Following up medical students who were healthy when they took the MMPI twenty-five years ago, they found a higher rate of CHD and death in those whose answers had indicated the same hostility toward others. Impatience and hostility, then, may form the "core" of the type A personality and thus warrant further study.

On a more theoretical level, Glass (1977) has suggested that the essence of type A behavior is an attempt to control stressful events. When confronted by trying circumstances, a type A individual struggles to control them and thus appears hard driving and competitive. This active coping with the environment causes the physiological changes associated with type A behavior, such as a higher level of norepinephrine. In this way Glass's theory may account for both the behavioral and physiological manifestations setting apart the type A personality. The theory has another important implication: the environment of type As should be carefully assessed. If challenging events are not encountered, the type A behavior pattern will not come to the fore. Until now little research has been conducted on environmental factors that are linked to activation of the type A pattern; they would seem to be an important area for future inquiry.

"I don't care if they *are* moving better over there. This is the fast lane. This is where I live."

(Drawing by Handelsman; © 1983, The New Yorker Magazine, Inc.)

ASTHMA

A Characterization of the Disease

Purcell and Weiss (1970) have described asthma in the following way.

Asthma is a symptom complex characterized by an increased responsiveness of the trachea, major bronchi, and peripheral bronchioles to various stimuli, and is manifested by extensive narrowing of the airways which causes impairment of air exchange, primarily in expiration, [thus inducing] wheezing. [The airways may be narrowed] because of edema [an accumulation of excess watery fluid in the tissues] of the walls, increased mucus secretion, spasm of the bronchial muscles, or the collapse of the posterior walls of the trachea and bronchi during certain types of forced expiration (p. 597).

Asthma attacks occur intermittently and with variable severity; the frequency of some patients' attacks may increase seasonally when certain pollens are present. The airways are not continually blocked; rather the respiratory system returns to normal or near normal either spontaneously or after treatment, thus allowing asthma to be differentiated from chronic respiratory problems like emphysema (Creer, 1982). The major structures of the respiratory system are shown in Figure 8.1.

Most often, asthmatic attacks begin suddenly. The patient has a sense of tightness in the chest, wheezes, coughs, and expectorates sputum. Subjective reactions

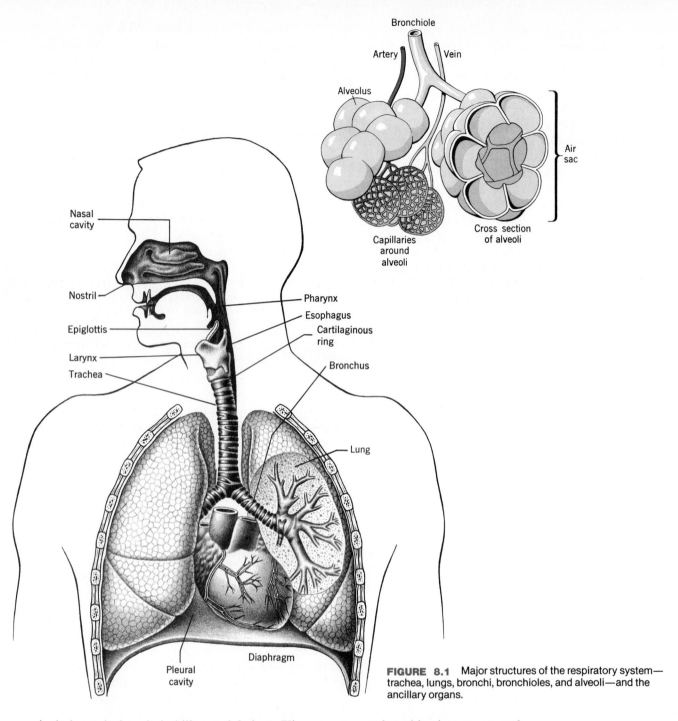

Bronchiole

Artery

Vein

Alveolus

Air
sac

Capillaries
around
alveoli

Cross section
of alveoli

Nasal
cavity

Nostril

Epiglottis

Larynx

Trachea

Pharynx

Esophagus

Cartilaginous
ring

Bronchus

Lung

Diaphragm

Pleural
cavity

FIGURE 8.1 Major structures of the respiratory system—trachea, lungs, bronchi, bronchioles, and alveoli—and the ancillary organs.

include panic-fear, irritability, and fatigue (Kinsman et al., 1974). A severe attack is a very frightening experience indeed. The immense difficulty of getting air into and out of the lungs feels like suffocation, and the raspy, harsh noise of the gasping, wheezing, and coughing compounds the individual's terror. He or she may become exhausted by the exertion and fall asleep as soon as breathing is more normal.

The asthma sufferer takes a longer time than normal to expire air, and whistling sounds can be detected throughout the chest. These sounds are referred to as rales. Symptoms may last an hour or less or may continue for several hours or sometimes even days. Between attacks no abnormal signs may be detected when the individual is breathing normally, but forced, heavy expiration will often allow the rales to be heard through a stethoscope.

One patient, to be described in the following case history, had his first attack at age nine. His condition worsened until he was thirteen, after which he was symptom-free for ten years. From that time on, however, his condition deteriorated to an unusual degree, and the patient eventually died of respiratory complications—an outcome which fortunately is rare.

> Abundant data from this patient's life suggest the importance of emotional factors in precipitating exacerbations of his asthma. He gives a graphic description of developing wheezing and shortness of breath upon separation from his mother. Once, while away on a trip with either her or his grandmother (it is not clear which), in a strange hotel, separated from his companion by a wall, he suffered through the night, having the feeling that his wheezes might be loud enough to be heard and bring her in to rescue him.
>
> He described clearly the relationship of his symptoms to odors. His response to the scent of flowers may have had an allergic basis. That seems less likely in the case of the scent of "lovely ladies," which he stated also gave him asthma. So did certain "bad" smells, of asparagus and cigar smoke. . . . He had many conflicts around weeping, frequently described being dissolved in tears, but always with the implication that he never really was exhausting the reservoir of "sobbing." . . .
>
> At the time of his brother's marriage, the patient was jealous; he managed to forget to mail the 150 invitations to the ceremony that had been entrusted to him. In the church he was almost more prominent than the bride, walking down the aisle just before the ceremony, gasping for breath, and wearing a fur coat, although the month was July (Knapp, 1969, p. 135).

Somewhere between 2 and 5 percent of the population is estimated to have asthma. A third of asthma sufferers are children, and about two-thirds of these youngsters are boys (Graham et al., 1967; Purcell and Weiss, 1970). Williams and McNicol (1969) studied 30,000 seven-year-old Australian schoolchildren. They found a high correlation between the age of onset of the symptoms and the length of time the disorder lasted. If the age of onset was less than one, 80 percent were found to

be still wheezing five years later. With ages of onset from three to four, 40 percent were still wheezing five years later, and with an onset age of five or six, only 20 percent were still wheezing five years later. Thus the earlier the disorder begins, the longer it is likely to last.

The Etiology of Asthma

Much of the debate concerning the importance of psychological factors in the development of asthma relates to whether or not emotionality is always implicated. To investigate the etiology of asthma, Rees (1964) divided the various possible causes into three categories, allergic, infective, and psychological. The cells in the respiratory tract may be especially sensitive to one or more substances or allergens such as pollen, molds, fur, and dust, bringing on asthma. Respiratory infections, most often acute bronchitis, can also make the respiratory system vulnerable to asthma. Anxiety, tension produced by frustration, anger, depression, and anticipated pleasurable excitement are all examples of psychological factors that may, through induced emotionality, disturb the functioning of the respiratory system and thus cause asthma.

Rees studied 388 asthmatic children admitted consecutively to the asthmatic outpatient clinic of St. David's Hospital, Cardiff, Wales. The part played by allergic factors was assessed through the case histories that were taken and by making cutaneous and inhalation reaction tests with suspected allergens. Patients were also exposed to suspected allergens and inert substances without their knowing which was which. The importance of infective factors was determined through the case histories and X-rays, by examining sputum, and by searching for pus or other evidence of infection in the nose, sinuses, and chest. The potential importance of psychological factors was assessed through the case histories and by direct behavioral observations. The principal results of Rees's study demonstrate the importance of conceptualizing asthma as a disease with multiple causes. As can be seen from Table 8.3, psychological factors were considered a dominant cause in only 37 percent of the cases. And in 30 percent of the cases psychological variables were regarded as totally unimportant— a conclusion at odds with the popular notion that asthma is always psychosomatic.

Rees's data showed also that the different causes of asthma varied in importance depending on the age of the individual. For those asthmatic individuals less than five years of age, the infective factors predominated. From ages six to sixteen the infective factors still pre-

TABLE 8.3 Relative Importance of Allergic, Infective, and Psychological Factors in the Etiology of Asthma   *(from Rees, 1964)*

Factors	Relative Importance, percent		
	Dominant	Subsidiary	Unimportant
Allergic	23	13	64
Infective	38	30	32
Psychological	37	33	30

dominated, but psychological variables increased in importance. In the range from ages sixteen to sixty-five, psychological factors decreased in importance until about the thirty-fifth year, thereafter becoming more consequential again.

Psychological Factors Producing Asthma

Rees's studies have demonstrated that some, but by no means all, cases of asthma have psychological factors as a primary cause. Yet even when asthma is originally induced by an infection or allergy, psychological stress can precipitate attacks. Kleeman (1967) interviewed twenty-six patients over an eighteen-month period. According to the reports of these patients, 69 percent of their attacks began with an emotional disturbance.

Dekker and Groen (1956) were able to produce asthma attacks in the laboratory using the following procedure. Before the actual investigation twelve asthmatic patients had described environmental situations that precipitated attacks. When these situations were reproduced in actual or pictorial form in the laboratory, three of the twelve patients developed full-blown asthma attacks, and three others had less severe respiratory symptoms. The stimuli to which the subjects ascribed their asthma included the national anthem, perfume, the sight of dust, horses, and waterfalls.

Finally, another study indicates the "power of suggestion" in inducing asthma attacks, even in individuals whose allergic reactions are regarded as the primary cause of their disorder (Luparello et al., 1971). Forty asthmatics and a control group of another forty persons were told that they were participating in a study of air pollution. The experimenter explained to each subject that he wanted to determine what concentrations of various substances would induce wheezing. The asthmatics were told that they would inhale five different concentrations of an irritant or allergen that had previously been established as a contributing cause of their asthma

attacks. They were led to believe that each successive sample would have a higher concentration of the allergen, but in fact they were given only five nonallergenic saline solutions to inhale. The control subjects were told that they were inhaling pollutants which could irritate the bronchial tubes and make it difficult for them to breathe. Fourteen out of the forty asthmatic patients reacted with significant airway obstruction, and twelve went on to develop full-fledged attacks. None of the controls had any pathological respiratory reactions. Later the twelve subjects who had developed asthma attacks were given the same saline solution to inhale but were told that the solution was a bronchodilator. The condition of all twelve improved, confirming the role of suggestion in some asthmatics.

Classical Conditioning

The two investigations just described suggest the possibility that asthma may be induced in a variety of situations as a result of conditioning. One conditioning experiment done with human beings as subjects had almost completely negative results, however. Dekker, Pelser, and Groen (1957) paired a known allergen with a neutral solvent. The classical conditioning hypothesis would argue that through repeated pairings of the CS and UCS, the CS should acquire the ability to elicit the asthmatic reaction. In this study, after repeated pairings, only two of a hundred subjects were found to have been successfully conditioned. Moreover, "In a personal communication dated October, 1961, Dekker reported that he was unable to replicate even these results" (Purcell and Weiss, 1970, p. 607). At this time there is no support for a classical conditioning account of asthma.

The Role of the Family

Several researchers have considered parent-child interactions to be important in the etiology of asthma. The investigators at the Children's Asthma Research Institute and Hospital in Denver routinely categorize their patients into those for whom psychological factors are considered the primary cause and those whose respiratory tracts are more greatly disturbed by other factors. In one investigation Purcell and his colleagues (1969) chose a group of twenty-two children. For thirteen children psychological factors were considered the principal precipitants of their asthma. For the other nine allergic or infective factors were considered more significant. These twenty-two children were studied over a considerable length of time which was subdivided into four periods. The first was an initial baseline period during which the children lived as usual with their families. In

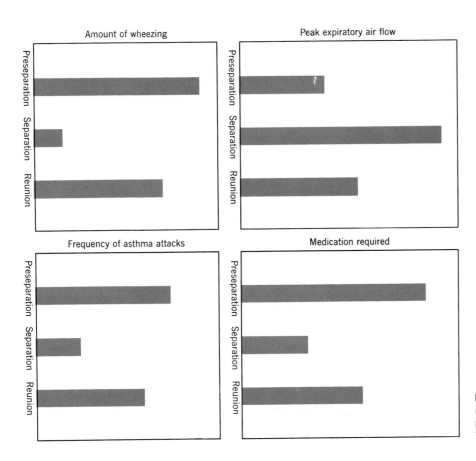

FIGURE 8.2 Improvement on several measures of asthma in children who were predicted to do well after being separated from their parents. After Purcell et al., 1969.

the second period the children still lived with their families, but all were informed that all family members except for the asthmatic child would soon be moved out for a two-week period. In the third period the children lived in their own homes but with a substitute mother, and in the fourth they were reunited with their parents. If the psychological factor disturbing one subgroup was the parent-child relationship, these children should improve when their parents lived apart from them. The children whose asthma was considered induced principally by allergic or infective factors would show no such improvement. The data supported the predictions remarkably well. Daily measurements and observations were made of the following variables: peak expiratory air flow, the force with which the individual can expel air; amount of medication required; wheezing; and frequency of asthma attacks. Seventy percent of the group who were predicted to do well without their parents improved during the separation phase (Figure 8.2). Of the nine children whose condition was not predicted to improve with their parents away, only one benefited from the separation.

Another study by Rees (1963) supports the theory that disturbed parent-child relationships may be associated with asthma. He classified the attitudes of the parents of hospitalized asthmatic children as either satisfactory—the parents promote feelings of security and are affectionate and accepting; or unsatisfactory—parents are rejecting perfectionists. Only 44 percent of the parents of asthmatics were rated as having satisfactory attitudes, whereas 82 percent of the parents of control children, accident cases in the same hospital, were rated in this way.

Not all research, however, finds that parent-child relationships figure in asthma. Gauthier and his co-workers (1977, 1978) studied young asthmatic children and their mothers through a battery of questionnaires and interviews and by making observations in the home. Most of the children and their mothers were well adjusted. The children's level of development was normal for their age, and they were independent and successful at coping with their surroundings.

The research we have reviewed is thus not completely consistent regarding the role that the home life of asthmatics plays in their illness. Furthermore, even if we allow that family relations are consequential in asthma, we cannot always tell whether the various familial variables are causal agents or maintaining agents. Although certain emotional factors in the home may be important in eliciting early asthmatic attacks in some children, in others the illness may originally develop for nonfamilial reasons, and then the children's parents may unwittingly reward various symptoms of the syndrome. For example, the parents may cater to the child and treat him specially because of his asthma. Current recommendations for the treatment of asthmatic children supply indirect support for this thesis. Doctors prescribe no special treatment and no overprotection. Instead, asthmatic children are urged to lead as normal a life as possible, even to the extent of participating in athletic events. An attempt is made, then, to keep the children from considering their sickness as the dominating factor in their lives. This attitude is well illustrated in the following interaction presented by Kluger (1969).

Patient: I can't go to school today because my asthma is worse.

Doctor: I know, but since it's not contagious why can't you be in school?

Patient (irritated): Because I'm having trouble breathing!

Doctor: I can see that, but you'll have trouble breathing whether you go to school or not. Remaining in bed won't help your breathing.

Patient (Disgustedly): Boy, they don't even let you be sick in this hospital! (p. 361).

Personality and Asthma

It has often been suggested that particular constellations of personality traits are linked to asthma. Several investigators have found that asthmatic individuals have a great many so-called neurotic symptoms: dependency and maladjustment (Herbert, 1965); meekness, sensitivity, anxiety, meticulousness, perfectionism, and obsessions (Rees, 1964). But most of this work consisted of comparing asthmatics to a normal control population. Neuhaus (1958) compared the personality test scores of asthmatic children to those of both a normal group of children and a group of children with cardiac conditions. As in other studies, the asthmatics were found to be more neurotic than those who were normal. But, and this is the important point, *the cardiac children were also more neurotic than normal children.* Thus the increased neuroticism of asthmatic children may reflect only reactions to a chronic illness; neuroticism scores on personality tests are always higher the longer the patient has been sick (Kelly and Zeller, 1969).

Physiological Predisposition

Now that the importance of various stresses in eliciting asthmatic attacks has been documented, we must attempt to account for the fact that not all individuals exposed to such stressors develop asthma. Rees (1964) found that 86 percent of the asthmatics examined had had a respiratory infection before asthma developed. Only 30 percent of his control subjects had been so afflicted. This study can be regarded as evidence that inheriting a weak organ, establishing a reaction pattern, or both may figure in the etiology of asthma. Individuals whose asthma is primarily allergic may have an inherited hypersensitivity of the respiratory mucosa, which then overresponds to usually harmless substances such as dust or pollen. There is evidence that the incidence of asthma has a familial pattern consistent with genetic transmission of a diathesis (Konig and Godfrey, 1973). Finally, there is some indication that asthmatics have a less than normally responsive sympathetic nervous system (Miklich et al., 1973; Mathe and Knapp, 1971). Activation of the sympathetic nervous system is already known to reduce the intensity of an asthmatic attack.

In conclusion, a diathesis-stress explanation once again seems to fit the data on a psychophysiological disorder. Once the respiratory system is predisposed to asthma, any number of psychological stressors can interact with the diathesis to produce the disease.

THERAPIES FOR PSYCHOPHYSIOLOGICAL DISORDERS

Since psychophysiological disorders are true physical dysfunctions, sound psychotherapeutic practice calls for close consultation with a physician. Antacids relieve the discomfort of ulcers, and anticholinergic drugs, which act like the sympathetic nervous system, decrease the secretion of gastric juice. Whether high blood pressure is organically caused or, as in essential hypertension, linked to psychological stress, the diuretic chlorthalidone will increase excretion by the kidneys of sodium chloride and thus reduce its presence in arterial walls and in turn their constriction. Reserpine has a sedative effect and also reduces arterial pressure. Asthma attacks can be alleviated by oral inhalation or injection of agents that dilate the bronchial tubes, one of the most effective being epinephrine. The help that drugs provide in ameliorating the damage and the discomfort in the particular body systems cannot be underestimated. Mental health and medical professionals recognize, however, that most drug interventions treat only the symptoms; they do not deal with the fact that the person is reacting emotionally to psychological stress. Although the evidence suggests that the predisposition for a particular organ breakdown is inherited or at least somatically based, nonetheless, the manner in which a person responds psychologically probably is not, and it is to this realm that psychotherapeutic interventions are directed.

Therapists of various persuasions agree in the most general terms that reducing anxiety is the best way to alleviate the suffering from psychophysiological disorders. The particular disorder, whether it be ulcer, essential hypertension, coronary heart disease, or an asthma attack, is considered a consequence of anxiety or to be linked with it in some way. Psychoanalytically oriented workers employ techniques such as free association and dream analysis, as they do with other anxiety sufferers, in their efforts to help the egos of their patients confront the supposed infantile origins of their fears. Ego analysts, however, like Franz Alexander, consider specific emotional states to underlie the several disorders and try to strengthen present functioning. Thus they would encourage someone with essential hypertension, viewed as laboring under a burden of undischarged anger, to assert himself and thereby siphon it off.

Client-centered therapists similarly regard people beset with psychophysiological disorders as needing to reduce anxiety, but they place special blame on the individual's conflict with society. Ulcers, hypertension, and coronary heart disease are considered the physiological evidence of the stress felt by those who comply with an establishment whose values go against their own best interests. The goal of the attentive listening and empathic reflection of client-centered therapists is to help clients see the physiological price paid for social conformity and make responsible decisions about changing their mode of living.

Behavior therapists employ their usual range of procedures for reducing anxiety—systematic desensitization, rational-emotive therapy, and assertion training—depending on the source of tension. If the person does not know how to act in a particular situation, behavior rehearsal and shaping may help him or her acquire necessary skills.

Behavioral medicine, a new area of specialization in behavior therapy, focuses on psychological factors that are linked to physical problems. Obviously psychophysiological disorders are of special interest to these mental health workers. Several forms of relaxation training are given as a part of medical treatment for hypertension, asthma, and other of these disorders. Treatments are also devised to lessen habits known to contribute to illness. For example, one important area of research is to help people stop smoking cigarettes, which has been linked to a host of medical problems. These therapists also work on methods to help people lose weight (Marston and Marston, 1980). Carrying around extra pounds, especially as people grow older, can contribute to coronary heart disease and to hypertension. One way to help asthma patients is to teach them how to discriminate better when they are having an attack. Many patients do not recognize their own symptoms and do not respond appropriately. But they can become more attuned to them and thereby better able to follow a treatment regimen (Creer, Renna, and Chai, 1982).

In recent years behavioral researchers have been exploring the clinical uses of *biofeedback* as a means of improving somatic functioning. Biofeedback provides people with prompt and exact information, otherwise unavailable, on heart rate, blood pressure, brain waves, skin temperature, and other autonomic bodily functions. The particular internal physiological process is detected and amplified by a sensitive electronic recording device. The person knows instantaneously, through an auditory or visual signal, the rate of the process, whether it is too high or too low or just right. Numerous studies have shown that most people, if given the task, for example, of raising their heart rates or lowering their blood pressure, can do so with the help of biofeedback (Elmore and Tursky, 1978; Shapiro, Tursky, and Schwartz, 1970). What is not yet clear is whether through biofeedback they can achieve results that are of

Biofeedback procedures are being applied in the treatment of number of psychophysiological disorders. Demonstrated here is a technique sometimes used to relieve headaches.

BOX 8.3

MIGRAINE HEADACHE AND BIOFEEDBACK

When I am in a migraine aura (for some people the aura lasts fifteen minutes, for others several hours), I will drive through red lights, lose the house keys, spill whatever I am holding, lose the ability to focus my eyes or frame coherent sentences, and generally give the appearance of being on drugs, or drunk. The actual headache, when it comes, brings with it chills, sweating, nausea, a debility that seems to stretch the very limits of endurance. That no one dies of migraine seems to someone deep into an attack, an ambiguous blessing. (From Joan Didion, The White Album, *pp. 170—171. Copyright © 1979, by Joan Didion. Reprinted by permission of Simon and Schuster, a Division of Gulf and Western Corporation.)*

Migraine headaches are estimated to afflict up to 10 percent of the general population. Some people have these attacks as often as every few days, others only a few times in their lives. The headache pain itself is usually on one side, almost as though the head were divided in two by an impermeable wall. It has been said that only those actually afflicted with the most common of psychophysiological disorders can know how extreme is the suffering associated with migraine.

A distinction is usually made between classic migraine and common migraine. In classic migraine the person has prodromal symptoms, symptoms experienced before the onset of the headache itself. They take the form of tension, wakefulness, declining energy and drive, and sometimes visual disturbances which are seen first as a shimmering haze, then as zigzag lines. In both types of migraine it is known that the headache itself is caused by sustained dilation, or increase in size, of the extracranial vasculature, principally of the temporal artery which trifurcates to supply the side of the head. Almost universally, the headache is initially a pulsing pain on one side of the head, coinciding with each heartbeat as the blood is pumped through the expanded extracranial arteries. The pain is caused by these dilated arteries triggering pain-sensitive nerve fibers in the scalp. As the headache progresses, the pain becomes steadier. The arteries thicken and rigidify, making stimulation of the extracranial nerve fibers constant rather than pulsing (Elmore, 1979). Recent evidence indicates that the scalp arteries of migraine victims are more sensitive to autonomic

nervous stimulation than those of normal people. Other evidence points to a general instability in vasomotor control, which appears to be the inherited diathesis that predisposes these unfortunates to reacting to stress with this debilitating disorder.

For many years there has been a controversy about the causes of the extracranial vascular dilation. In classic migraine, it will be recalled, visual disturbances are among the prodromal symptoms. These precursors to the headache itself, according to some researchers, are caused by intense constriction, or narrowing, of the internal carotid artery and its branches, the cranial arteries supplying blood to the brain and to the visual system. Somehow, the theorizing goes, this initial constriction of the internal cranial arteries produces the subsequent dilation of the external carotid artery and its branches, in particular of the temporal arteries, that is the immediate cause of the migraine headache itself.

Consequently, there are two competing schools of thought regarding the best way to treat migraine: one concentrates on the intracranial vasoconstriction during the prodromal stage, the other on the extracranial vasodilation of the headache phase. The first tries to dilate internal arteries by reducing sympathetic activity, the second to constrict external arteries by increasing sympathetic activity. Sympathetic activity can be reduced through such psychological techniques as deep-muscle relaxation training (Jacobson, 1929); autogenic training, a method promoting relaxation through suggestions of heaviness and warmth* (Luthe and Schultz, 1969); and a Westernized version of transcendental meditation (Benson, 1975). Of particular importance for our present discussion are studies that employ biofeedback to increase finger temperature as a means of promoting vasodilation in the body generally. Clinical reports of research conducted originally at the famous Menninger Clinic in Topeka, Kansas (Sargent, Green, and Walters, 1972, 1973), claimed marked improvement in a number of migraine patients who were taught to warm their hands through biofeedback training and then to initiate hand warming on their own at the slightest warning that a headache was coming on. Unfortunately, these studies were flawed by serious methodological problems. Nothing indicated that patients actually learned to warm their hands, and the judgments of improvement were unsystematic and

clinical significance. Several studies have demonstrated improvement in essential hypertension (Blanchard and Miller, 1977) and in tension headache (Budzynski et al., 1973), but perhaps other factors, such as relaxation training, have been responsible for the favorable results obtained. Biofeedback will be evaluated in greater depth in Chapter 19. Box 8.3 presents a recent example of promising clinical research.

Researchers in behavioral medicine also address the challenge of altering the driven, overcompetitive patterns of the type A individual, who has been shown to be at higher risk for heart disease. Within the past ten years or so, about a dozen studies have been conducted on how to lessen or change type A behavior. Because most of them have provided a narrow treatment of short duration, for example, a few sessions of relaxation trainimpressionistic (Elmore, 1979). The Menninger reports, however, did stimulate a series of more rigorous clinical studies.

The second treatment for migraine focuses on increasing sympathetic activity in order to halt extracranial artery dilation. Through biofeedback the individual is trained to reduce the amplitude of pulsations in the superficial temporal arteries, in other words to constrict the arteries at the site of the actual migraine headache.

Graham and Wolff (1938) had earlier given migraine sufferers ergotamine tartrate, a powerful vasoconstrictive drug, and found significant lowering of pulse in the superficial temporal arteries and in the occipital, the extracranial arteries at the side and rear of the head; patients also reported less headache pain. As with many drugs, however, the very vasoconstriction that appeared to alleviate the migraine had some serious side effects, such as nausea and numbness and even gangrene in the extremities. These side effects encouraged work on psychological methods of constricting just the extracranial arteries. A number of researchers have demonstrated that patients find relief from migraine by learning to lower extracranial artery pulse via biofeedback (for example, Friar and Beatty, 1976).

From an examination of the migraine treatment literature, Elmore and Tursky (1981) concluded that a study was needed to compare the two competing approaches to treatment. They also wanted to demonstrate by careful physiological measurement that whatever response was asserted to have been acquired via biofeedback was in fact acquired; and to determine whether therapy gains were maintained by following up patients for a period of time after their training.

Elmore and Tursky divided a sample of twenty-three adults suffering from migraine into two groups: one received eight sessions of biofeedback training to raise hand temperature, the other eight sessions of biofeedback training to lower temporal pulse. Both groups had a ninth session without feedback to test whether members could perform the learned response on their own. To achieve the respective goals of their groups, raising hand temperature or lowering temporal pulse, subjects were to generate images of warmth or coolness, or to adopt any technique, other than tensing the muscles, that seemed to work for them. They were also encouraged to practice these strate-

gies every day for about fifteen minutes and at the slightest warning that a headache was about to begin. For a month before and following treatment all subjects recorded the occurrence and intensity of headache in a specially designed pain and discomfort diary. If the people lowering temporal pulse did better than the hand-warming people, it could be concluded that migraine should be treated by *increasing sympathetic* nervous system activity. To relieve migraine headaches people need merely constrict the extracranial arteries. Superiority of hand warming, in contrast, would indicate that earlier on vasodilation is necessary in order to prevent the intracranial vasoconstriction believed by the Menninger group to trigger the later extracranial vasodilation.

Physiological measurements taken during the biofeedback training showed that members of each group did in fact learn the skill they were being taught. Moreover, the subjects lowering temporal pulse showed a pattern of general sympathetic nervous system activation, the hand-warming group deactivation of this system, demonstrating that the respective training procedures had the intended effects on the autonomic nervous system. Finally, the all-important treatment results: the people lowering temporal pulse achieved significantly more improvement during the one-month posttreatment evaluation than did the hand-warming subjects. Specifically, they reported fewer than half the headaches suffered before treatment, ingested significantly less headache medication, and tended to rate as less painful whatever headaches they had. In contrast, members of the hand-warming group rated their posttreatment headaches as significantly more painful and somewhat longer lasting than those suffered before treatment. The results, then, pose a serious challenge to the view that migraine is caused by sympathetic overarousal and that, generally speaking, people with this disorder should try to reduce their sympathetic nervous activity through relaxation training or tension-reducing drugs. Rather, treatment should be aimed more directly at constriction of the extracranial arteries.

*A series of six exercises train patients to regulate their breathing and heart rates and to make their extremities feel heavy and warm, the stomach warm, the forehead cool. Autogenic training is considered a combination of relaxation training and self-hypnosis.

ing, not surprisingly their results have been modest (Price, 1982). A significant exception is the Recurrent Coronary Prevention Project (Friedman et al., 1982), funded by the National Heart, Lung, and Blood Institute.

The overall purpose of this project was to see whether the type A behavior of men who had suffered a heart attack could be changed in the direction of type B,

and whether fewer of these patients than those given only cardiological counseling would then have a second heart attack. The treatment expected to improve subjects the most attempted to alter their type A behavior as well as the environmental, cognitive, and physiological factors believed to contribute to their personality. Thus subjects practiced talking more slowly and listening to others more closely instead of interrupting them, a change in behavior. They watched fewer television programs featuring violence and competitiveness, an environmental switch. They attempted to alter their silent, internal self-talk by believing that events are not necessarily direct challenges to them, a cognitive improvement. And they complied with their physicians' drug and diet prescriptions, to better their physiological state. Results were encouraging: type A behavior can be measurably changed. Moreover, after three years of treatment, for men who had received type A counseling the risk of a second heart attack was 2.5 percent annually, compared to 5 percent for type A men who received only cardiological counseling.

But there are many obstacles to reducing type A patterns in our culture. Price (1982) enumerates two. First, in an industrialized and competitive society such as ours, type A behavior pays off, at least in the short run, in increased productivity and achievement, even though personal happiness may be sacrificed. Second, being a type A person is in many ways a cultural norm in the United States and in other countries as well. Often it takes a heart attack to force a type A person even to consider giving up the aggressive, individualistic struggle to gain as many material rewards as possible in the shortest amount of time, and instead to treasure leisure time and to value people, including the self, for their intrinsic worth rather than for their achievements and status.

Some work by Matthews (for example, 1978) has assessed type A behavior in children and the ways in which young people learn the values and behavior of the type A personality. She has found, for example, that mothers of type A boys continually "up the ante" for reinforcement. The child is set ever-higher goals for the same degree of reward from the mother. The mass media and most of our schools exhort children to "Be number one." "Don't make mistakes." "Don't waste time." "Increase your production." "Upward and onward." It seems likely that developmental psychologists will find more and more evidence that type A behavior is taught to youngsters from early childhood on.

Thus shifting from type A behavior in an effort to prevent or at least reduce the incidence of coronary heart disease challenges the very essence of our advanced and advancing society. A perhaps unintended consequence of the burgeoning literature and research on the type A personality may well be a searing examination of some of the most basic values upon which modern Western civilization is built. Surely, however, psychology can advocate that different values be presented in schools and in the mass media. And the Recurrent Coronary Prevention Project, in which patients were encouraged to place less emphasis on achievement and on rushing and more on pausing to smell the flowers, to enjoy the moment, on living life in the slow lane rather than the fast one, indicates that through their own efforts individuals can alter their type A personalities and in the process make themselves happier as well as healthier.

SUMMARY

Psychophysiological disorders are physical diseases produced by psychological factors, primarily stress. Such disorders usually affect organs innervated by the autonomic nervous system, such as those of the respiratory, cardiovascular, gastrointestinal, and endocrine systems. Research has questioned how psychological stress produces a particular psychophysiological disorder. Some workers have proposed that the answer lies in the specifics of the stressor. One piece of evidence singles out great personal responsibilities as creating enough pressure to give an individual an ulcer. Theories and some evidence link inhibition of aggression to hypertension, the type A personality to heart attacks. Other theories propose that stress must interact with a physiological diathesis; for ulcers the diathesis may be a tendency of the stomach to secrete too much acid, for hypertension a labile circulatory system, for heart attacks a sympathetic nervous system that releases too much norepinephrine, and for asthma a respiratory system that overresponds to an allergen or one that has been weakened by prior infection. Although we have spoken of psychological stress affecting the body, it must be remembered that the *mind* and the *body* are best viewed as two different ways of talking about the same organism.

Because psychophysiological disorders represent true physical dysfunctions, medications are usually called for. The general aim of psychotherapies for these disorders is to reduce anxiety. Behavioral medicine, a new field of specialization in behavior therapy, tries to find psychological interventions that can improve the patient's physiological state. It has developed ways of helping people to relax, smoke less, eat fewer fatty foods, and, via biofeedback, gain control over various autonomic functions, such as heart rate and blood pressure. One study has developed methods by which type A victims of heart attacks can abandon their angry, driving ways.

James Strombotne, *The Group*, 1960
Collection of The Whitney Museum of American Art, New York. Juliana Force Purchase

AFFECTIVE DISORDERS

Melancholia, a term derived from the Greek words *melan* meaning black and *choler* meaning bile, and mania, derived from the Greek word *mainesthai*, to be mad, were two of the three types of mental disorder recognized by Hippocrates in the fourth century B.C. By the second century A.D. the physician Aretaeus of Cappadocia had suggested a relationship between melancholia and the apparently opposite emotional state of mania. In the late nineteenth century, as we have seen, the famous German psychiatrist Emil Kraepelin listed two major types of psychoses. One, schizophrenia, will be discussed in Chapter 14. The other, *manic-depressive illness*, which was considered to be the disturbance of all patients showing "affective excess," is one of the principal disorders discussed in this chapter.

GENERAL CHARACTERISTICS OF DEPRESSION AND MANIA

Depression

"Depression is the common cold of psychopathology, at once familiar and mysterious" (Seligman, 1973). Just as most people experience at least moments of anxiety every week of their existence, so will each of us probably have more than an ample amount of sadness during the course of our lives, although perhaps not to the degree or with the frequency that the diagnosis depression is warranted. Often depression is associated with other psychological problems and with medical conditions. The man who has trouble maintaining his erection during intercourse can become depressed about his sex life. The woman who has had a hysterectomy may suffer depression over what she incorrectly believes to be a loss of her femininity. Agoraphobics may become despondent because of their inability to venture out of their homes. Alcoholics may be depressed by their inability to control their drinking and by the social and employment problems that their drinking has provoked. In these and many other instances depression is best viewed as secondary to another condition. Our discussion of depression in this chapter will focus on people for whom this affective disorder is the *primary* problem.

The following eloquent account is from a person who would be regarded as suffering from profound depression. Clearly, anxiety also plays a part in deepening the despair.

I was seized with an unspeakable physical weariness. There was a tired feeling in the muscles unlike anything I

had ever experienced. A peculiar sensation appeared to travel up my spine to my brain. I had an indescribable nervous feeling. My nerves seemed like live wires charged with electricity. My nights were sleepless. I lay with dry, staring eyes gazing into space. I had a fear that some terrible calamity was about to happen. I grew afraid to be left alone. The most trivial duty became a formidable task. Finally mental and physical exercises became impossible; the tired muscles refused to respond, my "thinking apparatus" refused to work, ambition was gone. My general feeling might be summed up in the familiar saying "What's the use." I had tried so hard to make something of myself, but the struggle seemed useless. Life seemed utterly futile (Reid, 1910, pp. 612–613).

Depression has been studied from several perspectives in addition to such phenomenological reports. To be discussed are psychoanalytic views, which emphasize the unconscious conflicts associated with grief and loss; cognitive theories, which focus on the depressed person's self-defeating thought processes; learning theories, which contend with the curtailment of activity associated with depression; and physiological theories, which concentrate on what the central nervous system is doing at the neurochemical level.

There is general agreement on the most common signs and symptoms of depression (Robins and Guze, 1970; American Psychiatric Association, 1980).

1. Sad, depressed mood.

2. Poor appetite and weight loss or increased appetite and weight gain.

3. Difficulties in sleeping (insomnia); not falling asleep initially, not returning to sleep after awakening in the middle of the night, and early morning awakenings; or in some depressed patients a desire to sleep a great deal of the time.

4. Shift in activity level, becoming either lethargic (psychomotor retardation) or agitated.

5. Loss of interest and pleasure in usual activities.

6. Loss of energy, great fatigue.

7. Negative self-concept; self-reproach and self-blame, feelings of worthlessness and guilt.

8. Complaints or evidence of difficulty in concentrating, such as slowed thinking and indecisiveness.

9. Recurrent thoughts of death or suicide.

Paying attention is an exhausting effort for the depressed. They cannot take in what they read and what other people say to them. Conversation is also a chore, for many prefer to sit alone and to remain silent. They speak slowly, after long pauses, using few words and a low, monotonous voice. Others are too agitated and cannot sit still. They pace, wring their hands, sighing and moaning all the while or complaining. When depressed individuals are confronted with a problem, no ideas for its solution occur to them. Every moment has a great heaviness, and their heads fill and reverberate with self-recriminations. Depressed people may also neglect personal hygiene and appearance and make numerous hypochondriacal complaints of aches and pains that apparently have no physical basis. Utterly dejected and completely without hope and initiative, they may be apprehensive, anxious, and despondent much of the time.

A single individual seldom shows all the aspects of depression; the diagnosis is typically made if at least a few signs are evident, particularly a *mood* of profound sadness that is out of proportion to the person's life situation. Fortunately, most depression, although recurrent, tends to dissipate with time. But an average untreated episode may stretch on for six to eight months or even longer. When depression becomes chronic, the patient does not always snap back to an earlier level of functioning between bouts.

Mr. J. was a fifty-one-year-old industrial engineer who, since the death of his wife five years earlier, had been suffering from continuing episodes of depression marked by extreme social withdrawal and occasional thoughts of suicide. His wife had died in an automobile accident during a shopping trip which he himself was to have made but had canceled because of professional responsibilities. His self-blame for her death, which became evident immediately after the funeral and was regarded by his friends and relatives as transitory, deepened as the months, and then years, passed by. He began to drink, sometimes heavily, and when thoroughly intoxicated would plead to his deceased wife for forgiveness. He lost all capacity for joy—his friends could not recall when they had last seen him smile. Once a gourmet, he now had no interest in food and good wine, and on those increasingly rare occasions when friends invited him for dinner, this previously witty, urbane man could barely manage to engage in small talk. As might be expected, his work record deteriorated markedly. Appointments were missed and projects haphazardly started and then left unfinished.

Depression was Marilyn Monroe's frequent adversary and a disrupter of her personal and professional life. She fought many bouts of it throughout her career and earlier and then lost a final one.

Mania

Some people who suffer from episodic periods of depression also at times suddenly abound with joyful elation and become hyperactive, overconfident, and full of impractical, grandiose plans. Although there are clinical reports of individuals who experience *mania* but not depression, such a condition is apparently quite rare. Mania has the following signs and symptoms.

1. Elevated, expansive, or irritable mood.

2. Extraordinary increase in activity level—at work, socially, or sexually.

3. Unusual talkativeness, rapid speech, and the subjective impression that thoughts are racing.

4. Less than the usual amount of sleep needed.

5. Inflated self-esteem; belief that one has special talents, powers, and abilities.

6. Distractibility; attention easily diverted.

7. Involvement in activities that are likely to have undesirable consequences, such as reckless spending.

The manic stream of remarks is loud and incessant, full of puns, jokes, plays on words, rhyming, and interjections about nearby objects and happenings that have attracted the speaker's attention. This speech is very difficult to interrupt. It also reveals the manic's so-called *flight of ideas*. Although small bits of talk are coherent, the individual shifts rapidly from topic to topic. The manic need for activity may cause the individual to be annoyingly sociable and intrusive, constantly and sometimes purposelessly busy, and unfortunately oblivious to the obvious pitfalls of his or her endeavors. Any attempt to curb all this momentum can bring quick anger and even rage. Mania usually comes on suddenly, over the period of a day or two. Untreated episodes may last from a few days to several months.

The following description of a case of mania comes from our files. The irritability that is often part of this state was not found in this patient.

Mr. M., a thirty-two-year-old postal worker, had been married for eight years. He and his wife lived comfortably and happily in a middle-class neighborhood with their two children. In retrospect there appeared to be no warning for what was to happen. On February the twelfth Mr. M. let his wife know that he was bursting with energy and ideas, that his job as a mail carrier was unfulfilling, and that he was just

wasting his talent. That night he slept little, spending most of the time at a desk, writing furiously. The next morning he left for work at the usual time but returned home at eleven a.m., his car filled to overflowing with aquaria and other equipment for tropical fish. He had quit his job and then withdrawn all the money from the family's savings account. The money had been spent on tropical fish equipment. Mr. M. reported that the previous night he had worked out a way to modify existing equipment so that fish " . . . won't die anymore. We'll be millionaires." After unloading the paraphernalia, Mr. M. set off to canvass the neighborhood for possible buyers, going door to door and talking to anyone who would listen.

The following bit of conversation from the period after Mr. M. entered treatment indicates his incorrigible optimism and provocativeness.

Therapist: Well, you seem pretty happy today.

Client: Happy! Happy! You certainly are a master of understatement, you rogue! (Shouting, literally jumping out of his seat.) Why I'm ecstatic. I'm leaving for the West coast today, on my daughter's bicycle. Only 3100 miles. That's nothing, you know. I could probably walk, but I want to get there by next week. And along the way I plan to contact a lot of people about investing in my fish equipment. I'll get to know more people that way—you know, Doc, "know" in the biblical sense (leering at therapist seductively). Oh, God, how good it feels. It's almost like a nonstop orgasm.

FORMAL DIAGNOSTIC LISTINGS

Two major *affective disorders* are listed in DSM-III, *major depression* and *bipolar disorder*. The symptoms of major depression, sometimes also referred to as *unipolar depression*, are the profoundly sad mood and disturbances of appetite, weight, sleep, and activity level just described. Major depression is one of the most widespread of the disorders considered in this book. Approximately 8 to 11 percent of men and 18 to 23 percent of women will be clinically depressed at least once in their lives (Weissman and Myers, 1978; Woodruff, Goodwin, and Guze, 1974). The disorder is more frequent among members of the lower socioeconomic classes (Hirschfeld and Cross, 1982). The critical symptoms of bipolar disorder are the elated or irritable mood, talkativeness, and hyperactivity of mania, as well as episodes of depression. Interestingly, people who suffer only manic episodes are diagnosed as having bipolar disorder. The incidence of bipolar disorder is much lower than that of major depression—about one percent of the population (for example, Weissman and Myers, 1978).

The Bases for Distinguishing Major (Unipolar) Depression and Bipolar Disorder

There is abundant evidence that the bipolar-unipolar distinction is an important one. Those suffering the two disorders differ in ways other than whether they have manic episodes. For example, when bipolars are depressed, they typically sleep more than usual and are lethargic, whereas unipolars have insomnia and are agitated. Unipolar depression usually has a later age of onset than does bipolar disorder, the average ages being thirty-six and twenty-eight, respectively. Moreover, more relatives of individuals with bipolar disorder have affective disorders than do the relatives of those with unipolar depression. Lithium carbonate (see pages 219 and 558) is more therapeutic for bipolars who are currently depressed than it is for unipolars. All these differences add to the validity of the bipolar-unipolar distinction (Depue and Monroe, 1978).

Heterogeneity Within the Categories

A problem remaining in the classification of affective disorders, however, is their great heterogeneity. Some bipolar patients, for example, suffer the full range of symptoms of both mania and depression almost simultaneously or, alternating rapidly, every few days. Other patients have only the symptoms of either mania or depression during a clinical episode. So-called bipolar II patients have episodes of major depression but only a less severe form of mania, called *hypomania*; they also have family members with bipolar disorder. Some researchers advocate diagnosing these individuals as having bipolar disorder itself, but the evidence that they should be is still insufficient (Depue and Monroe, 1978).

Unipolar depression too has great heterogeneity. In the previous edition of the DSM, attempts were made to deal with this diversity. The factors distinguishing among various types of unipolar depression were age of onset, the presence or absence of stress, and whether or not the patient was psychotic. Involutional melancholia, one of the DSM-II categories, was thought to occur at the "change of life," when both men and women go through physiological changes that make it less likely that they will be able to reproduce. Stress was not viewed as an important etiological factor; rather physiological (hormonal) changes were believed to cause this kind of depression. But no evidence substantiates this belief. We know that, in addition to somatic changes, individuals in their forties and fifties face considerable other difficulties: doubts about sexual attractiveness, realization that certain life goals may never be achieved, and loss of contact with children. All are likely contributors to depression in people of this age. In two other DSM-II diagnoses, neurotic and psychotic depression, a life event was assumed to have brought on the reactions. But deciding whether depression was indeed caused by environmental stress proved troublesome.

DSM-III retains the option of diagnosing a depressed patient as psychotic but drops the notion of neurotic depression. Depressed patients are diagnosed as psychotic if they are subject to delusions and hallucinations. Among such depressives delusions and hallucinations are usually *mood-congruent*. Psychotically depressed patients may believe that they are being punished for past sins. Or their feelings of inadequacy may be elaborated into delusions of past incompetencies and failures. Sometimes they think that the world is coming to an end. The presence of delusions appears to be a useful distinction among unipolar depressives (Nelson and Bowers, 1978; Glassman and Roose, 1981): depressed patients with delusions do not generally respond well to the usual drug therapies for depression, but they do respond favorably to these drugs when they are combined with the drugs commonly used to treat other psychotic disorders such as schizophrenia.

Finally, according to DSM-III, some unipolar depressives may also have melancholic symptoms. They find no pleasure in any activity and are unable to feel better even temporarily when something good happens. Their depressed mood is distinctly different from "normal" grief and is worse in the morning. They awaken about two hours too early, lose appetite and weight, have strong feelings of guilt, and are either lethargic or extremely agitated. The validity of the distinction between depressions with or without melancholia is at present unknown. Depression with melancholia, however, is similar to an older concept, endogenous depression, which did seem to be useful (for example, Mendels and Cochrane, 1968).

Chronic Affective Disorders

DSM-III lists two long-lasting disorders in which affective disturbances are predominant. Although the symptoms of individuals with either of these disorders have been evident for at least two years, they are *not* severe enough to warrant a diagnosis of major depression or bipolar disorder. The person with *cyclothymic disorder* has frequent periods of depression and hypomania. These periods may be mixed, alternate, or be separated by periods of normal mood lasting as long as several months. Cyclothymics have paired sets of symptoms in their periods of depression and hypomania. During their depression they feel inadequate; during their hypomania their self-esteem is inflated. They withdraw from people, then seek them out in an uninhibited fashion. They sleep too much and then too little. Depressed cyclothymics have trouble concentrating, but during hypomania their thinking becomes sharp and creative; their productivity decreases and then increases.

The person with *dysthymic disorder* is chronically depressed, either persistently or with periods of normal mood lasting a few days or weeks, never more than a month or two at a time. Besides feeling blue and losing pleasure in usual activities and pastimes, the person has at least several other signs of depression, such as insomnia or sleeping too much; feeling inadequate, ineffective, and drained of energy; pessimism; being unable to concentrate and to think clearly; avoiding the company of others.

Both of these chronic mood disorders may occur in people who also, from time to time, have full-blown episodes of major depression or bipolar disorder. The prognosis for patients with major depression who also have dysthymic disorder has been found to be especially poor (Keller et al., 1982).

PSYCHOLOGICAL THEORIES OF DEPRESSION

As is true of theorizing about other abnormal syndromes, that concerning depression points to both psychological and physiological factors. It will be seen that each theoretical position emphasizes one or another aspect of depression at the expense of others. In this section we discuss several theories that are couched in psychological terms.

Psychoanalytic Theory

It is not always easy to distinguish between sadness, which is normal, and depression, which is not. The contrast between normal grief and abnormal depression is the focal point of Abraham's (1911) original attempt to interpret depression through psychoanalytic theorizing

and of Freud's (1917) celebrated paper, "Mourning and Melancholia." Abraham was Freud's student. They both saw self-centeredness as differentiating depression from normal grief. Freud's work was an elaboration of Abraham's theorizing.

Predictably, Freud saw the potential for depression being created early in childhood. He theorized that during the oral period the child's needs may be insufficiently or oversufficiently gratified. The person therefore remains "stuck" in this stage and dependent on the instinctual gratifications particular to it. With this arrest in psychosexual maturation, this fixation at the oral stage, he or she may develop a tendency to be excessively dependent on other people for the maintenance of self-esteem.

From this happenstance of childhood, how can the adult come to suffer from depression? The reasoning is complex, assuming as it does that several unconscious processes are a part of mourning. Freud hypothesized

An analysis of the psychological mechanisms of bereavement led Abraham and Freud to formulate the psychoanalytic theory of depression.

that after the loss of a loved one the mourner first *introjects* or incorporates the lost person: he or she identifies with the lost one, perhaps in a fruitless attempt to undo the loss. Because, as Freud asserted, we unconsciously harbor negative feelings against those we love, the mourner now becomes the object of his or her own hate and anger. In addition, the mourner also resents being deserted and feels guilt for real or imagined sins against the lost person. The period of introjection is followed by the period of *mourning work*, during which the mourner recalls memories of the lost one and thereby separates himself from the person who has died and loosens the bonds that introjection has imposed.

The grief work can go astray in overly dependent individuals and develop into an ongoing process of self-abuse, self-blame, and depression. Such individuals do not loosen their emotional bonds with the person who has died, continuing to castigate themselves for the faults and shortcomings perceived in the loved one who has been introjected. The mourner's anger toward the lost one continues to be directed inward. This theorizing is the basis for the widespread psychodynamic view of depression as anger turned against oneself.

One further point must be made. Since many people can become depressed and remain so without having recently suffered the loss of a loved one, it became necessary to invoke the concept of "*symbolic loss*" in order to keep the theoretical formulation intact. For example, a person may unconsciously interpret a rejection as a total withdrawal of love.

We see numerous problems in this formulation. First, since the person presumably both hates and loves the individual he or she has lost, why is it that only the hate and anger are turned inward and not the love that is also there? Since the depressed person is said to have introjected the loved one, thus directing inwardly the feelings previously directed to the loved one, why do anger and resentment predominate? If the mourner directed positive feelings about the lost one inwardly, he or she would be a happy person rather than a depressed one. Psychoanalytic theorists have tried to resolve this inconsistency by postulating that the loss of a loved one is viewed as a rejection or withdrawal of affection. Interpreted in this way, a negative emotional state is more likely to predominate. The crucial point, though, is the absence of direct evidence that depressives do interpret death as rejection by the deceased.

A second difficulty is common to all Freud's hypotheses that involve the concept of fixation at an earlier psychosexual stage of development. Freud states that fixation at the oral stage can come about *through either too little or too much gratification*. How much, it could be asked, is enough to prevent fixation? Freud's theory, being nonquantitative, does not deal adequately with this question.

The concept of "symbolic loss" presents a third problem. From our critical perspective, this concept is introduced only after the fact to account for depression when no actual object loss can be specified. The concept would not be invoked for people who are not depressed. If it is inferred only *after* a diagnosis of depression and only *after* no actual object loss can be discerned, the diagnostician is engaging in the kind of confused reasoning referred to as *post hoc, ergo propter hoc*, after this, therefore because of this.

Little research has been generated by psychoanalytic points of view, neither Freud's nor those of others that are not discussed here. The little information available does not support the theory. Dreams and projective tests should theoretically be means of expressing unconscious needs and fears. Beck and Ward (1961) analyzed the dreams of depressed people and found themes of loss and failure, not of anger and hostility. An examination of responses to projective tests established that depressives identify with the victim, not the aggressor. Other data also contradict the views of Abraham and Freud. If depression comes from anger turned inward, we would expect depressed people to express little hostility toward others. This was not found to be the case; depressed individuals often express intense anger and hostility toward people close to them (Weissman, Klerman, and Paykel, 1971).

At the same time, however, psychoanalytic ideas have found their way into more recent theorizing. For instance, irrational self-statements such as "It is a dire necessity that I be universally loved and approved of," to which Ellis attributes much human suffering, might plague Freud's "oral personality" in the deepening depression following the loss of a loved one. Although Freud cloaked his clinical impressions in theoretical terms that have been rejected by many contemporary writers, we must appreciate that some of his basic suppositions have a continuing influence.

Cognitive Theories

Discussions of the feeling of helplessness in Chapter 6 and of Ellis's concept of irrational beliefs in Chapter 2 and elsewhere indicate that cognitive processes play a decisive role in emotional behavior. In some theories of depression as in some concerning anxiety, thoughts and beliefs are regarded as causing the emotional state. In a way Freud is a cognitive theorist too, for he viewed depression as resulting from a person's belief that loss is a withdrawal of affection.

Beck's Theory

Perhaps the most important contemporary theory of depression to regard thought processes as causative factors is Aaron Beck's (1967). His central thesis is that depressed individuals feel as they do because they commit characteristic errors in logic. From an examination of his therapy notes, he found that his depressed patients tended to distort whatever happened to them in the direction of self-blame, catastrophes, and the like. Thus an event interpreted by a normal person as irritating and inconvenient, for example, the malfunctioning of an automobile, would be interpreted by the depressed patient as yet another example of the utter hopelessness of life. Beck's position is not that depressives think poorly or illogically in general. Rather, depressives draw illogical conclusions and come to evaluate negatively themselves, their immediate world, and their future. They see only personal failings, present misfortunes, and overwhelming difficulties ahead.

According to Beck, in childhood and adolescence, depressed individuals have learned, through loss of a parent or an unrelenting succession of tragedies, through the social rejection of peers, the criticisms of teachers, the depressive attitude of a parent, a negative schema or negative schemata. All of us have schemata of many kinds; by these perceptual sets, these "mini-paradigms," we order our lives. The negative schemata that depressed persons have acquired are activated whenever new situations they encounter resemble in some way, perhaps only remotely, the conditions in which the schemata were learned. Moreover, the negative schemata of depressives fuel, and are fueled by, certain illogical errors; together they distort reality. Thus an ineptness schema can make depressives expect to fail most of the time; a self-blame schema burdens them with responsibility for all misfortunes; and their negative self-evaluation schema constantly reminds them of their worthlessness. The following list gives the principal errors and the illogical conclusions drawn by a person whose schema of negative self-evaluation is operating.

1. **Arbitrary inference.** A conclusion drawn in the absence of sufficient evidence or of any evidence at all. For example, a man concludes that he is worthless because it is raining the day that he is hosting an outdoor cocktail party.

2. **Selective abstraction.** A conclusion drawn on the basis of but one of many elements in a situation. A worker feels worthless when a product fails to function, even though she is only one of many people who have produced it.

3. **Overgeneralization.** An overall sweeping conclusion drawn on the basis of a single, perhaps trivial, event. A student regards his poor performance in a single class on one particular day as final proof of his worthlessness and stupidity.

4. **Magnification and minimization.** Gross errors in evaluating performance. A woman, believing that she has completely ruined her car (magnification) when she sees that there is a slight scratch on the rear fender, regards herself as good for nothing; or a man still believes himself worthless (minimization) in spite of a succession of praiseworthy achievements.

These errors in logic could of course be used within a schema of positive self-evaluation, by a person who distorts what he sees so as to *enhance* his view of himself. For example, he can selectively abstract from the success of a project, on which he worked with many others, the conclusion that he himself has great ability and was primarily responsible for the good outcome. The depressed person, however, by these errors in thinking, confirms his self-deprecatory schema and finds himself unworthy and responsible for calamities.

It is important to appreciate the thrust of Beck's position. Whereas many theorists have seen people as victims of their passions, creatures whose intellectual capacities can exert little if any control over feelings—this is Freud's basic position—in the theory just outlined, the cause-effect relationship operates in the opposite direction. Our emotional reactions are considered to be a function of how we construe our world, and indeed the interpretations of depressives are found not to mesh very well with the way most people view the world. Beck sees depressives as the victims of their own *illogical self-judgments*.

At least two points need to be demonstrated when evaluating Beck's theory. First, depressed patients, in contrast to nondepressed individuals, must actually judge themselves in the illogical ways that Beck has enumerated. This first point was initially confirmed by Beck's clinical observations, which suggest that depressed patients do, in fact, manifest at least some of the errors in logic listed by him (Beck, 1967).

More recent support for this general proposition comes from a number of sources. Questionnaires have been developed to assess depressive-distorted cognitive biases in reacting to stories about college students in problematic situations (Krantz and Hammen, 1979) and to allow subjects to report negative automatic thoughts (Hollon and Kendell, 1980). In general, depressives' responses to these questionnaires agree with expectations based on Beck's theory. As indicated in Chapter 4, an experiment employing the Articulated Thoughts During Simulated Situations procedure found the thinking of depressive patients illogical (White, Davison, and White, 1985). In perceiving and recalling information, depressives would seem to have negative schemata, for they perceive information in more negative terms (Roth and Rehm, 1980) and recall their incorrect answers better than their correct ones (Nelson and Craighead, 1977).

Second, it should be demonstrated that the cognitive distortion of depressives does not follow upon an emotional disturbance, that it does in fact *cause* the depressed mood. Many studies in experimental psychology have in a general way shown that a person's feelings can be influenced by how he or she construes events. A study by Geer, Davison, and Gatchel (1970), for example, found that people are less aroused when they believe that they have control over painful stimulation, even when the belief is false. But manipulating affect has also been shown to change thinking (for example, Isen et al., 1978). No study that we know of directly demonstrates that the various emotional and physical aspects of depression are truly secondary to, or a function of, the negative schemata and the errors in logic that Beck believes operate in this disorder. Beck has found that depression and cognitive distortions are *correlated*, but a specific causal relationship cannot be determined from such data; depression could cause negative and illogical thoughts, or negative and illogical thoughts could cause depression.

Indeed, one longitudinal study of the relationship between cognition and depression found that negative and illogical thinking did not precede depression (Lewinsohn et al., 1981). A large sample of community residents completed a battery of tests measuring cognition and depression and were then followed-up eight months later. Of particular interest were the results of the earlier tests assessing the thinking of people who later became depressed.

Prior to becoming depressed, [future depressives] did not subscribe to irrational beliefs, they did not have lower expectancies for positive outcomes or higher expectancies for negative outcomes . . . nor did they perceive themselves as having less control over the events in their lives (p. 218).

In our view the relation in all likelihood works both ways: depression can probably make thinking negative and illogical, and negative, illogical thinking can probably cause depression.

In spite of these irresolutions, an important advantage of Beck's theory is that it is testable and has encouraged considerable research on depression. Even more important, as discussed later in this chapter (see page 215), it has encouraged therapists to work directly on depressed patients' thinking in order to change and alleviate their feelings (Beck, 1976).

Learned Helplessness:
A Cognitive-Learning Theory

In recent years Martin Seligman's (1974) *learned-helplessness* theory of depression has been of considerable interest. Seligman suggests that although anxiety is the initial response to a stressful situation, it is replaced by depression if the person comes to believe that control is unattainable. In some ways this model is similar to the ego-analytical view of Bibring (1953), who proposed that depression follows ". . . the ego's shocking awareness of its helplessness in regard to its aspirations" (p. 39).

Initially Seligman's view was a mediational learning theory, formulated to explain the behavior of animals who received painful electric shock in two different situations. In the first part of the experiment some dogs are put in a box with electric grids in the flooring and subjected to numerous painful electric shocks from which they cannot escape. In the second part these animals, as well as dogs who did not have this prior experience with inescapable shock, are placed in a similar apparatus. Now painful shock can be avoided if the dogs learn to leap over a partition to another compartment of the so-called shuttle box as soon as they hear a warning buzzer or see a light come on. The behavior of the dogs is markedly affected by whether they were earlier exposed to inescapable shock. Animals who have not had the earlier experience become quite upset when they receive the first few electric shocks but fairly soon thereafter learn to leap over the partition when they hear or see the conditioned stimulus, and thereby avoid further painful shock. The animals who have had the earlier experience with inescapable shock behave quite differently. Soon after receiving the first shocks, they stop running around in a distressed manner; instead they seem to give up and passively accept the painful stimulation. Not surprisingly, they do not acquire the avoidance response

TABLE 9.1 Sample Items from the Beck Depression Inventory *(after Beck, 1967)*

Attitudes		Depression Inventory
Sadness*	0	I do not feel sad.
	1	I feel sad.
	2	I am sad all the time and I can't snap out of it.
	3	I am so sad or unhappy that I can't stand it.
Pessimism	0	I am not particularly discouraged about the future.
	1	I feel discouraged about the future.
	2	I feel I have nothing to look forward to.
	3	I feel that the future is hopeless and that things cannot improve.
Guilt	0	I don't feel particularly guilty.
	1	I feel guilty a good part of the time.
	2	I feel quite guilty most of the time.
	3	I feel guilty all of the time.
Self-dislike	0	I don't feel disappointed in myself.
	1	I am disappointed with myself.
	2	I am disgusted with myself.
	3	I hate myself.
Self-accusations	0	I don't feel I am any worse than anybody else.
	1	I am critical of myself for my weaknesses or mistakes.
	2	I blame myself all the time for my faults.
	3	I blame myself for everything bad that happens.
Suicidal ideas	0	I don't have any thoughts of killing myself.
	1	I have thoughts of killing myself, but I would not carry them out.
	2	I would like to kill myself.
	3	I would kill myself if I had the chance.

*The words to the left do not appear in the actual inventory but are given here to indicate what attitudes each group of items is meant to measure.

as efficiently and effectively as the control animals do. Most of them in fact lie down in a corner and whine. Such experiments imply that animals can acquire what might be called a "sense of helplessness" when confronted with uncontrollable aversive stimulation. This helplessness later tends seriously and deleteriously to affect their performance in stressful situations that *can* be controlled. They appear to lose the ability and motivation to learn to respond in an effective way to painful stimulation.

On the basis of this and other work on the effects of uncontrollable stress, Seligman felt that learned helplessness in animals can provide a model for at least certain forms of human depression. He noted similarities between the manifestations of helplessness observed in animal laboratory studies and at least some of the symptoms of depression. Like many depressed people, the animals appear passive in the face of stress, failing to initiate action that might allow them to cope. They develop anorexia, having difficulty in eating or retaining what is eaten, and lose weight. On the physiological level, one of the neurotransmitter chemicals, norepinephrine, was found to be depleted in Seligman's animals (see Box 9.4, page 212). Drugs that increase levels of norepinephrine have been shown to alleviate depression in human beings. Although effectiveness of treatment does not, as we have often indicated, prove etiology, the fact that depression is reduced by a drug that increases the level of norepinephrine is consistent with the finding that learned helplessness in animals is associated with lower levels of the chemical.

Experiments with human beings have yielded results similar to those of experiments done with animals. People who have been subjected to inescapable noise, or inescapable shock, or who have been confronted with unsolvable problems, fail later to escape noise and shock and solve simple problems (for example, Hiroto and Seligman, 1975; Roth and Kubal, 1975). Moreover, the performance of tasks by college students who rate as depressed on the Beck Depression Inventory (BDI; Table 9.1) is similar to that of nondepressed students who have earlier been subjected to these same helplessness-inducing experiences (Miller, Seligman, and Kurlander, 1975; Klein and Seligman, 1976). This is very important, for it suggests that we can, in a laboratory setting, elicit from nondepressed subjects behavior similar to that observed in depressed individuals (Figure 9.1).

In 1978 a revised version of the learned-helplessness

[1]Miller and Norman (1979) have independently published a theory very similar to this reformulation.

FIGURE 9.1 Subjects who were depressed and those who were not depressed but had experienced inescapable noise acted more slowly to escape noise than did those in the other two groups. After Klein and Seligman, 1976.

D-NN: *Ss* rated as depressed on Beck Depression Inventory; were not previously subjected to noise.
ND-NN: *Ss* rated as nondepressed; were not previously subjected to noise.
ND-IN: *Ss* rated as nondepressed; were previously subjected to inescapable noise (the "helpless" group).
ND-EN: *Ss* rated as nondepressed; were previously subjected to escapable noise.

model was proposed by Abramson, Seligman, and Teasdale,[1] for several inadequacies of the theory and unexplained aspects of depression had become apparent. Many of life's misfortunes are beyond our control, but they do not sadden us to the extent that we become depressed. In addition, many depressed people hold themselves responsible for their failures. If they regard themselves as helpless, how can they blame themselves? And why do depressed people have so little self-esteem? The essence of the revised theory lies in the concept of *attribution* (Weiner et al., 1971), and in this way it blends cognitive and learning elements. Given a situation in which the individual has experienced failure, he or she will try to attribute the failure to some cause. In Table 9.2 the Abramson, Seligman, and Teasdale formulation is applied to indicate the ways in which a college student might attribute his failure on the mathematics portion of the Graduate Record Examination. Three questions are asked. Are the reasons for failure believed to be internal (personal) or environmentally caused (universal)? Is the problem believed to be stable or short-term? How global or specific is the inability to succeed perceived to be?

The attributional revision of helplessness theory postulates that the way the person attributes failure will determine its subsequent effects. Global attributions should increase the generality of the effects of failure. Attributions to stable factors will make them long-term. Finally, attributing the failure to internal characteristics is more likely to diminish self-esteem, particularly if the personal fault is also global and persistent.

People then become depressed when they believe either that desired outcomes are unattainable or that negative outcomes are unavoidable. Whether self-esteem collapses too depends on whether they blame the bad outcome on their own inadequacies. The generality and chronicity of their depression and loss of self-esteem depend on the globality and persistence of the characteristic blamed. In fact, the depression-prone individual is thought to show a "depressive attributional style," a tendency to attribute bad outcomes to personal, global, stable faults of character. When persons with this style have unhappy, adverse experiences, they become depressed and self-esteem shatters (Peterson and Seligman, 1984; see Box 9.1).

Some research gives direct support to the reformulated theory. Seligman and his colleagues (1979) have devised the Attributional-Style Questionnaire (ASQ; Table 9.3) and, as predicted by the theory, found that

TABLE 9.2 Attributional Schema of Depression: Why I Failed My GRE Math Exam

	Internal (Personal)		**External (Universal)**	
Degree	Stable	Unstable	Stable	Unstable
Global	I lack intelligence.	I am exhausted.	These tests are all unfair.	It's an unlucky day, Friday the thirteenth.
Specific	I lack mathematical ability.	I am fed up with math.	The math tests are unfair.	My math test was numbered "13."

BOX 9.1

DEPRESSION IN WOMEN: A CONSEQUENCE OF LEARNED HELPLESSNESS?

Depression appears to occur more often in women than in men. Why? A large-scale survey carried out by the National Institute of Mental Health Center for Epidemiologic Studies (Radloff, 1975) suggests some reasons.

More than 2500 men and women of all ages and from a broad range of educational and socioeconomic backgrounds were interviewed in two American cities. Among the questions asked were twenty that comprised a self-report measure of depression, such as how often had the person slept restlessly during the previous week, and how often had he or she felt sad.

Several of the numerous findings are important for our present purposes.

1. Consistent with work done previously, married men were found to be significantly less depressed than married women.

2. Contrary to earlier thinking (for example, Gove and Tudor, 1973; Bernard, 1973), however, it is concluded that the role of housewife per se does not account for the higher levels of depression in married women, for working wives were also more depressed than married men. Having a job outside the home, then, does not appear to insulate married women from depression. Indeed, working wives were no less depressed than those who did not have outside employment.

3. Contrary to the findings of previous studies, the working wives were not more depressed than working men because they felt overworked by having two jobs, one as homemaker and one outside the house. Although the working wives did more housework than working husbands, this was not associated with their higher levels of depression.

Radloff speculates that the higher levels of depression among women are best explained as a consequence of learned helplessness. The feminist literature would agree (for example, Bernard, 1973; Chesler, 1972), for it blames the greater incidence of mental problems among women on their lack of personal and political power. Feminists take the position that more women than men become depressed because their social roles do not encourage them to feel competent. What women do does not seem to count compared to the greater power that men have in society. In fact, it may be that little girls are *trained* to be helpless (Broverman, Broverman, and Clarkson, 1970). And the more helpless woman, unable to tolerate the single life (Bernard, 1973), is probably more likely to marry.

These are interesting hypotheses, even plausible ones. But we need to know, for example, whether a woman's depression is preceded by a series of events that force her to recognize a feeling of helplessness already instilled in her. This and other questions have to be dealt with before lending too much credence to a helplessness explanation of depression in women. Learned helplessness may, however, prove a fruitful framework within which to conduct research on the depression of women.

depressed college students did indeed more often attribute failure to personal, global, persistent inadequacies than did nondepressed students.

Metalsky and his colleagues (1982) have linked attributional style to depressed mood. A study was conducted with college students taking a course in abnormal psychology. Early in the semester the students completed the ASQ, an adjective checklist assessment of current mood, and a questionnaire concerning their grade aspirations. Eleven days later they again completed the adjective checklist assessing mood. Finally, five days later, after the midterm exam grade was returned, the students reported on their mood for a third time.

According to the reformulated helplessness theory, a tendency to attribute negative events to personal, global, and persistent inadequacies, as determined by the ASQ, should predict a more depressed mood in

TABLE 9.3 Instructions and Sample Item from the Attributional-Style Questionnaire
(from Seligman et al., 1979)

Please try to vividly imagine yourself in the situations that follow. If such a situation happened to you, what would you feel would have caused it? While events may have many causes, we want you to pick only one—the *major* cause if this event happened to *you*. Please write this cause in the blank provided after each event. Next we want you to answer some questions about the *cause* and a final question about the *situation*. To summarize, we want you to:

1. Read each situation and vividly imagine it happening to you.
2. Decide what you feel would be the *major* cause of the situation if it happened to you.
3. Write one cause in the blank provided.
4. Answer three questions about the *cause*.
5. Answer one question about the *situation*.
6. Go on to the next situation.

YOU HAVE BEEN LOOKING FOR A JOB UNSUCCESSFULLY FOR SOME TIME.

1. Write down *one* major cause _____.

2. Is the cause of your unsuccessful job search due to something about you or something about other people or circumstances? (Circle one number)

Totally due to other people or circumstances						Totally due to me
1	2	3	4	5	6	7

3. In the future when looking for a job, will this cause again be present? (Circle one number)

Will never again be present						Will always be present
1	2	3	4	5	6	7

4. Is the cause something that just influences looking for a job, or does it also influence other areas of your life? (Circle one number)

Influences just this particular situation						Influences all situations in my life
1	2	3	4	5	6	7

5. How important would this situation be if it happened to you? (Circle one number)

Not at all important						Extremely important
1	2	3	4	5	6	7

those students who received a poor grade. Students were divided into two groups, one consisting of those receiving good grades, another of those receiving poor grades. "Good" and "poor" depended on how their actual grades compared to their aspirations. A poor grade was defined as one equal to or less than the grade the student had earlier indicated he or she would be *un*happy with. A good grade was one equal to or greater than that the student had said he or she would be pleased with. For each group correlations were then computed between measures from the ASQ and change in depressed mood from before to after the midterm exam. Consistent with the theory, correlations within the good-grade group were not significant, for an increase in depressed mood requires *both* a particular attributional style *and* a negative event. For the poor-grade group two of three measures—internality and stability of faults—from the ASQ did predict an increase in depression. Students who were prone to attribute negative events to personal and persistent inadequacies became more depressed after a negative event, a poor grade, as predicted by the theory.

Over the past several years the original learned-helplessness theory and its attributional reformulation have clearly been at the forefront of psychological research on depression. In fact, in 1978 an entire issue of a major professional publication, the *Journal of Abnormal Psychology*, was devoted to theoretical and experimental studies on depression and learned helplessness. Although the theory is promising, some problems do need to be addressed in future work.

1. **Which type of depression is being modeled?** In his original paper Seligman attempted to document the similarity between learned helplessness and "reactive depression," depression indicated in DSM-II to be brought on by stressful life events. But Depue and Monroe (1978) have demonstrated that learned helplessness resembles the symptoms of a bipolar patient in a depressive episode more than it does those of any form of unipolar depression. Clearly, neither Seligman's dogs nor human beings in helplessness studies have exhibited both mania and depression. Seligman's (1978) solution to this problem is to bypass the traditional classification schemes and regard learned helplessness as a model for "helplessness depression." In so doing, he proposes a new diagnosis based on presumed etiology. Only future research will tell whether his solution is more than a circular statement.

2. **Can college student populations provide good analogues?** Although some research on learned helplessness has been done with clinical populations (for example, Abramson et al., 1978), many studies have examined college students who are selected on the basis of scores on the Beck Depression Inventory. This inventory was not, however, designed to *diagnose* depression, only to allow an assessment of severity in a clinically diagnosed group. Indeed, accumulating evidence indicates that selecting subjects solely on the basis of elevated BDI scores does not yield a group of people who can serve as a good analogue for those with clinical depression. Hammen (1980), for example, found that high scorers, with a mean of 18.37, were, when retested two to three weeks later, down to an average of only 10.87. This transient nature of a high BDI score is particularly important because it is common research practice to test potential subjects with the BDI and then have them participate in a research study several weeks or even months later. Hammen's results, then, caution us that some subjects designated as depressed on the BDI might not in fact be depressed by the time the actual study takes place.

3. **Are the findings specific to depression?** This issue is raised by the results of a learned-helplessness study that Lavelle, Metalsky, and Coyne (1979) conducted with subjects classified as having high or low test anxiety. The subjects with high test anxiety performed a task poorly after going through a laboratory situation inducing helplessness. Thus the learned-helplessness phenomenon may not be specific to depression. Similarly, highly anxious persons blame their failures on themselves, just as depressives do (Doris and Sarason, 1955).

4. **Are attributions relevant?** At issue here is the underlying assumption that people actively attempt to explain their own behavior to themselves and that the attributions they make have subsequent effects on behavior. Some research indicates that making attributions is not a universal process. For example, Hanusa and Schulz (1977) allowed subjects in a helplessness experiment to make open-ended attributions about their successes or failures. Subjects did not spontaneously report them, and even after probing, the attributions given did not fall into specific categories. Furthermore, relating attributions to behavior has been difficult. Indeed, in a series of experiments Nisbett and Wilson (1977) showed that people are frequently unaware of the causes of their behavior.[2]

Even if we allow that attributions are relevant and powerful determinants of behavior, we should note that many findings supporting the learned-helplessness theory have been gathered by giving individuals the ASQ or by determining how they attribute laboratory-induced successes or failures. When depressives were asked about the five most stressful events of their lives, however, their attributions did not differ from those given by normal subjects (Hammen and Cochran, 1981; see Box 9.2).

---

[2]The attribution literature makes the basic assumption that people *care* what the causes of their behavior are. This central idea is the brainchild of psychologists whose business it is to explain behavior. It may be that psychologists have projected their own need to explain behavior onto other people! Laypeople may simply not reflect on why they act and feel as they do to the same extent that psychologists do.

BOX 9.2

LIFE STRESS AND DEPRESSION

In Chapter 8 we described research on the relationship between life stress and the occurrence of various physical illnesses. A great deal of similar research has been done showing that life stress is also linked to the onset of depression. Many of these studies have used the same general methodologies that we described earlier: a group of depressed people and a control group are given a life events checklist and asked to indicate those that they had experienced in the past six months or year. The data consistently show that depressives report more stressful events (Paykel, 1979), although it remains possible that their recall is biased by their current psychological state. More recently, investigators studying life events and depression, like their counterparts studying life events and illness, have turned their attention to possible moderators of the stress-depression relation. Billings, Cronkite, and Moos (1983), for example, found that depressives have fewer social resources available to them and are less likely to try to solve the problems they face.

In an attempt to study similar issues and at the same time to improve the quality of data, Brown and Harris (1978) began a large-scale study of depressed women in London. Instead of using a life events checklist, they constructed a detailed interview and carefully trained interviewers to question subjects about any recent adversities that had distressed them. The truthfulness of the women's reports was checked by interviewing relatives. Furthermore, trained members of the research staff rated the stressfulness of the events, rather than letting the respondents estimate it. Using these methods, Brown and Harris found that 61 percent of depressive women but only 25 percent of the control subjects had experienced a severely disturbing life event in the nine months prior to the interview. The majority of these misfortunes were long-term and wrenching, such as separation from a key person, for example, her husband, a life-threatening illness of someone close, a major disappointment, or loss of her job. Social supports were also found to be crucial. When the women were divided into those who had an intimate friend in whom they confided and those who did not, the effects of stress were quite different. Only 10 percent of the women with an intimate relationship who experienced a misfortune became ill; the corresponding figure for the women without a confidant was 37 percent! Thus stress has a much greater impact on women with few social supports.

5. **Some research has provided clear refutations of some aspects of the theory.** In a series of studies, Alloy and Abramson (1979) examined one of its central points, that depressed people perceive themselves as having little control over their lives. Subjects were placed in various experimental situations manipulated by the experimenter to give set percentages of contingency between their responses and an outcome. After subjects had experienced some actual percentage or level of control, they were asked how much control they *believed* that they had had. Contrary to the theory, depressed students did not underestimate their degree of control. Using a classic experimental situation to induce helplessness in subjects, Ford and Neale (1985) found that they did not underestimate their control on the subsequent task.

One key assumption of the revised learned-helplessness theory is that the depressive attributional style is a persistent part of the makeup of depressed people. Using a battery of measures, including the ASQ, Hamilton and Abramson (1983) tested carefully diagnosed depressives on two occasions, first while they were in the midst of an episode of depression, and sec-

Having a close friend to confide in makes it less likely that a person will become depressed after experiencing some major life stress.

ond just before they were discharged from the hospital. Results from the first assessment revealed the expected depressive pattern on the ASQ. But the information gathered just before the patients were discharged indicated that the pattern was no longer present.

Depression Through Reduction in Reinforcement: A Learning Theory

One current learning conceptualization of depression bears some resemblance to Freud's theory, although, of course, the metaphors differ. Freud proposed as a causative factor the loss of a loved one by people whose oral dependencies retained from childhood make them particularly vulnerable to a lessening of external supports. It seems but a short step to connect depression to the reduction in activity that occurs when accustomed reinforcement is withdrawn. When a loved one dies, an important source of positive reinforcement is certainly lost.

For some learning theorists, the concept of *reduction in reinforcement and activity* is central (Eastman, 1976); unconscious mourning processes and introjection of the lost loved one play no part in their explanation of depression. Once people stop behaving as they used to do before the loss, when reinforcement was plentiful (Ferster, 1965; Lazarus, 1968b), the new lower level of activity and social participation may itself be reinforced (Ullmann and Krasner, 1975). For example, depressed people may receive sympathy or special dispensations from others, who expect less of them than they did before the loss of the loved one. The outlook for improvement is all the more bleak for those who lack social skills for acquiring in new or different ways the rewards that used to be available. In fact, this learning theory explains more directly than did Freud the depression that is not preceded by the loss of a loved one; accustomed reinforcements may be cut off for a number of reasons, for example, changes in occupational status or of locale.

The learning conceptualization attributing depression to a reduction in activity when reinforcement is lacking has been elaborated on and researched by Lewinsohn and his colleagues (for example, Lewinsohn, 1974). Figure 9.2 is a schematic representation of Lewinsohn's model of depression. The following assumptions are made.

1. The feeling of depression and other symptoms of the clinical syndrome, such as fatigue, are elicited when behavior receives little reinforcement.

2. This "thin" schedule of positive reinforcement, in turn, tends to reduce activity even more, and then reinforcements are even fewer.

3. The amount of positive reinforcement likely to be available is a function of three sets of variables: (*a*) the individual's personal characteristics, such as age, sex, and attractiveness to others; (*b*) the environment that the person is in, such as being at home rather than in prison; and (*c*) the person's repertoire of behavior that can gain reinforcement, for example, vocational and social skills.

FIGURE 9.2 Lewinsohn's model of depression, which takes into account the inactivity and dejection of the depressive. After Lewinsohn, 1974.

As Figure 9.2 indicates, a low rate of positive reinforcement reduces still further the activities and expression of qualities that might be rewarded. Both social participation and rewards decrease in a vicious cycle.

Research evaluating Lewinsohn's theory has generally assessed the relation between self-reports of mood and the number of pleasant events subjects indicate they have participated in. The items that people check off each day on the Pleasant Events Schedule (MacPhillamy and Lewinsohn, 1973), a list of 320 events generally regarded as pleasurable—such as talking about sports, playing in a musical group—assess the frequency of reinforcement. These studies show that the more depressed people are, the fewer pleasant events they report taking part in (Lewinsohn and Libet, 1972); the data indicate as well that depressed people declare having fewer pleasant experiences than do nondepressed people (MacPhillamy and Lewinsohn, 1974).

This information, however, constitutes only weak support for the theory. First, there is the problem of ascertaining the direction of these correlational relationships. Depressed mood could precede rather than follow a reduction in the number of pleasant experiences: a depressed person might report few pleasant events because his gloomy mood alters the way he feels about participating in them. Second, pleasant events are not necessarily reinforcers. A reinforcer is defined as having the capacity to make behavior more frequent. Some pleasant events will have this reinforcing property for particular individuals, but it cannot be assumed that each event on the Pleasant Events Schedule is each time a reinforcer. Finally, the accuracy of the self-reports being collected can be questioned. There is reason to doubt the reliability of depressed people's recollections of pleasant occasions (Nelson and Craighead, 1977).

The depressed person often surmises that others reject him or her, a suspicion which may well have some basis in fact. Coyne (1976), for example, found that a twenty-minute telephone conversation with a depressive made the mood of the callers more negative. Similarly, Gotlib and Robinson (1982) analyzed videotaped one-to-one interactions between students who were not depressed and either a mildly depressed student or another nondepressed student. Students interacting with a depressed student were less verbal and less supportive and smiled less. Clearly, the disheartening effects of a depressed person on others could play a role in *maintaining* the disorder. Indeed, clinicians working with depressed patients sometimes "catch" their mood. This clinical phenomenon may be useful for it can help clinicians recognize how depressed the patient is. But it may

also interfere with good therapeutic efforts; clinicians lose some effectiveness if they cannot ward off the somber mood that the morose, hopeless client instills.

PSYCHOLOGICAL THEORIES OF BIPOLAR DISORDER

Bipolar disorder has been neglected by both psychological theorists and researchers, probably because only between 5 to 10 percent of depressions are found in people who also have bouts of mania. In general, theories of the depressive phase of bipolar disorder are similar to theories of unipolar depression. The manic phase of the disorder is seen as a defense against a debilitating psychological state. The specific negative state that is being avoided varies from theory to theory. One of our own cases illustrates why many theorists have concluded that the manic state serves a defensive function.

> A forty-two-year-old male was currently in his third manic episode. During each he had had the classic pattern of manic symptoms, and much of his manic behavior centered around a grandiose delusion that he was the world's greatest businessman. "Did you know that I've already bought twenty companies today?" he stated at the beginning of a therapy session. "Not even Getty or Rockefeller have anything on me." From sessions between episodes, it was apparent that success in business was indeed a central concern to the patient. But he was far from successful. His parents had loaned him money to start several companies, but each had gone bankrupt. He was obsessed with matching the business successes of his wealthy father, but as the years passed his opportunities to do so were slipping away. It seemed, therefore, that his manic grandiosity was protecting him from a confrontation with his lack of business success—a realization that would likely have plunged him into a deep depression.

Clinical experience with manics as well as studies of their personalities when they are in remission indicate that they appear well adjusted between episodes. But if mania is a defense, it must be a defense against something, although probably not a characteristic that would be readily self-reported. Winters and Neale (1985) have recently tested the notion that manics, even when between episodes, have little self-esteem, and they devised means other than a conventional paper-and-pencil test to reveal these feelings.

Manics, unipolar depressives, and normal subjects were given two tests, a self-esteem inventory and a pragmatic inference test. The second was meant to be a subtle measure of the manics' expected low self-esteem. In the pragmatic inference test subjects first read a paragraph describing a series of events. Some of these brief stories had a positive outcome, the others a negative one. Subjects were then given a test that appeared to measure their recall of each story. Some items actually assessed recall of facts, but others forced the subject to go beyond the information and draw an inference. For example, one story concerned a man who was currently out of work. The reason for his unemployment was not stated directly, but the story was constructed to allow either of two inferences to be drawn. The subject could infer that the man was unemployed through no fault of his own but because the economy was poor. Or the subject could infer that the man's poor work record kept him unemployed. People with little self-esteem were expected to make the second inference. The important aspect of the test is that subjects do not discern that they are being required to draw inferences. They see the test as a simple measure of memory.

The results agreed exactly with expectation. On the paper-and-pencil measure of self-esteem, both the manics and normal subjects scored higher than the depressives. But on the pragmatic inference test the manics performed like the depressives; both groups drew the second inferences and revealed their low self-esteem. Thus the self-esteem of manics may be very low. Generally, however, their feelings of inadequacy are successfully defended against.

PHYSIOLOGICAL THEORIES OF AFFECTIVE DISORDERS

Since physiological processes are known to have considerable effects on moods, it is not surprising that investigators have sought physiological causes for depression and mania. Moreover, disturbed physiological processes must of course be part of the causal chain if a predisposition for an affective disorder can be genetically transmitted. Evidence indicating that an affective disorder is, in part, inherited would, then, provide some support for the view that the disorder has a physiological basis.

The Genetic Data

Research on genetic factors in unipolar depression and bipolar disorder has used both the family and twin methods. Estimates of the frequency of affective disorders in first-degree relatives of bipolars range from about 10 to 20 percent (Slater, 1938; Perris, 1969; Brodie and Leff, 1971; Hays, 1976). These figures are higher than those for the general population. Notably, among the first-degree relatives of bipolar index cases, there are more cases of unipolar depression than bipolar disorder. For example, James and Chapman (1975), in a thorough study conducted in New Zealand, found the morbidity risk estimates for the first-degree relatives of bipolars to be 6.4 percent for bipolar disorder and 13.2 percent for unipolar depression. Allen (1976) has reviewed concordance data for bipolar disorder in twins. Overall, the concordance rate for bipolar disorder in identical twins was 72 percent, in fraternal twins only 14 percent. The evidence supports the notion that bipolar disorder may have a heritable component (see Box 9.3).

The information available on unipolar depression indicates that genetic factors, although important, do not figure to the same extent that they do in bipolar disorder. Perris (1969), for example, found that more of the first-degree relatives of unipolar index cases than those of control cases had also experienced a depressive episode. The relatives of unipolar cases were not at high risk for bipolar disorder. Weissman, Kidd, and Prusoff (1982) found more than twice as many cases of depression in the first-degree relatives, particularly the female relatives, of depressive index cases than in the first-degree relatives of normal subjects. Rates of depression in the first-degree relatives were sometimes fivefold higher when the depression of the index cases was severe. Studies of unipolar depression in twins usually report MZ concordances of about 40 percent and DZ concordances of about 11 percent (Allen, 1976).

Earlier we mentioned the great heterogeneity of unipolar depressions. Some of the genetic data collected over the past decade bear on this issue. Winokur (1979) has noted differences in the disorders found in the first-degree relatives of unipolars. Both male and female first-degree relatives of men whose depression occurs for the first time rather late in life, after age forty, are at about equal risk for depression. But for male and female first-degree relatives of women whose first episode of depression begins earlier, the pattern is different. The female relatives are at greater risk for depression than male relatives, who are at greater risk for alcoholism and sociopathy. Although these data are not yet fully understood, they do suggest that the diagnosis unipolar depression may actually cover several disorders with different etiologies.

Taken together, the family and twin studies suggest that both *bipolar disorder* and *unipolar depression have*

BOX 9.3

A THEORY OF THE GENETIC TRANSMISSION OF BIPOLAR DISORDER

Throughout this book we have often been faced with theories couched in sufficiently vague terms to be untestable. A notable exception is the proposal of Winokur and his colleagues at the University of Iowa, that bipolar disorder is caused by a dominant gene on the X chromosome, one of two which together determine the sex of the fetus. The theory is easily tested. According to Mendelian genetics, the forty-six chromosomes in the body cells of human beings, and the genes they carry, act together in pairs. A dominant gene is one that will find expression, regardless of the other gene it is paired with. Women have a pair of similar sex chromosomes, XX, men a dissimilar pair, XY. The fetus gets one of its pair from the ovum of the mother and one from the spermatozoan of the father; each of these sex cells contains only twenty-three chromosomes, for the pairs have earlier divided. The mother, then, always contributes an X chromosome. If the father also contributes an X chromosome, the child will be female. If the father contributes a Y chromosome, the child will be male.

Winokur's theorizing grew out of an early study of the family histories of patients with affective disorders (Winokur and Clayton, 1967). The patients were separated into two groups, those whose families had incidences of affective disorders and those whose families did not. In the first group 96 percent of 112 probands were bipolars. In the second only 3 percent of 129 probands were bipolars. The relatives of bipolar probands were obviously at high risk. To investigate bipolar patients further, Winokur, Clayton, and Reich (1969) collected a new sample of 89 index cases. The data from this investigation are shown in Table 9.4. The A part of the table indicates that female relatives were at much higher risk than males, which would bear out the prediction that bipolar disorder is controlled by a dominant gene on the X chromosome. Part B of the table shows no instances of father-son pairs of bipolars. Again, this is precisely what Winokur's theory predicts. The reasoning is as follows. The gene causing bipolar disorder in the father is on his X chromosome. Since the father gives only his Y chromosome to a male child, his son cannot be affected.

Winokur's data supported his theory, but before long disconfirmations appeared. Goetzl and his colleagues (1974), Hays (1976), and James and Chapman (1975) have all reported father-son pairs of bipolars. Therefore Winokur's theory cannot account completely for the genetics of bipolar disorder. It may be, however, that bipolar disorder is etiologically heterogeneous, in which case Winokur's theory might apply to a subset of bipolar patients.

TABLE 9.4 A Study of the First-Degree Relatives of Bipolar Probands *(from Winokur, Clayton, and Reich, 1969)*

A.	Morbidity Risk of Relative of a Proband	
	Relationship to proband	*Risk, percent*
	mother	55
	father	17
	sister	52
	brother	29
B.	**Relationship of Depressive Pairs**	**Number of Pairs**
	father—son	0
	father—daughter	13
	mother—son	17
	mother—daughter	17

heritable components. And this conclusion is further supported by studies that have used the adoption method. Mendlewicz and Rainer (1977) found more affective disorders in the biological parents than in the adoptive parents of bipolar adoptees. Similarly, Cadoret (1978a) found more affective disorders in adopted children whose biological parents had an affective disorder.

Biochemistry and Affective Disorders

Two major theories have been proposed relating depression to *neurotransmitters* (see Box 9.4). One theory suggests that depression results from low levels of *norepinephrine*; the other points to low levels of *serotonin*. The norepinephrine theory also postulates that an excess of this neurotransmitter causes mania (Schildkraut, 1965).

The actions of drugs provided the clues on which both theories are based. In the 1950s two particular groups of drugs, the *tricyclics* and the *monoamine oxidase inhibitors* (see page 557), were found to be effective in relieving depression. Studies revealed that they also

BOX 9.4

COMMUNICATION IN THE NERVOUS SYSTEM

The nervous system is composed of billions of neurons. Although differing in some respects, each neuron has four major parts (Figure 9.3): (1) the cell body; (2) several dendrites, its short and thick extensions; (3) one or more axons, but usually only one, long and thin, extending a considerable distance from the cell body; and (4) terminal buttons on the many end branches of the axon. When a neuron is appropriately stimulated at its cell body or through its dendrites, a nerve impulse, which is a change in the electric potential of the cell, travels down the axon to the terminal endings. Between the terminal endings of an axon and other neurons there is a small gap, the synapse (Figure 9.4). For a nerve impulse to pass from one neuron to another, it must have a way of bridging the synaptic space.

The terminal buttons of each axon contain synaptic vesicles, small structures which are filled with chemicals called neurotransmitters. A neuron synthesizes and stores only one principal neurotransmitter. Neuropeptides, which serve as auxiliary neurotransmitters, may be stored by themselves in a neuron, with another neuropeptide, or with a principal neurotransmitter, whose action it supports or modifies. The nerve impulse causes the synaptic vesicles to release their transmitter substances, which flood the synapse and can then stimulate an adjacent neuron. The molecules of a transmitter fit into receptor sites in the postsynaptic neuron and thereby transmit the impulse.

Several principal transmitters have been identified; those belonging to two major compound groups, the catecholamines and the indoleamines, have been implicated in mood and emotion and therefore in psychopathology. Substances in both groups are monoamines, which means that their molecules contain a single amino group (NH_2). The catecholamines, each with a catechol portion ($C_6H_6O_2$), are norepinephrine, epinephrine, and dopamine. The two indoleamines, each with an indole portion (C_8H_7N), are serotonin and tryptamine. Serotonin and tryptamine are found in greater quantities in other bodily tissues than in the central nervous system. Serotonin, for example, occurs in large amounts in cells of the mucous membranes of the intestines. Its release from these cells helps to regulate peristal-

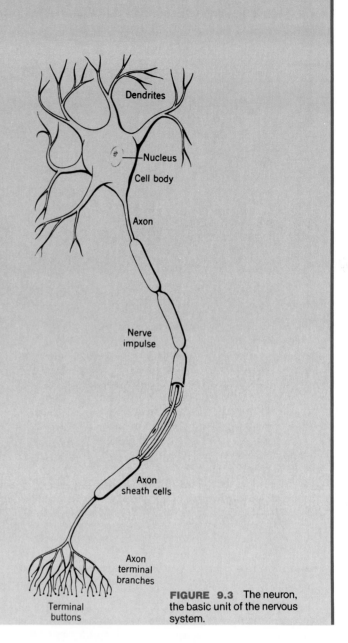

FIGURE 9.3 The neuron, the basic unit of the nervous system.

increase the levels of both serotonin and norepinephrine in the brains of animals. This information only suggested that depression is caused by low levels of these substances, but it encouraged further explorations. Another piece of evidence favoring both theories was provided by reserpine, a drug sometimes used in the treatment of hypertension. Early in the same decade reserpine had been isolated by a research team working in Switzerland. It is an alkaloid of the root of *Rauwolfia serpentina*, a shrub which grows in India. Hindu physicians have for centuries administered powdered rauwolfia as a treatment for mental illness. Reserpine became one of the compounds to initiate the modern era of psychopharmacology and to revolutionize the care and treatment of mental patients. This drug and chlorpromazine (see page 555) were given to schizophrenics to sis. Norepinephrine is a neurotransmitter of the peripheral sympathetic nervous system. Of these monoamines, norepinephrine, epinephrine, dopamine, and serotonin appear for certain to be neurotransmitters of the central nervous system. At least some of the particular pathways in the brain served by these transmitters have been identified.

To understand the theory and research relating neurotransmitters to psychopathology, we need to know how these substances are synthesized within the neuron from the amino acids tryosine and tryptophan. Table 9.5 presents this information. Finally, we need to consider the mechanisms by which the neurotransmitters are inactivated following their release. The catecholamines norepinephrine and dopamine are for the most part pumped back into the presynaptic neuron. The remainder of these substances is deactivated in the synapse by the enzyme catechol-O-methyltransferase (COMT). Catecholamines within the presynaptic neuron can be deactivated by the enzyme monoamine oxidase (MAO), which is present in the mitochondria, the powerhouses supplying the energy for the activities of all cells. Serotonin is also taken up again into the presynaptic neuron. It is deactivated within the presynaptic neuron and in the synapse by MAO.

FIGURE 9.4 A synapse showing the terminal buttons of two axon branches in close contact with a very small portion of the cell body of another neuron.

TABLE 9.5 Biosynthesis of the Catecholamines and Indoleamines

Catecholamines	Indoleamines
Tyrosine	Tryptophan
↓ tyrosine hydroxylase*	↓ tryptophan hydroxylase →→ tryptophan decarboxylase → Tryptamine
Dopa	5-Hydroxytryptophan
↓ dopa decarboxylase	↓ dopa decarboxylase
Dopamine	Serotonin
↓ dopamine-β-hydroxylase	
Norepinephrine	
↓ norepinephrine-N-methyltransferase	
Epinephrine	

*The substances on the arrows are the enzymes that catalyze the reactions.

calm their agitation. Reserpine did indeed relax and sedate them but was soon contraindicated, for a serious side effect in about 15 percent of the patients taking it was depression (for example, Lemieux, Davignon, and Genest, 1965). Reserpine was discovered to reduce levels of both serotonin and norepinephrine and of all the brain amines. It impairs the process by which these substances are stored within the synaptic vesicles and allows them instead to become degraded by monoamine oxidase.

So far we have examined *indirect* evidence for each theory. It would be ideal if the levels of norepinephrine, serotonin, or both could be measured within the brains of depressed people. This is not possible with existing technology, so we must take another tack. Two approaches have been used. The first measures metabolites of these neurotransmitters, the by-products of the breakdown of serotonin and norepinephrine, as they are found in urine, blood serum, and the cerebrospinal fluid. The problem with such measurements is that they are not direct reflections of *brain* levels of either serotonin or norepinephrine, since serotonin is involved in other bodily processes and norepinephrine acts in the peripheral nervous system.

A second strategy would be to choose drugs other than the antidepressants and reserpine that are known either to increase or to decrease the brain levels of serotonin and norepinephrine. A drug raising the level of a neurotransmitter should alleviate depression; one reducing it should deepen depression or induce it in normal subjects. This strategy also has its problems, however. Most drugs have multiple effects, making it difficult to choose one that accomplishes a specific purpose without complicating side effects.

These problems notwithstanding, what can be said of the validity of these theories that blame low levels of norepinephrine or serotonin for depression and high levels of norepinephrine for mania? First, a series of studies conducted by Bunney and Murphy and their colleagues at the National Institute of Mental Health monitored closely urinary levels of norepinephrine itself in a group of bipolar patients as they cycled through stages of depression, mania, and normalcy. Urinary levels of norepinephrine decreased as patients became depressed (Bunney et al., 1970) and increased during mania (Bunney, Goodwin, and Murphy, 1972). It has become clear, however, that the theory that a lack of norepinephrine causes depression applies to only a subset of depressed patients. Several lines of evidence support this conclusion. 3-Methoxy-4-hydroxyphenyl glycol (MHPG) is considered to be norepinephrine's principal metabolite. According to the theory, low levels of norepinephrine should be reflected by low levels of urinary MHPG. Although depressed bipolars have generally been shown to have low levels of urinary MHPG, the amount of MHPG in the urine of unipolars is more variable (for example, Muscettola et al., 1984).

Researchers have also linked urinary MHPG levels to the way unipolar patients respond to different tricyclic antidepressants. It is now known that some tricyclics, for example imipramine, block reuptake of norepinephrine, whereas others, such as amitryptyline, have this effect on serotonin. Therefore unipolar patients with low levels of MHPG, and, presumably, low levels of norepinephrine, should respond best to a tricyclic like imipramine. Research has generally supported this prediction (for example, Schatzberg et al., 1983), al-

though the relation between low levels of MHPG and good response to imipramine does not appear strong enough to be used in making clinical decisions about treatment (Muscettola et al., 1984).

Studies of serotonin rely on 5-hydroxyindoleacetic acid (5-HIAA), a major metabolite of serotonin which is present in cerebrospinal fluid. It can be measured to determine the level of the transmitter in the brain and spinal cord. A fairly consistent body of data indicates that 5-HIAA levels are low in the cerebrospinal fluid of depressives (Ashcroft, Crawford, and Eccleston, 1966; Mendels et al., 1972; Van Praag, Korf, and Schut, 1973). Studies also show that ingestion of L-tryptophan, which acts as a serotonin precursor, relieves depression, especially when used in combination with other drugs (Coppen et al., 1972; Mendels et al., 1975). Furthermore, p-cholorophenylalanine (PCPA), which suppresses serotonin synthesis by blocking tryptophan hydroxylase, reduces the therapeutic effect of drugs that usually lessen depression (Shopsin, Friedman, and Gershon, 1976).

We have already indicated that effective antidepressants increase levels of norepinephrine and serotonin and that knowledge of this formed a keystone of the norepinephrine and serotonin theories of depression. It now appears that the therapeutic effects of tricyclics and MAO inhibitors do *not* depend on an increase in the levels of neurotransmitters. The earlier findings were not incorrect; tricyclics and MAO inhibitors do indeed increase levels of norepinephrine and serotonin *when they are first taken*. But after several days the levels of neurotransmitters return to what they had been earlier. This information is crucial because it does *not* fit with our knowledge of the time that must pass before antidepressants become effective. Both tricyclics and MAO inhibitors take from seven to fourteen days to relieve depression! Thus a simple increase in norepinephrine or serotonin is not a plausible mechanism (Heninger, Charney, and Menkes, 1983).

What is the impact of these new findings on the old theories? Researchers are now examining whether tricyclics and MAO inhibitors may act against depression by making postsynaptic receptors more sensitive. Preliminary evidence indicates that these antidepressants do increase the sensitivity of both norepinephrine and serotonin receptors, and that the time when this happens fits with the known course of the therapeutic effects of these drugs (Heninger, Charney, and Menkes, 1983; Charney, Heninger, and Sternberg, 1984). Thus patients, even though their levels of norepinephrine or serotonin are low once again, are apparently able to put the neurotransmitters to good use because the receptors receiving them have become more sensitive. This attention to receptors means that new methodologies must be developed to study receptor sensitivity in human beings. Most of our current knowledge of the functioning of receptors comes from animal studies. As yet, the methods used in human studies are of course indirect. The next few years of research will undoubtedly see further refinements so that receptor functions can be more thoroughly explored.

These biochemical data lend some support to theories that affective disorders have physiological causes. Does this mean that psychological theories are irrelevant or useless? Not in the least. To assert that behavioral disorders have a basis in somatic processes is to state the obvious. No psychogenic theorist would deny that behavior is mediated by some kinds of bodily changes. The question rather is how psychological and physiological factors interact. We have already grappled with this philosophical issue in Chapter 8. It may well be, for example, that depletion of norepinephrine does cause certain kinds of depression, but that an earlier link in the causal chain is "the sense of helplessness" or "paralysis of will" that psychological theorists have proposed as the disabler.

THERAPY FOR AFFECTIVE DISORDERS

Most episodes of depression lift after a few months, although the time may seem immeasurably longer to the depressed individual. That most depressions are self-limiting is fortunate. But this circumstance has not allowed mental health workers to forsake the depressed person. Depression is too widespread and too incapacitating, not only to the person[3] but to those around him or her, not to treat the disorder. Current therapies are both psychological and somatic. Singly or in combination, they turn out to be quite effective.

Psychological Therapies

Because depression is considered derived from anger unconsciously turned inward, psychoanalytic treatment tries to help the patient achieve insight into the repressed conflict and often encourages outward release of the hostility supposedly working inward. In the most gen-

eral terms, the goal of analytic therapy is to uncover latent motivations for the patient's depression. A man may, for example, blame himself for the death of a loved one, as did the engineer described earlier, but repress this belief because of the pain it causes. The patient must first be guided to confront the fact that he holds this belief, after which the therapist can help him realize that his guilt is unfounded. The recovery of memories of stressful circumstances of the patient's childhood, when feelings of inadequacy and loss may have developed, should also bring relief.

Research on the effectiveness of dynamic psychotherapy in alleviating depression is sparse. The few investigations carried out have not found such treatment making a significant impact on the problem (Hollon and Beck, 1979). For example, psychoanalytic therapy combined with tricyclic drugs, which have proved useful, does not lift mood any more than do the drugs by themselves (Daneman, 1961; Covi et al., 1974).

In keeping with their cognitive theory of depression, that the profound sadness and shattered self-esteem of depressed individuals are caused by errors in their thinking, Aaron Beck and his associates have worked for several years to devise a cognitive therapy aimed at altering aberrant thought patterns. The therapist tries to persuade the depressed person to change his or her opinions of events and of the self. When a client states that she is worthless because "Nothing goes right. Everything I try to do ends in a disaster," the therapist offers examples contrary to this overgeneralization, such as competences that the client is either overlooking or discounting. The therapist also instructs the patient to monitor her "private monologues" with herself and to identify all patterns of thought that contribute to depression. She is then taught to think through her negative prevailing beliefs, to understand how they prevent her from making more realistic and positive assumptions and from more accurately interpreting adversity.

Although developed independently of Ellis's rational-emotive method, Beck's analyses are similar to it in some ways. For example, he suggests that depressed people are likely to consider themselves totally inept and incompetent if they make a mistake. This can be considered an extension of one of Ellis's irrational beliefs, that the individual must be competent in all things in order to be a worthwhile person.

Beck also includes more strictly behavioral components in his treatment of depression. Especially when patients are severely depressed, Beck encourages them to *do* things, such as getting out of bed in the morning, and discourages them from doing other things, such as

---

[3]Depression can be more than a serious inconvenience. It can be life-threatening, for the risk of suicide is especially great in depressed individuals. The last section of this chapter is devoted to suicide.

BOX 9.5

AN EXISTENTIAL THEORY OF DEPRESSION AND ITS TREATMENT

In 1959 a remarkable book, *From Death Camp to Existentialism*, was published by Viktor Frankl, an Austrian psychiatrist who during World War II had spent three horrible years in Nazi concentration camps. His wife, brother, and parents, imprisoned with him, all lost their lives. Revised since its initial appearance and retitled *Man's Search for Meaning* (1963), Frankl's book vividly describes the humiliation, suffering, and terror experienced by camp prisoners. Frankl goes on to tell how he and others managed to survive psychologically in the brutalizing conditions of the death camps.

Frankl concluded that he was sustained emotionally by having succeeded somehow in finding meaning in his suffering and relating it to his spiritual life. The spirit gives the individual freedom to transcend circumstances, and freedom makes him responsible for his life. Maddi's concept of existential neurosis would suggest (see page 49) that each human being has the responsibility to find purpose and meaning in life, even when the external world provides little evidence of them. Frankl believes that psychopathology, particularly depression, ensues when a person has no purpose in living. He developed out of his concentration camp experiences a psychotherapeutic approach called *logotherapy*, after the Greek word *logos*, translatable as meaning.

The task of logotherapy is to restore meaning to the client's life. This is accomplished first by accepting in an empathic way the subjective experience of the client's suffering, rather than conveying the message that suffering is sick and wrong and should therefore not be regarded as normal. The logotherapist then helps the client make some sense out of his or her suffering by placing it within a larger context, a philosophy of life in which the individual assumes responsibility for his or her existence and for pursuing the values inherent in life. Nietzsche has said, "He who has a why to live for can bear with almost any how."

It may be useful to relate Frankl's views on depression and its treatment to learned helplessness. Certainly the con-centration camp induced helplessness and hopelessness, an utter disbelief that an individual could exert any control over his or her life. Profound depression was commonplace. Logotherapy might be an effective way to reverse the helplessness depressed people experience in contemporary society, under less horrific and brutal conditions. By accepting responsibility for their lives and by seeking some meaning even in trying circumstances, they may achieve a sense of control and competence indispensable to forging an acceptable existence.

Viktor Frankl's best-known technique is called paradoxical intention. Patients are told to indulge their symptoms intentionally. If a depressed man has been unable to leave his bed until noon, he should stay there until evening. Exaggeration can bring this symptom under conscious control.

attempting suicide. Beck gives his patients activity assignments that will provide them with successful experiences and allow them to think well of themselves. But the overall emphasis is on cognitive restructuring, on persuading the person to think differently. If a change in overt behavior will help in achieving that goal, fine. Behavioral change by itself, however, without altering the errors in logic that Beck asserts depressed people commit, cannot be expected to alleviate depression in any significant way.

A widely cited comparative therapy study by Rush and his colleagues (1977), discussed in Chapter 19 (page 515), has indicated that Beck's cognitive therapy is more successful in alleviating depression than the common regimen of administering an antidepressant drug, the tricyclic imipramine (Tofranil). This superiority, maintained at a six-month follow-up and also at twelve months (Kovacs et al., 1981), has encouraged many other researchers to adopt the therapy and to develop it further. Previous research had shown imipramine to be

Assertiveness training can be used in treating depression. In this workshop, sponsored by the National Organization for Women, participants are engaging in an exercise in which they say positive things about themselves to the person next to them.

superior to insight-oriented psychotherapy in treating depression, which renders all the more impressive the finding that Beck's cognitive therapy was better than a standard course of pharmacotherapy.[4]

Sometimes a person has reason to be depressed. A woman who is disheartened because of the way that she is treated by men might be better advised by a feminist therapist, who will encourage her to resist continued subjugation by an overbearing spouse or boss, than by an equally well-intentioned cognitive therapist, who might try to teach her that the treatment she receives from husband or supervisor is not all that bad. As with forms of therapy for a wide range of human problems, the therapist must confront the moral and political implications of his or her work. Should I help the client alter her life situation, or should I help her adjust? Indeed, the very fact that the woman is depressed may indicate that she is ready for a change in her social and personal relations with others. The depression, then, may be a healthy sign, one which should be heeded as a signal that all is not well in her life.

[4]Beck's therapy for depression is examined in greater depth on page 514.

Although Seligman's learned-helplessness theory is a widely held conception of depression, as yet no specific program of therapy based on this view has been developed. Seligman did undertake to cure his helpless dogs, but it proved difficult. Removing the partition in the shuttle box did not encourage the animals to move, nor did supplying food on the side with the safe floor. When the buzzer or light came on, signaling that a painful shock was forthcoming, they still cowered in the corner on the unsafe side and then passively absorbed shock. Finally, the dogs were leashed and dragged to the other side when the buzzer or light came on. Some dogs started moving on their own after twenty-five draggings, others only after two hundred. They had to be forced to experience success in avoiding shock before they were able to move on their own. The growing research literature on learned helplessness has sensitized therapists in a general way to the need that many depressed people have to achieve a sense of competence and of control over events in their lives, and indeed to the need that all human beings have to believe that they command their own destinies (see Box 9.5).

Because Lewinsohn considers depression to be brought on by the reduction of activity and social participation when important sources of reinforcement are withdrawn, therapy based on his view focuses on behavioral deficits. Depressed people are asked to engage in more activities, such as shopping, participating in hobbies, and talking to other people. They are also trained to behave in ways that are likely to be regarded more positively by others. Assertion training, role playing, and modeling are all important methods of helping them develop the necessary social skills. In contrast to Beck's therapy, what people are thinking as they make changes in their overt behavior is not explicitly considered.

A study by Shaw (1977) compared four groups of depressed people. One group received training in social skills, based on Lewinsohn's theory; the second, Beck's cognitive-restructuring therapy. Members of the third, called an attention-placebo group, had nondirective discussions with a therapist about their feelings and the possible reasons for them. This group was included in order to evaluate what gains depressed people might make through the *placebo effect* (see page 474), through hoping and expecting to be helped by an interested and sympathetic professional. The fourth group was not treated. After sixteen hours of therapy, members of the cognitive-treatment group were less depressed than all the others, and those in the social-skills group were no better off than the attention-placebo subjects. Methodological problems have been mentioned for this study (Wilson and O'Leary, 1980), but nonetheless it did indicate that training people in social skills is not an especially effective treatment for lifting depression.

Somatic Therapies

There are a variety of somatic therapies for depression and mania. Perhaps the most dramatic, and controversial, treatment for depression is *electroconvulsive therapy* (ECT). Carried out usually in a hospital, ECT is the deliberate induction of a seizure and momentary unconsciousness by passing a current of between 70 and 130 volts through the patient's brain. Electrodes were formerly placed on each side of the forehead, but now the standard procedure is to put one on the temple of the nondominant cerebral hemisphere. In the past the patient was usually awake until the current triggered the seizure, and the electric shock often created frightening contortions of the body, sometimes even causing bone fractures. Now the patient is given a short-acting anesthetic, then an injection of a strong muscle relaxant before the current is applied. The convulsive spasms of the body muscles are barely perceptible to onlookers, and

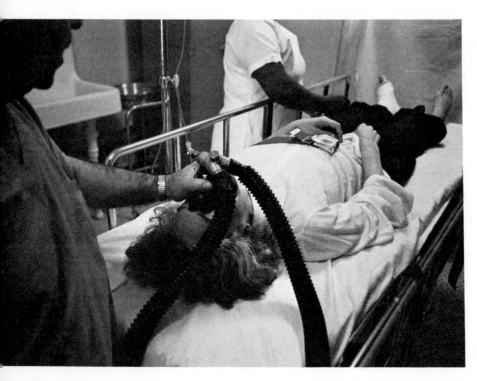

This woman has just undergone shock treatment. Oxygen is being administered because the muscle relaxant given earlier interferes with breathing.

the patient awakens a few minutes later, remembering nothing about the treatment.

Inducing a seizure still remains a drastic procedure, however. Why should anyone in his right but depressed mind agree to undergo such radical therapy, or how could a parent or a spouse consent to such treatment if the patient is judged legally incapable of giving consent? The answer is simple: ECT may be the optimal treatment for severe depression (Klerman, 1972). Most professionals, though, acknowledge the risks involved—memory loss which can be prolonged, although unilateral ECT to the nondominant hemisphere now erases fewer memories than did bilateral ECT; confusion; perhaps even some brain damage when shocks are administered repeatedly. Clinicians resort to ECT only after less drastic treatments have been tried and found wanting. In considering *any* treatment that has negative side effects, the person making the decision must be aware of the consequences of not providing any treatment at all. Given that suicide is a real possibility among depressed people, and given a moral stance that values the preservation of life, the use of ECT, at least after other treatments have failed, is regarded by many as defensible and responsible.

A variety of *antidepressant drugs* are available. Even if a chemical agent manages to alleviate a bout of depression only temporarily, that benefit in itself should not be underestimated, given the suicide potential in depression and given the extreme anguish and suffering borne by the individual, and usually by the family as well. Moreover, the judicious use of a drug may make unnecessary an avenue of intervention and control that many regard as very much a last resort, namely being placed in a psychiatric hospital.

The two major categories of antidepressant drugs are the tricyclics, such as imipramine (Tofranil) and amitriptyline (Elavil), and the monoamine oxidase (MAO) inhibitors, such as Parnate. Since the MAO inhibitors have by far the more serious side effects, the tricyclics are more widely used. These medications, discussed more fully in Chapter 20 (page 558), have been established as effective in a number of double-blind studies (Morris and Beck, 1974). Patients and their families must be forewarned, however, that one to several weeks may elapse before any therapeutic effect is observed. This delay can make for a difficult waiting period and points up once again the need to intervene psychologically as well as somatically. Practitioners do not rely exclusively on drugs like Tofranil for another reason. Once the patient has withdrawn from the drug, relapse is more often the rule than the exception (Klerman, 1975).

"Symptomatic relief" is, as already stated, of no small importance in problems like depression, but the patient should be able to stop taking the drug during periods when symptoms have lessened. The simple truth is that, at least so far, no chemical has been found that can "cure" depression.

People with the mood swings of bipolar disorder are often helped by carefully monitored dosages of *lithium*, an element, taken in a salt form, *lithium carbonate*. The fact that lithium carbonate cannot be patented like other drugs discouraged pharmaceutical companies for years from marketing it; only minimal profits are to be made. Lithium is now taken regularly and prophylactically, that is every day in the absence of problems in order to prevent radical shifts in mood (Davis, 1976). One of the consequences of the medication, however, is that it prevents bipolars from feeling extremely good on occasion (Honigfeld and Howard, 1978), and it is not always easy for them to forgo occasional euphoria. Because of possibly serious, even fatal side effects, lithium has to be prescribed and used very carefully.

SUICIDE

In classical Rome, in the period just preceding the Christian era, the quality of life was viewed as far more important than how long one lived. "Living is not good, but living well. The wise man, therefore, lives as well as he should, not as long as he can. . . . He will always think of life in terms of quality not quantity" wrote the first-century Roman Stoic philosopher Seneca (as cited in Shneidman, 1973, p. 384). Then in its first centuries, Christianity was a persecuted religion; many early Christians committed suicide in acts of martyrdom (Heyd and Block, 1981). Western thought changed radically in the fourth century, when St. Augustine proclaimed suicide a crime because it violated the Sixth Commandment, Thou shalt not kill. St. Thomas Aquinas elaborated on this view in the thirteenth century, declaring suicide to be a mortal sin because it usurped God's power over life and death. So, although neither the Old Testament nor the New explicitly forbids suicide, the Western world came to regard it as a crime and a sin (Shneidman, 1973). The irony is that the Christian injunctions against suicide, deriving from a profound respect for life, contributed to persecution of those who attempted to take their own lives. Indeed, as late as 1823 anyone in London who took his own life was buried with a stake pounded through his heart, and not until

1961 did suicide cease to be a criminal offense in England.

Suicide is discussed in the present chapter because many depressives have suicidal thoughts and sometimes make genuine attempts to take their own lives; moreover, it is generally believed that more than half of those who try to kill themselves are depressed and despondent at the time of the act. A significant number of people who are not depressed, however, make suicidal attempts and commit the act. An adequate understanding of suicide cannot come by concentrating only on the tendency of many depressed people to think about suicide.

Facts about Suicide

No single theory is likely to take into account all the available information about suicide. The diversity of

Suicide is a leading cause of death among college students. This peer support center at the University of Massachusetts offers a hot line so that students contemplating suicide have someone to contact and talk with.

known facts may help us appreciate how complex and multifaceted self-intentioned death is (Resnik, 1968; Gibbs, 1968; Douglas, 1967; Holinger, 1979; Shneidman, 1973; Seiden, 1974).

1. Every thirty minutes someone in the United States kills himself, and this rate—over 25,000 a year—is probably a gross underestimate.

2. As many as 200,000 in this country attempt suicide each year. There is one suicide for every eight attempts.

3. About half of those who commit suicide have made at least one previous attempt.

4. Three times as many men kill themselves as women, although the ratio may be approaching twice as many men as women, for women are becoming a higher-risk group.

5. Three times as many women as men attempt to kill themselves but do not die.

6. Divorced men are three times more likely to kill themselves than married men.

7. Suicide is found in both the very old and the very young—even in those older than ninety years and younger than ten years.

8. Suicide is found at all social and economic levels but is especially frequent among psychiatrists, physicians, lawyers, and psychologists.

9. No other kind of death leaves in friends and relatives such long-lasting feelings of distress, shame, guilt, puzzlement, and general disturbance. Indeed, these survivors are themselves victims, having an especially high mortality rate in the year following the suicide of their loved one.

10. Guns are the most common means of suicide in the United States. Men usually choose to shoot or hang themselves. Women are more likely to use sleeping pills. Elsewhere in the world methods vary by country. For example, coal gas is often chosen in England; gas and hanging are common means in Austria, pills and poisons in the Scandinavian countries.

11. Suicide ranks tenth as a leading cause of death among adults and second, after accidents, among college students.

12. Most of the people who kill themselves in the United States are native-born Caucasian males between forty-five and sixty years of age.

BOX 9.6

SOME MYTHS ABOUT SUICIDE

There are many prevalent misconceptions about suicide (Pokorny, 1968; Shneidman, 1973).

1. *People who discuss suicide will not commit the act.* The fact is that up to three-quarters of those who take their lives have communicated the intent beforehand, perhaps as a cry for help, perhaps to taunt. On the other hand, the vast majority of people who contemplate suicide do not actually attempt to kill themselves.

2. *Suicide is committed without warning.* The falseness of this belief is readily indicated by the preceding statement. The person usually gives many warnings, such as saying that the world would be better off without him, or making unexpected and inexplicable gifts to others, often of his most valued possessions.

3. *Only people of a certain class commit suicide.* Suicide is actually neither the curse of the poor nor the disease of the rich. People in all classes commit suicide.

4. *Membership in a particular religious group is a good predictor that a person will not consider suicide.* It is mistakenly thought that the strong Catholic prohibition against suicide makes the risk that Catholics will take their lives much lower. This is not supported by the evidence, perhaps because an individual's formal religious identification is not always an accurate index of true beliefs.

5. *The motives for suicide are easily established.* The truth is that we do not fully understand why people commit suicide. For example, the fact that a severe reverse in finances precedes a suicide does not mean that the reversal adequately explains the suicide.

6. *All who commit suicide are depressed.* This fallacy may account for the tragic fact that signs of impending suicide are overlooked because the person does not act despondently. Many of the people who take their lives are *not* de-

pressed. In fact, some people appear calm and at peace with themselves after having decided to kill themselves.

7. *A person with a terminal physical illness is unlikely to commit suicide.* A person's awareness of impending death does not preclude suicide. Perhaps the wish to end their own suffering or that of their loved ones impels many to choose the time of their death.

8. *To commit suicide is insane.* Although most suicidal persons are very unhappy, most do appear to be completely rational and in touch with reality.

9. *A tendency to commit suicide is inherited.* Since suicides often run in families, the assumption is made that the tendency to think in terms of self-annihilation is inherited. There is no evidence for this.

10. *Suicide is influenced by seasons, latitude, weather fronts, barometric pressure, humidity, precipitation, cloudiness, wind speed, temperature, and days of the week.* There are no good data to substantiate any of these myths.

11. *Suicide is influenced by cosmic factors such as sunspots and phases of the moon.* No evidence confirms this.

12. *Improvement in emotional state means lessened risk of suicide.* The fact is that people often commit the act after their spirits begin to rise and their energy level improves; this appears to be especially true of depressed patients.

13. *Suicide is a lonely event.* Although the debate whether to commit suicide is waged within the individual's head, deep immersion in a frustrating, hurtful relationship with another person—a spouse, a child, a lover, a colleague—may be a principal cause.

14. *Suicidal people clearly want to die.* Most people who commit suicide appear to be ambivalent about their own deaths (Kovacs and Beck, 1977).

---

13. It is estimated that each year upwards of 10,000 American college men and women attempt to kill themselves.

14. The rates for suicide among whites and native American youths are more than twice those for blacks. Indeed, between 1970 and 1980 the rates for young white men increased by 50 percent for ages fifteen to twenty-four, by nearly 30 percent for ages twenty-five to thirty-four.

15. The rates of suicide for adolescents and children in the United States are increasing. As many as 1600

young people between the ages of fifteen and nineteen are believed to kill themselves each year, and attempts are made by children as young as six. But the rates are far below those of adults.

16. Hungary is the country with the highest rate of suicide in the world. Czechoslovakia, Finland, Sweden, and Austria also have high incidences.

17. Suicide rates go up during depression years, remain stable during years of prosperity, and decrease during war years.

Theories of Suicide

In imagining a suicide, we usually think of a person deliberately performing a dramatic act explicitly chosen to end life almost immediately—the woman on the ledge of the tall building, the man with the gun next to his temple, the child with the bottle of mother's sleeping pills. But suicidologists also regard people as being suicidal when they act in self-destructive ways that can cause serious injury or kill them only after a period of time, such as the diabetic who neglects his insulin and dietary regimen; the alcoholic who will not seek help, despite his awareness of the damage being done to his body; the poor swimmer who repeatedly ventures out into the surf, although lifeguards warn of strong riptides. Sometimes termed subintentioned death, these apparent suicides complicate still further the task of understanding suicide and gathering statistics on it (Shneidman, 1973).

Mintz (1968) has summarized the numerous motivations for suicide mentioned in the literature: aggression turned inward; retaliation by inducing guilt in others; efforts to force love from others; efforts to make amends for ''perceived'' past wrongs; efforts to rid oneself of unacceptable feelings, such as sexual attraction to members of one's own sex; the desire for reincarnation; the desire to rejoin a dead loved one; and the desire or need to escape from stress, deformity, pain, or emotional vacuum. Two traditional theoretical positions, the psychoanalytic and Émile Durkheim's (1858–1917) sociological theory, have influenced suicidologists.

Psychoanalytic Theories of Suicide

Freud proposed two major hypotheses to account for suicide. One is an extension of his theory of depression and basically views suicide as murder. When a person loses someone whom he or she has ambivalently loved and hated, and introjects that person, aggression is directed inward. If these feelings are strong enough, the person will commit suicide. The second theory postulates that the death instinct, Thanatos, can turn inward and make the person take his or her life.

Freud's views on suicide are subject to many of the problems raised earlier in this text about psychoanalytic theorizing. Moreover, a careful analysis of suicide notes by Tuckman, Kleiner, and Lavell (1959) provides information that is in marked disagreement with the psychoanalytic position. They found that only a minority of the notes expressed hostility. In fact, about half expressed gratitude and affection for others. A possible rebuttal—which we find unsatisfactory—might be that a suicide note, written at the conscious level, could not be expected to reflect repressed hostility.

The Buddhist flag covers the body of a young girl who set herself on fire. Self-immolation is a form of altruistic suicide.

Durkheim's Sociological Theory of Suicide

Durkheim (1897), after analyzing the records of suicide for various countries and during different historical periods, viewed self-annihilation as a sociological phenomenon and distinguished three different kinds. *Egoistic suicide* is committed when a person has too few ties to the society and community. These people feel alienated from others, cut off from the social supports that are important to keep them functioning adaptively as social beings. *Altruistic suicides*, in contrast, are viewed by Durkheim as responses to societal demands. Some people who commit suicide feel very much a part of a group and sacrifice themselves for what they take to be the good of society. The self-immolations of Buddhist monks and nuns to protest the fighting during the Vietnam War would fit into this category. Some altruistic suicides, such as the hara-kiri of the Japanese, are literally required as the only honorable recourse in the circumstances. Finally, *anomic suicide* may be triggered by a sudden change in a person's relations to society. A successful businesswoman who suffers severe financial reverses may experience *anomie*, a sense of disorientation, because what she believed to be her normal way of living is no longer possible for her. Anomie can pervade a society in disequilibrium, making suicide more likely.

As with all sociological theorizing, Durkheim's hypotheses have trouble accounting for the different reactions of individuals in a given society to the same demands and conditions. Not all those who unexpectedly lose their money commit suicide. It appears that Durkheim was aware of this problem, for he suggested that individual temperament would interact with any of the social pressures that he found causative.

Perhaps at the most general level a person's suicide may be regarded as what he or she considered the best means for withdrawing from a particular and apparently unsolvable problem in living, from an unrelentingly painful emotional state described by Herman Melville in *Moby Dick* as "insufferable anguish." Even this suggestion, however, is inadequate, for it does not explain why person A chooses suicide whereas person B withdraws from stress by "going crazy." All explanations remain strictly *post hoc* until and unless a theory better predicts why individuals differ in their reactions to the same set of social conditions.

Prediction of Suicide from Psychological Tests

Psychologists have attempted to predict suicide on the basis of scores on psychological tests. It would of course

Jo Roman, in her early sixties and suffering from breast cancer that was not yet critical, methodically planned her death for fifteen months. She was determined to spare herself and her dear ones the pain and great emotional strain of a terminal illness. While she could still "function to my satisfaction," she bid her husband, daughter, and a close friend goodnight and farewell, swallowed thirty-five sleeping pills and a glass of champagne, and went quietly to bed.

be of immense theoretical and practical advantage to be able to predict from the results of tests who might consider the act. Theoretically, knowing what characteristics a potential suicide has would help us understand what makes people contemplate killing themselves. On practical, social-action grounds, being able to detect who is likely to make an attempt would obviously help those who wish to intervene and save lives.

Many investigators have studied the personality characteristics of those who have attempted suicide. An unavoidable difficulty with this kind of research stems from the fact that personality tests can seldom be given to numbers of people who may *later* kill themselves. Furthermore, in addition to this problem of obtaining data before a suicide attempt has been made, it is impossible to collect information, other than biographical accounts from relatives and a few other sources, after the deed has been done. Much of the literature, then, consists of reports of psychological tests given to people *after* they have made an aborted attempt at suicide. Clearly, the information obtained from such tests will reflect the fact that those tested have recently tried and failed to kill themselves. Their state of mind is likely to be quite different from what it had been before the attempt. For example, many who have tried unsuccessfully to take their lives feel extremely guilty and embarrassed. It is impossible to know with any exactness how test scores and interview behavior are affected by such postattempt factors.

Although these problems might have affected the results, several studies have found significant correlations between suicide intent and hopelessness. For example, Beck, Kovacs, and Weissman (1975) found that hopelessness, as measured by the Hopelessness Scale, was more highly correlated with suicide intent than was depression. The expectation that, at some point in the future, things may look no better than they do right now seems to be more instrumental than depression per se in propelling a person to take his or her life. Beck and his group have also developed the Suicidal Intent Scale (Beck, Schuyler, and Herman, 1974) and the Scale for Suicide Ideation (Beck, Kovacs, and Weissman, 1979), both of which show promise in helping us to understand and predict those at high risk for serious suicide attempts.

Another avenue of research has focused on the cognitive characteristics of people who attempt suicide. It has been suggested that suicidal individuals are more rigid in their approach to problems (for example, Neuringer, 1964), less flexible in their thinking (Levenson, 1972). Constricted thinking could account for their apparent inability to seek solutions to life problems other than taking their own lives. Others have suggested that such people may also be impulsive, the assumption being that they would not attempt to kill themselves were they to reflect carefully on their behavior. A study by Patsiokas, Clum, and Luscomb (1979) addressed some of these questions. They administered several tests to a group of psychiatric patients who had been admitted to a hospital for having attempted suicide, as well as to a control group made up of psychiatric patients with no history of having tried to take their own lives. Flexibility of thinking was measured by the Alternative Uses Test (Wilson et al., 1975), in which the person has to list as many different uses for a series of common objects as possible. Also given was the Matching Familiar Figures Test (Kagan, 1965). Each item of this test has at the top a picture of a familiar object. The person chooses the correct matching figure from six below, one of them

identical and the other five varying in a minute detail difficult to detect. The impulsive person supposedly responds too quickly and makes many errors, rather than taking the time to reflect and examine the figures closely.

In general, the results confirmed the hypothesis that people who attempt suicide are more rigid than control subjects, lending support to the clinical observation that they seem almost myopically incapable of thinking of alternative solutions to problems and might therefore tend to settle on suicide as the only way out. Little evidence linked impulsiveness to attempted suicide, however. The researchers speculate that the measure used may not be a valid index of impulsiveness as it relates to suicide. Another interpretation, more plausible to us, is that taking one's own life is not an impulsive act at all but is generally done after considerable reflection and doubt.

Suicide Prevention

Suicide prevention centers rely on demographic factors (Shneidman, Farberow, and Litman, 1970). Workers receiving phone calls from people in suicidal crises have before them a checklist to guide their questioning of each caller, for they must immediately assess how great the risk of suicide may be. For example, a caller would be regarded as a lethal risk if he is male, middle-aged, divorced, and living alone and has a history of previous suicide attempts. And usually the more detailed and concrete the suicide plan, the higher the risk. More details on suicide prevention centers are provided in Chapter 20 (page 545). Box 9.7 discusses some general clinical issues and gives guidelines for handling suicidal patients.

Another procedure is the *"psychological autopsy,"* pioneered at the Los Angeles Suicide Prevention Center (Shneidman, Faberow, and Litman, 1970). In effect, these workers analyze information obtained from crisis phone calls, from interviews with relatives and friends of those who are thinking about suicide or who are believed to have committed the act, and sometimes from notes left behind by those who have died. The purpose is to determine the actual mode of death and, if judged intentional, the reasons for it.

Of particular interest is a study (Shneidman and Farberow, 1970) of notes left by people who subsequently committed suicide. In the Los Angeles area, at the time this work was done, about 15 percent of suicides left notes, and the contents of these notes were analyzed by judges trained to rate them on the presence or absence of instructions and specific themes, such as self-blame, dis-

BOX 9.7

DEALING WITH SUICIDE

Although it is not true, as stated at the beginning of this section, that people are invariably depressed when they commit suicide or attempt to do so, suicide must always be considered a danger when working with those who are profoundly depressed. The despair and utter hopelessness of their existence may make them see suicide as the only solution, the only exit. In fact, sometimes the sole reason a depressed individual does *not* attempt suicide is that he or she cannot summon the energy to formulate and implement a suicide plan. In working with a seriously depressed individual, the clinician must be especially careful as the patient *emerges from* the low point of depression, for the sadness and hopelessness may still be strong enough to make self-annihilation appear the only option *and* now the person begins to have enough energy to do something about it. Because so many who commit suicide are depressed, treatment of this condition is at the same time an intervention that clinicians hope will reduce the risk of suicide.

Clinicians have to work out for themselves an ethic regarding a person's right to end his or her life. What steps is the professional willing to take to prevent a suicide? Confinement in a straitjacket on the back ward of a hospital? Or, as is more common in these modern times, sedation administered against the patient's wishes and strong enough that the person is virtually incapable of taking any action at all? And for how long will extraordinary measures be taken? The clinician realizes, of course, that many, perhaps even most, suicidal crises pass; the suicidal person is likely to be grateful afterward that he or she was prevented from destroying the self when it seemed the only course.* But to what extremes is the professional prepared to go in the interim in order to prevent a suicide attempt?

The therapist should not hesitate to inquire directly whether the client has thought of suicide. Experienced clinicians and suicidologists do not believe that the idea can be put into another person's head, that the risk of suicide can be increased merely by asking about it. On the contrary, opening up the topic for discussion can be the first step of a therapeutic intervention (Beck et al., 1979). It is important to adopt a phenomenological stance, to view the suicidal person's situation as he sees it, rather than convey in any way that he is a fool or is crazy to have settled on suicide as a solution to his woes. This Rogerian empathy for suicidal people is sometimes referred to as "tuning in" by those who work in suicide prevention centers. In addition, the clinician treating a suicidal person must be prepared to devote more energy and time than he or she usually does, even to psychotic patients. Late-night phone calls and visits to the patient's home may be frequent. Finally, the therapist should realize that he or she is likely to become a singularly important figure in the suicidal person's life—and be prepared both for the extreme dependency of the patient and for the hostility and resentment that sometimes greet efforts to help.

*Shneidman (1973) suggests that even at the peak of a suicidal crisis, the person may be intensely ambivalent. "It is possible—indeed probably prototypical—for a suicidal individual to cut his throat and to cry for help at the same time" (p. 384A).

comfort, death as relief, and the like. Having determined that such ratings could indeed be made reliably by independent judges, Shneidman and Farberow compared these actual suicide notes with simulated notes prepared for them by individuals who were *not* oriented toward killing themselves but who were matched to those who had on such demographic variables as age, sex, and social class. These control subjects had been instructed to write as *if* they were about to commit suicide. The genuine notes contained a greater number of instructions, such as suggestions about raising the children and explicit orders about how to dispose of the body; there was also evidence of significantly more anguish and hostility in the genuine notes.

As is the case in nearly all areas of abnormal psychology, not as much is known about suicide as we would like. In this instance the lack of information is all the more worrisome, since the very existence of many people is at stake. Fortunately, those who have devoted their professional lives to preventing suicide are not waiting for all the data to come in before attempting to intervene. The absence of a good theory does not preclude action. Working principles can be derived from available statistical studies, which already identify at least some of the individuals who are likely to make lethal attempts.

SUMMARY

DSM-III lists two principal affective disorders. In major or unipolar depression the person experiences profound sadness as well as a number of related problems, such as sleep and appetite disturbances, loss of energy and self-esteem. In bipolar disorder the person has episodes either of mania alone or of both mania and depression. With mania the person's mood is elevated or irritable, and he or she becomes extremely active, talkative, and distractible.

Psychological theories of depression have been couched in psychoanalytic, cognitive, and learning terms. Psychoanalytic formulations stress unconscious identification with a loved one whose desertion of the individual has made him or her turn anger inward. Beck's cognitive theory ascribes causal significance to negative and illogical self-judgment. According to Seligman's cognitive-learning appraisal, early experiences in inescapable, hurtful situations instill a sense of helplessness which can evolve into depression. These individuals are likely to attribute failures to their own general and persistent inadequacies and faults. Operant learning theorists trace depression to an unrewarding, inactive existence. These same theories are applied to the depressive phase of bipolar disorder. The manic phase is considered to be a defense against a debilitating psychological state. Physiological theories suggest an inherited predisposition for bipolar disorder in particular and relate the phenomena of depression and mania to abnormally depleted and copious amounts of the neurotransmitters that pass on neural impulses in particular nerve tracts of the brain.

There are a number of psychological and somatic therapies for affective disorders and especially for depression. Psychoanalytic treatment tries to give the patient insight into childhood loss and inadequacy and into later self-blame. The aim of the cognitive therapy of Beck is to uncover negative and illogical patterns of thinking and teach more realistic ways of viewing events, the self, and adversity. The learned-helplessness theory of depression, although not generating as yet a particular set of therapy procedures, does make therapists aware of the apparent need of people to believe that they exercise control over their lives. The existential logotherapy encourages depressed people to make spiritual sense of their suffering, to feel free and responsible for their lives, and to find meaning and purpose in existence. Finally, behavioral therapists encourage greater levels of activity in the belief that more frequent reinforcement will lighten the sad mood and encourage more social participation by depressed individuals.

A range of somatic treatments is also available; often used in conjunction with a psychological treatment, they can be very effective. Electroconvulsive shock and several antidepressant drugs have proved their worth in lifting depression. It has become possible for patients to avoid the excesses of manic and depressive periods through careful administration of lithium carbonate.

Finally, the topic of suicide was explored, although self-annihilative tendencies are not restricted to those who are depressed. A review of the facts and myths about suicide indicates that any single theory is unlikely to account for its great diversity, but that the information already gathered can be applied to prevent it.

Most large communities have suicide prevention centers, and most therapists at one time or another have to deal with patients in suicidal crisis. Clinical evidence suggests that suicidal persons need to have their fears and concerns understood but not judged, and that workers must gradually and patiently point out to them that alternatives to self-destruction are there to be explored.

PART THREE

Edvard Munch, *Ashes*, 1894

CHAPTER 10

James G. Davis, *The Fight*, 1984 Courtesy Yares Gallery, Scottsdale, Arizona

PERSONALITY DISORDERS AND SOCIOPATHY

Personality disorders, sometimes called "character disorders," are a group of diagnoses based on a trait approach to personality (see page 77). DSM-III puts it this way.

. . . When personality traits are inflexible and maladaptive and cause either significant impairment in social and occupational functioning or subjective distress . . . they constitute Personality Disorders. The manifestations of Personality Disorders are generally recognized by adolescence or earlier and continue throughout most of adult life, though they often become less obvious in middle or old age.

Many of the features characteristic of various Personality Disorders . . . may be seen during an episode of another mental disorder, such as Major Depression. The diagnosis . . . should be made only when the characteristic features are typical of the individual's long-term functioning and are not limited to discrete periods of illness (p. 305).

According to DSM-III, *personality disorders* are to be indicated on axis II, which means that their presence or absence is to be considered whenever a diagnosis is made. Personality disorders have been shown to possess little diagnostic reliability as they were defined in previous editions of the DSM (for example, Beck et al., 1962). Although DSM-III changed a number of the names given to specific personality disorders and attempted to improve the clarity of the definitions, in the field trials of DSM-III the reliability of diagnoses of personality disorders was lower than that of most other categories. And this rather low reliability figure was for personality disorders *as a class* rather than for the specific disorders. Even though personality disorders are diagnosed frequently—over 50 percent of the patients in field trials of DSM-III—the reliabilities of some of the individual personality disorders are totally inadequate. In addition, Frances (1980) has pointed out that the personality disorders represent the extremes of personality traits that are evident in many people. Thus they raise the problem of where to draw the line on a continuum; the lack of clear-cut guidelines on how to distinguish between normal and abnormal undoubtedly contributes to the low reliability. DSM-III, for example, states that the personality disorders are to be diagnosed when personality traits are "inflexible" or "maladaptive." But the terms "inflexible" and "maladaptive" are not defined, leaving the diagnoses open to the vagaries of individual clinician judgments.

Critics could also point to the problems of basing a diagnostic category on a trait conception of personality. As indicated in Chapter 4, saying that someone has a particular trait is not always a powerful predictor of behavior. Perhaps, though, personality disorders reflect the phenomenon discovered by Bem and Allen (1974): people who believe themselves to be consistent, and those with personality disorders may be among them, do indeed behave consistently enough in a wide range of situations to be described as having traits. A final problem is that there is simply very little information available on many of the personality disorders, not enough to indicate whether they are valid diagnoses.

(Drawing by Opie; © 1981, The New Yorker Magazine, Inc.)

SPECIFIC PERSONALITY DISORDERS

Personality disorders are grouped into three clusters in DSM-III. Individuals with the first three in the following list seem odd or eccentric, those with the next three dramatic, emotional, or erratic, and those with any of the last cluster of four disorders anxious or fearful.

Paranoid personality disorder The *paranoid personality* is suspicious of people. He or she expects to be mistreated by others and thus becomes secretive and is continually on the lookout for possible signs of trickery and abuse. Such individuals are extremely jealous and tend to blame others even when they themselves are at fault. Paranoid personalities are also overly sensitive, quick to take offense, argumentative, and tense. Their emotional responses are shallow, and they appear cold and humor- s to others.

Schizoid personality disorder The *schizoid personality* has difficulties in forming social relationships and usually has few close friends. He or she appears dull and aloof and without warm, tender feelings for other people. Indifferent to praise, criticism, and the sentiments of others, individuals with this disorder are "loners" and pursue solitary interests. They may daydream a great deal and sometimes seem "not with it," but they, unlike the schizophrenic, are basically in good contact with reality.

Schizotypal personality disorder The *schizotypal personality* usually has the interpersonal difficulties of the schizoid personality. But along with these are a number of other symptoms that are more eccentric, although they are not severe enough to warrant a diagnosis of schizophrenia (see Chapter 14). Schizotypal personalities may have *"magical thinking"*—superstitiousness, beliefs that they are clairvoyant and telepathic; and perceptual disturbances such as depersonalization, derealization, and recurrent *illusions*—they may sense the presence of a force or a person not actually there. Speech may also contain words used in unusual and unclear fashion. Under stress such persons can appear psychotic. Schizotypal personality disorder and schizophrenia are probably related to each other through genetic transmission of a predisposition. More first-degree relatives of schizophrenics are given the diagnosis than are relatives of individuals in control groups; the disorder may thus be a mild form of schizophrenia (Spitzer, Endicott, and Gibbon, 1979).

Borderline personality disorder The *borderline personality* reveals instability in relationships, mood, and self-image. For example, attitudes and feelings toward other people may vary considerably and inexplicably over short periods of time. Emotions are also erratic and can shift abruptly, particularly to anger. Borderline personalities are argumentative, irritable, and sarcastic. Their unpredictable and impulsive behavior, such as gambling, spending, sex, and eating sprees, is potentially self-damaging. These individuals have not developed a clear and coherent sense of self and remain uncertain about their values, loyalties, and choice of career. They cannot bear to be alone. So they tend to have a series of intense one-to-one relationships which are usually stormy, transient, and brief, for they also have little capacity to evaluate others and no real concern for them. Subject to chronic feelings of depression and emptiness, they may make manipulative attempts at suicide. Like the schizotypal personality, these persons can appear psychotic under emotional stress.[1]

Clinicians and researchers have used the term borderline personality for some time, but they have given it many meanings. Originally, the term implied that the patient was on the borderline between neurosis and schizophrenia; recent research, however, has not supported this view.

The current conceptualization of borderline personality derives from several sources. After reviewing the available literature and interview studies of borderline personalities, Gunderson, Kolb, and Austin (1981) devised an interview for collecting information necessary for the diagnosis. They also proposed a set of specific diagnostic criteria similar to those that ultimately appeared in DSM-III. The DSM-III criteria for borderline personality were established through a study done by Spitzer, Endicott, and Gibbon (1979). They began by examining research done in Denmark on whether heredity figures in schizophrenia. This genetic research had found more schizophrenia in the relatives of schizophrenics than in the general population and had also shown that these relatives had high rates of other disorders. These disorders were termed the schizophrenia spectrum or borderline schizophrenia. By carefully analyzing these cases, Spitzer and his colleagues determined that one particular clinical syndrome *did* appear to be related to schizophrenia through an inherited predisposition. This syndrome became DSM-III's schizotypal personality disorder. They also identified another syndrome not related to schizophrenia through a predisposition, and this became DSM-III's borderline personality disorder.

Much controversy still surrounds the diagnosis of borderline personality disorder. It has become apparent that borderline personalities make up a very heterogeneous group. For example, Pope and his co-workers (1983) found that about half of their sample of borderline personalities also had either major depression or bipolar disorder. These people responded well to the usual somatic treatments for these affective disorders. In addition, their first-degree relatives had a higher incidence of affective disorders than that of the general population. Pope and his colleagues found too that most of their borderline personalities could also be diagnosed as having another personality disorder—histrionic, narcissistic, or antisocial. Although Pope and his colleagues

---

[1]Patients with both borderline and schizotypal personality disorders would probably have been diagnosed as schizophrenic using DSM-II criteria. Designating the behavior of these people as the criteria for these two personality disorders is one way that DSM-III has narrowed the schizophrenia diagnosis (see Chapter 14).

have not yet replicated their study, the data do suggest a large overlap among the various personality disorders, an undesirable state of affairs given that these are viewed as distinct diagnoses.

This heterogeneity notwithstanding, what further can we say about borderline personality? It is an intriguing disorder which is both common and serious, hence the attention given it; it begins in adolescence; and it is more frequent in women than in men (McGlashan, 1983). Furthermore, the disorder runs in families, with high rates in first-degree relatives of index cases (Loranger, Oldham, and Tulis, 1983). Finally, the prognosis is not good; except for those who also have an affective disorder, response to treatment is poor (Pope et al., 1983). Clearly, much remains to be learned about this syndrome.

Histrionic personality disorder   The diagnosis *histrionic personality*, formerly called hysterical personality, is applied to people who are overly dramatic and always drawing attention to themselves. These individuals, emotionally expressive to an unusual degree, are also given to angry overreactions to minor annoyances and to quick boredom with normal routines. Interpersonal problems are frequent and include manipulativeness, seductiveness, dependence, and constant demands on others. The histrionic personality, found far more frequently in women than in men, is sometimes regarded as

"I used to think I was highly motivated. By the time I found out I was merely compulsive, I'd already made my pile."

(Drawing by Stevenson; © 1975, The New Yorker Magazine, Inc.)

superficially charming by other people, but also as vain, shallow, ungenuine and inconsiderate.

Narcissistic personality disorder   *Narcissistic personalities* have a grandiose view of their own uniqueness and abilities. They are preoccupied with fantasies of great successes and crave the admiration and attention of others. To say that they are self-centered is almost an understatement. Their interpersonal relationships are disturbed by their lack of empathy; by exploitiveness, taking advantage of others; and by feelings of entitlement, expecting others to do special, not-to-be-reciprocated favors for them.

The diagnosis of narcissistic personality disorder has its roots in modern psychoanalytic writings. Kernberg (1970) described the grandiosity and egocentric behavior of narcissists as a defense against the rage that they feel toward their parents, whom they perceive as cold and indifferent. Kohut (1966) has proposed that the narcissistic personality develops as a way of coping with perceived shortcomings in the self that rankle, because parents do not provide support and empathy. The child who receives such help learns to deal with his or her shortcomings more adaptively. Although these etiological speculations have not been empirically tested, the descriptions of narcissism by these psychoanalytic writers had a major impact on the DSM-III diagnosis (see Box 18.2, page 480).

Advoidant personality disorder   *Avoidant personalities* are keenly sensitive to the possibility of social rejection and humiliation and are therefore reluctant to enter into relationships, even though they yearn for closeness and for the affection and acceptance of others. They suffer from low self-esteem, being dismayed by their own personal shortcomings and devaluing all their achievements.

Dependent personality disorder   *Dependent personalities* lack self-confidence and self-reliance, passively allowing their spouses to assume responsibility for deciding where they should live, what jobs they should hold, with whom they should be friendly. They are unable to make demands on others, and they subordinate their own needs to ensure that they do not break up the protective relationships they have established. Submission is part of the traditional stereotype for feminine behavior; more women than men are diagnosed as having dependent personalities. Their belittlement of themselves brings to mind the colloquialism "inferiority complex."

Compulsive personality disorder   *Compulsive personalities* are perfectionists, preoccupied with details, rules, schedules, and the like. They are work- rather than pleasure-oriented and have inordinate difficulty making decisions and allocating time. Their interpersonal relationships are often poor because they demand that everything be done their way. They are generally serious and formal and are unlikely to express warmth and friendliness.[2] This dysfunctional attention to work and productivity is, not surprisingly, found more often in men than women.

Passive-aggressive personality disorder *Passive aggressive personalities* indirectly resist the demands of others, both in social situations and at work. The resistance, which is thought to be aggression in disguise, takes the form of thoroughgoing stubbornness and ineffectuality. They are habitually late for appointments, do not return phone calls, procrastinate, and "forget." This persistent behavior pattern usually provokes further problems, such as marital discord and not being offered promotions. The dawdling of passive-aggressive personalities can be considered a hostile way of controlling others without assuming responsibility for their own anger.

The personality disorders make up what many workers regard as an unreliable, cluttered grab bag of a category. Ironically, the descriptions of them may seem to fit some of the members of our own families and some of our acquaintances, not to mention ourselves! Each of us develops over the years some apparently persistent means of dealing with life's challenges, a certain "style" of relating to other people. One person is overly dependent, another challenging and aggressive; yet another is very shy and avoids social contact, and another is more concerned with appearances and bolstering his or her precious ego than with relating honestly and on a deep level with others. To be sure, DSM-III would not have these personalities diagnosed unless the patterns of behavior are long standing, pervasive, and dysfunctional, but the essential disturbances listed for the various personality disorders no doubt bring to mind the shortcomings of friends, colleagues—and oneself.

The reader may also have noticed that descriptions of some of the personality disorders are similar to those of diagnostic categories discussed elsewhere. Generally speaking, a person judged to have, for example, a para-

noid personality disorder is less disturbed than a person with paranoid schizophrenia or a paranoid disorder (see pages 344–345). People given one of these three diagnoses, however, all have in common a tendency to be overly suspicious, guarded, and thin-skinned. But it can be very difficult to distinguish personality disorders from others that bear a resemblance (Nathan et al., 1968), underlining once again their problematic status as a separate group of psychological disturbances.

Although data are few on the disorders just described, one personality disorder omitted from the foregoing list is more reliably diagnosed and has attracted the attention of workers for many years. *Antisocial personality disorder* is unfortunately a prevalent diagnosis. The rest of this chapter will be devoted to what is known about the disruptive and essentially self-destructive individuals whose deep-seated ethical and moral maladjustments frequently bring them into serious conflict with their associates and with society.

ANTISOCIAL PERSONALITY DISORDER (SOCIOPATHY)

In current usage the terms *sociopath* and *psychopath* appear interchangeably with antisocial personality. The concept has an interesting history. At the very beginning of the nineteenth century, Philippe Pinel conceived of *manie sans délire*. Pinel chose this term to indicate that the patient he described was violently insane (*manie*) but did not show other symptoms (*sans délire*) common among the insane. In 1835 James Prichard, an English psychiatrist, described the disorder "moral insanity" in an attempt to account for behavior so far outside the usual ethical and legal codes that it seemed a form of lunacy. The man whose nature prompted Pinel's term was an easily angered aristocrat who had whipped a horse, kicked a dog to death, and thrown a peasant woman into a well. Since the early concept was used to explain a wide range of strange behavior, it is not surprising that it came to function somewhat as a wastebasket diagnosis, encompassing those inclined not only to violence but to unconventional practices as well.

Three percent of adult American men and one percent of women are estimated to have antisocial personalities. Business executives, politicians, and physicians, plumbers, salespeople, carpenters, and bartenders—they are to be found in all walks of life. Prostitutes, pimps, confidence men, murderers, and drug dealers are by no means the only sociopaths.

[2]It may occur to the reader that these traits can be very adaptive in certain situations. It is a standing joke, for example, that success in graduate school goes to those who are compulsive. The issues are more serious, however, for they go to the heart not only of the appropriateness of considering such people to have a mental disorder, but also of the demands placed on people working for advanced degrees. Consider as well the kinds of people selected for graduate study, and the kinds of professionals these students are likely to become.

Before considering current views of antisocial personality, we shall examine excerpts from two case histories that illustrate the scope of sociopathic reactions. The first case illustrates many of the classic characteristics of the sociopath but is unusual in that the person described was neither a criminal nor in psychiatric treatment at the time that the data for the case study were collected. This is an important point, for the majority of sociopaths who are the subjects of research studies have broken the law and been caught for doing so. Only rarely do we have the opportunity to examine in detail the behavior of an individual who fits the diagnostic definition but yet has managed not to break the law. The second case history presents the more usual picture of the criminal sociopath.

The Case of Dan

This case history was compiled by a psychologist, Elton McNeil (1967), who happened to be a personal friend of Dan's.

Dan was a wealthy actor and disc jockey who lived in an expensive house in an exclusive suburb and generally played his role as a "personality" to the hilt. One evening, when he and McNeil were out for dinner, Dan made a great fuss over the condition of the *Shrimp de Johnge* that he had ordered. McNeil thought that the whole scene had been deliberately contrived by Dan for the effect it might produce, and he said to his companion,

"I have a sneaking suspicion this whole scene came about just because you weren't really hungry." Dan laughed loudly in agreement and said, "What the hell, they'll be on their toes next time." "Was that the only reason for this display?" . . . "No," he replied, "I wanted to show you how gutless the rest of the world is. If you shove a little they all jump. Next time I come in, they'll be all over me to make sure everything is exactly as I want it. That's the only way they can tell the difference between class and plain ordinary. When I travel I go first class."

"Yes, . . . but how do you feel about you as a person—as a fellow human being?"

"Who cares?" he laughed. "If they were on top they would do the same to me. The more you walk on them, the more they like it. It's like royalty in the old days. It makes them nervous if everyone is equal to everyone else. Watch. When we leave I'll put my arm around that waitress, ask her if she still loves me, pat her on the fanny, and she'll be ready to roll over any time I wiggle my little finger" (p. 85).

Another incident occurred when a friend of Dan's committed suicide. Most of the other friends whom Dan and McNeil had in common were concerned and called the psychologist to see whether he could provide any information about why the man had taken his life. Dan did not. Later, when McNeil mentioned the suicide to Dan, all he could say was "That's the way the ball bounces." In his public behavior, however, Dan's attitude toward the incident appeared quite different. He was the one who collected money and presented it personally to the new widow. In keeping with his character, however, Dan remarked that the widow had a sexy body that really interested him.

These two incidents convey the flavor of Dan's behavior. McNeil had witnessed a long succession of similar events, which led him to conclude that

[The incidents] painted a grisly picture of life-long abuse of people for Dan's amusement and profit. He was adept at office politics and told me casually of an unbelievable set of deceptive ways to deal with the opposition. Character assassination, rumor mongering, modest blackmail, seduction, and barefaced lying were the least of his talents. He was a jackal in the entertainment jungle, a jackal who feasted on the bodies of those he had slaughtered professionally (p. 91).

In his conversations with Dan, McNeil was also able to inquire into Dan's life history. One early and potentially important event was related by Dan.

I can remember the first time in my life when I began to suspect I was a little different from most people. When I was in high school my best friend got leukemia and died and I went to his funeral. Everybody else was crying and feeling sorry for themselves and as they were praying to get him into heaven I suddenly realized that I wasn't feeling anything at all. He was a nice guy but what the hell. That night I thought about it some more and found that I wouldn't miss my mother and father if they died and that I wasn't too nuts about my brothers and sisters for that matter. I figured there wasn't anybody I really cared for but, then, I didn't need any of them anyway so I rolled over and went to sleep (p. 87).

The moral depravity described long ago by Pinel and Prichard clearly marks Dan's behavior. A person may be otherwise quite rational and show no loss of contact with reality and yet behave in a habitually and exceedingly unethical manner. The final excerpt illustrates Dan's complete lack of feeling for others, a characteristic that will later be seen to have considerable relevance in explaining the behavior of the sociopath.

The Case of Jim

Jim, the fourth child in a family of five, grew up in the lower social class of a small Midwestern town. During his childhood the member of his family who made the greatest impression on him was his older brother, whom he described as follows.

He was always a bully, promiscuous, and adventurous. He was always involved with some local girl, before I was even old enough to realize what was going on. He started drinking early, and had several scrapes with the law. He had rough companions, whom I later inherited, who helped me on my way.

He married a tramp, ended up in a stolen car, and was given the choice of jail or the army, as this was the Korean war time. I cannot directly link him to my life of crime, although he introduced me to those who later helped me along. Also, he condoned some of my early petty thievery (Bintz and Wilson, as reprinted in Milton and Wahler, 1969, p. 92).

During early adolescence Jim engaged in many petty antisocial acts. For example, on one occasion he stole some change from his mother's pocketbook. His father reacted by whipping both brothers until Jim confessed. Once Jim had admitted taking the money, however, the punishment ended. This became standard practice for the family, with Jim being able to avoid punishment by confessing as soon as he was accused of misbehavior, regardless of whether or not he was guilty. Moreover, the petty thievery that Jim committed in the community was generally successful, and even when he was caught consequences were minimal.

Jim's first serious trouble with the law occurred when he was charged with raping a young woman whom he had picked up at the local skating rink. He was sentenced to five years at a reform school but received an immediate parole on the condition that his sentence would be activated if he violated it. After several parole violations such as petty theft, and being detained for speeding, he was sentenced to one year at the reform school. By the time he returned to his hometown a year later, he had become a young hoodlum. Jim himself stated that the principal consequence of the year in reform school had been the opportunity afforded him to fraternize with more experienced thieves. Shortly thereafter Jim and a friend committed their first major theft, stealing $1700 from a tavern safe. Then the same pair attempted to burglarize a lumberyard but were unable to open the safe. The next day they were

arrested, and the burglary tools were found in Jim's car. He served a ninety-day sentence for attempted burglary. Three months after being released, Jim was incarcerated again, this time for statutory rape. As soon as he was free again, he and a friend planned another robbery. They reasoned that a bootlegger would be a good target for a holdup for, being outside the law himself, he would be reluctant to report the incident to the police. They bungled the job badly, however, and both were sentenced to five-year terms. Jim served three of the five years and upon his release met the woman he was soon to marry. He described her as follows.

Diane was a tramp, I could tell from the start. She forced the introduction and the first date. I had sexual relations with her on the first date, she was my third sexual partner on that particular day. She was neat, but not really attractive. The next four and a half months we were intimate almost every night. She wanted to marry, I did not. I could not see myself married to this plain-looking tramp. In fact, toward the last, I was trying to think of a scheme to get rid of her . . . (p. 100).

During this period Jim held a job, but he soon began to sink deeper and deeper into debt. Eventually, an opportunity for another theft presented itself. Again the job was spectacularly unsuccessful and Jim was sentenced to ten years in the state penitentiary. While in the county jail, before the trial, he was visited often by Diane and finally married her just before going to prison. As a substitute for a wedding ring, Jim had the words "Love me, Diane" tattooed on his penis.

Cleckley's Concept of Sociopathy

Both of these case histories illustrate many of the symptoms of the sociopathic syndrome as it has been defined by Hervey Cleckley in his classic book of the subject, *The Mask of Sanity* (1976). On the basis of his vast clinical experience, he formulated a set of criteria by which to recognize the disorder. Cleckley's work continues to be accepted as providing the classic description of sociopathy.

1. Considerable superficial charm and average or above average intelligence.

2. Absence of delusions or other signs of irrational thinking.

3. Absence of anxiety or other "neurotic" symptoms; considerable poise, calmness, and verbal facility.

4. Unreliability, disregard for obligations; no sense of responsibility, in matters of little and great import.

5. Untruthfulness and insincerity.

6. Lack of remorse, no sense of shame.

7. Antisocial behavior which is inadequately motivated and poorly planned, seeming to stem from an inexplicable impulsiveness.

8. Poor judgment and failure to learn from experience.

9. Pathological egocentricity, total self-centeredness; incapacity for real love and attachment.

10. General poverty of deep and lasting emotions.

11. Lack of any true insight, inability to see oneself as others do.

12. Ingratitude for any special considerations, kindness, and trust.

13. Fantastic and objectionable behavior, after drinking and sometimes even when not drinking—vulgarity, rudeness, quick mood shifts, pranks.

14. No history of genuine suicide attempts.

15. An impersonal, trivial, and poorly integrated sex life.

16. Failure to have a life plan and to live in any ordered way, unless it be one promoting self-defeat.

Cleckley's indicators of sociopathy are somewhat different from DSM-III's criteria for the diagnosis of antisocial personality disorder. The DSM-III criteria refer to more specific aspects of behavior, such as inability to hold a job and be a responsible parent and failure to honor financial obligations. But DSM-III also omits some of the characteristics that Cleckley would regard as being of central importance, such as lack of shame and inability to learn from experience. Furthermore, although Cleckley says specifically that sociopaths have no anxiety or other "neurotic" symptoms, DSM-III states that they do complain of tension and personal distress. Information gathered by Hare (1980) highlights other characteristics of the antisocial personality. Hare has developed a checklist to aid in the diagnosis of sociopathy. Besides showing that the diagnosis can be made reliably using the instrument, Hare was able to determine the failings most indicative of the disorder. Lack of empathy and lack of concern for others, incapacities that are *not* listed specifically in DSM-III's criteria for

antisocial personality disorder, were the most important.

For the concept of sociopathy to be useful, it must be easily differentiated from criminal behavior. A definition that focuses on the reactions of the individual to his or her own antisocial behavior accomplishes this purpose. Thus Cleckley's criteria *no sense of responsibility* and *no sense of shame* are particularly important. The sociopath is viewed as not responding emotionally after committing an act that generally elicits shame and guilt in most people. Hare's (1980) research has also verified these two faults as indicative of sociopathy.

Lack of shame and guilt is presumably linked to the sociopath's inability to learn from experience, in particular to avoid punishment. The sociopath continues to engage in the same antisocial activities, even though they prove unsuccessful, and even though his or her intelligence is perhaps above average. Learning to avoid actions that continually fail may be mediated by emotional arousal; because sociopaths do not become emotionally aroused, they may be less likely to suffer from and to change their unproductive and antisocial ways.

Before examining the existing research on the sociopathic syndrome, we should emphasize again that most of it has been conducted on sociopaths who have already been convicted as criminals. Individuals such as Dan have rarely been studied in research settings. We must therefore keep in mind that the available literature may not allow us to generalize about the behavior of sociopaths who elude arrest and the subsequent label of criminal.[3]

THEORY AND RESEARCH ON THE ETIOLOGY OF SOCIOPATHY

The Role of the Family

Since much sociopathic behavior violates social norms, it is not surprising that many investigators have focused on the primary agent of socialization, the family, in their search for the explanation of such behavior. McCord and McCord (1964) concluded, on the basis of a classic

[3]Nor indeed are all criminals sociopaths. In fact, the majority of criminals cannot be described as sociopathic. We consider it important to draw a distinction between sociopathy and criminal behavior. *Criminality* refers to law breaking as defined by a given society at a given point in time. Crime in general is much too extensive a subject to be covered in a textbook on abnormal psychology. Whenever possible, we restrict our discussion to sociopathy, taking special note when investigators have studied criminality rather than sociopathy.

review of the literature, that lack of affection and severe parental rejection were the primary causes of sociopathic behavior. Several other studies have related sociopathic behavior to the parents' inconsistencies in disciplining their children and in teaching them their responsibilities to others (Bennet, 1960). Furthermore, the fathers of sociopaths are likely to be antisocial in their behavior.

But such data on early rearing must be interpreted with extreme caution. They were gathered by means of *retrospective reports*; we have already seen (see page 119*n*) that the information obtained in this way may be of little value. When people are asked to recollect the early events in the life of someone who is now known to be a sociopath, their knowledge of adult status may have some effect on what they remember or report about childhood events. Potentially deviant incidents are more likely to be recalled, whereas those that do not dovetail with the person's current behavior may be overlooked.

One way of avoiding the problems of retrospective data is to follow up in adulthood a large group of individuals who as children were seen at a child guidance clinic. In one such study very detailed records had been kept on the children, including the type of problem that had brought them to the clinic and considerable information relating to the family (Robins, 1966). Ninety percent of an initial sample of 584 cases were located thirty years after their referral to the clinic.[4] In addition to the clinic cases, 100 control subjects who had lived in the same geographic area served by the clinic but who had not been referred to it were also followed up in adulthood.

By interviewing the now-adult people chosen for both the experimental and control samples, the investigators were able to diagnose and describe any maladjustments of these individuals. Then adult problems were related back to the characteristics that these people had had as children to find out which of them predicted sociopathic behavior in adulthood. Robins summarized these as follows.

If one wishes to choose the most likely candidate for a later diagnosis of sociopathic personality from among children appearing in a child guidance clinic, the best choice appears to be a boy referred for theft or aggression who has shown a diversity of antisocial behavior in many episodes, at least one of which could be grounds

for Juvenile Court appearance, and whose antisocial behavior involves him with strangers and organizations as well as with teachers and parents . . . more than half of the boys appearing at the clinic [with these characteristics were later] diagnosed sociopathic personality. Such boys had a history of truancy, theft, staying out late, and refusing to obey parents. They lied gratuitously, and showed little guilt over their behavior. They were generally irresponsible about being where they were supposed to be or taking care of money (p. 157).

In addition to these characteristics, aspects of family life mentioned earlier were again found to be consequential. Both inconsistent discipline and no discipline at all predicted sociopathic behavior in adulthood, as did antisocial behavior of the father.

In sum, the research we have reviewed emphasizes the importance of child-rearing practices. The fathers of sociopaths appear to provide a model for antisocial behavior. We must caution, however, that poor training in socialization has been implicated in the etiology of a *number* of clinical syndromes, including delinquent, neurotic, and even psychotic behavior (Wiggins, 1968), and that many individuals who come from what appear to be similarly disturbed social backgrounds do *not* become sociopaths or develop any other behavior disorders. This point is important: adults may have no problems whatsoever in spite of the inconsistent and

Vandalism, truancy, and other antisocial activities in childhood are among the best predictors of adult sociopathy.

[4]It should be appreciated that being able to track down this large a percentage of individuals thirty years after their contact with the clinic is an incredible feat.

otherwise undesirable manner of their rearing. Thus, although family experience is probably significant in the development of sociopathic behavior, it can not be the whole story.

Genetic Correlates of Sociopathic Behavior

Twin and Adoptee Studies

Most of the studies concerned with the possible genetic basis for socipathic behavior have focused on criminality or antisocial behavior rather than on sociopathy per se. The data collected are therefore difficult to interpret since, as already emphasized, not all sociopaths are criminals nor are all criminals sociopaths. Lange's research (1929) comparing concordance rates for criminality in identical and fraternal twins showed them to be a great deal higher for identical twins, supporting the theory that genetic factors may be involved. Kranz (1936), in a study that used better sampling procedures, found the following patterns of concordance: identical twins, 66 percent; fraternal twins of the same sex, 54 percent; fraternal twins of the opposite sex, 14 percent. Although at first glance these data also seem to support the notion that genetic factors are important, they in fact give only slight support to this hypothesis. The critical piece of information is the marked *difference* in concordance rates of fraternal twins of the same sex and those of fraternal twins of the opposite sex. Both of these pairs of twins are equally alike genetically, but we can expect the parental rearing practices to which they are exposed to be markedly different. Fraternal twins of the same sex are probably treated more alike than are fraternal twins of the opposite sex. This evidence, in point of fact, implicates environmental factors.

But more recent adoptee studies suggest that heredity may indeed play a role in both criminality and sociopathy. With the help of the extensive social records kept in Denmark, Hutchings and Mednick (1974) and Mednick, Gabrielli, and Hutchings (1984) examined rates of criminality in the adoptive and biological relatives of adoptees who had acquired criminal records. Schulsinger (1972) performed a similar study with sociopathy as the misconduct of interest. Both studies of criminality found it at a higher rate in the biological relatives of criminals than in the adoptive relatives. Schulsinger found more sociopathy in the biological relatives of sociopaths. Studies done in the United States of adopted children whose biological parents were antisocial personalities also point to a genetic predisposition (Crowe, 1974; Cadoret, 1978b).

More complicated studies have examined both the criminality and the alcoholism of adoptees (Bohman et al., 1982; Cloninger et al., 1982). A large sample of adopted individuals were classified according to whether they had criminal records, a history of alcoholism, both, or neither. Criminals who were also alcoholic repeatedly committed violent offenses; risk for criminality in these individuals was linked to their own alcoholism but not to any criminal behavior of their biological parents. Nonalcoholic criminals tended to commit petty crimes, such as property offenses; their risk for criminality was associated with their biological parents' history of committing similar crimes as well as with instability in their placements before they were finally adopted. Thus these data again suggest that some forms of criminal behavior may have a genetic component.

Central Nervous System Activity and Sociopathy

Many early studies examined patterns of brain wave activity (see Box 10.1) in sociopaths and various groups of control subjects. Ellingson (1954) reviewed these studies and reported that in thirteen out of fourteen of them, investigating a total of about 1500 sociopaths, between 31 and 58 percent of the sociopaths showed some form of electroencephalogram (EEG) abnormality. The most frequent form of abnormality was *slow-wave activity*, which is typical of the infant and young child but not of the normal adult. The slow waves were widespread throughout the brain. There is, however, some evidence that among extremely impulsive and aggressive sociopathic individuals the EEG abnormalities are localized in the temporal lobes of the cerebral hemispheres (Hill, 1952). Finally, some individuals who respond with impulsive, aggressive, and destructive acts to seemingly trivial stimuli show what are referred to as *positive spikes*. These occur in the temporal area of the brain and consist of bursts of activity with frequencies of 6 to 8 cycles per second (cps) and 14 to 16 cps.

More recent findings reviewed by Syndulko (1978) generally agree with the earlier ones. Most studies report rather high frequencies of EEG abnormalities in sociopaths and the presence of slow waves and positive spikes in particular. Not all sociopaths show EEG abnormalities, however, and it is unclear whether those who do differ in any other way from those who do not. It should also be borne in mind that the EEG is a very gross measure of brain function, reflecting the mass action of hundreds of thousands of neurons. Furthermore, the brain waves of sociopaths are not abnormally

BOX 10.1

THE ELECTROENCEPHALOGRAM

The *electroencephalogram* or EEG is a graphic recording of the electrical activity of the brain. The brain is known to be continuously active, chemically and electrically, throughout life, even in sleep. Individual neurons of the central nervous system fire spontaneously at regular or irregular intervals, creating differences in electric potentials, that is, fluctuations in voltage. The fluctuations in voltage in the cortex, the portion of the brain immediately below the skull, can be picked up by two or more sensitive electrodes pasted to the scalp. The recording machine, the *electroencephalograph*, amplifies the pulsations one to two million times and connects them to a pen recorder (or recorders) which registers them on a continuously moving role of graph paper as a pattern of oscillations. The spontaneous activity of the brain, known as its waves, varies in different cortical areas and in the other, less accessible portions of the brain. Perhaps most importantly, the dominant brain waves reflect the degree to which the brain has been aroused.

In a normal adult subject, awake but resting quietly with eyes closed, the dominant rhythm has a frequency of between 8 and 13 pulsations or cycles per second (cps) and an amplitude of from 40 to 50 microvolts. This low-frequency, high-voltage wave is called the *alpha* rhythm. When a stimulus is presented, the alpha rhythm is replaced by a high-frequency (14 to 25 cps), low-voltage rhythm, the *beta* rhythm. If very low-frequency waves are found dominant in the awake adult, they are considered abnormal. These slow waves, which are sometimes found in sociopaths while they are awake, are referred to as the *theta* (4 to 7 cps)

and the *delta* (less than 4 cps) rhythms. Delta rhythms occur during deep sleep; theta waves are commonly recorded from subcortical parts of the brain. Examples of these various rhythms as well as the positive spikes referred to in the text may be seen in Figure 10.1.

The electroencephalograph records fluctuations in electrical activity from the cortex. Here the patient reclines with eyes closed while the operator checks the brain waves as they are recorded on graph paper.

Adult, relaxed wakefulness (alpha waves) interrupted by attentiveness (beta waves)	alpha beta alpha
Adult, deep sleep (delta waves)	
Adult, abnormal slow wave (theta waves)	
Positive spikes, 6 cps	
Positive spikes, 14 cps	

FIGURE 10.1 Patterns of electrical activity in the brain recorded by the electroencephalograph. After Hare, 1970.

slow in all experimental contexts. Hare and Jutai (1985), for example, found the usual high levels of slow-wave activity when sociopaths were resting, but later, when they played an exciting videogame, their brain waves were the same as those of normal subjects.

Specific interpretations of the sociopath's EEG abnormalities remain highly speculative at this time. Hare (1970), for example, interprets the high frequency of slow-wave activity to indicate a dysfunction in inhibitory mechanisms which, in turn, lessens the sociopath's ability to learn to forestall actions that are likely to get him or her into trouble. Although this interpretation is consistent with studies of the negligible effects of past punishment on sociopaths, it certainly is not the only one possible. But the *inability* of sociopaths *to learn to avoid* or escape from *punishment* has been an important subject of research.

Avoidance Learning, Punishment, and Sociopathy

As we have previously noted, in defining the sociopathic syndrome, Cleckley pointed out the inability of these persons to profit from experience; thus they do not try to avoid the negative consequences of social misbehavior. Cleckley also remarked that they were not neurotic and seldom anxious. Lykken (1957) deduced that sociopaths may have few inhibitions about committing antisocial acts because they experience so little anxiety. He performed several tests to determine whether sociopaths do indeed have low levels of anxiety. One of these tests involved avoidance learning.

A group of male sociopaths, judged to be so on the basis of Cleckley's criteria, were selected from a penitentiary population. Their performance on an avoidance learning task was compared to that of nonsociopathic penitentiary inmates[5] and of college students. It was of course critical that only avoidance and not learning mediated by other possible rewards be tested. If a subject perceives that his task is to learn to avoid pain, he may be motivated not only by the desire to avoid the pain but also by a desire to demonstrate his cleverness to the investigator. To ensure that no other motives would become manifest, Lykken made the avoidance learning task *incidental*. He used the following apparatus. On a panel in front of the subject there were four red lights in

a horizontal array, four green lights below each of the red ones, and a lever below each column, as illustrated in Figure 10.2. The subject's task was to learn a sequence of twenty correct lever presses, but for each he first had to determine by trial and error which of the four alternatives was correct. The correct lever turned on a green light. Two of the remaining three incorrect levers turned on red lights, indicating an error. The third incorrect lever delivered an electric shock to the subject. The location of the correct lever was of course not always the same. The subject was told simply to figure out and to learn the series of twenty correct lever presses. He was not informed that avoiding shock was desirable or possible, only that shock was randomly administered as a stimulant to make him do well. Thus the task yielded two measures of learning: the total number of errors made before the subject learned the correct sequence of twenty presses and the number of errors made that produced shock. Avoidance is measured by this second index.

FIGURE 10.2 The apparatus devised by Lykken (1957) for his study of avoidance learning in sociopaths.

For the first lever press assume that lever 3 is correct, that is, that pressing it lights the green bulb; that levers 1 and 4 are incorrect, lighting red bulbs; and that pressing lever 2 lights a red bulb and gives the subject a shock. For the second lever press the meaning of the levers may change entirely; for example, lever 2 may be correct, levers 3 and 4 incorrect, and lever 1 may give the shock. The subjects had to learn a sequence of twenty correct lever presses.

In terms of the overall number of errors made, there were no significant differences among any of the groups in Lykken's study. The college students, however, were apparently best able to remember the sequence of presses that produced shock and thus sharply decreased their proportion of shocked errors. The sociopaths made the most shocked errors, but the differences be-

---

[5]In the literature such people are sometimes referred to as neurotic sociopaths. We have avoided using this confusing term since, by definition, a sociopath is not neurotic.

tween their shocked errors and those of the other penitentiary inmates only approached statistical significance. The results of Lykken's investigation therefore tentatively support the hypothesis that sociopaths operate under lower levels of anxiety than do normal individuals.

Lykken also tried to verify his reduced-anxiety hypothesis by giving his subjects standard psychological tests for measuring anxiety, such as the Taylor Manifest Anxiety Scale. On these tests the sociopaths did indeed show lower levels of anxiety.

Lykken's pioneering work was subsequently followed up by Schachter and Latané (1964). These investigators reasoned that if sociopaths fail to learn to avoid unpleasant stimuli because they have little anxiety, a procedure that increases their anxiety should help them learn to shun punishment. Inasmuch as anxiety is viewed as being related to activity of the sympathetic nervous system, they injected Adrenalin, an agent whose effects mimic sympathetic activity, in order to increase anxiety.

Sociopathic and nonsociopathic prisoners from a penitentiary were studied with the same task and apparatus that had been devised by Lykken. This time each subject was tested twice. The subjects were led to believe that the effects of a hormone on learning were being investigated. Half received a placebo injection on the first day of testing and half an injection of Adrenalin. On the second day of testing, the injections received by the subjects were reversed.

The results of Schachter and Latané's experiment were important in several ways. First, the overall number of errors provided confirmation for Lykken's results: no difference was found between the sociopathic and nonsocipathic prisoners in the total number of errors committed in learning the sequence, whether they had been injected with Adrenalin or the placebo. Second, the nonsociopathic prisoners injected with the placebo markedly reduced their proportion of shocked errors after a number of runs, but the sociopaths injected with the placebo showed no such improvement. In this part of the study, the difference between the performances of the two groups of prisoners was greater than that revealed in Lykken's experiment and considerably larger than the amount necessary for statistical significance. Third, and most important, when injected with Adrenalin, the sociopaths showed a great reduction in the number of shocked errors, but the prisoners who were not sociopaths were adversely affected by the Adrenalin and did not learn to avoid the shock in their state of high arousal (Figure 10.3). Thus the hypothesis

Stanley Schachter, social psychologist at Columbia University, known for his theory that emotion has both cognitive and physiological aspects. He has investigated the relation between arousal in the autonomic nervous system, emotion, and sociopathy.

of the anxiety-free and *underaroused* sociopath received considerable support from the work of Schachter and Latané.[6]

Chesno and Kilmann (1975) have provided further confirmation of Schachter and Latané's work. Sociopaths, as well as several other groups of subjects, participated in a shock avoidance learning test. While they performed the task, the subjects were exposed to bursts of noise which varied in intensity. One-third of the subjects in each group were exposed to noise of 35 decibels, one-third to 65 decibels, and the remainder to 95. The varying levels of noise were expected to produce different levels of arousal, as had the Adrenalin injections in Schachter and Latané's work. And the sociopaths were expected to learn to avoid shock more readily as noise became more intense, which is exactly what happened.

An avoidance learning study by Schmauk (1970) qualifies the findings of Lykken as well as those of the other studies we have discussed. He showed that a particular kind of punishment, losing money, can have an

[6]The finding that the Adrenalin injection apparently worsened the avoidance learning performance of the nonsociopathic prisoners is difficult to interpret. A follow-up test by Schachter and Latané did not reproduce this effect.

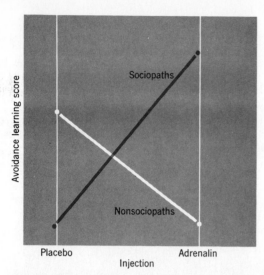

FIGURE 10.3 Results of Schachter and Latané's study (1964) of the effects of Adrenalin on avoidance learning in sociopathic and nonsociopathic prisoners. Higher scores reflect better avoidance learning; arousal through Adrenalin helped the sociopaths to learn to avoid shock by activating their otherwise under-aroused autonomic nervous systems.

effect on sociopaths. He tested three groups, sociopathic prisoners, nonsociopathic prisoners, and a control group consisting of farmworkers and hospital attendants. As in the previous studies, an avoidance learning task was devised, but this time three different aversive stimuli could be avoided: a physical punishment—electric shock; a tangible punishment—losing a quarter from an initial pile of forty; and a social punishment—the experimenter's saying "wrong" to the subject. There were again no differences among the groups in the total number of errors made before the task was mastered. The major finding of this study (Figure 10.4) indicated that the sociopath's avoidance performance varies with the nature of punishment. When the punishments confronting them were physical and social, the members of the control group were vastly superior to the sociopaths in learning to avoid punishment. But the sociopaths outdid them in learning to avoid the tangible punishment of losing a quarter. The nonsociopathic prisoners did better than the sociopaths in learning to avoid physical punishment but less well in avoiding social punishment.

It appears then that sociopaths *can* learn to avoid punishment. The differences found between sociopaths and nonsociopaths in previous investigations may reflect *not* a general deficit in avoidance learning ability but rather the fact that some punishments have no

meaning for the sociopath. Evidently, sociopaths will learn to avoid punishment that is relevant to their system of values, and money may very well be particularly important to them.

In the avoidance learning studies discussed thus far, punishment was inevitable if a particular incorrect response was made. But many crimes remain unsolved, so in real life the sociopath is actually in a situation in which punishment is uncertain. According to some clinicians, the sociopath almost magically believes that his antisocial behavior will not be punished. Therefore it may be that sociopaths are particularly insensitive to *uncertain punishment*. Siegel (1978) examined this notion by testing sociopaths, nonsociopathic prisoners, and college students in a card game in which different probabilities of losing poker chips, which could be redeemed for money, were the punishment. As expected, punishment had the least impact on sociopaths when its probability was in the middle range, from 40 to 70 percent. And the sociopaths also underestimated the likelihood of subsequently losing poker chips after a session in which the probability of loss was in the midrange. In these circumstances the nonsociopathic prisoners and the college students were not so cavalier about chancing the loss of chips. As in previous studies, then, sociopaths were affected less by punishment; more impor-

FIGURE 10.4 Mean avoidance learning scores plotted for three subject groups confronted by three different punishments, physical, tangible, and social. The sociopaths readily learned to avoid punishment when it cost them money. After Schmauk, 1970.

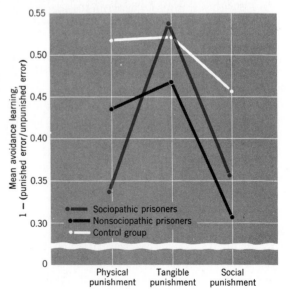

tantly, they behaved as though they believe punishment to be unlikely when it does not certainly follow a misstep.

Underarousal, Defective Planning and Inhibition, and Sociopathy

Sociopaths have often been described as not responding emotionally when confronted by both familiar and new situations that most people would find either stressful or unpleasant. Cleckley (1976) has written about this aspect of their behavior.

Regularly, we find in [the sociopath] extraordinary poise rather than jitteriness or worry, a smooth sense of physical well-being instead of uneasy preoccupations with bodily functions. Even under concrete circumstances that would for the ordinary person cause embarrassment, confusion, acute insecurity, or visible agitation, his relative serenity is likely to be noteworthy (p. 340).

This description is remarkably consistent with the Schachter and Latané finding that sociopaths do not ordinarily avoid electric shock but that they do so when their autonomic arousal is increased by injections of Adrenalin. Because of the assumed central role of the autonomic nervous system in states of emotion, several investigators have examined sociopaths both for their resting levels of autonomic activity and for their patterns of autonomic reactivity to various classes of stimuli.

Most studies indicate that in resting situations sociopaths have lower than normal levels of skin conductance. Furthermore, their skin conductance is less reactive when they are confronted with intense or aversive stimuli. A different picture emerges, however, when heart rate is examined. The heart rate of sociopaths is like that of normal people under resting conditions, and their heart rate reactivity to neutral stimuli is also unremarkable. But in situations in which sociopaths anticipate a stressful stimulus, their hearts beat faster than those of normal people anticipating stress.

These physiological reactions indicate that the sociopath cannot be regarded as simply underaroused, for measurements of skin conductance and heart rate are inconsistent. Basing his theorizing in part on Lacey's work (1967), Hare (1978) focuses on the *pattern* of psychophysiological responses of sociopaths. Faster heartbeats are viewed as a concomitant of gating out or reducing sensory input and thus lowering cortical arousal. Thus the increased heart rate of sociopaths who are anticipating an aversive stimulus would indicate that they are "tuning it out." Their skin conductance is then less

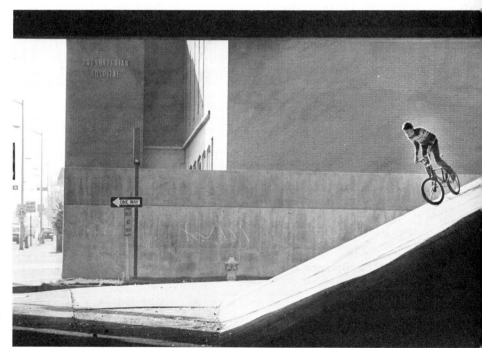

Some research suggests that the thrill seeking of sociopaths is an attempt on their part to make up for a level of arousal that is chronically too low.

reactive to an aversive stimulus because they have been able effectively to ignore it. That is, with skin conductance considered an index of anxiety, that of sociopaths does not increase to any extent after expected aversive stimulation because they have already dealt with it by screening it out.[7] This interpretation of the physiological reactions of sociopaths is plausible and consistent with the studies reviewed earlier on avoidance learning. Further research by Hare and his associates has confirmed that both in their behavior (Jutai and Hare, 1983) and in their physiological responses (Hare, in press) psychopaths are particularly adept at ignoring stimuli.

The fact that sociopaths are underaroused or are better able to control their arousal has additional implications. Quay (1965) has suggested that the impulsiveness, thirst for excitement, and inability to tolerate routine and boredom of sociopaths are fostered by their lesser emotional reactivity and by their ability to block out arousing sensory input and thus stem cortical arousal. Quay's reasoning is based on the hypothesis that there is an optimal level of arousal for human beings. When arousal is too high an individual will take steps to reduce it, and when it is too low the individual will take steps to increase it. Much of the sociopath's "thrill seeking" behavior could then be viewed as an attempt to increase his or her arousal enough to approach this optimal state.

If it is true that sociopaths seek excitement to raise their arousal levels, we might expect their performance on a tedious and monotonous task to be especially poor. Orris (1967) tested prisoners on such a task. The findings bore out the prediction. Sociopathic prisoners performed less well than did the others. We might also predict that given a choice, sociopaths will prefer novel and complex stimuli. Such stimuli are generally viewed as having high-arousal properties, and thus the sociopath might be expected to show a preference for them. Skrzypek (1969) tested this hypothesis on a sample of sociopathic and other prisoners and found that sociopaths indeed showed a somewhat greater preference for novelty and complexity than did the other prisoners.

We have indicated before that sociopaths have few plans and few inhibitions. Much of sociopathic behavior could be described as just this, a failure to plan and to control the self through inhibition. That is, whatever inhibits antisocial behavior in most of us does not appear to function in sociopaths. Gorenstein (1982) chose neuropsychological tests given to assess deficits associated with damage to the frontal lobes. These tests are relevant because frontal lobe lesions impair patients' capacity for foresight, planning, and the regulation of impulses.

As anticipated, hospitalized sociopaths differed from others receiving psychiatric treatment and from college students, having incapacities similar to those of patients with frontal lobe lesions, although their own brains were intact. The sociopaths were less able to switch on command from sorting cards by the color of the figures on them—red, yellow, green, or blue; to sorting them by the particular figure on each—stars, crosses, triangles, or circles; to sorting them by the number of figures on each. They were less able to remember, when shown cards one by one bearing either a plus or a minus, the sign on the card shown two cards back. And the Necker cube, the two-dimensional drawing of a cube that switches perspective when a subject stares at it, did so more frequently for them. Whatever plans, intentions, and short-term memories sociopaths may have are comparatively vulnerable to disruptions by entrenched habits and their own ways of responding, by their drives, and by salient stimuli. Sociopaths seem not to have the full power of planning, flexibility, and inhibition to control their actions.

The case histories, studies, and theories that we have reviewed show the sociopath to be an individual who does not react as most of us do. In particular, he has almost no anxiety, so it can have little deterrent effect. Moreover, because the sociopath is in greater control of his negative emotional reactions, arousal is actually sought. And because the sociopath is deficient in planning and in inhibition, he behaves impulsively. These are possible reasons for the sociopath's misconduct without regret and for his thrill seeking without regard for society's rules.

[7]Psychophysiological studies of sociopathy have also focused on what is called *recovery time*, the period it takes for the level of skin conductance to return to baseline after the body has responded to a stimulus. Slow recovery time is associated with criminal behavior and is even found in children of aggressive fathers (Mednick and Hutchings, 1978). The recovery time of sociopaths is more complicated. Hare (1978) found them to have slow recovery only when conductance from their left hands was checked and only when the stimuli had been unexpected or aversive. Slow recovery could be another indication of the greater ability of sociopaths to ignore or "tune out" aversive stimuli like punishment.

THERAPIES FOR PERSONALITY DISORDERS

There is as little information on treating personality disorders as there is on how they develop. Research on drug therapies for the various personality disorders is for the most part inconclusive. Few people with personality disorders even go to therapists, for they regard their behavior as "natural" and in no need of professional attention. It has even been asserted that their disorders, if such they be, cause them little if any discomfort (Nathan and Harris, 1980). Because disordered personalities do not believe that they need help and relate no better to the therapist than they do to others, they take no responsibility and make no effort in their own treatment. In fact, they may terminate it in short order.

Behavior Therapy for Disturbed Personalities

Behavior therapists, in keeping with their attention to situations rather than to traits, have no specific treatments as such for histrionic personality, borderline personality, or any of the other personality disorders designated by DSM-III. Rather they analyze the problems that, taken together, might be considered by an enthusiast of DSM-III to reflect a personality disorder. For example, the man diagnosed as having a paranoid personality will be very sensitive to criticism. This sensitivity may be treated by systematic desensitization or rational-emotive therapy. His argumentativeness and hostility when he disagrees with other people will push them away from him and provoke counterattacks from them. The behavior therapist may practice with the man more adaptive ways of disagreeing with other people.

One aspect of a personality disorder commands the attention of any skilled behavior therapist, as well as that of any other professional helper, namely, the alleged deeply ingrained, long-standing, and pervasive nature of the problem. A man will bear the diagnosis of paranoid personality only if his tendency to be suspicious and guarded is chronic and permeates his overall psychological functioning. Any therapist working with him must therefore consider the broad implications of his problem. Before a highly suspicious person can express emotion openly and appropriately, he must make major and difficult changes in his assumptions about people and in his general mode of functioning. In other words, therapy must take into consideration the pervasive, wide-ranging nature of a person's particular personality disorder and, in addition, the person's general intractableness.

35 YEARS IN THE SAME LOCATION

(Drawing by C. Barsotti; © 1985, The New Yorker Magazine, Inc.)

Therapy for Sociopathy

As for the treatment of antisocial personality disorder, there is unusual—and unfortunate—agreement among therapists of varying theoretical persuasions: sociopathy is virtually impossible to treat (Cleckley, 1976; McCord and McCord, 1964).

It may be that people with the classic symptoms listed by Cleckley are, by their very natures, incapable of benefiting from any form of psychotherapy. The most likely reason is that they are unable to form any sort of trusting, honest relationship with a therapist. A person who lies almost without knowing it, who cares little for the feelings of others and understands his own even less, who appears not to realize that what he is doing is morally wrong, who lacks any motivation to obey society's laws and mores, and who, living only for the present, has no concern for the future is all in all an extremely poor candidate for therapy. In fact, one clinician, experienced in working with sociopaths, has suggested three general principles.

A prison is widely regarded as more of a school for crime than as an effective agent of rehabilitation.

First, the therapist must be continually vigilant with regard to manipulation on the part of the patient. Second, he must assume, until proven otherwise, that information given him by the patient contains distortions and fabrications. Third, he must recognize that a working alliance develops, if ever, exceedingly late in any therapeutic relationship with a psychopath (Lion, 1978, p. 286).

To be sure, many valiant attempts have been made to establish tenable connections with sociopaths, but both the published literature and informal communications among mental health professionals support the conclusion that true sociopathy cannot be reached through clinical efforts. Similar negative conclusions are to be drawn as well about somatic methods—electroconvulsive shock, drugs such as Dilantin, stimulants, and sedatives, and psychosurgery.[8] There is, however, some

---

[8]An ethical problem can arise from this notion that sociopaths have a poor prognosis. If a prisoner is considered a sociopath, those in charge of decisions about parole and release are naturally concerned whether he has really changed his ways. His good behavior in prison may merely reflect his manipulativeness and ability to "con" people. The person designated a sociopath may thus be at a serious disadvantage in obtaining just treatment from the judicial system.

evidence that antianxiety agents can, in large doses, reduce hostility in sociopaths (Kellner, 1982).

Since many sociopaths spend time in prison for crimes that they have been convicted of, the discouraging results of imprisonment as rehabilitation are traced at least in part to the inability to modify sociopathic behavior. As criminologists have stated repeatedly (for example, Wilkins, 1969), our prison system seems to operate more as a school for crime than it does as a place where criminals, and sociopaths, can be rehabilitated. Ramsey Clark, a former United States attorney general, put it this way: "Prisons in the United States today are more often than not manufacturers of crime . . . [They] are usually little more than places to keep people—warehouses of human degradation" (1970, p. 213). For a time in the 1970s, there was interest in developing new therapy programs for prisoners. Operant conditioning regimens, usually token economies, were established for especially violent prisoners, and different kinds of group therapy tried to encourage the more tractable prisoners to assume some responsibility for their behavior. For a variety of reasons, including the claims of civil liberties groups that therapy in a prison setting is unconstitutional, fewer therapeutic efforts are now made on be-

BOX 10.2

AGGRESSION ALONE DOES NOT A SOCIOPATH MAKE

The social-learning literature on both the acquisition and elimination of aggressive behavior is extensive. Some writers (for example, Mahoney, 1980) refer to this theory and research in an effort to understand both the etiology and possible treatment of sociopathy. In our view, however, the kind of aggressive behavior studied by social-learning theorists is very different from that of an antisocial personality. Social-learning theorists (for example, Bandura, 1973) conduct experiments showing that basically normal children and adults can acquire sometimes complex and novel patterns of aggressive behavior by watching models perform such actions. The tendency to imitate has been shown to be related to how the model is rewarded for being aggressive, the status of the model, and how the observer is reinforced for aggression. Such research is informative about aggression in normal people under normal circumstances, but it does not address the issue of sociopathy. For example, none of the social-learning experiments on aggression has assessed whether subjects who imitate an aggressive model feel guilt or shame. Nor do these studies really touch on the *persistent* and *pervasive* monstrous cruelty that is a true hallmark of sociopathy and is clearly something apart from ordinary aggression. As for treatment, prosocial behavior may indeed be fostered in delinquent adolescents by systematically rewarding them for it in a homelike environment (see page 385). But the natures and inclinations of the young people living in residential treatment settings must be scrutinized. Although they have clearly run afoul of the law and stand every chance of spending many of their adult years in prison, very few, if any, of these youngsters can be described as incipient sociopaths.

half of prisoners. Indeed, the trend seems to be to regard imprisonment as simply punishment for transgression against society. Little attention is paid to trying to help those convicted so that they will "go straight" upon release.

An interesting argument in favor of incarceration is that psychopaths often "settle down" in middle age and thereafter (Craft, 1969). Whether through physiological changes, eventual insight into their self-defeating natures, or simply becoming worn out and unable to continue in their finagling ways, many sociopaths grow less disruptive as they approach forty. Prison, therefore, protects society from the antisocial behavior of "active" sociopaths, with release considered more plausible when the prisoner enters a stage of life in which the excesses of his sociopathy are less in evidence (see Box 10.2).

SUMMARY

The category of personality disorders is an extremely broad and heterogeneous one. There is little information on most of them. The notable exception is sociopathy, the dominant pattern of which is repeated antisocial behavior without regret or shame. In addition, sociopaths are thought to be unable to learn from experience, to have no sense of responsibility, and to establish no genuine emotional relationships with other people. Research on their families indicates that sociopaths had fathers who themselves were antisocial and that discipline was either absent or inconsistent. Genetic studies, particularly those using the adoptee method, suggest that a predisposition to sociopathy is inherited. The core problem of the sociopath may be that impending punishment creates no inhibitions about committing antisocial acts. A good deal of overlapping evidence supports this view: (1) sociopaths have abnormal amounts of slow-wave EEG activity, which may reflect a failure of the usual inhibitory processes; (2) sociopaths are slow at learning to avoid shock, a deficit which can be reduced by heightening the sociopath's level of physiological arousal; (3) sociopaths, according to their electrodermal responses, show little anxiety but, as indicated by their faster heart rates, seem better able than normal people to tune out aversive stimuli; and (4) sociopaths, according to tests of their frontal lobe capacities, do not have full control of themselves through planning and flexibility.

Little is known about effective therapy for the various personality disorders, for several reasons. The poor reliability of the diagnoses and the tendency to use the category as a grab bag make it difficult to evaluate reports of therapy. Therapy for the sociopath in particular holds little promise for a successful outcome. In addition to the pervasiveness and apparent intractability of the uncaring and manipulative life style, the antisocial personality is by nature a poor candidate for therapy. People who habitually lie and lack insight into their own or others' feelings—and have no inclination to examine emotions—will not readily establish a trusting and open working relationship with a therapist.

Larry Rivers, *Bad Witch*, 1970 Courtesy Marlborough Gallery, New York

SUBSTANCE USE DISORDERS

Alcoholism
Sedatives and Stimulants
Nicotine and Cigarette Smoking

Marijuana
LSD and Other Psychedelics

From prehistoric times humankind has used various substances in the hope of reducing physical pain or altering states of consciousness. Almost all peoples have discovered some intoxicant that affects the central nervous system, relieving physical and mental anguish or producing euphoria. Whatever the aftermath of taking such substances into the body, their effects are usually pleasing, at least initially.

Alcoholic beverages from the fermentation of many fruits and grains, of milk, honey, and molasses, and even of tree sap; opium, the dried milky juice obtained from the immature fruit of the opium poppy; hashish and marijuana from *Cannabis*, the hemp plant; and cocaine, an alkaloid extracted from coca leaves—these are the major natural drugs that have a long history of both use and abuse, and that continue today to present problems for society. In the United States and other Western countries, morphine, an alkaloid extracted from opium, and heroin, derived from morphine, are more prevalent than the raw opium, and dried marijuana is used more often than hashish. Also available are a number of newer synthetic and synthesized drugs, most importantly the barbiturates, the amphetamines, LSD, and PCP. Of all the potentially dangerous drugs, the one craved by the greatest number of people is nicotine, the principal alkaloid of tobacco. DSM-III has a separate section for these problems, Substance Use Disorders.

The pathological use of substances that affect the central nervous system falls into two categories, *substance abuse* and *substance dependence*. A person is considered to abuse a substance when he or she is, for example, often intoxicated from it throughout the day and, despite all efforts, unable to cut consumption in any consistent way. The state of intoxication reached will be deep enough that the person fails in important obligations to friends and family and at work. And he or she may also get into legal difficulties by causing harm when intoxicated or by behaving criminally in order to secure money to purchase the substance. The abuse must be of at least a month's duration to be considered a disturbance, according to DSM-III. A yearly New Year's Eve binge on the part of a person who during the rest of the year drinks in only moderate amounts is clearly not substance abuse.

Substance dependence is a more severe form of disorder in which there is evidence of physiological dependence on the drug, in addition to the abuser's other problems. Dependence in this sense, or *addiction* as we prefer to call it, is the physiological process by which the body responds to certain drugs. When addicting drugs are ingested for prolonged periods of time, greater and greater amounts of them are *tolerated*: the bodily systems habituate to the particular chemical so that larger and larger doses are necessary to maintain similar intoxicating effects. Then when the frequency of ingestion or the amount of the drug is suddenly decreased, the person suffers *withdrawal reactions*. The prolonged use of the drug has so altered the physiological conditions of the body that it is disturbed when the drug is not administered. For example, an addict who suddenly ceases to take morphine usually suffers from hypertension and cramps, is restless, and sweats profusely. The physiological mechanisms responsible for *tolerance* and withdrawal reactions are not well understood.

But not all drugs, even if they are taken regularly, bring on either tolerance or the later withdrawal reactions when their use is terminated. For this reason the term *psychological dependency*[1] is often applied to reliance on drugs that are not addicting. A drug may be taken because its effects make stressful or anxiety-provoking situations more bearable. But the dosage of the drug does not have to be continually increased to produce these effects, nor is there a withdrawal reaction if the drug is not taken. This is not to say that the individual with a psychological dependence on a drug feels no unpleasant effects when the drug is not available. If people are deprived of *anything* that they have come to rely on, they are likely to react negatively to its absence by becoming restless, nervous, or otherwise upset. These reactions sometimes resemble the withdrawal symptoms obtained with addictive drugs, but they should not be regarded as such *unless* there is also evidence of tolerance.

Many of those who abuse drugs use more than one drug at any given time. *Polydrug abuse* poses a serious health problem because the effects of some drugs when taken together are synergistic, that is, the effects of each interact to produce an especially strong reaction. For example, mixing barbiturates with alcohol is a common means of suicide, be it intentional or accidental. Alcohol is believed to have contributed to deaths from heroin as well, for evidence indicates that alcohol can dramatically reduce the amount of narcotic that need be taken for it to be a lethal dose. Many early studies found that

---

[1]The term psychological dependency must not be confused with DSM-III's use of the word dependence, which is, as noted, synonymous with addiction. But, generally speaking, drugs that are not known to be addictive, such as LSD, nonetheless can interfere greatly with people's lives, for their immoderate use can create the problems described for substance abuse. Therefore finding a person to be psychologically dependent on a substance is equivalent to the substance abuse diagnosis of DSM-III.

heroin addicts disliked alcohol, using it only as a substitute during withdrawal. In recent years, however, addicts seem to alternate between alcohol and heroin because the price of heroin is so high.

The DSM-III section Substance Use Disorders considers only the *behavior* associated with the regular use of substances that interfere with everyday life. If a person who is addicted to a drug is denied it and therefore thrown into withdrawal, a diagnosis in addition to substance dependence would also be applicable. In the Organic Mental Disorders section are listed *substance-induced organic mental disorders,* an example of which is *alcohol withdrawal delirium*, commonly known as the DTs (see page 257). In this chapter, then, which covers all psychological and physical problems created by drugs, we necessarily deal with facets of drug abuse that DSM-III puts into more than one major section.

ALCOHOLISM

Written reports of the use of wines, beers, and other alcoholic beverages date back to 3000 B.C., but not until about 800 B.C. was the distillation process applied to fermented beverages, making possible the preparation of the highly potent liquors that are available today. Alcohol consumption has risen, both in America and in most other countries. In 1940, for example, 30 percent of the American population were drinkers and 2 percent problem drinkers. By 1970 68 percent of the population drank, 9 percent problematically (Caddy, 1983). Fortunately, the overall use of alcohol has not increased much since 1970, although among some groups it has.

There are about 200,000 new cases of *alcoholism* each year, and in this last decade teenage alcoholism has greatly increased. In older studies male alcoholics outnumbered females by about four to one. But this gap is diminishing and, particularly among younger age groups, women's consumption of alcohol is on the upswing (Becker and Kronus, 1977). Although most of the people who have a drinking problem do not seek professional help, alcoholics do constitute a large proportion of new admissions to mental and general hospitals. The suicide rate of alcoholics, especially of women alcoholics, is much higher than that of the general population. A third of all suicides have alcohol as a contributing cause. Moreover, some estimate that alcohol is implicated in at least 25,000 highway deaths each year, about half the total number. Alcohol may be a factor as well in airplane crashes, industrial accidents, and mishaps in the home. Alcohol also presents law enforcement problems, for about one-third of all arrests in the United States are for public drunkenness. Homicide is an alcohol-related crime—over half of all murders are believed committed under its influence—and so too are parental child abuse, spouse abuse, and sexual offenses (Brecher, 1972; National Institute on Alcohol Abuse and Alcoholism, 1983).

Teenage drinking has been increasing steadily in recent years.

As in the more general diagnoses of substance abuse and dependence, DSM-III distinguishes between *alcohol abuse* and *alcohol dependence*. The second is applied when there are classic signs of addiction—either tolerance or withdrawal reactions, such as morning "shakes" and malaise which can be relieved only by taking a drink. Persons who begin drinking early in life develop their first withdrawal symptoms in their thirties or forties. For both diagnoses the pattern of drinking must indicate that it is out of control. Individuals will need to drink daily, being unable to stop or cut down despite repeated efforts to abstain completely or to restrict drinking to certain periods of the day. They may go on occasional binges, remaining intoxicated all through two, three, or more days. Sometimes they consume a fifth of spirits at a time. They suffer "blackouts" of the events that took place during a bout of intoxication; their craving may be so overpowering that they are forced to drink alcohol in a nonbeverage form, such as hair tonic. Such drinking of course causes social and occupational difficulties, and signs of them are necessary for both diagnoses: quarrels with family or friends, violence when intoxicated, frequent absences from work or loss of job, and arrest for intoxication or for traffic accidents.

Many researchers in the field of alcoholism have opted to emphasize the *continuity* of dependence on alcohol and of alcohol-related disabilities. The World

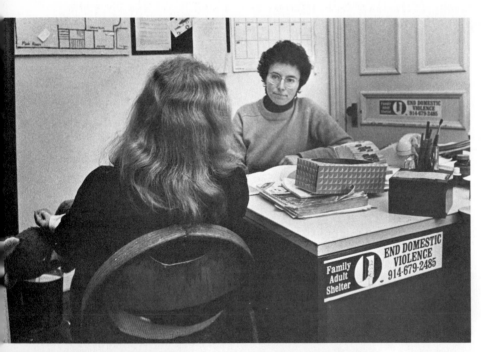

Alcohol abuse has serious negative effects not only on the abuser but also on family members and friends.

TABLE 11.1 Constituent Elements of the Alcohol Dependence Syndrome   *(from Edwards et al., 1977)*

Elements	Interpretation, Examples
Narrowing of the drinking repertoire	The drinking pattern tends to become a regular schedule of almost continuous daily consumption.
Salience of drink-seeking behavior	Drinking is given higher priority than other activities, in spite of its negative consequences.
Increased tolerance to alcohol	More and more alcohol is required to produce behavioral, subjective, and metabolic changes; large amounts of alcohol can be tolerated.
Repeated withdrawal symptoms	The individual is subject to tremulousness, sweatiness, nausea, and so on after short periods of abstinence.
Relief drinking	Withdrawal symptoms are relieved or avoided by further drinking, especially in the morning.
Compulsion to drink	The individual is subjectively aware of a craving for alcohol and has little control over the quantity and frequency of intake.
Readdiction liability	The syndrome is rapidly reinstated when drinking recommences after a period of abstinence.

Health Organization proposes an alcohol dependence syndrome (Table 11.1), consisting of several characteristics of alcohol abuse. The severity of dependence is related to the number of characteristics present, which can be measured by instruments designed to assess them (for example, Skinner and Allen, 1982).

Short-Term Effects of Alcohol

Physiological Effects

After being swallowed, alcohol does not undergo any of the processes of digestion. A small part of the alcohol ingested passes immediately into the bloodstream through the stomach walls, but most of it goes into the small intestines and from there is absorbed into the blood. It must then be metabolized in a series of steps; in the liver alcohol is first converted to acetaldehyde, then to acetate. About 75 percent of acetate is then transported to other tissues, where oxidation to water and carbon dioxide is completed.[2] The oxidation of alcohol is catalyzed by several enzymes—alcohol dehy-

drogenase, microsomal ethanol-oxidizing enzymes, and catalase. The liver can break down about one ounce of 100 proof (that is, 50 percent alcohol) whiskey per hour. Quantities in excess of this amount remain in the bloodstream. Whereas absorption of alcohol can be very rapid, removal is always slow. Many of the effects of alcohol vary directly with the level of concentration of the drug in the bloodstream, which in turn depends on the amount ingested in a particular period of time, the presence or absence in the stomach of food to retain the alcohol and reduce its absorption rate, the size of the individual's body, and the efficiency of the liver.

Because the drinking of alcoholic beverages is accepted in most societies, alcohol is rarely regarded as a drug, especially by those who drink. But it is indeed a drug, affecting the central nervous system. Alcohol, acting as a depressant, first numbs the higher brain centers, those that are primarily inhibiting. Thus the initial effect of alcohol is stimulating. Tensions and inhibitions are reduced, and the individual may experience an expansive feeling of sociability and well-being. Some people, though, become suspicious and even violent. Larger amounts interfere with complex thought processes; then motor coordination, balance, speech, and vision are impaired. At this stage of intoxication, some individuals become depressed and withdrawn. Alcohol is capable of blunting pain and in larger doses of inducing sedation and sleep. Before modern techniques of anesthesia were discovered, liquors were often administered to a patient about to undergo surgery.

[2]Various types of alcohol differ in the rate at which they can be oxidized. Ethyl alcohol, the type found in alcoholic beverages, oxidizes the most rapidly, whereas methyl or wood alcohol oxidizes much more slowly. Because of slow oxidation, large amounts of methyl alcohol may accumulate in the blood, causing death or blindness. Another type of alcohol, denatured alcohol, is a deadly poison because of the toxic substances added to it.

Behavioral Effects

Studies have determined that the short-term effects of alcohol on social drinkers are complex. Jones and Parsons (1975) reviewed a number of experiments that suggest, among other things, that effects vary depending on whether the person is becoming drunk or sobering up. In one such experiment Jones and Parsons (1971) assessed the abstract problem-solving ability of drinkers. Those on the downward part of the curve, that is, drinkers becoming sober, performed significantly better with a particular level of alcohol in their blood than did those who were getting high and had the same level. A person apparently thinks better, at a given stage of intoxication, if he or she is becoming less drunk than if becoming more so. The short-term memories of those becoming sober appear to be similarly good and those becoming intoxicated to be similarly poor (Jones, 1973).

Studies of alcohol's effects on sexual responding confirm Shakespeare's observation that "Lechery, sir, it provokes, and it unprovokes: it provokes the desire but it takes away the performance" (*Macbeth*, Act II, Scene 3). In the first experiment published on the effects of alcohol on the physiology of sexual responding, a plethysmograph was used to determine genital blood flow (see Box 12.2, page 294). Farkas and Rosen (1976) showed male subjects an erotic film after they had drunk one of four concentrations of alcohol ranging from 0 percent (pure orange juice) to 0.075 percent, which corresponds to about five drinks of straight whiskey. In each case the amount of alcohol could not be detected by the taste of the drink. The more alcohol the men ingested, the less the penile erection. Thus, in a laboratory setting, the more alcohol drunk, the more it took away from "performance."

Do women respond in the same way? Wilson and Lawson (1976) confirmed that their physiological sexual arousal was also reduced by drinking a large amount of alcohol. But when the women *believed* that they had drunk alcohol, they reported feeling sexually aroused even though, if the amount was large, their vaginal blood flow indicated little arousal. As psychologists have learned more than once, the Bard of Avon had great insight into the workings of humankind.

It now appears that some of the short-term effects of ingesting small amounts of alcohol are more strongly related to beliefs about the effects of the drug than to its chemical action on the body. For example, alcohol is commonly thought to stimulate aggression, reduce anxiety, and increase sexual responsiveness. Recent research has shown, however, that these reactions may not be caused by alcohol itself but by beliefs about alcohol's effects. Subjects are told that they will be consuming a quantity of alcohol but, in fact, are given an alcohol-free beverage with its taste disguised so that they will not see through the ruse. They subsequently become more aggressive (Lang et al., 1975), more sexually aroused (Wilson and Lawson, 1976), and less anxious (Wilson and Abrams, 1977). Indeed, subjects who merely believe that they have drunk alcohol, but have not, sometimes act the same way as subjects who have actually consumed the drug. Once again, cognitions have a demonstrably powerful effect on behavior.

Long-Term Effects of Prolonged Alcohol Use

The possible long-term effects of prolonged drinking are vividly illustrated in the following case history.

> At the time of his first admission to a state hospital at the age of twenty-four, the patient, an unmarried and unemployed laborer, already had a long history of antisocial behavior, promiscuity and addiction to alcohol and other drugs. . . . There had been eight brief admissions to private sanatoria for alcoholics, a number of arrests for public intoxication and drunken driving, and two jail terms for assault.
>
> The patient had been born into a wealthy and respected family in a small town. The patient's father, a successful and popular businessman, drank excessively and his death at the age of fifty-seven was partly due to alcoholism. The mother also drank to excess. The parents exercised little control over the patient as a child, and he was cared for by nursemaids. His father taught him to pour drinks for guests of the family when he was very young and he reported that he began to drain the glasses at parties in his home before he was six; by the time he was twelve he drank almost a pint of liquor every weekend and by seventeen was drinking up to three bottles every day. His father provided him with money to buy liquor and shielded him from punishment for drunken driving and other consequences of his drinking.
>
> The patient was expelled from high school his freshman year for striking a teacher. He then attended a private school until the eleventh grade, when he changed the date on his birth certificate and joined the Army paratroops. After discharge, he was unemployed for six months; he drank heavily and

needed repeated care at a sanatorium. When a job was obtained for him he quit within a month. On his third arrest for drunken driving he was jailed. His father bailed him out with the warning that no more money would be forthcoming. The patient left town and worked as an unskilled laborer—he had never acquired any useful skills—but returned home when his father died. During the next few years he was jailed for intoxication, for blackening his mother's eyes when he found a male friend visiting her, and for violating probation by getting drunk. He assaulted and badly hurt a prison guard in an escape attempt and was sentenced to two additional years in prison. When released, he began to use a variety of stimulant, sedative and narcotic drugs as well as alcohol (Rosen, Fox, and Gregory, 1972, p. 312).

Behavioral Effects

The life histories of male alcoholics were once considered to share a common progression. On the basis of an extensive survey of 2000 such men, Jellinek (1952) described the male alcoholic as passing through four stages on the way to his addiction. In the *prealcoholic* phase the individual drinks socially and also on occasion rather heavily to relieve tension and to forget about his problems. In the second *prodromal stage* drinking may become furtive and may also be marked by blackouts. The drinker remains conscious, talks coherently, and carries on other activities, without even appearing to be greatly intoxicated, but later he has no recall of the occasion. Alcohol begins to be used more as a drug and less as a beverage.

Jellinek terms the third phase *crucial*, choosing this adjective because he sees the alcoholic in this stage as being in severe danger of losing everything that he values. He has already lost control of his drinking. Once he takes a single drink, he continues to consume alcohol until he is too sick or in too much of a stupor to drink anymore. The individual's social adjustment also begins to deteriorate. He starts to drink during the day, and this becomes evident to his employer, family, and friends. The alcoholic neglects his diet, has his first bender, a several-day period of excessive drinking, and may experience hallucinations and delirium when he stops drinking. At this stage the individual still has the ability to abstain. He can give up alcohol for several weeks or even months at a time, but if he has just one drink the whole pattern will begin again.

In the final *chronic stage* drinking is continual, and benders are frequent. The individual lives only to drink.

Betty Ford and Dick Van Dyke are among the growing number of prominent people who have made public their problems with alcohol and the treatments that they have sought to curb their alcohol abuse.

His bodily systems have become so accustomed to alcohol that they must be supplied with it or he suffers withdrawal reactions. If liquor is not available to him, he will consume any liquid he can find that contains alcohol— shaving lotion, hair tonic, various medicinal preparations, whatever. He suffers from malnutrition and other physiological changes. He neglects his personal appearance and, having lost his self-esteem, feels little remorse about any aspect of his behavior. Finally, he ceases to

Advertisement for a nineteenth-century play which portrayed the evils of alcohol.

care at all about family and home, about friends, occupation, and social status.

Jellinek's description has been widely cited, but the available evidence is not always corroborative. One study found that blackouts do *not* occur in conjunction with modest drinking and that many alcoholics have never experienced a blackout (Goodwin, Crane, and Guze, 1969). Data now available also question the commonly accepted notion that a single drink stimulates an irresistible impulse to continue drinking (Marlatt, Demming, and Reid, 1973). Alcoholics "primed" with an initial drink, one they believed to be nonalcoholic, later consumed no more alcohol than did social drinkers. Finally, there is much less consistency in the progression from problem drinking to alcoholism than Jellinek implied. In a four-year follow-up of problem drinkers, Clark and Cahalan (1976) found much variability in outcome.

A growing body of evidence also indicates that Jellinek's account does not apply to alcoholic women. Alcoholism usually begins at a later age in women than in men and very often after an inordinately stressful experience, such as the death of a husband or a serious family crisis. For women the time interval between the onset of problem drinking and alcoholism is briefer. Alcoholic women tend more than men to be steady drinkers and to drink alone; they are also less likely to engage in binge drinking (Hill, 1980; Wolin, 1980).

Physiological Effects

In addition to the psychological deterioration brought on by alcoholism, severe physiological damage is a serious consequence of chronic drinking. Almost every tissue and organ of the body is affected by the prolonged consumption of alcohol. The malnutrition suffered may be severe. Because alcohol provides calories—a pint of 80 proof spirits supplies about half a day's caloric requirements—alcoholics often reduce their intake of food. But the calories provided by alcohol are "empty"; they do not supply the nutrients essential for health. Alcohol also contributes directly to malnutrition by impairing the digestion of food. In the older chronic alcoholic a deficiency of B-complex vitamins is believed to cause severe memory loss (Korsakoff's psychosis, page 602). A drastic reduction in the intake of protein contributes to the development of cirrhosis of the liver, a disease in which some liver cells become engorged with fat and protein, impeding their function, and some cells die, triggering an inflammatory process. In the next stage scar tissue develops and blood flow is obstructed. Cirrhosis ranks eighth among causes of death in the United States, and for many years deaths from alcohol-related cirrhosis have remained constant at approximately 5 per 100,000 of the population (Malin et al., 1982). The disease is more common in women alcoholics than in male. Alcohol per se also disturbs liver functions and damages liver cells. Other common physiological changes include damage to the endocrine glands and pancreas, heart failure, hypertension, and capillary hemorrhages, which are responsible for the swelling and redness in the face, and especially of the nose, of chronic alcoholics. Prolonged use of alcohol also appears to damage brain cells, especially those in the frontal lobes, causing cortical atrophy and other changes in structure (Parsons, 1975).

Heavy alcohol consumption during pregnancy can retard the growth of the fetus and infant and can cause cranial, facial, and limb anomalies as well as mental retardation. The condition is known as *fetal alcohol syndrome*. Even moderate drinking can produce less severe but undesirable effects on the fetus, leading the National Institute on Alcohol Abuse and Alcoholism to counsel total abstention during pregnancy as the safest course (*Alcohol, Drug Abuse and Mental Health Administration News*, May 2, 1980).

The effects of the abrupt withdrawal of alcohol from an alcoholic may be rather dramatic, for the body has become profoundly accustomed to the drug. Subjectively, the patient is often frightened, depressed, weak, restless and unable to sleep. Tremors of the muscles, especially of the small musculatures of the fingers, face, eyelids, lips, and tongue, may be marked, and there is an elevation of pulse, blood pressure, and temperature. The patient sweats profusely, and the pupils of his eyes react slowly to changes in light. An alcoholic who has been drinking for a number of years may also suffer from _delirium tremens_ (DTs) when the level of alcohol in the blood drops suddenly. He becomes delirious as well as tremulous. His hallucinations are primarily visual, but they may be tactile as well. Unpleasant and very active creatures—snakes, cockroaches, spiders, and the like—may appear to be crawling up the wall or all over the alcoholic's body, or they may fill the room. Feverish, disoriented, and terrified, the alcoholic may claw frantically at his skin to rid himself of the vermin, or he may cower in the corner to escape an advancing army of fantastic animals.

If body heat continues to rise, a significant percentage of brain cells may be destroyed. Indeed, the nervous system may be so disturbed that physiological functioning becomes erratic. Breathing may stop and the body may be thrown into convulsions. Death is imminently possible if the alcoholic in withdrawal from the drug is not hospitalized and given immediate medical care.

The delirium and physiological paroxysms caused by withdrawal of alcohol indicate that the drug is addictive. Increased tolerance is also evident. Mello and Mendelson (1970) found that some alcoholics could drink a quart of bourbon a day without showing signs of drunkenness. Moreover, levels of alcohol in the blood were unexpectedly low after what would usually be viewed as excessive drinking.

Although changes in the liver enzymes that metabolize alcohol can account to some extent for tolerance, most researchers now believe that the central nervous system is implicated. Alcohol can, for example, increase the fluidity of nerve cell membranes and by this process alter electrical conduction in the brain (National Institute on Alcohol Abuse and Alcoholism, 1983).

In short, _the psychological, physiological, and social consequences of prolonged consumption of alcohol are extremely serious._ Because the alcoholic's own functioning is so severely disrupted, the people he interacts with are also deeply affected and hurt by his conduct. Society too suffers, for the alcoholic is unlikely to be able to hold a job. The accumulated costs—the money spent on liquor, the time lost in work efficiency, the damage of traffic accidents, the expense of physicians and psychologists—run to tens of billions of dollars each year. The human tragedy, much more devastating, is virtually incalculable.

Theories of Alcoholism

In trying to understand alcoholism, we must draw a distinction between conditions that induce a person to _start_ drinking and those that play the central role in _maintaining_ the behavior. Chronic drinking can become an addiction; an alcoholic eventually continues drinking because his or her body demands alcohol. But the later physical need does not explain why an individual initially develops a drinking habit. Those who attempt to explain the origins of habitual drinking refer to either psychological or physiological factors. Within each of these two broad categories there are several theories.

Psychological Theories
Psychoanalytic views   Most analytic accounts of alcoholism point to _fixation at the oral stage_ of development as the precipitating cause. Early mother-child interactions supposedly either frustrate dependency needs during this stage of maturation or satisfy them to too great an extent. The various psychoanalytic theories therefore differ in the function attributed to excessive drinking. For example, Knight (1937) proposed that the male alcoholic's experience with an overprotective mother has developed a strong need to remain dependent. When this need is frustrated, he becomes angry and aggressive and feels guilty about his impulses. He drinks heavily to reduce these impulses and also to punish those who withhold affection from him. Fenichel (1945), in contrast, stated that being neglected by the mother turns the young male child toward his father, which in turn produces unconscious homosexual impulses. These repressed impulses compel him to drink in bars with other men, an activity that supposedly allows the alcoholic to obtain some of the emotional satisfaction he has not received from women. (It is not clear what the psychodynamic significance of solitary drinking would be.) Bergler (1946), emphasizing the self-destructive nature of alcoholism, hypothesized that alcohol addiction is a means of attempting to destroy a bad mother with whom the individual has identified. Little evidence is available to support these hypotheses.

Other analytic accounts of alcoholism describe excessive drinking as a defense mechanism adopted to reduce emotional conflicts or eliminate guilt. A common analytic quip defines the superego as the part of the personality that is soluble in alcohol.

Learning views   The notion that the consumption of alcohol can *reduce distress* is also advanced in learning-based accounts of alcoholism. An early experiment by Conger (1951) demonstrated that alcohol can relieve fear. First, animals were trained in a classic approach-avoidance situation: after having been trained to feed in a particular place, the animals were subjected to shock when they approached their food. Half of the animals were then injected with alcohol. These animals were found to approach the food more readily than did the controls. The fear that had become associated with the goal was apparently decreased by the alcohol in the bloodstream of the animals. Other investigations have replicated this work and also shown that conflict could increase alcohol consumption (Freed, 1971; Von Wright, Pekanmaki, and Malin, 1971).

Generalizing from these studies, we might argue that drinking alcohol is a learned response that is acquired and maintained because it reduces distress. Alcohol, however, has other effects besides the immediate allaying of tension, as our review of the long-term deleterious effects of continual drinking has revealed. Should not these extremely serious long-term negative effects outweigh the transient relief from stress felt when alcohol is first consumed? Dollard and Miller (1950) offered as a solution to this seeming paradox the concept of a *delay of reward gradient*. According to this formulation, the effectiveness of both rewards and punishments, in terms of their impact on any particular behavior, tends to decrease as they become farther and farther removed in time from the response. Thus a small but immediate reward exerts a more powerful effect than a larger one that does not immediately follow the response. Similarly, an immediate punishment is a much more effective agent of change than a punishment imposed several days, weeks, or even months later. In this sense the short-term reduction of distress offered by alcohol is seen as a rather large and immediately reinforcing benefit. Conversely, the longer-term effects of alcohol are of no avail in discouraging its consumption because they are suffered so long after the actual drinking.

The theory that the alcoholic drinks because alcohol reduces tension does not appear to account for the continuation of drinking over long periods of time. For example, Nathan and his colleagues (1970) reported a study in which alcoholics residing in a specially designed hospital ward were carefully observed. The patients were allowed to work to obtain points which could later be exchanged for alcohol. Although the patients themselves reported that they drank to relieve anxiety and depression, an assessment of their moods by means of a self-report adjective checklist indicated that they were actually *more* anxious and depressed after drinking. Similar results were reported by Mendelson (1964).

A recent study, however, does support the theory that people begin drinking to dampen tension. Sher and Levenson (1982) studied alcohol's tension-reducing properties in two groups of young men. One group was assumed to be at high risk for developing alcoholism, based on their responses to a set of forty-nine MMPI items that are able to detect future alcoholics. The second group scored low on the test and thus were assumed to be at low risk. Subjects were given either a moderate dose of alcohol or none at all, and stress was manipulated by telling them that they were soon to experience an electric shock or be forced to make a self-disclosing speech. Alcohol indeed reduced tension in this study, both by the subjects' self-reports and on a number of physiological measures made while they awaited the moment when they would be shocked or have to make a speech. But it did so only for the young men assumed to be at high risk for becoming alcoholics.

Investigators have also developed more specific versions of the theory. One of these is Hull's proposal that alcohol decreases self-awareness by interfering with the cognitive processes that select information about the self. Alcohol could therefore *indirectly* reduce tension if the person was troubled by negative thoughts about the self. Hull (1981) has marshaled evidence for his theory. He has shown, for example, that alcohol reduces the frequency with which people make self-focused statements while delivering a speech, assumed to be a measure of self-awareness. Similarly, other research demonstrates that alcohol lessens awareness of poor performance on an experimental task (Lubin, 1977). Finally, Hull reports that highly self-conscious subjects, after they have gone through a laboratory-induced failure, consume more alcohol than subjects with little self-consciousness. They apparently drink as a means of coping with failure and the negative thoughts about self that failure brings. Hull's promising refinement of the tension reduction theory, and other efforts in the same vein, will likely keep the theory active.

The sociocultural view   It has been argued that ethnic groups such as the Jews, Italians, and Chinese, who specify appropriate ceremonial, nutritional, or festive uses of alcohol, have lower rates of alcoholism. Although these people condone the drinking of alcohol under specified circumstances, they frown on overindulgence. For other national groups, such as the Irish and

The Passover seder is a socially sanctioned, ceremonial use of alcohol.

the English, the circumstances in which the consumption of alcohol is deemed appropriate are less clear. Empirically, there is a strong relation between the level of use of alcohol in a culture and the frequency of alcohol problems. Indeed, of all the sociocultural variables examined in a comprehensive study, the average level of alcohol use was the most important predictor of alcohol-related damage (Frankel and Whitehead, 1981).

A study carried out by McCord, McCord, and Gudeman (1959, 1960) reveals the importance of *ethnic and cultural backgrounds* in the etiology of alcoholism of males in the United States. Young men who had been intensively studied several years earlier as adolescents were followed up. In examining the earlier histories of those who had become alcoholics, the investigators found the relation of alcoholism and ethnic background to be significant. More young men with American Indian, western and eastern European, and Irish backgrounds were alcoholic than were those of Italian and other Latin extractions. The investigators also found a relation between alcoholism and social class: more of the alcoholics were from the middle class than from the lower class.

Although social and cultural factors are clearly important, they obviously cannot be the only ones. The relationship between ethnic background and alcoholism is not one to one; some Jews are alcoholics, and not every Irishman is addicted to the beverage. Furthermore, comparisons of various countries reveal a pattern of alcoholism not entirely consistent with this view. The rate of alcoholism in Ireland, for example, is actually quite low, and Italians have the second highest rate.

Epidemiologists pursue their own methods when studying alcoholism and examine the broad social contexts in which people live. Fillmore and Caetano (1980) found unusually high levels of alcoholism among sailors, railroad workers, and people in the "drink trade"—restaurant owners, bartenders, waiters, and liquor dealers. In all these occupations heavy drinking is normative, that is, almost expected as part of the job, and alcohol is readily available to these men. A survey of occupational drinking by Mannello and Seaman (1979) showed that 14 percent of railroad workers drank on the job, 5 percent came to work drunk or got drunk on duty, and 20 percent reported to work with hangovers. These are alarming statistics, considering the fact that railroad personnel are responsible for the physical safety of hundreds of thousands of people each day. Improvements in working conditions might help, such as more generous allowances for sick leave and modifying the requirement that railroad workers be on call for eight hours following every work shift.

Physiological Theories

Inasmuch as chronic alcoholism becomes a physiological addiction, theorists point to physiological factors in attempting to explain why some people begin a drinking pattern that eventuates in addiction. Among animals a preference for alcohol or indifference to it varies with the species. By selective mating within a species showing a preference, animals that greatly prefer alcohol to other beverages can be bred (Segovia-Riquelme, Varela, and Mardones, 1971). And there is evidence that alcoholism in human beings runs in families. A number of studies indicate that relatives and children of alcoholics have higher than expected rates of alcoholism. Studies indicating greater concordance for alcoholism in identical twins than in fraternal also point toward a possible role of heredity. Although these findings are consistent with the genetic transmission of a predisposition, these individuals might also have become alcoholics through exposure to drinking.

One study, however, examined alcoholism in the adopted offspring of alcoholics, thus allowing the role of heredity to be more precisely specified (Goodwin et al., 1973). One hundred seventy-four subjects were chosen from an initial pool of 5483 male babies who were adopted in Copenhagen between 1924 and 1947. Subjects were divided into the three following experimental and control groups.

1. $N = 67$: One and sometimes both biological parents of each subject (proband) in the experimental group had been hospitalized for alcoholism. The probands had been adopted within six weeks of birth by nonrelatives and had had no subsequent contact with biological relatives.

2. $N = 70$: Each subject in this control group was matched for age and time of adoption with a subject in group 1. None of the biological parents of these control subjects had a record of psychiatric hospitalization.

3. $N = 37$: The subjects in this control group were matched for age and time of adoption with subjects in group 1. At least one biological parent of each of these control subjects had been hospitalized for a psychiatric condition other than alcoholism or schizophrenia.

When this original sample was followed up, 133 subjects were located and interviewed. (Those who could not be located or who refused to be questioned were proportionately distributed across groups.) The subjects, who had a mean age of thirty at the time of the follow-up, were interviewed by a psychiatrist blind to their group assignment. Questions covered their drinking practices, psychopathology, and demographic variables. Since the subjects in the two control groups did not differ on any of the classificatory variables except having or not having a parent with a record of psychiatric hospitalization, they were combined into one comparison group for purposes of analysis. Problems that significantly discriminated between the experimental group and the comparison group are given in Table 11.2.

TABLE 11.2 The Alcohol-Related Problems of Offspring of Alcoholics, Adopted and Raised by Others, Compared with Those of Controls
(from Goodwin et al., 1973)

Problems	Probands, percent ($N = 55$)	Controls, percent ($N = 78$)
Ever divorced	27	9
Any psychiatric treatment	40	24
Psychiatric hospitalization	15	3
Drinking problems		
Hallucinations (as withdrawal symptons)	6	0
Loss of control	35	17
Repeated morning drinking	29	11
Treated for drinking	9	1
Alcoholic diagnosis	18	5

As can be seen, the two groups are easily distinguished one from the other on the basis of alcohol-related measures. Thus the results suggest that in men a predisposition toward alcoholism can be inherited.

Subsequent research has generally confirmed Goodwin's findings for adopted males (for example, Cadoret, Cain, and Grove, 1980). The results of studies with adopted daughters, however, are less clear. Goodwin and his colleagues (1977) found little evidence for any genetic contribution, but Bohman, Sigvardsson, and Cloninger (1981) found adopted daughters to be susceptible to alcoholism if their biological mother was alcoholic.

In speculating on what might be inherited as a diathesis for alcoholism, Goodwin (1979) proposes the ability to tolerate alcohol. To become an alcoholic, a person first has to be able to drink a lot, in other words, be able to tolerate large quantities of alcohol. Some ethnic groups, notably Orientals, may have a low rate of alcoholism because of their physiological intolerance. Indeed, about three-quarters of Orientals experience unpleasant effects from small quantities of alcohol.

Noxious effects of the drug may then protect a person from alcoholism.

Goodwin's hypothesis focuses on short-term effects, possibly on how alcohol is metabolized or on how the central nervous system responds to alcohol. Animal research indicates that genetic components are at work in both these processes (Schuckit, 1983). Even more interesting is a study comparing people with alcoholism in their family history—thus a high-risk group—and those with none. After an overnight fast these two groups of subjects came to the laboratory and were given a moderate dose of alcohol to drink. For the next five hours the levels of acetaldehyde were about two times higher in subjects with a family history of alcoholism, suggesting that some aspect of alcohol metabolism is deviant in people with a genetic predisposition (Schuckit and Rayses, 1979).

Therapy for Alcoholism

The havoc created by alcoholism, both for the drinkers themselves and for their families, friends, employers, and communities, makes this problem the most serious public health issue in this country. As already mentioned, no dollar figure can be put on the human tragedy that is a direct result of this most prevalent form of drug abuse. For these reasons industry spends large sums of money in support of various alcohol rehabilitation programs for employees, in the knowledge that for every dollar spent in this way, many more dollars will be returned in improved functioning of workers. Television and radio carry public service messages about the dangers of alcoholism, in attempts to discourage people from beginning to drink to excess and to encourage those already addicted to own up to their problem and seek help. Calling excessive drinking a disease is believed preferable to holding persons responsible for their drinking; presumably this lessens guilt and allows them to mobilize their resources to seek help and combat their alcoholism.

Traditional Hospital Treatment

Both public and private hospitals around the world have for many years provided retreats for alcoholics, sanctums where individuals can "dry out" and avail themselves of a variety of individual and group therapies, which they will need. The withdrawal from alcohol—*detoxification*—can be very painful, both physically and psychologically, and even fatal if not done under medical supervision. Tranquilizers are sometimes given to ease the anxiety and general discomfort of withdrawal.

Because many alcoholics misuse tranquilizers, some clinics try gradual tapering off without tranquilizers rather than sudden cutoff of alcohol. The alcoholic will need carbohydrate solutions and B vitamins either way and perhaps an anticonvulsant.

Disulfiram, or Antabuse, can discourage the patient from drinking; it causes violent vomiting should the person drink alcohol. Many alcoholics are naturally reluctant even to take the drug, but if they can be motivated to do so, Antabuse can be an effective therapy (Bourne, Alford, and Bowcock, 1966). The effects of Antabuse last about four days. If the alcoholic patient agrees to take the drug every four days, he is fairly certain not to drink. This buys times, a precious commodity. For the first time in a long while, the person has the chance to live without booze, to experience a football game without beer, a business luncheon without a martini, an evening at home without cocktails. Problems underlying the reliance on alcohol can become more evident. The therapist will be better able to evaluate what needs to be worked on in treatment, and with any luck the patient may begin to see the possibility of dealing with his problems without alcohol (Goodwin, 1982).

Alcoholics Anonymous

The largest and most widely known self-help group in the world is Alcoholics Anonymous (AA), founded in 1935 by two recovered drinkers. It currently has 30,000 chapters and a membership numbering more than a mil-

Alateen provides support for teenagers who live with an alcoholic parent.

lion people in the United States and ninety-one other countries throughout the world. An AA chapter runs regular and frequent meetings at which newcomers rise to announce that they are alcoholics, and older sober members give testimonials, relating the stories of their alcoholism and indicating how their lives are better now. The group provides emotional support, understanding, and close counseling for the alcoholic and a social life to relieve isolation. Members are urged to call upon one another around the clock when they need companionship and encouragement not to relapse into drink.

The belief is instilled in each AA member that alcoholism is a disease one is never cured of, that continuing vigilance is necessary to resist taking even a single drink lest uncontrollable drinking begin all over again. The important religious and spiritual aspect of AA is evident in the twelve steps of AA shown in Table 11.3. Two related self-help groups are of more recent origin. The relatives of alcoholics meet in Al-Anon Family Groups for

TABLE 11.3 Twelve Suggested Steps of Alcoholics Anonymous

1. We admitted we were powerless over alcohol—that our lives had become unmanageable.
2. Came to believe that a power greater than ourselves could restore us to sanity.
3. Made a decision to turn our will and our lives over to the care of God *as we understood Him*.
4. Made a searching and fearless moral inventory of ourselves.
5. Admitted to God, to ourselves, and to another human being the exact nature of our wrongs.
6. Were entirely ready to have God remove all these defects of character.
7. Humbly asked Him to remove our shortcomings.
8. Made a list of all persons we had harmed, and became willing to make amends to them all.
9. Made direct amends to such people wherever possible, except when to do so would injure them or others.
10. Continued to take personal inventory and, when we were wrong, promptly admitted it.
11. Sought through prayer and meditation to improve our conscious contact with God *as we understand Him*, praying only for knowledge of His will for us and the power to carry that out.
12. Having had a spiritual awakening as the result of these steps, we tried to carry this message to alcoholics and to practice these principles in all our affairs.

Source: The Twelve Steps and Twelve Traditions. Copyright © 1952, by Alcoholics Anonymous World Services, Inc. Reprinted with permission of Alcoholics Anonymous World Services, Inc.

mutual support in dealing with their alcoholic family members. Alateen is for the offspring of alcoholics, who also require support and understanding.

Unfortunately, the claims made by AA about the effectiveness of its treatment have rarely been subjected to scientific scrutiny. Available findings indicate that they should be viewed with some caution. For example, as many as 80 percent of people who join AA drop out (Edwards et al., 1967). Furthermore, without follow-up it is impossible to know how enduring are the short-term changes that AA may effect. Since return to excessive drinking is the norm rather than the exception for alcoholics, the absence of such information prevents an adequate evaluation of what many regard as the best treatment for alcoholism.

Aversion Therapy

Behavioral researchers have been studying the treatment of alcoholism for many years. In fact, one of the earliest articles on behavior therapy concerned aversive "conditioning" of alcoholism (Kantorovich, 1930). With these procedures a problem drinker is shocked or made nauseous while looking at, reaching for, or beginning to drink alcohol. The aversive stimulus may also be vividly imagined in a procedure called *covert sensitization* (Cautela, 1966). The alcoholic is instructed to imagine being made violently and disgustingly sick by his or her drinking.

Ethical considerations inhibit investigators in their selection of aversive procedures, for they entail, by their very nature, an assault on the person being treated. Although some drinkers who have undergone chemical *aversion therapy* in the context of a hospital program drink less or not at all at the end of treatment (Wiens and Menustik, 1983), it is doubtful that they do so because of conditioning (Kazdin and Wilson, 1978). Aversion therapy for alcoholism may well work because of the nonspecific, placebo effects of the treatment.

Behavioral Contracting

Making a contract with the alcoholic is somewhat more promising. An alcoholic in an institution agrees to refrain from excessive drinking in exchange for particular rewards, such as weekend passes or better living conditions on the ward. Provided a given patient can be persuaded to enter into the necessary contract, there is some evidence that control over drinking can be achieved (Nathan and Goldman, 1979).

Controlled Drinking

Until recently it was generally agreed that alcoholics had to abstain completely if they were to be cured, for they were said to have no control over their imbibing once they had taken that first drink. Although this continues to be the abiding belief of Alcoholics Anonymous, the research mentioned earlier calls the supposed constitutional weakness into question: drinkers' *beliefs* about themselves and alcohol may be as important as the physiological addiction to the drug itself. Indeed, considering the difficulty in our society of avoiding alcohol altogether, it may even be *preferable* to teach the problem drinker to imbibe with moderation. A drinker's self-esteem will certainly benefit from being able to control a problem and from feeling in charge of his or her life.

In the earliest training for controlled drinking, an outpatient was allowed to drink to a moderate level of intoxication and blood alcohol. He or she was then informed if the level of blood alcohol rose above a certain percent (Lovibond and Caddy, 1970). Thereafter when the person drank, he or she was supposedly able to keep the blood level of alcohol low.

Findings of one treatment program suggested that at least some alcoholics can learn to control their drinking and improve other aspects of their lives as well (Sobell and Sobell, 1976, 1978). Alcoholics attempting to control their drinking were shocked when they chose straight liquor rather than mixed drinks, gulped their drinks down too fast, or took large swallows rather than sips. They were also given problem-solving and assertiveness training, watched videotapes of their inebriated selves, and identified the situations precipitating their drinking so that they could settle on a less self-destructive course of action. Their improvement was greater than that of alcoholics who tried for total abstinence and were shocked for any drinking at all. Several years later, however, these findings came under sharp attack. Many controlled-drinking patients did in fact continue to drink heavily and were not open with follow-up interviewers about their drinking practices (Pendery, Maltzman, and West, 1982). This issue is quite controversial (Marlatt, 1983). Many workers in the field continue to question the wisdom of *controlled drinking* for alcoholics, being concerned that for many the belief that they can imbibe with moderation will prove to be an illusion.

There may be a way to resolve this apparent inconsistency in findings and philosophy. Investigators at the Rand Corporation, a research institute in Santa Monica, California, determined that for some patients—alcoholics under forty with relatively little dependency on alcohol—controlled drinking seemed a better goal in rehabilitation than total abstinence. The opposite was true for older, more addicted drinkers, however (Armor,

Polich, and Stambul, 1976, 1978). Of particular interest is the finding that moderate drinking rather than abstinence seems to work for some alcoholics who have gone through a total-abstinence program (Marlatt, 1983). In other words, although their treatment goal had been to cease all drinking, some of the patients adopted a pattern of moderate, off-and-on drinking while maintaining employment and other common indicators of any successful therapy.[3]

Contemporary controlled-drinking treatment programs do much more than the earliest ventures, which concentrated on teaching patients to monitor their blood alcohol levels. Patients are taught other ways of responding to situations that might lead to excessive drinking. Learning to resist social pressures to drink; assertivenes, relaxation, and stress management training, sometimes including biofeedback and meditation; and exercise and better diets will all help to bolster them. They are also taught that a lapse will not inevitably precipitate a total relapse and can be regarded as a learning experience. Sources of stress in their work, family, and relationships are examined. To be able to control their drinking, they must become active and responsible in anticipating and resisting situations that might tempt excesses (Marlatt, 1983).

Clinical Considerations

A general problem with attempts to treat alcoholism has been the therapist's often unstated assumption that all people who drink to excess do so for the same reasons. Thus an analyst may assume that problem drinkers are trying to escape from intolerable feelings of dependency. A humanistic theorist may hold that the excessive drinker escapes into the haze of alcohol because he or she lacks courage to face problems and deal with them in an open, direct fashion. A behavior therapist favoring aversive treatment believes that reducing the attraction alcohol or its taste has for drinkers will help them abstain. As is true of people with other human problems, however, those who drink are not likely to be this simple (Lazarus, 1965). A more sophisticated and comprehensive clinical assessment considers the place that drinking

---

[3]There is a definitional issue here. Are these younger drinkers really alcoholics? Some show no signs yet of tolerance and withdrawal. They might be called "problem drinkers" (Lang and Marlatt, 1982), people whose lives are seriously disrupted by periods of drunkenness but who have no clear signs of physical addiction. But to those who regard alcoholism as a progressive disease with an inexorable course of ever stronger addiction, such drinkers are incipient alcoholics, for whom total abstinence is the only sensible goal.

occupies in the person's life. A woman in a desperately unhappy marriage, with meaningless time on her hands at home, now that her children are in school and no longer need her constant attention, may seek the numbing effects of alcohol just to help the time pass and to avoid facing her life dilemmas. Making the taste of alcohol unpleasant for this woman by pairing it with shock or an emetic seems neither sensible nor adequate. The therapist should concentrate on the marital and family problems and try to reduce the psychological pain that permeates her existence. Since she is probably a true addict, she will also need help in tolerating the withdrawal symptoms that come with reduced consumption. And without alcohol as a reliable anesthetic, she will need to mobilize other resources to confront her hitherto avoided problems. Social-skills training may help her to do so.

In addition, alcoholism is sometimes associated with other mental disorders, in particular affective disorders and sociopathy (Goodwin, 1982). The clinician must conduct a broad-spectrum assessment of the patient's problem, for if heavy drinking stems from the desperation of deep depression, a regimen of Antabuse or any other treatment focused only on alcohol is unlikely to be of lasting value.

Early advertisement from the Bayer Company, illustrating the legal sale of heroin as a medicant for coughing.

SEDATIVES AND STIMULANTS

Until 1914 addiction to drugs was disapproved in the United States, but it was tolerated. The 1914 Harrison Narcotics Act changed this, making the unauthorized use of various drugs illegal and those addicted to them criminals. The drugs to be discussed, not all of which are illegal, may be divided into two general categories. The major *sedatives*, called "downers," slow the activities of the body and reduce its responsiveness. In this group of drugs are the organic narcotics—opium and its derivatives morphine, heroin, and codeine—and the synthetic barbiturates. The second group, the *stimulants* or "uppers," act on the brain and the sympathetic nervous system to increase alertness and motor activity. The amphetamines are synthetic stimulants; cocaine is a natural stimulant extracted from the coca leaf.

Sedatives

Narcotics

Opium, originally the principal drug of illegal international traffic, was known to the people of the Sumerian civilization dating back to 7000 B.C. They gave the poppy that supplied this narcotic the name by which it is still known and which means "the plant of joy." Opium is a mixture of about eighteen alkaloids, but until 1806 people had no knowledge of these substances to which so many natural drugs owe their potency. In that year the alkaloid *morphine*, named after Morpheus, the Greek god of dreams, was separated out from raw opium. This bitter-tasting powder proved to be a powerful sedative and pain reliever. Before its addictive properties were noted, it was commonly used in patent medicines. In the middle of the century, when the hypodermic needle was introduced in the United States, morphine began to be injected directly into the veins to relieve pain. Many soliders wounded in battle and those suffering from dysentery during the Civil War were treated with morphine and returned home addicted to the drug. Concerned about administering a drug that could disturb the later lives of patients, scientists began studying morphine. They thought that part of its molecule might be responsible for relieving pain and another part for its addictiveness. In 1874 they found that morphine could be converted into another powerful pain-relieving drug, which they named *heroin*. It was used initially as a cure for morphine addiction and was substituted for morphine in cough syrups and other patent medicines. So many maladies were treated with heroin that it came to be known as G.O.M. or "God's own medicine" (Brecher, 1972). Heroin proved to be even more potent than morphine, however, acting more quickly and with greater intensity, and it is more addictive. By 1909 President Theodore Roosevelt was calling for an international investigation of opium and the opiates.

Opium and its derivatives morphine and heroin produce euphoria, drowsiness, reverie, and sometimes a lack of coordination. Heroin has an additional initial effect, the "rush," a feeling of warm, suffusing ecstasy immediately following an injection. The addict sheds worries and fears and has great self-confidence for four to six hours. Then letdown, bordering on stupor. Because these drugs are central nervous system depressants, they relieve pain. All three are clearly addicting in the physiological sense, for users show both increased tolerance of the drugs and withdrawal reactions when they are unable to obtain another dose.

Our understanding of the process of addiction to opiates has increased greatly over the past decade. In the early 1970s several laboratories reported the presence in vertebrate brains of what appeared to be specific opiate receptors, that is, cell components to which opiates bind to produce euphoria and analgesia. Because it seemed unlikely that such receptors had been developed to interact with opiate alkaloids in the environment, a search began for internally produced (endogenous) opiates. By 1975 such compounds, called _endorphins_, had been discovered in several species, including human beings (Goldstein, 1976). Apparently we all can produce our own opiates. Endorphins are thought to be the body's own pain relievers and may play a crucial role in addiction. Ingesting an exogenous opiate, such as heroin, may halt the normal production of endorphins. If later the exogenous substance is no longer supplied, an individual could be left with no opiates in the body, either exogenous or endogenous, precipitating withdrawal reactions.

Reactions to not having a dose of heroin may begin within eight hours of the last injection, at least after high tolerance has built up. During the next few hours the individual will typically have muscle pain, will sneeze, sweat, become tearful, and yawn a great deal; the symptoms resemble influenza. Within thirty-six hours the withdrawal symptoms have become more severe. There may be uncontrollable muscle twitching, cramps, chills alternating with excessive flushing and sweating, and a rise in heart rate and blood pressure. The addict is unable to sleep, vomits, and has diarrhea. These symptoms typically persist for about seventy-two

hours and then diminish gradually over a five- to ten-day period.

The use of heroin in the United States increased greatly in the 1960s, but since then addiction has remained relatively constant, at about 400,000 cases (Dogoloff, 1980). A new kind of heroin has been described by the staff of the Haight-Ashbury Clinic in San Francisco (as reported by Leibtag, 1980). Imported from Iran, "Persian" is considerably more potent than other forms of street heroin—92 percent pure as compared with the usual 2 to 4 percent. Persian is usually smoked or "snorted" rather than injected. This kind of ingestion of the drug presents new hazards of pulmonary complications as well as of rapid addiction. Withdrawal from Persian, as might be expected, is markedly more severe than that from weaker preparations of the drug. Dealers have been trying to meet this new competition by mixing their weaker heroin with instant coffee, to give it the brown, powdery appearance of Persian. More ominously—because heroin depresses breathing—they have been selling cleaner heroin, up to 50 percent pure.

Even more serious than the physical effects are the social consequences of narcotic addiction. The drug and obtaining it become the center of existence, structuring all activities and social relationships. Since narcotics are illegal, addicts must deal with the underworld in order to maintain their habits. The high cost of the drugs—addicts must often spend $100 and more per day for their narcotics—means that they must either have great wealth or acquire money through illegal activities, such as prostitution or selling drugs themselves.[4] Thus the correlation between addiction and criminal activities is rather high, undoubtedly contributing to the popular notion that drug addiction per se causes crime.

Barbiturates and Other Sedatives

Barbiturates were synthesized as aids for sleeping and relaxation. The first was produced in 1903, and since then hundreds of derivatives of barbituric acid have been made. Two types are usually distinguished—long-acting barbiturates for prolonged sedation and short-acting barbiturates for prompt sedation and sleep. The short-acting drugs are usually viewed as addicting. Initially, the drugs were considered highly desirable and were prescribed very frequently. In the 1940s, however, a campaign was mounted against them because they were discovered to be addicting, and physicians prescribed barbiturates less frequently. Today in the United States they are manufactured in vast quantities, enough, it is

[4]Recent indications are that heroin use is increasing in the upper socioeconomic classes.

Several aspects of drug abuse. (Top left) A medical team trying to revive a heroin OD case. (Right) A "shooting gallery" which had just been raided by the police. (Bottom left) A cocaine hot line at a New Jersey hospital.

ing a mildly euphoric state. With excessive doses, however, speech becomes slurred and gait unsteady. Impairment of judgment, concentration, and ability to work may be extreme. The user loses emotional control and may become irritable and combative before falling into a deep sleep. Very large doses can be fatal because the diaphragm muscles relax to such an extent that the individual suffocates. As we have indicated in Chapter 9, barbiturates are frequently chosen as a means of suicide. But many users accidently kill themselves by drinking alcohol, which potentiates, or magnifies, the depressant effects of barbiturates. With prolonged excessive use the brain can become damaged and personality deteriorates.

Increased tolerance follows prolonged use of the barbiturates, and the withdrawal reactions after abrupt termination are particularly severe and long lasting and can even cause sudden death. The delirium, convulsions, and other symptoms resemble those following abrupt withdrawal of alcohol. Properly prescribed and used, barbiturates can be safe and effective. If a user purchases them on the street, however, he or she is vulnerable to being sold other drugs packaged to look like barbiturates, or drugs made by amateur home chemists

estimated, to supply each man, woman, and child with fifty pills per year. Many are shipped legally to Mexico and then brought back into the country and trafficked illegally. The majority of polydrug abusers choose a barbiturate or other sedative as one of their drugs.

Barbiturates—the street for the most part offers pentobarbital, secobarbital, and amobarbital—are depressants,[5] relaxing the muscles and in small doses producing

[5]Methaqualone, a sedative sold under the trade names Quaalude and Sopor, is similar in effect to barbiturates and has become a popular street drug. Besides being addictive, it has other dangers—internal bleeding, coma, and even death from overdose.

who may not know how to remove potentially poisonous by-products.

Three types of barbiturate abusers—and abusers of other sedatives such as methaqualone, diazepam (Valium), and meprobamate (Miltown)—can be distinguished. The first group fits the stereotype of the illicit drug abuser: adolescents and young adults, usually male and often antisocial, who use the drugs to alter their moods and consciousness, sometimes mixing them with other drugs. The second group consists of middle-aged, middle-class, "respectable" individuals who begin their use of sedatives under a physician's orders, to alleviate sleeplessness and anxiety, and then come to use larger and larger doses until they are addicted. These people rely less on street purchases because they are generally able to obtain refills of their drug prescriptions whenever they wish, sometimes switching doctors so as not to raise suspicion. The third group are health professionals, physicians and nurses, who have easy access to these drugs and often use them to self-medicate for anxiety-related problems (Shader, Caine, and Meyer, 1975; Liskow, 1982).

Stimulants

Amphetamines

In seeking a treatment for asthma, the Chinese-American pharmacologist Chen studied ancient Chinese descriptions of drugs. He found a desert shrub mahuang commended again and again as an effective remedy. After systematic effort Chen was able to isolate an alkaloid from this plant which belongs to the genus *Ephedra*; ephedrine did indeed prove highly successful in treating asthma. But relying on the shrub for the drug was not viewed as efficient, and so a search began for a synthetic substitute. The *amphetamines* were the result of this search (Synder, 1974).

The first amphetamine, Benzedrine, was synthesized in 1927. Almost as soon as it became commercially available in the early 1930s as an inhalant to relieve stuffy noses, the public discovered its stimulating effects. Physicians thereafter prescribed it and the other amphetamines soon synthesized to control mild depression and appetite. During World War II soldiers on both sides were supplied with the drugs to ward off fatigue; today amphetamines are sometimes used to treat hyperactive children (see page 379).

Amphetamines such as Benzedrine, Dexedrine, and Methedrine produce effects similar to those of norepinephrine in the sympathetic nervous system. They are taken orally or intravenously and can be addicting. Wakefulness is heightened, intestinal functions are inhibited, and appetite is reduced—hence their use in dieting. The heart rate is increased and blood vessels in the skin and mucous membranes constrict. The individual becomes alert, euphoric, and more outgoing and is possessed with seemingly boundless energy and self-confidence. Larger doses can make the person nervous, agitated, and confused, subjecting him or her to palpitations, headaches, dizziness, and sleeplessness. Sometimes the high-level user becomes so suspicious and hostile that he or she can be dangerous to others. There are some reports that large doses taken over a period of time induce a state quite similar to paranoid schizophrenia, including its delusions. This state can persist beyond the time that the drug is present in the body. Frequent ingestion of large amounts of amphetamines is also believed to cause brain damage.

Tolerance develops rapidly so that mouthfuls of pills are required to produce the stimulating effect. As tolerance increases, the user may stop taking pills and inject Methedrine, the strongest of the amphetamines, directly into the veins. The so-called speed freaks give themselves repeated injections of the drug and maintain intense and euphoric activity for a few days, without eating or sleeping, after which they are exhausted and depressed and sleep or "crash" for several days. Then the cycle starts again. After several repetitions of this pattern, the physical and social functioning of the individual will have deteriorated considerably. Behavior will be quite erratic and hostile, and the speed freak may become a danger to himself and to others. Of particular concern is the fact that as many as 20 percent of high school students have taken amphetamines at least once, and its use among younger adolescents is on the increase (Goodwin and Guze, 1984).

Cocaine

The Spanish conquistadors introduced coca leaves to Europe. The Indians of the Andean uplands, to which the coca shrubs are native, chew the leaves, but the Europeans chose to brew them instead in beverages. The alkaloid *cocaine* was extracted from the leaves of the coca plant in 1844 and has been used since then as a local anesthetic. In 1884, while still a young neurologist in Vienna, Sigmund Freud began using cocaine to combat his depression. Convinced of its wondrous effects, he prescribed it to a friend with a painful disease and published one of the first papers on the drug, "Song of Praise," which was an enthusiastic endorsement of the

BOX 11.1

OUR TASTIEST ADDICTION—CAFFEINE

What may be the world's most popular drug is seldom viewed as a drug at all, and yet it has strong effects, produces tolerance in people, and even subjects habitual users to withdrawal. Users and nonusers alike joke about it, and most readers of this book have probably had some this very day. We are of course referring to caffeine, a substance found in coffee, tea, cocoa, cola and other soft drinks, in some cold remedies, and in some diet pills.

Coffee, introduced from Arabia and Turkey in the fifteenth and sixteenth centuries, was, like tobacco, initially considered abhorrent to Europeans and Americans. "Proper" people regarded it as hazardous and drinking it unseemly because of its stimulating effects, which sometimes included "blasphemous" speech. And yet its popularity spread. People found that it "quickens the spirits," and they liked its taste, which improved with the addition

Caffeine is part of many everyday activities. The powerful effects of this drug are now becoming more widely known.

of sugar, making the beverage even more popular. In 1652 the first London coffeehouse was established. In 1854 the first coffeehouses appeared in Constantinople. It is impossible to picture present-day Western culture and much of Eastern without the ceremony and sociability of moments shared over cups of coffee (Brecher, 1972).*

Two cups of coffee, containing between 150 and 300 milligrams of caffeine, affect most people within half an hour. Metabolism, body temperature, and blood pressure all increase; urine production goes up, as most of us will attest; there may be hand tremors, appetite can diminish, and, most familiar of all, sleepiness is warded off. Extremely large doses of caffeine can cause headache, diarrhea, nervousness, severe agitation, even convulsions and death. Such deaths, though, are virtually impossible unless the individual grossly overuses tablets containing caffeine, for the drug is rapidly excreted by the kidneys without any appreciable accumulation.

Habitual users find it difficult to begin their day without their usual mug or two of the brew and, when they cannot, sometimes suffer such withdrawal symptoms as headaches, irritability, and mood changes. Although parents usually deny their children access to coffee and tea, often they do allow them to imbibe caffeine-laden cola drinks, hot chocolate, and cocoa, and to eat chocolate candy and coffee- and chocolate-flavored ice cream (Berger and Dunn, 1982). Thus our addiction to caffeine can begin to develop as early as six months of age, the form of it changing as we move from childhood to adulthood.

*Some of these cups of coffee are these days decaffeinated, as health-conscious consumers try to avoid or escape from the craving for caffeine. But it is not unusual to hear regular, caffeinated coffee referred to as "real" coffee. In turn, decaffeinated versions endeavor valiantly to establish themselves as legitimate coffee beverages.

exhilarating effects he had experienced.[6] One of the early products using coca leaves in its manufacture was Coca-Cola, the recipe for which was concocted by an

[6]Freud subsequently lost his enthusiasm for cocaine after nursing a physician friend, to whom he had recommended the drug, through a night-long psychotic state brought on by it.

Atlanta druggist in 1886. For the next twenty years Coke was the real thing, but in 1906 the Pure Food and Drugs Act was passed and the manufacturer switched to coca leaves from which the cocaine had been removed.

In addition to its pain-reducing effects, cocaine acts rapidly on the cortex of the brain, heightening sensory awareness and inducing a thirty-minute state of euphoria. Sexual desire is accentuated, and feelings of self-confidence, well-being, and indefatigability suffuse the user's consciousness. An overdose may bring on chills, nausea, and insomnia, as well as a paranoid breakdown and terrifying hallucinations of insects crawling beneath the skin. As users take larger and larger doses of the purer forms of cocaine now available, they are more often rushed to emergency rooms and may die of an overdose (Kozel, Crider, and Adams, 1982).

Cocaine can be sniffed (''snorted''), smoked in pipes or cigarettes, swallowed, or even injected into the veins like heroin; some heroin addicts in fact mix the two drugs in a combination known as ''speedball,'' which is taken orally. In the 1970s cocaine devotees in this country adopted a practice similar to that used in parts of South America for enhancing the effects of the drug. To separate, or free, the most potent component of cocaine, they heat cocaine with ether. When purified by this chemical process, the cocaine base—or ''freebase''—is extremely powerful. Called white tornado, baseball, or snow toke, it is usually smoked in a water pipe or sprinkled on a normal or marijuana cigarette. Rapidly absorbed into the lungs and carried to the brain in a few seconds, the freebase induces an intense, two-minute high, followed by restlessness and discomfort. Some freebase smokers go on marathon binges lasting up to four days (Goodwin and Guze, 1984). The freebasing process is hazardous, however, because ether is flammable. Comedian Richard Pryor nearly died from the burns he suffered when the ether he was using ignited.

Cocaine use has soared in the 1970s and into this decade. The dramatic increase in use is evident in these statistics. In 1974 it was estimated that 5.4 million Americans had tried cocaine at least once; in 1982 this figure had risen to 21.6 million. Current users of the drug numbered 1.6 million in 1974; in 1982 they numbered 4.2 million (National Institute on Drug Abuse, 1983; Blanken, Adams, and Durell, in press, as cited in Adams and Durell, 1984). In 1984 cocaine use among high school seniors increased slightly, all regions considered, but it jumped by over 40 percent among seniors in the Northeastern states. More than 10 percent of high school seniors in this region reported being current users (*The New York Times*, January 8, 1985).

The economics of cocaine provides staggering figures for money spent by those using it heavily. In 1982 people snorting cocaine once a day spent $1000 a week for the drug. Others using it more often reported spending between $2000 and $12,000 a week, being able to

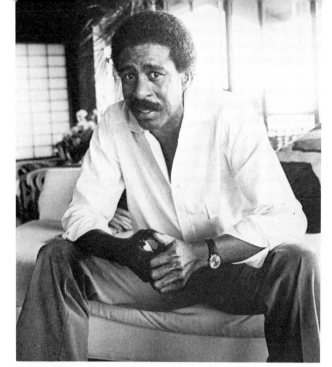

After Richard Pryor's accidental burning, he gave up both cocaine and alcohol.

support their expensive habit because they themselves sold the drug or were independently wealthy (Siegel, 1982). In the early 1980s cocaine cost $2000 an ounce, making it approximately five times more expensive than gold. It was a status symbol in the 1920s among Hollywood performers, and in the 1980s it has reemerged with similar meaning for actors, athletes, and others in the better-paid strata of our society. Now the cost of cocaine has begun to decrease, and people from all segments of society are using it (Adams and Durell, 1984).

Is cocaine addicting? Until very recently it was strongly believed not to be. Opinion, however, has begun to shift, and the question is hotly debated and scientifically complex (Jones, 1984). In our own judgment the data accumulating over the next several years will in fact confirm that cocaine is an addictive drug.

But *even if* cocaine is not truly addicting, it certainly induces in heavy users an extreme reliance and what we earlier termed a psychological dependency, so that the drug becomes the center of the user's life. Current laboratory research as well as field-based research indicates more and more that this drug can take hold of people with as much tenacity as has been demonstrated for years with the established addictive drugs. Animals will select cocaine over access to food and water, even to the extent that they die. Nor do the mass media lack for reports of the social, psychological, economic, and legal damage that some will subject themselves to in order to continue taking the drug (Grabowski, 1984).

Theories of the Origins of Drug Addiction

Physiological Theories
Many have regarded the physiological changes in the body effected by drugs as the most important factor in drug addiction. Because the physiology of the body has been changed by the drug, it reacts when the substance to which it has become accustomed is no longer administered. To avoid withdrawal reactions, the addict continues taking the drug. Physiological alterations are, in turn, viewed as having been established through accident or curiosity. A person may take the drug by chance or because he or she wants to experience its effects. With enough repetition—how much is not known—the person is ensnared by changes in bodily chemistry and the concomitant severity of withdrawal reactions. The addict is regarded as an unwitting victim of physiological reactions, continuing to use the drug to ward off the distress of withdrawal.

Ausubel (1961a) has challenged this interpretation by alleging that the effects of withdrawal from heroin, for example, are in reality no more severe than a bad case of influenza. Anecdotal evidence exists to support Ausubel's claim that the effects of withdrawal are not as severe as is often imagined. As noted earlier, however, the apparent increase in availability of purer forms of heroin is likely to exacerbate the withdrawal problems of addicts.

Psychological Theories
Psychological theories of the origin of drug addiction usually emphasize reduction of distress and the pleasant feeling and euphoric state that the drugs produce. These theories also attempt to explain why particular kinds of people seem to "need" these effects. An association has often been noted between criminality, drug abuse, and antisocial personality disorder. In this context drug abuse may be considered as part of the thrill-seeking behavior of the sociopath discussed in Chapter 10. We might also expect narcotics to be used by anxious individuals in order to reduce their distress. Drug addicts have also been found to be deviant on various personality questionnaire measures. But we must question whether these personality characteristics antedated the addiction and caused it. For example, we might find that drug addicts tend to be more suspicious than nonusers. To conclude that suspiciousness contributes to the use of drugs would not be justified, for it might well be the addict's *reaction* to his illegal status as a drug user.

Some similarities in family background have been identified in the life histories of drug addicts (Chein et al., 1964). In many cases the father is absent from the home of the future addict. If the father is present, he tends to be a shadowy figure or to be overtly hostile and distant. If present he may also serve as a model for criminal behavior, and the relations between the mother and father are likely to be stormy. Chein and his colleagues therefore proposed that the personality defects of the drug addict, whatever they are, were developed through family background. Initial experiences with addicting drugs were also shown to be nonaccidental. Most addicts were found to have been introduced knowingly to the drugs, not by an adult but rather by a member of their peer group, suggesting the importance of peer pressure and curiosity. Boredom and aggravation are probably contributing factors. In ghettoes where narcotics are readily available, and the culture of the streets prevails, the incidence of drug use is especially high.

An intriguing explanation of ghetto drug use and drug dealing has been proposed by Preble and Casey (1969). In their eyes addiction and all that goes with it become a challenge and a full-time occupation. In order to maintain his or her habit, the addict must be actively and resourcefully engaged in a variety of money-making enterprises, such as theft, fencing stolen property, selling drugs, and prostitution. The addiction, then, becomes the organizing principle of life, providing a focus for how the person, now a fully committed hustler, spends his or her days and nights.

Therapy for the Use of Illicit Drugs

Central to the treatment of those who use illicit drugs is detoxification, withdrawing the person from the drug itself. Heroin withdrawal reactions range from relatively mild bouts of anxiety, nausea, and restlessness for several days, to more severe and frightening bouts of delirium and apparent madness, depending primarily on the purity of the heroin that the individual has been using. Someone high on amphetamines can be brought down by appropriate dosages of one of the phenothiazines, a class of drugs more commonly used to treat schizophrenics (see page 555), although it must be kept in mind that the speed freak may also have been using other drugs in conjunction with amphetamines. As for barbiturates, withdrawal reactions from these drugs, as already noted, are especially severe, even life-threatening; they begin about twenty-four hours after the last dose and reach their maximum two or three days later. They have usually abated by the end of the first week, but they may last a month if doses have been large. Withdrawal from these drugs is best done gradually, not "cold turkey," and should take place under close medical supervision (Honigfeld and Howard, 1978).

Withdrawal is but the first way in which therapists try to help the addict or drug abuser, and perhaps ironically it is the easiest part of the rehabilitation process. Finding a way to enable the drug user to function on his or her own, without drugs, is an arduous task which promises more disappointment and sadness than success for both helper and client. Nonetheless, a great number of efforts are made, many of them financed heavily by federal and state governments.

Two widely used drug therapy programs for heroin addiction are the administration of *heroin substitutes* and of *heroin antagonists*. In the first category are *methadone* and methadyl acetate, both synthetic narcotics. Originally developed by Dole and Nyswander (1966), these agents are designed to take the place of heroin. Since they are themselves narcotics, successful treatment merely converts the heroin addict into a methadone addict. The addict must come to a clinic once a day and swallow methadone in the presence of a staff member, three times a week for methadyl acetate, thereby improving his or her lot by no longer having to resort to needles or to criminal activity to satisfy a physical need. Although early reports were encouraging, problems have been noted as well. For one thing, since methadone does not give the addict a euphoric high, many will return to heroin if it becomes available to them. In addition, when methadone is injected, rather than taken orally as it is supposed to be, its effects on some addicts are similar to those of heroin (Honigfeld and Howard, 1978). Not surprisingly, an illegal market in methadone has developed, which would seem to be defeating the purpose of its use. Finally, a great number of people drop out from methadone programs.

Cyclazocine and naloxone are heroin antagonists. After being gradually withdrawn from heroin, addicts receive increasing dosages of either of these drugs, which prevents them from experiencing any high should they later take heroin. The drugs have great affinity for the cells that heroin usually binds to. Their molecules occupy the cells, without stimulating them, and heroin molecules have no place to go. The antagonist, then, changes the whole nature of heroin; it simply will not produce the euphoric effect that the addict seeks. As with methadone, however, addicts must make frequent and regular visits to the clinic, which requires motivation and responsibility on their part. In addition, addicts do not for some time lose the actual craving for heroin.

Drug abuse, though, cannot be dealt with solely by some form of chemotherapy. People turn to drugs for many reasons, and even though in most instances their current drug taking is controlled primarily by a physical addiction, the entire pattern of their existence is bound to be influenced by the drug and must therefore command the attention of whoever would hope to remove the drug from their lives.

Drug abuse is treated in the consulting rooms of psychiatrists, psychologists, and other mental health workers. The several kinds of psychotherapy are applied to drug use disorders as they are to the other human maladjustments. Little can be said, however, about the relative efficacy of psychoanalytic, behavioral, and humanistic therapies in helping people to break their dependence on drugs (Liskow, 1982).

Self-help residential homes or communes, with which most readers are familiar, are the most widespread psychological approach to heroin addiction and other drug abuse. Modeled after Synanon,[7] a therapeutic community of former drug addicts founded by Charles Dederich in Santa Monica, California, in 1958, these residences are designed to restructure radically the addict's outlook on life so that illicit drugs no longer have a place. Daytop Village, Phoenix House, Odyssey House, and other drug rehabilitation homes share the following features.

1. A total environment in which drugs are not available and continuing support is offered to ease the transition from regular drug use to a drug-free existence.

2. The presence of often charismatic role models, former addicts who appear to be meeting life's challenges without drugs.

---

[7]Like its founder, Charles Dederich, who in 1980 pleaded no contest to a charge of attempting to murder a lawyer for Synanon members, by placing a poisonous snake in his mailbox, Synanon has fallen on hard times. Emulated by others, Synanon itself eventually lost its mission. It grew large and wealthy through its business enterprises, and it has been brought to court for acts of violence and for holding residents against their will.

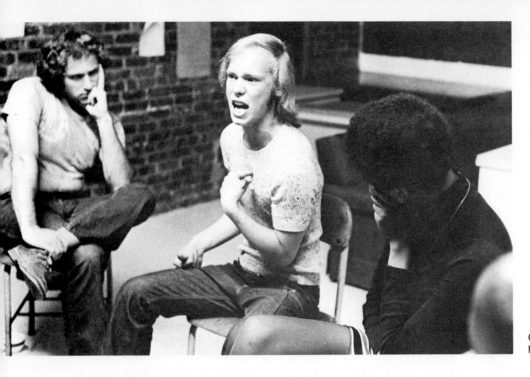

Group therapy in drug rehabilitation homes is usually confrontational.

3. Direct, often brutal confrontation in group therapy, in which the addict is goaded into accepting responsibility for his problems, and for his drug habit, and urged to take charge of his life.

4. A setting in which the addict is respected as a human being rather than stigmatized as a failure or a criminal.

5. Separation of the addict from previous social contacts, on the assumption that these relationships have been instrumental in fostering the addictive life style.

There are several obstacles to evaluating the efficacy of residential drug treatment programs. First, since entrance is voluntary and the dropout rate high, those who remain cannot be regarded as representative of the population of people addicted to hard drugs. Their motivation to go straight is probably much higher than average; therefore any improvement they might make will in part reflect their uncommon desire to rid themselves of their habit, rather than the specific qualities of the treatment program. Second, the role of mental health professionals is either nonexistent—because of an explicit antagonism toward "shrinks" and social workers—or very

marginal; adequately designed research on the outcomes of these programs has not been undertaken.

NICOTINE AND CIGARETTE SMOKING

The history of tobacco smoking bears much similarity to the use of other addictive drugs (Brecher, 1972). Its popularity spread through the world from Columbus's commerce with the native American Indians. It did not take long for sailors and merchants to imitate the Indians' smoking of rolled leaves of tobacco—and to experience, as the Indians did, the increasing craving for the stuff. When not smoked, tobacco was chewed or else ground into small pieces and inhaled as snuff.

Some idea of the addictive qualities of tobacco can be appreciated by considering how much people would sacrifice to maintain their supplies. In sixteenth-century England, for example, tobacco was exchanged for silver ounce for ounce. Poor people squandered their meager resources for their several daily pipefuls. Even the public tortures and executions engineered as punishment by the Sultan Murad IV of Turkey during the seventeenth century could not dissuade those of his subjects who were addicted to the weed.

Prevalence and Consequences of Smoking

The threat to health that smoking poses has been documented convincingly by the United States Surgeon General in a series of reports since 1964. Among the medical problems associated with, and almost certainly caused or exacerbated by, long-term cigarette smoking are lung cancer, emphysema, cancer of the larynx and of the esophagus, and a number of cardiovascular diseases. Among the many statistics on the health hazards of smoking is the estimate that thirty- to thirty-five-year-old, two-pack-a-day cigarette smokers have a mortality rate twice that of nonsmokers. And as with alcohol, the socioeconomic cost to society-at-large is considerable: smokers compile each year over 80 million extra days of lost work and 145 million extra days of disability. Health costs associated with cigarettes in the United States run about $30 billion annually, and about 350,000 people die prematurely each year as a result of smoking.

These ill tidings appear, after many years, to be having some limited influence on smokers and their consumption of tobacco. Since the first Surgeon General's report there has been a welcome decrease in smoking among adults (Warner, 1977). And yet about 54 million American adults still smoke about 620 billion cigarettes a year. What is even more alarming, smoking among teenage boys did not at once change and that among teenage girls actually *increased*. Perhaps of even greater concern is that children have been taking up the habit at earlier ages.

The attraction of smoking for young people has caused concern, for smoking is very difficult to give up once the habit and the addiction have been established. In the early 1980s, however, cigarette smoking finally began to decline among young people. Researchers surmise that the widely publicized health dangers of smoking may be making an impact. Through peer pressure and social support not to smoke, the "macho" image of the male smoker and the supersophisticated image of the female smoker seem to be losing their appeal.[8]

Most people who smoke acknowledge that it is hazardous to their health, and yet they continue to engage in what might be viewed as suicidal behavior. Perhaps one of the most tortured addicts was Sigmund Freud, who continued smoking up to twenty cigars a day in the full knowledge that they were seriously taxing his heart and causing cancerous growths in his mouth. With his

jaw later almost entirely removed and replaced by an awkward artificial one, Freud suffered great difficulty swallowing and endured excruciating pain. But he was still unable to bear the anguish of abstaining. Although many heavy smokers do succeed in stopping, Freud's tragic case was certainly not the exception.

The health hazards are not restricted to those who smoke. The smoke coming from the burning end of a cigarette, the so-called sidestream smoke, contains higher concentrations of ammonia, carbon monoxide, nicotine, and tar than does the smoke actually inhaled by the smoker. Nonsmokers can suffer lung damage, possibly permanent, from extended exposure to cigarette smoke (Bennett, 1980). At the very least, many nonsmokers greatly dislike the smell of smoke from burning tobacco, and some have allergic reactions to it. Moreover, when mothers-to-be smoke, their infants are more likely to be born prematurely and to have lower birth weights and birth defects.

In recent years various local governments have passed, or tried to pass, ordinances regulating where cigarettes may or may not be smoked in public places and work settings. New Jersey's new regulations are perhaps the most comprehensive in the country. Smoking is banned in supermarkets and on buses and other public conveyances. Restaurants must post signs indicating whether they have an area for nonsmokers. Workplaces with more than fifty employees must either ban smoking on the premises or restrict it to designated areas. Many nonsmokers express enthusiastic approval of such measures, but pressure from smokers and from the tobacco industry sometimes defeats efforts to enact laws. Some smokers object virulently to what they view as undue infringement on their rights.

Is Smoking an Addiction?

For some people smoking is a pleasurable accompaniment to their relaxing activities, and for others a necessary aid to their coping with challenging situations in our achievement-oriented society (Mausner, 1973). A smoker receives satisfaction from handling the pack, removing the cigarette, perhaps tapping one end against a firm surface to pack the tobacco more firmly, an act which probably has no real effect, especially on a filter cigarette; lighting the cigarette and perhaps sharing the match with a friend; and taking puffs at intervals during a relaxing conversation or an exhilarating task requiring

---

[8]But young people emulate their familial elders as well as their peers. If both parents and an older sibling smoke, a youngster is four times as likely to do so than if none of the other family members smokes.

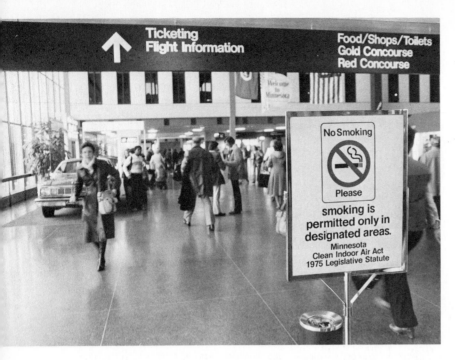

Recognizing the undesirable effects of cigarette smoke on bystanders, some municipalities have established restrictions on smoking in public.

concentration, such as reading a psychology textbook. Such social and psychological factors are not to be overlooked in attempts to understand why people begin and continue to smoke. Nonetheless, there is growing evidence that the _nicotine_ in tobacco is a powerful addictive drug. It is important to distinguish among different kinds of smokers. Those smoking more than two packs a day may well be addicted to nicotine, whereas those who limit smoking, for example, to social situations, and consume less than a pack a day do indeed smoke from habit, but they may not be addicted.

Although upwards of four million American smokers are estimated to quit on their own each year, over three-quarters of them return to smoking within twelve months. Regular smokers trying to escape from the weed report problems such as disruption of sleep, nausea, headaches, constipation, excessive eating, increased anxiety, difficulty in concentrating, irritability—in short, all the signs and symptoms we are accustomed to seeing portrayed humorously by screen characters or displayed by friends and loved ones in the throes of "nicotine fits." And these withdrawal symptoms can persist for many weeks, even months. As with other addictions, the most readily available relief is a bit more of the same—another cigarette and the nicotine "hit" it provides to a body grown dependent on it. Nonsmokers

tend to berate the nicotine addict with allegations of no will power and lack of concern for self and others. From all we know, however, these people are waging an extremely difficult battle with a true addiction (Jarvik, 1979). In fact, it has been estimated that one out of five people who have refrained from smoking for as long as nine years continues at least occasionally to crave a cigarette (Fletcher and Doll, 1969).

Evidence collected in Stanley Schachter's laboratory at Columbia University more clearly supports the notion that smoking is an addiction to nicotine. He has shown that smokers adjust their habit to maintain a relatively constant level of nicotine in their systems (Schachter, 1977) and has suggested further that their rate of smoking is controlled by the pH (a measure of acidity-alkalinity) of the urine. Said another way, "The smoker's mind is in his bladder" (Schachter, Silverstein, and Perlik, 1977). Urinary pH is related to smoking in the following way. When urine is acidic, nicotine is excreted at a greater rate than when urine is nonacidic. Therefore when urine is acidic, there should be more smoking to replace the nicotine being excreted. This prediction was confirmed in a study in which smokers ingested vitamin C; their urine was acidified and their rate of smoking increased (Schachter, Kozlowski, and Silverstein, 1977). Furthermore, if Schachter's thesis is correct, smoking should also increase in other circumstances that acidify the urine. Stress appears to operate in this fashion, increasing both the acidity of the urine and smoking (Silverstein, Kozlowski, and Schachter, 1977; Schachter et al., 1977). The usual effects of stress can even be short-circuited via a manipulation that prevents urine from becoming too acidic. After drinking sodium bicarbonate, which makes urine more alkaline, subjects under stress did not increase their smoking (Schachter, Silverstein, and Perlik, 1977).

A study by Schneider, Jarvik, and Forsythe (1984) supplies corroborative evidence. Heavy smokers stopped and either chewed nicotine gum to replace that lost by not smoking or chewed a placebo, thereby experiencing true abstinence from nicotine. The second group reported significantly more withdrawal symptoms than the first, such as restlessness and craving for a cigarette.

The rather general agreement that nicotine is addictive, and that at least heavy smokers are addicted, has raised concern about the proliferation of low-nicotine cigarettes. Smokers who switch to such cigarettes in the numbers they are accustomed to smoke each day will experience acute withdrawal symptoms, as happens to smokers who stop "cold turkey" in an effort to abstain from cigarettes altogether (Schachter, 1977). Regular smokers will therefore smoke more of these "improved" cigarettes or take greater numbers of puffs and inhale more deeply than they did when smoking those containing higher levels of nicotine. Thus Schachter (1978) questions current social policy that encourages the development and marketing of low-nicotine cigarettes. Since the products of incomplete combustion of tar during the smoking process itself, rather than nicotine, are the principal agents causing cancer and other harm, it might be preferable to develop low-tar–*high*-nicotine cigarettes; these would provide the nicotine addict with the drug he or she craves but at the same time reduce the risks associated with tar. Nicotine may, however, through stimulation, contribute to or exacerbate cardiovascular disease. All things considered, it is better not to begin smoking at all, or, if the habit is established, to concentrate personal and professional efforts on reducing or eliminating it.

Treatment and Prevention of Cigarette Smoking

Of the thirty million smokers who have quit since 1964, it is believed that 95 percent did so without professional help (National Cancer Institute, 1977; U.S. Department of Health and Human Services, 1982).[9] Some smokers attend smoking clinics or consult with professionals for specialized smoking reduction programs. The American Cancer Society and the Church of the Seventh Day Adventists have been especially active in offering programs to help people stop smoking. And, as mentioned earlier, more and more nonsmokers object to people smoking in restaurants, trains, airplanes, and public buildings. The social context, then, provides many more incentives and support to stop smoking than existed twenty years ago, when the Surgeon General first warned of the serious health hazards associated with cigarette smoking. Even so, it is estimated that not more than half of those who go through smoking cessation programs succeed in abstaining by the time the program is over; and only about one-third of those who have succeeded in the short term actually remain away from cigarettes after a year (Hunt and Bespalec, 1974).

The most encouraging results come from behavioral programs, especially those employing the so-called *rapid-smoking treatment* (Lando, 1977; Lichtenstein and Danaher, 1977). The procedure calls for a smoker to sit in a poorly ventilated room and puff much faster than normal, perhaps as often as every six seconds. After a number of such daily sessions, many smokers report less desire to smoke; in fact, as might be expected, the rapid-smoking sessions make most of the participants ill. In aversive-conditioning terms rapid smoking uses the natural consequences of the act, smoke, as an aversive UCS to discourage puffing on a cigarette. What appears to be a promising behavior therapy procedure may, however, also be dangerous to the health of some smokers, especially those with cardiopulmonary disease—ironically those who most need to stop smoking (Horan, Linberg, and Hackett, 1977).

Unfortunately, research on smoking cessation is marred by numerous methodological errors and procedural oversights; in particular, most studies fail to include a placebo group, in order to assess the contributions of faith and expectancy (Pechacek, 1979). When placebo effects are not evaluated, even meager achievements cannot be attributed to the program or method being examined.

[9]Investigations have begun on these large numbers of people who quit without being in a formal program. What enables a particular individual to stop? How does this person survive the withdrawal from nicotine, a hellish period of time that can last for months, some say even years? What homegrown techniques do these people use? What commonalities exist among these do-it-yourselfers?

BOX 11.2

NICOTINE GUM AND NICOTINE FITS

Each of the thousands of "hits" that the smoker administers to himself or herself each day during the consumption of a pack or two of cigarettes delivers nicotine to the brain in seven seconds. Gum containing nicotine, sold under the trade name Nicorette, may help smokers endure the nicotine withdrawal that accompanies any effort to stop smoking. The nicotine in gum is absorbed much more slowly and steadily. The rationale is that providing the addicting drug by gum will help unlink the act of smoking from the nicotine "hit." At the same time cessation of smoking is disconnected from the nicotine "fit" or withdrawal. The long-term goal, of course, is for the former smoker to be able to cut back on the use of gum as well, eventually eliminating reliance on nicotine altogether. Experts argue, however, that even were the smoker to stay with the gum indefinitely, his or her situation would be healthier than obtaining nicotine by smoking.

Some well-controlled, double-blind studies suggest that nicotine gum is useful in a limited way. Jarvis and his coworkers (1982) in Great Britain found better abstinence at one-year follow-up by people chewing nicotine gum than by those chewing a placebo gum. A series of studies at the University of California at Los Angeles by Schneider, Jarvik, and their associates (1983) had less positive outcomes. The greatest difference between nicotine and placebo gum groups was found early in treatment, between weeks 3 and 6, and at six months. After one year the nicotine gum group had relapsed noticeably—only 30 percent of them were still abstinent—and yet they were still better than the control group, only 20 percent of whom were still abstinent.

A closer analysis of the UCLA data revealed an interesting finding. The logic of chewing nicotine gum is that it will help a person stop smoking by supplying the nicotine otherwise obtained from cigarettes. This implies that a person who is highly dependent on cigarettes will benefit more than a person less so, for there will be a better fit between the state of the smoker, who has a great need for nicotine, and the drug treatment, in which the gum supplies nicotine. Jarvik and Schneider (1984) divided the smokers in the just-described study into those with great and little dependence, based on their answers to a questionnaire by Fagerstrom

(1978). People were asked how much they inhale, whether they smoke when sick or in forbidden places, and whether their cigarettes contain large or small amounts of nicotine. Table 11.4 shows the number of smokers abstinent at one-year follow-up as a function of whether they were rated as having great or little dependence on nicotine. The difference is significant statistically, confirming the hypothesis and replicating a similar study by Fagerstrom (1982). Moreover, no such relation was observed for subjects who used the placebo gum, and none was expected because the gum contained no nicotine. The 41 percent abstinence rate for people dependent on nicotine is considerably higher than the 30 percent success rate when subjects were considered without regard for their nicotine dependence.

TABLE 11.4 Numbers of Abstainers and Smokers as a Function of Nicotine Dependence *(after Jarvik and Schneider, 1984)*

	Great Dependence	Little Dependence
Abstinent	7	0
Smoking	10	8

The authors suggest that "clinic support" is also important. This entails monitoring the use of the gum for the first week, daily encouragement, and discussion of coping skills. The gum itself provided only limited help in cutting back on smoking, once the first few weeks of treatment had passed. Nicotine gum may help heavy smokers through some of the withdrawal at the beginning of treatment, but something other than replacement of cigarette nicotine is clearly necessary to keep people from later smoking. As time goes on, smokers have to learn psychological ways of dealing with stress and otherwise negotiating their way in life without the "companion" that the cigarette may have become over many years of smoking.

Behavioral treatments have thus far focused on the overt act of smoking. Given the addictive nature of the smoking habit, the disappointing results are not surprising. Until more is known of how to eliminate the addiction or at least of how ex-smokers might learn to tolerate withdrawal symptoms for long periods of time, it is unrealistic to expect great advances in treatment. Box 11.2

describes research on a promising new method of withdrawing from the nicotine of cigarettes, by chewing nicotine gum.

And yet, as important as addiction is in heavy smoking, smoker A may also have trouble quitting for psychological reasons, and they may be quite different from those plaguing smoker B. When two such smokers are exposed to the same treatment package, it is unlikely to help both. Unfortunately, in their zeal to make an impact on the smoking problem, workers have for many years put smokers in standardized programs. Since there are probably a number of reasons why people have trouble quitting, there will have to be diverse methods to help them stop.

In light of the difficulties in desisting from smoking once the habit and addiction are established, *prevention* of smoking, developing ways of discouraging young people even from experimenting with tobacco, has become a top priority among health researchers, with encouragement from the Surgeon General. What measures hold promise for persuading young people to resist smoking? Although many young people now apparently do fear disastrous consequences later in life and resist cigarettes, smokers, young and old alike, seem able to discount the possiblity that they are at higher risk of coronary heart disease or lung cancer—the "It won't happen to me" syndrome. Indeed, although heavy smokers are eleven times as likely as nonsmokers to develop lung cancer, large numbers of heavy smokers live longer and healthier lives than do nonsmokers. In addition it is the nature of young people to have a limited time perspective. Teenagers would seem to be more concerned with next Saturday evening's festivities or next Friday's math exam than with their life situation at age sixty.

The fact that more and more adults are quitting may influence young people. Whether an admired teacher or health professional smokes can be expected to affect a young person's decision to begin or continue. An interesting disparity between the actual and believed rate of smoking among teachers suggests an intervention. In one survey close to 70 percent of teenagers thought it likely that their teachers smoked (Jarvik et al., 1977). Another survey, however, found that only about 20 percent of teachers do in fact smoke (American Cancer Society, 1976). Perhaps conveying more accurate information to students would allow them to regard teachers as nonsmoking models.

Recent programs in the public schools may prove effective. Aware of the effects of peer pressure, Evans and his co-workers (1981) have developed films that portray teenagers resisting appeals from friends to try smoking. The hope is that youngsters will acquire assertive ways and refuse invitations to partake. McAlister, another researcher, has focused on enhancing the self-esteem of young people, on the assumption that, feeling good about themselves, they will be better equipped to stand up to social pressure and perhaps even ridicule (*ADAMHA News*, November 2, 1979).

Millions of Americans, most of them reasonable and intelligent, smoke cigarettes from packages bearing the ominous label "Warning—The Surgeon General Has Determined That Cigarette Smoking Is Dangerous to Your Health." Behavioral and medical scientists have the important and formidable challenge of understanding better why people begin smoking, why they continue, and why it is so very difficult for most of them to give up the habit.

MARIJUANA

Marijuana consists of the dried and crushed leaves and flowering tops of the hemp plant, *Cannabis sativa*. It is most often smoked, but it may be chewed, prepared as a tea, or eaten in baked goods. *Hashish*, much stronger than marijuana, is produced by removing and drying the resin exude of the tops of high-quality cannabis plants. Both marijuana and hashish have been known for thousands of years, and their poor reputation among the general public dates back many centuries. For example, the English word assassin comes from the Arabic word *hashishāshīn*, which means those addicted to hashish, and which was the name given an order of Muslims who took hashish and murdered Christians at the time of the Crusades. In early American history the plant was extensively cultivated, not for smoking but for its fibers, which were used in the manufacture of cloth and rope. By the nineteenth century the medicinal properties of *Cannabis* resin were noted, and it was a recommended treatment for rheumatism, gout, depression, cholera, and neuralgia, as well as being smoked for pleasure. Until 1920 marijuana was little seen in the United States, but with the passage of the Eighteenth Amendment, which prohibited the sale of alcohol, marijuana began to be brought across the border from Mexico and smoked for intoxication by members of the lower classes. Unfavorable reports in the press attributing crimes to marijuana use led to the enactment of a federal law against the sale of the drug in 1937. It is today illegal in most countries, many of which are bound by a United Nations treaty prohibiting its sale (Goodwin and Guze, 1984).[10]

---

[10]As will be seen in this section, the marijuana story is full of ironies. One is that marijuana is the biggest cash crop in agriculture-rich California.

Early recreational use of hashish in a fashionable apartment in New York City. An 1876 issue of the *Illustrated Police News* carried this picture with the title "Secret Dissipation of New York Belles: Interior of a Hasheesh Hell on Fifth Avenue."

Frequency of Marijuana Use

Periodically the National Institute of Drug Abuse (NIDA), a federal agency charged to investigate drug use in this country by encouraging investigators through awards of grants, publishes the results of surveys taken of youths, ages twelve to seventeen; young adults, eighteen to twenty-five; and those over twenty-six. They are questioned about current drug use, past use, frequency of use, range of drugs used, and so forth. In general, trends over the past fifteen years suggest that the use of marijuana peaked in 1979 and is now showing a slight decline. For example, the following percentages of those between the ages of twelve and seventeen reported having used marijuana at least once: 14 percent in 1972, 31 percent in 1979, and 27 percent in 1982 (*Marijuana Research Findings: 1980*; *National Survey on Drug Abuse, 1979*; *National Survey on Drug Abuse, 1982*). Among adults ages eighteen to twenty-five, the figures were 39 percent in 1971, 53 percent is 1974, 68 percent in 1979, and 64 percent in 1982. It is estimated that around 13 percent of Americans of all ages are current users of marijuana.

These statistics indicate that the smoking of marijuana is very prevalent, from the elementary schools on up. Other findings show that people from all socioeconomic classes use the drug, although more of those living in the West and in the Northeast do so than individuals in other parts of the United States.

Reasons for Use

In the middle and late 1960s, when social activism was prevalent among young people, use of marijuana appeared to have political and generational significance. Along with psilocybin and LSD, marijuana was declared to be a drug of the young, and its illegality may have enhanced its appeal among those who were in their then magical years below the age of thirty. By the same token, the harsh penalties meted out to those unlucky enough to be caught may have reflected the antipathy felt by the "establishment" toward the long-haired, raucous, and politically radical youth counterculture, which appeared to pose a threat to standards and institutions.

Marijuana remains popular because of its pleasurable effects. People report enjoying good feelings of being "high" and relaxed, usually without the hangover common with alcohol. They generally find that space seems larger, time is drawn out, and perceptions are enhanced; a feeling of serene detachment and composure is created. Many consider marijuana an easy escape from their everyday lives; and many value the sociality of sharing joints, and the accompanying camaraderie—sitting quietly with friends and acquaintances, touching, conversing, and listening to music. Devotees of rock concerts and science fiction movies assert that more interesting and intense experiences are available to them if they get high before or during performances. When penalties for use of marijuana were reduced and people in all walks of life numbered themselves among its champions, the sweet scent of marijuana in parks and even some theaters became almost commonplace in some parts of the country.

Effects of Marijuana

A great deal of research has been conducted on marijuana in recent years. Like most other drugs it is apparently not without its risks. Science has generally found that the more we learn about a drug, the less benign it turns out to be. Marijuana is no exception.

Psychological Effects of Marijuana

The intoxicating effects of marijuana, as of most drugs, depend in part on potency and size of the dose. We have already stated that smokers of marijuana find it makes them feel relaxed and sociable. Large doses have been reported to bring rapid shifts in emotion, to dull attention, fragment thoughts, and impair memory. Extremely heavy doses have sometimes been found to induce hallucinations and other effects similar to those of LSD, including extreme panic. People who have had psychological problems before using any psychoactive drug are generally believed to be at highest risk for having negative reactions to it.

The major active chemical in marijuana has been isolated and named delta-9-tetrahydrocannabinol (THC). Since 1974 the marijuana available in this country has come from Jamaica, Mexico, and Colombia and has been very potent, as much as ten times stronger than that sold earlier.[11] Thus in the early 1970s the most widely available domestic *Cannabis* contained about 0.4 percent THC; samples studied in 1979, in contrast, averaged more than 4 percent and in the early 1980s as much as 6 percent. Hash oil, a concentrated liquid marijuana extract only recently available on the street, has been found to be as much as 28 percent THC. The picture is complicated, however, by the fact that *Cannabis* contains more than 400 compounds in addition to THC. Many of these compounds are believed to exert psychological effects either by themselves or in conjunction with one another and with THC.

Let us examine more closely the psychological effects of marijuana. An abundance of scientific evidence indicates that marijuana interferes with a wide range of cognitive functions. And since *Cannabis* available in recent years is stronger, actual short-term effects on people's minds are probably greater than they were found to be in the laboratory studies, which were conducted for the most part in the late 1960s. A number of tests—digit-symbol substitution (substituting symbols for numbers), reaction time tests, repeating series of digits forward and backward, arithmetic calculations, reading comprehension and speech tests—all revealed intellectual impairment (*Marijuana Research Findings: 1980*). Of special significance are loss of short-term memory and state-dependent learning, the inability, when sober, to recall material learned when high. Given both the numbers of high school students who use marijuana regularly and the strength of *Cannabis* today, it would seem that significant numbers of students may be seriously hindering their learning.

Several studies have demonstrated that being high on marijuana diminishes complex psychomotor skills necessary for driving. And highway fatality and drive arrest figures indicate that marijuana plays a role in a significant proportion of accidents and arrests; a study in California, for example, found that of 1800 blood samples taken from people arrested for driving while intoxicated, 24 percent had detectable levels of marijuana (Reeve, 1979, cited in *Marijuana Research Findings: 1980*). Marijuana has similarly been found to impair manipulation of flight simulators. Some performance decrements can persist even after a person believes he or she is no longer high, creating the very real danger that people will attempt to drive or to fly when they are not functioning adequately.

Does long-term use of marijuana affect intellectual functioning in any sort of consistent way? Studies requiring memory and problem solving that were conducted in Egypt and in India in the late 1970s indicated some deterioration in users compared to nonusers (Soueif, 1976; Wig and Varma, 1977). It is impossible to know, however, whether these differences existed before heavy drug use and whether they might have been associated with poor diet. American college students do not show these deficits, so it would be premature to conclude that chronic use of the drug brings intellectual deterioration.

Somatic Effects of Marijuana

Some preliminary, tentative evidence indicates that marijuana may be harmful to reproduction. Two studies of

[11]The potency of the leaves is thought to vary with the region in which the hemp plant is cultivated. The leaves of plants grown in hot, relatively dry climates contain larger amounts of THC.

male chronic users found lower sperm counts and less motility of the spermatozoa, suggesting that fertility might be decreased, especially in men who are already marginally fertile (Hembree, Nahas, and Huang, 1979; Issidorides, 1979). It is conceivable, notes the 1980 Public Health Service Marijuana Report, that negative effects on sperm may be greatest in young smokers. The junior high and high school male students of today may be tampering with their present and future fertility.

As for female reproduction, a study with female "street users" yielded consistent findings, namely frequently failure to ovulate normally and shortened fertility periods. Moreover, researchers have discovered that marijuana constituents can cross the placental barrier[12] in rats and thus may affect the development of a fetus (Vardaris et al., 1976). Experiments with female rhesus monkeys, using THC levels comparable to fairly heavy use by human beings, found abnormally frequent loss of the fetus in those who became pregnant (Sassenrath, Chapman, and Goo, 1979). Marijuana also shows up in the milk of squirrel monkeys to whom the drug is administered, thus raising the possibility that nursing mothers may pass on its effects to their babies (Chao et al., 1976). All these studies have their share of methodological problems, but the outcomes for animals and human beings do raise the possibility that moderate and heavy use of marijuana interferes with reproduction. People interested in bearing children need to exercise caution and prudence with *any* drug.

In the short term, marijuana makes the eyes bloodshot and itchy, dries the mouth and throat, increases appetite, and may raise blood pressure somewhat. There is no evidence that smoking marijuana has untoward effects on the normal heart. The drug apparently poses a danger to people with already abnormal heart function, however, for it does elevate heart rate, sometimes dramatically. As a NIDA report suggests, this fact may become of particular concern as present smokers grow older. The relatively healthy thirty-year-old marijuana users of today are the fifty-year-olds of tomorrow, with a statistically greater chance of having a cardiovascular system impaired for other reasons, such as heart disease. If they are still using the drug then, their hearts will be more vulnerable to its effects. In addition, it is possible that long-term use of marijuana, like the chronic use of tobacco, may be harmful in ways that cannot be predicted from the short-term effects studied so far (Jones, 1980).

Indications are that long-term use of marijuana may seriously impair lung structure and function. Even though marijuana users smoke far fewer cigarettes than do persons using tobacco, most inhale marijuana smoke more deeply and retain it in their lungs for much longer periods of time. Any harmful elements present in marijuana smoke may exert effects far greater than would be expected were only the absolute number of cigarettes or pipefuls considered. What are these unfavorable pulmonary effects? First, a research team at the University of California at Los Angeles found that the amount of air a person can expel following a deep breath, called vital capacity, is reduced as much from smoking one marijuana cigarette a day as from smoking sixteen conventional cigarettes a day (Tashkin, Clavarese, and Simmons, 1978). Second, since marijuana cigarettes are generally "homemade," they are not filtered as are most tobacco cigarettes nowadays; the smoke contains significantly higher levels of tar which, like the tar from conventional cigarettes, has been found to cause cancer when applied to the skin of laboratory animals. Moreover, marijuana smoke contains 70 percent more benzopyrene, another known cancer-causing agent, and 50 percent more carcinogenic polyaromatic hydrocarbons than does the smoke from regular cigarettes (Cohen, 1981). The risk of lung cancer from regular, prolonged use of marijuana cannot be overlooked. Although not yet clearly demonstrated in human beings, another potential hazard is increased susceptibility to infection, specifically a serious form of pneumonia; marijuana smoke reduces the antibacterial defense systems of the lungs.

Whether marijuana is addictive has been a matter of some interest. Recent information suggests that indeed marijuana may be, contrary to widespread earlier belief that it is not. It began to be suspected that tolerance could develop when American servicemen returned from Vietnam accustomed to concentrations of THC that would be toxic to domestic users. Controlled observations have confirmed that habitual use of marijuana does produce tolerance (Nowland and Cohen, 1977).[13]

[13]The question whether marijuana is physically addicting is complicated by "reverse tolerance." Experienced smokers need only a few "hits" or puffs to become high from a cigarette that a less experienced user puffs many times in order to reach a similar state of intoxication. Reverse tolerance is directly opposite to tolerance for an addicting drug like heroin. The substance THC, after being rapidly metabolized, is stored in the body's fatty tissue and then released very slowly, over as long a period of time as a month, which may explain people's reverse tolerance for it.

[12]The placenta is the porous membrane forming the sac in which a fetus develops. In studying whether a chemical in the pregnant woman's body might affect the fetus, scientists try to determine whether it can penetrate the placenta or whether this membrane filters it out. If the agent can get through this barrier, there is presumptive—suggestive but not definite—evidence that the fetus is affected.

BOX 11.3

THE STEPPING-STONE THEORY—FROM MARIJUANA TO HARD DRUGS

A concern prevalent for some time is expressed in the so-called "stepping-stone theory" of marijuana use. According to this view, marijuana is dangerous not only in itself but as a first step that can lead young people to become addicted to hard drugs like heroin. In the late 1960s, when information on the harmfulness of marijuana was scant, the issue was basically a political and generational one. People in their teens and college years believed that the older generation, lacking scientific data to discourage marijuana use, had concocted the stepping-stone theory, which itself lacked empirical support, in order to justify harsh legal penalties for marijuana use and sale. Since there was little disagreement that the hard drugs were very harmful, marijuana was said to be so too because it was a first step to a career of abusing these drugs.

Studies done in the late 1970s and early 1980s established several specific dangers from using marijuana, as we have seen, but the stepping-stone theory is still being discussed (for example, O'Donnell and Clayton, in press). Survey information published in 1982 by the NIDA lends support to the hypothesis, finding a typical sequence in which young people, at ages twelve to seventeen, begin with alcohol and cigarettes, then sometimes add marijuana to their repertoire, and in young adulthood, at ages eighteen to twenty-five, begin turning to LSD, PCP, cocaine, or heroin.

Most youths, however, do *not* follow this sequence of drug use, although most young adults who use the more dangerous drugs do report having earlier smoked marijuana. At least for certain teenagers, then, marijuana may indeed act as a stepping-stone to further involvement with drugs, but its use is clearly not the only factor operating.

Whether long-term users suffer physical withdrawal when accustomed amounts of marijuana are not available is less clear. When subjects abstain after a period of heavier-than-normal smoking in the laboratory, appetite is lost and other withdrawal symptoms such as irritability, nausea, and diarrhea do develop (Jones, 1977; Jones and Benowitz, 1976). Withdrawal was also found in a study in which users selected their own number of joints, smoked in their usual manner, and then stopped (Mendelson, Rossi, and Meyer, 1974).

Ours is known to be a drug-taking culture. At any one time many individuals have circulating in their bloodstreams one or more chemicals that have been swallowed, injected, sniffed, or smoked. How drugs *interact* with one another, the combination of marijuana and alcohol in particular, is of no little concern. People often take these two drugs together or close enough in time for them to be mixing in the body.

Evidence from studies of both animals and human beings indicate that simultaneous use of alcohol and marijuana more seriously impairs perception, cognition, and motor activity than does either drug alone. The synergistic effect also extends to physiological processes; for example, heart rate is faster and eyes become more bloodshot. Marijuana can enhance the effects of other drugs such as barbiturates and amphetamines. Although this interactive force of THC is complex and inadequately understood, people should be aware of it and govern themselves accordingly (Siemens, 1980).

Therapeutic Effects of Marijuana

In a seeming irony, therapeutic uses of marijuana have come to light during the same period that negative effects of regular and heavy usage of the drug have been indicated. In the 1970s a number of double-blind studies (for example, Sallan, Zinberg, and Frei, 1975) showed that THC and related drugs can reduce for some cancer patients the nausea and loss of appetite that accompany chemotherapy. Marijuana often appears to reduce nausea when other antinausea agents fail. It is also a treatment for glaucoma, a disease in which outflow of fluid from the eyeball is obstructed. Abnormally high pressure builds up and vision gradually fails. A 1971 study by Hepler and Frank had shown that smoking marijuana reduced intraocular pressure in normal subjects. This discovery led to clinical trials. Oral ingestion of delta 9-THC, especially when combined with conventional treatment of the eye disease, reduces intraocular pressure in glaucoma sufferers (Hepler, Frank, and Petrus, 1976).

Research continues on these and other therapeutic uses of marijuana, but as yet none is regarded as standard medical practice (Cohen, 1980). Moreover, since such medical treatments tend to be attempted with older people, the potential benefits have to be measured against physical risks. It will be unfortunate if the illegality of marijuana in many states hinders scientific study of its positive uses, especially for serious medical conditions inadequately dealt with by conventional treatments.[14]

LSD AND OTHER PSYCHEDELICS

In 1943, a Swiss chemist, Albert Hofmann, recorded a description of an illness he had seemingly contracted.

Last Friday . . . I had to interrupt my laboratory work . . . I was seized with a feeling of great restlessness and mild dizziness. At home, I lay down and sank into a not unpleasant delirium, which was characterized by extremely exciting fantasies. In a semiconscious state with my eyes closed . . . fantastic visions of extraordinary realness and with an intense kaleidoscopic play of colors assaulted me (cited by Cashman, 1966, p. 31).

Earlier in the day Dr. Hofmann had manufactured a few milligrams of *d*-lysergic acid diethylamide, a drug which he had first synthesized in 1938. Reasoning that he might have unknowingly ingested some and that this was the cause of his unusual experience, he deliberately took a dose and confirmed his hypothesis.

After Hofmann's experiences with *LSD* in 1943, the drug was referred to as psychotomimetic because it was thought to produce effects similar to the symptoms of a psychosis. Then the term *psychedelic*, from the Greek words for soul and to make manifest, was applied to emphasize the subjectively experienced expansion of consciousness reported by users of LSD and two other drugs, *mescaline* and *psilocybin*.[15] In 1896 mescaline, an alkaloid and the active ingredient of peyote, was iso-

lated. Peyote is obtained from small, disklike growths of the top of the peyote cactus, most of which extends below ground. The drug has been used for centuries in the religious rites of Indian peoples living in the Southwest and northern Mexico. Psilocybin is a crystalline powder which Hofmann isolated from the mushroom *Psilocybe mexicana* in 1958. The early Aztec and Mexican cultures called the sacred mushrooms "god's flesh," and the Indians of Mexico still use them in their worship today.

During the 1950s these drugs were given in research settings to study what were thought to be psychotic experiences. In 1960 Timothy Leary and Richard Alpert of Harvard University began an investigation of the effects of psilocybin on institutionalized prisoners. The early results, although subject to several confounds, were encouraging: released prisoners who had a psilocybin trip proved less likely to be rearrested. At the same time the investigators started taking trips themselves and soon had gathered around them a group of people interested in experimenting with psychedelic drugs. By 1962 their activities had attracted the attention of law enforcement agencies. As the investigation continued, it became a scandal, culminating in Leary and Alpert's departure from Harvard. The affair seemed to give tremendous impetus to the use of the *hallucinogens*, particularly since the manufacture of LSD and the extraction of mescaline and psilocybin were found to be relatively easy and inexpensive.

After leaving Harvard, Leary and Alpert founded the International Foundation for Internal Freedom, an organization which emphatically espoused the desirability of psychedelic trips. It can probably be said that the proselytizing efforts of Leary and Alpert shifted attention from the supposedly psychotic experiences induced by the drugs to their mind-expanding effects.[16] The user's state of consciousness and intensification of sensory perceptions were considered extremely positive and beautiful. Among the mind expansions often cited and

---

[14]And yet additional risks may have to be considered even for very ill cancer patients. Dr. Steve Kagen (as reported by *The New York Times*, February 19, 1981) found that marijuana contains a fungus particularly dangerous to people whose immune systems are impaired, and those of cancer patients undergoing chemotherapy are. In the lungs of a healthy person the immune system fights off the fungus, and the individual suffers mild cough or fever. Patients with immune systems weakened by the drugs fighting their cancer may develop a more serious version of the infection, which can cause death.

[15]A new psychedelic joined the ranks of illegal drugs on an emergency basis on July 1, 1985. Ecstasy, whose scientific name is 3,4-methylenedioxymethamphetamine, had become alarmingly popular with the *Big Chill* generation in California, Texas, south Florida, and the North-

eastern states. Users say that Ecstasy enhances self-insight, empathy, and aesthetic awareness and intensifies emotions. It can also cause muscle tension, rapid eye movements, nausea, faintness, chills or sweating, and anxiety, depression, and confusion. The Drug Enforcement Administration considers the use of Ecstasy to be unsafe and a serious threat to health.

[16]Like many of the "old timers" in the psychedelic drug revolution, Alpert now espouses an Eastern meditation philosophy that urges people to forsake drugs and work instead on creating their own meaningful "trips" without the aid of chemical agents. Known as Baba Ram Dass, he has lectured and written eloquently about the possibility of cultivating expanded states of consciousness; those who would devote the necessary time and energy to meditation techniques will be open to such experiences, according to Ram Dass.

sought after are a marked slowing of time; the feeling that the body and limbs have lost their boundaries with space; a dreamy light-headedness and detachment from reality; gratifying and illuminating images seen in great richness and profusion of colors; occasional synesthesias, the merging of one sense modality with another so that, for example, colors are heard and sounds seen; enlightenments; ecstasy; and a sense of being in empathic connection with all of humankind.

Research on the Effects of Psychedelics

The typical dose of LSD is extremely small, from about 100 to 350 micrograms, administered as a liquid absorbed in sugar cubes or as capsules or tablets; for psilocybin the usual dose is about 30,000 micrograms; and for mescaline the usual dose is between 350,000 and 500,000 micrograms. The effects of LSD and mescaline usually last about twelve hours, those of psilocybin about six.

The effects of varying doses of LSD were studied by Klee and his associates (1961). Neither the subjects nor the observers knew the amounts of drug that had been administered. Nonetheless, experienced observers could readily judge the dose levels ingested by a particular subject from his reports of visual effects and from his somatic or bodily reactions, particularly of the sympathetic nervous system; intellectual impairment and also confusion increased with higher doses. There is no indication that LSD or the other psychedelics are addicting.

The effects of the psychedelics, like those of other kinds of drugs, depend on a number of psychological variables in addition to the dose itself. A subject's set, that is, attitudes, expectancies, and motivations about taking drugs, are widely held to be important determinants of reactions to psychedelics. Among the most prominent dangers of taking LSD is the "bad trip." Some aspect of experience after taking the drug creates anxiety, which escalates and then amplifies into a full-blown panic attack. Often the specific fear is of going crazy. These panics are usually short-lived and subside as the drug is metabolized. A minority of people, however, go into a psychotic state which can require hospitalization and extended treatment.

Some of the individual studies on psychological sets of people taking psychedelics have been relatively simple, others complex. Expectancies were examined by Metzner, Litwin, and Weil (1965). Before receiving 25,000 to 30,000 micrograms of psilocybin, subjects were asked, "How apprehensive are you about taking the drug?" and "How good do you feel about taking the drug today?" Reports of greater apprehension about taking the drug correlated significantly with increased anxiety, headache, and nausea during the drug experience itself. Other studies confirm the great importance of the person's psychological set to the nature of the drug effects (Linton and Langs, 1964; Klee and Weintraub, 1959; Von Felsinger, Lasagna, and Beecher, 1956).

Pahnke (1963) performed a considerably more remarkable and original piece of research. He attempted to maximize all the situational variables that might contribute to a religious or mystical experience. Subjects in his investigations were theological students who first attended a meeting at which they were told of the possibilities of having religious experiences after taking psilocybin. Twenty students were given psilocybin and twenty an active placebo by a double-blind procedure. Nicotinic acid was given as the placebo because it does produce some effects, such as a tingling sensation in the skin. After receiving the drug or the placebo, each subject participated in a two-and-a-half-hour-long religious service which included meditation, prayers, and the like. To heighten the significance of the occasion, Pahnke had chosen to conduct the experiment on Good Friday. After the service each subject wrote a description of his experience and answered an extensive questionnaire. The mystical and transcendental experiences of the group who took psilocybin were found to be significantly greater than those of the group who took the placebo.

The Problem of Flashbacks

One of the principal concerns about ingesting LSD is the possibility of *flashbacks*—"the transient recurrence of psychedelic drug symptoms after the pharmacologic effects of such drugs have worn off and [there has been] a period of relative normalcy" (Heaton and Victor, 1976, p. 83). Little is known about these flashback "trips" except that they cannot be predicted or controlled. The available evidence does not support the hypothesis that they are caused by drug-produced physical changes in the nervous system. For one thing, only 15 to 30 percent of users of psychedelic drugs are estimated ever to have flashbacks (for example, Stanton and Bardoni, 1972). Moreover, there is no independent evidence of measurable neurological changes in these drug users. The flashback, which seems to have a force of its own and may come to haunt people weeks and months after they have

BOX 11.4

NOT AN UPPER OR A DOWNER BUT AN INSIDE-OUTER

In 1956 Parke Davis and Company, a large pharmaceutical firm, synthesized a new anesthetic. Although effective in large doses, it was found to cause agitation and disorientation as the patient regained consciousness. When administered in smaller doses, it induced a psychoticlike state. In 1965 this new drug, *phencyclidine*, was taken off the market, and by 1978 its legal manufacture was discontinued in the United States.

Phencyclidine (PCP) was first seen in illegal use in Los Angeles in 1965. It soon turned up in the Haight-Ashbury district of San Francisco under the name "PeaCe Pill" and was sold as a psychedelic, but it quickly gained a bad reputation because many users had negative reactions. In the late 1960s and early 1970s the drug spread to other parts of the country until, by 1979, it had turned up in most states.

As sold on the street, PCP is known by dozens of names—among which are angel dust, elephant tranquilizer, cadillac, cozmos, Detroit Pink, embalming fluid, Killerweed, horse crystal, PeaCe Pill, wac, and zombie—and has been marketed falsely as LSD, psilocybin, cocaine, and other drugs. It is available in many forms and degrees of purity and in most colors. In granular form it contains between 50 and 100 percent phencyclidine. This angel dust is usually available as mint or parsley that has been sprinkled with PCP powder or liquid and sealed in zip-lock plastic bags. The most popular ways to take PCP are in mint or parsley joints and in commercial cigarettes that have been dipped in liquid PCP or had a string dipped in liquid PCP passed through them. But the drug can also be injected intravenously, swallowed, put in the eyes as drops, "snorted" like cocaine, and smoked in a pipe.

The effects of PCP depend largely on the dosage. The user generally has jerky eye movements (nystagmus) alternating with a blank stare, is unable to walk heel-to-toe in a straight line (gait ataxia), and has great rigidity of the muscles. Hallucinations and delusions are also experienced by some. All the sensory systems become overly sensitive so that users are extremely susceptible to any stimulation and are best left alone. When touched, they are likely to flail and become so agitated and combative that it takes several people to restrain them. Their incoherence and lack of communicativeness do not allow them to be "talked down" from their high. With very high dosages—actually, as little as a single gram—there are usually a deep and prolonged coma, seizures, apnea or periods of no breathing, sustained high blood pressure, and sometimes even death from heart and lung failure or from ruptured blood vessels in the brain. No medication to reverse the effects of PCP has yet been found. People seldom remember afterward what happened while they were on the drug.

Phencyclidine is not an upper or a downer, nor is it a psychedelic. Some workers refer to it as an "inside-outer," a term which to some extent conveys the bizarre and extreme nature of its effects, which bear similarities to those of drugs as different from one another as alcohol, barbiturates, stimulants, and hallucinogens.

How long do the effects of PCP last? The way it is ingested and the dosage seem to play a role. Onset is usually between one and five minutes after smoking a treated cigarette; effects peak after about half an hour and then do not dissipate for up to two days. Since PCP remains in the body for several days, it can accumulate if ingested repeatedly. Chronic users who have taken the drug several times a week for six months experience cognitive distortions and disorientation for several months afterward, even for as long as two years after use has ceased. In addition, the personality often changes, there can be memory loss, and the person may experience severe anxiety, depression, and aggressive urges.

Organ damage has not yet been linked to chronic use of this drug. More than 100 deaths were reported in Los Angeles County in 1978 alone, however. These fatalities were caused in a number of ways. One man who was swimming drowned because he lost his spatial orientation; others have expired because of severe respiratory depression or uncontrollable increase in body temperature. Information about the drug is too limited at this time to know more about its long-term effects. Its addictiveness and other consequences are likely to be difficult to determine because most PCP users take other drugs as well.

Those who use PCP frequently are apparently very young, averaging fifteen years of age. The drug is often used with alcohol. Abusers tend to be arrested more often for substance-related offenses than those taking the other drugs discussed in this chapter, and they tend as well to have overdosed on more occasions. The PCP user, then, seems to be more socially deviant, perhaps more often sociopathic, than abusers of other illicit substances. Evidence indicates that PCP use is very much on the rise (Berger and Dunn, 1982).

In light of how terrifying and dangerous the drug is, why does its use increase? A number of reasons have been proposed, but given the relative recency of PCP abuse, they are very tentative indeed. The drug is inexpensive and both readily available and easily synthesized in a home laboratory, making it a quick and easy escape from unpleasant realities. Peer pressure may be great among the young to show that one is "tough" enough to stay in control. The sheer intensity of the experience is enticing, and the euphoria it can induce has been described as "a dream world" and a "perfect escape" (Berger and Dunn, 1982). The fact that scare tactics have been applied with other illicit drugs throughout the years may also reduce the credibility of warnings about PCP.*

*Most of the foregoing is based on *Phencyclidine Abuse Manual*, published in 1980 by the University of California Extension, Los Angeles, pursuant to a contract from the State of California Department of Alcohol and Drug Abuse.

taken the drug, is a very upsetting phenomenon for those it besets.

Heaton and Victor (1976) determined to explore a possible psychological explanation of flashbacks. Heaton had been mindful of previous evidence indicating that extreme relaxation and sensory deprivation can produce in some people sensations and experiences closely similar to those reported during flashbacks. In an earlier study (1975) he had demonstrated that *expectancy* of a flashback increased the chances that former LSD users, after swallowing a placebo capsule and then undergoing mild sensory deprivation, would report such experiences, whether or not they had previously had flashbacks. The belief that they had taken a drug that would produce a flashback proved more important than a past history of such phenomena.

Heaton and Victor therefore speculated that some drug users, believing that flashbacks are likely, may *attend selectively* to naturally occurring altered states of consciousness and then *label* them flashbacks of a previous drug trip. But why would they allow their thinking to take such a course? Employing various scales from the MMPI, the two researchers developed measures of thinking in a logical, reality-oriented fashion and in a looser, inner-fantasizing mode. They then recruited thirty male volunteer drug users from clinics and counseling agencies serving young people, including "street people," in a Western metropolitan area. Half claimed no previous history of flashbacks; the others reported such experiences. The two groups, satisfactorily matched on classificatory variables such as age and the number of times that they had previously taken psychedelics, were tested on the selected MMPI scales. Then all subjects swallowed a capsule, which they were told would probably produce a flashback in experienced drug users like themselves, and underwent brief sensory deprivation. On a second occasion all subjects were given a different capsule, this time with the expectation that it would *not* produce a flashback. Both capsules were placebos.

The group of LSD users reporting earlier flashbacks did show significantly more loose fantasizing, as measured by the MMPI scales. They were also found to have poorer social and sexual adjustment, an uneven school and work history, and often a history of bizarre thinking. And the subjects who scored especially high in loose thinking did indeed report many flashback experiences during the sensory deprivation, even when they had been told that the capsule ingested would *not* produce such effects.

Although it is impossible to know whether the personality described predated the tendency to have flashbacks, the results are useful. They suggest that

Under environmental conditions which pull for altered states of consciousness anyway, [loose-thinking] subjects have less ability (and possibly less desire) to maintain reality-oriented mental activity. . . . [Furthermore,] if the subject labels his initial sensations as the beginning of a flashback, expectations . . . are self-fulfilling to the extent that they selectively direct attention to psychedelic sensations (Heaton and Victor, 1976, p. 89).

SUMMARY

Using substances to alter mood and consciousness is virtually a human characteristic, and so also is the tendency to abuse them. DSM-III follows contemporary practice in distinguishing between substance abuse and substance dependence. Abuse is usage that interferes with a person's customary functioning. Substance dependence, or addiction, is a physiological dependence on a drug in which tolerance builds up—ever-increasing amounts are required to achieve a particular effect—and there are withdrawal reactions should the person desist from taking the drug.

Alcohol has a variety of short-term and long-term effects on human beings, and many are tragic in nature, ranging from poor judgment and motor coordination, and their dire consequences for the alcoholic and society, to addiction, which makes an ordinary productive life impossible and is extremely difficult to overcome. As with other addicting drugs, people come to rely on alcohol less for how good it makes them feel than for an escape from feeling bad.

Less prevalent but more notorious, perhaps because of their illegality, are the so-called hard drugs, the narcotic heroin and the barbiturates such as Seconal, which are sedatives, and the amphetamines and cocaine, which are stimulants. Heroin has been of special concern in recent years because stronger varieties have become available. Barbiturates have for some time been implicated in both intentional and accidental suicides; they are especially lethal when alcohol is taken at the same time. Cocaine use has risen dramatically in the past few years. Its extremely high cost and elaborate paraphernalia made it a rather "trendy" drug in some circles, but now it costs somewhat less and is used by all segments of society.

Nicotine, especially when taken into the body via the inhaled smoke from a cigarette, has worked its addictive power on humankind for centuries and, in spite of somberly phrased warnings from public health officials, continues in widespread use. Of special concern is the smoking of school-aged youngsters and teenagers. Each year the government and private individuals spend millions of dollars to dissuade people from beginning the habit or to help those already addicted to desist from smoking; and each year millions of dollars are spent by the government and private individuals promoting the cultivation and sale of tobacco products. Neither the psychological-medical nor economic-political issues have easy solutions.

Marijuana is smoked by a great number of young Americans. Arguments for deregulation of marijuana have stressed its supposed safety, in comparison to the known harm caused by the habitual use of alcohol, which is a legal and integral part of our culture. But currently available evidence indicates that marijuana when used with regularity is not benign. Significantly stronger varieties of marijuana are now available than were in the early 1970s. Furthermore, there is evidence that marijuana constituents may adversely affect fertility, fetal development, heart function in people who already have coronary problems, and pulmonary function. The debate continues whether marijuana is addicting; although withdrawal has not been conclusively demonstrated, it does appear that tolerance develops over time. Ironically, at the same time that the possible dangers of this drug began to be uncovered, marijuana was found to ease the nausea of cancer patients undergoing chemotherapy and to reduce the excessive intraocular pressure of glaucoma sufferers.

Phencyclidine, known as PCP or angel dust, is a newcomer on the drug abuse scene. Concern about it dwarfs that surrounding other illicit drugs, for people on PCP are unpredictable and often violent and have such seriously impaired judgment that they can inadvertently kill themselves.

The so-called psychedelics, LSD, mescaline, and psilocybin, are taken by many to alter or expand consciousness. Their continuing popularity attests to humankind's desires not only to escape from unpleasant realities but probably to explore inner space as well.

Therapies to discourage usage of many of these drugs are often confrontational in nature. Residential and outpatient programs confront alcoholics and other drug addicts with the immorality or stupidity of their behavior and encourage in them a resolve to alter the mode of their lives, leaving no room for chemical crutches. Behavioral clinicians, until fairly recently, employed primarily aversive techniques with abusers of alcohol and tobacco, but they now include in their repertoire procedures designed to reduce anxiety and enhance social skills. Anxiety and the lack of such skills may be underlying reasons why people turn to drugs as a means of coping with life.

CHAPTER 12

Caravaggio, *Bacchus*, c. 1595 Art Resource

PSYCHOSEXUAL DISORDERS: GENDER IDENTITY DISORDERS AND THE PARAPHILIAS

William V. is a twenty-eight-year-old computer programmer who currently lives alone. He grew up in a rural area within a conservative family with strong religious values. He has two younger brothers and an older sister. William began to masturbate at age fifteen; his first masturbatory experience took place while he watched his sister urinate in an outdoor toilet. Despite considerable feelings of guilt, he continued to masturbate two or three times a week while having voyeuristic fantasies. At the age of twenty he left home to spend two years in the navy.

On a summer evening at about 11:30 P.M., William was arrested for climbing a ladder and peeping into the bedroom of a suburban home. Just before this incident he had been drinking heavily at a cocktail lounge featuring a topless dancer. When he had left the lounge at 11:15 P.M. he had intended to return to his home. Feeling lonely and depressed, however, he had begun to drive slowly through a nearby suburban neighborhood, where he noticed a lighted upstairs window. With little premeditation, he had parked his car, erected a ladder he found lying near the house, and climbed up to peep. The householders, who were alerted by the sounds, called the police, and William was arrested. Although this was his first arrest, William had committed similar acts on two previous occasions.

The police referred William's case for immediate and mandatory psychological counseling. William described a lonely and insecure life . . . to his therapist—six months before the arrest, he had been rejected in a long-term relationship, and he had not recovered from this emotional rejection. As an unassertive and timid individual, he had responded by withdrawing from social relationships, and increasing his use of alcohol. His voyeuristic fantasies, which were present to begin with, became progressively more urgent as William's self-esteem deteriorated. His arrest had come as a great personal shock, although he recognized that his behavior was both irrational and self-destructive (Rosen and Rosen, 1981, pp. 452–453).

Of all the aspects of human suffering that command the attention of psychopathologists and clinicians, few touch the lives of more people than problems involving sex. Oftentimes the human suffering is exacerbated by bad counsel and misinformation—such as the belief held not so long ago that masturbation should be avoided at all costs because it was immoral and might even weaken the mind. This chapter and the next consider the full range of human sexual thoughts, feelings, and actions that are generally regarded as abnormal and dysfunctional and are listed in DSM-III as *psychosexual disorders* (Table 12.1). In the present chapter our study is of the *gender identity disorders*, the *paraphilias*, and *ego-dystonic homosexuality*, all of them sexual problems that are viewed as particularly serious and aberrant and that are found in only a small minority of people. The next chapter focuses on *psychosexual dysfunctions*, disruptions in normal sexual functioning to be found among many people who are in otherwise reasonably sound psychological health.

When workers speculate on how people become *disordered* in their sexual lives, the impression is conveyed that we rather fully understand how people develop *nor-*

TABLE 12.1 Psychosexual Disorders *(from DSM-III)*

A. Gender Identity Disorders
1. Transsexualism.
2. Gender identity disorder of childhood.
3. Atypical gender identity disorder.

B. Paraphilias
1. Fetishism.
2. Transvestism.
3. Zoophilia.
4. Pedophilia.
5. Exhibitionism.
6. Voyeurism.
7. Sexual masochism.
8. Sexual sadism.
9. Atypical paraphilia (for example, coprophilia, frotteurism, necrophilia).

C. Psychosexual Dysfunctions
1. Inhibited sexual desire.
2. Inhibited sexual excitement.
3. Inhibited female orgasm.
4. Inhibited male orgasm.
5. Premature ejaculation.
6. Functional dyspareunia.
7. Functional vaginismus.
8. Atypical psychosexual dysfunction.

D. Other Psychosexual Disorders
1. Ego-dystonic homosexuality.
2. Psychosexual disorder not elsewhere classified.

mally as sexual beings. Actually, we know little of how or why a physically mature male has both the desire and ability to interact with a physically mature woman, so that, at some point, he will insert his penis into her vagina and one or both of them will have an orgasm after a period of thrusting. The most widely held belief is that people are "doin' what comes naturally." This may be true in some limited degree, but left out of such an explanation are the complex rules we all learn about how to initiate a sexual encounter, what makes it sexually stimulating, how it is paced, what meaning it has for us.

GENDER IDENTITY DISORDERS

"Are you a boy or a girl?" "Are you a man or a woman?" For virtually all people—even those with serious mental disorders such as schizophrenia—the answer to such questions is immediate and obvious. Also unequivocal is the fact that others will agree with the answer given. Our sense of ourselves as male or female, or what is called *gender identity*, is so deeply ingrained from earliest childhood that, no matter the stress suffered at one time or another, the vast majority of people are certain beyond a doubt of their gender.

Some people, however, and more often they are men, feel deep within themselves from early childhood that they are of the opposite sex. The evidence of their anatomy—normal genitals and the usual secondary sex characteristics, such as beard growth for men and developed breasts for women—does not persuade them that they are what others see them to be. A male transsexual, then, can look at himself in a mirror, see an ordinary man, and yet announce to himself that he is a woman. Furthermore, he will often try to convince the medical profession to bring his body in line with his gender identity; many transsexuals undergo genital surgery and hormone treatment to make their bodies assume as much as possible the anatomy of the opposite sex.

Transsexualism

DSM-III defines a *transsexual* as an adult who has a persistent, deep sense of discomfort in his (less often her) anatomic sex, often wishes to be rid of his genitals and live as a woman, and has felt this way for more than two years. This last stipulation excludes people who may, under specific stress, temporarily reject their anatomic gender. Excluded also are schizophrenics who on very rare occasions claim to be of the other sex, as well

as people who are biologically intersexed, that is, possess both male and female sex organs, as in *hermaphroditism*.

Transsexuals, sometimes called "gender dysphorics," generally suffer from anxiety and depression, not surprising in light of their psychological predicament. A male transsexual's interest in men will be interpreted by him as a conventional heterosexual preference, given that he is "really" a woman. Predictably, transsexuals often arouse the disapproval of others when they choose to cross-dress in clothing of the other sex. Indeed, for a man to dress as a women is illegal in many states. Many male-to-female transsexuals who are getting ready to undergo sex-reassignment surgery carry letters from their physicians or therapists informing police authorities that their cross-dressing is an important early aspect of treatment. Cross-dressing is less of a problem for female-to-male transsexuals because contemporary dress fashions allow women to don clothing very similar to that worn by men.

The question is often raised whether it is not delusional for a person with a penis to believe he is a woman. DSM-III asserts that "The insistence by an individual with Transsexualism that he or she is of the other sex is, strictly speaking, not a delusion since what is invariably meant is that the individual *feels like* a member of the other sex rather than truly believing he or she *is* a member of the other sex" (p. 263). Case studies of many transsexuals reveal, however, that such people express the conviction that they are, in fact, members of the opposite sex. Their statements imply more than the "as if" feelings that DSM-III claims are prevalent. Research has provided conflicting findings (for example, Langevin, Paitich, and Steiner, 1977; Hunt, Carr, and Hampson, 1981). But perhaps it matters little whether transsexuals are delusional or not; their condition remains what it is.

The long-standing and apparently unchangeable nature of the transsexual's incongruous gender identity has led researchers to speculate that transsexuals are hormonally different from those with normal gender identity. Perhaps a woman who believes that she is a man has an excess of androgens such as testosterone and androsterone, hormones known to promote the development of and maintain male secondary sex characteristics. In a review of several such investigations, Meyer-Bahlburg (1979) found the results to be equivocal: some female transsexuals have elevated levels of male hormones, but most of them do not. Differences, when they are found, are difficult to interpret. Many transsexuals use sex hormones in an effort to alter their bodies in the direction of the sex to which they believe they belong. Even though a researcher studies only transsexuals who have not taken such exogenous hormones for a few months, relatively little is known at present about the long-term effects of earlier hormonal treatment. In any event, the available data do not support an explanation of transsexualism in terms of hormones. Even less conclusive is the research on possible chromosomal abnormalities.

Gender Identity Disorder of Childhood

Virtually all transsexuals who have been studied by sex researchers report retrospectively that they engaged in cross-gender behavior as young children. An examination of *gender identity disorder of childhood* might therefore provide clues to the etiology of transsexualism. The children given this diagnosis are profoundly feminine boys and profoundly masculine girls, youngsters whose behavior, likes, and dislikes do not fit our culture's rules for what is appropriate for the two sexes. Thus a boy may not like rough-and-tumble play, may prefer the company of little girls, don women's clothing, and insist that he will grow up to be a girl. He may even claim that his penis and testes are disgusting. The onset of the disorder is before the age of six.

The very categorization of boys and girls as having their own masculine and feminine ways is so heavily laden with value judgments and stereotyping that considering opposite behavioral patterns abnormal may seem unjustified. But some evidence suggests that these patterns can come from a physical disturbance. Human and other primate offspring of mothers who have taken sex hormones during pregnancy may frequently behave like the opposite sex *and* have anatomical abnormalities. For example, girls whose mothers took synthetic progestins during pregnancy, to prevent uterine bleeding, were found to be "tomboyish" during their preschool years (Ehrhardt and Money, 1967). Progestins are considered precursors of androgens, the male sex hormones. Other young tomboys also had genitalia with male characteristics, which suggests a link between the progestins taken by their mothers and male physical features (Green, 1976). Young boys whose mothers ingested female hormones when they were pregnant were found to be less athletic as young children and to engage less in rough-and-tumble play than their male peers (Yalom, Green, and Fisk, 1973). Although such children were not necessarily abnormal in their gender identity, the prenatal sex hormones did give them higher than usual levels of cross-gender interests and behavior.[1]

The cross-gender behavior that many, perhaps most, little children engage in now and then may in some homes receive too much attention and reinforcement from parents and other relatives. Interviews with the parents of children who have become atypical frequently reveal that they did not discourage, and in many instances clearly encouraged, cross-dressing behavior. This is especially true for feminine boys. Many mothers, aunts, and grandmothers found it "cute" that the little fellow enjoyed putting on mommy's old dresses and high-heeled shoes, and very often they instructed the youngster on how to apply lipstick, eyeshadow, and rouge. Family albums often contain photographs of the young boys fetchingly attired in women's clothing. Such reactions on the part of the family of an atypical child have probably contributed in a major way to the conflict between his or her anatomical sex and the acquired gender identity (Green, 1974).

Research with infants and very young children whose genitals have both male and female characteristics and who often undergo surgery to correct the problem indicates that by the age of three a child has achieved a sense of gender identity that is virtually impossible to change later on (Money, Hampson, and Hampson, 1955). Indeed, the gender assigned several of these children was later found to conflict with at least one anatomic sex criterion, such as the indication of sex by their chromosomes. Such children already over the age of three kept the gender to which they had been assigned. The web of evidence, then, points to the criticalness of how a very young child, under three years of age, is treated by the adults around him. Dressing a child as a boy, giving him (or her!) a male name, and encouraging him to engage in traditional masculine activities are major influences on the development of gender identity. In contradiction to widespread belief, anatomy is not always destiny.

These findings, however, should *not* be interpreted to mean that encouraging gentleness in a little boy or assertiveness, even aggressiveness, in a little girl will probably lead to a gender identity disorder. Indeed, *most GID children do not become transsexual in adulthood, even without professional intervention* (Zucker et al., 1984). Investigators working in this field are very much aware of the culture-relative aspects of masculinity and

---

[1]Research fails to show that exposure to opposite-sexed hormones necessarily causes gender dysphoria, yet researchers do continue to seek the etiology of gender identity disorders in sex hormone imbalances. To our minds this means that many sex researchers have a hidden bias, that psychological factors could not possibly account for a gender identity disturbance.

femininity, and of the difference between enjoying activities more typical of the opposite sex and actually believing that one *is* of the opposite sex. We do know that the vast majority of little boys engage in varying amounts of "feminine" play and little girls in varying amounts of "masculine" play with no identity conflicts whatsoever (Green, 1976). Gender identity disorder of childhood and the adult disorder of transsexualism are rare, far less prevalent than could be expected from the numbers of little boys who play with dolls and of little girls who engage in vigorous, physical-contact sports.

Indeed, Sandra Bem (1984) takes the view that we need not consider any behavior or interest as gender-related except those that concern anatomy or reproduction. She argues that children should enjoy the freedom to behave in both conventional and nontraditional ways without risking punishment from parents or peers. A little boy who shows tenderness to a doll and a little girl who does not should not be made to worry and doubt themselves. Taking the argument a step further, would transsexuality itself disappear if sex-role stereotyping ceased to exist? Then a man would regard his traditionally feminine traits and interests as a normal *masculine* variation, rather than as a pathognomonic sign of being a woman trapped in a man's body (see Raymond, 1979). He would need to be more accepting of any sexual attraction to members of his own sex, however, an attraction which transsexuals regard as heterosexual.

Therapies for Gender Identity Disorders

Sex-Change Surgery

Innovations in surgical procedures, coupled with advances in hormonal treatments and a sociocultural atmosphere that would permit their implementation, have allowed many transsexuals to pursue their wish to become in some respects a member of the opposite sex. The treatments to be described, however, do *not* biologically transform a man or woman into the opposite sex.

In *sex-change surgery* for men, the genitalia are almost entirely removed, with some of the tissue retained to form an artificial vagina. At least a year before the operation, appropriate female hormones are given to develop the breasts, soften the skin, and change the body in other ways; they have to be taken indefinitely after the surgery (Green and Money, 1969). Most male-to-female transsexuals have to undergo extensive and costly electrolysis to remove beard and body hair, however, and they receive training to raise the pitch of their voice; the female hormones prescribed do not make

hair distribution and the voice less masculine. Some male-to-female transsexuals also have plastic surgery on their chin, nose, and Adam's apple to rid them of masculine largeness. At the same time the transsexual begins to live as a female member of society in order to experience as fully as possible what it is like. The genital surgery itself is not done until a one- or two-year trial period has been completed. Conventional heterosexual intercourse is possible for male-to-female transsexuals, although pregnancy is out of the question since only the external genitalia are altered.

For female-to-male transsexuals the process is more arduous and the outcomes more problematic. The penis that can be constructed is small and not capable of normal erection; artificial supports are therefore needed for conventional sexual intercourse. An operation now available extends the urethra into the newly constructed penis to allow the person the social comfort of being able to use public urinals. Less cosmetic follow-up is needed than for male-to-female transsexuals because the male hormones prescribed make drastic, masculinizing changes, such as altering fat distribution and stimulating the growth of beard and body hair. The relatively greater ease of the female-to-male change may come in part from our society's lesser focus on the physical attributes of men. A small, soft-spoken man is more acceptable to society than a large, hulking woman.

DSM-III indicates that the ratio of male transsexuals to female transsexuals ranges from eight to one to two to one. In the first comprehensive book on female-to-male transsexuals, Lothstein (1983) reports that each year more and more women are applying for sex-reassignment surgery. His work indicates that the ratio is closer to two to one.

The first sex-change operation took place in Europe in 1930, but the surgery that attracted worldwide attention was performed on an ex-soldier, Christine (originally George) Jorgensen, in Copenhagen in 1952. Some years later Jan (originally James) Morris, a well-known journalist, published *Conundrum* (1974), a sensitive and highly personal account of her life as a man and her subsequent alteration to a woman.

For many years the Gender Identity Clinic at Johns Hopkins University School of Medicine was a leading American facility for these operations, but in the 1980s their sex-change program was terminated. A study by Meyer and Reter (1979) found that transsexuals on whom surgeons had operated failed to show better life adjustment than those who did not have surgery. These negative findings were embraced so readily by the Johns Hopkins Clinic and several hospitals that they seemed,

A 1960 picture of James Morris, who after sex-change surgery became Jan Morris, shown in a 1974 photograph.

so to speak, "exactly what the folks wanted to hear" in order to justify, on scientific grounds, terminating their sex-change surgery programs. The Meyer-Reter study, however, was strongly criticized by Fleming, Steinman, and Bocknek (1980) on a number of methodological grounds. The outcome for sex-reassignment surgery remains quite unclear and may not be as bleak as portrayed by the study. In any event, sex-change programs continue elsewhere; it is estimated that each year in the United States upwards of 1000 transsexuals are surgically altered to the other sex.

The long-term effectiveness, or even wisdom, of sex transformation surgery is difficult to evaluate (Lothstein, 1980). Given that people who go to great lengths to have this surgery performed claim that their future happiness depends on the change, should this surgery be evaluated in terms of how happy such people are afterward? If so, it can be safely said that some transsexuals who have crossed over anatomically are better off, others are not. But as people make their way through life, many events bring them a greater or lesser amount of fulfillment or even just ease. If a surgically altered transsexual becomes dismally unhappy, is the venture to be indicted as antitherapeutic? Transsexuals who under-

take these procedures often cut their ties to former friends and family members and to aspects of their previous lives—"Was it *I* who played tailback on the football team?" Considerable stress is the fate of those who choose to divorce themselves from the past, for the past contributes to our sense of ourselves as people, as much as do the present and the future. A transsexual who has surgery, then, confronts challenges few others have occasion to face; adjustment to the new life should perhaps be evaluated more leniently.

All experienced therapists, whatever their theoretical persuasion, are wary of a client who says "If only . . . ." The variations are legion: "If only I were not so fat. . . ." "If only I were not so nervous. . . ." "If only I had not left school before graduation. . . ." Following each "if only" clause is some statement indicating that life would be far better, even wonderful . . . if only. Most of the time the hopes expressed are an illusion; things are seldom so simple. The transsexual, understandably focusing on the discrepancy between gender identity and biological makeup, blames his or her present dissatisfactions on the horrible trick nature has played. But he or she usually find that sex change falls short of solving life's problems. It may handle this one set of them, but it usually leaves untouched other difficulties that all human beings are subject to.

Even proponents of sex-change surgery have for some time advocated psychotherapy to help transsexuals adjust to their new lives. Instructional materials for transsexuals, their friends, and relatives are available from the Harry Benjamin Gender Dysphoria Association, named after the New York endocrinologist who in the 1950s was a pioneer in his clinical work with transsexuals. Whether transsexuals choose sex-change surgery or not, they need a good deal of supportive psychotherapy and counseling to help them through their conflicts, anxiety, and depression (Roberto, 1983).

Alterations of Gender Identity

Are sex-change operations indeed the only option? They used to be considered the only viable treatment, for psychological attempts to shift gender identity had consistently failed. Gender identity was assumed too deep-seated to alter. Apparently successful procedures for altering gender identity through behavior therapy have now been reported, however. One treatment (Rekers and Lovaas, 1974) was of a five-year-old boy who, since age two, had been cross-dressing and showing the other familiar signs of gender identity disorder. Concurring with the therapist's judgment that conforming to societal standards of masculinity would benefit the boy in both the short and long run, the child's parents began, as instructed, to compliment and otherwise support him whenever he played with traditionally male toys, rather than those commonly preferred by girls, and whenever he engaged in other little-boy activities. Feminine mannerisms were to be discouraged. After only six months of intensive treatment, the boy was typically masculine, and he was still so at a two-year follow-up. Although it might be objected that encouraging play with guns while discouraging play with dolls only reinforces cultural stereotypes (Winkler, 1977), this child may have been spared considerable psychological hardship by bringing his gender identity into conformity with his biological makeup.[2]

An even more dramatic reversal of gender identity was reported by Barlow, Reynolds, and Agras (1973). In their behavioral treatment of a seventeen-year-old male transsexual, gender role was broken down into concrete components, such as mannerisms, interpersonal behavior, and fantasies, and the client was given training to change each component. He was initially made aware of the effeminate manner in which he stood, sat, walked, and talked. Then through modeling, rehearsal, and video feedback, and through voice retraining, he was taught the ways of doing them judged masculine by the culture. Almost immediately the staring and ridicule of his peers lessened, and he returned to high school part time. The young man's social skills improved as he was taught to make eye contact and conversation and to express his positive feelings through appropriate smiles and other means.

He still felt himself to be a female, however, and had fantasies and urges to have intercourse with men. Therapy then focused on his fantasy life. During training sessions a female therapist encouraged him to imagine himself in sexual situations with attractive women; she also embellished his fantasies by describing foreplay in explicit detail. He was instructed to generate such fantasies when encountering women as he went about his daily activities. After thirty-four training sessions over a period of two months, the client's desire to change sex dropped dramatically, and fantasies about men decreased in number as those about women increased. He was now beginning to think of himself as a man, and the attraction he still occasionally felt toward men took place without gender role reversal, that is, the attraction was that felt by one man toward another.

Measures of sexual arousal with the penile plethysmograph (see Box 12.1) more definitely revealed that he was still attracted to men and not women, so therapeutic effort was now devoted to increasing the arousal felt toward women and decreasing that felt toward men. Slides of women were paired with slides of men, the idea being to classically condition sexual arousal to women by associating them with the arousal felt toward slides of males. This procedure, followed by aversion therapy sessions to reduce the attractiveness of slides of males, promoted the desired change to a heterosexual pattern of arousal. Interestingly, during this period the young man's manner of standing, sitting, and walking became even more traditionally masculine. He also felt much better about himself and had returned to high school on a full-time basis. Five months after the end of treatment, the young man reported for the first time masturbating to orgasm while imagining himself with a woman. A one-year follow-up found him going steady with a woman and engaging in "light petting." He no longer thought of himself as a woman. Five years later the man's gender identity continued to be masculine, his sexual orientation heterosexual (Barlow, Abel, and Blanchard, 1979).

[2]We have stated that most GID children do not become transsexuals, even without special treatment. Not knowing whether this particular child would "grow out of it," the parents and the therapists decided to intervene.

BOX 12.1

PSYCHOPHYSIOLOGICAL ASSESSMENT OF SEXUAL AROUSAL

Let us examine closely some important innovations in physiological measurement. In 1966 Masters and Johnson startled researchers and lay people alike by their direct physiological assessments of men and women during states of great sexual arousal. The measures they used primarily were muscle tension and blood volume in various parts of the cardiovascular system. In addition, they employed ingenious photographic devices to record changes in the color of various tissues of the vagina during the sexual arousal of women. More recently behavioral researchers have been using two genital devices for measuring sexual arousal in men and in women, and each of them enjoys validation in giving rather specific measurements of sexual excitement. Both are sensitive indicators of vasocongestion of the genitalia, that is, the flooding of their veins with blood, a key physiological process in sexual arousal.

The penile plethysmograph (Freund, 1963; Bancroft, Jones, and Pullan, 1966) has been used successfully to measure the sexual arousal of men in a variety of experiments. A plethysmograph is a device that measures blood flow. The most widely used penile plethysmograph is a strain gauge, consisting of a very thin rubber tube filled with mercury or a circular piece of light surgical steel, either of which can be placed around the penis (Barlow et al., 1970) with ease and in privacy. As the penis fills with blood during sexual excitement, the tube or steel stretches, changing the electrical resistance of the mercury or steel; through appropriate wiring the increase in resistance is transformed into tracings on a complex apparatus called the polygraph. Increase in the length of the penis correlates fairly well with increase in circumference, and both of them are a function of engorgement of the penis with blood during sexual excitement. The strain gauge, then, provides a useful measure of sexual responding in men.

Similarly direct and specific measurement of female sexual arousal was not at first possible. Only indirect measures such as those used by Masters and Johnson were available, and these are unsatisfactory for both aesthetic and practical reasons. Fortunately, a vaginal plethysmograph was eventually invented by Sintchak and Geer (1975). This device is shaped like a small menstrual tampon and has a light at the tip. The light reflected from the vaginal walls is recorded and provides a measure of the amount of blood they contain. Like the penile strain gauge, the vaginal probe is easily put in place by subjects in total privacy. An important validational study of this device was reported

by Geer, Morokoff, and Greenwood (1974). They showed female undergraduates erotic and nonerotic films, a young man and a young woman having an explicit sexual encounter, and *The Crusades*, depicting battle scenes and court life during the time of the Crusades. Since each film was readily identified as erotic or nonerotic, any differences between the measurements of the two groups of subjects during the viewings could be taken as evidence that the vaginal probes do provide a valid measure of sexual excitement. The women watching the sexual film showed much greater blood flow than did the subjects watching the control film. It is of interest that heart rate measurements taken concurrently did not differentiate the two groups of subjects, confirming the desirability of specific genital measures.

Subjects soon become relatively unaware of the presence of genital plethysmographs on their bodies and of the wiring to the polygraph. This degree of unobtrusiveness, desirable in any assessment procedure, is particularly important in studying sexual behavior, about which many people are self-conscious. The technical innovations and availability of these devices have spurred a remarkable volume of research on human sexual behavior. Of course, it would be naive to assert that these genital devices have no effect on how subjects respond in a laboratory. Furthermore, volunteers for such studies have had more sexual experiences than those who do not volunteer (Wolchik, Spencer, and Lisi, 1983); hence findings based on their reactions cannot be reliably generalized.

The physiology of the human body presents problems for the assessment of sexual arousal by genital plethysmographs. In the earliest stages of arousal, the penis lengthens faster than it grows in circumference (Davidson et al., 1981); the circumference, which is what the strain gauge measures, can initially *decrease* as the penis lengthens. Many studies of male sexual arousal focus on these early stages, what may be termed sexual *interest*. In turn, the vaginal plethysmograph is extremely sensitive to temperature; the body temperature of women is known to fluctuate, depending on the phase of the menstrual cycle (Beck, Sakheim, and Barlow, 1983).

Not all sexuality can be measured in terms of genital responding. And yet the data being collected by sex researchers around the world are beginning to shed light on an area of human conduct previously shrouded in mystery, embarrassment, and an often harmful mythology.

The work of Barlow and his colleagues represents the first successful change of gender identity in an adult transsexual and as such raises the possibility that cross-sex identity is amenable to change. The clinicians themselves acknowledge that this particular client might have been different from other transsexuals because he did consent at the outset to participate in a therapy program aimed at changing his gender identity. Most transsexuals refuse such treatment as inappropriate; for them sex-reassignment surgery is the only legitimate goal.[3]

THE PARAPHILIAS

The term paraphilia denotes that there is a deviation (*para-*) in what the person is attracted to (*-philia*). In those suffering the disorders,

. . . unusual or bizarre imagery or acts are necessary for sexual excitement. Such imagery or acts tend to be insistently and involuntarily repetitive and generally involve either: (1) preference for use of a nonhuman object for sexual arousal, (2) repetitive sexual activity with humans involving real or simulated suffering or humiliation, or (3) repetitive sexual activity with nonconsenting partners. . . . [The paraphilias] in varying degrees may interfere with the capacity for reciprocal affectionate sexual activity (DSM-III, pp. 266, 261).

This definition of paraphilias indicates that a person need not actually engage in overt acts to be given the diagnosis; the unconventional sexual activity may be solely imaginal, as when certain fantasies or pictorial materials are relied on for sexual arousal during masturbation. The deviant components of a paraphilia are *necessary* for sexual excitement, not merely a variation that a person may on occasion choose to lend variety to his or her sex life. Paraphilias may, according to DSM-III, be multiple rather than single and also be an aspect of other mental disorders, such as schizophrenia or one of the personality disorders. Finally, the fact that in some of these patterns of existence nonconsenting partners are specifically sought indicates that they will have legal consequences.

Fetishism

A fetishist, almost always a male, is sexually enthralled by some inanimate object or some specific nongenital part of a person. His disorder of *fetishism* takes the form of using

[3]In their follow-up report on the seventeen-year-old transsexual, Barlow, Abel, and Blanchard (1979) described two additional cases treated in the same way. These two men, in their mid-twenties, were on the route to sex-change surgery but then had second thoughts. The behavioral retraining succeeded again in altering gender identity but not their attraction to men.

"Believe me, Harry—It's become *more* than just another fetish."

nonliving objects (fetishes) as a repeatedly preferred or exclusive method of achieving sexual excitement. The diagnosis is not made when the fetishes are limited to articles of female clothing used in cross-dressing, as in Transvestism, or when the object is sexually stimulating because it has been designed for that purpose, e.g., a vibrator (DSM-III, p. 268).

Beautiful shoes, sheer stockings, gloves, toilet articles, fur garments, and especially underpants are common sources of arousal for fetishists. Some can carry on their fetishism by themselves in secret by fondling, kissing, smelling, or merely gazing at the adored object as they masturbate. Others need their partner to don the fetish as a stimulant for intercourse. Fetishists sometimes become primarily interested in making a collection of the desired objects, and they will burgle week after week to add to their hoard.

Other individuals make fetishes of parts of the female body. Locks of hair, feet, ankles, hands, fingernails, delicately shaped ears, and large bosoms may be the narrowed focus of all passion. To secure contact with them, the fetishist may engage in rather extraordinary maneuvering—such as working as a shoe salesman, even though he could qualify for a better-paying position—and may even commit assault.

A transvestite imitating Marilyn Monroe
in a Parisian nightclub act.

early in his sexual experiences, masturbate to pictures of women dressed in black leather. Indeed, one experiment (Rachman, 1966) lends some mild support to learning propositions. Male subjects were repeatedly shown slides of nude and alluring females interspersed with slides of women's boots. The subjects were eventually aroused by the boots alone. The "fetishistic attraction" induced, however, was weak and transient.

Box 6.3 (page 122) discussed the possibility that people are "prepared" to learn to become phobic to certain objects. It is also possible that human beings are prepared to learn to be sexually stimulated by certain classes of stimuli. If mere association with sexual stimulation were all there is to acquiring a fetishism through classical conditioning, would not objects such as ceilings and pillows be found high on the list of fetishes (Baron and Byrne, 1977)? At this point it would be premature to conclude that fetishisms are established through classical conditioning.

Transvestism

When a man is sexually aroused by dressing in the clothing of the opposite sex while still regarding himself as a member of his own sex, the term *transvestism* is applied to his behavior. A transvestite may also enjoy appearing socially as a woman; some female impersonators become performers in nightclubs, catering to the delight that many sexually conventional people take in skilled cross-dressing. When arousal is the primary motivation of transvestites, they often masturbate when cross-dressed. Transvestism should not be confused with homosexuality; transvestites are heterosexual, and only a few homosexuals ever on occasion "go in drag." As mentioned earlier, it is illegal in many jurisdictions to appear cross-dressed in public.

Transvestites, who are always males according to DSM-III, by and large cross-dress episodically rather than on a regular basis. They tend to be otherwise masculine in appearance, demeanor, and sexual preference. Most are married. The cross-dressing usually takes place in private and in secret and is known to few members of the family. The compulsion to cross-dress may become more frequent over time but only rarely develops to a change in gender identity, that is, to the man's believing that he is actually a member of the female sex.

Case histories of transvestites often refer to childhood incidents in which the little boy was praised and fussed over for looking "cute" when wearing female attire. Learning accounts assume the disorder results from the conditioning effects of repeatedly masturbating

Subjectively, the attraction felt by the fetishist toward the object or part of the body is involuntary and irresistible. Because it has such a strong, compulsive quality, the fetishism may be a dominant force in the man's life. The degree of the erotic focalization distinguishes fetishisms from the ordinary attraction that high heels and net stockings may hold for heterosexual men and from their normal appreciation of beautiful hair, bosoms, and thighs. The disorder usually begins by adolescence, although the fetish may have acquired special significance even earlier, during childhood. It may have some association with a person toward whom the fetishist had as a child felt an intimate connection.

Psychoanalytic theorists generally consider fetishisms and the other paraphilias to serve some sort of defensive function, warding off castration anxiety about normal sexual contacts. Learning theorists usually invoke some kind of classical conditioning in the person's social-sexual history. For example, a young man may, when cross-dressing, similar to the supposed classical conditioning connection between arousal and the object adopted as a fetish. Some clinicians believe transvestism represents for a beleaguered male a refuge from the responsibilities he sees himself bearing solely by virtue of being male in our society. Female clothing, then, is believed to have *meaning* for transvestites that is more complex and encompassing than sheer sexual arousal; trying to explain transvestism solely in sexual terms may therefore be an oversimplification.

Incest

The taboo against <u>incest</u> seems virtually universal in human societies (Ford and Beach, 1951). A notable exception were the marriages of Egyptian pharoahs to their sisters or other females of their immediate families. In Egypt it was believed that the royal blood should not be contaminated by that of outsiders. Some anthropologists consider the prohibition against incest to have served the important function of forcing more widely spread social ties and consequently greater social harmony than would have been likely had family members chosen their mates only from among their own. The incest taboo makes sense according to present-day scientific knowledge. The offspring from a father-daughter or a brother-sister union has a greater probability of inheriting a pair of recessive genes, one from each parent. For the most part, recessive genes have negative rather than positive physiological effects; they may cause serious birth defects. The incest taboo, then, has adaptive evolutionary significance (Geer, Heiman, and Leitenberg, 1984).

Incest,[4] which includes all forms of sexual contact, seems most common between brother and sister. The next most common form, which is considered more pathological, is between father and daughter. In a well-known study on sex offenders, Gebhard and his associates (1965) found that most fathers who had relations with physically mature daughters tended to be very devout, moralistic, and fundamentalistic in their religious beliefs. Fathers who commit incest may be sexually frustrated in their marriage yet feel constrained, for religious reasons, from seeking gratification through masturbation, prostitutes, or extramarital affairs. For them it is preferable to keep sexual contacts within the family (Frude, 1982). Other evidence, however, indicates that incestuous relationships can be found in families of all

religious and socioeconomic backgrounds (Rosen and Rosen, 1981). Very few instances of mother-son incest are reported.

Statistics on the incidence of incest are notoriously difficult to collect; family members are very reluctant to report the offenders to the authorities, sometimes from fear of violence from the offending father, particularly when he drinks heavily (Mey and Neff, 1982). Family members may also realistically fear that the child or father can be legally removed from the home, which would have a major negative impact on the very existence of the family. Incest is now acknowledged to happen much more often than had earlier been assumed. A study of 796 college students found that an astounding 19 percent of the women and 8.6 percent of the men has been sexually victimized as children. Of the victimized women, 28 percent had had incestuous relations, of the men, 23 percent (Finkelhor, 1979). When states pass more effective legislation on reporting incidents of incest, confirmed cases increase 50 to 500 percent. The number of confirmed incest cases that came to the attention of child welfare departments in Texas in 1974 was 214; in 1976, 630; and in 1977, 1153. The Child Sexual Abuse Treatment Program in Santa Clara County, California, received 36 incest referrals in 1971, 180 in 1974, and 600 in 1977 (Justice and Justice, 1979).

Explanations of incest run the gamut from sexual deprivation to the Freudian notion that human beings have basic human desires for such relationships. Some older explanations tended to "blame the victim" (Ryan, 1971): Bender and Blau (1937) described a number of children who had been involved in incestuous relationships as having "unusually attractive and charming personalities" (p. 511) and, because of their seductiveness, as not being totally innocent parties. In addition to being morally repugnant, this hypothesis is refuted by the information available (Meiselman, 1978).

Gagnon (1977) speculates that an incestuous relationship between father and daughter can begin when the father is under considerable stress outside the home and receives insufficient emotional and sexual support from his wife. He turns to an available, sometimes prepubescent daughter, who takes on the role of substitute wife. Whether the incest continues depends in large measure on the response of the man's wife, who may choose to ignore what is going on in the interest of keeping the family together. The reactions of the daughter are, of course, highly variable and can be expected to change over time. Perhaps initially flattered that she can take good care of daddy, the growing young woman may later feel degraded and trapped by the whole affair and run away from home. Or she may become pregnant,

[4]For some reason incest does not appear in DSM-III.

thus *forcing* other family members to deal with the father's behavior.

There is little firm evidence bearing on the long-term effects of incest on either children or parents. A number of studies reviewed by Geer, Heiman, and Leitenberg (1984) suggest that the adverse psychological impact on the child can be serious, evidenced by later prostitution, promiscuity, drug abuse, depression, and psychosexual dysfunction. At the same time, however, it is important to point out, without minimizing the problem, that incest does not necessarily lead to lasting psychological difficulties (Mey and Neff, 1982).

Pedophilia

Pedophiles are adults, usually men at least as far as police records indicate, who derive sexual gratification through physical and often sexual contact with prepubertal children. Older adolescents may also be pedophiles, although the disorder most frequently begins in middle age. Violence is seldom a part of the molestation, but society's reaction to pedophiles is far more punitive than it is toward rapists, who employ physical force. Sometimes the pedophile, or child molester, is content to stroke the child's hair, but he may also manipulate the child's genitalia, encourage the child to manipulate his, and less often, attempt intromission. The molestations may be repeated over a period of weeks, months, or years if they are not discovered by other adults or protested by the child.

Two major distinctions are drawn between incest and pedophilia. First, by definition, incest is between members of the same family. Second, and more importantly, incest victims tend to be older than the object of a pedophile's desires. It is more often the case that a father becomes interested in his daughter when she begins to mature physically, whereas the pedophile is interested in the youngster precisely because she is sexually immature.

Pedophiles tend to be rigidly religious and moralistic. As with most of the aberrant sexual behavior that has been described there is a strong subjective feeling of compulsion in the attraction that draws the pedophile to the child. According to Gebhard and his colleagues (1965), pedophiles generally know the children they molest, being a next-door neighbor or friend of the family. Most older heterosexual pedophiles are or have been married at some time in their lives.

As with incest, it is not known with any degree of precision how widespread child molestation is; since most instances occur between the child and someone known to him or her and to the family, many more cases are assumed to go unreported to authorities than come to their attention. Indeed, in 1984 several day-care centers across the country were alleged to be the sites of ongoing child molestation by the owners and staff, heightening public awareness of, and outrage at, the extent of the problem.

It has been suggested that the drive to approach a child sexually can reflect a sense of having failed in the adult world, socially and professionally as well as sexually. Occasionally, though, an adult predisposed toward pedophilia may be aroused by a child's innocent, uninhibited show of affection. Unbeknown to the child, the pedophile perceives sexual overtones in demonstrativeness. In defining pedophilia, state laws prescribe an upper age limit for those who are to be considered children, making it a crime to approach sexually any younger person. The age varies in different states.

When a child tells a parent that an adult has fondled him or her, the parents face the dilemma of how to react. Many experts feel that the child tends not to interpret the interaction in the same sexual terms that adults do (Gagnon, 1977). Even if the molester has an orgasm, it is not always clear to the child what has happened, and to react with adult alarm can lend needless negative meaning to an unfortunate incident. But at the same time the young child must be protected from a prolonged and harmful sexual relationship with an adult.

Voyeurism ("Peeping")

Now and then a man may by chance happen to observe a nude woman without her knowing he is watching her. If his sex life is primarily conventional, his act is voyeuristic, but he would not generally be considered a voyeur. *Voyeurism* is

repetitive looking at unsuspecting people, usually strangers, who are either naked, in the act of disrobing, or engaging in sexual activity, as the repeatedly preferred or exclusive method of achieving sexual excitement. The act of looking ("peeping") is for the purpose of achieving sexual excitement, and no sexual activity with the person is sought. Orgasm, usually produced by masturbation, may occur during the voyeuristic activity, or later in response to the memory of what the individual has witnessed. Often these individuals enjoy thinking about the observed individuals' being helpless and feeling humiliated if they knew they were being seen (DSM-III, pp. 272–273).

The surreptitious voyeur, unable to manage closer sexual encounters, invades from a distance the privacy of a disrobing stranger.

A true voyeur, who is almost always a man, will not find it particularly exciting to watch a woman who is undressing for his special benefit. The element of risk seems important, for he is excited by his anticipation of how the woman would react if she knew he was watching.[5] Some voyeurs derive special pleasure from secretly observing couples having sexual relations. As with all categories of behavior that are against the law, frequencies of occurrence are difficult to assess, since the majority of *all* illegal activities go unnoticed by the police.

From what we know, voyeurs tend to be young, single, submissive, and fearful of more direct sexual encounters with others (Katchadourian and Lunde, 1972; McCary, 1973). Their peeping serves as a substitute gratification and possibly gives them a sense of power over those watched. They do not seem to be otherwise dis-

[5]That voyeurs have an impoverished social life and engage in surreptitious peeping instead of making conventional sexual and social contacts with women suggests another way to understand their preference for spying on unaware women. If the woman were to be aware of the man's actions and continue nonetheless to allow herself to be watched, the man might well conclude that she has some personal interest in him. This possibility would be very threatening to the voyeur and, because of his fear, less sexually arousing. Perhaps then it is not the risk of being discovered that arouses the voyeur. Rather, undiscovered peeping, because it protects the heterosexual voyeur from a possible relationship with a woman, is the least frightening way for him to have contact with her.

turbed, however. After all restrictions against the sale of pornographic materials to adults had been lifted in Denmark, one of the few observed effects of this liberalization was a significant reduction in peeping, at least as reported to the police (Kutchinsky, 1970). It may be that the increased availability of completely frank pictorial and written material, which is typically used in masturbation, satisfies the needs that had earlier made some men without other outlets voyeurs.

Exhibitionism

Voyeurism and exhibitionism together account for close to a majority of all sexual offenses that come to the attention of police. It should come as no surprise that exhibitionists are frequently arrested for what is legally termed "indecent exposure"; the very nature of their disorder compels them to expose themselves to people who are shocked or at least offended by the act. Again, the frequency of *exhibitionism* is much greater among men. A quip holds that a man surreptitiously looking at a nude woman is a voyeur, but that a woman looking at a naked man is watching an exhibitionist. Like many statements about human sexuality, this one implies that women are less sexual than men. The exhibitionist repeatedly exposes

the genitals to an unsuspecting stranger for the purpose of sexual excitement, with no attempt at further sexual activity with the stranger. The wish to surprise or shock the observer is often consciously perceived or [is] close to conscious awareness, but these individuals are usually not physically dangerous to the victim. Sometimes the individual masturbates while exposing himself (DSM-III, p. 272).

The urge to expose seems overwhelming and virtually uncontrollable to the exhibitionist or "flasher" and is apparently triggered by anxiety and restlessness as well as by sexual arousal. Because of the compulsive nature of the urge, the exposures may be repeated rather frequently and even in the same place and at the same time of day. Apparently exhibitionists are so strongly driven that, at the time of the act, they are oblivious to the social and legal consequences of what they are doing (Stevenson and Jones, 1972). In the desperation and tension of the moment, they may suffer headache and palpitations and have a sense of unreality. Afterward they flee in trembling and remorse (Bond and Hutchison, 1960). Only rarely does the exhibitionist seek physical contact with his unwilling observer; even less often is a more violent sexual offense, such as rape, a danger (Rooth, 1973). Generally, the exhibitionist is immature in his approaches to the opposite sex and has difficulty in interpersonal relationships. Over half of all exhibitionists are married, but their sexual relationships with their wives are not satisfactory (Mohr, Turner, and Jerry, 1964).

Younger exhibitionists may not manifest other kinds of psychopathology, but some of those who expose themselves come from the ranks of the mentally retarded and the senile. Some who exhibit do so while having a temporal lobe epileptic seizure (see page 602). Because the behavior of these men may be without deliberation and intent and sometimes even awareness, it is problematic whether they should be considered exhibitionists. When the label of exhibitionism is applied, not only overt behavior but also intent should be established, which may be difficult.

The fact that the exhibited penis is sometimes flaccid (Langevin et al., 1979) raises interesting questions about the *sexual* aspects of the act. How sexually arousing can it be for a man to expose himself if his penis is not erect when doing so? The exhibitionist, deficient as he seems to be in more conventional social skills, may regard his act of exposure as the best social interaction that he can manage. The fact that a nonchalant reaction on the part of the observer is not satisfying to the exhibitionist confirms that he is seeking to startle those to whom he exposes himself.

The search to determine how exhibitionism develops has turned up very little. One of many psychodynamic theories views the problem as stemming from a re-

Sexually explicit materials are readily available in many cities. One study suggests that voyeurism may decline through public access to pornography.

pressed fear of castration and the exhibitionist's need to reassure himself that he is still a man. Such speculations are unsupported by any data, nor have they contributed to the development of effective therapies. An intriguing learning hypothesis emphasizes the reinforcing aspects of masturbation. McGuire, Carlisle, and Young (1965) reported on the development of exhibitionism in two young men who were surprised during urination by an attractive woman. When the embarrassment had passed and they were in private, the thought of being discovered in this way aroused them and they masturbated while fantasizing the earlier experience. After repeated masturbating to such fantasies, they began to exhibit. The report suggests that repeated association of sexual arousal with images of being seen by a woman classically conditioned the men to become aroused through exhibiting. No controlled evidence, however, clearly supports a learning explanation of exhibitionism.

Rape

The Crime

Few other antisocial acts are viewed with more disgust and anger than the obtaining of sexual gratification from an unwilling partner through *forcible rape*. A second category, *statutory rape*, refers to sexual intercourse between a male and any female who is a minor. The typical age of consent, as decided by state statutes, is eighteen years. It is assumed that a younger person should not be held responsible for her sexual activity, but it has been suggested in recent years that the age be lowered. A charge of statutory rape can be made even if it is proved that the girl entered into the situation knowingly and willingly. Thus statutory rape need not involve force, being simply a consummated intercourse with a female minor that was reported to the police. The focus here is on rape other than statutory.

In the past rape was considered an offense not against the victim but against the property rights of the woman's husband, father, or brothers. Even now in most states a forcible sexual assault by a husband on his wife is not legally recognized as rape. Moreover, certain women have ''bad'' reputations with the police of their communities. Under these circumstances a truly forceful and even violent rape may not be categorized as such in the station house, especially when the status in the community of the man involved is higher than that of the victim. Thus a biased incidence of rape, as well as of other unconventional sexual behavior, may be obtained if attention is restricted to police records. Overriding

these considerations, however, is the unfortunate fact that the woman may feel that great shame is attached to her involuntary role in rape. Perhaps as many as twenty rapes occur for every one reported to the police; but even though underreported, the incidence of rape is increasing faster than incidences of murder, assault, and robbery. Rape is the fastest-growing violent crime in the United States.[6]

Noteworthy too is the frequency with which men subject women to coerced sexual activity that stops short of rape. In a survey of undergraduate men, Rapaport and Burkhart (1985) found that many had sexually manhandled women against their will. For example, 37 percent had placed their hand on a woman's breast, 31 percent had removed or disarranged underclothing, and 30 percent had touched the genital area of a protesting woman.

The Victim and the Attack

A prevalent belief is that the victims of rape are always young and attractive. This is a myth. Although many victims do indeed fit this description, many others do not. Age and physical appearance are no barriers to some rapists; they may choose children as young as one year old and women in their eighties. In almost all instances of forced rape, there is sexual intercourse, but other activities as well—fellatio and cunnilingus—are sometimes demanded of or performed on the victim. In what is sometimes termed sadistic rape, the rapist inflicts serious physical harm on the victim's body, such as inserting foreign objects into the vagina or pulling and burning her breasts. Some rapists murder and mutilate (Holmstrom and Burgess, 1980). Little wonder then that rape is considered as much an act of violence and aggression as a sexual act.

Rape victims are often traumatized by the experience, both physically and mentally. In the minutes or seconds preceding rape, the woman begins to recognize her dangerous situation but can scarcely believe what is about to happen to her. During the moments of the attack, she is first and foremost in great fear for her life. The physical violation of her body and the ripping away of her freedom of choice are enraging. But the victim also feels her vulnerability in not being able to fight off her stronger attacker and usually finds her capacity for resistance seriously compromised by her terror. For weeks following the rape, many victims are extremely

---

[6]In many jurisdictions the definition of rape includes not only vaginal penetration but oral and anal entry as well (Geis, 1977).

tense and deeply humiliated; they feel guilt that they were unable to fight harder and have angry thoughts of revenge. Many have nightmares about rape. In a study of women admitted to a large city hospital for emergency treatment immediately following rape, Burgess and Holmstrom (1974) found that half ultimately changed their place of residence or at least their telephone number. A large number had trouble in their sexual relationships with husbands or lovers. Masters and Johnson (1970) too found among their dysfunctional couples a number of women who had developed negative attitudes toward sex with their husbands following rape. Some victims of rape develop phobias about being outdoors or indoors, or in the dark, depending on where the rape took place. They may also for a time fear being alone or in crowds or having anyone behind them. For good reason DSM-III mentions rape as one of the traumata that can give rise to posttraumatic stress disorder.

The Rapist

The vast majority of rapes are almost surely planned—it is inaccurate to say that rape is the spontaneous act of a man whose sexual impulses have gone out of control (Harrington and Sutton-Simon, 1977). The rapist may have a sadistic streak, but unlike the sadist he often does not know the victim beforehand and attacks someone who is unwilling. Moreover, the sadist usually has an established, ongoing relationship with a masochist. In many cases a pattern of repeated rape is part of a sociopathic life style.

The incidence of sexual dysfunction during rape may be high. Interviews with 170 men convicted of sexual assault revealed that erectile failure as well as premature and retarded ejaculation had in their criminal act been considerable problems for a third of these men, although almost none reported having them in his consenting sexual relations. Only one-fourth of the men gave no evidence of sexual dysfunction during rape (Groth and Burgess, 1977). One interpretation of such reactions is that rape is not invariably sexual. In fact, because rape is a mixture of both sex and aggression, the motivation is difficult to determine.

Sexism and the subjugation of women through rape were explored in depth by Susan Brownmiller (1975) in her best-selling book *Against Our Will*. Her thesis is that rape is "nothing more or less than a conscious process of intimidation by which all men keep all women in a state of fear" (p. 5). She garners evidence from history, both ancient and modern. In the Babylonian civilization (3000 B.C.), for example, a married woman was the property of her husband. If she was raped, both she

and the rapist were bound and tossed into a river. The husband could choose to save her, or he could let her drown, just punishment for "her adultery." The views of the ancient Hebrews were no more enlightened; a married woman who had been raped was commonly stoned to death along with her attacker. When an unbetrothed virgin was raped within the walls of the city, she was similarly stoned, for it was assumed that she could have prevented the attack simply by crying out.

These penalties that different societies have imposed on raped women, together with the fact that men with their generally superior strength can usually overpower women, buttress Brownmiller's argument that rape has served in the past and still serves to intimidate women. The Crusaders raped their way across Europe in the eleventh through thirteenth centuries on their holy pilgrimages to free Jerusalem from the Muslims, the Germans in World War I raped as they rampaged through Belgium, and American forces raped in Vietnam as they "searched and destroyed." Brownmiller contends that rape is actually *expected* in war. In her view, membership in the most exclusive males-only clubs in the world—the fighting forces of most nations—encourages a perverse sense of masculine superiority and creates a climate in which rape is acceptable.

Who is the rapist? Is he primarily the psychopath who seeks the thrill of dominating and humiliating a woman through intimidation and often brutal assault? Is he an ordinarily unassertive man with a fragile ego who, feeling inadequate after disappointment and rejection in work or love, takes out his frustrations on an unwilling stranger? Or is he the teenager, provoked by a seductive and apparently available young woman who, it turns out, was not as interested as he in sexual intimacy? Is he a man whose inhibitions against expressing anger have been dissolved by alcohol? The best answer is that the rapist is all these men, probably in a combination of several of these circumstances.

If we rely for information on crime reports, men arrested for rape tend to be young—usually between fifteen and twenty-five years of age—poor, unskilled, and not well educated. They come from the lower classes, in which, sociologists assert, violence is more the norm than in the middle class. About half of them are married and living with their wives at the time of the crime. A fourth to a third of all rapes are carried out by two or more men. Given the knowledge that rape is seriously underreported, however, it would be a mistake to generalize about rapists from information gleaned from police files. Indeed, in some instances the rapist is the victim's husband (Russell, 1982).

Some theoreticians believe that rape is part and parcel of the cultural stereotypes of masculinity and femininity, whereby the male's role in sexual relationships is to be aggressive, the female's passive yet seductive. The woman is expected to resist the man's advances; the man is expected to overcome her resistance. It may be that some acts of rape are committed through faulty communication between the man and the woman. The woman's "Maybe" is interpreted as "Yes" by the man, who proceeds on the assumption that the woman "really" wants to be intimate, only to be sorely disappointed and unable to accept her ultimate refusal (Gagnon, 1977). This view of rape would of course apply only to instances in which the two people know each other—in more than a third of reported rapes they do—not to the large number of assaults that occur on streets and through forced entry into the woman's home. Nor does this view account for the extreme brutality that is often part of the assault.

Emerging from the study of rape, and of other patterns of unconventional sexual behavior, is the fact that sexuality can serve many purposes. Indeed, an act we label as sexual because it involves the genitalia may sometimes be better understood in nonsexual terms. The classic study of sex offenders (Gebhard et al., 1965) concluded that up to 33 percent of rapists carried out the act to express aggression rather than for sexual satisfaction. Rapists, in the opinion of many (for example, Brownmiller, 1975; Gagnon, 1977), aggress against others for reasons having only remotely to do with sex per se (see Box 12.2). Many feminist groups object to the classification of rape as a *sexual* crime at all, for it can mask the basically assaultive and typically brutal nature of the act, and it creates an atmosphere in which the sexual motives of the *victim* are questioned. Although a person who is beaten and robbed (without being sexually abused) is hardly suspected of secretly wanting to be attacked, by cruel irony the victims of rape must often prove their moral "purity" to husbands, friends, police—even to themselves. What, after all, did *they* do that might have contributed to the incident, especially if the rapist is not a complete stranger? But there are indications that the stigma of rape is being lessened by more enlightened views, coming in large measure from women's liberation groups and from books such as Brownmiller's.

Sexual Sadism and Sexual Masochism

The majority of *sadists*, as indicated earlier, establish relationships with masochists to derive mutual sexual gratification. Sadomasochism is found in both hetero-

sexual and homosexual relationships. The sadist may derive full orgastic pleasure by inflicting pain on his or her partner, and the masochist may be completely gratified by being subjected to pain. For other partners the sadistic and masochistic practices are a prelude to sexual intercourse. A married couple seen for behavior therapy had practiced the following ritual.

As a prelude to sexual intercourse, the young man would draw blood by cutting a small incision on the palm of his wife's right hand. She would then stimulate his penis, using the blood of her right palm as a lubricant. Normal intercourse will then ensue, and the moment the wife felt her husband ejaculating, she was required to dig her nails deep into the small of his back or buttocks (Lazarus and Davison, 1971, pp. 202–203).

Masochists seem to outnumber sadists, however. For this reason "bondage and discipline" services may constitute a considerable portion of the business of a house of prostitution. The manifestations of sexual masochism are also varied. Some of course are self-inflicted.

Some sadists murder and mutilate. Fortunately, however, most of the time sadism and masochism are restricted to fantasies and are not then regarded as disorders, according to DSM-III. The increasing number of "sex shops" in large cities do a lucrative business in providing pictorial and written materials to those who need at least the vicarious experience of pain in order to satisfy themselves sexually.

The shared activities of a sadist and a masochist are heavily "scripted." Pain, humiliation and domination, or both take place as part of a story that the two agree to act out together. Themes of submission-domination appear to be as important as inflicting physical pain. The masochist, for example may be a mischievous child, who must be punished by a discipline-minded teacher; or a slave from ancient times, recently sold to a powerful sultan. The activities of the masochist and sadist, then, assume for both parties a certain fictional *meaning* which heightens sexual arousal. Cognitive theorists like Gagnon and Simon (1973) hold that any explanation of sadomasochistic sexual patterns must take into account the fabrications that the partners weave into their actions.

How can it happen that a person, often quite normal in other respects, must inflict or experience suffering, directly or vicariously, in order to become sexually aroused? If it is assumed, as some psychoanalysts do, that pain provides sexual pleasure, the answer is readily available; unfortunately, this "explanation" really explains nothing. Another psychoanalytic theory, re-

BOX 12.2

A PSYCHOPHYSIOLOGICAL ANALYSIS OF RAPE

Discussions of rape are based almost entirely on the work of historians, sociologists, political analysts, and journalists. Recently, experimental psychologists have been trying to bring something of the phenomenon into the laboratory. The work of Abel and his colleagues (1977) is a good example of this kind of research.

In their initial study these workers developed a methodology that relied on the penile plethysmograph to help them distinguish between rapists and nonrapists. Most of the rapists had long histories of forcible sexual assaults on women, and some on men as well. Control subjects had histories of other types of unconventional sexual behavior, such as exhibitionism, pedophilia, and homosexuality.

The independent variable in the experiment consisted of two kinds of erotic audiotapes. The story recorded on one tape was of mutually enjoyable intercourse with a suitable partner; the other audiotape was of a rape of that same partner. The enjoyable scene of intercourse portrayed the partner as willing, loving, and utterly involved with the subject. In the rape scene the victim resisted and was in physical as well as emotional pain. According to the plethysmograph, rapists were significantly more aroused by the rape tape than were the nonrapist subjects, the expected pattern. But interestingly, the rapists were highly aroused by the mutually enjoyable intercourse tape as well! In fact, this tape aroused them no less than the rape scene. And the nonrapists, although much more aroused by the lovemaking than by the rape, nonetheless showed some mild arousal when listening to the rape story.

Abel then went on to use the same method to investigate the rapist's response to aggression. Are rapists aroused by aggression if the incident does not conclude with sexual assault? How does arousal from aggression relate to arousal from rape? Some of the rapists already studied listened to three additional tapes. One of them depicted a rapist slapping, hitting, and holding a woman down against her will, but without ensuing intercourse. On the second the man had forcible intercourse with the same victim. The rapists also listened to a tape of nonviolent sexual intercourse with a willing partner. Results revealed that the aggression scene generated some sexual arousal, but only 40 percent of that generated by the rape scene and an even smaller percentage of that generated by the tape of mutually satisfying nonaggressive intercourse.

Abel and his colleagues then compared the plethysmograph records of individual rapists with their case histories. Some case histories indicated a preference for conventional intercourse, with rape resorted to if the victim was unwilling. These men had relatively small erections to the aggression story, greater response to the rape, and the greatest response to the conventional intercourse. For other rapists, whose histories showed repeated, often sadistic assaults on women, erections to mutually enjoyable intercourse were minimal, but arousal was markedly augmented when aggression was added to sex to equal rape. Moreover, high levels of arousal were elicited by the aggression tape. Hence the picture is not a simple one. Some men apparently resort to rape only when loving intercourse is unavailable, whereas others seem to *require* violence-with-sex forced on an unwilling and frightened victim.

How does this sort of research relate to the discussions in the text? Consider, for example, Brownmiller's thesis that rape is man's way of intimidating, even denigrating, women. Her historical-political analysis might at first appear a world apart from the laboratory research of Abel. But this is not really the case, even though investigators like Brownmiller and experimentalists seldom converse. Abel and his colleagues have shown that some rapists do, indeed, become sexually aroused by scenes depicting aggression, and that this arousal can be greater than that they experience when scenes of conventional intercourse are presented. The question this kind of laboratory research does not address—and can probably *never* address—is *why*. Why are certain men sexually stimulated when pain is inflicted on an unwilling victim? What is there about the one-down relationship between a rapist and his victim that excites him? Brownmiller and others find the causes in the broad sweep of history and more particularly in the power relationship between men and women. Their independent variables, if you will, are male machismo, the deliberate degradation of women, and the desire to intimidate by aggression. Abel and others in their laboratory work examine men at the end of a long shaping process. The rapists they have studied are products of their social-learning history. To figure out *why* they aggress is the larger, more important question. The search should take investigators into the domain of sociologists, political scientists, and historians.

stricted to men, holds that the sadist has a castration complex and inflicts pain to assure himself of his power and masculinity. It may also be that in childhood or adolescence sadomasochistic elements were present while orgasms were experienced. Although it is plausible to suggest that classical conditioning may have occurred, there are as yet no data to support this theory. A related hypothesis suggests that the physiological arousal from inflicting and experiencing pain is not, in fact, dissimilar to sexual excitement. In the early stages of being sexualized, discriminations may be difficult to make, especially if the pain-inducing act also includes sexual elements. In this way the individual may learn to label pain-produced arousal as sexual. Interesting as it may be, this hypothesis is also purely speculative at this point.

Atypical Paraphilias

The paraphilias of the final category are called atypical; they are a miscellaneous group of unconventional activities, all of them having impressive and mysterious names, none of them being well understood. In each instance the act is necessary for sexual excitement, not merely a variation of conventional behavior. Among them are the following.

Coprophilia. Obtaining sexual gratification from handling feces.

Frotteurism. Obtaining sexual gratification by rubbing against another person, without engaging in sexual intercourse.

Klismaphilia. Achieving sexual excitement by means of an enema administered by another person.

Necrophilia. Being sexually intimate with a corpse.

Telephone scatologia. Making obscene phone calls for sexual gratification.

Sexual oralism. Exclusive reliance on oral-genital sex.

Sexual analism. Exclusive reliance on anal sex.

Gerontosexuality. Marked preference for older people as sexual partners.[7]

Therapies for the Paraphilias

Neither the psychoanalytic school nor the humanistic has made notable contributions to therapy for paraphilias, although interesting case studies abound in their clinical literatures.

---

[7]This paraphilia highlights the subjectivity or cultural relativism that permeates psychiatric diagnosis. How much older must a person's sex partner be for the relationship to be considered abnormal? Widespread ignorance of how sexually active people can be well into their eighties (see page 459) may be the reason why a diagnosis pertaining to this preference was ever suggested.

In the earliest stages of behavior therapy, paraphilias were narrowly viewed as attractions to inappropriate objects and activities. Looking to experimental psychology for ways to reduce these attractions, workers fixed on aversion therapy. Thus a boot fetishist would be given shock or an emetic when looking at a boot, a transvestite when cross-dressing, a pedophile when gazing at a photograph of a nude child, and so on. Sometimes these negative treatments were supplemented by training in social skills and assertion, for many of these individuals only poorly relate to others in ordinary social situations and even more poorly if at all through conventional sexual intercourse. There is some reason to believe that aversion therapy can alter pedophilia, transvestism, exhibitionism, and fetishism (Marks and Gelder, 1967; Marks, Gelder, and Bancroft, 1970) although to what extent the improvements are achieved through the placebo effect is unclear.

More recently the aversive stimulus has been presented in imagination, via covert sensitization (Cautela, 1966). Instead of being shocked or made nauseous with a drug while confronting the objects or situations to which he is inappropriately attracted, the paraphiliac, with assistance and encouragement from the therapist, pairs in imagination the pleasurable but unwanted

"When I said you were allowed one phone call, I did not mean another obscene one."

(Drawing by Charles Addams; © 1974, The New Yorker Magazine, Inc.)

arousal and an aversive stimulus. In a variation called covert punishment, the fantasized aversive stimulus may concern the aftermath of his act. The pedophile may imagine that his wife and daughter catch him fondling a little girl, that the police arrest him in the street, that his crime is reported in the newspapers, that he loses his job and goes to jail.

Paraphiliacs have also been behaviorally treated by _orgasmic reorientation_, which attempts to help them respond sexually to stimuli or situations that for them do not have the accustomed appeal. Individuals are confronted with a conventionally arousing stimulus while they are responding sexually for other, undesirable reasons. In an early clinical demonstration of this technique, Davison (1968a) instructed a young man troubled by sadistic fantasies to masturbate at home in the following manner.

When assured of privacy in his dormitory room . . . he was first to obtain an erection by whatever means possible—undoubtedly with a sadistic fantasy, as he indicated. He was then to begin to masturbate while looking at a picture of a sexy, nude woman (the "target" sexual stimulus). . . . If he began losing his erection, he was to switch back to his sadistic fantasy until he could begin masturbating effectively again. Concentrating again on the . . . picture, he was to continue masturbating, using the fantasy only to regain erection. As orgasm was approaching, he was at all costs to focus on the . . . picture . . . (p. 84).

The client was able to follow these instructions and over a period of weeks began to find conventional pictures, ideas, and images sexually arousing. The therapist, however, had to complement the orgasmic procedure with some covert sensitization for the sadistic imaginings. The follow-up after a year and a half found the client capable of conventional arousal, although he apparently reverted to his sadistic fantasies every now and again. This dubious outcome has been reported for other instances of orgasmic reorientation, but behavior therapists continue to explore its possibilities.

A sensible program of treatment must always consider the multifaceted nature of a particular disorder. Individual A may cross-dress for one reason, individual B for another. An exhibitionist, for example, may experience a great deal of tension in connection with his urge to expose himself; it would therefore make sense to desensitize him to women of the type who appeal to him. After imagining them in a succession of street and other public scenes, until they no longer make him anxious, he may be more relaxed when he encounters appealing women in public places and so may not feel the urge to expose (Bond and Hutchison, 1960). Other paraphiliacs might be questioned about social situations and aspects of relating to women that cause them undue discomfort. They could be desensitized to these, in hopes of making them generally less anxious.

The paraphilias have been the focus of considerable behavior therapy research. The evidence that aversion therapy, assertion training, social-skills training, covert sensitization, desensitization, and other behavior therapy procedures can effect enduring and significant changes in the paraphilias is meager when the usual standards of scientific evidence are applied (see Chapter 5). In our zeal to be rigorous, however, we should not dismiss the fact that behavior therapy has, for whatever constellation of reasons, proved far more effective than either psychoanalysis or humanistic-existential therapies in treating these very difficult and resistant human problems. Although the role of insight per se appears important in treating anxiety and depression, clinical and experimental reports reveal that for the paraphilias a focused, action-oriented, directive program, especially one that includes the teaching of specific social skills, may be the most appropriate.

Therapy for Rape

Unlike most of the disorders dealt with in this book, rape has the dubious distinction of presenting two different challenges to the mental health professional: treating the man who has committed the act and treating the woman who has been the victim.

A number of therapy programs have been developed to reduce the tendency of men to rape. In some prisons group therapy of a confrontational nature has been employed in efforts to encourage convicted rapists to take responsibility for their violence toward women and to explore more decent ways of handling their anger and relating to the opposite sex. But the effectiveness of these programs has for the most part not been studied. Most rapists perpetrate their assaults many times in their lives, and prison terms have little demonstrable effect on reducing the future incidence of rape. Therapists who try to help men who rape have to consider a wide range of causes that might underlie the problem—loneliness, deficient social skills, fear of dealing with women in conventional ways, actual hatred for women, inability or unwillingness to delay gratification, perhaps especially after excessive drinking, and exaggerated conceptions of masculinity that relegate women to an inferior position.

A number of surgical and hormonal treatments for rapists, and for child molesters as well, have been tried. They all have in common, which turns out to be their principal problem, eliminating the offender's ability to have sexual intercourse. He is castrated, either surgically by removing the testes or chemically by administering female hormones. When the sexual drive is lessened, it is lessened indiscriminately, however, leaving the man unable to explore more conventional avenues of sexual intercourse. This denial of alternatives can itself generate other antisocial and psychological problems for the former rapist and ethical problems for society. It should be borne in mind as well that erectile capacity is not necessary for rape; the violence itself is not directly addressed by these drastic medical measures (Geer, Heiman, and Leitenberg, 1984).

Considerable effort is expended in helping the victims of sexual assaults (for example, Peters, 1977; Sutherland and Scheri, 1977). A number of rape crisis centers and telephone hot lines have been established across the country, some of them associated with existing hos-

pitals and clinics, others operating on their own. Staffed both by professionals and by female volunteers, who may themselves have been rape victims in the past, these centers offer support and advice. Women from the center accompany the rape victim to the hospital and to the police station, where they help her with the legal procedures and with recounting the events of the attack. They may later arrange for examinations for pregnancy and venereal disease and for psychological counseling. These empathic companions help the victim get started in expressing her feelings about her ordeal, and they urge her to continue her venting with her own relatives and friends. If the attacker or attackers have been apprehended, the women from the center urge the victim to go through with the prosecution. They attend both her meetings with the district attorney and the trial itself.

As already indicated, rape victims, far more than the victims of other violent crimes, tend to examine their own role in provoking or allowing the attack; counseling, therefore, has to concentrate on alleviating the woman's feelings of responsibility and guilt. When long-term counseling is available, attention is often paid to the woman's ongoing relationships, which may be dis-

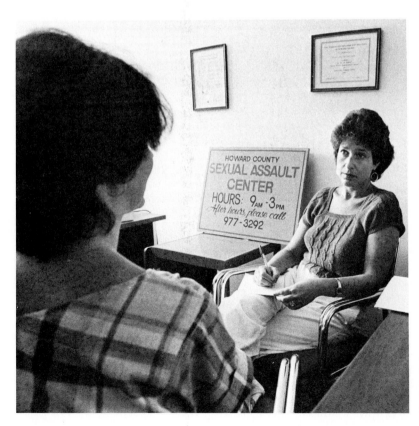

Rape counseling centers not only help women with the legal procedures of reporting and prosecuting a rape but also provide therapy for the traumatic aftereffects which plague and often devastate victims.

BOX 12.3

IMPRISONED SEX OFFENDERS: A PROBLEM FOR SOCIETY

Sex offenders, those who are convicted of rape, child molesting, voyeurism, and exhibitionism, are usually imprisoned. Sometimes, but not always, specially designed treatment programs are available to help the prisoner with his problem, but the success rates are not encouraging.

To begin with, virtually all therapies require the active cooperation of the patient. They generally have little chance of succeeding when forced on a person. Moreover, when therapy takes place in a prison, conditions may be too restrictive for the prisoner to become truly involved in his treatment. Finally, above and beyond the inherently coercive surroundings, professional knowledge of how to treat unconventional patterns of sexuality is quite limited. Until recently, therapeutic efforts were very punitive in nature, consisting for the most part of aversion therapy. Many critics believe that such radical treatments reflected society's wish to punish the offender for his heinous acts rather than any desire to help him.

The 1970s saw a curtailment of treatment. Lawsuits were brought on behalf of prisoners who objected to certain therapeutic interventions on the grounds that their civil rights were being violated. And indeed, some sex offenders were being subjected to extremely painful and unethical practices in the name of behavior modification. Actions by the courts have brought much-needed protection to many prisoners, but at the same time it may have a price: clinicians have been discouraged from developing treatments that could conceivably have controlled behavior threatening to society as well as to the offender himself. Finally, the descriptions of sex offenders indicate the complexity of their behavior. A man who feels compelled to exhibit himself to unwilling observers would seem to suffer from a host of underlying psychological problems. If he is a lonely person, unable to initiate even casual, let alone intimate, relationships with women, chances are that many areas of his life require careful attention. Such work requires much skill, patience, and time—which our society does not have in abundance when it comes to treating the imprisoned sex offender.

BOX 12.4

HOMOPHOBIA AND EXCLUSIVE HOMOSEXUALITY

Those who argue that heterosexuality is normal and homosexuality abnormal often make the statement that exclusive homosexuality is unknown in the animal kingdom when members of the opposite sex are available. It is also proposed that heterosexual contacts are maximized in all species so that adequate reproduction can take place. Moreover, it is apparently the case that in no human culture has exclusive homosexuality been encouraged for sizable numbers of people.

These arguments are cogent, but they overlook one essential characteristic of human sexuality, namely that *bisexuality is more prevalent than exclusive homosexuality* (Kinsey, Pomeroy, and Martin, 1948). Churchill (1967) made the provocative suggestion that exclusive homosexuality may well be encouraged by antihomosexual societies such as our own. Because sexual contacts between members of the same sex are so severely condemned, some bisexuals may be forced into making a choice and *thereby* become committed to contacts with members of their own sex rather than continuing to find sexual relationships with members of both sexes meaningful. What some call *homophobia* (Weinberg, 1972) may actually help create exclusive homosexuality.

rupted or otherwise negatively affected by the rape. Husbands and lovers often acquire the culture's suspicion of the victim and must be kept from viewing their loved one as guilty or tainted by the experience.

Attitudes and support systems now encourage the victim to report rape and pursue the prosecution of the alleged rapist, but the legal situation is still problematic. Estimates are that only a very small percentage of rapists are convicted of their crimes. Any familiarity of the victim with her assailant argues strongly against his ultimate conviction. The victim's role in her own assault continues to be examined. And many rapists rape hundreds of times, even though they are occasionally imprisoned for an offense. Society must be attentive and active to ensure that the victim's rights are defended by the legal system.

EGO-DYSTONIC HOMOSEXUALITY

From the time that DSM-II was published in 1968 until 1973, it listed *homosexuality* as one of the "sexual deviations." During 1973 the Nomenclature Committee of the American Psychiatric Association, under pressure from many professionals, and particularly from gay activist groups, recommended to the general membership the elimination of the category homosexuality and the substitution of *sexual orientation disturbance*. This new diagnosis was to be applied to gay men and women who are "disturbed by, in conflict with, or wish to change their sexual orientation." The members of the psychiatric association voted on the issue, in itself a comment on the conduct of science in the twentieth century. The change was approved, but not without vehement protests from a number of renowned psychiatrists who had for some time been identified with the traditional view that homosexuality reflects a fixation at an early stage of psychosexual development and is inherently abnormal.

The controversy continued among mental health professionals, but as DSM-III was being developed during the late 1970s, it became increasingly clear that the new nomenclature would maintain the tolerant stance toward homosexuality that had become evident in 1973. The current category, *ego-dystonic homosexuality*, refers to a person who is homosexually aroused, finds this arousal to be a persistent source of distress, and wishes to become heterosexual.

The New Category

As for all categories of disorder, DSM-III contains for ego-dystonic homosexuality a discussion of predisposing factors.

Since homosexuality itself is not considered a mental disorder, the factors that predispose to homosexuality are not included in this section [or anywhere in DSM-III]. The factors that predispose to Ego-dystonic Homosexuality are those negative societal attitudes toward homosexuality that have been internalized. In addition, features associated with heterosexuality, such as having children and [a] socially sanctioned family life, may be viewed as desirable and incompatible with a homosexual arousal pattern (p. 282).

What do these statements mean? Consider the plight of the homosexual growing up in contemporary society.

To suggest that a person comes voluntarily to change his sexual orientation is to ignore the powerful environmental stress, oppression if you will, that has been telling him for years that he should change. To grow up in a family where the word "homosexual" was whispered, to play in a playground and hear the words "faggot" and "queer," to go to church and hear of "sin" and then to college and hear of "illness," and finally to the counseling center that promises to "cure," is hardly [to live in] an environment of freedom and voluntary choice. The homosexual is expected to want to be changed and his application for treatment is implicitly praised as the first step toward "normal" behavior (Silverstein, 1972, p. 4).

DSM-III takes the position then that a homosexual is abnormal if he or she has been persuaded by this prejudiced society-at-large that his or her sexual orientation is inherently deviant, something which DSM-III itself asserts is not the case! Ego-dystonic homosexuality could also develop when a homosexual is frustrated or hurt by societal prejudices against his or her desire to establish a home with another person of the same sex. If DSM-III's explicit support of homosexuality is able to help win for the life style greater acceptance than it has today, eventually there will be fewer social and legal sanctions against homosexual partners' setting up households and raising children, whether they be adopted or the offspring of earlier heterosexual liaisons of one or both of them. The homosexual will then be able to enjoy more of what is now the heterosexual "package." The DSM will have influenced itself out of this new category, ego-dystonic homosexuality.

A Comment on Past Theory and Research

For many years theories have been proposed, and data collected, on the origins of homosexuality. Psychoanalysts, learning theorists, and physiologically oriented workers have compared homosexuals with heterosexuals for differences in their psychological or physical makeup. Perhaps the most widely cited study is that carried out by Bieber and several of his colleagues (1962). Case records of 106 homosexual patients were compared with those of 100 heterosexual patients. These two groups were being seen by 77 New York psychoanalysts. Among the differences found was that the homosexual male analysands more often had "close-binding intimate mothers" and emotionally detached, hostile fathers. Overlooking for present purposes a number of methodological flaws in the study—the most important being that all the 106 homosexuals were being analyzed and were not representative of homosexuals en masse, most of whom are not in therapy—we ask whether these differences demonstrate that homosexuality per se is pathological and that having such parents is pathogenic, that is, causes illness.

BOX 12.5

SEXUAL PREFERENCE AND OUR UNDERSTANDING OF HUMAN BEHAVIOR

The Kinsey reports (Kinsey, Pomeroy, and Martin, 1948; Kinsey, Pomeroy, Martin, and Gebhard, 1953) documented for the first time that a great many men and women have homosexual feelings at various times in their lives. So it became less and less defensible to divide people up into two mutually exclusive categories based on the gender of their sexual partners. A continuum seemed more appropriate. But, as Gagnon has pointed out, the very fact that homosexuality and heterosexuality appear at opposite ends of Kinsey's continuum reveals an *assumption* that human behavior will be better understood if individuals are placed somewhere on a continuum of sexual preference. An infinite array of characteristics might have anchored Kinsey's scale:

In United States culture the gender of one's sexual partner is crucial, and therefore leads to a key label; however, let us think of a society where gender does not matter, but where it is very important what emotions one feels during sex. People would then divide up by the kind of feeler that they

are . . . love-feelers or lust-feelers (the former would obviously be "better" people). In our studies we would find that there are many love-feelers in the society and only just a few lust-feelers; in the middle we would find bi-feelers. Soon we would have theories about why people felt lust (and not love); their childhoods would be studied; the fact that they were not able to feel correctly would tell us that they were immature, neurotic, perhaps even criminal. (From Human Sexualities, *p. 236. Copyright © 1977, by Scott, Foresman and Company. Reprinted by permission.)*

Is Western society's long-held concern with sexual orientation a useful one? Is our understanding of Michelangelo's genius furthered by our knowing that he had strong homosexual interests? Many have remarked that his sensitive sculpture "David" is a manifestation of his homosexuality, that his brilliant representation of a young man came from his sexual love for men and for the person who was the model for the sculpture. Are we then to "explain" the beauty of the Sistine Chapel in a similar fashion?

BOX 12.6

GENDER IDENTITY AND HOMOSEXUAL PREFERENCE

Psychoanalytic theory and to a degree behavioral theories as well hold male homosexuality to be a problem in gender identity: a man can become homosexual because he has not adopted his society's definition of manhood. Making love to a man rather than to a woman is assumed to be possible only for men who do not share a given society's conception of masculinity.

Other theorists and writers dispute whether homosexuals have an inappropriate gender identity. Churchill (1967), for example, refers to the comradeship and homosexual love that existed among many Greek warriors; Plato commented on the military advantages of homosexual relationships, for they seemed to foster great ferocity in battle on the part of men driven to protect their lovers. Is it reasonable to regard a brave soldier as lacking a masculine gender identity?

Moreover, in the Bieber study (1962) only 2 percent of the homosexuals were rated by their analysts as "effeminate"; this finding of masculinity among male homosexuals was borne out in a study by Evans (1969), in which 95 percent of the homosexuals rated themselves as "moderately or strongly masculine." Indeed, in his renowned

"Three Contributions to the Theory of Sex" (1905), Freud asserted, "In men, the most perfect psychic manliness may be united with . . . homosexuality."

Many male homosexuals have a firm identification of themselves as men (Silverstein, 1972); the same holds true for lesbians, who usually identify themselves as women (Martin and Lyon, 1972). To be sure the stereotype of the limp-wristed, lisping "fag" probably contributes to the misconception, or at least overgeneralization, of male homosexuality as feminine behavior. And the stereotype of the "butch" or "dyke" who wears her hair clipped and dresses in tailored clothing similarly fosters the misconception that the lesbian is somehow less of a woman, more of a man. But we must bear in mind that homosexuals grow up in the same cultures as everyone else! They learn that preferring a same-sexed partner implies being less of a man or less of a woman, and they may consciously adopt traits of the opposite gender. To explain homosexuality itself as simply an error in gender identity is probably wrong. "Gender roles are not a mold in which we pour our sexuality" (Gagnon, 1977, p. 242).

Bieber and his colleagues clearly believe so.

[The close-binding intimate mother] exerted an unhealthy influence on her son through preferential treatment and seductiveness on the one hand and inhibiting, over-controlling attitudes on the other. In many instances, the son was the most significant individual in her life and the husband was usually replaced by the son as her love object. . . .[8] We are led to believe that . . . maternal close-binding intimacy and paternal detachment-hostility is the "classic" pattern and most conducive to promoting homosexuality . . . in the son (pp. 47, 144).

The implication of this study and of many others is that any differences found between homosexuals and heterosexuals constitute evidence that homosexuality is abnormal and that the difference itself is pathogenic. Is there anything wrong with this line of reasoning?

Let us take an analogous situation. Suppose we found that women who are now good golfers had as children attended public schools more often than did women who are poor golfers. Suppose also that the difference in their golfing ability is the only consistent one between the two groups. Under what circumstances would we conclude that childhood experiences in private schools are pathogenic, causing pathology or illness? The answer is simple: going to a private school is pathogenic if its outcome, being a poor golfer, has already been judged pathological. If we do not make this a priori judgment, we cannot talk of a difference between two groups as indicative of pathology in one of the groups, and we cannot regard the presumed cause a pathogenic one. The most we can say is that the two groups are *different* from each other.

This logic can be applied to Bieber's study.

One cannot attach a pathogenic label to a pattern of child rearing unless one a priori labels the adult behavior pattern as pathological. . . . What is wrong with [a "close-binding intimate mother"] unless you happen to find her in the background of people whose current behavior you judge beforehand to be pathological? (Davison, 1976, p. 159).

Future Research

If the mental health professions take seriously the DSM-III position that homosexuality itself is not pathological

unless a person internalizes society's views that it is, research into ego-dystonic homosexuality should not concern itself with finding reasons why attraction to same-sexed partners develops. Rather, the search should be for the reasons why some homosexuals cannot resist pressures from others to believe that homosexuality is abnormal. And, as discussed in Box 21.7 (page 594), mental health workers might well spend less time trying to make homosexuals into heterosexuals and more time trying to eliminate the prejudices of society against homosexuality. If such efforts succeed, we can expect laws discriminating against homosexuals to be eliminated, and social prejudices may mollify as well. In short, the very societal conditions that bring on ego-dystonic homosexuality may disappear and with them, as indicated earlier, the last vestige of homosexuality from the list of mental disorders.

SUMMARY

In this chapter we examined three categories of psychosexual disorders. The gender identity disorders—transsexualism and gender identity disorder of childhood—are deep and persistent convictions of individuals that their anatomic sexual makeup and the psychological sense of self as a man or a woman and as a boy or a girl are discrepant. Thus a man who is a transsexual is masculine in his physical endowment but considers himself a woman and would like to live as such. Early child-rearing practices may have encouraged the young child to believe that he or she was of the opposite sex. These problems are of significant theoretical interest, for they illustrate the early plasticity of our beliefs about ourselves as males and females. For a time the only kind of help available to such individuals was sex-change surgery, to bring their bodies into line in some degree with gender identity. Now, however, behavior therapy has been able to alter specific aspects of the transsexual's behavior—mannerisms, tone of voice, sexual fantasies—and bring gender identity into line with anatomy.

In the paraphilias unusual imagery and acts are necessary for sexual excitement or gratification; fetishism, transvestism, pedophilia, incest, and sexual sadism are examples of such problems. Rape, although it is not described in DSM-III, is a pattern of behavior of considerable social and psychological trauma for the victim. The very inclusion of rape in a discussion of human sexuality is a matter of some controversy, for many workers regard rape as an act of aggression and violence rather

---

[8]The presumed replacement of the father by his son as a "love object" did not refer to explicit sexual activities.

than of sex. The most promising treatments for the paraphilias are behavior therapies, such as aversion therapy to reduce unwanted attraction and training in social skills to help the person have ordinary relations with members of the opposite sex.

DSM-III's new diagnosis, ego-dystonic homosexuality, is given to people whose homosexuality is a source of persistent distress and who clearly wish to be heterosexual. The inclusion of this category in the new nomenclature and descriptive statements about it are not completely logical, but they may eventually help eliminate prejudice against homosexuality.

Edvard Munch, *Ashes*, 1894 Nasjonalgalleriet, Oslo

PSYCHOSEXUAL DYSFUNCTIONS

In the preceding chapter the unconventional patterns of sexual behavior of a small minority of the population were described. But many "ordinary" people are likely to have problems that interfere with conventional sexual enjoyment at least to some extent during the course of their lives. Our concern in this chapter is with a range of sexual problems that are considered to represent inhibitions in the normal sexual response cycle.

A psychological problem has consequences not only for the individual but also for those with whom he or she is involved. Individuals unable to interact socially with others are inevitably cut off from many opportunities in life and, furthermore, often have low opinions of themselves. They can be a source of frustration and guilt for a spouse, a child, or a friend. This aspect of human emotional problems is especially important in our consideration of *psychosexual dysfunctions*, for they are usually evident in intimate personal relationships. A marriage is bound to suffer if one or both of the partners fear the sexual situation. And most of us, for better or for worse, base part of our self-concept on our sexuality. Do we please the people we love, do we gratify ourselves, or, more simply, are we able to enjoy the fulfillment and relaxation that can come from a pleasurable sexual experience? Sexual difficulties can be of such severity that tenderness itself is lost, let alone the more intense satisfaction of sexual activity. It will be helpful to keep these points in mind in this review of the various sexual dysfunctions and, at the end of the chapter, of some of the therapies for them.

THE SEXUAL RESPONSE CYCLE

We begin by describing the *sexual response cycle*. It has been conceptualized in several ways. Havelock Ellis (1906), one of the earliest sexologists, spoke of *tumescence* and *detumescence*—the flow of blood into the pelvic area during arousal and orgasm and its flow out of the areas afterward. A three-stage model—desire, excitement, and orgasm—has been proposed by Helen Singer Kaplan (1974), a noted sex therapist. What is significant about her model is the inclusion of "desire" as the initial stage.

William H. Masters and Virginia Johnson (1966), in their highly publicized research, overlooked the importance in everyday life of an inclination or decision by the individual to begin sexual activity in the first place. The four-stage cycle of sexual arousal delineated by them (Figure 13.1) was based on direct observations of normal volunteers who consented to be observed and to have their physiological responses to sexual stimulation recorded in a laboratory.[1] The responses of men and women were found to be unexpectedly similar.

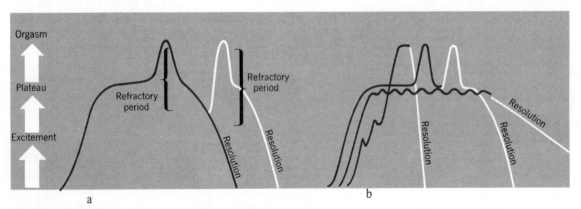

FIGURE 13.1 Graphs of (a) male and (b) female sexual response cycles. The blue lines indicate the most common patterns of response, the white lines variations. The female cycle does not always climb to orgasm, but when it does, there is not the inevitable refractory period found in the male cycle. Many women are able to have multiple orgasms in fairly rapid succession. After Masters and Johnson, 1966, p. 5.

[1]Although it is generally assumed that the data collected by Alfred Kinsey in the 1940s and 1950s were based almost entirely on interviews, John Gagnon, formerly associated with Kinsey's Institute for Sex Research in Bloomington, Indiana, has called attention to the extent to which Masters and Johnson built on work done earlier at the Institute. Many findings of the Kinsey group, published later in the Kinsey reports, were obtained through the direct observation and filming of sexual activity. The social climate of the day, however, discouraged Kinsey from acknowledging that this group had, in fact, gathered information on human sexuality through direct observation (Gagnon, 1977).

Havelock Ellis (1859–1939), a British writer on the psychology of sex and a humane and discerning man, understood at the turn of the century the sexual capacities of women and children and old people.

ing swelling. Of course these basic physiologic responses take on a different appearance in a man than they do in a woman. Interestingly enough, the basic physiologic sexual responses remain the same regardless of the stimulation—coital, manipulative, mechanical, or fantasy (Belliveau and Richter, 1970, pp. 33–34).

It is important to note that the various sexual response phases pointed out by Masters and Johnson do not represent actual quantitative changes in any particular physiological or psychological dimension. Heart rate, or vaginal lubrication, or engorgement of the penis does not steadily increase during excitement, remain constant during plateau, shift markedly upward during orgasm, and slowly diminish during resolution. Nor did Masters and Johnson claim to have shown the sexual interest of their subjects to wax and wane in this manner. What they and Ellis and Kaplan have proposed are schemes for talking about human sexuality. The scheme is an *invention* of the scientist, a device for organizing

Desire is the first phase in the sexual response cycle, preceding the excitement, plateau, orgasmic, and resolution phases.

The excitement phase *is initiated by whatever is sexually stimulating to a particular individual. If stimulation is strong enough, excitement builds up quickly, but if it is interrupted or if it becomes objectionable, this phase becomes extended or the cycle may be stopped. If effective sexual stimulation is continued, it produces increased levels of sexual tension. . . . This increased tension is called the* plateau phase. *If the individual's drive for sexual release in this phase is not strong enough, or if stimulation ceases to be effective or is withdrawn, the man or woman will not experience orgasm, but will enter a long period of gradually deceased sexual tension. The climactic or* orgasmic phase, *a totally involuntary response, consists of those few seconds when the body changes resulting from stimulation reach their maximum intensity. During the* resolution phase, *after the orgasm, there is a lessening of sexual tensions as the person returns to the unstimulated state. Women are capable of having another orgasm if there is effective stimulation during this phase. The resolution period in the male includes a time, which varies among individuals, when restimulation is impossible. This is called the* refractory period. *In both sexes, the basic responses of the body to sexual stimulation are myotonia (increased muscle tension) and vasocongestion (filling of the blood vessels with fluid), especially in the genital organs, caus-*

The noted sex researchers and therapists, William H. Masters and Virginia Johnson. Their pioneering work helped launch a more candid and scientific appraisal of human sexuality.

physiological research can tell us little about the *psychological* components of human sexuality. Masters and Johnson were nonetheless able to provide firm data on certain controversial points and to dispel a few myths.

1. Although the *clitoris* (Figure 13.2) is very important in transmitting sexual stimulation in the female, it has been a mistake to advise men to try to stimulate it continually during intercourse. During the plateau phase the clitoris retracts, making access to it extremely difficult and even painful for some women. In point of fact, it is very difficult to have intercourse without stimulating the clitoris *indirectly*, which is the type of stimulation that some women seem to prefer.

2. Masters and Johnson were able to document that orgasms in women obtained from stimulation of the clitoris, without entrance into the vagina, are as intense as and indeed physiologically indistinguishable from orgasms obtained by having an erect penis in the vagina.

   Probably few pieces of misinformation have caused more consternation than Freud's insistence that the vaginal orgasm is superior to the clitoral orgasm. He asserted, and practitioners have parroted to hundreds of thousands of people for years since, that a woman who can have an orgasm only by stimulation of her clitoris is settling for second best; further, that failure to have an orgasm via stimulation of the vagina by the man's penis is a sign of psychosexual fixation and immaturity. The Freudian theory is explained nicely by John Gagnon.

   Everyone goes through certain psychosexual stages, one of which involves masturbation as the important overt sexual activity. This stage occurs early in life as part of the parade of changes toward heterosexual genital maturity, that is, intercourse with a person of the opposite sex. Masturbation is infantile; intercourse is mature; being mature is better than being infantile. When women masturbate, they touch the clitoris; when women have intercourse, they have a penis in the vagina. Since masturbation is infantile, pleasures achieved by touching the clitoris are infantile. Sexual maturity [therefore] requires that women move from having orgasms produced by touching the clitoris to having orgasms produced by the penis in the vagina. The site of sensation [is] supposed to move from clitoris to vagina. (From Human Sexualities, *p. 138. Copyright © 1977, by Scott, Foresman and Company. Reprinted by permission.)*

and discussing a body of information (Gagnon, 1977). It is also worth mentioning that sex researchers speak in terms of group averages, which after all are by definition a convenient way to summarize a *range* of scores or experiences. So a given individual's responses can differ noticeably from a group average without being considered deviant or abnormal.

The impact of Masters and Johnson's work was considerable, contributing to our knowledge of the physiology of human sexuality. Perhaps more important, it helped make the scientific study of sex legitimate and acceptable. Even before their book was published, the information obtained through research was being put to use in the treatment phase of their work (Masters and Johnson, 1970). By knowing how the body functions to achieve maximum sexual response, Masters and Johnson were able to elaborate methods of treating sexual dysfunction. These and other treatments are discussed later in this chapter.

The artificial circumstances in which Masters and Johnson gathered their findings limit their generality somewhat, however. And we should be mindful that

Even before the work of Masters and Johnson, some sexologists had been trying to disabuse people of this notion (for example, A. Ellis, 1961), pointing out that the walls of the vaginal barrel are poorly supplied with sensory nerve endings, whereas the clitoris, like the glans of the penis, is amply supplied. The fact that orgasms achieved by masturbation and manual manipulation by the partner, both of which typically concentrate on the clitoris and surrounding areas, were found to create at least as much excitation as intercourse pretty much puts to rest the bugaboo about clitoral orgasms.

Many authorities now believe that all female orgasms are evoked by stimulation of the clitoris, whether the friction is applied directly or through coitus. The orgasm itself, however, is expressed by rhythmic contractions of vaginal muscles. This dichotomy may be the source of the myth of clitoral and vaginal orgasms (Kaplan, 1974). Of course these findings in no way imply that the insertion of the penis and the movements of coitus are not extremely enjoyable to women.

3. Having simultaneous orgasms, a goal held up in numerous marriage manuals as indicating true love and compatibility, was not shown to be a mark of superior sexual achievement. In fact, it can often distract each of the partners from his or her own sexual pleasure.

4. It was also found that not only do most women *not* object to intercourse during menstruation, but they even tend to enjoy it more, particularly during the second half of the period.

5. During the second three months of pregnancy, women seem to desire intercourse at least as much as when not pregnant. Although there is some danger of spontaneous abortion in the early stages, particularly for women who have a history of spontaneous miscarriage, most women continue to desire sexual stimulation, sometimes until they go into labor. At any rate, little harm seems to come to the woman and to the fetus in the uterus through intercourse, at least during the first six months of pregnancy.

FIGURE 13.2 Exterior view of female genitalia, cross section of male. (From Alvin Nason and Robert DeHaan, *The Biological World.* New York: Wiley, 1973.)

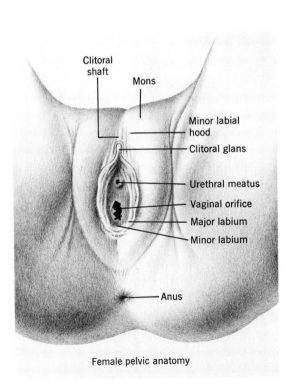

Female pelvic anatomy

Clitoral shaft
Mons
Minor labial hood
Clitoral glans
Urethral meatus
Vaginal orifice
Major labium
Minor labium
Anus

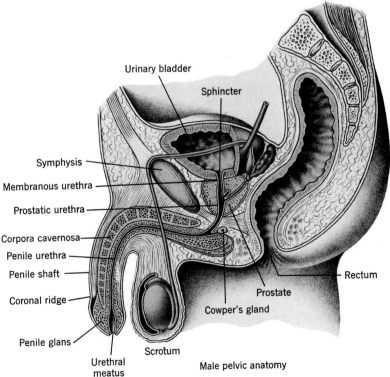

Male pelvic anatomy

Urinary bladder
Sphincter
Symphysis
Membranous urethra
Prostatic urethra
Corpora cavernosa
Penile urethra
Penile shaft
Coronal ridge
Penile glans
Urethral meatus
Scrotum
Prostate
Cowper's gland
Rectum

6. Various facts about the male's penis were also confirmed. The size of a man's erect penis was not found to be a factor in the enjoyment he can derive himself and impart to his sexual partner. The vagina is a potential not an actual space; that is, it distends just enough to accommodate the penis. Hence a very large penis will not create more friction for the man or the woman than a smaller one. Furthermore, penises that are small when flaccid may double in size when erect, whereas penises that are large in the limp state increase less proportionately. In other words, there does not seem to be as much variation in the size of the *erect* penis as had been assumed. The idea that the size of a man's penis is an index of his virility was completely dispelled.[2]

THE SEXUAL DYSFUNCTIONS: DESCRIPTIONS AND CAUSES

There have been several attempts to classify *sexual dysfunctions* (see LoPiccolo and Hogan, 1979, for a comprehensive review). Although no scheme is universally accepted, that of DSM-III is as reasonable as any others that have been proposed.

In general, the categories listed represent disturbances in one or more of the phases of the response cycle, as viewed by DSM-III: the appetitive phase, the equivalent of Kaplan's stage of desire; the excitement stage; the orgasm; and the resolution. DSM-III omits the plateau stage described by Masters and Johnson, and it indicates that inhibition of the resolution phase is rarely of clinical significance. A particular disorder may be lifelong, or it may have been acquired after a period of normal functioning; it may be generalized, or it may occur only in particular situations or with certain partners; and it may be total or partial. Each of the disorders may show up either during sexual activity with another person or during masturbation. DSM-III does not state whether the sexual partner is of the opposite sex or same sex, a sign of the growing liberalization of the attitude of the mental health professions toward homosexuality. The prevalence of these disturbances is believed to be very great, so great in fact that people should not assume that they need treatment only because they sometimes experience one or more of these problems. In the diagnostic criteria for each sexual dysfunction, DSM-III uses the phrase "recurrent and persistent" to underscore the fact that a problem must be serious indeed before a diagnosis is made.[3]

In our discussions of DSM-III categories of sexual dysfunctions, we describe what is believed to cause these human problems. It is important to bear in mind, however, that most of these generalizations about etiology are based on clinical reports of investigators like Masters and Johnson (1970), Kaplan (1974), and other sex therapists. As with all clinical reports, information provided by clients and interpreted by therapists is subject to distortion and selective attention. Moreover, no studies compare groups of dysfunctional patients with appropriate control groups for the presence or absence of causative factors. For example, an unpleasant experience with a prostitute at age seventeen may seem to be a major cause of a thirty-year-old man's erectile problem, but countless other men have had a similar negative experience *without* developing a sexual problem.

Any points made about etiology are therefore necessarily tentative. Although this caveat can be issued for any section of this book, it is particularly appropriate to bear in mind here, considering the likelihood that the lives of many readers will be touched in some way by what is being discussed.

Inhibited Sexual Desire

The psychosexual dysfunction *inhibited sexual desire* did not appear in DSM-II. Its presence in DSM-III reflects a formal recognition that some people are troubled by what they, and especially their partners, perceive to be abnormally little interest in initiating or having sexual intimacies. The colloquialism is "low sex drive."

Of all the sexual dysfunctions covered by DSM-III, this one seems to be the most problematic. How frequently "should" a person be interested in sex? How often "should" a person actually have intercourse or masturbate? The diagnosis inhibited sexual desire may owe its very existence to the greater openness about sex in contemporary society—and perhaps to the higher expectations people are acquiring about being sexual.

[2]Some women have voiced disagreement with Masters and Johnson's conclusion about the merit of a large penis. No doubt psychological variables, as well as the purely physiological ones that Masters and Johnson have dealt with, play a part in determining how an individual woman reacts.

[3]What is defined as normal and desirable in human sexual behavior varies with time and place. Contemporary views, as reflected in DSM-III, point to *inhibitions* of sexual expression as causes of abnormality. In contrast, during the nineteenth and early twentieth centuries the Western world regarded *excess* as the culprit. It is well to keep these varying temporal and cultural norms in mind as we continue our study of human sexual dysfunction.

Sexual disinterest was formerly thought to be rare and found only in women. Contemporary sex researchers and therapists recognize the phenomenon in men as well, and among those who seek help at some sex therapy centers inhibited sexual desire is more and more often the diagnosis. In extreme cases a person may have an actual aversion to sex altogether.

We know little about the causes. Probably the most definite evidence is that certain drugs, especially sedatives and narcotics, can dull a person's sexual desires. Sexual dysfunctions of the partner may also be implicated: a woman who is constantly frustrated by her partner's erectile problems or inept lovemaking may decide that sex is just not worth the aggravation and disappointment. Interpersonal problems of the partners can also be expected to affect their interest in sex with each other. In general, the importance that sex has in someone's life can vary tremendously. Unlike hunger and thirst, an "appetite" for sex need not be satisfied or even exist in order for the individual to survive and, it seems, to live happily.

Inhibited Sexual Excitement

DSM-II referred to "impotence" in the male. Its equivalent in women would be "frigidity." The problem of inhibition during the excitement stage of the response cycle is, according to DSM-III, evidenced

In males, *[by] partial or complete failure to attain or maintain erection until completion of the sexual act, or*

In females, *[by] partial or complete failure to attain or maintain the lubrication-swelling response of sexual excitement until completion of the sexual act (p. 279).*

The diagnosis *inhibited sexual excitement* is appropriate only if "the individual engages in sexual activity that is adequate in focus, intensity, and duration" (p. 279). Should a woman, for example, be unresponsive to the overtures and technique of a man whom she does not particularly like, the diagnosis is not made.

Helen Singer Kaplan (1974) has outlined a wide range of erectile problems for men. Some get an erection

easily but lose it as they enter the woman's vagina. Others are flaccid when intercourse is imminent but maintain an erection easily during fellatio. Some men are erect when the partner dominates the situation, others when they themselves are in control. Some suffer complete erectile failure, being unable to maintain an erection under any circumstances. Others have problems only with people they care for deeply. Moreover, an obvious aspect of the problem is that it is, in fact, obvious. A woman can at least go through the motions of lovemaking, but sexual intercourse is usually stalemated if the man is not erect. A great deal is at stake if the penis becomes flaccid when it "should" be erect.[4] For this reason, perhaps, an "impotent" male is sometimes and unfortunately regarded as less than a man.

The causes of erectile problems are many. Possible organic factors include certain medications, such as Mellaril, one of the phenothiazines used in treating psychoses; some drugs for hypertension, angina, and heart disease; alcohol in large amounts; obesity; and generally any disease or hormonal imbalance that can affect the nerve pathways or blood supply to the penis (Geer, Heiman, and Leitenberg, 1984). If one of these is believed to be the sole cause, a diagnosis of a psychosexual dysfunction is not made, according to DSM-III. And yet it is important to realize that physical causes sometimes play a major role when a man loses or does not have any erection at all. The majority of erectile difficulties, however, are believed to be psychological in nature (Rosen and Rosen, 1981), brought on by performance fears and other preoccupations that distract men from "egoless" involvement in and enjoyment of sexual relations. The inhibition of sexual excitement in women is discussed in the following section on inhibited female orgasm.

Inhibited Female Orgasm

Sometimes called orgasmic dysfunction or anorgasmia, the persistent inability of a woman to have orgasms following sexual stimulation judged adequate for a climax is to be diagnosed as *inhibited female orgasm*, according

---

[4]Male erectile problems are complicated and important. Although an extended discussion is beyond the scope of this book, a few additional observations would seem in order. The fact that the state of a man's penis is evident both to him and to his partner is generally regarded as placing a unique set of pressures on him that are not the fate of a woman who suffers from inhibited sexual excitement. True enough, but the woman's situation is not easy either. The very fact that she can have sexual relations without being aroused has no doubt contributed to neglect of the woman's needs and desires. Moreover, the man's self-esteem is not the only one threatened if he becomes flaccid; the partner too, whether it be a woman or another man, often has doubts

about sexual adequacy—is she not sexy enough, not lovable enough, not creative or "liberal" enough? Finally, replacement of impotence and frigidity by the phrase inhibited sexual excitement can be considered an advance. Impotence implies that the man is not potent, or in control, or truly masculine, and negatively backs up the macho conception of masculinity that many people are challenging. Frigidity implies that the woman is emotionally cold, distant, unsympathetic, unfeeling. Both terms are derogatory and encourage as well a search for causes *within* the person, rather than focusing attention on the relationship, the domain contemporary investigators explore for answers and solutions.

to DSM-III. Oftentimes a woman also has difficulty during the excitement phase and would therefore receive the diagnosis of inhibited sexual excitement as well.

Until recently a distinction was not generally made between problems a woman may have in becoming sexually aroused and those she may have in reaching an orgasm. Although as many as 20 percent of all adult women rarely if ever experience an orgasm (Kinsey et al., 1953), far fewer are believed to remain unaroused during lovemaking. Kaplan (1974) argues that this distinction, made too in DSM-III, is an important one, for "As a general rule, women who suffer from orgasmic dysfunction are responsive sexually. They may fall in love, experience erotic feelings, lubricate copiously, and also show genital swelling" (p. 343). In fact, she argues that failure to have orgasms should not be regarded as a disorder at all, rather as a normal variation of female sexuality.

Numerous reasons have been put forward to explain anorgasmia. Perhaps many women, unlike men, have to *learn* to become orgasmic. That is, the capacity to have an orgasm may not be innate in females as it is in males. In men ejaculation, which almost always is accompanied by orgasm, is necessary for reproduction. A woman may to some extent learn to have coital orgasms through earlier masturbation; survey findings indicate that women who masturbated little or not at all before they began to have intercourse were much more likely to be inorgasmic than women who had (Kinsey et al., 1953; Hite, 1976; Hoon and Hoon, 1978). These are, of course, correlational data; some third factor may be responsible both for infrequent masturbation and for diminished ability to have orgasms. Lack of sexual knowledge also appears to play a role according to clinical data; many inorgasmic women, as well as those who experience little excitement during sexual stimulation, are unaware of their own genital anatomy and therefore have trouble communicating their needs to a partner or to themselves.

Women have different "thresholds" for orgasm. Although some have orgasms quickly and without much clitoral stimulation, others seem to need intense and prolonged stimulation, whether during foreplay or intercourse. The reaction of a woman's partner can contribute to the problem; a man may conclude that he and his penis are inadequate if the female asks for manual stimulation of her clitoris during intercourse.

Another factor may be fear of losing control. The French have an expression for orgasm, *le petit mord*, the little death. Some women fear that they will begin screaming uncontrollably, make fools of themselves, or faint. A related source of inhibition is a belief, perhaps poorly articulated, that to let go and allow the body to take over from the conscious, controlling mind is somehow unseemly. The state of a relationship is also not to be overlooked: although some women can enjoy making love to a person they are angry with, or even despise, most hold back under such circumstances.

Inhibited Male Orgasm

Masters and Johnson (1970) used the somewhat pejorative term ejaculatory incompetence for the inability of the man to ejaculate within the vagina. The DSM-III diagnosis *inhibited male orgasm* would be applied to problems of ejaculating during intercourse, masturbation, manual or oral manipulation by a partner, and anal intercourse.

Difficulty in ejaculating is relatively rare, although some have suggested it is becoming more prevalent as men deem it desirable to delay their orgasms for long periods of time (Rosen and Rosen, 1981); indeed, sex without orgasm has even been proposed in recent years as an ultrasophisticated form of male sexuality. It may be that some men are learning the skill too well! More prosaic causes have also been put forth: fear of impregnating a female partner, withholding love, expressing hostility, and, as with female anorgasmia, fear of letting go. In rare instances the problem may be traced to a physical source, such as taking certain tranquilizers (Munjack and Kanno, 1979).

Premature Ejaculation

Masters and Johnson (1970) define ejaculation as being premature when a man is unable to inhibit his orgasm long enough for his female partner to climax in 50 percent of their sexual encounters. Many people have been concerned about stipulating the male problem of *premature ejaculation* in terms of a *partner's* responsiveness. In DSM-III this difficulty is handled as follows: "Ejaculation occurs before the individual wishes it, because of recurrent and persistent absence of reasonable voluntary control of ejaculation and orgasm . . ." (p. 280). The focus is now on the preference of the man himself.[5] As with many other of the sexual dysfunctions, considerable judgment is required by clinicians who employ the DSM, for they must take into account such factors as the man's age, whether the sexual partner is new, and how often the man customarily has intercourse.

---

[5]It would be naive, however, to overlook the extent to which a partner may influence the man's judgment that ejaculation is occurring before he wishes it.

Premature ejaculation is probably the most prevalent sexual dysfunction among males, occurring also on an occasional basis, in which case the diagnosis is not appropriate. In general, the problem is associated with considerable anxiety. Sometimes the man ejaculates even before he penetrates the vagina but more usually within a few seconds of intromission. Although the human being is more than a relatively hairless ape, evolutionary theory informs us that rapid ejaculation has survival value, for any animal is particularly vulnerable to surprise attack when copulating. Hence the more quickly copulation can occur, the better. Kinsey, himself a biologist, suggested that ejaculating quickly should not be regarded as a problem in human beings. Such a view, however, considers only the reproductive function of intercourse, ignoring its recreational and interpersonal functions (Rosen and Rosen, 1981). Indeed, concern about ejaculating "too soon" may be regarded as part and parcel of the undue emphasis placed on coitus as the ultimate in sexual behavior. The problem for couples who prize conventional sexual intercourse above all other sexual activities is that erection is slowly lost after an ejaculation, with many men finding continued stimulation unpleasant and sometimes painful. If lovemaking stops when the penis is no longer hard, ejaculation may indeed sometimes be premature. But if, as sex therapists advise, couples expand their repertoire of activities to include techniques not requiring an engorged penis, gratification of the partner is eminently possible *after* the man has climaxed. Indeed, when the focus is removed from penile-vaginal intercourse, a couple's anxieties about sex usually diminish sufficiently to permit greater ejaculatory control in the male and sexual intercourse of longer duration. As mentioned earlier, nowadays less and less emphasis is placed on simultaneous orgasms during conventional sexual intercourse. It will be interesting to observe whether shifts in sexual norms and practices alter the concept of premature ejaculation.

Functional Vaginismus

During sexual excitement, especially when intercourse or other sexual intimacy is imminent, some women have involuntary spasms of the musculature of the outer third of the vagina. Coitus or even the insertion of a finger becomes impossible. This condition, *functional vaginismus*, is not strictly sexual in nature, for the woman usually cannot undergo a routine pelvic examination, which entails insertion of a speculum. The adductor muscles of the thighs may also be subject to spasms, preventing their separation when intercourse or an examination is

attempted. Nor can the woman herself insert an object into her vagina.

Since the spastic contractions of the muscles prevent intercourse, it is not surprising one theory supposes that the woman wishes, perhaps unconsciously, to deny herself, her partner, or both the pleasures of sexual intimacy. As plausible as this idea may seem, no evidence supports it. Indeed, women with this problem can often have sexually satisfying lives through clitoral stimulation, if the partner is so inclined. Clinical reports also suggest fear of pregnancy and negative attitudes about sex in general. Masters and Johnson found that for a number of couples the man's inability to maintain an erection preceded the development of vaginismus in his wife; for some women, then, the sexual problems of their partners are so anxiety-provoking that a condition like vaginismus may develop.

Functional Dyspareunia

Sometimes a man or a woman finds it painful to have intercourse. If this problem is not caused exclusively by a physical disorder, or if, in a woman, there are no vaginal spasms or lack of lubrication—which would indicate functional vaginismus or inhibited sexual excitement—DSM-III says *functional dyspareunia* is to be diagnosed. Masters and Johnson, as well as other authorities on sexual dysfunctions, however, have found dyspareunia to be caused almost always by physical problems, such as infections of the vagina, cervix, and uterus and of the glans of the penis; pulled ligaments in the pelvic region; and scar tissue in the vaginal opening from incisions made during childbirth.

THEORIES OF PSYCHOSEXUAL DYSFUNCTIONS: GENERAL CONSIDERATIONS

Earlier Sexology

Psychoanalytic views have assumed that sexual dysfunctions are symptoms of underlying repressed conflicts. The analyst considers the symbolic meaning of the "symptom" both to understand its etiology and to guide treatment. Since sexual dysfunctions bring discomfort and psychological pain to both the individual and to his or her partner, and since unimpaired sexuality is inherently pleasurable, the theme of repressed anger and aggression competing with the gratification of sexual needs pervades psychoanalytic writings. Thus a man who ejaculates so quickly that he frustrates his female

BOX 13.1

PSYCHOSEXUAL DYSFUNCTION: A BIOENERGETIC APPROACH

Wilhelm Reich (1942), an Austrian psychoanalyst, agreed with Freud in placing human sexuality at the center of psychology but, unlike Freud, he studied sexual functioning directly. He concluded that the basis for all anxiety was the inability to achieve full and repeated sexual satisfaction. Thus the goal of therapy was to teach people to achieve sexual satisfaction by releasing muscular tension and allowing the free flow of sexual energy. Although one of Reich's extreme notions—that a vital energy "orgone" pervades nature and can be accumulated for bodily use by sitting in a specially designed box—discredited his other theories in the early fifties, they reemerged in the work of Alexander Lowen (1958). The *bioenergetic movement* is a force in American psychology and psychiatry, especially on the West coast.

According to the bioenergetic view, sexual dysfunctions such as premature ejaculation and inhibited orgasm are caused by chronic tensions as they affect the muscles of the body. These chronic tensions are said to develop when powerful emotions like fear, anger, and sexual excitation are "blocked." The "blocking" is described as being not only cognitive but physical. Bioenergetic analysts speak of such phenomena as "the dead pelvis" in describing the body posture of those individuals who do not experience orgasm as the full and rhythmic involuntary pelvic movements indicative of sexual satisfaction. The task of bioenergetic therapy is to teach people to relax the body's musculature and establish freedom of movement during sex.

Bioenergetic therapy generally proceeds at both the cognitive and physical levels. At the cognitive level the therapist employs traditional psychodynamic procedures to help the patient achieve insight into the thoughts and feelings maintaining a rigid and sexually dysfunctional body posture. At the physical level the patient is instructed in a series of exercises designed to remove body tensions and breathing irregularities and to promote freedom of pelvic movement. Some bioenergetic therapists loosen tense areas of the body through deep-muscle massage. While the patient is being massaged, he or she is encouraged to recall and express any emotions that are experienced in order to ensure that emotional blocks and muscle tensions are not reinstated.

Bioenergetics, following Reich, places sexual dysfunction at the heart of all emotional and behavioral problems and has the same therapy goal for all clients, the restoration of sexual functioning. This goal may be appealing to some, but others have criticized it as contributing to a cultural obsession with sexual gratification and kindling unrealistic expectations of sexual fulfillment (Keen, 1979).

Because bioenergetic therapy has not been properly evaluated in controlled studies, its effectiveness is difficult to judge. Bioenergetics does, however, offer a unique view of human sexual inadequacy.

Bioenergetic therapy considers sexual dysfunctions to be caused by chronic anxiety and tension. Here Alexander Lowen performs deep-muscle massage to remove tension.

partner may be expressing repressed hostility to women who remind him unconsciously of his mother. A woman with vaginismus may be expressing her repressed penis envy by threatening to castrate a man who would hope to enter her vagina. There is little evidence for the validity or even the usefulness of psychoanalytic theories of psychosexual dysfunctions. In fact, many contemporary psychoanalysts now recognize the inability of their therapy to help people with sexual dysfunction and supplement it with the more direct techniques of behavior therapy (LoPiccolo, 1977).

Humanists view psychosexual dysfunctions in the same way that they do other disorders. A sexual dysfunction is considered to reflect the crippling anxiety and inhibition of a person who is failing to fulfill his or her own potential (see Box 13.1).

Most contemporary sexologists appear to operate within a social-learning framework, although it is not always labeled as such. The most comprehensive account of the etiology of human sexual dysfunction was offered by Masters and Johnson in their widely acclaimed book *Human Sexual Inadequacy* (1970). Let us first examine their suggestions and then consider modifications and extensions of their ideas that have been proposed more recently.

The Findings of Masters and Johnson

Current Factors

Masters and Johnson discovered in the backgrounds of their patients a number of untoward attitudes and events which they consider responsible for sexual problems. The two researchers distinguish between these *historically* relevant factors and two *currently* relevant variables, which they believe underlie the *maintenance* of all human sexual inadequacies. Sexual disorders are maintained, they suggest, because during intercourse one or both of the participants either adopt a *spectator role* or have crippling *fears about performance*. These two attitudes focus undue attention on performance rather than allowing a relatively passive and uncritical acceptance of sexual stimulation, which if unimpeded leads naturally to sexual enjoyment, including orgasm. As Masters and Johnson have stated, "fear of inadequacy is the greatest known deterrent to effective sexual functioning, simply because it so completely distracts the fearful individual from his or her natural responsivity by blocking reception of sexual stimuli . . ." (1970, pp. 12–13).

Historical Factors

How do people come to adopt the spectator role and

FIGURE 13.3 Historical and current causes of human sexual inadequacies, according to Masters and Johnson.

harbor performance fears? Masters and Johnson proposed that unfortunate attitudes instilled by upbringing and difficult experiences of earlier years feed into the current causes of sexual problems (Figure 13.3).

Religious orthodoxy One or both partners may have negative attitudes toward sex because they have been brought up with strict religious beliefs that denigrate sexual enjoyment. For example, a woman with vaginismus who was interviewed by Masters and Johnson had been

. . . taught that almost any form of physical expression might be suspect of objectionable sexual connotations. . . . She was prohibited when bathing from looking at her own breasts either directly or from reflection in the mirror for fear that unhealthy sexual thoughts might be stimulated by visual examination of her own body. Discussion with a sibling of such subjects as menstruation, conception, contraception, or sexual functioning were taboo. . . . Mrs. A. entered marriage without a single word of advice, warning, or even good cheer from her family relative to marital sexual expression. The only direction offered by her religious advisor relative to sexual behavior was that coital connection was only to be endured if conception was desired (p. 254).

Psychosexual trauma Some patients trace their fears of sexual contact to particularly frightening or degrading experiences during initial sexual exposures. One young man had been assured by a prostitute that "He would never be able to get the job done for any woman—if he couldn't get it done here and now with a pro." One woman could date her vaginismus to a gang rape from which she suffered severe physical and psychological damage.

Homosexual inclinations Men with erectile problems and inorgasmic women may be unable to enjoy heterosexual relations because they have homosexual inclinations.[6]

[6]When Masters and Johnson published their clinical report on the nature and treatment of "human sexual inadequacy" in 1970, the sociopolitical climate was not as accepting of homosexuality as it is today. Their treatment program was exclusively heterosexual in its focus; hence the presence in one of the partners of a homosexual preference was seen as an etiological factor. The alternative view that the problem lay with a decision of the homosexual partner to try to maintain a heterosexual marriage was not explicitly considered. Similarly, until recently professionals have not attended systematically to sexual dysfunctions in homosexual relationships; contributions like Silverstein's *A Family Matter: A Parent's Guide to Homosexuality* (1977) are likely to redress the imbalance and help focus attention on homosexual interests, practices, and concerns.

Inadequate counseling Bad advice from professional workers may create or exacerbate sexual inadequacies. Some men were told by physicians that erectile problems are incurable, others that they are a natural part of the aging process. A few had been warned by clergymen that their problem was God's punishment for sins.

Excessive intake of alcohol An erectile problem sometimes begins with undue concern about a normal reduction in sexual responsiveness brought on by excessive drinking (see page 254). In the typical pattern suggested by Masters and Johnson, a man who works very hard may develop a habit of drinking a good deal. Large amounts of alcohol are known to interfere with erections, while at the same time, ironically, lowering inhibitions. Having drunk too much, the man may find later in bed that no erection develops. Instead of attributing his lack of sexual arousal to his drinking, however, he begins to ruminate. Fear accumulates, and after a number of failures he may become unable to have an erection. The wife often attempts to be understanding and supportive of the husband. He, for any number of reasons, interprets this solicitude as further questioning of his masculinity. Or the wife, concerned that she may no longer be sexually attractive to her husband, pushes for sexual encounters and aggravates the situation. Soon she may refrain from any physical contact whatsoever, even affectionate hugs and kisses, for fear that the husband will interpret this as a demand for intercourse. The communication of the couple worsens, intensifying the man's anxiety and setting a pattern difficult to reverse without professional assistance.

Vaginismus As yet another example of the intimate relation between the sexual reactions of the two partners, Masters and Johnson found that some men develop erectile problems because of the partner's vaginismus.

Physiological causes Some of the disorders are attributable to physical damage. As indicated earlier, clitoral or vaginal infections, torn ligaments in the pelvic region, scar tissue at the vaginal opening from incisions made during childbirth (episiotomies), and—especially in older, postmenopausal women—insufficient lubrication of the vagina may make intercourse painful for women. Infection of the glans of the penis, which can develop when it is not kept clean, may cause dyspareunia in men. A minority of men with erectile problems are found to suffer from metabolic disturbances through diabetes, and in some sexual arousal is dulled by the use of certain tranquilizers.[7]

Sociocultural factors Especially in female dysfunctions, cultural biases play a role. ''Sociocultural influence more often than not places the woman in a position in which she must adapt, sublimate, inhibit, or even distort her natural capacity to function sexually in order to fulfill her genetically assigned role. Herein lies a major source of woman's sexual dysfunction'' (p. 218). The man has the blessing of society to develop sexual expressiveness, but the woman, at least until recently, has not had this freedom, and her needs have often been ignored. And of course compounding her difficulties is the fact that she does not require sexual arousal in order to function adequately as a partner during sexual intercourse.

According to laboratory studies reported in *Human Sexual Response*, women seem capable both of multiple orgasms and of more sustained, more frequent, and more physiologically intense sexual arousal than men, which makes the neglect of their sexuality particularly ironic.

Other Contemporary Views

Figure 13.3 illustrates graphically the distinction that Masters and Johnson made between the several historically relevant factors in the development of sexual problems and the two variables believed to operate in the here and now, spectator role and fear of performance. One question that suggests itself is whether causes alleged to be of only historical importance might not be of more immediate concern to some people. Might not a woman's *current* religious beliefs inhibit her involvement in and enjoyment of sexual relations? Or consider the woman who was traumatized as a teenager by a gang rape. Might not the memory of that incident intrude itself upon her consciousness whenever she finds herself in an intimate situation? Masters and Johnson would reply that a religious belief or memory acts on the present by making the person a spectator rather than an uncriti-

cal participant, thus preserving the integrity of their theoretical model. Be that as it may, religious beliefs and sexual traumas might conceivably hinder a person's sexual behavior in a very direct and immediate way.

Masters and Johnson considered sexual dysfunctions as problems in and of themselves and not inevitably caused by deeper-seated intrapsychic or interpersonal difficulties. The couples whose treatment formed the basis of their second book, *Human Sexual Inadequacy* (1970), had marriages which, in spite of the sexual problems, were marked by caring and closeness. But as the Masters and Johnson general orientation became widespread and their therapy techniques were applied by others, sex therapists saw people whose relationships were seriously impaired. It is not difficult to imagine why a marriage or other relationship might deteriorate when the couple has not had intercourse for years. By the time a therapist is consulted, he or she is faced with the chicken-and-egg conundrum. It is impossible to know whether the hostility between the two people caused the sexual problem or vice versa. The working assumption of most therapists is that couples have both sexual and interpersonal problems. Clearly, it is unrealistic to expect a satisfying sexual encounter when, for example, the man is angry with the woman for spending more and more time outside the home, or when the woman resents the man's insensitive dealings with their children. Such negative thoughts and emotions can in-

Marital distance and distress are commonly associated with sexual dysfunctions and are therefore often targets of sexual therapy.

[7]Spinal cord lesions, depending on how complete they are and where they are located, may cause paralysis and loss of sensation either in the legs (paraplegia) or in both arms and legs (quadraplegia). A person who cannot move his or her arms and legs is sometimes considered incapable of sexual excitement. This is not so. A review by Higgins (1978) documents erections and ejaculation in a number of paralyzed men.

trude themselves into the sexual situation and thereby inhibit whatever arousal and pleasure might otherwise be found.

As with other disorders, Albert Ellis (1971) emphasizes the role of irrational thinking in the development and maintenance of sexual dysfunctions. Thus a woman who cannot have orgasms during intercourse is assumed to be *demanding* of herself that she have one. Indeed, the often-used phrase "achieve an orgasm" may reflect our society's maladaptive view of sexual satisfaction as something to be pursued and won, much as people chase after approval and recognition. Ellis's term for this kind of self-defeating, demanding thinking—"musturbation"—seems appropriate here. Many sexologists, including Masters and Johnson, appreciate that such thoughts can preclude sexual enjoyment.

"Why doesn't he touch me more there, rather than here?" "Why does she stop stroking just as I'm getting excited?" As mentioned earlier, people may lack knowledge of sexual anatomy and functioning and more specifically be unaware of the likes and dislikes of a partner. Unfortunately, just caring for the partner may not be enough in establishing a mutually satisfying sexual relationship. People who have sexual problems are often found to lack knowledge and skill (LoPiccolo and Hogan, 1979). A woman may be left "hanging" short of orgasm by a lover who does not appreciate the importance of clitoral stimulation; the husbands of inorgasmic women are often reported to be awkward lovers (Kaplan, 1974; LoPiccolo, 1977).

A related problem is poor communication between partners. For any number of reasons—embarrassment, distrust, dislike, resentment, depression, to name but a few—one lover may not inform the other of his or her preferences, likes, and dislikes. Then he or she often misinterprets the failure of the partner to anticipate or mind-read as not really caring. Although sexual communication is frequently inadequate in distressed marriages and is therefore tended to in marital therapy (see page 534), it can also be poor in people who are otherwise compatible. Open discussions of sex by partners, among friends, in the media, and even in professional training programs are after all relatively recent phenomena.

Finally, as with many of the other psychological problems dealt with in this book, it is not known why some people have in their backgrounds or in their present lives one or more of the factors believed to be of etiological significance and yet do not have a sexual dysfunction. Why a person develops one sexual dysfunction rather than another is also a puzzle.

BEHAVIORAL AND COGNITIVE THERAPIES FOR PSYCHOSEXUAL DYSFUNCTIONS

Perhaps in no area of psychotherapy have behavioral and cognitive therapies been more notably successful than in treating psychosexual dysfunctions. Therapists, some of whom specialize as sex therapists, work directly with the sexual problems in question, paying relatively little attention to the intrapsychic and personality problems focused on by psychodynamic and humanistic therapists. To date a few adequately controlled outcome studies (for example, Obler, 1973; Heiman and LoPiccolo, 1983) plus the overwhelming weight of clinical evidence indicate the greater effectiveness of learning and cognitive approaches in treating sexual dysfunctions.

LoPiccolo and Hogan (1979) offer a useful scheme for describing the treatment of sexual dysfunctions. Sex education, techniques for reducing anxiety, skills and communication training, procedures to change attitudes and thoughts, shifts in routines, marital therapy, psychodynamic techniques, and medical and physical procedures are all considered as means. A therapist may choose only one technique to treat a given case, but the multifaceted nature of sexual problems usually demands several.

Sex education Because many dysfunctional people are ignorant of basic facts about human sexuality, most therapists devote time and effort to educating their clients in sexual anatomy and the physiological processes of intercourse. An unintentional but important effect of such instruction is to make legitimate the explicit discussion of sex, taking it out of the realm of unspoken taboo and mystery and dismissing some of the anxiety and embarrassment surrounding this previously avoided topic.

Anxiety reduction techniques Well before the publication of the Masters-Johnson therapy program (see Box 13.2), behavior therapists appreciated that their frightened clients needed gradual and systematic exposure to anxiety-provoking aspects of the sexual situation. Wolpe's systematic desensitization and *in vivo desensitization*, that is, by real-life encounters, have been employed with apparently high degrees of success (Hogan, 1978; Andersen, 1983), especially when they are combined with skills training; people highly anxious about sex have often failed to learn to do a number of necessary and preliminary things. In vivo desensitization would appear to be the principal technique of the Masters-Johnson program, although additional components probably contribute to its overall effectiveness.

Skills and communication training   To improve sexual skills and communication, therapists assign written materials, show clients videotapes and films that demonstrate explicit sexual techniques, discuss techniques with them, and encourage them to express their likes and dislikes to their partners (for example, McMullen and Rosen, 1979). All these training procedures also expose the client to anxiety-laden material; this desensitizing aspect appears to be an additional benefit.

Procedures to change attitudes and thoughts   In what are called *sensory-awareness procedures*, the client is encouraged to tune in to the pleasant sensations that accompany even incipient sexual arousal. The sensate-focus exercises described in Box 13.2, for example, are a way of opening the individual to truly sensual and sexual feelings. Rational-emotive therapy tries to substitute less self-demanding thoughts for "musturbation," the "I must" thoughts often making a catastrophe of things for sexually dysfunctional people.

Shifts in routines   Therapists may encourage a couple to make "dates" with each other, to take the phone off the hook, hang a "Do Not Disturb" sign on the bedroom door, or agree not to have intercourse for a given period of time. The assumption is that any such specific shifts from habitual behavior can have positive reinforcing consequences and be beneficial to the sexual relationship.

Marital therapy   As noted earlier, sexual dysfunctions are often embedded in a distressed marital or other close relationship. Troubled couples usually need special training in communication skills. Marital therapy is discussed in more detail in Chapter 20.

Psychodynamic techniques   A man may not at first admit that he cannot have an erection, in which case the therapist must listen between the lines of what he says. A woman may be thought reluctant to take the initiative in sexual encounters because, although she may not verbalize it to the therapist, she considers such assertiveness unseemly and inappropriate to her traditional female role. In such instances the general analytic view of clients as often unable to express clearly to their therapists what truly bothers them can help in proper assessment and planning for behavioral treatment. Kaplan (1974) articulates well the blend of psychodynamic therapy with direct behavioral treatment. No doubt elements of nonbehavioral therapy are to be found in the actual practices of sex therapists, even if they are not made explicit by these workers when they discuss their techniques in journals or with colleagues. Readers may wish

Sensate focus, in which partners give pleasure to each other through touching, is one of the techniques used in early phases of therapy for sexual dysfunction.

to hearken back to the earlier discussion of eclecticism in therapy (Box 2.4, page 52) to remind themselves of the complexity of the therapeutic enterprise.

Medical and physical procedures   Although our study of sexual dysfunctions has referred to relatively few underlying somatic problems, therapists must not ignore their possibility, especially if dyspareunia and complete erectile dysfunction are the disorders. When depression is part of the clinical picture and has severely diminished sex drive, antidepressant drugs can be helpful (Winokur, 1963). Tranquilizers are also used as an adjunct to anxiety reduction techniques, although the depressant effects of these drugs may be detrimental to sexual functioning. Most therapists use drugs only when psychological procedures are found wanting.

The self-help trend is quite evident among sexually dysfunctional people as well as among those who strive to enhance already satisfying sex lives. For greater

BOX 13.2

THERAPY FOR PSYCHOSEXUAL DYSFUNCTIONS BY MASTERS AND JOHNSON

In 1970 the publication of Masters and Johnson's *Human Sexual Inadequacy* generated an excitement in the mental health community that is seldom encountered. This book reported on a therapy program carried out with close to 800 sexually dysfunctional people. Each couple had traveled to St. Louis and spent two weeks attending the Reproductive Biology Research Foundation for intensive therapy by day and doing sexual homework in a motel at night. Away from home, they were free of domestic distractions and able to make their stay a sort of second honeymoon. Many of the Masters and Johnson techniques had been used by therapists for some time; and, although some methodological problems have been uncovered by workers who have examined their report closely (Zilbergeld and Evans, 1980), other therapists using their techniques have had the same high rates of success (Andersen, 1983). Masters and Johnson virtually created the sex therapy movement, and their work therefore deserves a detailed description.

The therapy attempts to reduce or eliminate fears of performance and to take the participants out of their maladaptive roles as spectators. Then, it is hoped, the couple will be able to enjoy sex freely and spontaneously.

Each day the couple meets with a dual-sex therapy team, the assumption being that men best understand men and women best understand women. For the first several days the experiences of all couples are the same, regardless of their specific problem. An important stipulation is that for the time being any sexual activity between the two partners is expressly forbidden. A complete social and sexual history is obtained during the first two days, and physical examinations are conducted so that any organic factors can either be excluded or be found and dealt with.

In the assessment interviews considerable attention is paid to the so-called *sexual value system*, the ideas of each partner about what is acceptable and needed in a sexual relationship. Sometimes this sexual value system must be changed for one or both partners before sexual functioning can improve. For example, if one partner regards sexuality as ugly and unacceptable, it is doubtful whether even the most powerful therapy can help that person and the partner enjoy sex.

On the third day the therapists begin to offer interpretations about why problems have arisen and why they are continuing. In all cases the emphasis is on problems in the relationship, not on particular difficulties of either partner. A basic premise of the Masters and Johnson therapy is that ". . . there is no such thing as an uninvolved partner in any marriage in which there is some form of sexual inadequacy" (1970, p. 2). Whatever the problem, the couple is encouraged to see it as their mutual responsibility. At this time the clients are introduced to the idea of the spectator role. They are told, for example, that a male with erectile problems usually worries about how well or poorly he is doing rather than participating freely. It is pointed out to the couple that this pattern of observing himself, although totally understandable in context, is blocking his natural responses and greatly interfering with sexual enjoyment.

At the end of the third day an all-important assignment is given to the couple, namely to engage in *sensate focus*. The couple is instructed to choose a time when they feel "a natural sense of warmth, unit compatibility . . . or even a shared sense of gamesmanship" (Masters and Johnson, 1970, p. 71). They are to undress and give each other pleasure by touching each other's bodies. The co-therapists appoint one marital partner to do the first "pleasuring" or "giving"; the partner who is "getting" is simply to enjoy being touched. The one being touched, however, is *not* required to feel a sexual response and, moreover, takes responsibility for immediately telling the partner if something becomes distracting or uncomfortable. Then the roles are switched. Attempts at intercourse are still forbidden. To Masters and Johnson this approach is a way of breaking up the the frantic groping common among these couples. The sensate-focus assignment may promote contact where none has existed for years; if it does, it is a first step toward gradually reestablishing sexual intimacy.*

Sensate focusing may uncover deep animosities that have hitherto remained hidden. Most of the time, however, partners begin to realize that encounters in bed can be intimate without necessarily being a prelude to sexual intercourse. On the second evening the partner being pleasured is instructed to give specific encouragement and direction

---

arousal and ecstatic enjoyment of sex, some people rely on chemicals. Amyl nitrite is a peripheral vasodilator, but unfortunately it sometimes has the potentially fatal side effect of heart failure. Amyl nitrite is inhaled from a small glass vial, usually by men, just before orgasm to intensify and prolong it. Alcohol disinhibits in small amounts; marijuana, hashish, cocaine, LSD, and other psychedelics have effects that are variable and often dramatic. Other chemicals are touted for their presumed aphrodisiac, or sexually stimulating, properties. For example, cantharides or Spanish fly, a preparation of powdered blister beetles which is taken internally, creates inflammation and itching in the genitals, sensations experienced by some people as sexually arousing. The by placing his or her hand on the hand of the giving partner in order to regulate pressure and rate of stroking. The touching of genitals and breasts is also now allowed. Still, however, there is no mention of an orgasm, and the prohibition on intercourse remains in effect. Diagrams are presented if the partners are ignorant of basic female and male anatomy, as they often are. After this second day of sensate focusing, treatment branches out according to the specific problem or problems of the couple. As an illustration, we will outline the therapy for orgasmic dysfunction in the female.

After the sensate-focus exercises have made the couple more comfortable with each other in bed, the wife's attention is directed to maximizing her own sexual stimulation without trying to have an orgasm. As a result her own sexual excitement usually builds. The therapists give explicit instructions about generally effective means of manually manipulating the female genital area, although ultimate decisions are made by the female partner, who is encouraged to make her wishes clear to the man, moment by moment. In the treatment of other dysfunctions, as in the treatment for this one, it is emphasized that at this stage having orgasms is not the focus of interaction between partners.

After the woman has begun to enjoy being pleasured in this way, the next step is to move the source of sensate pleasure from the man's hand on her body to his penis inside her vagina. She is told to place herself on top of the man and gently insert the penis; she is encouraged simply to tune in to her feelings. When she feels inclined, she can begin slowly to move her pelvis. She is encouraged to regard the penis as something for her to play with, something that will provide her with pleasure. The male can also begin slowly to thrust. At all times, however, the wife must be able to decide when and what should happen next.

When the couple is able to maintain this containment for minutes at a time, without the man's thrusting forcefully toward orgasm, a major change has usually taken place in their sexual interactions: for perhaps the first time the woman has been allowed to feel and think sexually, and indeed selfishly, about her own pleasure. In their subsequent encounters most couples begin to have mutually satisfying intercourse.

Clinicians must be extremely sensitive in presenting these various treatment procedures to a couple whose problems may stretch back many years. Sometimes the couple discuss sex for the very first time at the Masters and Johnson clinic. The calm and open manner of the therapists puts the couple at ease, encouraging in them both a commitment to follow certain instructions and a more open attitude toward sex and the activities that people may engage in together when making love. Although behavioral prescriptions are specific, the therapists can never lose sight of the atmosphere that must be maintained in the consulting room and, it is hoped, transferred over to the privacy of the bedroom, where much of the *actual* therapy takes place. As in other forms of behavior therapy, there is a strong emphasis on technique, but interpersonal factors set the stage for behavior to change.

Sex clinics have sprung up everywhere, based in general on the Masters and Johnson model, and many mental health professionals have incorporated direct sex therapy techniques into their practices. Researchers have investigated various aspects of the treatment package. One question is whether a dual-sex therapy team is really necessary for all couples; this does not seem to be the case (Fordney-Settlage, 1975; Husted, 1975). Another question concerns the effectiveness of daily intensive therapy as compared to the more usual outpatient practice of once-weekly sessions; data indicate no advantage to the intensive Masters-Johnson regimen (Heinman and LoPiccolo, 1983). Some clinicians now rely on electrically powered vibrators when treating female orgasmic dysfunction; with proper instructions many inorgasmic women first learn to enjoy orgasms through self-stimulation with these little machines (Barbach, 1975; Dodson, 1974). The pursuit and enhancement of sexual pleasure for its own sake is being legitimized. Although some are concerned about this trend and dub it "sexual athletics," on the whole the relaxation of strictures regarding sexuality promises greater satisfaction for most people (Gagnon and Davison, 1974).

*Details of other direct therapies, some of them going beyond what Masters and Johnson describe, are available in LoPiccolo and LoPiccolo, 1978; Rosen and Rosen, 1981; Gagnon, 1977; Kaplan, 1974.

most that can be said about any of these drugs is that their efficacy is yet to be established, although their benefits to some people under some circumstances, as well as their dangers to others, are attested to by enthusiastic testimonials and by dire warnings.

Implanting a rigid plastic rod or a system of hydraulic tubes in a chronically flaccid penis and removal of the clitorial hood, in hopes of enhancing clitoral stimulation, are surgical procedures. These are radical steps to take, but implantations in the penis will allow the physically disabled man to have an erection—if they work. Major medical complications have been reported for a significant number of such operations (Malloy, Wein, and Carpiniello, 1980). Alterations of the female genitalia is seemingly unnecessary, since the clitoris can be gently rubbed either during or separately from intercourse. Finally, simple physical exercise may have some favorable impact on sexual difficulties, although the effects may be general and placebo in nature; people who jog or otherwise maintain their bodies in good physical condition probably feel generally better about themselves and may thereby improve their sex lives. One set of exercises does appear to have some specific benefit for inorgasmic women, namely the Kegel (1952) exercises for regularly contracting and thereby strengthening the pubococcygeal musculature surrounding the vagina.

SUMMARY

Few emotional problems are of greater interest to people nowadays than the psychosexual dysfunctions, disruptions in the normal sexual response cycle which seem to be caused by inhibitions and which rob many people of sexual enjoyment. DSM-III categorizes these disturbances as occurring in one or more of four phases of the response cycle: the appetitive phase (whether the person wishes to have sex), the excitement phase (whether the individual can respond with arousal to stimulation he or she deems acceptable), orgasm, and resolution. Disorders can vary in severity, in chronicity, and in their pervasiveness, occurring generally or only with certain partners and in particular situations. In no instance should a person believe himself or herself to have a psychosexual dysfunction unless the difficulty is persistent and recurrent; all of us quite normally experience sexual problems on an intermittent basis throughout our lives.

The particular sexual dysfunctions were described and their presumed causes discussed. Although organic factors must be considered, especially for instances of dyspareunia and complete erectile failure, the etiology of the disorders usually lies in a combination of unfavorable attitudes, difficult earlier experiences, fears of performance, assumption of a spectator role, and lack of specific knowledge and skills. Sex-role stereotypes may play a part in some dysfunctions: a man who has trouble maintaining his erection is often called impotent, the implication being that he is not much of a man; and a woman who does not have orgasms with regularity is often termed frigid, the implication being that she is generally cold and unresponsive. The problems of females in particular appear to be linked to cultural prejudices against their sexuality, ironic in light of laboratory data indicating that women are capable of more frequent sexual enjoyment than men.

Information on the causes of psychosexual dysfunction derives almost entirely from uncontrolled case studies and must therefore be viewed with caution. The absence of solid data on etiology has not deterred therapists from devising seemingly effective behavioral and cognitive interventions. Direct sex therapy, behavioral in nature and aimed at reversing old habits and teaching new skills, was propelled into public consciousness by the appearance of the Masters and Johnson book *Human Sexual Inadequacy* in 1970. Their method, anticipated by several behavior therapists years earlier, hinges on gradual, unthreatening exposure to increasingly intimate sexual encounters and the sanctioning of sexuality by credible and sensitive therapists. Education in sexual anatomy and physiology; anxiety reduction techniques; skills and communication training; procedures to change attitudes and thoughts; shifts in routines; marital therapy, when the sexual problem is embedded, as it often is, in a snarled relationship; psychodynamic techniques; and a variety of medical and other physical procedures are other means applied by sex therapists. Controlled data are only just beginning to appear, but there is good reason to be optimistic about the ultimate ability of the mental health professions to help most people achieve at least some relief from crippling sexual inhibitions.

PART FOUR

Frederico Castellón, *The Dark Figure*, 1938

THE SCHIZOPHRENIAS

SCHIZOPHRENIA

All of a sudden things weren't going so well. I began to lose control of my life and, most of all, myself. I couldn't concentrate on my schoolwork, I couldn't sleep, and when I did sleep, I had dreams about dying. I was afraid to go to class, imagined that people were talking about me, and on top of that I heard voices. I called my mother in Pittsburgh and asked for her advice. She told me to move off campus into an apartment with my sister.

After I moved in with my sister, things got worse. I was afraid to go outside and when I looked out of the window, it seemed that everyone outside was yelling "kill her, kill her." My sister forced me to go to school. I would go out of the house until I knew she had gone to work; then I would return home. Things continued to get worse. I imagined that I had a foul body odor and I sometimes took up to six showers a day. I recall going to the grocery store one day, and I imagined that the people in the store were saying "Get saved, Jesus is the answer." Things worsened—I couldn't remember a thing. I had a notebook full of reminders telling me what to do on that particular day. I couldn't remember my schoolwork, and I would study from 6:00 P.M. until 4:00 A.M., but never had the courage to go to class on the following day. I tried to tell my sister about it, but she didn't understand. She suggested that I see a psychiatrist, but I was afraid to go out of the house to see him.

One day I decided that I couldn't take this trauma anymore, so I took an overdose of 35 Darvon pills. At the same moment, a voice inside me said, "What did you do that for? Now you won't go to heaven." At that instant I realized that I really didn't want to die, I wanted to live, and I was afraid. I got on the phone and called the psychiatrist whom my sister had recommended. I told him that I had taken an overdose of Darvon and that I was afraid. He told me to take a taxi to the hospital. When I arrived at the hospital, I began vomiting, but I didn't pass out. Somehow I just couldn't accept the fact that I was really going to see a psychiatrist. I thought that psychiatrists were only for crazy people, and I definitely didn't think I was crazy yet. As a result, I did not admit myself right away. As a matter of fact I left the hospital and ended up meeting my sister on the way home. She told me to turn right back around, because I was definitely going to be admitted. We then called my mother, and she said she would fly down on the following day (O'Neal, 1984, pp. 109–110).

Although the diagnosis of schizophrenia has existed now for about a century and the disorder has spawned more research than any other, we remain far from understanding this serious mental disorder. The massive and extreme disruptions of thoughts, perceptions, emotions, and behavior that are schizophrenia are what people generally refer to as madness. In this chapter we consider first how schizophrenia is and has been diagnosed and in so doing find that through the decades there have been widespread disagreements. Then we examine research on the etiology of schizophrenia and therapies for the disorder.

HISTORY OF THE CONCEPT

Kraepelin's and Bleuler's Early Descriptions

The concept of *schizophrenia* was initially formulated by two European psychiatrists, Emil Kraepelin and Eugen Bleuler. Differences in their approaches to schizophrenia and their definitions of the disorder have continued to have a major impact and have produced a good deal of controversy. Kraepelin first presented his concept of *dementia praecox*, the early term for schizophrenia, in 1898. Two major groups of endogenous, or internally caused, psychoses were differentiated, manic-depressive illness and dementia praecox. Dementia praecox included several diagnostic concepts—dementia paranoides, catatonia, and hebephrenia—already singled out and regarded as distinct entities by clinicians in the few previous decades. The term dementia praecox is itself descriptive of two major aspects of the disorder: an early onset (praecox) and a progressive intellectual deterioration (dementia). Among the major symptoms that Kraepelin saw in such patients were hallucinations, delusions, negativism, attentional difficulties, stereotyped behavior, and emotional dysfunction. Thus Kraepelin focused on both course and symptoms in defining the disorder, although he often emphasized the former over the latter.

Kraepelin did not move much beyond a descriptive level. In the eighth edition of his textbook, for example, he grouped the symptoms of dementia praecox into thirty-six major categories, assigning hundreds of them to each. He made little effort to interrelate these great numbers of separate symptoms and stated only that they all reflected dementia and a loss of the usual unity in thinking, feeling, and acting. In contrast to Kraepelin's descriptive approach, the view of the next major figure,

Eugen Bleuler, represented both a specific attempt to define the "core" of the disorder and a move away from Kraepelin's emphasis on prognosis in defining the disorder.

In describing schizophrenia, Bleuler broke with Kraepelin on two major points, for he believed that the disorder in question did not necessarily have an early onset and that it did not inevitably progress toward dementia. Thus Bleuler was much less. attentive to the *course* of the disorder than was Kraepelin, and the label dementia praecox was no longer considered appropriate. In 1908 Bleuler proposed his own term, schizophrenia, to capture what he viewed as the essential nature of the condition.

Psychoanalytic theory had a major influence on Bleuler's view of schizophrenia. First, he thought that Freudian concepts could account for the specific content of symptoms such as delusions and hallucinations. They were viewed as efforts to replace the existing world from which the schizophrenic had retreated. Second, and even more importantly, Bleuler was led to attempt for schizophrenia what Freud had tried to accomplish for the neuroses—to specify underlying psychological processes that might be at the root of the various disturbances of schizophrenic patients.

Bleuler, like Kraepelin, had noted the great range of distress and dysfunction evident in schizophrenic patients. But Bleuler went much further than Kraepelin in trying to specify a common denominator or essential property that would link the various disturbances together. The metaphorical concept that he adopted for this purpose was the "breaking of associative threads." For Bleuler associative threads joined not only words but thoughts. Thus goal-directed, efficient thinking and communication were possible only when these hypothetical structures were intact. The notion that associative threads are disrupted in schizophrenics was then used to "account" for other problems. The attentional difficulties of schizophrenics, for example, were viewed by Bleuler as resulting from a loss of purposeful direction in thought, which in turn caused passive responding to objects and people in the immediate surroundings. In a similar vein, blocking, a seeming total loss of a train of thought, was considered a complete disruption of the associative threads for the subject under discussion.

Kraepelin's writings then fostered a narrow definition of schizophrenia and an emphasis on description. Although he recognized that a small percentage of patients who originally manifested symptoms of dementia praecox did not deteriorate, he preferred to limit this diagnostic category to patients who had a poor prognosis. Bleuler's work, in contrast, led to a broader concept of

Emil Kraepelin (1856–1926), the German psychiatrist whose descriptions of dementia praecox have proved remarkably durable in the light of contemporary research.

Eugen Bleuler (1857–1939), the Swiss psychiatrist who contributed importantly to our conceptions of schizophrenia and coined the term.

schizophrenia and a more pronounced theoretical emphasis. He placed patients with a good prognosis in his group of schizophrenias and even proposed the existence of "latent" schizophrenia, a term to be applied to patients who "have the disorder" but do not manifest overt schizophrenic symptoms. In addition, he included as schizophrenic "many atypical melancholias and manias of other schools, especially hysterical melancholias and manias, most hallucinatory confusions, some 'nervous' people and compulsive and impulsive patients, and many prison psychoses" (1923, p. 436).

The Broadened American Concept

Bleuler had a great influence on the American conception of schizophrenia. Over the first part of the twentieth century, its breadth was extended considerably. At the New York State Psychiatric Institute, for example, about 20 percent of patients were diagnosed schizophrenic in the 1930s. The numbers increased through the 1940s and in 1952 peaked at a remarkable 80 percent. In contrast, the European concept of schizophrenia remained narrower. The percentage of patients diagnosed schizophrenic at Maudsley Hospital in London stayed relatively constant, at 20 percent, for a forty-year period (Kuriansky, Deming, and Gurland, 1974).

The reasons for the increase in the frequency of American diagnoses of schizophrenia are not difficult to find. Several prominent figures in the history of American psychiatry, following Bleuler's lead, expanded the concept of schizophrenia to an even greater extent and also diverted attention from diagnosis itself.

Adolf Meyer (1866–1950), considered by many to have been the dean of American psychiatry (for example, Zilboorg and Henry, 1941), argued that diagnostic categories were often arbitrary and artificial (for example, Meyer, 1917, 1926). His approach to schizophrenia was flexible and did not rely on either specific symptoms or progressive deterioration for a definition of the disorder. He viewed it as an accumulation of faulty habits which had been building for a very long period of time. What he called substitutive reactions had replaced the ones appropriate to daily living and become established as the person settled into a rut of least resistance.

The American conception of schizophrenia was also broadened by investigators who suggested additional schizophrenic subtypes.[1] For example, in 1933 Kasanin described nine patients who had all been assigned diagnoses of dementia praecox. The onset of the disorder had been sudden for all of them and their recovery relatively rapid. Noting that theirs could be said to be a combination of both schizophrenic and affective symptoms, Kasanin suggested the term "schizoaffective psychosis" to describe the disturbances of these patients.

---

[1]Both Kraepelin and Bleuler had suggested that schizophrenia could be divided into specific types, but the subtypes discussed here went considerably beyond their proposals.

This diagnosis subsequently became part of the American concept of schizophrenia, being listed in DSM-I (1952) and the DSM-II.

The schizophrenia category was further expanded by Hoch and his colleagues, who argued that schizophrenia often "masquerades" as other disorders. They suggested the terms "pseudoneurotic schizophrenia" (Hoch and Polatin, 1949) and "pseudopsychopathic schizophrenia" (Hoch and Dunaif, 1955) to describe anxious, withdrawn persons with serious interpersonal problems who also have neurotic or psychopathic symptoms. Hoch argued that even though these patients often lack the more classic symptoms of schizophrenia, they reveal, on closer examination, the cognitive and emotional disorganization he considered the hallmark of the disorder. As a result of such opinions, many patients who would otherwise have been diagnosed as suffering from neuroses, affective disorders, and personality disturbances came in this country to be considered schizophrenic.

In the 1960s and 1970s the *process-reactive* dimension was another key means of maintaining the broad concept of schizophrenia in the United States. As soon as Bleuler had observed that the onset of schizophrenia was not always at a young age and that deterioration was not a certain course, clinicians began to observe other differences between those whose onset was later and who sometimes recovered and those whose onset was earlier and who usually deteriorated further. Some schizophrenics had been relatively deviant, apathetic individuals for many of their young years, suffering gradual but insidious depletion of thought, emotion, interests, and activity. Others, usually later in life, had a rather rapid onset of more severe symptoms. The term *process*, indicating some sort of basic physiological malfunction in the brain, was chosen for insidiously developing schizophrenia and *reactive* for what appeared suddenly after stress. For the last thirty years in the United States the process-reactive dimension has been extensively studied. Earlier social and sexual adjustment, as measured, for example, by the Phillips Scale (1953), became a means of distinguishing schizophrenics and determining their chances for recovery. Those with a *good premorbid* adjustment were more likely to have only an episodic problem and to have a good prognosis. Process schizophrenia, then, which has followed an earlier poor adjustment of patients at school, work, and in their sexual and social lives, may be equated with Kraepelin's original description of dementia praecox. The inclusion of reactive patients in the definition helped extend the American concept.

A prevailing interest in treatment also played a role in broadening the American conception of schizophrenia. Both Bleuler and Meyer had rejected the notion that deterioration was inevitable, thus allowing the possibility of intervention and the restitution of reason. Harry Stack Sullivan (1892–1949) shared this optimistic view and became the first major theorist to develop a systematic psychological treatment for schizophrenia. He emphasized the *underlying* emotional and cognitive factors motivating what he considered to be the schizophrenic's withdrawal from interpersonal relationships. Other behavior did not play an important role in Sullivan's definition of the disorder. Because he believed that personality could be observed only in interpersonal relations, he, in fact, maintained that there were *no* fundamental critieria for the disorder (Sullivan, 1929).

The DSM-III Diagnosis

With the publication of DSM-III, the American conception of schizophrenia has moved considerably from the excessively broad definition we have been discussing. The new definition narrows the range of patients diagnosed schizophrenic in four ways. First, the diagnostic criteria are presented in explicit and considerable detail. Second, patients with symptoms of an affective disorder are excluded. Many patients with a DSM-II diagnosis of schizophrenia actually had an affective disorder (Cooper et al., 1972). Schizophrenia, schizoaffective type, is now listed as *schizoaffective disorder*[2] in a new separate section, Psychotic Disorders Not Elsewhere Classified. Third, DSM-III requires that the person have continuous signs of schizophrenia for at least six months. Thus are eliminated patients who have a brief psychotic episode, often stress-related, and then recover quickly. DSM-II's acute schizophrenic episode is now diagnosed as either *schizophreniform disorder* or *brief reactive psychosis*, which are also listed in the new section. In schizophreniform disorder the psychotic symptoms—emotional turmoil, fear, confusion, vivid hallucinations—must not persist for more than six months or for fewer than two weeks. A brief reactive psychosis must not last longer than two weeks and is brought on by stress that would devastate almost anyone. Fourth, what DSM-II may have regarded as mild forms of schizophrenia are now diagnosed as personality disorders—schizotypal and borderline—as we saw in Chapter 10 (page 231n).

It cannot be concluded, however, that with the appearance of DSM-III we have reached a final answer to the problem of diagnosing schizophrenia. The DSM-III criteria are not accepted universally, and in fact, a number of different sets of diagnostic criteria are still frequently used. Endicott and her colleagues (1982) compared diagnoses made by the sets of criteria of ten different diagnostic systems. The number of patients identified as schizophrenic ranged from a low of six to a high of forty-four! Thus the breadth of the schizophrenia concept remains an issue even in contemporary research.

The foregoing has served as background for a more detailed description of the behavior of schizophrenics. The diagnostic symptoms to be presented rely heavily on the DSM-III criteria as well as on information collected in a large-scale investigation of schizophrenia, the International Pilot Study of Schizophrenia (IPSS), conducted by the World Health Organization (Sartorius, Shapiro, and Jablonsky, 1974).

CLINICAL SYMPTOMS OF SCHIZOPHRENIA

The symptoms of schizophrenic patients can be organized into disturbances in several major areas—thought, perception and attention, motor behavior, affect or emotion, and life functioning. The range of problems of people diagnosed as schizophrenic is very extensive, although patients who are so diagnosed will typically have only *some* of them. DSM-III determines for the diagnostician how many problems must be present, and in what degree, to justify the diagnosis. Unlike most diagnostic categories that we have considered, there is *no essential* symptom that must be present. Thus schizophrenic patients differ from one another more than do patients with other disorders. The heterogeneity of schizophrenia suggests that it would be appropriate to try to subdivide schizophrenics into types who manifest particular constellations of problems. After reviewing the major symptoms, we shall examine the types of schizophrenia.[3]

---

[2]Schizoaffective disorder is to be diagnosed only when the clinician cannot decide between an affective disorder and schizophrenia or schizophreniform disorder. Onset and usually recovery are rapid, as indicated earlier.

[3]Although we describe the symptoms of schizophrenia in detail, it must be kept in mind that diagnostically the duration of the disorder is regarded as at least as important, if not more so, in allowing schizophrenia to be distinguished from the symptomatically similar schizophreniform disorder and brief reactive psychosis.

Disorder of Thought

The term *thought disorder* refers to problems both in the *form* of thought—the organization of ideas, speaking so that a listener can understand; and in its *content*—the actual ideas that are expressed. We examine first the form of thought in schizophrenia.

Disorders of thought form In response to an initial, seemingly simple question to a schizophrenic patient, this conversation ensued:

> "How old are you?"
>
> "Why I am centuries old, sir."
>
> "How long have you been here?"
>
> "I've been now on this property on and off for a long time. I cannot say the exact time because we are absorbed by the air at night, and they bring back people. They kill up everything; they can make you lie; they can talk through your throat."
>
> "Who is this?"
>
> "Why, the air."
>
> "What is the name of this place?"
>
> "This place is called a star."
>
> "Who is the doctor in charge of your ward?"
>
> "A body just like yours, sir. They can make you black and white. I say good morning, but he just comes through there. At first it was a colony. They said it was heaven. These buildings were not solid at the time, and I am positive that this is the same place. They have others just like it. People die, and all the microbes talk over there, and prestigitis you know is sending you from here to another world. . . . I was sent by the government to the United States to Washington to some star, and they had a pretty nice country there. Now you have a body like a young man who says he is of the prestigitis."
>
> "Who was this prestigitis?"
>
> "Why, you are yourself. You can be prestigitis. They make you say bad things; they can read you; they bring back Negroes from the dead" (White, 1932, p. 228).

This excerpt illustrates the *incoherence* sometimes found in the conversation of schizophrenics. Although the patient may make repeated references to central ideas or a theme, the images and fragments of thought are not connected. it is difficult to understand exactly what the patient is trying to tell the interviewer. In addition, the patient used the word "prestigitis" several times, a *neologism* or new word which he has made up himself and which is probably meaningless to the listener.

Thought may also be disordered by *loose associations*, in which case the patient may be more successful in communicating with a listener but has difficulty sticking to one topic. He or she seems to drift off on a train of associations evoked by an idea from the past. Schizophrenic patients have themselves provided descriptions of this state.

My thoughts get all jumbled up. I start thinking or talking about something but I never get there. Instead, I wander off in the wrong direction and get caught up with all sorts of different things that may be connected with things I want to say but in a way I can't explain. People listening to me get more lost than I do. . . .

My trouble is that I've got too many thoughts. You might think about something, let's say that ashtray and just think, oh! yes, that's for putting my cigarette in, but I would think of it and then I would think of a dozen different things connected with it at the same time (McGhie and Chapman, 1961, p. 108).

Another aspect of the schizophrenic's associative problems is termed *clang associations*. The patient's speech contains many rhyming words, for example, "How are you today by the bay as a gay, Doctor?" The words follow one another because they rhyme, not because they make grammatical or logical sense. Other disturbances in thought form are *poverty of speech*—the amount of discourse is reduced; *poverty of content*—the amount of speech is adequate but it conveys little information; *perseveration*—words and ideas are persistently repeated; and *blocking*—a train of speech is interrupted by silence before an idea is completed and then the thought being conveyed cannot be recalled.

Disturbances in the form of thought were regarded by Bleuler as the principal clinical symptom of schizophrenia and remain one of the DSM-III criteria for the diagnosis. But recent evidence indicates that the thinking of some schizophrenics is not faulty in form. Furthermore, the presence of thought disorder does not discriminate well between schizophrenics and other psychotic patients, such as some of those with affective disorders (Andreasen, 1979).

Disorders of thought content Deviance in *content* of thought seems more central to schizophrenia than confusion in form of thought. The thoughts of 97 percent of schizophrenics in the IPSS were found disordered in a very fundamental way, through "*lack of insight*." When asked what they thought was wrong or why they had been hospitalized, schizophrenics seemed to have no appreciation of their condition and little realization that their behavior was unusual. In addition, many schizophrenics are subject to *delusions*, holding beliefs that the rest of society would generally disagree with or view as misinterpretations of reality.

No doubt each of us is, at one time or another, rather concerned because we believe that others think badly of us. Perhaps much of the time this belief is well justified. Who, after all, can be universally loved? Fortunately, we either learn to live with this belief, or, if it is false, are readily able to dispel it. Consider for a moment, however, what life would be like if you were firmly convinced that numbers of people did not like you, indeed that they disliked you so much that they were plotting against you. Some of these persecutors have sophisticated listening devices which allow them to tune in on your most private conversations and gather evidence in a plot to discredit you. None of those around you, including your loved ones, is able to reassure you that these people are not spying on you. In fact, even your closest friends and confidants are gradually joining your tormentors and becoming members of the persecuting community. You are naturally quite anxious or angry about your situation, and you begin your own counteractions against the imagined persecutors. Any new room you enter must be carefully checked for listening devices. When you meet a person for the first time, you question him or her at great length to determine whether he or she is part of the plot against you.

Simple *persecutory* delusions were found in 65 percent of the IPSS sample. Schizophrenics' delusions may also take several other forms. Some of the most important of these have been described by the German psychiatrist Kurt Schneider (1959). The following catalogue of these delusions is drawn from Mellor (1970).

1. **Delusional percept.** A normal perception, for some reason, takes on a special significance for the patient and an often elaborate delusional system quickly develops. To give an example of such a transformed percept,

A young Irishman was at breakfast with two fellow-lodgers. He felt a sense of unease, that something frightening was going to happen. One of the lodgers pushed the salt cellar towards him (he appreciated at the time that this was an ordinary salt cellar and his friend's intention was innocent). Almost before the salt cellar reached him he knew that he must return home, "to greet the Pope, who is visiting Ireland to see his family and to reward them . . . because Our Lord is going to be born again to one of the women. . . . And because of this they [all the women] are all born different with their private parts back to front" (p. 18).

Kurt Schneider, a German psychiatrist, proposed that particular forms of hallucinations and delusions, which he calls first-rank symptoms, are central to defining schizophrenia.

2. **Somatic passivity.** The patient is a passive, unwilling recipient of bodily sensations imposed by an external agency.

A twenty-nine-year-old teacher described "X-rays entering the back of my neck, where the skin tingles and feels warm, they pass down the back in a hot tingling strip about six inches wide to the waist. There they disappear into the pelvis which feels numb and cold and solid like a block of ice. They stop me from getting an erection" (p. 16).

3. **Thought insertion.** Thoughts, which are not the patient's own, have been placed in his or her mind by an external source.

A twenty-nine-year-old housewife said "I look out of the window and I think the garden looks nice and the grass looks cool, but the thoughts of Eamonn Andrews come into my mind. There are no other thoughts there, only his. . . . He treats my mind like a screen and flashes his thoughts on it like you flash a picture" (p. 17).

4. **Thought broadcast.** The patient's thoughts are transmitted, so that others know them.

A twenty-one-year-old student [found that] "As I think, my thoughts leave my head on a type of men-

tal ticker-tape. Everyone around has only to pass the tape through their mind and they know my thoughts'' (p. 17).

5. **Thought withdrawal.** The patient's thoughts are "stolen" from his or her mind by an external force, suddenly and unexpectedly.

   A twenty-two-year-old woman [described such an experience]. "I am thinking about my mother, and suddenly my thoughts are sucked out of my mind by a phrenological vacuum extractor, and there is nothing in my mind, it is empty . . ." (p. 16–17).

The next three delusions pertain to the experiencing of feelings and the carrying out of actions and impulses that have been imposed on the patient by some external agent.

6. **"Made" feelings.** *A twenty-three-year-old female patient reported, "I cry, tears roll down my cheeks and I look unhappy, but inside I have a cold anger because they are using me in this way, and it is not me*

"I demand to know what hidden forces are impeding my progress and strewing my path with obstacles!"

(Drawing by Sempé; © 1982, The New Yorker Magazine, Inc.)

who is unhappy, but they are projecting unhappiness onto my brain. They project upon me laughter, for no reason, and you have no idea how terrible it is to laugh and look happy and know it is not you, but their emotions'' (p. 17).

7. **"Made" volitional acts.** *A twenty-nine-year-old shorthand typist described her [simplest] actions as follows: "When I reach my hand for the comb it is my hand and arm which move, and my fingers pick up the pen, but I don't control them. . . . I sit there watching them move, and they are quite independent, what they do is nothing to do with me. . . . I am just a puppet who is manipulated by cosmic strings. When the strings are pulled my body moves and I cannot prevent it''* (p. 17).

8. **"Made" impulses.** *A twenty-nine-year-old engineer [who had] emptied the contents of a urine bottle over the ward dinner trolley [tried to explain the incident]. "The sudden impulse came over me that I must do it. It was not my feeling, it came into me from the X-ray department, that was why I was sent there for implants yesterday. It was nothing to do with me, they wanted it done. So I picked up the bottle and poured it in. It seemed all I could do.''* (p. 18).

Disorders of Perception and Attention

Schizophrenic patients frequently report that the world seems somehow different or even unreal (derealizations) to them. Some mention changes in the way their bodies feel. Parts of their bodies may seem too large or too small, objects around them too close or too far away. Or there may be numbness or tingling and electrical or burning sensations. Patients may feel as though snakes are crawling inside the abdomen. Or the body may become so depersonalized that it feels as though it is a machine. Some patients become hypersensitive to sights, sounds and smells. They may find it torment to be touched. Light may seem blinding and noise becomes an agony. Others remark that their surroundings are not as they used to be, that everything appears flat and colorless. Some schizophrenics report difficulties in attending to what is happening around them.

I can't concentrate on television because I can't watch the screen and listen to what is being said at the same time. I can't seem to take in two things like this at the same time especially when one of them means watching and the other means listening. On the other hand I seem to be always taking in too much at the one time, and then I can't handle it and can't make sense of it. . . . [Or, as another patient stated] When people are talking,

I just get scraps of it. If it is just one person who is speaking, that's not so bad, but if others join in then I can't pick it up at all. I just can't get in tune with the conversation. It makes me feel all open—as if things are closing in on me and I have lost control (McGhie and Chapman, 1961, p. 106).

The most dramatic distortions of perception are called *hallucinations*, sensory experiences in the absence of any stimulation from the environment. They occur most often in the auditory modality and less often in the visual. Seventy-four percent of the IPSS sample reported having auditory hallucinations.

As with delusions, some hallucinations are thought to be particularly important diagnostically because they occur more often in schizophrenics than in other psychotic patients. Schneider (1959) has described these, and we again rely on Mellor (1970) for examples.

1. **Audible thoughts.** *A thirty-two-year-old housewife complained of a man's voice speaking in an intense whisper from a point about two feet above her head. The voice would repeat almost all the patient's goal-directing thinking—even the most banal thoughts. The patient would think, "I must put the kettle on" and after a pause of not more than one second the voice would say "I must put the kettle on." It would often say the opposite "Don't put the kettle on"* (p. 16).

2. **Voices arguing.** *A twenty-four-year-old male patient reported hearing voices coming from the nurse's office. One voice, deep in pitch and roughly spoken, repeatedly said "G.T. is a bloody paradox," and another higher in pitch said "He is that, he should be locked up." A female voice occasionally interrupted, saying "He is not, he is a lovely man"* (p. 16).

3. **Voices commenting.** *A forty-one-year-old housewife heard a voice coming from a house across the road. The voice went on incessantly in a flat monotone describing everything she was doing with an admixture of critical comments. "She is peeling potatoes, got hold of the peeler, she does not want that potato, she is putting it back, because she thinks it has a knobble like a penis, she has a dirty mind, she is peeling potatoes, now she is washing them . . ."* (p. 16).

Motor Symptoms

Disturbances in motor activity are obvious and bizarre. The schizophrenic may grimace or adopt strange facial expressions. He or she may gesture repeatedly, using pe-

Painting done by a patient while in a residential treatment center for adolescents. He described the painting as showing the ghost he used to see all the time.

culiar and sometimes complex sequences of finger, hand, and arm movements—which often seem to be purposeful, odd as they may be. Some schizophrenics manifest an unusual increase in the overall level of activity. There may be much excitement, wild flailing of the limbs, and great expenditure of energy similar to that seen in mania. At the other end of the spectrum is *catatonic immobility*: unusual postures are adopted and maintained for very long periods of time. A patient may stand on one leg, with the other tucked up toward the buttocks, and remain in this position virtually all day. The limbs of catatonic patients may have what is referred to as *waxy flexibility*. Another person can move them about and put them into strange positions that will then be maintained.

Affective Symptoms

Two affective abnormalities are found in a number of schizophrenic patients. In some affect is said to be *flat*; virtually no stimulus can elicit an emotional response. The shallowness or complete blunting of emotion renders the schizophrenic apathetic. The patient may stare vacantly, the muscles of his face flaccid, his eyes lifeless.

A pose assumed in catatonic posturing is held for hours at a time.

When spoken to he answers in a flat and toneless voice. Flat affect was found in 66 percent of the IPSS schizophrenics. Other patients have *inappropriate affect*. The emotional responses of these individuals are out of context—the patient may laugh on hearing that her mother has just died or become enraged when asked a simple question about how a new garment fits. These schizophrenics are likely to shift rapidly from one emotional state to another for no discernible reason. Although this symptom is quite rare, when it does appear it is of considerable diagnostic importance.

Impairments in Life Functioning

Besides the specific symptoms that have been described, schizophrenics have many impairments of what should be the daily routines of their lives. In adolescence the preschizophrenic usually has few social skills, few friends, and no intimates. Dating is infrequent and academic difficulties are common. After leaving high school most schizophrenics are relatively unsuccessful in

obtaining and holding a job. And they become ever more seclusive and actively avoid the company of other people. They even keep a definite physical distance and may have difficulty looking people in the eye. Personal hygiene and grooming may become quite cursory. Later, after they have experienced full-blown episodes of schizophrenia, they continue to have many similar problems even between episodes.

SUBCATEGORIES OF SCHIZOPHRENIA

Three of the types of schizophrenic disorders that are now included in DSM-III—*hebephrenic, catatonic,* and *paranoid*—were initially proposed by Kraepelin many years ago. The present descriptions of Kraepelin's original types provide further information on what schizophrenia is like and on the great diversity of behavior that relates to the diagnosis.

Disorganized Schizophrenia

Kraepelin's hebephrenic form of schizophrenia is called *disorganized* schizophrenia by DSM-III and is characterized by a number of rather diffuse and regressive symptoms. Hallucinations and delusions—sexual, hypochondriacal, religious, and persecutory—are profuse and less organized than those of the paranoid schizophrenic. The patient may be subject to bizarre ideas, often involving deterioration of the body. He is constantly changeable, breaking into inexplicable fits of laughter and crying. Much of the patient's behavior is marked by a pattern of silliness and absurdity. He may grimace or have a meaningless smile on his face. He giggles childishly and speaks incoherently, stringing together similar-sounding words and inventing neologisms. All in all, his life seems a tangled skein of delusions, mannerisms, and busy, inconsequential rituals. He may tie a ribbon around his big toe or move incessantly, pointing at objects for no apparent reason. He frequently deteriorates to the point that he becomes incontinent, voiding anywhere and at any time. And he completely neglects his appearance, never bathing, brushing his teeth, or combing his hair.

Catatonic Schizophrenia

The most obvious symptoms of the *catatonic* type of schizophrenia are the motor disturbances discussed earlier. Such individuals typically alternate between catatonic immobility and wild excitement, but one or the other type of motor symptoms may predominate. The onset of catatonic reactions may be more sudden than other forms of schizophrenia, although the person has probably already shown some apathy and withdrawal from reality. The limbs of the immobile catatonic may become stiff and swollen; in spite of apparent obliviousness, he or she may later relate all that has happened during the stupor. In the excited state the catatonic may shout and talk continuously and incoherently, all the while pacing with great agitation. This form of schizophrenia is seldom seen today, perhaps because drug therapy works effectively on these bizarre motor processes (Arieti, 1955).

Paranoid Schizophrenia

A more common diagnosis is paranoid schizophrenia. The key to this diagnosis is the presence of prominent delusions. Usually they are of persecution, but sometimes they may be *grandiose* delusions. Individuals may have an exaggerated sense of their own importance, power, knowledge, or identity. Or they may be plagued by *delusional jealousy*, believing the sexual partner to be unfaithful. Vivid auditory and visual hallucinations may also accompany the delusions. These patients often develop what are referred to as *ideas of reference*: they incorporate unimportant events within a delusional framework, reading personal significance into the seemingly trivial activities of others. They think that phrases of overheard conversations apply to them, and the continual appearance of a person on a street where they customarily walk means that they are being watched. What they see of television or read in magazines also somehow refers to them. Paranoid schizophrenics are agitated, argumentative, angry, and sometimes violent. But they remain emotionally responsive, although they may be somewhat stilted, formal, and intense with others. And they are more alert and verbal than other schizophrenics; their thought processes, although deluded, have not fragmented (see Box 14.1)

Positive and Negative Symptoms

The Kraepelinian types still form the basis of current diagnostic systems, yet many have questioned their usefulness. Diagnosing types of schizophrenia is extremely difficult, which often means that diagnostic reliability is dramatically reduced. Furthermore, the types have little predictive validity: knowing that a patient has been diagnosed as having one or another form of schizophrenia does not give us information that will be helpful in treatment or in predicting the course of the problems. Finally, there is considerable overlap among types. For example, patients with all forms of schizophrenia may have delusions. Thus the Kraepelinian system of subtyping has not proved to be an optimal way of trying to deal with the variability in schizophrenic behavior.

Supplemental types that have been added by the DSM are also flawed, as definitions of the *undifferentiated* and *residual* types will indicate. The undifferentiated type is for patients who either have psychotic symptoms that do not fit into any other type or have symptoms of more than one of them. The diagnosis residual schizophrenia "should be used when there has been at least one episode of Schizophrenia but the [current] clinical picture . . . is without prominent psychotic symptoms, though signs of the illness persist" (DSM-III, p. 192). Clearly, schizophrenia is a disorder with a wide range of possible symptoms. Indeed, Bleuler wrote of the "group of schizophrenias," implying that it is not one but a set of disorders, each perhaps with a different etiology.

There is continuing interest in establishing types of schizophrenia, even though earlier ones have not proved helpful in treatment and prognosis. The system currently attracting much interest distinguishes between positive and negative symptoms. *Positive symptoms* consist of excesses, such as hallucinations, delusions, and bizarre behavior. *Negative symptoms* consist of behavioral deficits. In contrast to positive symptoms, negative symptoms are not thoroughly assessed in standard interviews. Andreasen (1982) has therefore developed a new instrument, the Scale for the Assessment of Negative Symptoms, so that they can be reliably rated. This scale assesses five negative symptoms.

1. **Affective flattening**. A blunting of emotions.

2. **Alogia**. A group of language deficits, including poverty of speech, poverty of content of speech, blocking, and long delays before responding.

3. **Avolition-apathy**. A lack of interest, drive, and energy manifested as inattention to grooming and hygiene, difficulty in seeking and keeping a job, and general activity.

4. **Anhedonia-asociality**. An inability to experience pleasure and feel intimacy, together with little interest in recreational activities, sex, and social relationships.

5. **Attentional impairment**. An inability to focus, indicated by inattentiveness at work and to the testing done during the patient's hospitalization.

With reliable ratings of both positive and negative symptoms, it becomes possible to divide schizophrenic patients into those with positive symptoms, negative symptoms, and "mixed" symptoms. Andreasen and Olsen (1982), for example, evaluated fifty-two patients

BOX 14.1

PARANOID DELUSIONS AND REPRESSED HOMOSEXUALITY

According to DSM-III, paranoid delusions are the most obvious symptom of both paranoid schizophrenia and the *paranoid disorders*. A person with a paranoid disorder is troubled by persistent persecutory delusions or by delusional jealousy, the unfounded conviction that the spouse or lover is unfaithful. But unlike the paranoid schizophrenic, he or she has no thought disorder, no hallucinations, and no bizarre delusions. The person speaks and reasons coherently and carries out daily responsibilities. A circumscribed delusional system is the one and fundamental loss of contact with reality. People with paranoid disorder rarely seek treatment through their own volition, but when they become contentious and initiate series of litigations, others may bring them for care.

Freud's theory, commonly accepted even today, is that paranoid delusions result from repressed homosexual impulses which are striving for expression. The anxiety stemming from their threatened expression is handled primarily by the defense mechanism of projection, attributing to others feelings that are unacceptable to one's own ego (Freud, 1915). The basic unconscious thought is, "I, a man, love him" or "I, a woman, love her." Freud considered the common paranoid delusions of persecution and grandiosity to derive from distortions, and then projection, of this basic homosexual urge.

In *delusions of persecution* the homosexual thought "I, a man, love him," being unacceptable to the ego, is converted into the less threatening statement "I, a man, hate him." Since the emotion expressed by this premise is also less than satisfactory, it is further transformed by projection into "He hates me, so I am justified in hating him." The final formulation may be "I hate him because he persecutes me." Freud asserted that the persecutor is always a person of the same sex who is unconsciously a love object for the individual.

Delusions of grandiosity (megalomania) begin with a contradiction of the homosexual impulse. The sentence "I,

a man, love him" is changed into "I do not love anyone." But since libido must be invested in or attached to something or someone, the psychic reality becomes "I love only myself."

One of Freud's lesser-known cases of a patient with paranoid delusions is of special interest, for it seems initially to challenge Freud's basic tenet that the persecutor must be a person of the same sex. The kinds of inferences that constitute the argument of this case study are typical of those made by Freud in his attempts to understand his clinical data and to test his hypotheses.

Freud was consulted by a lawyer in Vienna who had been hired by a woman to sue a male business associate for making indecent allegations about her. She stated that the man had had photographs taken of them while they were making love and was now threatening to bring disgrace upon her. Because of the unusual nature of her allegation, the lawyer had persuaded her to see Freud so that he could offer an opinion.

The woman, about thirty years of age, was an attractive single person who lived quietly with her mother, whom she supported. A handsome man in her firm had recently begun to court her. After much coaxing he had persuaded her to come to his apartment for an afternoon together. They became intimate, at which point she was frightened by a clicking noise coming from the direction of a desk in front of the window. The lover told her that it was probably from a small clock on the desk. As she left the house that afternoon, she encountered two men, one of them carrying a small package. They appeared to whisper something to each other secretively as she passed. By the time she reached home that evening, she had put together the following story. The box was a camera, the men were photographers, and her lover was an untrustworthy person who had arranged for photographs to be taken of them while they were undressed. The following day she began to berate the lover for his untrustworthiness, and he tried equally hard

---

diagnosed as schizophrenics according to DSM-III and found that sixteen could be regarded as having negative symptoms, eighteen positive symptoms, and eighteen mixed. Evidence relevant to the validity of this distinction will be given when we discuss the possible roles of dopamine and brain pathology in the etiology of schizophrenia.

RESEARCH ON THE ETIOLOGY OF SCHIZOPHRENIA

We have now considered *how* schizophrenics differ from

normal people in the ways they think, speak, perceive, and imagine. We are now ready to ask *what* can explain the scattering and disconnections of their thoughts, their wanting or inappropriate emotions, their misguided delusions and bewildering hallucinations. In contrast to other disorders considered in this book, broad theoretical perspectives like psychoanalysis and learning theory have not had much of an impact on research in schizophrenia. Therefore we provide only a brief overview of major theoretical positions, in Box 14.2. The specific areas of etiological research are examined in detail, however.

to rid her mind of her unfounded suspicions. Freud read one of the letters that the man had written to the woman. It struck him that the lover was indeed sincere and honest in denying involvement in such a plot.

At this point Freud faced a dilemma common in scientific inquiry. What should the investigator do when confronted by an instance that negates his hypothesis? The persecutor of the young woman appeared to be a member of the opposite sex. Freud could, of course, have completely abandoned his theory that paranoid delusions originate in homosexual impulses. Instead, he looked more closely into the case to see whether there were subtle factors that would allow him, in the end, to preserve the integrity of his theory.

During the second meeting with Freud, the woman changed the story somewhat. She admitted that she had visited the man twice in his apartment, not once, and that only on the second occasion had she heard the suspicious noise. After the first and uneventful visit—as far as her paranoia was concerned—she had been disturbed by an incident that she had witnessed at the office. The next day she had seen her new lover speaking in low tones to an older woman who was in charge of the firm. The older person liked the younger woman a great deal, and the younger woman in turn found that her employer reminded her of her own mother. She was therefore very concerned about their conversation and became convinced that her suitor was telling the woman about their lovemaking the previous afternoon.

Then it occurred to her that her lover and her employer had been having a love affair for some time. At the first opportunity she berated her lover for telling their employer of their lovemaking. He naturally protested and after a while succeeded in undoing her suspicions. Then she made her second visit to his apartment and heard the reputed clicking.

Let us examine Freud's comments on this portion of the case history.

These new details remove first of all any doubts as to the pathological nature of her suspicion. It is easy to see that the white haired elderly manageress is a mother-substitute, that in spite of his youth the lover had been put in the place of the father, and that the strength of the mother-complex has driven the patient to suspect a love-relationship between these ill-matched partners, however unlikely such a relation might be. Moreover, this fresh information resolves the apparent contradiction with the view maintained by psychoanalysis, that the development of a delusion of persecution is conditioned by an overpowerful homosexual bond. The original persecutor—the agency whose influence the patient wishes to escape—is here again not a man but a woman. The manageress knows about the girl's love-affairs, disapproves of them, and shows her disapproval by mysterious allusions. The woman's attachment to her own sex hinders her attempts to adopt a person of the other sex as a love object (1915, p. 155).

To protect herself unconsciously from her own homosexual impulses, the young woman is presumed to have developed a paranoid delusion about the man and her employer. A crucial aspect of the case, according to Freud, was the click that the woman had heard and interpreted as the sound of a camera shutter. Freud assumed that this click was actually a sensation or beat in her clitoris. Her sexual arousal, then, provided the basis for her paranoid delusion of being photographed.

Freud allowed himself a remarkable amount of unverified inference in this particular case. Because he wanted to hold to a homosexuality-based theory of paranoia, he inferred that the woman regarded her female superior as a substitute for her mother, that she had an undue homosexual attachment to her own mother and by generalization to this older woman, and that the click that she had heard and construed in paranoid fashion to be the sound of a camera shutter was really sexual excitement.*

---

*A more general problem with the psychoanalytic theory of paranoia is that many paranoids are *aware* of their homosexual interests. If so, they should have no need unconsciously to form defensive projections.

Social Class and Schizophrenia

Numerous studies have shown a relation between social class and the diagnosis of schizophrenia. The highest rates of schizophrenia are found in central city areas inhabited by the lowest socioeconomic classes (for example, Hollingshead and Redlich, 1958; Srole et al., 1962). The relationship between social class and schizophrenia does not show a continuous progression of higher rates of schizophrenia as the social class becomes lower. Rather, there is a sharp, decided difference between the number of schizophrenics in the lowest social class and those in others. In the ten-year Hollingshead and Redlich study of social class and mental illness in New Haven, Connecticut, the rate of schizophrenia was found to be twice as high in the lowest social class as in the next to the lowest (see Box 14.3). The findings of Hollingshead and Redlich have been confirmed cross-culturally by similar community studies carried out in countries such as Denmark, Norway, and England (Kohn, 1968).[4]

---

[4]There is perhaps one exception to this finding: the relationship may disappear in nonurban areas (Clausen and Kohn, 1959).

BOX 14.2

MAJOR THEORETICAL POSITIONS ON THE ETIOLOGY OF SCHIZOPHRENIA

Psychoanalytic Theory

Because Freud himself dealt primarily with neuroses, he had relatively little to say about schizophrenia. He did occasionally speculate on its origins, though, using some of the psychoanalytic concepts that he applied to all disordered personalities. His basic notion was that schizophrenics have regressed to a state of "primary narcissism," a phase early in the oral stage before the ego has differentiated from the id. There is thus no separate ego to engage in reality testing—a crucial function whereby the ego takes actions that test the nature of its social and physical environment. By regressing to narcissism, schizophrenics have effectively lost contact with the world; they have withdrawn the libido from attachment to any objects external to themselves. Freud thought that the cause of the regression was an increase, during adulthood, in the intensity of id impulses, especially sexual ones. Contemporary psychoanalytic theorists give primacy to aggressive impulses. Whether the threats of the intense id impulses provoke schizophrenia or a neurosis depends on the strength of the ego. Neurotics, having developed a more stable ego, will not regress to the first psychosexual stage, as schizophrenics do, and consequently will not lose contact with reality.

Few data bear on the psychoanalytic position. The theory has generated intriguing and speculative analysis of case history material but little research. Studies showing that schizophrenics have cognitive deficits could be said to demonstrate that the egos of schizophrenics have been impaired. But even so, ego impairment need not be precipitated by an increase in id impulses, nor need it end in a regression to a childhood state. Finally, no one has presented evidence that ego impairments cause schizophrenia.

Labeling Theory

In a radical departure from the traditional conceptualization of schizophrenia, Scheff (1966) has suggested that the disorder is a learned social role. This position, also known as *labeling theory*, is essentially unconcerned with etiology. Rather, Scheff argues that the crucial factor in schizophrenia is the act of assigning a diagnostic label to the individual. Presumably this label then influences the manner in which the person will continue to behave, based on the stereotypic notions of mental illness, and at the same time determines the reactions of other people to the individual's behavior. The social role, therefore, *is* the disorder, and it is determined by the labeling process. Without the diagnosis, Scheff argues, deviant behavior—or to use his term, residual rule breaking—would not become stabilized. It would presumably be both transient and relatively inconsequential.

By residual rules Scheff means the rules that are left over after all the formal and obvious ones, about stealing and violence and fairness, have been laid down. They concern ways of behaving that are so taken for granted that they are rarely if ever stated and come to mind only when they are breached. "Do not stand still staring vacantly in the middle of a busy sidewalk." "Do not talk to the neon beer sign in the delicatessen window." "Do not spit on the piano." The examples are endless. Scheff believes that one-time violations of residual rules are fairly common. Normal people may think that they know when they can safely violate such rules, but through bad luck or poor judgment they are caught in their acts and the diagnoses assigned them take over. Then they are very likely to accept the social role of being mentally ill. Once judged so, they find it very difficult to rejoin the sane, for employment will be denied them and other people will know about their pasts. In the hospital they will receive attention and sympathy and be free of all resonsibilities. So once there they actually perceive themselves as mentally ill and settle into acting crazy as is expected of them.

The correlations between social class and schizophrenia are consistent, but they are still difficult to interpret in causal terms. Some people believe that being in a low social class may in itself cause schizophrenia. This is called the *sociogenic hypothesis*. The degrading treatment a person receives from others, the low level of education, and the unavailability of rewards and opportunity, taken together, may make membership in the lowest social class such a stressful experience that the individual develops schizophrenia.

But another explanation of the correlation between schizophrenia and low social class has also been suggested, the *social-drift theory*. During the course of their developing psychosis, schizophrenics may "drift" into the poverty-ridden areas of the city. The growing cognitive and motivational problems besetting these individ-

Scheff's theory has some intuitive appeal. Most people who have worked for any amount of time at a psychiatric facility have witnessed abuses of the diagnostic process. Patients are sometimes assigned labels that are poorly justified. Many factors other than symptomatology can influence both the diagnostic and hospitalization processes, such as the number of beds available.

Scheff's theory has a number of serious problems, however, indicating that it is, at most, of secondary importance to our understanding of schizophrenia. First of all, Scheff refers to deviance as residual rule breaking, and as described it is indeed merely that. Violating cultural norms governing the nature of interpersonal interaction is, however, very different from the phenomena included in most definitions of schizophrenia and certainly from Schneider's descriptions of delusions and hallucinations. Calling schizophrenia residual rule breaking trivializes a very serious disorder. Second, very little evidence indicates that unlabeled norm violations are indeed transient, as Scheff implies. Third, information regarding the detrimental effects of the social stigma associated with mental illness is inconclusive at best (Gove, 1970). Thus holding that schizophrenia may most usefully be thought of as simply a label arbitrarily assigned to hapless rule breakers is not a satisfactory position.

An Experiential Theory

Ronald Laing, a Scottish existential psychiatrist, has offered a view of schizophrenia that is similar in some respects to labeling theory. For him schizophrenia is not an illness but a label for another kind of problematic experience and behavior.

> . . . The experience and behavior that gets labelled schizophrenic is a special sort of strategy that a person invents in order to live in an unlivable situation . . . the person has come to be placed in an untenable position. He cannot make a move or make no move without being beset by contradictory pressures, both internally, from himself, and externally, from those around him. He is, as it were, in a position of checkmate (1964, p. 186).

Under such stress he will no longer masquerade as the false outer self society expects of him. Rather he retreats from reality backward into his inner world. There he passes through regressive changes, but it is a voyage of discovery on which he may meet and make peace with his true inner self. Then he may emerge again into reality with a whole and authentic identity. Laing considers the family to be the primary culprit producing the behavior that is labeled schizophrenia. In what Laing calls *mystification*, the parent has systematically stripped the child's feelings and perceptions about himself and the world of all validity, so that he has come to doubt his hold on reality.

Rather than trying to remove the patient's symptoms, Laing argues that we should accept his or her experience as valid, understandable, and potentially meaningful and beneficial. The schizophrenic is on a psychedelic trip, necessitated by untenable environmental demands, and is in need of guidance—not control—if the destination of that trip is to be a state of enlightenment.

Laing's ideas are popular among those who object to what they consider to be hypocrisies of society and of the mental health establishment. Those who experience the suffering associated with schizophrenia may also take comfort in the belief that they are going through a positive growth process. At this point, however, there is little evidence that experiencing schizophrenia can make a "better person" of the patient. When released from the hospital, most schizophrenics who had a poor premorbid adjustment live a marginal existence, isolated from social relationships. But, as we shall see, there is some evidence to support Laing's assertion that schizophrenia is caused in part by familial experiences.

In sum, none of the major theoretical positions discussed has much support. Freud's views of regression to the oral stage; labeling theory, which postulates that schizophrenia is role taking reinforced by the attitudes of diagnosticians and mental hospital staff; and Laing's hypothesis that schizophrenia is a trip to improved functioning—all are without substantiating evidence.

uals may so impair their earning abilities that they cannot afford to live elsewhere. Or they may by choice move to areas where little social pressure will be brought to bear on them and where they can escape intense social relationships.

One way of resolving the conflict is to study the social mobility of schizophrenics. Three studies (Schwartz, 1946; Lystad, 1957; Turner and Wagonfeld, 1967) have found that schizophrenics are downwardly mobile in occupational status. But an equal number of studies have shown schizophrenics *not* to be downwardly mobile (Hollingshead and Redlich, 1958; Clausen and Kohn, 1959; Dunham, 1965). Kohn (1968) has suggested another way of examining this question. Are the fathers of schizophrenics also from the lowest social class? If they are, this could be considered evi-

BOX 14.3

THE ADEQUACY OF INDICES OF SCHIZOPHRENIA

Perhaps the most important decision facing a researcher interested in the relationship between social class and schizophrenia is determining how schizophrenia will be indexed. Many studies use hospital admission rates, especially those of state hospitals. But lower-class individuals are more likely to come to a public hospital than to a private one. Furthermore, many studies have shown that some people who suffer serious mental disorders never enter a mental hospital at all.

Researchers have attempted to make their sampling more complete by picking individuals from all treatment facilities in a given area. But the same kind of problem holds. For example, there are social class differences between people who have been treated for mental illness and severely impaired people who have never had any kind of treatment (Srole et al., 1962). Thus using treatment as an index of schizophrenia is suspect.

An alternative approach is to go into the community and examine everyone, or a representative sample of everyone. The problem of relying exclusively on treatment is solved, but other difficulties are raised. Operating in the community makes diagnostic reliability and even the defi-

nition of abnormal behavior a difficult proposition. The raters employed in the community studies have usually received much less training than those who conduct studies in psychiatric facilities. In addition, community studies settle for what is termed *prevalence* rather than *incidence* data. Incidence refers to the number of new cases found in various population groups during a particular period of time and thus is theoretically the most relevant measure in an investigation of this sort. In community studies, however, a simple count of the number of abnormal people is made. This prevalence measure is somewhat inappropriate, for it reflects both incidence and duration of illness. Since there is a correlation between duration of illness and social class (Hollingshead and Redlich, 1958), we cannot determine from prevalence data whether a correlation between social class and schizophrenia reflects incidence or duration of the disorder.

All in all, however, workers have continued to find a relation between social class and schizophrenia, whatever the methodologies employed, indicating that their data can be accepted.

dence in favor of the hypothesis that lower-class status is conducive to schizophrenia, for class would be shown to *precede* schizophrenia. If the fathers are from a higher social class, the drift hypothesis would be the better explanation.

Goldberg and Morrison (1963) conducted such a study in England and Wales. The occupations of male schizophrenic patients were found to be less remunerative and prestigious than those of their fathers. Turner and Wagonfeld (1967) conducted a similar study in the United States and found evidence for both the sociogenic and drift hypothesis. Fathers of schizophrenics were more frequently from the lowest social class, supporting the sociogenic hypothesis. But at the same time many schizophrenics were lower in occupational prestige than their fathers, supporting the drift hypothesis. Thus it appears that both theories are partially correct. Some, but not all, of the relationship between social class and schizophrenia can be accounted for by the drift hypothesis. Social class appears to play a causal role, but the exact way in which the stresses associated with it exert their effect remains unknown.

The Role of the Family

Many theorists have regarded family relationships, especially those between a mother and her son, as crucial in the development of schizophrenia. The view has been so prevalent that the term "*schizophrenogenic mother*" has been coined for the supposedly cold and dominant, conflict-inducing parent who is said to produce schizophrenia in her offspring (Fromm-Reichmann, 1948). These mothers have also been characterized as rejecting, overprotective, self-sacrificing, impervious to the feelings of others, rigid and moralistic about sex, and fearful of intimacy.[5]

Another prominent theory is the *double bind* proposed by Bateson and his colleagues (1956). These writers believe that an important factor in the development of schizophrenic thought disorder is the constant subjection of an individual to a so-called double-bind situation. A double bind has the following aspects.

[5]It is noteworthy that most theories implicating family processes in the etiology of abnormal behavior focus almost exclusively on the mother. Sexism?

1. The individual has an intense relationship to another, so intense that it is especially important to be able to understand communications from the other person accurately so that the individual can respond appropriately.

2. The other person expresses two messages when making a statement, one of which denies the other.

3. The individual cannot comment on the mutually contradictory messages and cannot withdraw from the situation or ignore the messages.

The parent rarely communicates with the child in a simple and direct way. What a mother says to her son may be contradicted by how she says it, by what she does, or by emotion conveyed in other ways. And the child cannot complain that he does not understand, nor can he ask for clarification. It becomes impossible for him to order his thinking; his responses may eventually become even more confused than the communications he receives. In their original paper Bateson and his colleagues gave the following example.

A young man who had fairly well recovered from an acute schizophrenic episode was visited in the hospital by his mother. He was glad to see her and impulsively put his arm around her shoulders whereupon she stiffened. He withdrew his arm and she asked, "Don't you love me anymore?" He then blushed and she said, "Dear, you must not be so easily embarrassed and afraid of your feelings." The patient was able to stay with her only a few minutes more and following her departure he assaulted an aide. . . .

Obviously, this result could have been avoided if the young man had been able to say, "Mother, it is obvious that you become uncomfortable when I put my arm around you, and you have difficulty accepting a gesture of affection from me." However, the schizophrenic patient doesn't have this possibility open to him. An intense dependency in training prevents him from commenting upon his mother's communicative behavior, though she comments on his and forces him to accept and to attempt to deal with the complicated sequence. . . .

The impossible dilemma thus becomes: "If I am to keep my tie to my mother, I must not show her that I love her, but if I do not show her that I love her then I will lose her" (pp. 258–259).

Controlled studies evaluating these two theories have not yielded supporting data. Studies of families of schizophrenics have, however, revealed that they differ in

some ways from normal families. In an early review of this literature, Fontana (1966) drew two conclusions.

1. There is more conflict between the parents of schizophrenics than between the parents of control patients.

2. Communication between the parents of schizophrenics is less adequate than that between control parents.

But whether these family processes should be viewed as playing a causal role in the development of schizophrenia is questionable. It is equally plausible that the conflict and unclear communication are a response to having a young schizophrenic in the family. Indeed, some evidence favors this interpretation. For example, Liem (1974) had a number of families with a schizophrenic son and control families with a normal son participate in an object identification task. The "communicator" was given the task of describing common objects, such as lamp or match, and concepts, such as teacher or child, so that a listener could identify them. During a session five "communications" about each of three objects or concepts were tape-recorded. Each schizophrenic son and each normal son had a turn in the role of communicator. Each set of parents took the role together as a communicating pair. Later parents and sons responded to different tapes, giving an answer after each description. The parents responded to tapes made by their own son, by an unknown nonschizophrenic son, and by an unknown schizophrenic son. The sons responded to tapes made by their own parents, unknown parents of a normal son, and unknown parents of a schizophrenic son.

How does this study relate to the possible role of the family in the etiology of schiozphrenia? If unclear communication by the parents of a schizophrenic is assigned a *causal* role, we might expect their descriptions to be indeed inadequate and confusing to anyone who listens to them. In contrast, if the parents of a schizophrenic are *reacting* to their child's disorder, we would not expect their descriptions to be inadequate, but we would expect *all* parents to have difficulty interpreting the tape-recorded communications of a schizophrenic son. This second pattern is the one borne out by Liem's study.

On several measures of adequacy of communication, there were no important differences between the parents of normal and schizophrenic sons. The schizophrenic sons were inferior to normal sons, however, as would be expected from the fact that communication problems are part of the diagnostic concept of schizophrenia. All parents were confused by the descriptions formulated by schizophrenic sons, making more misidentifications when they listened to their own schizophrenic son's tape or that of an unknown schizophrenic son. In the author's own words,

The communication disorder of schizophrenic sons had an immediate, observable, negative effect not only on the parents of schizophrenic sons but on all parents who heard and attempted to respond to them. Disorder was not observed in the communications of parents of schizophrenic sons nor were their communications found to adversely affect sons who heard and responded to them (p. 445).

Studies like Liem's, however, may not accurately reflect actual everyday interactions between a schizophrenic and his or her parents. Therefore we cannot conclude that the faulty communications of parents play no role in the etiology of schizophrenia. Indeed, some recent findings suggest that they do. One of these studies is the Unversity of California at Los Angeles Family Project (Goldstein and Rodnick, 1975). In this project adolescents with behavior problems were studied intensively along with their families. A five-year follow-up revealed that a number of the young people had developed schizophrenia or schizophrenia-related disorders. The investigators were then able to relate these disorders discovered at follow-up to any deviance in the communications of parents that had been evident five years earlier. Communication deviances of parents were indeed found to be a powerful predictor of the later onset of schizophrenia in their offspring, supporting the significance of faulty family interactions in the etiology of the disorder (Norton, 1982).

A series of studies conducted in London indicate that the family can also have an important impact on the adjustment of patients *after* they leave the hospital. Brown and his colleagues (1966) conducted a nine-month follow-up study of a sample of schizophrenics who returned to live with their families after being discharged from the hospital. Interviews were conducted with the parents or spouses before discharge and rated for the number of critical comments made about the patient and for expressions of hostility toward or emotional overinvolvement with him or her. On the basis of this variable, called *expressed emotion* (EE), families were divided into those revealing a great deal, high-EE families, and those revealing little, low-EE families. At the end of the follow-up period, 10 percent of the patients returning to low-EE homes had relapsed. In marked contrast, 58 percent of the patients returning to a high-EE home had gone back to the hospital in the

same period! This research, which has since been replicated (Vaughn and Leff, 1976; Leff, 1976), indicates that the environment to which patients are discharged has great bearing on whether or not they are rehospitalized.

The Genetic Data

Suppose that you wish to select an individual who will one day be diagnosed as a schizophrenic and that no behavior patterns or other symptoms can be considered. This problem, suggested by Paul Meehl (1962), has one solution with at least an even chance of picking a potential schizophrenic. *Find an individual who has a schizophrenic identical twin.* There now exists a convincing body of literature indicating that a predisposition for schizophrenia is transmitted genetically. The major methods employed in this research, as in other behavior genetics research projects, are the family and twin studies. The findings obtained from them will be discussed first and thereafter studies of adopted children.

Family Studies

Table 14.1 presents a summary, compiled by Zerbin-Rüdin (1972), of the risk for schizophrenia in various relatives of schizophrenic index cases. In evaluating the figures of this table, bear in mind that the risk for schizophrenia in the general population is a little less than one percent. Quite clearly, relatives of schizophrenics are at increased risk, and the risk increases as the genetic relationship between index case and relative becomes

TABLE 14.1 Morbidity Risk for Schizophrenia Compiled from the Most Important Investigations of Various Authors   *(from Zerbin-Rüdin, 1972)*

Relationship to a Schizophrenic	Morbidity Risk, percent
Parents	
Children	9–16
Siblings	8–14
Children of two affected parents	40–68
Half-siblings	1– 7
Stepsiblings	1– 8
Grandchildren	2– 8
Cousins	2– 6
Nieces and nephews	1– 4
Uncles and aunts	2– 7
Grandparents	1– 2

closer. Therefore the data gathered by the family method support the notion that a predisposition for schizophrenia can be transmitted genetically. And yet relatives of a schizophrenic proband share not only genes but also common experiences. A schizophrenic parent's behavior could be very disturbing to a developing child. The influence of the environment cannot be discounted as a rival explanation for the higher morbidity risks.

Twin Studies

A summary of the available twin studies appears in Table 14.2. The concordance rates reported in the several studies of identical twins range with great variability from 6 to 86 percent. The rates of concordance for the fraternal twins range from 2 to 34 percent. Concordance for the identical twins is generally greater than that for the fraternal, but it is always less than 100 percent. This is important, for if genetic transmission were the whole story of schizophrenia and one twin was schizophrenic, the other twin would be guaranteed a similar fate because MZ twins are genetically identical.

Gottesman and Shields (1972) studied all twins treated at the Maudsley and Bethlem hospitals in London, England, between the years 1948 and 1964. One of the problems of any twin study of schizophrenia is how to judge concordance. Recognizing the potential problems and biases involved in making psychiatric diagno-

David Rosenthal, a psychologist who has made a major contribution to understanding the genetics of schizophrenia and of other mental disorders.

ses, often of people who were not hospitalized, Gottesman and Shields devised a three-grade system of concordance. All probands were, of course, hospitalized schizophrenics. The co-twins with the first grade of concordance were also hospitalized and diagnosed schizophrenic. Co-twins with the second grade of concordance were hospitalized but not diagnosed as schizophrenic; those with the third grade were abnormal but not hospitalized. Concordance rates for the MZ and DZ twins in the sample, figured cumulatively for the three grades,

TABLE 14.2 Concordance Rates in the Major Twin Studies of Schizophrenia *(after Rosenthal, 1970)*

Study	Country	Monozygotic Twins		Dizygotic Twins	
		Number of Pairs	Concordance, percent	Number of Pairs	Concordance, percent
Luxenburger, 1928, 1934	Germany	17–27	33–76.5*	48	2.1
Rosanoff et al., 1934–1935	United States and Canada	41	61.0	101	10.0
Essen-Möller, 1941	Sweden	7–11	14–71	24	8.3–17
Kallmann, 1946	New York	174	69–86.2	517	10–14.5
Slater, 1953	England	37	65–74.7	115	11.3–14.4
Inouye, 1961	Japan	55	36–60	17	6–12
Tienari, 1963, 1968	Finland	16	6–36	21	4–10
Gottesman and Shields, 1972	England	24	42	33	9
Kringlen, 1967	Norway	55	25–38	172	4–10
Fischer, 1973	Denmark	16	24–58	34	10–34
Hoffer and Pollin, 1970	United States	80	13.8	145	4.1

*The ranges in the concordance figures reflect different definitions of what would constitute a concordant pair.

TABLE 14.3 Concordance in MZ and DZ Twins as Defined in Three Ways *(from Gottesman and Shields, 1972)*

Definition of Concordance	Concordance, percent	
	MZ	DZ
1. Hospitalized and diagnosed schizophrenic	42	9
2. Hospitalized but not schizophrenic, plus those with first-grade concordance	54	18
3. Not hospitalized but abnormal, plus those with first-grade and second-grade concordance	79	45

are shown in Table 14.3. As the definition of concordance is broadened, its rate increases in both MZ and DZ pairs, but concordance of the MZs is always significantly higher than that of the DZs.

Gottesman and Shields have also examined the relationship between severity of schizophrenia in the proband and the rate of concordance. Severity was defined in terms of the total length of hospitalization and the outcome, that is, whether the patient recovered enough to leave the hospital and then engage in gainful employment. When one of a MZ pair was judged severely ill, concordance rates went up dramatically. For example, pairs of MZ twins were divided into two groups; in one group the probands had had less than two years of hospitalization, in the other more than two years of hospitalization. The concordance rate for the first group was 27 percent, for the second 77 percent.

Questions have been raised about the interpretation of data collected on twins. Some have argued that the experience of being an identical twin may itself predispose toward schizophrenia. If schizophrenia is considered an "identity problem," it might be argued that being a member of an identical pair of twins could be particularly stressful. But schizophrenia occurs about as frequently in single births as in twin births. If the hypothesis were correct, simply being twins would have to increase the likelihood of becoming schizophrenic—which it does not (Rosenthal, 1970).

But the most critical problem of interpretation remains. Since the twins have been reared together, a common deviant environment rather than common genetic factors could account for the concordance rates. A few

pairs of identical twins, at least one of whom developed schizophrenia, have been reared apart from very early childhood, enabling the relative contributions of heredity and environment to be separately determined. Of the sixteen cases in the literature, ten were concordant and six discordant (Rosenthal, 1970). The concordance rate of this limited sample was therefore 62.5 percent, a finding that certainly supports the view that a predisposition for schizophrenia is genetically transmitted. Because of the small sample size and the unsystematic way in which the sample was collected, however, the data cannot be regarded as conclusive.

A clever analysis, supporting a genetic interpretation of the high concordance rates found for identical twins, was performed by Fischer (1971). She reasoned that if these rates indeed reflected a genetic effect, the children of even the discordant, or nonschizophrenic, identical co-twins of schizophrenics should be at high risk for schizophrenia. These nonschizophrenic twins would presumably have the genotype for schizophrenia, even though it was not expressed behaviorally, and thus might pass along an increased risk for the disorder to their children. In agreement with this line of reasoning, the rate of schizophrenia and schizophreniclike psychoses in the children of nonschizophrenic co-twins of schizophrenic probands was 9.4 percent. The rate among the children of the schizophrenic probands themselves was only slightly and nonsignificantly higher, 12.3 percent. Both rates are substantially higher than those found in an unselected population.

Adoptee Studies

A study of children of schizophrenic mothers reared from early infancy by adoptive parents has provided more conclusive information on the role of genes in schizophrenia. This study too eliminated the possible effects of a deviant environment. Heston (1966) was able to follow up forty-seven people who had been born to schizophrenic mothers while they were in a state mental hospital. The infants were taken away from the mothers shortly after birth and given either to relatives or to foundling homes, which placed them in foster homes or arranged for their adoptions. Fifty control subjects were selected from among those placed through the same foundling homes that the children of schizophrenic mothers had been sent to. The follow-up assessment consisted of an interview, MMPI, IQ test, social class ratings, and the like. A dossier on each of these subjects was then rated independently by two psychiatrists, and a third evaluation was made by Heston. Ratings were made on a 0 to 100 scale of overall disability and, when-

TABLE 14.4 Subjects Separated from Their Schizophrenic Mothers in Early Infancy *(from Heston, 1966)*

Assessment	Offspring of Schizophrenic Mother	Control Offspring, Mothers Not Schizophrenic
Number of subjects	47	50
Mean age at follow-up	35.8	36.3
Overall ratings of disability (low score indicates more pathology)	65.2	80.1
Number diagnosed schizophrenic	5	0
Number diagnosed mentally defective	4	0
Number diagnosed sociopathic	9	2
Number diagnosed neurotic	13	7

ever possible, psychiatric diagnoses were offered. Ratings of disability proved to be quite reliable, and when the number of diagnostic categories was reduced to four—schizophrenia, mental deficiency, sociopathy, and neurosis—diagnostic agreement was also acceptable.

The control subjects were rated as less disabled than were the children of schizophrenic mothers. Similarly, thirty-one of the forty-seven children of schizophrenic mothers (66 percent) were given a psychiatric diagnosis, but only nine out of fifty control subjects (18 percent) were. None of the control subjects was diagnosed schizophrenic, but 16.6 percent of the offspring of schizophrenic mothers were so diagnosed.[6] In addition to this greater likelihood of being diagnosed schizophrenic, the children of schizophrenic mothers were more likely to be diagnosed mentally defective, sociopathic, and neurotic (Table 14.4). They had been involved more frequently in criminal activity, had spent more time in penal institutions, and had more often been discharged from the armed services for psychiatric reasons. Heston's study clearly supports the importance of genetic factors in the development of schizophrenia. Children reared without contact with their so-called "pathogenic mothers" were still more likely to become schizophrenic than were the controls.

Seymour Kety, a prominent figure in research into both the genetics and the biochemistry of schizophrenia.

[6]The 16.6 percent figure was *age-corrected*. By this process raw data are corrected to take into account the age of the subjects involved. If a subject in Heston's sample was only twenty-four at the time of the assessment, he might still have become schizophrenic at some later point in his life. The age correction procedure attempts to account for this possibility.

A study similar in intent to Heston's has been carried out in Denmark under Kety's direction (Kety et al., 1968, 1976). In Denmark a lifelong and up-to-date listing of the address of every resident is kept, and a National Psychiatric Register maintains records on every psychiatric hospitalization in the country. The starting point for the investigation was a culling of the records of all children who had been adopted at an early age between the years 1924 and 1947. All adoptees who had later been admitted to a psychiatric facility and diagnosed schizophrenic were selected as the index cases. From the remaining cases the investigators chose a control group who had no psychiatric history and who were matched to the index group on variables such as sex and age. Both the adoptive and the biological parents and the siblings and half-siblings of the two groups were then identified, and a search was made to determine who of them had a psychiatric history. As might be expected if genetic factors figure in schizophrenia, the biological relatives of the index cases were diagnosed schizophrenic more often than were members of the general population. The adoptive relatives were not.

Evaluation

All the data collected so far indicate that genetic factors play an important role in the development of schizophrenia. Earlier twin and family studies deserved the criticism of environmentalists, who found that investigators had not acknowledged upbringing as a possible contributing factor. But later studies of children of schizophrenic mothers and fathers, who were reared in foster and adoptive homes, plus the follow-up of relatives of adopted schizophrenics, indicate the importance of genetic transmission, for the potential biasing influence of the environment had been virtually removed. As Seymour Kety, the highly regarded schizophrenia researcher, has quipped, "If schizophrenia is a myth, it is a myth with a heavy genetic component" (1974).

We cannot conclude, however, that schizophrenia is a disorder completely determined by genetic transmission. The less than 100 percent concordance rate of identical twins would argue against this, and we must always keep in mind the distinction made between phenotype and genotype (see page 124). The diathesis-stress model, introduced in Chapter 2, seems appropriate for guiding theory and research into the etiology of schizophrenia. Genetic factors can only be predisposers for a disorder. Stress is required to render this predisposition an observable pathology. And yet the exact sources of stress are rather vague at this point. Low social class and certain patterns of family interaction are two areas we have already discussed. There is also some evidence that, in the weeks preceding hospitalization, schizophrenics experience an increased number of stressful life events (Brown and Birley, 1968). But, on the whole, additional research is needed on how particular environmental stressors trigger schizophrenia in an already predisposed person.

Biochemical Factors

Speculation concerning possible biochemical[7] causes of schizophrenia began almost as soon as the syndrome was identified. Kraepelin thought in terms of a chemical imbalance, as already indicated, for he believed that poisons secreted from the sex glands affected the brain to produce the symptoms. Carl Jung suggested the presence of "toxin X," which he thought would eventually be identified. The demonstrated role of genetic factors in schizophrenia also suggests that biochemicals should be investigated, for it is through the body chemistry and physiological processes that heredity may have an effect.

The extensive and continuing search for possible biochemical causes has a principal difficulty to overcome. If an aberrant biochemical is found in schizophrenics and not in control subjects, the difference in biochemical functioning may have been produced by a third variable rather than by the disorder. Most schizophrenic patients, for example, take tranquilizing medication. Although the effects of such drugs on behavior diminish quite rapidly once they are discontinued, traces of them may remain in the bloodstream for very long periods of time, making it difficult to attribute a biochemical difference between schizophrenic and control subjects to schizophrenia per se. Institutionalized patients may also smoke more, drink more coffee and have a less nutritionally adequate diet than various control groups. They may also be relatively inactive. All these variables can conspire to produce biochemical differences in schizophrenic and control patients that confound attempts to seek deviant biochemicals in the schizophrenics. Nonetheless, the search for biochemical causes of schizophrenia proceeds at a rapid rate. Tremendous advances now allow a much greater understanding of the relation between biochemistry and behavior. At present no biochemical theory has unequivocal support. But because of the great amount of effort that continues to be spent in the search for biochemical causes of schizophrenia, we shall review one for the best-researched factors.

Excess Dopamine Activity

The theory that schizophrenia is brought on by excess activity of the neurotransmitter dopamine is based prin-

[7]This section is necessarily technical, and for readers who have not studied biochemistry, it may be unusually difficult to follow. We want to provide the details, however, for those who have this background. For those who lack it, we hope at least to convey the logic and general trends in the research on biochemical factors.

cipally on information concerning the mode of action of drugs that are effective in treating schizophrenia. If the biochemical activity of a therapeutically effective drug is understood, or at least hypothesized, the process responsible for the disorder may be guessed at too.[8] The *phenothiazines* (see page 555), in addition to alleviating some symptoms of schizophrenia, produce side effects resembling Parkinson's disease. Parkinsonism is known to be caused, in part, by low levels of dopamine in a particular nerve tract of the brain (see page 606). It is therefore supposed that phenothiazines interfere with dopamine activity. Phenothiazine molecules are assumed, because of the structural similarities to the dopamine molecule (Figure 14.1), to fit into and thereby block postsynaptic receptors in dopamine tracts. From this speculation about the action of the drugs that help schizophrenics, it is but a short inductive leap to view schizophrenia as resulting from excess activity in dopamine nerve tracts.

Further indirect support for the theory of *excess dopamine activity* comes from the literature on amphetamine psychosis. Amphetamines can produce a state that closely resembles paranoid schizophrenia, and they can exacerbate the symptomatology of a schizophrenic (Angrist, Lee, and Gershon, 1974). The amphetamines are thought to act either by directly releasing catecholamines into the synaptic cleft or by preventing their inactivation (Snyder et al., 1974). We can be relatively confident that the psychosis-inducing effects of amphetamines comes from their impact on dopamine, rather than norepinephrine, for phenothiazines are antidotes to amphetamine psychosis.

Researchers are seeking biochemical causes of schizophrenia with ever-increasing technological sophistication.

FIGURE 14.1 Conformations of (a) chlorpromazine, a phenothiazine, and (b) dopamine and (c) their superimposition, determined by X-ray crystallographic analysis. Chlorpromazine blocks impulse transmission by dopamine by fitting into its receptor sites. Adapted from Horn and Snyder, 1971.

[8]Although the therapeutic effects of a drug may provide a *clue* to the causes of the disorder it helps to alleviate, we must be mindful once again that treatment effects cannot logically prove the case for etiology or even for the current causes of the problem in question.

Work has been done on monoamine oxidase, for a deficiency of this enzyme, which can inactivate dopamine within the presynaptic neuron, might explain excess dopamine activity. Murphy and Wyatt (1972) studied blood platelet MAO in thirty-three chronic schizophrenics and twenty-two normal controls matched for age and sex. The blood platelets of schizophrenics were much lower in MAO than those of the controls; a subsequent investigation with drug-free patients confirmed this result. But acute schizophrenics, those who had suddenly been beset with florid and obvious symptoms, were not found to differ from controls in platelet MAO levels (Carpenter, Murphy, and Wyatt, 1975). Moreover, Friedman and his colleagues (1974) studied platelet MAO of schizophrenics, depressives, and normal controls and found no significant differences. Postmortem studies of levels of MAO in the brains of eight schizophrenics and nine controls by Schwartz and his colleagues (1974) found no differences, nor did similar work done by Domino, Krause, and Bowers (1973).

The major metabolite of dopamine, homovanillic acid, has also been examined, with the expectation that it would be present in greater amounts in schizophrenics. Homovanillic acid can be measured in cerebrospinal fluid by treating patients with probenecid, a drug which prevents the transfer of homovanillic acid from cerebrospinal fluid to blood. But Bowers (1974) found that before drug treatment schizophrenics had lower levels of homovanillic acid than patients with affective illness, and that levels of homovanillic acid in schizophrenics increased when they were reassessed during treatment. Post and his colleagues (1975) found no differences in levels of homovanillic acid in schizophrenics and several control groups.

Meltzer, Sachar, and Frantz (1974) have also indirectly evaluated the excess-dopamine-activity hypothesis, by examining levels of the hormone prolactin. The dopaminergic system controls to some extent the release of prolactin inhibiting factor and thus prolactin levels in blood serum. If schizophrenics have excessive dopamine transmission, more inhibiting factor should be released and blood serum should contain less prolactin. Serum prolactin of thirty newly admitted drug-free patients was compared to that of a sample of normal controls, and no differences were found.

The theory of excess dopamine transmission is not strongly refuted by the evidence collected in the studies of MAO, homovanillic acid, and prolactin. Dopaminergic overactivity has not, perhaps, been specified precisely enough. The predictions of depleted MAO and increased levels of homovanillic acid assume that the dopamine-releasing neurons are overactive. But it may be that in schizophrenia dopamine *receptors* are overactive or oversensitive. In fact, the work on the phenothiazines' mode of action would suggest that the dopaminergic receptors are a more likely locus of disorder. Indeed, some postmortem studies of schizophrenics' brains have revealed that dopamine receptors may have either increased in number or been hyperactive (Lee and Seeman, 1977; Mackay et al., 1982). If increased activity of the dopaminergic receptors is the key to schizophrenia, the data concerning levels of MAO and homovanillic acid are not crucially relevant. As for serum prolactin, its levels are affected by a host of variables, including stress, and thus it is hazardous to conclude that they provide an accurate reflection of the activity of dopaminergic neurons.

Recent research on the excess-dopamine-activity theory has revealed that it may not be applicable to all schizophrenics. Some studies have now shown, for example, that amphetamines do not worsen the symptoms of all patients (for example, Kornetsky, 1976), and one study has even reported that symptoms lessen after an amphetamine has been administered (Kammen et al., 1977). Furthermore, phenothiazines have been shown to benefit only a subgroup of patients. In both instances the divergent results are related to the positive–negative-symptoms distinction noted earlier (see page 343). Amphetamines worsen positive symptoms and lessen negative ones. Phenothiazines lessen positive symptoms but have little or no effect on negative symptoms (Haracz, 1982). The dopamine theory appears in fact to be one applying only to schizophrenics with positive symptoms.

Even in this more limited context, the hypothesis cannot be regarded as having been proved, for it has difficulty handling some other effects. For example, phenothiazines gradually lessen positive schizophrenic symptoms over a period of several weeks. But the drugs rapidly block dopamine receptors, and after several weeks tolerance should have developed (Davis, 1978). This disjunction between the clinical and pharmacological effects of phenothiazines is difficult to understand within the context of theory. It is also puzzling that phenothiazines have to reduce dopamine levels or receptor activity to *below normal*, producing Parkinsonian side effects, if they are to be therapeutically effective. According to the theory, reducing dopamine levels or receptor activity to normal should be sufficient for a therapeutic effect. But apparently it is not. Thus, although the dopamine explanation remains the most actively researched biochemical position, it is not likely to be a complete theory of the biochemistry of schizophrenia.

Evaluation

The history of research on whether biochemicals figure in schizophrenia has been one of discovery followed by failures to replicate. Many methodological problems plague this research, and many confounds, unrelated to whether or not a subject is schizophrenic, can produce biochemical differences. Thus we must maintain a cautious attitude toward the excess-dopamine-activity theory. Furthermore, studies on biochemicals can indicate only that a particular substance and its physiological processes are associated with schizophrenia. Dopamine activity might become excessive *after* rather than *before* the onset of the disorder.

Neurological Findings

The search for a brain lesion that causes schizophrenia, like that for a biochemical, began as early as the syndrome was identified. But the research did not prove promising, for studies when replicated did not yield the same findings. Interest gradually waned over the years. In the last two decades, however, spurred by a number of methodological advances, the field has reawakened and yielded some promising evidence (Seidman, 1983; Weinberger, Wagner, and Wyatt, 1983). A percentage of schizophrenics—the exact number cannot be specified—have been found to have observable brain pathology.

Postmortem analysis of the brains of schizophrenic patients are one source of this evidence. These studies consistently reveal abnormalities in schizophrenics' brains, although the specific problems reported vary from study to study (Weinberger, Wagner, and Wyatt, 1983). Even more impressive are the images obtained in CAT scan studies. Researchers were quick to apply this new tool to the living brains of schizophrenics. Thus far these images of living brain tissue, with a resolution of less than one millimeter, have most consistently revealed that a proportion of schizophrenics have enlarged ventricles, suggestive of limbic or diencephalic pathology (see Box A.1 page 601). Large ventricles are in turn correlated with impaired performance on neuropsychological tests, poor premorbid adjustment, poor response to drug treatment, and the presence of negative symptoms

CAT scan images of the brain in horizontal section. The ventricles show up as dark areas toward the center. The ventricles of the brain of the schizophrenic (left) are clearly enlarged as compared to those of a normal brain (right).

(Weinberger et al., 1980; Andreasen et al., 1982). CAT scan images have also revealed evidence of cortical and cerebellar atrophies, although these lesions are not as frequent as enlarged ventricles.[9]

Seidman (1983) has collected neuropathological evidence disclosed by several other means. Schizophrenics have considerably more than the usual number of abnormalities in their EEGs, principally a diminution in the alpha rhythm; reduced metabolism in the frontal brain areas; and deficits on neuropsychological tests that are thought to reflect brain pathology. All the evidence suggests that these malfunctionings are likely to appear only in patients with chronic, negative symptoms. Thus investigators may be on the verge of isolating a subgroup of schizophrenic patients who have signs of brain pathology and suffer negative symptoms.

High-Risk Studies of Schizophrenia

How does schizophrenia develop? An earlier method of answering this question was to construct developmental histories by examining the childhood records of those who had later become schizophrenics. This research did indeed show that those who were to become schizophrenics were different from their contemporaries even before any serious problems were noted in their behavior. Albee and Lane and their colleagues repeatedly found preschizophrenics to have a lower IQ than members of various control groups, which usually consisted of siblings and neighborhood peers (Albee, Lane, and Reuter, 1964; Lane and Albee, 1965). Investigations of the social behavior of preschizophrenics yielded some interesting findings; for example, teachers have described male schizophrenics as being disagreeable in childhood, female schizophrenics as being passive (Watt et al., 1970; Watt, 1974). Both have been described as delinquent and withdrawn (Berry, 1967).

But these findings are gross and nonspecific; certainly the traits mentioned would also be found in children and adolescents who are not destined to become schizophrenic. The major limitation of this type of developmental research is that the data on which it relies were not originally collected with the intention of describing preschizophrenics or of predicting the development of schizophrenia from childhood behavior. More specific information is required if developmental histories are to be a source of new hypotheses.

[9]Enlarged ventricles and cortical and cerebellar atrophies are also found in the CAT scans of other psychotic patients and are not specific to schizophrenia (Rieder et al., 1983).

Perhaps the most desirable way of collecting information about the development of schizophrenia would be to select a large sample of individuals and follow them for the twenty to forty-five years that are the period of risk for the onset of schizophrenia. But such a method would be prohibitively expensive, for only about one individual in a hundred eventually becomes schizophrenic. The yield of data from such a simple longitudinal study would be small indeed. The *high-risk method* overcomes this problem; only individuals whose risk of becoming a schizophrenic in adulthood is greater than the average are selected for study. In most of the current research projects using this methodology, individuals who have a schizophrenic parent are selected as subjects for, as we saw earlier, having a schizophrenic parent increases a person's risk for developing schizophrenia.

This method has three other major advantages.

1. Variables that have direct relevance to the development of schizophrenia can be chosen for study.

2. The data are collected before the individual becomes schizophrenic. Therefore, unlike studies of hospitalized adult schizophrenics, these investigations will not be confounded by variables such as drugs, diet, and inactivity.

3. Finding variables that predict the occurrence of schizophrenia in adulthood may allow early intervention and the prevention of this serious disturbance.

In the early 1960s one of the first and most extensive high-risk studies was begun in Denmark by Sarnoff Mednick and Fini Schulsinger. Denmark was chosen because the registries of all people make it possible to keep track of them for long periods of time. Mednick and Schulsinger selected as their high-risk subjects 207 young people whose mothers were chronic schizophrenics and had had poor premorbid adjustment. It was decided that the mother should be the parent suffering the disorder because paternity is not always easy to determine and because schizophrenic women have more children than do schizophrenic men. Then 104 low-risk subjects, individuals whose mothers were not schizophrenics, were matched to the high-risk subjects on variables such as sex, age, father's occupation, rural-urban residence, years of education, and institutional upbringing versus rearing by the family. A summary of the design and expected results may be seen in Figure 14.2.

In the wake of Mednick and Schulsinger's pioneering efforts, a number of other high-risk studies were begun. These studies, however, have not yet reached the point at which the data collected on high-risk children can be linked to adult outcomes. Thus we will describe only the Mednick and Schulsinger findings. Even here we need to be mindful that the results, based on a small number of subjects, are tentative.

In 1972 the now-grown men and women of the high-risk sample and of the low-risk group were followed-up through a number of measures, including a diagnostic battery. Seventeen of the high-risk subjects, nine men and eight women, were diagnosed schizophrenic. None of the control men and women was so diagnosed. The follow-up also revealed that six high-risk subjects had committed suicide, as compared to none of the low-risk subjects. Looking back to the information collected on the subjects when they were children, the investigators found that several circumstances predicted the later onset of schizophrenia. For boys, separation from parents early in life and being brought up in an institution predicted later schizophrenia (Walker et al., 1982). Their separation from their parents was itself related to an early onset of schizophrenia in their mothers and to lower-class status. The heightened responsiveness of a boy's autonomic nervous system also predicted later schizophrenia. And the mothers of the boys with greater autonomic responsiveness had had more pregnancy and birth complications while carrying and delivering them. For girls, the only circumstance predicting schizophrenia was an early onset of the disorder in their mothers,

Sarnoff Mednick, of the University of Southern California, and Fini Schulsinger, of the University of Copenhagen, pioneers in applying the high-risk longitudinal method of studying schizophrenia.

which was in turn related to lower-class status (Mednick, Schulsinger, and Griffith, 1981).

These early returns, granted that they come from a small study, seem to suggest that the etiology of schizophrenia may differ for men and women. Even more important than the specific findings to date is the fact that the high-risk method is in a general sense yielding interesting findings. As subjects in other high-risk projects

FIGURE 14.2 Design and expected results of Mednick and Schulsinger's study (1968) of young people with a high risk of developing schizophrenia.

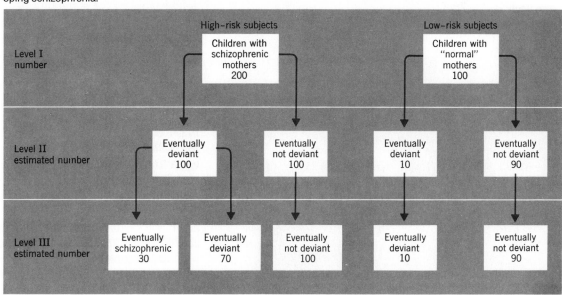

mature, we may indeed learn much about the development of schizophrenia.

THERAPIES FOR SCHIZOPHRENIA

The puzzling, often frightening array of phenomena that plague schizophrenics makes one wonder how they can possibly be helped. The history of psychopathology, reviewed in Chapter 1, is in many respects a history of humankind's efforts, often brutal and unenlightened, to deal with schizophrenia. Although some of the insane people condemned centuries ago as witches or confined in foul asylums may have suffered from problems as prosaic as food poisoning or syphilis (see pages 14 and 18), there seems little doubt that many, were they to be examined now, would carry a diagnosis of schizophrenia. Box 14.4 contains a general discussion of the mental hospital; until the advent of deinstitutionalization, somatic and psychological therapies for schizophrenia were for the most part administered within a hospital.

Somatic Treatments

The general warehousing of severely disturbed patients in mental hospitals earlier in this century, coupled with the shortage of professional staff, created a climate that

With the advent of neuroleptic medication, the drug table has become a major feature of mental hospitals.

allowed, perhaps even subtly encouraged, experimentation with radical somatic interventions. In the early 1930s the induction of a coma via large dosages of insulin was introduced by Sakel (1938), who claimed that up to three-quarters of the schizophrenics he treated showed significant improvement. But later findings by others were less encouraging, and *insulin coma therapy*, which presented serious risks to health, including irreversible coma and even death, was gradually abandoned.

In 1935 Moniz, a Portuguese psychiatrist, introduced the *prefrontal lobotomy*, a surgical procedure which destroys the tracts connecting the frontal lobes to lower centers of the patient's brain. His initial reports, like those of Sakel for insulin coma therapy, claimed high rates of success (Moniz, 1936), and for twenty years thereafter hundreds of mental patients underwent variations of psychosurgery, especially if their behavior was violent. Many of them did indeed quiet down and could even be discharged from hospitals. But during the 1950s this intervention too fell into disrepute, for several reasons. Many patients suffered serious losses in their cognitive capacities—which is not surprising, given the destruction of parts of their brain believed responsible for thought—became dull and listless, or even died. The principal reason for its abandonment, however, was the introduction of drugs that seemed to reduce the behavioral and emotional excesses of many patients.

Electroconvulsive therapy (ECT) has been in use since its development in 1938 by Cerletti and Bini. Electrodes are placed on both temples, more recently on only one temple, and a current of between 70 and 130 volts is applied for a fraction of a second. A seizure is thereby induced, followed by a period of unconsciousness. In the treatment of schizophrenia, ECT has, like psychosurgery, proved to be basically ineffective and has given way to the several psychotropic medications, although it remains an apparently effective treatment for profoundly depressed patients (see page 561).

Without question the most important development in the treatment of the schizophrenia disorders was the advent in the 1950s of several drugs collectively referred to as antipsychotic medications. They are also called *neuroleptics* because, in addition to their beneficial effects, they have side effects similar to the behavioral manifestations of neurological diseases. The phenothiazines, especially *chlorpromazine* (Thorazine), not only control the emotional and behavioral excesses of most mental hospital patients but also, in a manner still inadequately understood, improve the disordered thinking of many schizophrenics, often to the point that they can be released from confinement. And these beneficial consequences are over and above the ubiquitous placebo effect (Klein and Davis, 1969). Drugs are recognized to be more effective if the surroundings in which they are administered are supportive rather than impersonal or demeaning, pointing up once again the complex interplay between physiological and psychological variables (Simpson and May, 1982). Problems and unanswered questions still abound in the use of these antipsychotic drugs; additional details about them and the other somatic treatments just discussed are provided in Chapter 20.

Psychological Treatments

Efforts to treat schizophrenia have by no means all been somatic. Freud himself worked little, either in his clinical practice or through his writings, on adapting psychoanalysis to the treatment of schizophrenics; he believed them to be incapable of establishing the close interpersonal relationship that is essential for analysis. It was Harry Stack Sullivan, the American psychiatrist, who pioneered in doing psychotherapy with hospital patients. Sullivan established a ward at the Sheppard and Enoch Pratt Hospital in Towson, Maryland, in 1923 and developed a psychoanalytic treatment reported to be markedly successful. He held that schizophrenia reflected a return to early childhood forms of communication. The fragile ego of the schizophrenic, unable to handle the extreme stress of interpersonal challenges, had regressed. Therapy therefore requires the patient to learn adult forms of communication and achieve insight into the role that the past has played in current problems.[10] Sullivan advised the very gradual, nonthreatening development of a trusting relationship. For example, he recommended that the therapist sit somewhat to the side of the patient in order not to force eye contact, which is deemed too frightening in the early stages of treatment. After many sessions, and with the establishment of greater trust and support, the analyst begins to encourage the patient to examine his or her interpersonal relationships.

A similar ego-analytic approach was proposed by Frieda Fromm-Reichmann (1889–1957), a German psychiatrist who emigrated to the United States and worked for a period of time with Sullivan at Chestnut Lodge, a private mental hospital in Rockville, Maryland. Fromm-Reichmann was sensitive to the symbolic and uncon-scious meaning of behavior, attributing the aloofness of schizophrenics to a wish to avoid the rebuffs suffered in childhood and thereafter judged inevitable. She treated them with great patience and optimism, making it clear that they need not take her into their world or give up their "sickness" until they were completely ready to do so. Along with Sullivan, Fromm-Reichmann (1952) helped establish psychoanalysis as a major treatment for schizophrenia.

Paradoxes are inherent to psychoanalytic thought. Whereas Sullivan and Fromm-Reichmann trod gingerly and gently into the defensive structure of their patients, John Rosen (1946) in his *direct analysis* drives a Mack truck. He agrees with his analytic colleagues that therapy must establish communication and foster insight, but he parts company with them about the fragility of the schizophrenic's ego. Rosen believes it strong enough to handle direct, often brutal confrontation, although always in a supportive relationship.[11] The following excerpt describes part of a therapy session with a young male catatonic schizophrenic.

For the first hour, his productions were repetitious and revealed that he was actively hallucinating. He made reference to numerous sexual adventures. He spoke as follows: "This is a wonderful airplane. It's over the Atlantic Ocean. I can see her down there. My mother. She's floating. Here I go. A dive bomb. I have her centered. Here I go. Here I go."

Following this symbolic incestuous experience, the patient screamed in terror and appeared to plead for mercy with his father. "Don't cut off my balls. Please don't cut them off. Please, papa, please." Since the plea was directed toward "papa," the physician said he was "papa," that he had seen what happened and that everything would be all right. The patient received permission to have these thoughts about his mother and was promised that there would be no punishment (1946, p. 193).

Rosen becomes the omnipotent, nurturant protector of his patients. In some instances he actually feeds and caresses them to lend reality to their regression and enable them to reexperience problems from early childhood that are assumed to underlie their psychosis. Patients spend virtually all their waking hours in the company of the therapist and his assistants, being ha-

---

[10]Sullivan's work is discussed more generally in Chapter 18.

[11]Those who have worked with Rosen attest to his unusual ability to establish a supportive relationship with many patients so that they are not frightened or otherwise disturbed by his unorthodox techniques.

BOX 14.4

THE MENTAL HOSPITAL

Each year about two and a half million Americans are hospitalized for mental disorders. It has been estimated that one in ten people in this country will enter a mental hospital at least once (Atthowe, 1976). Treatment in public mental institutions is primarily custodial in nature, the existence of patients monotonous and sedentary for the most part. After Pinel's revolutionary work in La Bicêtre (see page 15), the hospitals established in Europe and in this country were for a time relatively small and privately supported. Patients had close contact with attendants, who talked and read to them and encouraged them to purposeful activity. Residents were to lead as normal lives as possible and in general take responsibility for themselves within the constraints of their disorders. This moral treatment, which is estimated to have achieved enviable discharge rates, had to be abandoned in the second half of the nineteenth century, however. The staffs of the large, public mental hospitals being built to take in the many patients for whom the private ones had no room could not provide such individual attention (Bockhoven, 1963). Moreover, these hospitals came to be administered by physicians, who were more interested in the physiological aspects of illness and in the physical well-being of mental patients. The money that had paid the personal attendants went into equipment and laboratories.

Mental hospitals in this country today are usually funded either by the federal government or by the various states. In fact, the term "state hospital" is taken to mean a *mental* hospital run by the state. They are often old, grim, and somewhat removed from major metropolitan centers. Their costs to society in economic terms are utterly staggering. Some Veterans Administration hospitals and general medical hospitals also contain psychiatric wards.

In addition, there are private mental hospitals. Sheppard and Enoch Pratt near Baltimore, Maryland, and McLean Hospital, in Belmont, Massachusetts, are two of the most famous. The physical facilities of private hospitals tend to be superior to those of state hospitals for one simple reason: the private hospitals have more money. The daily costs to patients in these private institutions can exceed $400 per day and may still not include individual therapy sessions with a member of the professional staff! Although some patients may have medical insurance, usually with a ninety-day limit, such hospitals are clearly beyond the means of most citizens.

A somewhat specialized mental hospital is reserved for people who have been arrested and judged unable to stand trial and for those who have been acquitted of a crime by reason of insanity (see page 565). They have not been sent to prison, but armed guards and tight security regiment their lives. Treatment of some kind is supposed to take place during their internment.

Many fine books and articles have been written about mental hospitals (Stanton and Schwartz, 1954; Goffman, 1961; Rosenhan, 1973; Moos, 1974). They agree with our own clinical experiences that, even in the best of hospitals, patients usually have precious little contact with psychiatrists or clinical psychologists. Most of a patient's days and evenings are spent either alone or in the company of other patients and of aides, individuals who often have little more than an elementary school education. As with imprisonment, the overwhelming feeling is of helplessness and depersonalization. Patients sit endless hours in hallways waiting for dining halls to open, for medication to be given out, and for consultations with psychologists, social workers, and vocational counselors to begin.

Except for the most severely disturbed, patients have access to the various facilities of a hospital, ranging from woodworking shops to swimming pools, from gymnasia to proverbial basketweaving shops. Most hospitals require patients to attend group therapy—here a general term indicating only that at least two patients are supposed to relate to each other and to a group leader in a room for a specific period of time. And for some patients there are the few sessions alone with a professional therapist.

One nagging problem is that institutionalization is difficult to reverse once people have resided in mental hospitals for more than a year. The mental hospital has certainly not proved its worth by preparing patients for their return to the community. We recall asking a patient who had improved markedly over the previous several months why he was reluctant to be discharged. "Doc," he said earnestly, "It's a jungle out there." Although we cannot entirely disagree with his view, there nonetheless appear to be at least a few advantages to living on the outside. But this man—a veteran and chronic patient with a clinical folder more than two feet thick—had become so accustomed to the restrictions and care of various Veterans Administration hospitals that the prospect of leaving was as frightening to him as the prospect of entering a mental hospital is to those who have never lived in one. Recent deinstitutionalization sweeps have greatly reduced the number of patients in mental hospitals, but the problems of the chronic patient have yet to be handled adequately.

One treatment now widely applied is *milieu therapy*, in which the entire hospital becomes a "therapeutic community" (for example, Jones, 1953). All its ongoing activities and all its personnel become part of the treatment program. Milieu therapy appears to be a return to the moral practices of the nineteenth century. Social interaction and group activities are encouraged so that through group pressure the patients are directed toward normal functioning. Patients are treated as responsible human beings rather than custodial cases (Paul, 1969). They are expected to participate in their own readjustment, as well as that of their fellow patients. Open wards allow them considerable freedom. Evidence of the efficacy of milieu therapy, however, is scant (Greenblatt et al., 1965; Fairweather, 1964). Indeed, the intensive involvement of hospital staff, a sine qua non of milieu therapy, may be harmful to some schizophrenics. They are believed to need, at least part of the time, a cessation of social stimulation and their own quiet solitude (Simpson and May, 1982; Spadoni and Smith, 1969).

In a milestone project at a unit in a new Illinois state mental health center, Paul and Lentz (1977) demonstrated encouraging improvement in twenty-eight chronic "hardcore" patients through *social-learning therapy*. A token economy, which reached into many details of the patients' lives, was combined with other behavior therapy interventions tailored to the particular needs of each resident. A host of measures were taken on the behavior of both staff and patients over four and a half years of treatment, with a later eighteen-month follow-up on patients who had since been discharged. The social-learning program was markedly more successful than both milieu therapy, carried out for a matched group at another unit of the mental health center, and routine hospital management of a second matched group in an older Illinois state hospital. Since mental hospitals will be needed for the foreseeable future, especially by people who demonstrate time and again that they have difficulty functioning on the outside, Paul's work is of special importance. It suggests specific ways the chronic patient can be helped to cope better not only within the hospital but during periods of discharge as well.

The dramatic contrast between private and state mental hospitals. (Top) A living room of the Sheppard and Enoch Pratt Hospital. (Bottom) The crowded quarters of a state institution.

rangued through threats and coaxed through promises to interpret and relinquish their psychotic behavior. Rosen is, understandably, a controversial figure, and his claims for a 100 percent cure rate do little to reduce the controversy.

Existential and humanistic therapies have made little if any impact on schizophrenic disorders. As writers in this tradition have themselves suggested (for example, Corey, 1977), to make responsible choices and thus become truly human, to face the existential realization that the individual is ultimately alone in the world are high-level demands and very probably beyond the capacities of the people described in this chapter. A schizophrenic's response to the expounding of existential-humanistic goals might well be "They should be my worst problems." When people must struggle even to reason logically, to avoid violating social norms, and to attend to the world as most people see it, rather than to their own of frightening demons and persecutors, they do not have the luxury of contemplating ultimate aloneness and the awesome responsibility of making choices, of creating existence anew every day. But empathic listening and efforts to reassure patients that they will not be hurt are certainly beneficial. Clinical lore, for example, tells us not to challenge the paranoid's delusions, lest we become part of them. The person who believes that the C.I.A. is broadcasting messages into his or her mind and keeping tabs on daily thoughts and activities needs an empathic ear.

The overall evaluation of insight-oriented psychotherapy with schizophrenics, although truly in its infancy, thus far justifies little enthusiasm for applying it with these severely disturbed people (Feinsilver and Gunderson, 1972). Earlier, great claims of success were made for the analyses done by Sullivan and Fromm-Reichmann, but a close consideration of the patients they saw indicates that many tended to be only mildly disturbed and might not even have been diagnosed schizophrenic by the strict DSM-III criteria for the disorder. What little research has been done on Rosen's direct analysis is methodologically flawed; in any event, it does not find value in this approach. A widely cited study by Carl Rogers and his associates (1967) examining client-centered therapy with schizophrenics indicated that empathic listening by an exceptionally genuine therapist can help establish a good therapeutic relationship, but no inroads on the actual clinical problems of schizophrenics were made (May, 1974). This failure to ease their condition is consistent with research indicating that client-centered therapy is most successful with people who can involve themselves deeply in ther-

apy from the outset. Expecting such involvement from schizophrenics is unrealistic (Shilling, 1984). Finally, a study by May (1968; May et al., 1976) failed to show that psychoanalysis added anything to a phenothiazine regimen. Although experienced clinicians often believe that they themselves, or other highly gifted therapists, can make a positive impact on certain schizophrenics, and this may indeed happen when some therapists work with some patients, evidence obtained through controlled scientific research does not indicate that insight into themselves and the past is of much help to schizophrenics.

Family therapy was conceived in the 1950s in response to theories of schizophrenia that proposed abnormal family relationships as causes. Whether or not they are, it is possible, once the problem exists, that the schizophrenic patient's symptoms may be relieved by correcting relationships within the home. If a parent sends conflicting messages to a schizophrenic son, the parent could be helped to clarify his or her statements, and the son could be taught that people do not always say to others what they really mean. The literature contains reports of improvement brought about by family therapy, but fundamental changes are rarely achieved. The research on family therapy suffers from methodological problems that preclude drawing firm conclusions (Massie and Beels, 1972). A more promising family therapy project, described in Chapter 20 (page 539), was designed to reduce stress in patients returning home after hospitalization.

In recent years behavior therapy has been developed for schizophrenia, particularly operant conditioning techniques. As discussed in greater detail in Chapter 19, hundreds of hospitalized patients, most of them carrying a diagnosis of schizophrenia, have lived in a token economy instituted to eliminate specific behavior, such as hoarding towels; to teach more socially appropriate responses, such as combing hair and arriving on time at dining halls; and to encourage activity, such as doing chores on the ward (Ayllon and Azrin, 1968). The study by Paul and Lentz (1977) demonstrated the potential of a carefully designed and meticulously implemented therapy program based on social-learning principles. Seriously ill schizophrenics were released to shelter care and three even to independent living.[12] At the present time it

[12]The criterion of being discharged from a mental hospital is more complicated than may appear on the surface. A treatment may help a person leave a hospital, yet that person may still be able to live only a marginal existence. Keith and his colleagues (1976) concluded that only half of schizophrenics who are released from mental hospitals are able to assume full occupational and social responsibilities.

is generally acknowledged among mental health professionals that therapy programs with a learning framework are the most effective psychological procedures for helping schizophrenics function better. But behavior therapy is seldom claimed to make such thoroughgoing changes that we can speak of curing people with this group of mental illnesses. These interventions do, however, reverse somewhat the effects of institutionalization, fostering social skills such as assertiveness in people whom attendants have reinforced for passiveness and compliance.

The justified enthusiasm for drugs that reduce hallucinations and delusions and even improve clarity of thought should not blind us to the always-existing need of patients to learn or relearn ways of interacting with their world, of dealing with the troubling emotional challenges all people face as they negotiate life. Schizophrenia is almost assuredly an illness that certain people are predisposed to develop when under stress. A wonder drug that alleviates symptoms still leaves untouched the basic tendency of the individual to react abnormally on later occasions. Perhaps schizophrenics can be taught effective coping skills so that, in the future, they will be able to keep their emotional reactions under better control. Well before all the answers are in on this puzzling and serious group of mental disorders, logic dictates that comprehensive treatment of schizophrenia be both somatic and psychological.

SUMMARY

The pioneering efforts of Kraepelin and Bleuler led to two views of schizophrenia. Kraepelin's work fostered a descriptive approach and a narrow definition, whereas Bleuler's theoretical emphasis led to a very broad diagnostic category. Bleuler had a great influence on the American conception of schizophrenia. His influence, together with the American interest in treatment and the addition of several poorly defined types of schizophrenia, served to make the American concept excessively inclusive. By mid-twentieth century the differences in the way schizophrenia was diagnosed in America and Europe were vast. With the advent of DSM-III, the American concept of schizophrenia has become narrower and more similar to a European view. The basic symptoms are disturbances in thought—incoherence, loose associations, lack of insight, and delusions; in perception and attention—derealization, distractibility, and hallucinations; in motor behavior—grimacing, gesturing, and

flailing of limbs or catatonia and waxy flexibility; and in affect—flat or inappropriate. Schizophrenics also have little social competence and considerable difficulty holding jobs. A review of the schizophrenic types proposed by Kraepelin and in DSM-III indicates the great variability in the behavior of schizophrenic patients. Schizophrenics have recently been typed by their positive symptoms—their excesses such as hallucinations, delusions, and outlandish behavior; and by their negative symptoms—their flattened emotions, poverty of speech, apathy, anhedonia, and inattentiveness.

Research has tried to determine the etiological role of specific variables such as social class, the family, genetic and biochemical factors, and brain pathology. The diagnosis of schizophrenia is more frequently applied to members of the lowest social class. Available information indicates this is so in part because the stresses of lower-class existence are great and in part because the disorder keeps schizophrenics from achieving higher social status. Vague communications and conflicts are evident in the family life of schizophrenics and probably contribute to their disorder.

The data on genetic transmission are impressive. The adoptee studies, which are relatively free from most criticisms that can be leveled at family or twin studies, show a strong relation between having a schizophrenic parent and the likelihood of developing the disorder. Perhaps the genetic predisposition has biochemical correlates, although research in this area permits only tentative conclusions. At this time the excess-dopamine-activity theory appears the most promising in helping to explain the schizophrenia of those with positive symptoms. The brains of schizophrenics with negative symptoms, however, have enlarged ventricles, cortical and cerebellar atrophies, a diminished alpha rhythm, and a reduced metabolism in the frontal areas.

Much of the information we have reviewed is consistent with a diathesis-stress view of schizophrenia. Investigators have turned to the high-risk method, studying children who are particularly vulnerable to schizophrenia by virtue of having a schizophrenic parent. Mednick and Schulsinger have found that circumstances predicting maladjustment in adulthood differ for boys and girls. Having mothers who suffered an early onset of schizophrenia and were poor predicted the development of schizophrenia in girls. As for boys, these circumstances plus their mothers' difficulties in carrying and delivering them, their labile autonomic nervous systems, and being brought up in an institution from early childhood predicted who would become schizophrenic.

There are both somatic and psychological therapies for schizophrenia. Insulin and electroshock treatments and even surgery were in vogue earlier in the century, but none is employed to any extent nowadays, primarily because antipsychotic drugs, in particular the phenothiazines, are now available. In numerous studies these medications have been found to have a major and beneficial impact on the disordered lives of schizophrenic patients. They have also been very much a factor in the deinstitutionalization of hospital patients. But drugs alone are unlikely to be the answer, for schizophrenics need to be taught or retaught ways of dealing with the challenges of everyday life, and perhaps as well to resolve the intrapsychic problems believed by some therapists to underlie their symptoms. Ego-analytic theory assumes that schizophrenia represents a retreat from the pain of childhood rejection and mistreatment; the relationship gradually and patiently established by the analyst offers the patient a safe haven in which to explore repressed traumas. Direct analysis agrees that childhood conflicts lie at the core of schizophrenia but regards the patient's ego as not too fragile for an assaultive analysis of defenses. Good evidence for the efficacy of these treatments is not plentiful, although case studies of dramatic cures are many in both the professional and popular literature. More recently behavioral treatments have helped patients discharged from mental hospitals to meet the inevitable stresses of family and community living, and, when discharge is not possible, to lead more ordered and constructive lives within an institution.

PART FIVE

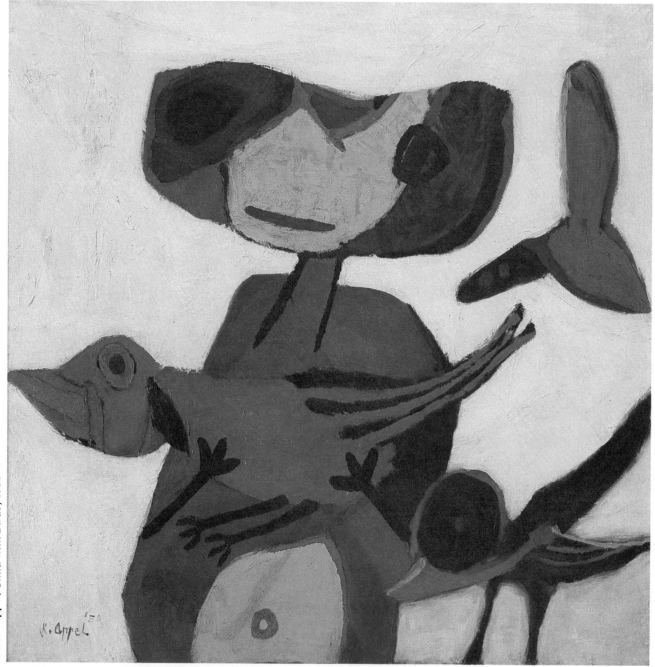

Karel Appel, *Child with Birds*, 1950

**DEVELOPMENTAL
DISORDERS**

Pablo Picasso, *First Steps*, 1943 Yale University Art Gallery, Bequest of Stephen Carlton Clark, B.A., 1903

SPECIFIC DISORDERS OF
CHILDHOOD AND ADOLESCENCE

Classification
Learning Disabilities
Disorders of Undercontrolled Behavior
Disorders of Overcontrolled Behavior
Eating Disorders

"Nothing is more precious than a young child" (O'Leary and Wilson, 1975, p. 39). And few events in an adult's life are more emotionally draining than being close to a child who is hurt, physically or psychologically. Until now in this book the psychological problems discussed have been those that beset a significant proportion of the adult population. As upsetting as it may be to have a friend or relative who suffers from depression, or from unpredictable bouts of anxiety, or from the myriad of thought and emotional disruptions of schizophrenia, it is much more disturbing to see these problems in a child. Children are judged to have few emotional resources with which to cope with problems. The extreme dependency of troubled children on their parents and guardians adds to the sense of responsibility that these people feel, and to their guilt, whether it be justified or not.

Most psychodynamic, behavioral, and even biological theories find childhood experience and development to be critically important to adult mental health. In addition, most theories regard children as more malleable than adults and thus more amenable to treatment. We would therefore expect the disorders of children to have been the focus of voluminous research into etiology, prevention, and treatment. Until recently, however, they have been given considerably less attention than adult problems.

Disorders associated with the course of adult development and aging have received even less attention than those of childhood. The disorders of these two periods, childhood and aging, can be treated together as a new research endeavor, the study of the problems of life-span development. In this chapter we discuss childhood and adolescent disorders that are relatively specific and focused, that is, disorders affecting a fairly narrow band of behavior, such as the inability of an otherwise normal child to master basic arithmetic skills. Chapter 16 covers more pervasive and serious disorders in development, namely mental retardation and infantile autism. In Chapter 17 the problems linked with aging are reviewed.

CLASSIFICATION

The classification of childhood disorders has changed radically over the last thirty years. Consistent with the scant research efforts then being expended on the problems of childhood, DSM-I and DSM-II treated them primarily as downward extensions of adult disorders. Children were often given diagnoses that had originally been created for adults. The major adult categories of psychoses, neuroses, and personality disorders of DSM-II, for example, were all applied to children as well. The only unique section for disorders of children was Behavior Disorders of Childhood and Adolescence. The ineffectiveness of this system is indicated by the fact that most children seen by mental health professionals received a diagnosis of adjustment reaction, a very broad one indeed, or no diagnosis at all (Achenbach, 1982).

Recognizing a need for change in the classification system, the Group for Advancement of Psychiatry (GAP), an organization of psychiatrists devoted to a careful scrutiny of their field, proposed a very different diagnostic scheme for children (GAP, 1966). Although the work was still linked to psychodynamic theory, the GAP committee began creating a developmentally oriented diagnostic system tailored specifically to childhood disorders. These efforts were incorporated and extended in DSM-III. Whereas DSM-II contained one section with seven specific diagnoses to be applied uniquely to children, DSM-III contains a section with forty specific diagnoses gathered in nine general groups. The expansion of childhood diagnoses in the three DSMs is traced in Table 15.1, which summarizes the schemes employed by each version.[1]

Although the validity of the broader and more detailed system employed by DSM-III has not yet been established, its reliability can be addressed at this time. Initial studies with childhood diagnoses of DSM-III indicate that overall reliability is moderate. For some specific categories—for example, attention deficit disorder with hyperactivity, separation anxiety, anorexia nervosa, enuresis—reliabilities are excellent. But for others, such as socialized conduct disorder, they are not (Werry et al., 1983). Indeed, the fact that reliability studies are being done at all is a positive sign for the new system, for no reliability studies were ever conducted on the section for childhood disorders of either DSM-I or DSM-II (Cantwell et al., 1979).

Factor analysis has also had a major influence on the classification of childhood disorders. Ratings of the behavior of disordered children are collected and analyzed, allowing clusters of symptoms that are related to one another to be separated out. These symptom clusters are called factors. A review of the major factor-analytic studies of disordered children found consistent evidence for at least two broad clusters of childhood symptoms. Children with symptoms from one cluster are called either undercontrolled or externalizers and are said to

[1]DSM-III still applies adult diagnoses to children if their symptoms meet the criteria. Affective disorders are one example.

TABLE 15.1 Diagnoses Applied Exclusively to Children in Three Versions of the DSM

Listings	DSM-I	DSM-II	DSM-III
Overall			
Major category	None	One	Nine
N of subcategories	Six	Ten	Forty
Psychoses			
Major category	None	None	Pervasive Developmental Disorders
N of subcategories	One	One	Three
Example	Schizophrenic reaction, childhood type	Schizophrenic reaction, childhood type	Infantile autism
Developmental Deviations			
Major category	None	None	Specific Developmental Disorders
N of subcategories	None	None	Six
Example	—	—	Developmental reading disorder
Problems of Undercontrol			
Major category	None	Behavior Disorders of Childhood and Adolescence	Attention Deficit Disorder
N of subcategories	One	Five	Three
Example	Adjustment reaction, conduct disturbance	Hyperkinetic reaction	Hyperactivity
			Conduct Disorders
			Five
			Undersocialized aggressive
Problems of Overcontrol			
Major category	None	Behavior Disorders of Childhood and Adolescence	Anxiety Disorders
N of subcategories	Two	Two	Three
Example	Adjustment reaction, neurotic traits	Withdrawing reaction	Separation anxiety
			Other Disorders
			Five
			Elective mutism
Other			
Major category	None	None	Eating Disorders
N of subcategories	Three	Three	Five
Example	Adjustment reaction of infancy	Adjustment reaction of infancy	Bulimia
			Stereotyped Movement Disorders
			Five
			Tourette's disorder
			Other Disorders with Physical Manifestations
			Five
			Stuttering

show behavior excesses. Children who have symptoms from the other cluster are said to be overcontrolled, to be internalizers, or to have behavior deficits[2] (Achenbach and Edelbrock, 1978). Although the names picked for the two broad clusters depend on theoretical orientation—we have chosen *undercontrolled* and *overcontrolled*—the key to the distinction between them lies in whether the child's ways of reacting, such as disobedience, creates more of a problem for others or, such as anxiety, affects the self primarily.

In this survey of childhood and adolescent disorders, we draw from both DSM-III listings and the undercontrolled-overcontrolled dimension for chapter organization. Learning disabilities will be reviewed first. This category, which DSM-III calls specific developmental disorders, covers extreme deviations from the average in a specific area of intellectual development, such as learning arithmetic and reading. Following this section are one each on undercontrolled and overcontrolled behavior and a final one on the eating disorders of anorexia nervosa and bulimia.

Before proceeding, it is important to note that childhood disorders differ from adult disorders in a very central way. Whereas most adults identify *themselves* as having a problem, most children are so identified *by others*. The difference between "I have a problem" and "You have a problem" is great. When people refer themselves for treatment, we can be reasonably sure that they have problems for which they desire help. When a child is referred for treatment, on the other hand, all we really know is that someone perceives this child as disordered. Why does the person see this child as needing treatment? Child mental health workers must continually ask themselves questions that are not readily answered. Is this boy really unmanageable or does he just remind his mother of her divorced husband? Is this girl really distractible or is she merely bored by school? The evidence indicates that although the child's actual behavior plays a major role in how adults perceive him or her, many other factors also enter into the perception (Ross, 1981).

LEARNING DISABILITIES

A group of problems found among children, and usually extending throughout their lives, are called the *specific developmental disorders*. They are coded on axis II, sep-

arate from the major clinical syndromes, because, says DSM-III, these developmental problems often occur along with other disorders and should not be overlooked. Better known as *learning disabilities*, these diagnoses are applied to children who differ from age-appropriate norms in a specific area of intellectual development, such as the acquisition of language. The children have significant impairment in acquiring the particular skill, not accounted for by chronological age, mental age, or inadequate schooling. In addition, they handle tasks requiring the skill in a way significantly below their intellectual capacity. The three specific developmental disorders having to do with language are twice as frequent in boys as in girls. If the problem is considered to be an integral part of another disorder, such as the language deficiencies of an autistic child, or if it is but one instance in a more general delay in development, as in mental retardation, no specific developmental disorder is diagnosed.

DSM-III lists four developmental disorders.

Developmental reading disorder   Children with *developmental reading disorder*, better known as *dyslexia*, have difficulty distinguishing between the letters b and d, o and c, M and W. Or they may confuse the subject and object of a sentence, reading "John sees Mary" as "Mary sees John." The reading of these children is slow and their comprehension less than it should be. When reading orally, they omit, add, and distort words. Having this disorder does not preclude great achievements. It is widely known that Nelson Rockefeller, former governor of New York and former vice-president of the United States, suffered from dyslexia.

Developmental arithmetic disorder   Less is known about *developmental arithmetic disorder*, perhaps because difficulties in arithmetic do not impart as much of a stigma in our society as do problems in reading and speaking (Wicks-Nelson and Israel, 1984). This disorder is also apparently not common.

Developmental language disorder   *Developmental language disorder* can be both receptive, wherein the child has trouble understanding spoken language, or expressive, wherein the child has difficulty expressing himself or herself in speech. A child with the receptive form may seem to be deaf, so deficient is he or she in comprehending what is being said. A youngster with the expressive form of the disorder may seem eager to communicate verbally but have inordinate difficulty finding the right words. Even at age four, the child speaks only in short phrases. Old words are forgotten when new ones are

---

[2]Narrower clusters have been found, but they can be covered by the broader terms of undercontrolled and overcontrolled.

learned, and the use of grammatical structures is considerably below age level.

Developmental articulation disorder Unlike the children who have trouble understanding and finding words, youngsters with *developmental articulation disorder* both comprehend a substantial vocabulary and express themselves in it, but their words sound like baby talk. ''Blue'' comes out ''bu,'' and ''rabbit'' ''wabbit.'' They have not learned articulation of the later-acquired speech sounds, such as r, sh, th, f, z, l, and ch.

Etiology of Learning Disabilities

Both physiological and psychological factors are possible causes of the several learning disabilities. Answers are far from in. Earlier the disabilities were linked to ''minimal brain damage.'' Nowadays there are vague hypotheses about defects in areas of the brain known to serve particular intellectual functions. People with language difficulties are believed to have damage in the left frontal lobes. Diet and environmental insults, such as lead poisoning, have also been implicated, as have genetic factors. Siblings and identical twins often have the same difficulties with reading (Benton, 1978).

Psychological theories explaining learning disabilities cluster around two major positions, *perceptual-deficit theory* and *academic-instruction theory* (Wong, 1979). Perceptual-deficit theory asserts that learning disabilities are caused by a dysfunction in one or more levels of perceptual processing. According to this theory, children fail to learn because they make errors in perceiving sensory stimuli. For example, one popular early hypothesis suggested that children with dyslexia *perceive* printed letters in reverse order or mirror image, mistaking one letter for another, for example, a *d* for a *b*. The learning-disabled child was believed actually to see the alphabet and words differently from other children. In fact, in the writing of these children letters are frequently reversed and words written backward. Although there has been a general failure to pinpoint perceptual deficits in many learning-disabled children (Wong, 1979), some researchers still continue the search (Cruickshank, 1977).

Academic-instruction theory proposes that a learning disability reflects a problem of teaching rather than a problem of learning (Englemann, 1969). The child is not incapable of learning; rather the teacher has failed to instruct properly.[3] As might be expected, those who

blame academic instruction are concerned more with identifying new methods of teaching than with describing learning-disabled children. Although it is doubtful that failures to teach properly explain many instances of presumed learning disability, the assumption that at least some of these children have not been properly taught certain skills has led to encouraging treatments.

Intervention with Learning Disabilities

Professional attempts to remedy learning disabilities have been subject to somatic, educational, and psychological fads—from the use of stimulants and tranquilizers; to training the child in motor activities believed to have been inadequately mastered at a younger age, in hopes of reorganizing neuronal connections in the brain; to psychoanalytic psychotherapy. The anxiety of parents whose otherwise normal child lags behind in reading or cannot speak effectively and normally for his or her age is not to be underestimated. At stake as well is the investment of local and federal moneys in remedial programs to bring such youngsters up to the achievement level of their age-mates, so that they can have a reasonable chance to participate in the rewards of our literate and technological society.

These learning-disabled children are systematically rewarded for signs of improvement in their academic skills.

---

[3]Explaining learning disabilities as a failure in academic instruction is a contradiction, for DSM-III specifies that a learning problem cannot be caused by inadequate schooling.

Even though many experts believe that at least some learning-disabled children suffer from subtle brain defects which interfere with their comprehension and handling of intellectual material, treatment is usually behavioral, teaching specific skills. For example, if a dyslexic child cannot distinguish between a U and a V, he is rewarded for saying "U" when he is shown this letter, but not if what he sees is a V. This is called discrimination training and is better viewed as educational than therapeutic.

One of the very earliest examples is a case study reported by Staats and Butterfield (1965). The client was a fourteen-year-old boy from a large Mexican-American family who was reading at only the second-grade level. His academic and occupational prospects were grim, and he had already been in trouble with the police. Staats and Butterfield broke down the task of learning to read into several small steps. The young man's first task was to master a number of words written on file cards. All the words were from a story that his therapists hoped to have him read as the next step. Using tokens that the boy could "cash in" later for things he wanted, they systematically reinforced him for correctly pronouncing each new word. Whenever the boy failed, the trainer said the word correctly and then returned to it somewhat later. When all the new words for the story had been learned, reinforcement was made contingent on reading entire paragraphs of the story correctly. The tokens given at this stage were worth more than those the young man had obtained earlier for reading single words. Ultimately the boy had to read stories silently and answer comprehension questions correctly in order to earn tokens. After forty hours of such individualized instruction over a period of four and a half months, the boy had advanced more than two grade levels in reading ability. Many programs modeled after Staats and Butterfield's pioneering work show promise in alleviating some of the problems of learning-disabled children (for example, Schwartz, 1977).

DISORDERS
OF UNDERCONTROLLED BEHAVIOR

The undercontrolled child lacks or has insufficient control over behavior that is expected in a given setting and is appropriate to the child's age. Because of such failings, the undercontrolled child is frequently an annoyance to both adults and peers. Two general categories of *undercontrolled behavior* are frequently differentiated, attention deficit disorder with hyperactivity and conduct problems.

Problems of undercontrol are defined by the type and form of the behavior, its *topography*. The high frequency of much "problem" behavior in the general population of children, such as fidgeting in class, makes it questionable, however, whether isolated incidents should be considered abnormal. Other behavior, such as assaulting a teacher, is by topography alone considered abnormal by most people.

Attention Deficit Disorder with Hyperactivity

Everybody probably knows at least one child considered to be hyperactive, and this child is most likely to be a school-age boy. These youngsters often behave impulsively or act before thinking, a pattern that may lead both to social friction and to academic failure. They have difficulty focusing on a single activity and often shift erratically from one task to another without finishing those projects they begin. Many of these children tend not to maintain the behaviors expected of them for more than a few minutes—whether this involves sustained attention to a task or game, patient waiting for a desired event, or modulation of spontaneous verbal and motor behaviors. They seem to have remarkably high energy levels, approaching activities with striking and sometimes formidable intensity.

A hyperactive child's mother might report that he has difficulty remembering not to trail his dirty hand along the clean wall as he runs from the front door to the kitchen. His peers may find that he spontaneously changes the rules while playing Monopoly or soccer. His teacher notes that he asks what he is supposed to do immediately after detailed instructions were presented to the entire class. He may make warbling noises or other strange sounds that inadvertently disturb anyone nearby. He may seem to have more than his share of accidents—knocking over the tower his classmates are erecting, spilling his cranberry juice on the linen tablecloth, or tripping over the television cord while retrieving the family cat—and thereby disconnecting the set in the middle of the Superbowl game.

A hyperactive child is all too frequently "in trouble"—with his peers, his teachers, his family, his community. His social faux pas do not seem to stem from negativism or maliciousness. In fact, he is often quite surprised when his behaviors elicit anger and rejection from others. Nor does he seem to have any basic deficits or disabilities—either in intellectual or in interpersonal spheres. He seems *almost* normal in every way, but yet he has inordinate and pervasive difficulties getting along in the everyday world. This is the puzzle of hyperactivity—a puzzle that continues to perplex and intrigue child health and education specialists. (Whalen, 1983, pp. 151–152).

As the foregoing description suggests, the term "hyperactive" is familiar to most people, especially to parents and teachers. Other diagnoses that have in the past been used to describe youngsters who are inattentive and impulsive include minimal brain damage, which clearly suggested that subtle brain dysfunction caused the behavioral problems, and hyperkinesis, which is from the Greek words *hyper* meaning over and *kinesis* meaning motion. DSM-III has replaced these terms with *attention deficit disorder*, either *with* or without *hyperactivity*. The focus now is on an inability to concentrate on the task at hand for an appropriate period of time. Hyperactivity is added to the diagnosis (ADD-H) when inattentive children seem to have particular difficulty controlling their activity in situations that call for sitting still, such as at school or at mealtimes. When required to be quiet, they appear unable to stop moving or talking. They are often described as being "on the go," as "running like a motor." They are also disorganized, erratic, and tactless, obstinate and bossy. All their activities and movements seem haphazard. They quickly wear out their shoes and clothing, smash their toys, and soon exhaust their family and teachers.

As Whalen (1983) cautions, it is important not to apply the ADD-H diagnosis to youngsters who are rambunctious, "overactive," or a bit distractible, for in the early school years children are often so. Those who worry that DSM-III diagnoses may stigmatize children unnecessarily (for example, Garmezy, 1977) remind us that words like "rambunctious" may really mean no more than that the child is more lively and more difficult to control than a parent or teacher would like. ADD-H is best reserved for truly extreme and persistent cases. Nor is the diagnosis to be applied to children who are judged to have severe or profound mental retardation or serious neurological impairment, for they in themselves can cause some of the behavior and symptoms associated with ADD-H.

Not surprisingly, the inattention and impulsiveness of ADD-H children are often associatd with academic difficulties. In fact, some workers believe that learning disabilities and ADD-H are so closely related that they are sometimes indistinguishable one from the other. To be sure, more than three-quarters of a sample of ADD-H children were found to have serious learning problems, and more than one-third of learning-disabled children to be hyperactive (Safer and Allen, 1976). But these same statistics also indicate that the overlap is not complete; some ADD-H children, for example, do very well in school. For the time being, efforts are being made to keep the two categories separate while acknowledging their relatedness (Whalen, 1983).

Misconduct at school is found in about 80 percent of hyperactive children (Satterfield et al., 1972). And they are commonly described by adults as immature. Many such children have inordinate difficulties getting along with peers and establishing friendships (Whalen, 1983), probably because their behavior is annoying to others. They may instead play with children younger than themselves and with toys inappropriate to their age; they also persist in baby talk (Weiss et al., 1971). The social relations of ADD-H youngsters are poor not because they do not know what to do; compared to normal children, they do not suffer from deficiencies in "interpersonal intelligence" or social reasoning abilities. Rather, they seem not as readily to *do* the right thing when the occasion arises (Paulauskas and Campbell, 1979; Whalen, 1983).

The problems of hyperactive children begin in early infancy: they are more likely than their peers to develop colic (Stewart et al., 1966), and they fail to reach developmental milestones, such as walking, at the expected ages (Denhoff, 1973). Furthermore, even during infancy there are deviations in activity level; some are overactive but others, interestingly enough, are too passive (Werry, Weiss, and Douglas, 1964). By the preschool years their inattentiveness and overactivity are evident. They do not follow through when given small chores by their parents, and they knock over their baby sister's pile of blocks when asked to play with her. At this stage in their lives, they are often considered temperamental and emotional children (Schain and Reynard, 1975). Their problems attract real notice when they enter school, probably because of the greater degree of structure evident in most elementary school settings. One study (Stewart et al., 1966) compared teacher ratings of the behavior of hyperactive and control children (Table 15.2). The actions and attitudes rated make a good catalogue of hyperactivity.

It is estimated that 8 to 9 percent of elementary school boys and 2 to 3 percent of girls have ADD-H (Miller, Palkes, and Stewart, 1973). At one time it was

BOX 15.1

ENURESIS

Infants have no bladder or bowel control and must continually be diapered. As the child becomes older, toilet training begins. Some children learn toileting at eighteen months, others at thirty months, and so on. When is it no longer "normal" to be unable to control the bladder? The answer, as determined by cultural norms and statistics, is fairly arbitrary.

DSM-III and other classification systems distinguish between those who wet during sleep, which is nocturnal enuresis, and those who wet themselves while awake with or without bed-wetting, which is called diurnal enuresis. Daytime continence is established earlier. When a child falls behind in bladder control, it is usually for the nighttime hours. Using census data and incidence rates at different ages, Baller (1975) projects what he calls a conservative estimate of close to four million bed wetters in the United States today! The majority of bed wetters are male; there are approximately two male enuretics for every female (DeJonge, 1973).

Figure 15.1 shows Lovibond's (1964) calculation of the incidence of bed-wetting in England as a function of age. Certainly the cutoff on this graph, after which bed-wetting is designated a problem, cannot be set at two years, when the rate is over 40 percent. In the United States the most commonly accepted cutoff is between three and four years of age, at which time the estimated incidence of bed-wetting is 10 to 15 percent of the age group (Baller, 1975). In contrast, Bettelheim (1969) reported that on an Israeli kibbutz 40 percent of the nine-year-olds wet their beds, but the caretakers do not consider this a problem. Apparently there is more bed-wetting but less enuresis in Israel!

Clearly, age is not the only factor that enters into a diagnosis of enuresis. Baller (1975) offers a four-part definition of nocturnal enuretics as

persons who (1) involuntarily wet the bed; (2) show no evidence of urinary, organic pathology; (3) are three and one half years of age or more; and (4) have simply continued the nighttime wetting habits of infancy ("primary enuresis") or have . . . fallen into a pattern of bed-wetting ("secondary enuresis") that averages more than twice a week (p. 15).

This fourth criterion is a commonly made distinction, one found also in DSM-III. Primary enuretics, who represent two-thirds of all enuretics (Starfield, 1972), have wet the bed from infancy, whereas secondary enuretics were once able to remain dry at night but have apparently lost the capacity.

One consistent finding about enuresis is that the likelihood of an enuretic having a first-degree relative who also wets is very high, approximately 75 percent (Bakwin, 1973), evidence for either physiological or psychological theories of etiology. Bed-wetting is usually done during the first third of the night, when the child is not dreaming. If it does take place during a period of dreaming, the child may later recall a dream having to do with urination. Hospitalization between the ages of two and four, the birth of a sibling, and entering school are predisposing stresses.

Theories of Enuresis

As many as 10 percent of all cases of enuresis are caused by purely medical conditions. The most common of the known physical causes is urinary tract infection. Approximately one in twenty female and one in fifty male enuretics have such an infection. Treatment of the infection oftentimes does not stop the enuresis, however. Other infrequent but known physical causes are chronic renal or kidney disease, tumors, diabetes, and seizures (Kolvin, MacKeith, and Meadow, 1973). Because of the substantial incidence of physical causes of enuresis, most professionals refer enuretics to physicians before beginning psychological treatment.

Some psychoanalytic theorists have suggested that enuresis serves as a symbol for other conflicts. Enuresis has been hypothesized to be both symbolic masturbation and a disguised means of demonstrating spite toward parents (Mowrer, 1950). A related notion considers enuresis a

FIGURE 15.1 Incidence of bed-wetting in England. After Lovibond, 1964.

thought that hyperactivity simply went away by adolescence. From a careful review of the literature, however, Wallander and Hubert (1985) offer the tentative conclusion that ADD-H-diagnosed young people continue to have adjustment problems throughout adolescence and some into young adulthood. Their overactivity tends to diminish in adolescence and adulthood, but these young people have more problems finishing school than normal adolescents. Their employment histories are comparable to those of normal individuals, perhaps because symptom of a more general psychological disorder. Many investigators disagree, however, finding other personal problems to be a reaction to the embarrassment and guilt of wetting, rather than being causes of enuresis. Children will of course lose self-esteem if their peers ostracize them and their parents become angry and rejecting. When bladder control is gained, most of the correlated emotional problems are also likely to disappear (Starfield, 1972; Baller, 1975).

Learning theorists propose that children wet when toilet training begins at too early an age, when training is lax and insufficient reinforcement is given for proper toileting, and more specifically when children do not learn to awaken as a conditioned response to a full bladder or to inhibit sufficiently relaxation of the sphincter muscle controlling urination (Mowrer and Mowrer, 1938; Young, 1965; Baller, 1975). Bladder control, the inhibition of a natural reflex until voluntary voiding can take place, is after all a skill of considerable complexity. Although no single learning theory has received much empirical support, treatments based on learning models have proved quite successful (Doleys, 1977).

Treatment of Enuresis

In the late 1930s Mowrer and Mowrer (1938) introduced the _bell and pad_, a treatment for nocturnal enuresis based on learning principles. Over the years the procedure has proved markedly successful in reducing or eliminating bedwetting. Although relapses can be common, it is estimated that 75 percent of enuretic children will learn to stay dry through the night with the help of this remarkably simple device (Doleys, 1977).

The bell and a battery are wired to the pad, which is composed of two metallic foil sheets, the top one perforated, separated by a layer of absorbent cloth (Figure 15.2). The pad is inserted into a pillowcase and placed beneath the child at bedtime. When the first drops of urine, which acts as an electrolyte, reach the absorbent cloth, the electric circuit is completed between the two foil sheets. The completed circuit sets off the bell, which awakens the child immediately or soon after he begins to wet. He is then able to stop urination, turn off the device, and go to the bathroom.

Mowrer and Mowrer (1938) viewed the bell and pad as a classical conditioning procedure wherein an unconditioned stimulus, the bell, wakes the child, the unconditioned response. The bell is paired with the sensations of a full bladder so that they eventually become a conditioned stimulus which produces the conditioned response of awakening, before the bell sounds. Others have questioned the classical conditioning theory, suggesting instead that the bell, by awakening the child, serves as a punisher and thus reduces the undesirable behavior of wetting.* Other methods that use an operant conditioning rationale instead of or in addition to the bell and pad procedure have also proved quite successful (Doleys, 1977).

A rather different learning treatment for enuresis is based on the theory that enuretics have an abnormally small functional bladder capacity. Children perform exercises to increase gradually the volume of urine that they can retain before voiding (Starfield, 1972). For instance, a child may be asked to drink a large glass of water and not to urinate for thirty minutes. The next day the time might be stretched to thirty-five minutes, and so on; rewards are provided for the steps along the way. In this manner the child's capacity to hold urine without voiding is gradually increased, the hope being that the enlarged capacity will reduce wetting. Although often useful, retention control training has not proved as effective as the bell and pad (Doleys, 1977).

---

*In actual practice the bell usually wakes the child's parents too; their reactions may serve as an additional incentive for the child to remain dry.

FIGURE 15.2 The bell and pad apparatus for halting bed-wetting, devised by Orval Hobart and Willie Mae Mowrer.

they are no longer in the highly structured and cognitively demanding school setting where ADD-H tends to show up prominently. And yet in adulthood some of these ADD-H people, mostly men, are more likely to abuse alcohol and to have greater numbers of car accidents than do individuals in the general population. Unfavorable outcomes are found both among those who were treated as youngsters and among those who were not.

In a series of important studies, Loney and her asso-

TABLE 15.2 Classroom Behavior of ADD-H and Control Children   *(from Stewart et al., 1966)*

Behavior	Control, percent ($N = 33$)	Hyperactive, percent ($N = 37$)
Overactive	33	100
Can't sit still	8	81
Fidgets	30	84
Leaves class without permission	0	35
Can't accept correction	0	35
Temper tantrums	0	51
Fights	3	59
Defiant	0	49
Doesn't complete project	0	84
Doesn't stay with games	3	78
Doesn't listen to whole story	0	49
Moves from one activity to another in class	6	46
Doesn't follow directions	3	62
Hard to get to bed	3	49
Unpopular with peers	0	46
Talks too much	20	68
Wears out toys, furniture, etc.	8	68
Gets into things	11	54
Unpredictable	3	59
Destructive	0	41
Unresponsive to discipline	0	57
Lies	3	43

ciates have identified some of the predictors of adolescent outcome in a large sample of hyperactive children. By factor-analyzing the symptoms, Loney, Langhorne, and Paternite (1978) identified two principal clusters. The first was called the hyperactivity factor and included hyperactivity, inattention, and deficits in judgment. The second, called the aggression factor, included aggression as well as problems of control and negative emotion. The better predictor of both hyperactivity and aggressive behavior at follow-up in adolescence was the aggression factor (Paternite and Loney, 1980). The aggressive aspect of ADD-H, then, can extend beyond childhood and may even be a lifelong problem.

Physiological Theories of ADD-H

The search for causes of ADD-H is complicated by the heterogeneity of children given this diagnosis; any factor found to be associated with the syndrome is perhaps linked with only one group of them. As with other psychopathologies, there are youngsters whose histories or biochemistry "should" have them suffering from the problem, but they do not.

A predisposition toward ADD-H may be inherited. Morrison and Stewart (1971), for example, found that 20 percent of hyperactive children had a parent who had been hyperactive. The corresponding figure for control children was 5 percent. Similar results have been reported by Gross and Wilson (1974), and the findings have held up in more methodologically sophisticated adoption studies (Morrison and Stewart, 1973; Cantwell, 1975).

A biochemical theory of hyperactivity, proposed by Feingold (1973), has enjoyed much attention in the popular press. He had been treating a woman for allergies while she was concurrently being seen by a psychiatrist for uncontrollable, frenetic behavior. Feingold thought that the patient might be allergic to aspirin and other salicylate compounds, so he prescribed a diet free of them. Both her allergic symptoms and her overactivity rapidly and dramatically diminished. Feingold soon noted the prevalence of salicylates and other similar chemicals in food additives and embarked on a study in which hyperactive children were kept on a diet free of food additives. Many responded favorably, and his work was subsequently replicated (Hawley and Buckley, 1974). Thus it seemed possible that the central nervous systems of some hyperactive children, perhaps through a genetically transmitted predisposition, are upset in some way by food additives. It is unlikely, though, that more than a small percentage of cases of hyperactivity are caused by sensitivity to food additives. Well-controlled studies of the Feingold diet have found that very few such children respond positively (Goyette and Conners, 1977).

There is some evidence that ADD-H children suffer from abnormally low levels of arousal in the central nervous system. For example, the cerebral spinal fluid of ADD-H children has low levels of homovanillic acid, the major metabolite of dopamine (Shaywitz, Cohen, and Shaywitz, 1978). But, as Whalen (1983) cautions, the cause-effect relations are not straightforward. For example, we know that stress can alter neurotransmitter metabolism; since many ADD-H children are probably under abnormally high levels of stress because of the troubles their behavior gets them into, their biochemical differences may be a consequence of, rather than a cause of, their hyperactive behavior. The underarousal theory, however, remains an important one for researchers to pursue.

ADD-H children show some signs of possible brain damage. Their mothers have often had difficult pregnancies (Pasamanick, Rogers, and Lilienfeld, 1956), and in infancy hyperactive children are more likely to have had seizures, encephalitis, cerebral palsy, and head injury (Conners et al., 1972). Furthermore, hyperactivity can be brought on by lead poisoning (Wiener, 1970). And many hyperactive children show abnormal EEGs (Gross and Wilson, 1974) in addition to "soft" neurological signs, such as clumsiness, confusion of right and left, and poor balance and coordination. All this evidence points to some brain malfunction, but what parts of the brain might be impaired? Unfortunately, no data currently available allow greater and more meaningful specification of the vague term brain damage (Sroufe, 1975).

The success of psychostimulant medication in treating hyperactive children was once considered to be additional evidence in support of a physiological theory of hyperactivity. Amphetamines, as discussed in Chapter 11, heighten the adult's sense of energy. Yet they have the effect of increasing attention and decreasing activity level in hyperactive children. This apparently paradoxical effect was taken as evidence for abnormal physiological processes in hyperactive children. Such an interpretation is no longer viable, for recent evidence demonstrates that normal children also respond to amphetamines with increased attention and decreased activity (Rapoport et al., 1978). The once presumed "paradoxical effect" has proved to be the normal response of children to psychostimulants.[4]

Psychological Theories of ADD-H

Bettelheim (1973) proposed a diathesis-stress theory, suggesting that hyperactivity develops when a predisposition to the disorder is coupled with unfortunate rearing by parents. A child with a disposition toward overactivity and moodiness is stressed further by a mother who easily becomes impatient and resentful. The child is unable to cope with the mother's demands for obedience, the mother becomes more and more negative and disapproving, and the mother-child relationship ends up a battleground. With a disruptive and disobedient pattern already established, the demands of school cannot

be handled, and the behavior of the child is often in conflict with the rules of the classroom.

The Fels Research Institute's longitudinal study of child development supplies some evidence that is consistent with Bettelheim's position (Battle and Lacey, 1972). Mothers of hyperactive children were found to be critical of them and relatively unaffectionate, even during the children's infancy. These mothers continued to be disapproving of their children and dispensed severe penalties for disobedience. The parent-child relationship, however, is bidirectional, the behavior of each being determined by the reactions of the other. The influence of hyperactive children's behavior on the actions of their mothers has also been demonstrated (Barkley and Cunningham, 1979). It is plausible, though, that a critical and unaffectionate mother might exacerbate the problems of a hyperactive child (Cunningham and Barkley, 1979).

Finally, although no comprehensive theory has been proposed, two ways in which learning might figure in hyperactivity should be mentioned. First, hyperactivity could be reinforced by the attention it elicits. Second, as Ross and Ross (1982) suggest, hyperactivity may be modeled on the behavior of parents and siblings.

Treatment of ADD-H

As already indicated, two somatic treatments for hyperactivity are in use. Stimulant drugs, especially methylphenidate or Ritalin, have been prescribed for this disorder since the early 1960s (Sprague and Gadow, 1976). One estimate is that during the school year 1 to 2 percent of American children are given Ritalin or one of the amphetamines in efforts to control their hyperactivity (Henker and Whalen, 1980). The other somatic intervention is the so-called Feingold diet, promulgated by Feingold's 1975 book, *Why Your Child is Hyperactive*, and by numerous parent associations throughout the country. These associations publish complete diets made up of foods that do not contain such things as artificial flavors and colorings, preservatives, and natural salicylates.

We have already said that few hyperactive children are helped by the Feingold diet. A number of controlled studies comparing stimulants with placebos in double-blind designs indicate short-term lessening of fidgeting and greater obedience in school (Cantwell and Carlson, 1978; O'Leary, 1980). Little research indicates that over the long haul such drugs favorably influence academic achievement, however (Weiss et al., 1975); in fact, they may sometimes *interfere with* academic performance

---

[4]In addition to this empirical disconfirmation, the reader is reminded of the logical fallacy of concluding etiology from the effectiveness of treatment.

when administered in doses strong enough to reduce hyperactivity (Sprague and Sleator, 1977).

Despite the absence of a comprehensive theory, treatments of ADD-H children based on learning principles have demonstrated at least short-term success in improving both social and academic behavior. In these treatments the behavior of the children is monitored both at home and in school, and they are reinforced for doing the appropriate thing, such as remaining in their seats and working on assignments. Point systems and star charts are frequently a part of these programs; the youngsters earn points and the younger children stars

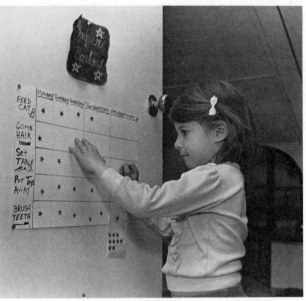

A hyperactive child looking at her star chart for the week. At the end of the week, stars are exchanged for tangible rewards.

for behaving in certain ways. They can then of course "spend" their earnings for backup rewards. It is of special interest that the focus of these operant programs is on improving academic work rather than on reducing signs of hyperactivity, such as running around and jiggling (O'Leary et al., 1976). The therapists devising them treat hyperactivity as a deficit in certain skills rather than as an excess of disruptive behavior. Although hyperactive children have proved very responsive to these programs, the optimal treatment for the disorder, discussed in more detail in Chapter 20, seems

to require the use of both stimulants and behavior therapy.

Conduct Disorders

The term *conduct disorders* encompasses a wide variety of undercontrolled behavior. There is no single definition. Rather, any undercontrolled behavior that is deemed noxious or unacceptable to others may be viewed as a conduct problem. Aggression, defiance, and disobedience, verbal hostility, lying, destructiveness, vandalism, theft, promiscuity, and early drug and alcohol use are attitudes and actions usually covered by the general, and rather vague, category of conduct disorders. The patterns and severity of the acts go beyond the mischief and pranks common among children and adolescents. A lack of concern for the feelings, wishes, and well-being of others is another serious shortcoming of those with conduct problems.

Two types of conduct disorders are commonly identified (Jenkins and Glickman, 1947; Quay, 1964). The diagnosis *socialized conduct disorder* applies to children who perpetrate frequent antisocial or delinquent acts—truancy, running away, serious lying, stealing—in the company of peers. *Undersocialized conduct disorder* is the diagnosis when the antisocial acts more closely resemble those of the adult antisocial personality—vandalism, rape, breaking and entry, fire setting, mugging, assault, extortion, purse snatching, armed robbery—and the children committing them have no stable bonds and apparently no concern for how their actions affect others. In fact, the disorder may be a precursor of antisocial personality, for many of these children will as adults have conflicts with the law (Robins, 1966).

Perhaps more than any other childhood disorder, conduct problems are defined by the impact of the child's behavior on people and surroundings. Schools, parents, and peers usually decide what undercontrolled behavior is unacceptable conduct. Preadolescents and adolescents are often identified as conduct problems by legal authorities. Indeed, as Herbert (1982) points out, moral judgments are inherent in our conception of conduct disorder, for the criteria concern rules of conventional social behavior, such as sympathy and respect for others, as well as honesty, attachment, and loyalty to peers. The very term "conduct" carries with it the connotation of "good" and "bad." Moreover, since much of the behavior considered a conduct problem has a high base rate in the general population, a certain level of aggression or disobedience must be "normal." Even delin-

TABLE 15.3 Frequency of Illegal Activities in Nondelinquent Male Populations *(from Short and Nye, 1958)*

Delinquent Act	Admit Committing Act, percent			Admit Committing Act More Than Once or Twice, percent		
	Midwestern Students	Western Students	Training School Boys	Midwestern Students	Western Students	Training School Boys
Driving a car without a license	81.1	75.3	91.1	61.2	49.0	73.4
Skipping school	54.4	53.0	95.3	24.4	23.8	85.9
Fist fighting	86.7	80.7	95.3	32.6	31.9	75.0
Running away	12.9	13.0	68.1	2.8	2.4	37.7
School probation or expulsion	15.3	11.3	67.8	2.1	2.9	31.3
Defying parents' authority	22.2	33.1	52.4	1.4	6.3	23.6
Stealing items worth less than $2	62.7	60.6	91.8	18.5	12.9	65.1
Stealing items worth from $2 to $50	17.1	15.8	91.0	3.8	3.8	61.4
Stealing items worth more than $50	3.5	5.0	90.8	1.1	2.1	47.7
Gang fighting	24.3	22.5	67.4	6.7	5.2	47.4
Drinking beer, wine, or liquor	67.7	57.2	89.7	35.8	29.5	79.4
Using narcotics	1.4	2.2	23.1	0.7	1.6	12.6
Having sexual relations	38.8	40.4	87.5	20.3	19.9	73.4

quency is difficult to define. As indicated in Table 15.3, a wide variety of illegal acts are committed by a significant proportion of "nondelinquent" populations.[5]

An excerpt from the case history of Tom serves to illustrate the difficulty of defining conduct disorders in terms of behavior alone.

> He entered the church, now, with a swarm of clean and noisy boys and girls, proceeded to his seat and started a quarrel with the first boy who came handy. The teacher, a grave, elderly man, interfered; then turned his back a moment and Tom pulled a boy's hair in the next bench, and was absorbed in his book when the boy turned around; stuck a pin in another boy, presently, in order hear him say "Ouch!" and got a new reprimand from his teacher (p. 454).

Based on this sample of Tom's behavior, are we to conclude that he has a conduct disorder? Certainly he is aggressive and disobedient, two of the more frequent indications. And the impact of Tom's behavior on his companions and the Sunday school session is a disruptive one, as we can be sure both Tom's Sunday school teacher and his classmates would report. The excerpt, however, was taken from *The Adventures of Tom Sawyer*, by Mark Twain (1876). Tom Sawyer a conduct problem? No! For over one hundred years Tom has been considered the prototypical all-American boy. Something about Tom, perhaps his cleverness and his affection for Becky, keeps us from thinking of him as a boy with conduct problems. Although he was devilish, even Aunt Polly acknowledged that Tom was not *really* a ruffian.

[5] "Juvenile delinquency" is a legal, not a psychological, term, referring to acts committed by a young person, usually less than eighteen years of age, that are either generally illegal, such as assault or robbery, or illegal only for people of a certain age, such as truancy. It is not surprising, then, that many youngsters who are diagnosed as conduct-disordered run afoul of the law and are judged to be juvenile delinquents by our system of juvenile justice. A young person with a conduct disorder, however, might well evade legal detection.

"But as I was saying," said Aunt Polly, *"he warn't bad, so to say—only mischievous. Only, just giddy, and harum-scarum, you know. He warn't any more responsible than a colt. He never meant any harm, and he was the best-hearted boy that ever was"* (p. 503).

The factors that make the actions of one child be considered a conduct problem and the same actions of another be accepted as "normal" are intriguing. Unfortunately, they are largely unspecified in the psychological literature. Fertile ground for speculation is provided by the contrast between Tom Sawyer and Huck Finn, who would likely be diagnosed as having a conduct disorder. "Huckleberry was cordially hated and dreaded by all the mothers of the town, because he was idle, and lawless, and vulgar and bad" (p. 464). The fact that Huck had no "proper" family may have been one factor swaying the opinions of the townspeople.

We do not wish to overstate the labeling bias of society, however. Many qualities of the child's behavior itself must be considered in the diagnosis of conduct disorders. Perhaps the two most important criteria for deciding whether a given act is aggressive or problematic are the frequency with which it occurs and the intensity of the behavior (Herbert, 1978). Thus one fight in a year is not a problem, but one fight per week is. (The percentage of young people committing a delinquent act the second time is sometimes dramatically less than those who do it once, as indicated in Table 15.3.) Similarly, stealing a candy bar is a minor incident; stealing a car is a felony. These criteria of frequency and intensity do not fully solve the problem of defining conduct disorders, but they are important considerations.

Because of the definitional difficulties, the prevalence of conduct disorders is impossible to estimate accurately. With little doubt, however, they are quite common. Approximately one-third of all referrals made to child guidance clinics are for conduct problems (Wiltz and Patterson, 1974). Furthermore, since it is estimated that most children with conduct problems do not receive treatment (Bahm, Chandler, and Eisenberg, 1961), clinic referrals would not reflect the true prevalence of these problems. If both of these suppositions are accurate, conduct disorders must be the most frequent psychological problem of childhood.

Conduct problems are from three to ten times more frequent in males than in females, although their incidence in females may be increasing (Herbert, 1978). Generally, the more serious the delinquent act, the greater the ratio of males to females committing it. Juvenile crime is a major problem, particularly in the more violent categories of robbery and aggravated assault. The rate of juvenile crime increased greatly in the 1960s and 1970s and has now leveled off at this high frequency.

The prognosis for children diagnosed as having conduct disorders is poor. Robins (1966, 1972), in her thirty-year follow-up study of adults who had as children been seen in a child guidance clinic (see page 237), found that fully 50 percent of them had in their younger years been incarcerated in correctional institutions, and that the majority of the people in this clinic sample continued to be antisocial in their behavior during adulthood. As is the case with hyperactivity, it is clear that conduct problems are not simply outgrown.

Etiology of Conduct Disorders

Numerous theories have been offered for the etiology of conduct disorders. Physiological explanations are suggested by the fact that a higher incidence of antisocial behavior is found in the relatives of delinquent children than in the general population (Cloninger, Reich, and Guze, 1975). Furthermore, twin studies show consistently higher concordance rates for antisocial behavior in identical pairs than in fraternal pairs (Eysenck, 1975). The effects of rearing are indicated by findings that families of these children frequently lack cohesiveness (Craig and Glick, 1963), and that they have experienced the stresses of marital discord and divorce (Rutter, 1971; Emery and O'Leary, 1979; see Box 15.2).

An important part of normal child development is the growth of moral awareness, acquiring a sense of what is right and wrong and the ability, even desire, to abide by rules and norms. Most people refrain from hurting others, not only because it is illegal but because it would make them feel guilty to do otherwise. Conduct-disordered children, like the sociopaths discussed in Chapter 10, seem to be deficient in this moral awareness, viewing antisocial acts as exciting, as rewarding, indeed as central to their very self-concept (Ryall, 1974). Some psychodynamic theorists have explained conduct problems and delinquency as a ". . . disorder(s) in the functioning of the superego" (Kessler, 1966, p. 303). In psychoanalytic theory the superego is the part of the psyche that governs behavior according to societal and parental rules; thus conduct problems are traced to a failure of conscience and moral development.

Research into the backgrounds of conduct-disordered youngsters has shown a pattern of family life lacking in factors believed to be central to the development of a strong moral sense. Strong affection between child and parents; making firm moral demands on the child; using sanctions in a consistent manner; punishing

BOX 15.2

THE ROLE OF MARITAL DISCORD IN CONDUCT DISORDERS

The role that separation and divorce play in fostering conduct problems and delinquency has been an issue of debate. The incidence of delinquency is greater in one-parent families than in two-parent families (for example, Glueck and Glueck, 1959). Some have argued that separation from a parent by itself causes deliquency (Bowlby, 1973). If this assumption is correct, parents would be wise to stay together "for the child's sake."

But research evidence contradicts this conclusion. McCord, McCord, and Thurber (1962) compared the rates of gang delinquency in the sons from three groups of homes. The three types consisted of happy single-parent homes, happy homes inhabited by both parents, and unhappy single-parent homes. The researchers found that rates of delinquency of sons from the two types of happy homes

were very similar, but the unhappy single-parent homes produced a greater percentage of delinquents. On the basis of this finding, they concluded that discord, not separation, was the more likely cause of delinquency. The confounding of two factors, separation and marital conflict, would explain the misinterpretations of the results of other studies. More recent evidence, including comparisons of homes broken by death with homes broken by divorce, supports the conclusion that discord is the important factor. A parent's death, unlike a parent's absence through separation or divorce, is not associated with a higher incidence of conduct disorder in the children (Felner, Stolberg, and Cowen, 1975; Rutter, 1979). Although the separation per se does have disruptive effects, family conflict is apparently the key contributor to delinquency and conduct problems.

These series of photographs demonstrate what effects watching an aggressive model have on the behavior of observers. The top panels show the model's attack on a Bobo doll, the two rows below the imitative pummeling of Bobo by two children who have observed her.

psychologically rather than physically, to induce anxiety and guilt rather than anger; and reasoning and explaining things to the child all help in this development (Herbert, 1982; Hoffman, 1970; Wright, 1971).

Several other psychological theories have merit. Learning theories that look to both modeling and operant conditioning have received considerable attention as explanations of the development and maintenance of conduct problems. Bandura and Walters (1963) were among the first to point out the obvious, that children can learn aggressiveness from parents who behave in this way. Children may also imitate aggressive acts that are seen elsewhere, such as on television (Liebert, Neale, and Davidson, 1973). Since aggression is an effective, albeit unpleasant, means of achieving a goal, it is likely to be reinforced. Thus, once imitated, aggressive acts will probably be maintained.

Bandura and Walters (1959) found that the families of antisocial adolescents use physical punishment more often than control families and are more likely to reward aggressive acts. A later study by Hetherington and Martin (1979) confirmed and extended these findings. Youngsters in treatment for aggressive or antisocial behavior were likely to have siblings and fathers who themselves had records of aggressive and criminal behavior. These studies, although limited by a cross-sectional design,[6] indicate that modeling and reinforcement are part of the etiology of at least some conduct problems.

Patterson and Reid (1970) have offered a more specific explanation of how conduct problems are rewarded in families. Their _coercion hypothesis_ is best demonstrated by an example from our clinical files.

Chris was an eight-year-old boy brought to the clinic by his mother, who described him as unmanageable. Whenever his mother refused to comply with Chris's requests, he became upset. At these times Chris would be stubborn, uncooperative, and verbally abusive. Occasionally he would throw a temper tantrum and lie down on the floor, kicking his feet and screaming. His mother usually ignored Chris's behavior for a few minutes, but she gave in to his demands when his tantrums became too difficult for her to bear. This sequence of agitation and giving in had become habitual, particularly when the mother was busy. When she felt rushed and perturbed, she gave in to Chris almost immediately.

The coercion hypothesis postulates that both Chris and his mother are rewarded in this sequence of events. Chris is rewarded by getting his own way, his mother by the cessation of Chris's obnoxious behavior. Through this mutual rewarding both Chris's conduct problems and his mother's acquiescence are likely to be maintained. Therapy based on the coercion hypothesis would direct the mother never to give in to Chris while he is misbehaving and thereby extinguish his conduct problem. The coercion hypothesis seems a likely model, but it explains only how obstreperous behavior is _maintained_, not how it first _develops_.

In any discussion of conduct disorders and delinquency, the work of sociologists must be recognized. Social class and urban living in particular are related to the incidence of delinquency. High unemployment, poor educational facilities, disrupted family life, and a subculture which deems delinquency acceptable have all been found to be contributing factors (Gibbons, 1975). Any comprehensive theory of delinquency and conduct disorders would need to include these consistent sociological findings.

Treatment of Conduct Disorders and Delinquency

The management of conduct disorders poses a formidable challenge to contemporary society. Sociologists and politicians, as well as community psychologists, working on the assumption that poor economic conditions create most of the problem, argue for a fairer distribution of income, for job programs and other large-scale efforts to alleviate the material deprivation of the lower classes, among whom, as previously noted, delinquency is often found.

As meritorious as such proposals might be on moral and political grounds, the broad sociological view gives too little consideration to two simple facts: only a minority of lower-class youngsters are "hoods," and conduct problems are to be found in sizable numbers among children and adolescents of middle- and upper-class families.[7] Mischief and crime of well-to-do young peo-

---

[6]The findings are only correlational. In such cross-sectional studies it is possible that the aggressiveness of the children elicits physical punishment from their parents. A longitudinal study would permit a cause-effect conclusion. Say, for example, a child is not aggressive at age five but lives in a home in which he is punished physically. By age ten he may have become an aggressive youngster. Because punishment preceded the child's aggression, we are better able to draw a causal inference.

[7]One view of the juvenile delinquency of young people from affluent backgrounds holds that, with time on their hands, they sometimes make the conscious choice to engage in antisocial acts, not out of any felt economic need but as a way to fill their leisure hours. They supposedly engage in a bit of deliberation, weighing the positive consequences against the negative. This view of antisocial behavior is inconsistent with considering it to have an underlying pathology (Richards, Berk, and Forster, 1979).

ple are underrepresented in police statistics because the status and social influence of their families often keep these children from being booked and incarcerated, as poorer youngsters are. Although sociological considerations may play some role in planning treatments, we emphasize here psychological methods aimed more at the particular individuals themselves.

Some of the young people with undersocialized conduct disorder are the sociopaths of tomorrow. Just as precious little in the way of effective psychological treatment has been found for sociopathy, so are there few ways to reach young people who commit violent and antisocial acts with little remorse or emotional involvement. These callous young individuals, most of them male, "graduate from" training schools and youth farms to lives of crime and dissoluteness, interrupted by extended periods of incarceration in prisons. Recidivism is the rule. One of society's most enduring problems is how to deal with people whose social consciences appear grossly underdeveloped.

Some behavior therapists find in people whose behavior violates societal norms

A failure to have learned . . . to postpone immediate and often unlawful gratification and . . . a lack of socially endorsed skills for finding alternate, legal forms of gratification. . . . It follows that intervention must be aimed at teaching needed controls and missing skills. [Furthermore,] the norm-violator may not have acquired the ability to discriminate between acceptable and unacceptable behavior, [hence] the logical treatment is the teaching of this discrimination (Ross, 1981, p. 148).

These therapists advocate positive reinforcement of new prosocial responses rather than the punishment of existing antisocial behavior. Two kinds of effort can be distinguished. First, therapists may try merely to change the behavior of residents while they are in an institution. Or they may try to create changes during institutionalization that generalize to life on the outside, so that discharged people will do better in school, hold jobs longer, and avoid legal hassles with the police. In light of the marital and familial problems of many of the parents of conduct-disordered youngsters, it is not surprising that they require therapeutic attention themselves (Herbert, 1982).

Several studies have demonstrated that systematically reinforcing prosocial acts can improve the overt behavior of young men with conduct disorders while they are in an institution (for example, Barkley et al., 1976). Improvement after release was demonstrated by

an architect, Harold Cohen, and his associates, who developed a one-year special program at the National Training School for Boys in Washington, D.C. The school is a federally run residential center for male teenagers who have been convicted of crimes such as robbery, auto theft, and even murder (Cohen and Filipczak, 1971). This project, referred to as CASE II, was a comprehensive educational program consisting of sixteen courses. The American Revolution, electronics, and remedial mathematics and reading are a sampling of those offered. The young men were able to earn money by demonstrating their competence; making grades 90 percent or better earned them extra points. They used their money to pay for special meals, private rooms, room furnishings, to order clothing, and to gain admittance to a recreational lounge. The residents became less aggressive as time went on, took care of their living quarters, and in general acted less like juvenile delinquents and more like young men in their teens without serious police records. After eleven months of the program, the average increase in IQ was 12.5 points. Upon release the young men applied the study skills that they had acquired to good advantage in the public school system. Moreover, for two years they had less trouble with the law; their recidivism rate the first year was only one-third of the average.

Delinquent youngsters who live at an Achievement Place, a small, familylike home supervised by live-in surrogate parents, attend regular schools in their community. They earn points for completing homework, for reading books and newspapers, for keeping neat and clean, and for helping with household tasks (Table 15.4). After sufficient improvement on the point system, they shift to the merit system. They are still carefully monitored, but their good behavior is rewarded now by praise, approval, and affection, and all privileges are free. The next step is the homeward-bound system. With continued good behavior the youngsters are able to spend a little more time at home each week. Eventually, they earn their release through their good behavior, and for two years their recidivism rates too are generally low. Repairing the academic and social deficits of youngsters seems a promising way to begin the attack on the serious social and psychological problem of delinquency.

Success in teaching specific skills suggests that taking preventive measures during earlier child rearing might prove useful in reducing the incidence of antisocial behavior. An exemplary program of clinical research on the families of aggressive boys has been conducted for a number of years by Gerald Patterson and

TABLE 15.4 Behavior That Earns and Loses Points at Achievement Place *(from Phillips, 1968)*

Behavior That Earns Points	Points
1. Watching news on TV or reading the newspaper	300 per day
2. Cleaning and maintaining neatness in one's room	500 per day
3. Keeping one's person neat and clean	500 per day
4. Reading books	5 to 10 per page
5. Aiding houseparents in various household tasks	20 to 1000 per task
6. Doing dishes	500 to 1000 per meal
7. Being well dressed for an evening meal	100 to 500 per meal
8. Performing homework	500 per day
9. Obtaining desirable grades on school report cards	500 to 1000 per grade
10. Turning out lights when not in use	25 per light
Behavior That Loses Points	**Points**
1. Failing grades on the report card	500 to 1000 per grade
2. Speaking aggressively	20 to 50 per response
3. Forgetting to wash hands before meals	100 to 300 per meal
4. Arguing	300 per response
5. Disobeying	100 to 1000 per response
6. Being late	10 per minute
7. Displaying poor manners	50 to 100 per response
8. Engaging in poor posture	50 to 100 per response
9. Using poor grammar	20 to 50 per response
10. Stealing, lying, or cheating	10,000 per response

his colleagues at the Oregon Social Learning Center (Patterson, Cobb, and Ray, 1973). Parents of young boys who could be considered "predelinquent" were trained to monitor their interactions with their aggressive sons; to desist from reinforcing their misbehavior with attention, a pattern often found in the families of aggressive youngsters; and to reward prosocial behavior more consistently. A follow-up study of a number of families with aggressive and coercive sons a year after treatment suggested that such interventions had been helpful for at least some of the youngsters (Patterson, 1974b). Behavioral treatments may help prevent the development of full-blown conduct disorders in children and adolescents.

DISORDERS OF OVERCONTROLLED BEHAVIOR

Overcontrolled behavior, as indicated earlier, usually creates more problems for the individual child than for others.[8] Unlike undercontrolled children whose behavior is judged by others, children with problems of overcontrol themselves frequently complain of bothersome fears and tenseness; of feelings of shyness, of being unhappy and unloved; and of being inferior to other children. Symptoms of overcontrolled behavior are similar to those of the adult problems of anxiety and depression. The three specific problems of overcontrol to be discussed are childhood fears, social withdrawal, and depression; they are frequently found in the same child (Quay, 1979). The first two problems are roughly equivalent to the DSM-III listings *separation anxiety disorder* and *avoidant disorder*. Childhood depression is not a specific diagnostic category in DSM-III; as will be seen, the evidence for depression in children is controversial.

---

[8]We must not, however, underestimate the toll taken on parents, family members in general, and teachers by the problems described in this section.

Childhood Fears

Most children have many fears that are apparently "outgrown" in the normal course of development. For example, Jersild, Markey, and Jersild (1933) interviewed 398 children of ages five to twelve. Fear of the following were expressed by substantial numbers: supernatural events, for example, ghosts and witches, 19.2 percent; being alone, in the dark, or in a strange place, being lost, 14.6 percent; attack or danger of attack by animals, 13.7 percent; bodily injury, falling, illness, operations, hurt and pains, 12.8 percent. The results of a similar study of generally younger children appear in Figure 15.3. Certain types of fears diminish as children become older. Experience with various everyday objects apparently takes away their fearsomeness. But imaginary fears magnify and are acquired by more and more children as they gain in months and years. Later on, by the time children are in the sixth grade, fears of imaginary creatures have been abandoned, but fears of bodily injury and physical danger have increased (Bauer, 1976).

The suffering experienced by a fearful child should not be underestimated. In contrast to adults, who are usually able to acknowledge that many of their fears are baseless, children do not have enough years behind them to adopt this realistic perspective (Wicks-Nelson and Is-

FIGURE 15.3 Relative frequency of fears of various kinds shown by children of different ages who were observed by parents and teachers in the Jersild and Holmes study (1935). After Gray, 1971.

The first day of school for an obviously frightened child.

School Phobia

One childhood fear has attracted the most attention, for not only it is disabling to the child and disruptive to the household, but it also appears to be a true phobia, an extreme avoidance that does not usually just go away with the passage of time. *School phobia*, furthermore, has serious academic and social consequences for the youngster. Waldfogel (1959) offers the following definition.

School phobia refers to a reluctance to go to school because of acute fear associated with it. Usually this dread is accompanied by somatic symptoms with the gastrointestinal tract the most commonly affected. . . . The somatic complaints come to be used as an auxiliary device to justify staying at home and often disappear when the child is reassured that he will not have to attend school. The characteristic picture is of a child nauseated or complaining of abdominal pain at breakfast and desperately resisting all attempts at reassurance, reasoning, or coercion to get him to school. In its milder forms, school phobia may be only a transient symptom; but when it becomes established, it can be one of the most disabling disorders of childhood, lasting even for years (pp. 35–36).

The frequency of school phobias has been estimated at 17 per 1000 children per year (Kennedy, 1965), and unlike most childhood disorders, they are more common in girls than in boys. School phobia is commonly thought to be rooted both in actual fear of being in school and in separation anxiety, but primarily in separation anxiety. Since the beginning of school is often the first circumstance that requires lengthy and frequent separations of children and their parents, separation anxiety is frequently a principal cause of school phobia. In fact, school phobia is listed in DSM-III as one of several manifestations of separation anxiety disorder.

If separation anxiety largely accounts for school phobias that commence with enrollment in school, how are the serious ones that develop later to be explained? Johnson and his colleagues (1941) have offered one interpretation.

First some environmental event, which may be related to the school setting itself, elicits increased anxiety in the child. At the same time the mother becomes increasingly anxious about some problem of her own. A dependent relationship between mother and child may then conspire to increase further the anxiety that occurs naturally when mother and child are separated by the child's going to school. Thus the child starts to avoid school, and the mother does not protest too strongly.

rael, 1984). As recounted in DSM-III, children's fears often affect them physically: they have headaches, stomachaches, and nausea, and they vomit. Children may have a near-obsessive concern that parents will be hurt during an absence, or that they will never see their parents again. They may be subject to nightmares and insomnia, indeed, to an overwhelming sense of dread and apprehension that permeates their young lives and robs them of the simple pleasures that childhood can bring. Perhaps the sense of helplessness spoken of earlier aggravates a situation already grim in the eyes of the child.[9]

[9]Some children have an entirely new fear, the fear that the world will be annihilated in a thermonuclear holocaust. Parents and professionals alike have difficulty providing the same kind of ironclad reassurance that they can offer when, for example, a youngster is afraid of the dark.

She may even unwittingly reward the child's nonattendance for her own purposes. Given that the dependent relationship works both ways, the child being dependent on the mother and the mother being dependent on the child, the mother may not wish to lose her child to the school each day. Several factors may therefore conspire to keep the child from school. Initial, perhaps realistic, fears may make the young child withdraw from school to seek the comforting figure of her mother. This dependency on her mother is consoling and reinforces both mother and daughter for avoiding the feared situation. Finally, since the object of fear is not confronted, actual fears are not reduced and may, in fact, be worsened.[10]

Treatment of Childhood Fears

How are childhood fears overcome? As Figure 15.3 indicates, many simply dissipate with time and maturation. Perhaps the most widespread means of helping children overcome fears, employed by millions of parents, is to expose them gradually to the feared object, often while acting simultaneously to inhibit their anxiety. If a little girl fears strangers, a parent takes her by the hand and walks her slowly toward the new person. Mary Cover Jones (see page 498) was the first psychologist to explain this bit of folk wisdom as a counterconditioning procedure.

Indeed, contemporary therapists have by and large built on folk wisdom in helping children overcome fears. *Exposure* is generally agreed to be the most effective way of eliminating baseless fear and avoidance. Modeling has also proved effective, both in laboratory studies (for example, Bandura, Grusec, and Menlove, 1967) and in countless clinical treatments; another child, one the fearful child is likely to imitate, demonstrates fearless behavior. Offering rewards for moving closer to a feared object or situation can also encourage a child to venture forth. When the fear and avoidance of a school phobic child are very great and of long duration, they may require desensitization through direct, graduated exposure plus operant shaping. In one of our cases, the therapist started with walks to school with nine-year-old Paul. Next the boy, one step at a time on successive days, entered the schoolyard, then an empty classroom after school, attended the opening morning exercises and then left, sat at the desk, spent time in school, all with the therapist beside him, then with the therapist out

of sight but still nearby. In the last steps, when anxiety seemed to have lessened, promises to play the guitar for Paul at night, comic books, and tokens that would eventually earn the boy a baseball glove were the enticements for attending school (Lazarus, Davison, and Polefka, 1965).

Finally, some new situations may be threatening, not only for children but for adults as well, because the person lacks the knowledge and skills to deal with them. Thus a child's fear of the water may very well be based on a reasonable judgment that danger lurks there because he or she cannot swim. Parents and therapists must see to it that children have the opportunity to acquire knowledge and relevant skills.

Social Withdrawal

Most classrooms have in attendance at least one or two children who are extremely quiet and shy. Oftentimes these same children will play only with family members or familiar peers, avoiding strangers both young and old. Their shyness may prevent them from acquiring skills and participating in a variety of activities that most of their age-mates enjoy, for they avoid playgrounds and games played by neighborhood children. Although some youngsters who are shy may simply be "slow to warm up," withdrawn children never do, even after prolonged exposure to new people. Extremely shy children may refuse to speak at all in unfamiliar social circumstances; this is called *elective mutism*. In crowded rooms they cling and whisper to their parents, hide behind the furniture, and cower in corners. At home they ask their parents endless questions about situations that worry them. Withdrawn children usually have warm and satisfying relationships with family members and family friends, and they do show an eagerness for affection and acceptance. Because the point at which shyness or withdrawal becomes a problem varies, no statistics of the frequency of *social-withdrawal disorder* have been compiled.

Theories of the etiology of social withdrawal are not well worked out. It is often suggested that anxiety interferes with social interaction and thus causes the child to avoid social situations. Or withdrawn children may simply not have the social know-how that facilitates interaction with their age-mates. The finding that isolated children make fewer attempts to structure peer relations and are less imaginative in their play may indicate a deficiency in certain social skills. Finally, isolated children may have become so because they have in the past spent

---

[10]For a general discussion of the etiology of phobias, the reader is referred back to Chapter 6, page 119.

Shy children keep to themselves in playgrounds, all the while wanting to join in.

most of their time with adults; they do interact more freely with adults than with other children (Scarlett, 1980).

Treatment for withdrawal or social avoidance disorders is similar to the treatment of childhood fears. In one innovative study youngsters were helped by viewing films in which other isolated children gradually engage in and come to enjoy play with their peers (O'Connor, 1969). Shy children may be given attention by day-care personnel and teachers as reinforcement for socializing with peers but none when they remain alone (Hart et al., 1968). They may also be taught skills needed for using play equipment, thus increasing the likelihood of social contact (Buell et al., 1968). Having peers serve as live models and then reward the shy child for social interactions has also proved effective (Furman, Rahe, and Hartup, 1979).

Affective Disorders in Childhood

Clinical reports in the literature describe what appear to be instances of both major depression and bipolar disorder in children. According to DSM-III, the symptoms of affective disorders of children are the same as those of adults. At the same time, however, there is controversy whether many children have affective disorders and how they should be defined (Lefkowitz and Burton, 1978).

Rutter, Tizard, and Whitmore (1970), using conservative criteria, conducted an extensive survey of children on the Isle of Wight; they found that fewer than one per-

cent were depressed. In marked contrast, some other studies (for example, Weinberg et al., 1973) have reported much higher figures. The discrepancy hinges on two points. First, some of the behavior defining adult depression is common in childhood. For example, 37 percent of girls and 29 percent of boys have poor appetite at age six (MacFarlane, Allen, and Honzik, 1954). Should this relatively frequent behavior of eating little be given clinical significance? Studies that do will find more childhood depression. Second, some researchers have chosen a very broad range of behavior to indicate the presence of childhood depression. To this range they couple the notion of "masked depression." Behavior not considered indicative of depression in adults—such as hyperactivity, psychophysiological reactions, school problems, aggression—is nonetheless thought to reflect an "underlying" depression in children. Clearly, such an expansive definition, which is unsupported by data, means that a large number of diagnoses will probably be invalid.

How shall we then conceptualize depression in children? Developmental psychologists remind us that children are *not* miniature versions of adults. It may therefore be unwise to assume that depression will take the same form in youngsters that it does in adults. In part, of course, the problem is to arrive at a consensual definition of childhood depression that will be useful in investigation and treatment. Achenbach and Edelbrock (1981) had parents bringing their children for mental health services and parents of control children rate them

on a number of items. The item "unhappy, sad, or depressed" was applied to no more than 13 percent of the
control children between the ages of four and sixteen.
But referred children had this item applied to them by
their parents with much greater frequency. Rates ranged
from 43 percent for four- and five-year-old boys to 80
percent for twelve- and thirteen-year-old girls. Other
items applied by parents that correlated strongly with
sad affect for children between the ages of six and eleven
were complaints of loneliness, feels too guilty, feels
worthless or inferior, nervous, sulks a lot, worrying, too
fearful or anxious, feels he or she has to be perfect, self-
conscious or easily embarrassed, fears he or she might
think or do something bad. As Achenbach (1982) comments, although these complaints and disconsolating
feelings are rather different from the DSM-III criteria
for depression in adults (see page 194), they do seem to
reflect depression.

Depression in young people heightens suicide risk,
especially for those between the ages of fifteen to nineteen. But even at much younger ages children, lacking
the time perspective that comes with maturity, can become so despondent, so completely without hope of
things becoming better, that they attempt to end their
lives. But as we have discussed previously (see page 220),
suicide is not always linked to depression. Adolescents
appear to commit suicide far less from depression than
from personal conflicts and developmental crises, such
as the breakup of a love affair (Achenbach, 1982; Cy-
tryn and McKnew, 1979). Suicide is the third most common cause of death among young people in the United
States, exceeded only by accidents and homicide. It
is conceivable that some of their deaths deemed accidental are actually suicides, a number of them subintentioned.[11]

EATING DISORDERS

Anorexia Nervosa

Anorexia nervosa is a life-threatening disorder unac-
counted for by any known physical disease. The term
anorexia means severe loss of appetite, nervosa, for

A young anorexic woman studying her body in an
attempt to overcome her belief that she is too fat.

[11]This loss of life is clearly tragic, but the fact that suicide is the third-
ranking cause of death in young people should be placed in perspective. Young people and children are far less likely than adults to die
from disease. Therefore their deaths are more likely to be from accidents and suicide. The *rates* of suicide in children and adolescents are
actually quite low, nowhere near those of adults.

BOX 15.3

**PLAY THERAPY AND FAMILY THERAPY: TWO GENERAL METHODS
OF TREATING CHILDHOOD PROBLEMS**

Many of the childhood disorders discussed in the present chapter, and even the more serious problems to be reviewed in the next, are treated by two general methods, *play therapy* and *family therapy*.

Children are usually less verbal than adults, at least in the sense that is needed for psychoanalytic and client-centered therapy. Moreover, children are often more reluctant than older clients to voice their concerns and complaints directly and openly. Through the pioneering work of Melanie Klein (1932) and Anna Freud (1946b), play became an analytic vehicle for delving into a child's unconscious, taking the place of the free association and recounting of dreams that means so much in analytic treatment of adults. It is assumed that in play therapy a child will express his or her feelings about problems, parents, teachers, and peers. A play therapy room is equipped with puppets, blocks, games, puzzles, drawing materials, paints, water, sand, clay, toy guns and soliders, and a large inflated rubber clown, Bobo, to punch. These toys will, it is hoped, help draw out inner tensions and concerns. A dollhouse inhabited by parental and child dolls is a common fixture. The therapist may encourage a young male client to place the figures in "any room you wish," to position the dolls in a way "that makes you feel good." The child may assemble members of the little family in the living room, except for the father, who is placed in his study. "What is Daddy doing?" the therapist will ask. "He's working. If he weren't

such a meanie, he'd come out and play with the kids." The therapist will then, as he or she would for an adult, interpret for the boy the wish he seems reluctant to express openly. Little in the way of controlled research has been done to evaluate the claims made for play therapy by its adherents. What evidence is available, however, does not find it to be notably effective (Barrett, Hampe, and Miller, 1978; Levitt, 1971).

Whatever ultimate purposes may be served by play therapy, at the very least it is likely to help the adult therapist establish rapport with a youngster. An adult client might respond favorably to a therapist who is empathic, kindly, and replete with professional degrees, but a little girl is likely to be suspicious and regard "Dr. X" as an ally of her parents or teacher, with no real interest in her. Therapists of varying persuasions, including behavior therapists who would eschew the symbolic significance an analytic worker might see in the child's play, commonly use a playroom to establish a relationship with a young client and perhaps also to determine from what the child says and does with toys the youngster's perspective of the problem.

Because children usually live with their parents and siblings, and because their lives are so inextricably bound up with them, many therapists examine and attempt to alter patterns of interactions in families rather than see the troubled child or young adolescent alone. Family therapy (page 534) too is practiced by therapists of all persuasions. Practi-

---

emotional reasons. Interestingly, the word anorexia is a misnomer because many anorexics do not initially so much lose their appetites as fear eating (Achenbach, 1982). Serious weight loss, an intense fear of becoming obese, and a refusal to eat sufficiently to gain or maintain body weight are three principal symptoms of this mysterious disorder. The self-starvation imposed by anorexics brings about physiological changes sometimes difficult to reverse; estimates vary, but approximately 5 percent die. Another 25 percent of anorexics continue in the unremitting course of their disorder at two-year follow-up, and the remainder gain weight back as a result of treatment and over the course of time (Hsu, 1980).

Anorexia is far more common in young women than in men. Ratios as high as twenty female anorexics for every male have been reported; approximately one of every 200 school-aged women is anorexic (Crisp,

Palmer, and Klucy, 1976). Onset of the weight loss most commonly begins during adolescence, shortly after the beginning of menstruation. Amenorrhea, failure to menstruate regularly, is reported in almost all anorexic young women, often before weight loss has become noticeable. They begin losing weight because, being a little plump or sometimes obese, they decide to diet; but the dieting continues far beyond reasonable bounds. Anorexics may take laxatives and exercise extensively and frantically to lose weight. The manic energy expended in excessive physical activity is amazing, considering their emaciation.

Anorexics are preoccupied with food, even when they are struggling not to ingest it. They become interested in its preparation, collecting cookbooks, trying new recipes, and planning and cooking elaborate meals of many courses and special dishes for others. Many anorexics do not admit to feeling any hunger, but others tioners hold that the child's problem has been caused or is maintained by disturbed relationships within the family. For example, the father may have defaulted on his own responsibilies, forcing a male child to take a more adult role than he feels ready to assume. As we have pointed out many times, however, treatments that help alleviate a problem may in no way indicate its etiology. The fact that clarifying and altering disturbed family relationships relieve the disorders of children does not mean that the disturbed relationships themselves caused their problems in the first place. Many clinical reports and the intrinsic plausibility of family therapy suggest that future studies will back up claims of success made by enthusiasts.

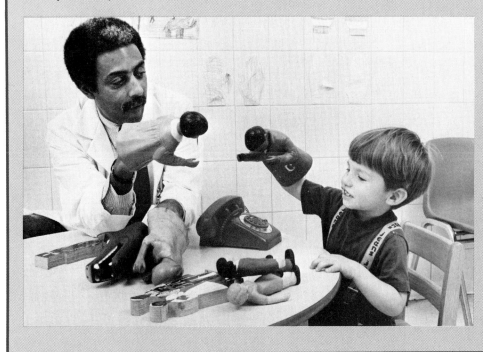

Play therapy, using common household objects and sometimes puppets, is a common tactic in treating disorders of childhood.

say they do feel hungry but force themselves not to eat. Admission to feeling hungry is associated with an eating pattern found in almost half of all anorexics, binge eating or bulimia, followed by self-induced vomiting. Anorexics who are also bulimic are more impulsive, depressed, and anxious than others and may be particularly difficult to treat (Caspar et al., 1980; Garfinkel, Moldofsky, and Garner, 1980). Indeed, anorexics in general deny having a problem that needs treatment.

A commonly reported phenomenon of anorexia is a distorted body image. Despite their protruding ribs and hipbones, their skull-like faces, their broomstick limbs, anorexics do not view themselves as being too thin. Rather, in frequent scrutinizings of their figures in mirrors, they either continue to see themselves as too fat or feel that they have finally arrived at an attractive weight. Anorexics are often described as "good girls." They are well-behaved, conscientious, quiet, and often perfectionistic. They frequently obtain better grades and score higher on IQ tests than controls (Bemis, 1978).

The Etiology of Anorexia Nervosa

Theories accounting for anorexia are varied and largely unsubstantiated. Some psychological explanations of the disorder have been based on Freud's notion that eating can be a substitute for sexual expression. Thus the anorexic's refusal to eat is thought to indicate fear of increasing sexual desires or perhaps of oral impregnation (Ross, 1977). Learning theorists have suggested that anorexia may be a weight phobia (Crisp, 1967) or a striving to effect the image of the beautifully slim woman so extensively modeled and emulated by our society (Bemis, 1978). Others view anorexia as a reflection of conflict, between wanting to attain independence and selfhood within the family and a fear of growing up.

BOX 15.4

BEHAVIORAL PEDIATRICS

An earlier discussion of behavior medicine (see page 189) enumerated several applications of psychological knowledge to the prevention and treatment of physical disease, for example, altering the type A behavior pattern as a way of reducing the incidence of later coronary heart disease. Recently, psychological attention has been paid to childhood and adolescent diseases.

Russo and Varni (1982) propose a normal person-abnormal situation (NPAS) model as a way of conceptualizing a field called *behavioral pediatrics*. An acutely or chronically ill child is a young person who may have psychological problems because he or she has been placed, by illness, in a complex and stressful predicament. Many sick children suffer considerable pain and sometimes defacement and have to spend long periods of time in a hospital, away from parents, siblings, and the comforting surroundings of their homes and neighborhoods.

In general, behavioral pediatrics combines behavior therapy and pediatrics to manage disease in children. It concerns itself with parent–child, school–child, and medical team–child relations (Varni and Dietrich, 1981). Some specific examples of recent work in behavioral pediatrics will convey the scope and aims of this burgeoning and promising field (Kellerman and Varni, 1982).

Only in recent years have many forms of childhood cancer, such as acute lymphoblastic leukemia, become treatable; some types can even be treated so effectively that they go into remission and the children are alive five years after the onset of cancer. With such improvement, however, come new problems of a psychological nature for both patients and families—learning to live with the disease and its treatment.

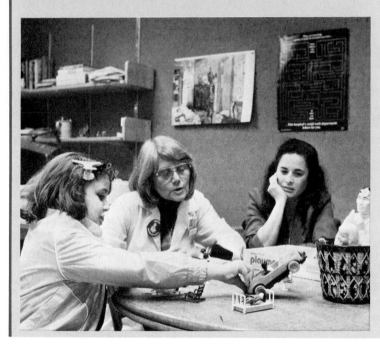

At the Sloan-Kettering Institute a counselor works with a young cancer patient and her mother.

Finally, a variety of organic explanations have been offered. Abnormal functioning of the part of the hypothalamus known to control how much we eat, sexual activity, and menstruation is perhaps the leading physiological theory, but specific abnormalities have not been found (Bemis, 1978).

Therapy for Anorexia Nervosa

The treatment of anorexia is really a two-tiered process. The immediate goal is to help the young woman gain weight in order to avoid medical complications and the possibility of death. An anorexic may have to be hospitalized if any food is to be gotten into her at all. And she

Concealing from a youngster the true nature of his or her illness, and how life-threatening it is, increases rather than decreases anxiety (for example, Spinetta, 1980). Open communication with the child is advocated. Research advises maintaining the child in his or her regular school as much as possible (Katz, 1980). Because cancer and its treatment can bring physical disfigurement, the child should be taught to handle the teasing that often awaits any youngster who looks different; assertion training and learning to ignore the hurtful remarks can be helpful. When radiation therapy makes the child's hair fall out, he or she may wish to wear a wig.

Pain accompanies both the diagnosis and treatment of childhood cancer. A child with leukemia must undergo frequent and regular bone marrow aspiration. The doctor inserts a long needle into the middle of the thigh bone and extracts some marrow. It hurts. And it is not the kind of pain that the individual readily habituates to (Katz, Kellerman, and Siegel, 1980). The experience takes a toll on the young patient, and on the parents as well. Specialists in behavioral pediatrics have developed hypnotic imagery techniques which teach the child to relax and thereby reduce the trauma of this inevitable medical event. Children who develop anticipatory anxiety before undergoing other painful medical procedures have been helped by viewing films of a coping model (Jay et al., 1982). Systematic desensitization to situations associated with the pain, such as entering the hospital and sitting in the waiting room, will reduce the level of anxiety with which a patient comes to the medical procedure and in turn to some extent the pain. Reducing anxiety can be of more general importance. An extremely anxious child, for example, may avoid the medical procedure or may begin to lose weight. Weight loss will decrease his or her chances of surviving cancer (Dewys et al., 1980).

Children and adolescents with other medical problems have also been helped by behavioral pediatrics. Chronic arthritic pain in the joints is a serious problem for hemophiliacs, people whose blood lacks a critical clotting factor. Varni (1981) has successfully treated such pain by hypnotic imagery techniques, teaching his patients both to relax and to increase blood flow to the affected joint. A higher surface temperature about the joint diminishes the need for pain medications, many of which have the undesirable side-effect of inhibiting platelet aggregation, thus worsening an already bad blood-clotting condition. When children with asthma are in no physical danger, paying little attention to their attacks can lessen their severity and duration (Creer, Weinberg, and Molk, 1974), although the asthma itself is by no means cured by this operant procedure.

Obesity in children is highly predictive of obesity in adulthood, which is, as we know, a major risk factor for such diseases as hypertension, heart disease, and diabetes. Behavioral investigators have been working to help overweight youngsters alter their eating habits, their exercise practices, and other aspects of their life styles that appear to contribute to the caloric intake and how it is or is not burned off (Epstein, Masek, and Marshall, 1978). For example, obese children, like obese adults, eat faster, take bigger bites, and chew their food less than do age peers of normal weight (Drabman et al., 1979). When their parents are also involved in treatment, weight can be lost permanently (Aragona, Cassady, and Drabman, 1975).

Another topic in behavioral pediatrics is known as *therapeutic compliance*. How can we get people to do the things that are necessary to prevent or manage an illness (Varni and Wallander, in press)? Juvenile diabetes serves as a good example of the challenge facing the youngsters and families affected. Urine must be tested several times a day to determine glucose (sugar) levels so that food intake and the amount of insulin can be adjusted. Indeed, diet itself poses a major challenge to youngsters. They must learn to resist the cultural blandishments to consume candy and other sweets. Their meals need to be timed to coincide with the peak action of an insulin injection so that the insulin does not lower glucose levels abnormally. Activity and exercise must also become part of the regimen, for they exert their own natural, insulinlike effect of utilizing glucose in the cells (Hobbs, Beck, and Wansley, 1984). With no cure of diabetes in sight, diabetics need to accept both their condition and the required regulation of some of the most basic of human drives. The complex set of self-care skills that a young person needs in order to cope with this serious but treatable disease is now benefiting from clinical research in behavioral pediatrics (Epstein et al., 1981).

has often become so weak and her physiological functioning so disturbed that she badly needs hospital treatment. Intravenous feeding will provide necessary nourishment in life-threatening situations. Behavior therapy programs in which the hospitalized anorexic is isolated as much as possible and given mealtime company, then periods of access to a television set, radio, or phonograph, walks with a student nurse, mail, and visitors as rewards for eating and gaining weight have been successful in producing immediate increases in body weight. The second goal of treatment, long-term maintenance of gains in body weight, is not reliably achieved by medical, behavioral, or traditional psychodynamic interventions (Bemis, 1978).

One mode of treatment that may be able to produce long-term gains for anorexics is family therapy. Like most other treatments, family therapy has been insufficiently studied for its long-term effects. One report, however, suggests that as many as 86 percent of fifty anorexic daughters treated with their families were still functioning well when assessed at times ranging between three months to four years after treatment (Rosman, Minuchin, and Liebman, 1976). Salvador Minuchin and his colleagues, who represent but one of several "schools" of family therapy, have done considerable work on anorexia nervosa. The treatment they have developed is called *the family lunch session*.

Before the specific treatment is described, a basic assumption in Minuchin's family treatment has to be made clear. He believes that "sick" family members, especially children, serve to deflect attention away from underlying conflict in family relationships. The illness is the family psychopathology become manifest, so to speak. In these families members are both rigid and deeply enmeshed in one another's lives, overprotect the children, and do not acknowledge conflicts. Thus the sickness acts to reduce friction surrounding these basic family disturbances. By providing an alternative focus of attention, the illness lessens the tension between family members. Minuchin believes that troubled families therefore act in a way that keeps the "sick" family member in the patient role (Minuchin et al., 1975). To treat the disorder, Minuchin attempts to redefine it as interpersonal rather than individual and to bring the family conflicts to the fore. Thus, it is theorized, the symptomatic family member is freed from having to maintain his or her problem, for it no longer deflects attention from the dysfunctional family.

Families of anorexics are seen by the therapist during mealtime, since the conflicts related to anorexia are believed to be most evident then. There are three major goals for these lunch sessions: (1) changing the patient role of the anorexic; (2) redefining the eating problem as an interpersonal one; and (3) preventing the parents from using their child's anorexia as a means of avoiding conflict. One strategy is to instruct each parent to try individually to force the child to eat. The other parent may leave the room. The individual efforts are expected to fail. But through this failure and the frustration of each, the mother and father may now work *together* to persuade the child to eat. Thus, rather than being a focus of conflict, the child's eating will produce cooperation and increase parental effectiveness in dealing with

the child (Rosman, Minuchin, and Liebman, 1975). Given the only moderate successes of other treatments devised for anorexics, family therapy appears promising.

Bulimia

For some time regarded as an occasional accompaniment to anorexia, *bulimia* has now been recognized by DSM-III as an eating disorder separate from anorexia nervosa. Bulimia is from the Greek words *bous* meaning head of cattle and *limos* meaning hunger. Often referred to as the binge-purge syndrome, it consists of episodes of gross overeating followed by induced vomiting or overdoses of laxatives to rid the body of the enormous amount of food just ingested. Unlike the anorexic, the bulimic seldom has abnormally low weight, but patients with both disorders do share an abnormal concern with body size, having a morbid fear of becoming fat. The anorexic and the bulimic both make persistent attempts to lose weight, but only the anorexic actually reduces food intake (Schlesier-Stropp, 1984).[12]

The foods bulimics choose have a texture that allows them to be eaten rapidly. They gobble them down, with little chewing, in a short span of time, and then may go in search of more food. A typical binge might consist of two packages of cookies and a loaf of bread, a gallon of milk and a half gallon of ice cream, a basket of fried chicken, and fistfuls of candy and pastries (*The New York Times*, October 20, 1981). Bulimics are painfully aware that their uncontrollable eating pattern is abnormal. They often feel disgust, helplessness, and panic while the binge is upon them. The purge is a source of relief for most victims.

The prevalence of bulimia is difficult to estimate because the eating and purging are done in private, in great secrecy, and body weight is generally within normal limits. The guilt-ridden victims are so careful to hide their disorder that those who live with them may not know of it. One estimate is that in the United States more than five million people, mostly women, are bulimic, binging-purging at least once a week, and sometimes spending upwards of a hundred dollars a day on food, usually high-calorie carbohydrates (Ely, 1983).

In her review of the bulimia literature, Schlesier-Stropp (1984) provides the following portrait of the typical binge eater. She is likely to be a Caucasian woman in her mid-twenties who began overeating at about age

[12]As noted earlier, aspects of both disorders are indeed found in some people; these individuals are sometimes referred to as bulimarexics.

BOX 15.5

DEPRESSION AND THE EATING DISORDERS

It had long been noticed that both anorexics and bulimics are often depressed, and now this depression is being examined. In a study by Ben-Tovim, Marilov, and Crisp (1979), of a group of twelve anorexics and nine bulimics, all the bulimics had clinical levels of depression, and one-third of the anorexics did. In a sample of 105 hospitalized anorexics, Eckert and his colleagues (1982) found high levels of depression, especially in the anorexics with the most severe eating difficulties. Winokur, March, and Mendels (1980) looked at the incidence of affective disorder in the families of anorexics and control subjects, the assumption being that they would be higher in the relatives of those with eating disorders if in fact depression and anorexia are linked. The hypothesis was confirmed. The fact that the affective problems of family members often antedated the onset of the patient's anorexia argues against the explanation that relatives became depressed as a reaction to the eating problem. In addition, Pope and Hudson (1984) have reported marked success in treating bulimia with antidepressant drugs. These lines of evidence point to a connection between depression and both anorexia and bulimia.

Let us assume that depression is indeed connected to anorexia and bulimia. But which is the cause and which the effect? If an anorexic loses 25 percent of her body weight, the drop in her body temperature and the starvation may cause biochemical changes that bring on depression. Similar harmful somatic changes can take place in bulimia. From a psychological point of view, the loss of control, guilt, and shame that accompany these eating disorders could easily eventuate in a clinical depression. On the other hand, depression could conceivably cause anorexia. Bruch (1980), a psychoanalytic theorist, suggests that a young woman may compensate for her depressed feelings by seeking to be thin and desirable; finding that as she loses weight her depression does not lift, she seeks to lose still more. Bruch (1981) also suggests that anorexia might be regarded as an adolescent female manifestation of depression. Looking to her appearance as both the cause and potential cure of her depression, the young woman loses more and more weight. These are all speculations. Certainly not all anorexics, and not all bulimics, are depressed, nor do all depressed young women become anorexic or bulimic. But with little doubt the relation between depression and both anorexia and bulimia is strong. What is needed are longitudinal studies that carefully observe young women over time for changes in their affective states as well as for the emergence of eating disorders (Hilterbrand, 1983).

---

eighteen and began purging, usually by vomiting, about a year later. She is usually within the normal weight range for her age and height, and her family history has an unusually high incidence of obesity and alcoholism. Several other points should be noted from Schlesier-Stropp's review: (1) very few men have been diagnosed as bulimic; (2) bulimia is a problem of adolescence and early adulthood, with very, very few cases beginning after age thirty; (3) overeating tends to precede purging by as much as three years; (4) the frequency of binging-purging cycles varies considerably, with some people doing so once a day, others once or so a week, still others as often as thirty times a week.

Bulimics also frequently suffer periods of depression (see Box 15.5) and anxiety as well as guilt over their inability to control binging. Their costly binge-purges can take up so many of their hours that social activities are restricted, financial resources squandered. Many bulimics are suicidal as well.

There are also physiological consequences, especially if the purging is done by vomiting. Sore throats, swollen salivary glands, and destruction of tooth enamel by the acidic vomitus have been reported in a significant number of bulimics; intestinal damage, nutritional deficiencies, and dehydration can also result. Menstrual irregularities, found frequently among female anorexics, are less severe among female bulimics (Ely, 1983; Schlesier-Stropp, 1984).

The behavior pattern of the bulimic is apparently not totally unlike the behavior of normal dieters. Herman and Polivy (1980) developed what they call the Restraint Scale to identify dieters. Subjects are asked how often are you dieting? What is the maximum amount of weight you lose in one month? Do you eat sensibly in front of others and splurge alone? What is your maximum weight gain within a week? Laboratory research with groups of subjects identified as restrained and unrestrained in their eating has offered interesting results. In one study participants were first given one, two, or no milk shakes and then free access to ice cream. Normal eaters' consumption of ice cream decreased, depending on how many milk shakes they had consumed earlier. Restrained eaters, however, showed the opposite pattern and ate more ice cream after two milk shakes than after none (Herman and Mack, 1975). Polivy (1976) has also shown that the eating of restrained eaters is cognitively controlled. That is, if told that they have eaten food high in calories, they subsequently eat more. From this information we may speculate that dieting to lose weight can actually set the stage for overeating, once the rules of the diet have already been violated. "Oh, well, I've already blown my diet today, so I might as well. . . ." In the extreme, such a mechanism might be relevant to bulimia.

What can be done for a person who is bulimic? Untreated, the problem is unlikely to go away. Systematic studies of different interventions are thus far few in number. Changing women's beliefs that equate thinness with success (Boskind-Lodahl and White, 1978), assertion training (White and Boskind-White, 1981), elaborate self-monitoring of food intake (Fairburn, 1980), and preventing the bulimic from vomiting after her binge (Rosen and Leitenberg, 1982) have all been tried. They have all had some successes, as have antidepressant drugs (Pope and Hudson, 1984). It must be concluded, however, that very little is known about the effective treatment of bulimia, reflecting our inadequate understanding of the disorder.

SUMMARY

DSM-III has greatly expanded the range of diagnosis applicable to children. Specific developmental disorders are diagnoses given children whose behavior differs from age-appropriate norms in a specific area of development. Children with these learning disabilities do poorly in reading, language, or mathematics, even though they are believed to have the intellectual capacity to achieve greater mastery. Theories of learning disabilities blame either perceptual deficits, for example, seeing letters reversed, or faulty instructional techniques. Special instruction coupled with dispensing rewards has been successful. Enuresis is diagnosed when children older than three and a half continue to wet the bed or themselves while awake. Although no theory of enuresis has strong support, a nighttime treatment based on learning principles and using a bell and pad is quite successful.

Attention deficit disorders and conduct problems are disorders of undercontrolled behavior. The attentional problems of hyperactive children, who are "running motors" in situations that call for sitting still, are now viewed as primary; DSM-III's diagnosis is attention deficit disorder with hyperactivity. Genetic studies, evidence of neurological problems and underarousal of the central nervous system, and the fact that hyperactivity can be induced by head injuries, brain diseases, and lead poisoning point to a physiological cause. The role of parents, either as causing or exacerbating the disorder, is also supported by some data. Stimulant drugs and rewards for sitting still and doing homework help to calm ADD-H children. Conduct disorders cover aggression, lying, theft, vandalism, and other acts and attitudes deemed unacceptable by others. A genetic predisposition, marital discord of parents, poor rearing in moral awareness, modeling and direct reinforcement of deviant behavior, and living in city slums are considered etiological factors. Reinforcement of prosocial behavior and teaching specific academic skills have proved promising interventions.

School phobia, social withdrawal, and depression are disorders of overcontrolled behavior. School phobia, a fear and refusal to go to school, is usually treated by gradual exposure to the feared situation, sometimes coupled with rewards for attending school. Children who withdraw socially are assumed to do so because of anxiety and poor social skills. The frequency of depression in children is not known for certain. Nor do we know for sure whether depressed children have symptoms different from those of depressed adults. Play therapy and family therapy are often applied to disorders of overcontrolled behavior. Behavioral pediatrics helps children adjust to serious illness.

The final disorders discussed are two enormously irregular eating patterns of adolescents. In anorexia nervosa the individual does not eat enough to maintain a healthy weight and, if not stopped, starves herself to death. It is much more common in adolescent women than men. None of the several theories of anorexia—fear of becoming sexually mature, weight phobia, striving for the slim image so esteemed by our society, conflict between wanting selfhood within the family and a fear of growing up, and physiological dysfunctions—has much support. Treatment of the disorder is difficult, although family therapy appears promising. In bulimia, sometimes found in anorexics but also considered to be a separate disorder, the individual indulges herself in binges of eating and then induces vomiting or takes a laxative to rid her body of the food. Although not as life-threatening as anorexia, bulimics suffer serious health consequences from their vomiting and forced bowel movements, such as tooth decay and damage to the intestines. In both eating disorders depression may play a role, not just as an understandable consequence but as a cause as well.

Karel Appel, *Child with Birds*, 1950 Oil on canvas, 39½″ × 39¾″.
Collection, The Museum of Modern Art, New York.   Mr. and Mrs. William B. Jaffe Fund.

MENTAL RETARDATION
AND INFANTILE AUTISM

Mental Retardation
Early Infantile Autism

Mental retardation and infantile autism are two very serious disorders of childhood. Because they interfere markedly with the normal developmental process, many of the children affected are unlikely to become well-functioning adults. Not only are these disorders lifelong but, if severe, they trammel all of a life. Mentally retarded and autistic children are similar in a number of respects. The majority of autistic children score significantly below average on intelligence tests, and many children with mental retardation make ritualistic hand movements, body-rock, and are injurious to themselves, actions which are even more frequent in those with autism. Educational interventions can also be similar for children with the two disorders. Both autism and the moderate, severe, and profound forms of mental retardation become evident in infancy or in very early childhood. Retardation and autism are, however, different disorders and different problems of development.

MENTAL RETARDATION

Kevin is a twenty-three-year-old man who was diagnosed in childhood as having moderate to severe mental retardation. He has been in educational programs since he was six years of age. At present he feeds and dresses himself but needs help in selecting clothing to wear and must be "checked" to ensure that everything is appropriate before going out. He finds his way around his community without getting lost, but he cannot take buses alone. He can go on errands to the grocery store about two blocks from his home, but he takes a note for the storekeeper and does not know whether he has been given the correct change. He is reliable in helping with simple household chores, such as making beds, setting the table, running the vacuum cleaner, and helping with simple tasks in the kitchen. His scores on the Wechsler Adult Intelligence Scale are very much below normal. The psychologist reported that Kevin did not respond on some verbal tasks, which had to be marked "Fail"; she did not know, however, whether he could have responded correctly were his speech better. Kevin's speech is indeed barely understandable, with many articulation problems, but he does respond to directions and requests. He functions adequately in a sheltered workshop on simple tasks, such as stuffing bags, simple assembly, and attaching stickers in

correct places. He understands that he is paid for work and talks about using the money he makes, but he must be supervised in selecting purchases. He functions socially at the level of a six-year-old (adapted from Grossman, 1983).

The Concept of Mental Retardation

DSM-III bases its definition of mental retardation and the criteria for its diagnosis on standards set by the American Association of Mental Deficiency in 1973. Their definition states mental retardation to be "significantly subaverage general intellectual functioning existing concurrently with deficits in adaptive behavior and manifested during the developmental period." Let us examine these several criteria.

Intelligence Test Scores as a Criterion

The first component of the definition requires a judgment of intelligence. Since there is no universal agreement on what constitutes general intellectual functioning, some might have difficulty accepting even this component. Most psychologists, however, rely on performance on standardized intelligence tests to determine intellectual functioning, although others have developed alternative testing procedures (see Box 16.1).

Performance on standardized intelligence tests may be used to determine a person's mental age, for items making up these tests are ordered by difficulty. National norms have been established to indicate the age levels at which most children are successful with the particular items. A person's mental age is the age level that is the norm for the items they are able to pass. For example, if a twelve-year-old girl is able to answer correctly items most nine-year-olds are able to pass, but not the items passed by the majority of older children, her mental age is nine.

Scores on IQ tests are standardized in such a way that 100 is the mean and 15 is the standard deviation, which is a measure of how scores are dispersed both above and below the mean. This means that approximately two-thirds of the population receive scores between 85 and 115. By the same token, a score of 130 means that the person is two standard deviations above the mean, placing him or her in the ninety-eighth percentile; and those with a score of 70 are the bottom 2 percent of the population. Basically, these statistical devices permit us to compare people to others, converting their actual test performance into standardized scores

BOX 16.1

NEW APPROACHES TO MEASURING IQ

Reuven Feuerstein, an Israeli psychologist and a former student of the renowned Swiss child psychologist Jean Piaget, had doubts about the construction and use of standardized IQ tests.

From his work with children from disadvantaged neighborhoods, he came to believe that many of them had more potential than their scores on IQ tests indicated. He believes, in addition, that children's performance after brief instructions should be the best indicator of their ability to learn. He has therefore developed the Learning Potential Assessment Device (LPAD) as an alternative to standardized IQ tests (Haywood et al., 1975; Feuerstein, 1980).

In order to minimize any potential bias caused by cultural or social class differences, Feuerstein selected only items that would be unfamiliar to all children. Figure 16.1 illustrates one of the problems on the LPAD. Although the items are similar to those found in standardized IQ tests, the testing procedure is not. The LPAD uses a test-train-retest process. First, the child's ability to solve the problems without any help is assessed. Next, the examiner provides brief training and instructions on how to solve the problems. Finally, the child is retested. Scores represent children's ability to learn following instructions, or their learning potential.

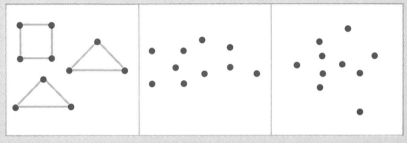

FIGURE 16.1 The object of this sample item from the Learning Potential Assessment Device is to find the square and the two triangles embedded in each set of dots. Each dot can be used just once, but the figures may overlap. The forms in the second and third boxes have exactly the same shapes and sizes as those in the first.

which tell us where a given individual falls in relation to others.

Testing children suspected of having mental retardation on standardized IQ tests presents several problems. First, the age norms were derived from samples of white, middle-class children. Generalizing to children from different racial or cultural backgrounds may not be valid. Second, few of the intelligence tests have been validated for IQ scores of less than 70. Individuals of low intellectual functioning were not adequately represented in the groups taking the tests when the scales were being compiled and standardized. Third, physical handicaps are not taken into account by several of the most reliable and frequently used IQ tests. Fourth, because a child with mental retardation may not be as familiar with the testing situation or be motivated to do well like other children, he or she may obtain a spuriously low IQ score.

From 1959 through 1973, the American Association of Mental Deficiency considered anyone who scored lower than one standard deviation below the mean on standardized IQ tests (IQ = 85) to have "significant subaverage general intellectual functioning." This criterion categorized approximately one-sixth of the population as mentally retarded. In 1973 the criterion was changed to approximately two standard deviations below the mean (IQ = 70). In essence, this definitional change reduced the incidence of mental retardation from 16.7 percent of the population to approximately 2.5 percent.

Adaptive Behavior as a Criterion

Adaptive behavior is taken to be the effectiveness or degree with which "an individual meets the standards of personal independence and social responsibility expected of his or her age and cultural group" (DSM-III, p. 37). The adaptive skills a child is expected to learn are caring for the self; acquiring concepts of time and money; being able to use tools, to shop, and to travel by public transportation; and becoming socially responsive and self-directive. The adolescent is expected to be able to apply academic skills, reasoning, and judgment to daily living and to participate in group activities. The adult, of course, is expected to be self-supporting and to assume social responsibilities.

Several tests have been constructed to assess adaptive behavior, the best known being the American Association of Mental Deficiency Adaptive Behavior Scale (ABS) (Nihira et al., 1974) and the Vineland Adaptive Behavior Scales, formerly the Vineland Scale of Social Maturity (Sparrow, Balla, and Cicchetti, 1984; Table 16.1).

TABLE 16.1 Sample Items from the Vineland Adaptive Behavior Scales *(from Sparrow, Balla, and Cicchetti, 1984)*

Age Level	Item
2 years	Says at least fifty recognizable words.
	Removes front-opening coat, sweater, or shirt without assistance.
5 years	Tells popular story, fairy tale, lengthy joke, or plot of television program.
	Ties shoelaces into a bow without assistance.
8 years	Keeps secrets or confidences for more than one day.
	Orders own meal in restaurant.
11 years	Uses the telephone for all kinds of calls, without assistance.
	Watches television or listens to radio for information about a particular area of interest.
16 years	Looks after own health.
	Responds to hints or indirect cues in conversation.

Although impairments in adaptive behavior have long been included in the definition of mental retardation, only recently have the tests been adequately standardized with firmly established norms. One problem with many assessments of adaptive behavior, however, is that they fail to consider the environment that the person must adapt to. A person who lives in a small rural community where everyone is acquainted may not need as complex skills as someone who lives in New York City. Youngsters who are quite competent working at farm chores, walking to school, and shopping at the local general store may, when transported to a city, be considered deficient in adaptive behavior if they are not able to ride the subway to school or buy groceries at a store where a foreign language is spoken. Since the requirements of one setting may be more complex than those of another, a criterion based on what the average,

middle-class white and urban child does may not be valid.[1] An effective and valid assessment of adaptive behavior should therefore consider the interaction between the child and the surroundings he or she must function in.

Another problem with assessing adaptive behavior is that the distinction between it and intelligence is sometimes blurred. Charlesworth (1976), an ethological psychologist who studies intelligence from an evolutionary perspective, believes that the ability to adapt to the environment is the hallmark of intelligence. According to this view, adaptive behavior scores are a more valid measure of intelligence than scores on IQ tests, which require more abstract thinking. Critics of the ethological perspective, however, point out that the cockroach has been best able to adapt to the environment, as evidenced by its length of time on earth, longer than that of any other creature. Not many people would be willing to claim that the cockroach is more intelligent than human beings.

Time of Onset as a Criterion

A final definitional criterion mandates that mental retardation be manifest before adulthood, that is, before age eighteen. This rules out classifying as mental retardation any deficits in intelligence and adaptive behavior from traumatic accidents or illnesses occurring later in life. For the majority of children with more severe impairments, diagnosis can usually be made during infancy, or sometimes even before the child is born. The majority of children considered mentally retarded, however, are not identified as such until they enter school. These children have no obvious physiological, neurological, or physical manifestations, and thus their problems become apparent only when they are not able to keep up with their peers in school. Once these mildly retarded children leave school and acquire a role in the community and work world, their mental retardation may become less evident once again. The increased prevalence of mental retardation in school-aged children has led some researchers to consider it a school phenomenon.

Classification of Mental Retardation

Four levels of mental deficiency are now recognized by DSM-III, each of them a specific subaverage range on the far left of the normal distribution curve of measured intelligence. The IQ ranges given are not of course the sole basis of diagnosis, for deficiencies in adaptive be-

[1]By the same token, city children may find themselves at a loss with some of the activities expected of youngsters living on a farm!

havior are also a criterion of mental retardation. Some persons falling in the mildly retarded range based on IQ may have no deficits in adaptive behavior and thus are not considered mentally retarded. The American Association on Mental Deficiency suggests that the IQ criterion be applied only after deficits in adaptive behavior have been identified. The following is a summary of how individuals at each level of mental retardation are described by Robinson and Robinson (1976).

Mild mental retardation (50 to 70 IQ) The mildly retarded comprise about 80 percent of all those who have IQs less than 70. They are not always distinguishable from normal youngsters until they enter school. By their late teens they can usually learn academic skills at about a sixth-grade level. As adults they are likely to be able to maintain themselves in unskilled jobs or in sheltered workshops, although they may need help with social and financial problems. Only about one percent are ever institutionalized, usually in adolescence for behavior problems. Most of the mildly retarded show no signs of brain pathology and are members of families whose intelligence and socioeconomic levels are low.

Moderate mental retardation (35 to 49 IQ) About 12 percent of those with IQs of less than 70 are moderately retarded. Brain damage and other pathologies are frequent. The moderately retarded may have physical defects and neurological dysfunctions that hinder fine motor skills, such as grasping and coloring within lines, and gross motor skills, such as running and climbing. During childhood these individuals are eligible for special classes in which the development of self-care skills rather than academic achievement is emphasized. The moderately retarded are unlikely to progress beyond the second-grade level in academic subjects and can manage this learning only in later childhood or as adults. They may, however, learn to travel alone in a familiar locality. Many are institutionalized. Although most can do useful work, few hold jobs except in sheltered workshops or in family businesses. Most live dependently within the family. Few have friends of their own, but they may be left alone without supervision for several hours at a time. Their retardation is likely to be identified in infancy or early childhood, for their sensorimotor coordination remains poor, and they are slow to develop verbal and social skills. In contrast to mildly retarded children, moderate retardates and those more seriously retarded are found in all socioeconomic groups.

Severe mental retardation (20 to 34 IQ) About 7 percent of those with IQs of less than 70 are severely retarded. They commonly have congenital physical ab-

normalities and limited sensorimotor control. Most are institutionalized and require constant aid and supervision. For children in this group to be able to speak and take care of their own basic needs requires prolonged training; the self-care training that is provided in the special classes within the school system is usually inadequate except for the upper portion of this group. As adults the severely retarded may be friendly but can usually communicate only briefly on a very concrete level. They engage in very little independent activity and are often lethargic, for their severe brain damage leaves them relatively passive and the circumstances of their lives allow them little stimulation. They may be able to perform very simple work under close supervision. Genetic disorders and environmental insults, such as severe oxygen deprivation at birth, account for most of this degree of retardation.

Profound mental retardation (below 20 IQ) Less than one percent of the retarded are profoundly so, requiring total supervision and often nursing care all their lives. Very little training is usually given them because it is assumed that they can learn little except possibly to walk, utter a few phrases, feed themselves, and use the toilet. Many have severe physical deformities as well as neurological damage and cannot get around on their own. There is a very high mortality rate during childhood.

Workers in a field called "special education" have developed parallel classification systems to aid in instructional programming. Labels such as "educable" and "trainable" are sometimes substituted for "mild" and "moderate" mental retardation, respectively. The present trend, however, is away from educational placement based on the student's degree of mental retardation and toward an individualized placement based on the person's strengths, weaknesses, and the amount of instruction needed. For example, in New York State a student who needs considerable one-on-one instruction because his intellectual functioning is deficient may be placed in the same classroom with a child who needs intensive instruction because she has emotional problems or physical handicaps. Thus students are identified by the classroom environment that they are judged to need. This approach can lessen the stigmatizing effects of being considered retarded.

Nature of Mental Retardation

Deficiencies in Adaptive Skills

A retarded person is generally limited at least to some

extent in six skills needed for daily living—communication, social skills, academic skills, sensorimotor skills, self-help skills, and vocational skills. A direct discussion of these adaptive skills provides a means of comparing degrees of mental retardation and the help that these children need.

Communication Although most children develop spontaneously the ability to speak and communicate, children with mental retardation may need help. Those with mild handicaps may require only minimal support to achieve effective communication, such as being assigned to a speech class. Children with more severe disabilities, however, may need years of intensive language training in order to express effectively their basic needs and feelings.

Through special training retarded children with rather severe disabilities can often acquire better language skill than was previously thought possible.

Some children are taught alternate means of communication, either to replace or to facilitate speech. Many children considered too disabled to use language can communicate effectively by sign language, communication boards and gestures, and photographs or drawings of common objects and actions (Fristoe and Lloyd, 1979).

Social skills It is not uncommon for children who are mildly retarded to have difficulties making and keeping friends. The more seriously retarded children show little awareness of social conventions. For example, many moderately and severely retarded youngsters seem overly friendly, wanting to be held and hugged by people whom they have just met. Children who are profoundly retarded may appear to be unaware of those who approach them.

Even children who are profoundly retarded, however, are capable of some social behavior. A child with multiple physical handicaps may be unable to talk or to reach out to someone but will smile at a favorite person. Because social behavior is not expressive does not mean that the person is not responding to social events. The individual may be experiencing more emotion than he or she is able to express.

Academic skills Academic skills, such as reading, writing, and mathematics, pose difficult problems for children with even mild mental handicaps. Still, they can learn enough arithmetic to shop effectively, to balance checkbooks, and to budget their money. They may also competently read recipes, how-to manuals, or just-for-fun books. Few teachers attempt to teach these skills, in their usual sense, to children with more severe handicaps. But many of these children have learned, with adequate instruction, "functional academics," for example, reading signs and labels frequently found on their daily route or using a calculator at a store.

Sensorimotor skills The degree of sensorimotor impairment is not consistently related to the degree of mental retardation. To be sure, many severely and profoundly retarded children have serious motor and sensory impairments. Children may also have physical disabilities but little or no mental impairment. Unfortunately, many children with physical disabilities, such as cerebral palsy[2] or hearing loss, may appear to be mentally retarded and subsequently be given an inappropriate educational curriculum. As clinicians become more aware of these problems and as assessment procedures become more sophisticated, fewer diagnostic errors are being made.

[2]Some people with cerebral palsy are very likely to be underestimated. Difficulties in walking and speaking, problems in using hands in a smooth, coordinated fashion, uncontrollable facial grimaces—these are frequently interpreted by others as signs that intelligence is defective. Although the majority of those with cerebral palsy do have IQs below the average, many individuals achieve uncommonly high levels of distinction which require superior intellectual functioning.

Self-help skills Self-help skills are exercised in the routine activities of daily living—bathing, dressing, eating, using a telephone. Many children with mild and moderate retardation have all these skills. Children with profound retardation often require extensive, arduous training and supervision in order to perform these basic tasks. But many of these children also have physical disabilities; a movement that is simple for a nonhandicapped person may pose a real challenge for someone with a limited range of motion.

Vocational skills One goal of education is to prepare children for a vocation. By the time most youngsters with mild mental retardation have finished school, they have acquired most of the skills needed to support themselves with a job in a competitive marketplace. In fact, children's mild handicaps may be quite apparent when they are confronted by academic subjects but disappear in the world of work. Children with moderate mental retardation may also have acquired some work skills, and many do get jobs. They are usually simple jobs, structured and supervised, in sheltered workshops or family businesses.

Retarded people do clerical, maintenance, and laundry work; packaging; electronic and other light assembly; cutting metals, drilling, and other machine work; farming, gardening, and carpentry. They are also in the domestic and food services and in other service fields. Some are taught to participate in the care and training of those more retarded than themselves and benefit greatly from the experience. Many retarded workers are very persistent, accurate, and punctual employees.

Deficiencies by Age Level

Often, rather than describing a person's performance by the degree of retardation, it is given by age level. An eighteen-year-old woman with severe mental retardation may be described as communicating at a six-year-old level. This means that her communicating abilities are comparable to those of the average six-year-old. Another person, scoring within the range of moderate retardation, may be expected to achieve social skills comparable to those of a seven- or eight-year-old and no better.

This type of description is based on certain assumptions. First, skills are assumed to develop in the same course for all people, regardless of their degree of mental handicap. Second, the ultimate level of performance reached by a person with mental retardation is assumed to be less than that of a nonretarded person. Finally, the age level reached in one skill, such as communication,

A retarded child is guided by her teacher in tracing letters, a beginning step in learning to read and write.

will be approximately the same as the age level reached in another, such as social skills.

These assumptions, although logically consistent, have not been substantiated. The way skills develop may depend in part on the primary cause of the mental retardation. For example, a fourteen-year-old boy diagnosed as moderately retarded and having specific brain damage may be unable to add one plus one yet have little problem reading and writing. Thus, although his academic performance may average out to that of a six-year-old, his and that of a normal six-year-old are really not comparable. In addition, by describing him as "at a six-year-old level," we are tempted to treat him as though he were six years old instead of fourteen. A boy of fourteen certainly has different experiences and emotions than a younger child, whether mentally retarded or not.[3]

Deficiencies in General Cognitive Abilities

Researchers who study mental retardation try to discover general cognitive abilities that are related to intelligence. They have assumed that defects in them are responsible for the observed deficits in adaptive behavior, and that significant improvements in cognitive functioning will be paralleled by improved adaptive behavior (Baumeister and Berkson, 1980).

---

[3]A normal six-year-old is also different in many ways from a retarded fourteen-year-old who is functioning at a six-year-old level.

Directed attention Zeaman and House (1963, 1979) have proposed that persons with mental retardation have problems in learning to do a task because they do not pay attention to the relevant dimensions. Several studies have compared children with mental retardation to normally achieving children on a discrimination learning task. The children were to select correctly between two objects on the basis of one or more specific dimensions, such as color, size, and shape. The results showed that mentally retarded children took longer to attend to the relevant dimensions of the objects. Once they did, their learning proceeded at the same rate as that of children without mental retardation. The researchers attributed the slower initial learning of the retarded children to their having attended to cues that were irrelevant for mastery.

Strategic processing Failure to use strategies in solving problems has been suggested as another general cognitive deficit of children with mental retardation (Detterman, 1979; Ellis, 1963, 1970). The number of items in short-term memory is limited, to about seven, and so is the length of time that they will be remembered. If not rehearsed, they usually fade in a few seconds. Long-term memory is a more permanent store with an almost infinite capacity. In 1963 Ellis proposed that children with mental retardation are not able to remember as many stimuli as normally achieving children of the same mental age. Many subsequent studies tried to specify more completely the nature of the memory differences. In general, the long-term memories of children with and without mental retardation were found to be the same, but not their short-term memories. Ellis interpreted the poor short-term memories of retarded children as a failure to rehearse items.

Several researchers have claimed that retarded children can apply strategic processes, but that they do not have spontaneous access to them and cannot coordinate them (Brown, 1974; Belmont and Butterfield, 1969, 1971). For example, if normally achieving children are given a list of ten items to remember, many will rehearse the items or find cues to help them remember them. Retarded children of comparable mental age do not do this on their own. But when the experimenter suggests repeating the words to themselves, they do so and remember as well as uninstructed, normally achieving youngsters.

Executive functioning Other researchers suggest that retarded children have general deficits in "executive functioning" (Borkowski, Reid, and Kurtz, in press; Butterfield and Belmont, 1977). The children fail to generalize strategies to other times and to other settings. Although the appropriate use of memory strategies is one aspect of executive functioning, it includes as well "metacognitive" activities such as knowing how to plan, to monitor progress, to solve problems, and to check outcomes for completeness and correctness. People with and without retardation may have strategic ability but not be able to apply it.

Control function of language Russian developmental psychologists have long been interested in discovering general cognitive deficits in individuals with mental retardation. Only recently has their work been translated into English and is therefore just beginning to be incorporated into experimental studies of mental retardation done in the United States. Lev Semenovich Vygotsky (1896–1934) had an extensive theory of thought and speech which regarded them as stemming from separate roots but later coinciding. He also theorized that private speech branches off from social speech and assumes a control function. The control function of language is crucial to intelligent behavior and develops in three stages (Vygotsky, 1978). A child's behavior is first controlled or regulated by instructions from other people. Then the child imitates these instructions aloud, and they serve as a cue or guide to behavior. The process is completed when the child's formerly spoken words become internalized, when they become inner speech. This natural internalizing process may break down in retarded children. Indeed, there is some evidence that retarded children as well as normal younger children are not proficient at using language to control their behavior (Meichenbaum and Goodman, 1969; Wertsch, 1979; Luria, 1961).

Etiology of Mental Retardation

Figure 16.2 illustrates the nature and etiology of mental retardation in three widening circles. The innermost circle represents the responsible causal agent. In only 25 percent of the mentally retarded population can this primary cause be specifically identified. The middle ring consists of the just-mentioned general cognitive abilities that people with mental retardation lack, at least to some extent. Because they have been found inadequate in people with all levels of mental retardation, it is tempting to view these deficiencies as causing the disability. The question remains, however, why are they lacking? The outer ring gives the six adaptive skills that are wanting in retarded children. Our focus in this section is on the innermost circle.

It is not known why, but mental retardation is nearly twice as common in boys as in girls. In general, persons with severe or profound mental retardation have an identifiable organic brain defect, whereas persons with less severe mental retardation do not. Persons whose mental retardation is associated with identifiable organic impairments are found in much the same percentages throughout all socioeconomic, ethnic, and racial groups. In contrast, persons with mild or moderate mental retardation are overrepresented in the lower socioeconomic classes.

No Identifiable Etiology

Two theories have been proposed to explain why people with no identifiable brain defect do not function within the normal range of intelligence. One, proposed by Edmund Zigler (1969), is called the developmental or social-deprivation theory. Basically, through cultural-familial deprivation, children's intelligence is thought to develop more slowly and to reach a lower ultimate level. Their deficiencies in adaptive functioning are considered both a direct result of the environment and a by-product of slower intellectual functioning. The higher incidence of mild and moderate mental retardation in the lower socioeconomic classes is consistent with the social-deprivation theory. Zigler's developmental position underlies the many education programs that have been implemented in efforts to bring mildly retarded children up to normal levels of intellectual and social functioning.

The alternate view is that brain damage, too slight to be detected by currently available methods, causes mild retardation. Baumeister and MacLean (1979), for example, propose that a trauma during the birth of infants, as well as other prenatal and perinatal conditions, damages the brain enough to cause mild retardation. But other factors, including the environment, may make the same degree of impairment manifest itself differently. The effects of the environment could explain the relatively few persons in the upper socioeconomic classes with mild retardation. Consider two persons with equal structural impairment, one from an upper socioeconomic level and one from a lower. The first individual's slight deficit could be compensated for by the enriched background. The second individual's deficit might be exaggerated by impoverished circumstances. To show signs of retardation, a socially advantaged person must have more extensive damage, which is impervious to help from an enriched upbringing.

Although researchers have attempted to determine the nature of the proposed physical brain impairment,

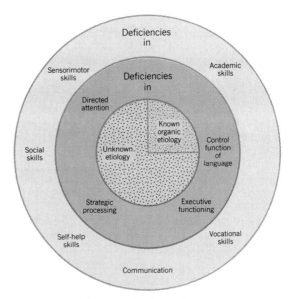

FIGURE 16.2 The causes of mental retardation and the adaptive skills and the general cognitive abilities that are wanting in retarded people.

results have thus far been inconclusive (Baumeister and MacLean, 1979; Karrer, Nelson, and Galbraith, 1979). Some evidence suggests, however, that the synaptic connections in the brains of children with mental retardation are less complex and less differentiated than those of normal children (Huttenlocher, 1974; Purpura, 1976). Unfortunately, the minor physical defects responsible for mild to moderate retardation are readily observable only in postmortem studies. Their presence is also somewhat of a chicken-and-egg question. Does the environmental deprivation or the structural deficit occur first? For example, studies of animals raised in a deprived environment find their brains smaller in size (Krech, Rosenzweig, and Bennett, 1966).

Genetic Conditons

The approximately 25 percent of people with mental retardation that has a *known* single organic cause inflate the incidence of retardation in the population over what would be statistically expected were no abnormal conditions present. These individuals create what is referred to as a ''bump'' at the bottom end of the normal curve (Figure 16.3). Genetic conditions, infectious diseases, accidents, prematurity, chemicals, and environmental hazards are six categories of organic impairment.

Chromosomal anomalies Four percent of all recognized pregnancies have chromosomal abnormalities. The majority of these pregnancies, however, end in spontaneous abortions or miscarriages. Only about one-

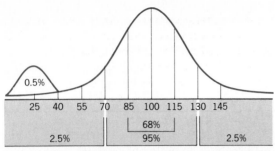

FIGURE 16.3 Normal curve showing the theoretical distribution of IQ scores. The bump on the left represents the actual frequency of severe and profound retardation, all of it with organic causes.

half of one percent of the babies who are born have a chromosomal abnormality (Smith, Bierman and Robinson, 1978). A significant proportion of these infants die soon after birth. Of the babies that survive, the largest percent have *Down's syndrome* or *trisomy 21*.

Down's syndrome is named after the British physician Langdon Down, who first described the clinical signs in 1866. In 1959 the French geneticist Jerome Lejeune and his colleagues identified its genetic basis. Human beings usually possess forty-six chromosomes, inheriting twenty-three from each parent by means of the germ cells. Individuals with Down's syndrome almost always have forty-seven chromosomes instead of forty-six. During maturation of the egg, something goes wrong so that the two chromosomes of pair 21, the smallest ones, fail to separate. If this egg is fertilized, uniting with a sperm, there will be three of chromosome 21; thus the technical term trisomy 21. Down's syndrome is found in approximately one out of 800 to 1200 live births.

All of a woman's eggs remain in prophase 1 of meiosis, basically in a suspended state of division, from the time that they were formed, when the woman was merely a fetus, until they begin to mature, usually one at a time, after puberty. The longer this period, the greater the chance for damage to pairs of chromosomes that would prevent their eventual separation. For this reason the incidence of Down's syndrome increases dramatically for mothers over the age of thirty-five; in 1973 women over thirty-five had little more than 13 percent of all pregnancies but bore more than one-half of the infants with trisomy 21.

Unlike women, men, after puberty, form new germ cells daily, fresh from the beginning. Recent research, however, indicates that in as many as 25 percent of Down's syndrome cases the father's sperm carries the extra chromosome (Magenis et al., 1977). Again, age at conception is implicated, especially rather advanced paternal age.

Fortunately, the amniotic fluid in which the fetus is immersed within the uterus contains cells and other substances from the fetus. A small amount of the fluid can be withdrawn by needle in the sixteenth week, a process called amniocentesis. The cells are cultured and later reveal whether chromosomes 21 are three. A new method, chorionic villi biopsy, can be performed even earlier, in the tenth week, an important advantage. The villi, tiny protrusions on the chorion, the outermost membrane surrounding the fetus, are tissue from the conceptus. They are taken by suction or clipping and removed directly through the mother's cervix. Cells of this tissue are cultured and then analyzed.

The IQs of people with Down's syndrome are in the mild to moderate range of mental retardation. In addition, they have many rather distinctive physical signs of their syndrome: short and stocky stature; oval, upward-slanting eyes; the epicanthic fold, a prolongation of the fold of the upper eyelid over the inner corner of the eye; sparse, fine, straight hair; a wide and flat nasal bridge; square-shaped ears; a large, furrowed tongue, protruding because the mouth is small and its roof low; short, broad hands with stubby fingers; a general loose-jointedness, particularly in the ankles; and a broad-based walk. Perhaps 40 percent of children with Down's syndrome have heart problems; a small minority may have blockages of the upper intestinal tract; and about one in six dies during the first year. Mortality after age forty is high; at autopsy brain tissue generally shows deterioration similar to that in Alzheimer's disease. Plastic surgeons have recently attenuated some of the more obvious facial distinctions of young people with Down's syndrome. Despite their mental retardation, most of these children learn to read, to write, and even to do math!

Within the past several years researchers have identified certain individuals with malformations of the X chromosome (Harvey, Judge, and Wiener, 1977). Specifically, the X chromosome may actually break in two—hence the name *fragile X*. Although the only physical symptom apparently associated with fragile X is enlargement of the testicles in males, the individual is consistently retarded. Females may be carriers of the fragile X chromosome without being mentally retarded. The incidence of mental retardation caused by fragile X has been estimated second to that caused by Down's syndrome (Gerald, 1980).

Recessive-gene diseases When a pair of defective recessive genes misdirect the formation of an enzyme, metabolic processes are disturbed. The problem may affect development of the embryo in the uterus or become important only much later in life.

In *phenylketonuria* (PKU) the infant, born normal, soon suffers from a deficiency of liver enzyme, phenylalanine hydroxylase, which is needed to convert phenylalanine, an amino acid of protein food, to tyrosine. Phenylalanine and its derivative phenylpyruvic acid build up in the body fluids, eventually giving the urine a musty odor and ultimately wreaking irreversible brain damage. The unmetabolized amino acid interferes with the process of myelination, the sheathing of neuron axons. This sheathing is essential for the rapid transmittal of impulses and thus of information; the neurons of the frontal lobes are particularly affected. Little wonder that mental retardation is profound.

Although a rare disease with an incidence of about one in 14,000 live births, it is estimated that one person in seventy is a carrier of the recessive gene. There is a blood test for prospective parents who have reason to suspect that they might be carriers. Fortunately too, after the PKU newborn has consumed milk for several days, an excess of unconverted phenylalanine can be detected in its blood. State laws require that the necessary test be given. If the test is positive, the parents are urged to provide the infant a diet low in phenylalanine. When the diet is restricted as early as the third month and until the age of six, when brain differentiation is relatively complete, cognitive development improves, sometimes to within the normal range (*Collaborative Study of Children Treated for Phenylketonuria*, 1975).

Tay-Sachs disease, a disorder of lipid metabolism transmitted by the pairing of single recessive genes, is found for the most part among Jewish families of northeastern Europe ancestry. In many metropolitan areas of the United States, large-scale screening programs provide Jewish couples with the blood tests that detect carriers. In Tay-Sachs disease an enzyme is missing in nerve cells, and fat accumulates in the nervous system. Analysis of substances in the amniotic fluid will reveal the absence of the enzyme.

The child born with Tay-Sachs disease suffers increasing muscular weakness, atrophy of the optic nerve, convulsions, and eventual blindness. One-fourth to one-half of these children are born to cousin marriages. They seldom live beyond the third year (Kolb, 1968).

Several hundred other recessive-gene diseases have been identified, many of them causing mental retardation. Only a very minor percentage of the cases of mental retardation is accounted for by any single disease. Genetic counseling can help future parents find out whether their backgrounds suggest that they are at risk

for carrying certain of these recessive genes. And amniocentesis and chorionic villi biopsy can reveal the presence of some of these problems in the fetus.

If the fetus is found to have genetic abnormalities, the parents usually have the option of abortion. Supporters of selective abortion refer to the poor quality of life of a retarded individual as well as to the emotional costs to the parents and the costs to society to provide care. Opponents of selective abortion claim that all life is sacred and that such fetuses have the right to life. It is not an easy issue.

Infectious Diseases

While in utero, the fetus is at increased risk of mental retardation from maternal infectious diseases. The consequences of these diseases are more serious during the first trimester of pregnancy, when the fetus has no detectable immunological response. In addition, the first trimester is a critical period in the brain's development. Cytomegalovirus, toxoplasmosis, rubella, herpes simplex, and syphilis are all maternal infections that may cause both physical deformities and mental retardation of the fetus. The mother may experience slight or even no symptoms from the infection, but the effects on the developing fetus can be devastating. Pregnant women

In amniocentesis a sample of fluid is withdrawn from within the amnion, the sac surrounding the fetus. The fluid can be analyzed and cultured to monitor the progress of fetuses suspected of being at risk for particular problems.

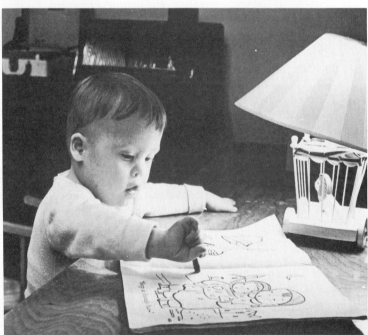

The development of a child with Down's syndrome, sensitively photographed by his father.

Prematurity, defined as delivery two or more weeks before term, together with the factors that cause it, puts the infant at risk for developing mental retardation.

who go to prenatal clinics are given a blood test for syphilis. Today women who contemplate having a child can take a blood test to determine whether they are immune to rubella; nearly 85 percent of American women are. A woman who is not should be vaccinated at least six months before becoming pregnant. The vaccine is routinely given to preschool children.

After birth, infectious diseases can also affect a child's developing brain. Encephalitis and meningococcal meningitis may cause irreversible brain damage and even death if contracted in infancy or early childhood. These infections in adulthood are usually far less serious, probably because the brain is largely developed by about the age of six. There are several forms of childhood meningitis, a disease in which the protective membranes of the brain are acutely inflamed and fever is very high. Even if the child survives and is not severely retarded, he or she is likely to be moderately or mildly so. Other disabling aftereffects are deafness, paralysis, and epilepsy.

Accidents

In the United States accidents are the leading cause of death and severe disability in children over one year of age. Falls and automobile accidents are among the most common mishaps in early childhood and may cause varying degrees of head injury and mental retardation. The institution of laws mandating that children riding in automobiles wear seat belts may play a major role in re-

ducing the incidence of mental retardation in young children.

Prematurity

A baby is considered premature if delivered two or more weeks before term. Prematurity and its associated problems are the number one cause of death in early infancy, before one year of age. Premature infants who survive have an increased risk of developing mental retardation. Although the relation between prematurity and mental retardation is quite high, it is difficult to substantiate prematurity per se as a causal factor. Many factors— poverty, teenage motherhood, inadequate nutrition, and poor prenatal care—all figure in prematurity. Additionally, premature infants may develop other medical problems that place them at increased risk for mental retardation.

There is some evidence, however, that preterm infants may not get off to a good start in intellectual development. Field and her colleagues (1979, 1980) have compared the patterns of mothers' interactions with their preterm infants to those of mothers with full-term infants. Those between mothers and preterm infants have less synchrony, less sensitivity, give and take, and turn taking. Field suggests that parents of preterm infants may be disappointed in their infants because they expect them to act their birth age, rather than their age since conception in the womb.

Noxious Chemical Substances

In the early 1960s a presumably harmless drug called thalidomide was prescribed in England, Canada, West Germany, and Scandinavia for pregnant women experiencing morning sickness. Thus they took the drug during the critical embryonic period. Many of the babies born to these mothers had arms and legs resembling the buds that precede limb development in the human embryo, a condition called phocomelia. Although thalidomide was quickly taken off the market, for thousands of infants the damage was already done.

The havoc wreaked by thalidomide was extreme, but it can serve to underscore the point that the ingestion of any chemical substance by a pregnant woman may cause the development of the fetus to diverge in a serious way from its normal track. One such chemical in widespread use is alcohol.

Consumption of even one or two glasses of wine each day during the first trimester of pregnancy increases by 10 percent the probability that the infant will be born with *fetal alcohol syndrome*. FAS consists of both physical symptoms—small head, widely spaced eyes, a flat nose, a deep upper lip, and a small stature which never catches up—and mental retardation. The risk of FAS increases with the amount of alcohol consumed. But even if the mother has only one or two alcohol binges during pregnancy, the infant may still develop FAS. As with many hazards, the risk to the fetus is greatest during the first trimester. Many women do not realize that they are pregnant until the later part of the first trimester. Thus, even if the mother quits drinking as soon as the pregnancy becomes known, some damage to the fetus may already have been done.

Environmental Hazards

Several environmental pollutants can cause poisoning and mental retardation. These include mercury, which may be transmitted through affected fish, and lead, which is found in lead-based paints, smog, and the exhaust from automobiles burning leaded gasoline. Lead poisoning can cause kidney and brain damage as well as anemia, mental retardation, seizures, and death. Lead-based paint is now prohibited, but it is still on the walls of lower-income housing and by this time old and flaking. The flakes have a sweet taste. Very young children absorb through the gastrointestinal track 40 percent of the lead they swallow, compared to the 5 to 10 percent of ingested lead absorbed by adults. They inhale two to three times as much airborne lead per unit of body weight as adults because of their higher metabolic rates and greater physical activity. A 1982 survey by the National Center for Health Statistics found excessive blood levels of lead in 4 percent of preschool children. In February 1985 the Federal Centers for Disease Control defined lead poisoning as a lead level of 35 micrograms per deciliter of blood, down from a previous level of 50 micrograms per deciliter, established in 1978. To lower the amount of lead in the air, the Environmental Protection Agency ruled in March 1985 that the maximum lead content of gasoline be reduced from 1.1 grams per gallon, the standard adopted in 1982, to 0.1 gram per gallon by January 1, 1986, a 91 percent cut. It also advanced by four years the date for the total ban of leaded gasoline, from 1992 to 1988.

The increasing technology of our society creates environmental hazards. The intent of a medical treatment is to do good, but an unforeseen consequence may be mental retardation. One such medical procedure—the diptheria-pertussis-tetanus (DPT) vaccine—carries such iatrogenic dangers, that is, problems induced inadvertently by the doctor. The DPT vaccine protects thousands of children from pertussis, a dangerous childhood disease more commonly known as whooping cough. The

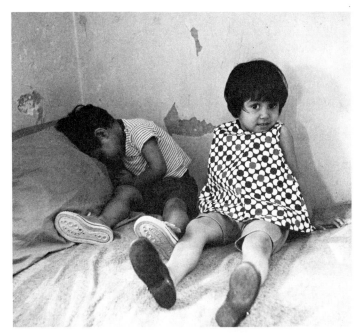

Eating sweet chips of lead-based paint can seriously damage the brain and cause mental retardation.

pertussis part of the vaccine, however, causes a high rate of adverse reactions in the children inoculated. These range from redness and swelling around the vaccinated area, to persistent crying or high-pitched screaming, to brain damage and sometimes even death. The DPT vaccine is estimated to be responsible for approximately fifty cases of severe mental retardation each year.

Although the potential side effects of the DPT vaccine were known in the early 1940s, the majority of the population remains unaware of the risks. A group of parents, Dissatisfied Parents Together, whose children have been adversely affected by the DPT vaccine, advocate federal legislation that would allow compensation for the families of DPT victims. The proposed legislation would also require doctors to give parents all the information available on the vaccine before it is administered and to report all adverse reactions.

Prevention of Mental Retardation

In the early 1960s a national effort was begun to prevent retardation. The President's Panel on Mental Retardation stated that if we would apply all the knowledge available, one-half of all new cases of mental retardation could be prevented (Begab, 1974). Prevention depends, in part, on understanding the factors causing retardation. The known organic causes present a fairly straightforward challenge and opportunity, and many of them can now be counteracted, as already indicated. For the majority of cases in which etiology is not as obvious, prevention becomes considerably more problematic.

Eugenics Movement

Historically, eugenics[4] has been practiced in an effort to decrease the numbers of mentally retarded people. Eugenics advocates that breeding be selective to increase, from one generation to another, the proportion of persons with better than average hereditary endowments. Social Darwinism had contributed the belief that mental retardation was caused largely by heredity. In 1903 the American Breeders Association was formed in order to devise guidelines and set up policies by which people

Project Head Start was designed as an early intervention to increase children's intellectual abilities.

should be allowed to conceive and bear children. Two remedies for mental retardation were advocated, segregation and sterilization.

Many large institutions were constructed where retarded individuals could live apart from the rest of the population. Most were no more than warehouses for anyone unfortunate enough to do poorly on newly con-

structed intelligence tests (Blatt, 1966). The majority of residents were newly arrived immigrants, members of racial minorities, children with physical handicaps, and indigents.

Although forced segregation reduced the number of children born to couples with one partner of questionable intelligence, it did not stop couples within institutions from bearing children. In Indiana, in 1907, the first mandatory sterilization law for women with mental retardation was passed. By 1930 twenty-eight states had these laws. Although their unconstitutionality was questioned, forced sterilization continued to be practiced in many institutions throughout the 1950s. In the 1960s safeguards were passed to protect the rights of individuals with mental retardation to marry and bear children.

Early Intervention

As the importance of environmental factors in the incidence of mental retardation became more widely recognized, prevention efforts turned to early intervention for children at risk through the impoverished circumstances of their rearing. Prevention of mild mental retardation depends on identifying susceptible people early and training them early, before they actually become retarded. Researchers are working both at improving the procedures for identifying children at risk and at designing the most effective preventive programs. Both children and parents may be given help, but most focus on preschool children.

Certainly the best-known, large-scale effort to raise the achievement and intellectual level of disadvantaged children is Project Head Start. Its purpose is to prepare children socially and culturally to succeed in the regular school setting by giving them experiences that they are missing at home. The impetus for Head Start came during the 1960s, when national attention was directed to problems of hunger and civil rights. If the thousands of children from culturally disadvantaged families were to have the same educational opportunities as other children, the poverty cycle would have to be broken and the standard of living raised considerably.

Project Head Start has served as an impetus for other preschool projects. One of the most comprehensive is the Abecedarian Project of the University of

[4]Eugenics should be distinguished from genetic counseling. Parents who learn through a counselor that they are at risk for giving birth to a sick infant are advised about the odds, the care that would be necessary for the child should it be born handicapped, and given other information that might help them reach a decision in a difficult predicament. In contrast, eugenics tries to create babies who, it is believed, will have certain qualities that may make them *superior*. During the

Third Reich the Nazis wanted to increase the numbers of blond, blue-eyed Aryan children. Nowadays there are ''sperm banks'' in which are stored the frozen sperm of men of uncommon professional distinction, such as brilliant scientists and writers, the hope being that, at some later time, a woman will apply to be impregnated by sperm judged to be genetically superior.

North Carolina. Launched in 1972, the Abecedarian Project was designed to lessen the degree of mental retardation or to prevent it in children considered to be at high risk (Ramey, MacPhee, and Yeates, 1982). The project directors identified 112 pregnant women whose social and economic resources were limited. They had received little education, and some had been malnourished during the pregnancy. The women were divided randomly into an experimental group and a control group. Since maternal malnutrition and poor medical care are known to be detrimental to infants, all families received medical and nutritional services after their child was born.

The infants in the experimental group began attending a preschool program before they were three months old. Care was provided all day long, for fifty weeks of the year. The aim of the program was to make certain that the children had opportunities to learn language and appropriate and adaptive social behavior, opportunities they might not be getting at home. Tests of experimental and control children were administered every three months during the first year and once a year thereafter.

Initial results, up to age three, revealed several differences between preschoolers enrolled in the Abecedarian program and the control children, who spent their days at home. Experimental children adapted more readily to unfamiliar situations and people, responded more appropriately and vigorously to task demands, and had more advanced speech. In general, these children were more adept at initiating and carrying out interactions with people and with objects at preschool. They were also able to attend to, comprehend, and carry out abstract and complex tasks. During laboratory play periods experimental children were better able to communicate their wants and needs to mother; their play periods also lasted longer and appeared more enjoyable to mother.

Control children whose mothers had been malnourished during pregnancy scored significantly lower on intelligence tests at three years of age than control children whose mothers had not. In contrast, the mother's earlier malnourishment did not affect the IQs of the experimental children, which suggests that the positive effects of the preschool program attenuated the negative effects of malnutrition.

The increasing use of day-care facilities by working mothers has recently received much public attention, for it is feared that the child's attachment to mother will suffer. The Abecedarian children's attachment to their mothers was therefore compared to their attachment to the preschool teacher. The preschool was found to have no negative effects. Preschool children demonstrated strong attachments to their mothers, preferring them to their preschool teacher.

Other unforeseen changes occurred in the Abecedarian families. First, more experimental mothers went back to school. Second, more experimental mothers obtained semiskilled or skilled jobs than did control mothers, who were more likely to be unemployed or else have an unskilled job. Although this was not a planned outcome, it should not be surprising. If the youngest, or only, child is in preschool for eight hours a day, the mother may have more time to pursue personal goals. Since a mother's lack of education often correlates with the incidence of mental retardation in her child, her pursuit of education and skilled work can be expected to benefit her child's intellectual development.

In spite of the initial significant positive effects of early intervention programs, the real test of their effectiveness is whether children are able to maintain their gains as they continue through school. Unfortunately, most follow-up studies of school-aged children, including those in Head Start and the Carolina Abecedarian Project, have found that once the intervention is withdrawn, experimental children regress toward the level of control children. Clearly, intervention programs should be continued during elementary school. In addition to what may be considered a moral imperative, the cost of preventing mental retardation must be far less than the thousands spent on caring for a retarded person throughout his or her life.

Treatment for Mental Retardation

Over the past two hundred years attitudes have swung like a pendulum from optimism and interest in educating the "feeble-minded" to bleak pessimism (Crissey, 1975). Édouard Seguin, a French physician and educator of the nineteenth century, was convinced that education was a universal right and that "idiots" were among the neediest. Considering mental retardation a weakness in the nervous system, he devised teaching methods to correct specific disabilities. After leaving Paris in 1848, he settled in Ohio and was instrumental in setting up special schools throughout the northeastern United States, one of them the Pennsylvania Training School for Idiots. (The reader will note how the connotative meanings of terms change. Nowadays health professionals would never use the word idiot, let alone include it in the name of an institution.) But disillusionment set in later in the century when the goals that had been confidently worked toward earlier were not attained. The children did not become normal, and the institutions grew and grew. Perhaps retarded individuals were just "born that way" and little could be done for them, except to maintain them and protect them from the intellectual demands of society. But now again, in the past few decades of this century, there have been serious and systematic attempts to educate retarded children to as full an extent as possible. Most retarded people can acquire the competencies needed to function effectively in the community.

Deinstitutionalization

Since the 1960s the trend has been to give retarded individuals educational and community services rather than institutional care. Like the emptying of mental hospitals, this is called "deinstitutionalization." According to the Developmentally Disabled Assistance and Bill of Rights Act, passed by Congress in 1975, retarded individuals have a right to appropriate treatment in the least restrictive residential setting. Ideally, moderately retarded people live in small- to medium-sized homelike residences, integrated into the community. A transition period gradually prepares the individual for the move from the institution to the community home. Medical care is provided the residents, and trained, live-in supervisors and concerned aides see to their special needs round the clock. Residents are encouraged to participate in the household routines to the best of their ability. Se-

Among the programs now offered retarded children are the Special Olympics.

Since the 1960s, many retarded adults have moved from large, isolated institutions to small, homelike group residences which are located in their communities.

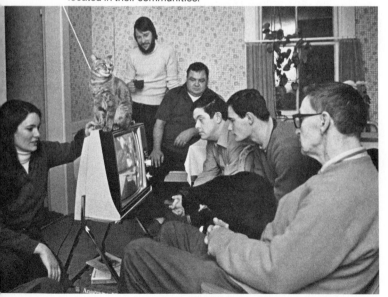

verely retarded children may live at home or in foster-care homes provided with educational and psychological services. Many mildly retarded persons who have jobs and are able to live independently have their own apartments. Others live together in semi-independent apartments of three to four retarded adults. The aid of a counselor is generally provided only in the evening.

Unfortunately, some large institutions have been closed down and the residents discharged without having a supervised community placement to go to. Other institutions have been renovated to provide a more homelike atmosphere. Residents are often clustered in cottages on the institution grounds. They are no longer living in barracks, but because institutions are often located outside the city limits, residents have few opportunities to shop in stores, take public transportation, and come in contact with normal people. At present, the majority who remain in institutions are severely and profoundly retarded people who have physical handicaps as well (Scheerenberger, 1984).

Public Law 94-142

In 1975 the United States Congress passed Public Law 94-142, the Education for All Handicapped Children

BOX 16.2

THE IDIOT SAVANT

One particularly interesting phenomenon, usually regarded as a special form of mental retardation, is the *idiot savant*, a retarded person with superior functioning in one narrow area of intellectual activity. A classic case history was reported by Scheerer, Rothman, and Goldstein (1945), who studied their subject intensively from his eleventh year through his sixteenth. During this period they gave the boy numerous problem-solving tasks and intelligence tests. L. was described as follows.

1. He had been failing at school, showing little interest in classroom activities and interacting minimally with classmates.

2. L. had developed the unusual talent of being able to provide, with little apparent thought, the day of the week for any date between 1880 and 1950. A favorite pastime was to ask people their birth dates and then immediately tell them on which day of the week they had been born and when their birthday would fall in any other given year, past or future. L. had been performing this feat since the age of seven. Scheerer and his colleagues point out, however, that he had no grasp of which of two people was the older, designating always the person whose birthday fell in an earlier part of the year. For example, he would regard anyone born on June 10 as being older than someone born on September 13, quite overlooking the year of birth or the physical appearance of the two people.

3. L. could quickly spell forward or backward practically any word pronounced to him, *but* without knowing its meaning or caring to.

4. The boy had a very well-developed but unusual musical ability. He could play many melodies on the piano by ear, that of Beethoven's "Moonlight Sonata," for example, but he seemed to have no grasp of what he was doing and took no enjoyment in it. He ignored any instructions or comments on his playing. Moreover, "He sings the accompaniment or the Italian words [to several operas] as they sound to him. Without knowing the language he reproduces it phonetically" (p. 2).

5. L.'s arithmetic ability was also unusual. He could, for example, add ten to twelve two-digit numbers as fast as they were recited to him, but he was unable to learn to add larger numbers. He could also count by 16 very rapidly—1, 17, 33, 49, and so on—but without any understanding of what the numbers meant; for instance, he could not state that 20 is larger than 8.

6. He easily learned the Gettysburg Address at age fourteen by rote memory, but without understanding its meaning.

Scheerer and his colleagues found L. to test at an IQ of 50 on the Binet scale. In their attempt to explain L.'s behavior, they rejected the idea that an idiot savant has a supernormal *ability* in one area. Rather they suggested that this kind of individual lacks the crucial ability to reason abstractly and that, given this serious handicap, he copes with the world by channeling his energy into rote memory feats. He develops rote skills to an unusually high degree because he can in essence do little else with his cortex. L.'s IQ rating was low because he could not perform tasks that children must handle in order to score in the normal range when they are eleven or older—namely tasks requiring abstract reasoning. For instance, shown an absurd picture of a man in the rain holding an umbrella upside down, the boy at age fifteen said "Yes, the man is holding an umbrella upside down. I don't know why, there is a lot of rain there" (p. 10). The overall problem was summarized by these workers as " . . . a general impairment of abstract capacity . . . , L. [even] succeeded in his own performance-specialties without having a genuine understanding of their meaning . . ." (p. 59).

Act. Passage of this law represented substantial gains for the educational rights of children with handicaps and, in addition, secured their integration into the community. Specifically, it includes five provisions.

1. **All handicapped children between the ages of three and twenty-one have the right to a free, appropriate public education.** Before the passage of this law, school districts could refuse to accept into their schools children with mental, emotional, or physical handicaps.

Parents of children with disabilities were often left with three choices: to pay for a private school, to attempt to care for their child at home, or to institutionalize the child. Because few parents could afford private schools or had the resources needed to care for their child at home, many children ended up in institutions. When P.L. 94-142 was instated, children with mental retardation could receive an appropriate education in a public school while their parents were given a break from caretaking responsibilities during the day.

2. Individual educational programs (IEPs) are mandated for each handicapped child, with annual reevaluations. The right of access to the public schools, in and of itself, does not guarantee that handicapped children will develop to their fullest potential. In fact, special-education classrooms have often been little more than daycare centers providing virtually no functional learning. Or, if instruction was provided, it was often not appropriate to the students' ages and levels of functioning and did not teach them the skills that they needed. P.L. 94-142 guarantees that training will be carefully tailored to the individual child. The goals for the children are determined at an IEP conference which must include, at the least, an administrator of the educational agency, the teacher, the children's parents, and, if possible, the students themselves. Further, P.L. 94-142 mandates that the goals for each IEP be reevaluated at least once a year to ensure that they continue to be relevant to what the child needs to learn and is capable of learning.

3. Students are entitled to education in the least restrictive environment. The "least restrictive environment" provision of P.L. 94-142 has been subject to differences in interpretation. In the abstract, the "least restrictive environment" is one that allows the handicapped student to develop mentally, physically, and socially with the fewest barriers while at the same time providing necessary support. To some the least restrictive environment is that of nonhandicapped peers. The children are educated at the same schools as normally achieving youngsters and are "mainstreamed" into some of their classrooms. Others would say that a segregated school provides the resources and intensive training required by retarded children.

The practice of mainstreaming children with severe mental retardation into classrooms with nonhandicapped peers is referred to as "social integration." At the very least, students with all levels of mental retardation are educated at the same schools as other same-aged students. They have the opportunity to encounter and interact with their peers on the playground, in the cafeteria, in the hallways. Special classes and teachers provide them their educational program. In essence, the students are socially integrated without being academically integrated.

Less severely retarded students may benefit from more pervasive integration. For example, students with mild or moderate mental retardation may cope effectively with their normally achieving peers in many nonacademic classes, such as art, gym, and home economics. Many students with only mild levels of retardation may even benefit from attending academic classes, supplemented by special classes geared to these students' special learning goals and learning styles.

Initial studies of how being mainstreamed with their peers affected mildly retarded children—examining achievement, self-esteem, social acceptance, and intelligence—found slightly positive effects, no effects, or even negative effects on their self-esteem (Gottlieb et al., 1983). Rather than giving up on mainstreaming after these initial reports, educators instead analyzed the reasons that results were not more positive. They devised a program to help the normally achieving students understand retarded children. The students watched a slide and sound presentation describing children with severe handicaps, followed by a question and answer period. Then they were given the opportunity to be a "Special Friend" to a student with severe handicaps. This system was compared to segregated schools and to integrated schools making no such effort. The normally achieving students in the school with the integration program had more positive attitudes toward children with severe handicaps and were more accepting of them. Those in the integrated schools without the special program were not as positive in their attitudes toward handicapped children but were more positive than students in completely segregated schools (Voeltz, 1980, 1982).

Programs sensitive to the problems inherent in mainstreaming appear likely to yield positive results for students both with and without mental retardation. Normal children can learn from early in life that there is tremendous diversity among human beings, that a child may be different in some very important ways and yet be worthy of respect and friendship. With support from parents and teachers, normal children may reach adulthood without the burden of prejudice of earlier generations. Such an eventuality would benefit both the normal child and his or her age-mate not blessed with as quick and receptive a mind.

4. The right to procedural due process is guaranteed. If the parents with a handicapped student or the students themselves believe that the education is not appropriate, or that the student's due process is being violated, they may protest to the proper school administrators. Often parents will believe that their child should be eligible for special services, but through the cutoff points of testing the child may not receive the necessary classification and thus miss out on the extra resources. Other parents may believe that the school is not teaching the students what they need to know when they graduate. P.L. 94-142 mandates that interested parties have the right to protest, to participate in hearings and appeals, and to have an attorney present.

The defendants in a legal case in Pennsylvania argued that some children who are severely and profoundly impaired tend to learn much more slowly than other children and tend much more quickly to forget what they have learned. The court concluded that a state rule limiting the school year to 180 days kept such children from obtaining an appropriate public education and, accordingly, violated P.L. 94-142. Year-round education was provided.

5. **States that comply with these statutes receive federal assistance.** Each state is required to report to the federal government whether or not its school districts are complying with the provisions of P.L. 94-142. When they do not comply, moneys are withheld from educational programming.

Teaching Strategies

Therapies based on the writings of Freud and Rogers, which rely heavily on verbal ability, indeed verbal facility, have had limited applicability in treating retarded people. But verbal exchanges with retarded individuals are of course possible and necessary. Moderately and mildly retarded children can use advice from a counselor or other adult; they all need to be reassured about the competencies that they have, and they can obtain encouragement and support from what kind and trustworthy people tell them (Robinson and Robinson, 1976). Play therapy has been adapted for treatment of retarded children, water and finger paints in unstructured sessions for the severely retarded, for example, coloring books and puzzles in more structured meetings with those less so (Leland and Smith, 1965).

Therapists treat retarded children with behavioral methods, in particular *applied behavior analysis*[5] and cognitive behavior therapy. Applied behavior analysis is most often used to teach severely and profoundly retarded children and those with autism the adaptive skills mentioned earlier: communication, self-help, social, and vocational skills. Children with mild and moderate mental retardation are given cognitive therapy to improve their general cognitive functioning.

Applied behavior analysis Children with severe and profound retardation usually need intensive instruction to be able merely to feed, toilet, and groom themselves. To teach a severely retarded child a particular routine, the therapist usually begins by analyzing and dividing the targeted behavior, such as eating, into smaller components: pick up spoon, scoop food from plate onto spoon, bring spoon to mouth, remove food with lips, chew and swallow food. Operant conditioning principles are then applied in order to teach the child these components of eating. For example, the child may be reinforced for successive approximations to picking up the spoon until he or she is able to do so. The chain may start at the first step of the sequence, picking up the spoon, and add further components till the last one is mastered; this is referred to as "forward chaining." Or the child may be taught the last step first, chewing and swallowing the food. Each time a step is mastered, the next-earlier step is taught. With this "backward chaining" procedure the student accomplishes the goal, actually eating the food, during each training period. The learning is slow and requires painstaking patience from the teacher. Nevertheless, both forward and backward chaining have been effective in teaching needed skills to children with severe and profound handicaps.

Applied behavior analysis is also used to reduce inappropriate and self-injurious behavior. Children with severe and profound mental handicaps who live in institutions are especially prone to stereotypies performed in isolation—repetitive, rhythmic, self-stimulatory motions, such as rocking back and forth, swaying, rolling the head—and to aggression against the self or toward other children and staff. These maladaptive movements and injurious actions can often be reduced by reinforcing substitute responses.

The significance of learning self-care and of reducing stereotypes and injurious actions must not be underestimated. Toilet-trained children, for example, are more comfortable, are liked better by the staff, and can leave the ward for other rooms and leave the building to play on the grounds. Mastering toilet training and learning to feed and dress themselves may even mean that severely retarded children can live at home. Most retarded people face discrimination from others, whose negative attitudes are based in part on the sometimes gross violations of norms committed by them. Being able to act more normally will increase their chances of interacting meaningfully with others. Moreover, the self-esteem that comes from learning to take better care of oneself is extremely bolstering.

Cognitive behavior therapy As we indicated earlier, retarded children fail to use strategies in solving problems, and when they do have strategies, they often do not apply them effectively. Self-instructional training, for example, teaches retarded children to guide their actions

[5]In the behavioral literature on mental retardation, this term is used more frequently than operant conditioning, but the two terms refer to the same kinds of assessments and interventions.

through speech. Meichenbaum and Goodman (1971) outline a five-step procedure based on a Russian theory for self-instructional training. First the instructor performs the task, speaking instructions aloud to herself while the child watches and listens. Then the child listens and performs the task while the instructor speaks instructions to him. The child repeats the task twice again, first giving himself instructions aloud, then whispering them. Finally, he is ready to perform the task while uttering self-talk instructions to himself.

Self-instructions have been employed to teach children self-control, to pay attention, as well as more academic tasks. Johnston and her colleagues (1980) have found self-instruction effective for teaching planning skills and addition and subtraction to mildly retarded children in a classroom. The children ask themselves, "How do I begin?" and "What kind of math problem is this?" They are also given answers to these questions. For example, "It's an add problem. I can tell by the sign." To self-instruct themselves in specific arithmetic techniques for carrying and borrowing, the children may learn to say, "I start with the top number in the one's column. Since it has two numbers, I have to carry." A question designed to foster monitoring or checking skills might be, "Is the answer right? I need to check it." Finally, the children learn to reinforce themselves for correct answers, "I got it right. I'm doing very well."

Ross and Ross (1973) implemented an exemplary program based on a finding by Milgram (1973) that retarded children do not use mediators to make associations as effectively as normal children do. They gave one group of children whose IQs ranged from 40 to 80 special game sessions in which they watched nonretarded children using sentences to link words together. Control retarded children continued in the usual curriculum of the school at which the study was being carried out. During the school year the special group of children showed marked increases in their measured IQ, and eleven of the thirty of them were actually transferred from the special classes to regular ones; the control children did not show such improvement.

EARLY INFANTILE AUTISM

Imagine that you are walking into a community group home for children with developmental disabilities. You are taking a class on mental retardation, and one of the requirements is to volunteer some time in this home. As several of the children rise to greet you, you become aware of some minor or major physical signs. One child has slanted eyes and a flat nose, characteristic of Down's syndrome. Another makes spastic movements, which you recognize as signs of cerebral palsy. A third child may call to you from a wheelchair with grunting noises and communicate with a combination of hand gestures and pictures. So far the children are as you expected from your readings.

Finally, you notice a fourth child in the room. He is standing in front of the fish tank. As you approach him, you notice that he has beautiful blue eyes, thick blond hair, and an impish smile. You think that he will probably be a popular high school football star in a few years. You naturally assume that he is a visitor to the group home or a sibling of one of the residents. You start talking to him about the fish. Instead of acknowledging your comment, or even your presence, he begins rocking back and forth while continuing to smile, as if enjoying a private joke. When the group home director enters the room, your first question is about the boy at the fish tank. The director tells you that he is autistic.

Descriptive Characteristics

From the time when it was first distinguished, _infantile autism_ has seemed to have a mystical aura about it. The syndrome was first identified in 1943 by a psychiatrist at Harvard, Leo Kanner, who noticed that eleven children who were not normal behaved in ways that were not common in children with mental retardation or with schizophrenia. He named the syndrome autism because he observed that, "there is from the start an _extreme autistic aloneness_ that, whenever possible, disregards, ignores, shuts out anything that comes to the child from the outside" (Kanner, 1943). Kanner considered autistic aloneness the most fundamental symptom, but he also found that the eleven had been unable from the beginning of life to relate to people in the ordinary way, were severely limited in language, and had a great obsessive desire that everything about them remain exactly the same.

Since Kanner's original description, others have tried to define the symptoms that differentiate autism from other related disorders. Rutter (1976) identified, in addition to a failure to develop social relations and to learn language, the ritualistic and compulsive activities of autistic children. Autism begins before the age of thirty months, indeed can be evident in the first weeks of life. The disorder was not accepted into official diagnostic nomenclature until the publication of DSM-III in 1980.

Autism occurs relatively infrequently in the general population, in approximately four or five infants out of

BOX 16.3

PERVASIVE DEVELOPMENTAL DISORDERS

There has been a good deal of confusion in the classification of serious disorders that begin in childhood. DSM-II used the diagnosis *childhood schizophrenia* for these conditions, implying that they were simply an early onset form of adult schizophrenia. But the available evidence did not support this supposition and instead demonstrated many differences between childhood and adult schizophrenia. For example, delusions and hallucinations did not seem to be prevalent among the children formerly considered schizophrenic. Although the sex ratio is about equal among adult schizophrenics, the so-designated schizophrenia of childhood was more common among males. Lotter (1966) indicated the ratio as 2.5 to 1, but Rutter (1967) placed it at 4.3 to 1. Moreover, unlike adult schizophrenia, the supposed childhood schizophrenia was not preponderant in the lower classes. Finally, in a well-executed, ten-year follow-up study of psychotic children, many of whom could be regarded as childhood schizophrenics, Lockyer and Rutter (1969) did not find that they had become adult schizophrenics. We must therefore conclude that the evidence does not favor viewing adult schizophrenia and the so-called childhood schizophrenia as two closely related disorders.

As a partial replacement for the earlier childhood schizophrenia diagnosis, DSM-III proposes *childhood onset pervasive developmental disorder*. The diagnosis is given children with profound disturbances in social relations and "oddities of behavior" that begin after thirty months but before twelve years of age. The children are not emotionally responsive, have little interest in their peers or in social relationships, and cling to their parents more than is appropriate for their age. They may have sudden episodes of intense anxiety and peculiar motor behavior, such as moving their hands and fingers in a stereotyped manner. Overresponsiveness or underresponsiveness to light, sound, and pain, self-mutilation, speech abnormalities, and an obsessive insistence on maintaining the same routines are other symptoms.

This new diagnosis is clearly applicable to some children who were formerly considered childhood schizophrenics. But children are not to be given the new diagnosis if they have delusions, hallucinations, or signs of thought disorder. According to DSM-III, children with such disturbances are to be diagnosed schizophrenic, for they meet the criteria that are applied to adults. Because of the diagnostic problems, we will not consider childhood onset pervasive developmental disorder any further but instead discuss in the text another pervasive developmental disorder, one which has intrigued and befuddled researchers and clinicians for several decades, infantile autism.

10,000. Studies indicate that about four times more boys have autism than girls. Autistic children are found in all socioeconomic classes and in all ethnic and racial groups.

Autism and Mental Retardation

Kanner believed that autistic children were probably of average intelligence. He based this conclusion on their good physical condition and on their skill at some tasks requiring rote memory or spatial ability. Empirical investigations indicate, however, that approximately 80 percent of autistic children score below 70 on standardized intelligence tests. Because of the significant number of autistic children who are also mentally retarded, it is sometimes difficult clearly to differentiate the two disabilities. For the most part, the information already presented about mental retardation accurately describes most autistic children as well.

But there are important differences. Although retarded children usually score consistently poorly on all parts of an intelligence test, the scores of autistic children may have a more differentiated pattern. In general, autistic children do worse on tasks requiring abstract thought, symbolism, or sequential logic, all of which may be associated with language. They usually obtain better scores on items requiring visual-spatial skills, such as matching designs in block design tests and in putting together disassembled objects (DeMyer, 1975; Rutter and Lockyer, 1967). In addition, like the idiot savant described earlier, they may have isolated skills reflecting great talent, such as multiplying two four-digit numbers rapidly in their heads. They may also have exceptional long-term memory, recalling the exact words of a song heard years earlier.

Because of the social nature of autistic children's disability, standard scores on intelligence tests have been questioned. In fact, autistic children are often referred to as "untestable." Although getting an autistic child into a testing situation is not an impossible task, managing to hold the child's attention long enough to indicate to him or her what is expected is another matter. Furthermore, most autistic children have little concern about how they score on an intelligence test and even less concern about showing the experimenter what they know. Indeed, autistic children can be very negativistic. In one study, for example, autistic children were asked to choose red or square objects from a stimulus array; each correct response was rewarded. Over 80 percent of the children tested made *fewer* correct responses than would be expected on the basis of chance alone. In other words, they actively avoided making correct responses (Cowan, Hoddinott, and Wright, 1965). Although these factors make testing difficult, mental health professionals do generally believe that the intellectual functioning of autistic children has significant deficits.

Extreme Autistic Aloneness

The fact that autism becomes evident before thirty months of age distinguishes it from schizophrenia and other disorders in which social withdrawal is a symptom. In a sense autistic children do not withdraw from society—they never joined it to begin with. Normal infants may show signs of attachment, usually to mother, as early as three months. In autistic children this early

When together, autistic children do not pay much attention to one another, preferring inanimate objects to the company of their peers.

attachment is virtually absent. They do not smile or reach out or look at their mothers when being fed. Infants may reject parents' affection by refusing to be held or cuddled, arching their back when picked up to minimize the contact normal infants—and parents—love. Although normal infants often coo or cry or fret in order to attract parental attention, autistic children seldom initiate contact with the caregiver, except when hungry or wet. Indeed, such children are often described as "good babies" because they make few demands. Autistic infants are content to sit quietly in their playpens, completely self-absorbed, never noticing the comings, goings, and doings of other people.

Impaired attachment to parents is not the only way in which the autistic child's social development is poor. He never approaches others and may look through or past people or turn his back on them. When play is initiated by someone else, however, the autistic child may be compliant and engage in the selected activity for a period of time. Physical play such as tickling and wrestling may actually appear to be enjoyable to the child.

Autistic infants may avert their gaze if parents try to communicate with them, and they are described as engaging in less eye contact than their peers. The sheer amount of eye gaze may sometimes be relatively normal, but not the way in which it is used. Normal children eyegaze to gain someone's attention or to direct the other person's attention to an object of regard. The autistic child generally does not do this (Mirenda, Donnellan, and Yoder, 1983).

Few autistic children may be said to have friends. Not only do they seldom initiate play with other children, but potential friends, like parents, usually receive little responsiveness from the autistic child. In fact, some autistic children appear not to recognize or distinguish one person from another. They do become preoccupied with and form strong attachments to keys, rocks, a wire mesh basket, light switches, a large blanket; to mechanical objects such as refrigerators and vacuum cleaners. If the object is something that they can carry, they walk around with it occupying their hands and keeping them from learning to do more useful things.

Parents may attribute their autistic infant's behavior to several factors. They may believe that the baby will "grow out of it" and become more responsive as it matures. They may adapt to the infant, believing that the behavior is normal, just different from what they expected. Other parents may realize that something is very wrong but be unable to admit it to themselves. Sometimes they fear that the baby is deaf. Parents may first realize that something is seriously awry when the infant misses an important developmental marker or when some abilities already acquired are lost. For example, an autistic infant may not say "Mama" or "Dada" as early as expected, if at all, or may begin to walk at the appropriate time but soon quit.

Communication Problems

Even before the period when language is usually acquired, autistic children have deficits in communication. Babbling, a descriptive term for the utterances of infants before they actually begin to use words, is less frequent in autistics and conveys less information than does that of other infants. Ricks (1972), for example, played tape recordings of the babbling of both autistic and mentally retarded infants to their own mothers and to other mothers. Although all mothers understood best the meaning of the noises of their own infants, the babbling of the autistic children was less meaningful to other mothers than was the babbling of the mentally retarded children.

By two years of age, most normally developing children are using words for meaningful objects in their surroundings and constructing one- and two-word sentences to express more complex thoughts. About 50 percent of all autistic children never learn to speak at all (Rutter, 1966). Even when they do, many peculiarities are found, among them *echolalia*. The child echoes, usually with remarkable fidelity and in a high-pitched monotone, what he or she has heard another person say. The teacher may ask an autistic boy, "Do you want a cookie?" The child's response will be, "Do you want a cookie?" This is immediate echolalia. In delayed echolalia the child may be in a room with the television on and with others conversing and appear to be completely uninterested. Several hours later or even the next day, the child may echo a word or phrase from the conversation or television program. Mute autistic children who later do acquire some functional speech through training must usually first pass through a stage of echolalia.

In the past most educators and researchers believed that echolalia served no functional purpose. Recently, Prizant (1983) and others have suggested that echolalia may actually be an attempt to communicate. The boy who was offered a cookie decides at a later time that he does want one. He will approach the teacher and ask, "Do you want a cookie?" Although the child may not know what each of the individual words means, he has certainly learned that the phrase is connected with getting a cookie.

Another abnormality common in the speech of autistic children is *pronoun reversal*. The children refer to themselves as "he," or "you," or by their own proper names; the pronouns "I" or "me" are seldom used and then only when referring to others. Pronoun reversal is closely linked to echolalia. Since autistic children often use echolalic speech, they will refer to themselves as they have heard others speak of them; pronouns are of course misapplied. For example,

Parent: "What are you doing, Johnny?"

Child: "He's here."

Parent: "Are you having a good time?"

Child: "He knows it."

If normal speech is built up, this pronoun reversal might be expected to disappear. It has been reported, however, to be highly resistant to change (Tramontana and Stimbert, 1970); some children have required very extensive training even after they have stopped parroting the phrases of other people.

Neologisms, made-up words or words used with other than their usual meaning, are another distinction of autistic children's speech. Neologisms may also be a consequence of echolalia. If a word or phrase heard earlier is repeated later by the autistic child, it may be inappropriate to the present situation. Autistic children may also change slightly the original words or phrase. These alterations may develop into made-up words.[6]

Two people talking together use some words that are abstract in meaning. Children with autism are very literal in their use of words. For example, a child who learned to say "Yes" when his father promised to put him on his shoulders if he said the word then used the word yes to mean only that he wanted to be placed on his father's shoulders. In the reverse, called metaphorical language, the child may say, "Do not drop the cat" to mean the more general "No," because his mother had used these emphatic words when he was about to drop the family kitten.

Communication deficiencies may leave a lasting mark of social retardation on the child. The link between social skills and language is made evident by the often spontaneous appearance of affectionate and dependent behavior in these children after they have been trained to speak (Churchill, 1969; Hewett, 1965).

---

[6]All children make up words in this fashion. Normal children, however, alter their idiosyncratic words as they listen to the speech of others and are corrected by those who care for them.

Compulsive and Ritualistic Acts

Autistic children become extremely upset over changes in daily routine and their surroundings. An offer of milk in a different drinking cup or a rearrangement of furniture may make them cry or bring on a temper tantrum. Even common greetings must not vary.

Each morning she had to be greeted with the set phrase, "Good morning, Lily, I am very, very glad to see you." If even one of the very's was omitted or another added she would start to scream wildly (Diamond, Baldwin, and Diamond, 1963. p. 304).

An "obsessional" quality, similar to the preservation of sameness, pervades the behavior of autistic children in other ways. In their play they may continually line up toys or construct intricate patterns out of household objects. They may become preoccupied with train schedules, subway routes, and number sequences. By adolescence full-blown obsessions sometimes appear.

Autistic children are also given to stereotypes, peculiar ritualistic hand movements and to other rhythmic movements, such as endless body rocking, hand flapping, and walking on tiptoe. They spin and twirl string, crayons, sticks, and plates, twiddle their fingers in front of their eyes, and stare at fans and spinning things. They may also become preoccupied with manipulating a mechanical object and be very upset when interrupted. Often toys are used in a compulsive and ritualistic manner rather than for their intended purpose.

This obsessional quality may be related to "overselectivity," an attentional problem studied by Lovaas and his colleagues (1971). Three cues, one visual, one auditory, and one tactile, were presented simultaneously to normal, autistic, and retarded children. They were taught to press a bar in response and were then rewarded with candy. Later only one cue was given at a time. The normal children had considered the situation in its entirety and were thus able to respond to each of the three separate cues. Retarded children pressed the bar for two of the cues, autistic children for only one. They had not attended to the entire pattern of stimulation, rather only one part of it.

Prognosis in Infantile Autism

What happens to such severely disturbed children when they reach adulthood? Kanner (1973) reported on the adult status of nine of the eleven children whom he had described in his original paper on autism. Two developed epileptic seizures; by 1966 one of them had died, and the other was in a state mental hospital. Four others had spent most of their lives in institutions.

Originally fighting for their aloneness and basking in the content that it gave them, originally alert to unwelcome changes and, in their own way, struggling for the status quo, originally astounding the observer with their phenomenal feats of memory, they yielded readily to the uninterrupted self-isolation and soon settled down to a life not too remote from a nirvanalike existence (p. 185).

Of the remaining three, one had remained mute but was working on a farm and as an orderly in a nursing home. The last two have made at least somewhat satisfactory recoveries. Although both still live with their parents and have little social life, they are gainfully employed and have some recreational interests. Other follow-up studies corroborate the generally gloomy picture of adult autistics (for example, Rutter, 1967; Treffert, McAndrew, and Dreifuerst, 1973; Lotter, 1974). From his review of all published studies, Lotter (1978) concluded that only 5 to 17 percent of autistic children had made a relatively good adjustment in adulthood, leading independent lives but with some residual problems, such as social awkwardness. Most of the others had limited lives, and about half were institutionalized.

Etiology of Infantile Autism

Psychological Bases of Autism

Since Kanner first described autism, researchers have of course been seeking its cause. Some of the same reasons that led Kanner to consider autistic children to be average in intelligence, their normal appearance and apparently normal physiological functioning, led others to regard autism as environmentally caused.

One of the best-known of the psychological theories was formulated by Bruno Bettelheim (1967). The basic supposition of his theory is that autism closely resembles the apathy and hopelessness found among inmates of German concentration camps during World War II (see page 130). Bettelheim hypothesizes that the young infant has rejecting parents and is able to perceive their negative feelings. He finds that his own actions have little impact on their unresponsiveness. The child comes to believe "that [his] own efforts have no power to influence the world, because of the earlier conviction that the world is insensitive to [his] reactions" (p. 46).

This experience of helplessness, which appears similar to the learned helplessness discussed earlier (see page 20), is viewed as extremely frustrating and frightening for the child. But he is unwilling to communicate his fears because he feels that nothing good can come from it. He never really enters the world but builds the "empty fortress" of autism against pain and disappointment. His only activities—his ritualistic hand movements and echolalic speech—are more a means of shutting out the world than of truly meeting it. An elaborate fantasy life is created, and insistence on sameness is the rule that brings permanence and order. Autistic children remain safe only if everything about them stays put. Since the essential purpose of activity is to bring about change, autistic children avoid any sort of action; their universe centers on a static environment, beyond which they will not move.

Social-learning theorists, like those who are psychoanalytically oriented, have postulated that certain childhood learning experiences cause autism. Ferster (1961), in an extremely influential article, suggested that the inattention of the parents, especially of the mother, prevents establishment of the associations that make human beings reinforcers. And because the parents have not become reinforcers, they cannot control the child's behavior, the end result being infantile autism. Ferster's reasoning is as follows.

1. Behavior is controlled primarily by its consequences.

2. Initially, the young child responds only to primary reinforcers, such as food and milk.

3. As children grow older, their behavior comes more under the control of secondary and generalized reinforcers, such as praise and love. These social rewards have acquired their reinforcing properties through contiguous association with primary rewards.

4. The behavior of autistic children is a consequence of not having adequate secondary and generalized reinforcers. Because their parents neglect them—for example, by being excessively involved in professional and other non-family-oriented activities—they have no opportunity to acquire generalized reinforcers.

5. Thus the children learn to function alone or autistically and never become responsive to human contact, having been deprived of it during the earlier stages of life.

It is clear that both Bettelheim and Ferster, and others, have implied that parents play the crucial role in the etiology of autism. Many investigators have studied the characteristics of these parents; for a psychogenic theory of a childhood disorder to have any plausibility at all, something very unusual and damaging about the parents' treatment of their children would have to be demonstrated.

In his early papers Kanner described the parents of autistic children as cold, insensitive, meticulous, introverted, distant, and highly intellectual (Kanner and Eisenberg, 1955). He summed up his theory of how such traits affect the children by saying that they are reared in "emotional refrigeration." Others (for example, Singer and Wynne, 1963; Rimland, 1964) have also noted the detachment of parents of autistic children, although Rimland has used less pejorative adjectives. Singer and Wynne have described several means by which these parents "disaffiliate" themselves from their children. Some are cynical about all interpersonal relations and are emotionally cold; others are passive and apathetic; and still others maintain an obsessive, intellectual distance from people.

Systematic investigations, however, have failed to confirm these earlier clinical impressions. For example, Cox and his colleagues (1975) compared the parents of autistic children to those of children with receptive aphasia (a disorder in understanding speech); the two groups did *not* differ in warmth, emotional demonstrativeness, responsiveness, and sociability. Similarly, De-Myer and her co-workers (1972) did not find the parents of autistic children to be rejecting, nor did Cantwell, Baker, and Rutter (1978) or McAdoo and DeMyer (1978) find psychiatric disorders in parents, using standard measures like the MMPI. The weight of the evidence is overwhelming: there is nothing remarkable about the parents of autistic children.

Even if we were to ignore these recent findings, the direction of a possible correlation between parental characteristics and autism is not easily determined. Any deviant parental behavior could be a reaction to the child's abnormality rather than the other way around. Moreover, although autism is a severe disorder, the parental behavior that has been discussed does not appear likely to be more than mildly damaging. It would seem that only very gross mistreatment, such as keeping the child in a locked closet, could precipitate severe problems so early in life. There have been few reports of exceedingly harsh treatment of autistic children (see Box 16.4).

It is commonly accepted in contemporary science that the failure to prove an effect does not mean it does not exist. Although investigations have not uncovered harmful parental influences on children of a sort that could reasonably cause infantile autism, this does not mean that such influences do not exist. In a purely logical sense, they may be operating, and so far we have simply failed to discover them. But in the meantime the very early onset of autism and an accumulation of neu-

BOX 16.4

THE PERNICIOUS NATURE OF PSYCHOGENIC THEORIES

Readers of this book have no doubt noticed that the authors are often critical of some psychogenic theories, both psychoanalytic and learning. In addition to our aspirations to provide as scientifically accurate a textbook as possible, we are conerned about the impact that theories may have on people. Consider, for a moment, what your feelings might be if a psychiatrist or psychologist were to tell you that your unconscious hostility has caused your child to be mute at the age of six. Or how would you feel if you were told that your commitment to professional activities has brought about the autistic behavior patterns of your child? The fact is, of course, that the truth of these allegations has yet to be demonstrated, and considerable information even contradicts these views. But in the meantime a tremendous emotional burden is placed on parents who have, over the years, been told that they are at fault.

As Rimland (1964) has suggested, considering autism psychogenic in origin may be not only an inadequate hypothesis but also a pernicious one.

rological and genetic evidence do imply a physiological basis for this puzzling disorder.

Physiological Bases of Infantile Autism

Genetic factors Genetic studies of autism are difficult to conduct because the disorder is so rare. Indeed, the family method presents special problems because autistic persons almost never marry. But autistics do often have siblings, so that the rate of autism in their brothers and sisters can be assessed. It turns out to be about 2 percent (Rutter, 1967). Although this is a small percentage in and of itself, it represents a fiftyfold increase in risk as compared to the morbidity risk in the general population.

Early twin studies of autism were seriously flawed, principally because of sampling bias. But evidence of the importance of genetic factors in autism is provided by a methodologically sound study conducted by Folstein and Rutter (1978). In ten pairs of fraternal twins, one of whom had autism, there was no concordance of the co-twins. But in the eleven pairs of identical twins, one of whom had autism, the concordance rate was 36 percent: four of the co-twins had autism. In addition to examining concordance for autism, Folstein and Rutter also looked for cognitive disabilities, such as delayed speech, problems in saying words properly, and low IQ, in the co-twins. Concordance for cognitive impairment was 82 percent for the MZ pairs and 10 percent for the DZ. Thus the identical twin of an autistic is very likely to have difficulties of speech and intellect, but the fraternal twin of an autistic is not. Autism is apparently linked genetically to a broader deficit in cognitive ability. Taken together, the evidence from family and twin studies supports a genetic basis for infantile autism.

Neurological factors Early on EEG studies of autistic children indicated that many had abnormal brain wave patterns (for example, Hutt et al., 1964). Neurological examinations have also revealed signs of damage in a large percentage of autistic children (Bosch, 1970; De-Myer et al., 1973; Gubbay, Lobascher, and Kingerlee, 1970). Thus a large proportion of autistic children appear to have a neurological dysfunction, as assessed by EEG and other neurological tests. The degree of neurological abnormality or central nervous system dysfunction seems to be related to the severity of the autistic symptoms. In adolescence 30 percent of autistic children begin having epileptic seizures. Furthermore, the prevalence of autism in children whose mothers had rubella during the prenatal period is approximately ten times higher than that in the general population of children. A syndrome similar to autism may follow in the aftermath of meningitis, encephalitis, and tuberous sclerosis and develop through PKU, all of which may affect central nervous system functioning. These findings, plus the degree of mental retardation, would seem to link autism and brain damage.

Autism cannot, however, be attributed to general brain damage for two reasons. First, not all autistic children show signs of brain damage. Although the EEGs of autistic children often indicate abnormal brain wave patterns, many are within the normal range. Second, many children have similar brain damage but no symptoms of autism. In fact, most children who are brain-damaged are not autistic.

Treatment of Infantile Autism

Special Problems in Treating Autistic Children

Educational programs for autistic children usually try to relieve their symptoms and improve their communication, social skills, and adaptive behavior so that they can become more independent. Autistic children have several problems that make teaching them difficult, however. First, they do not adjust to changes in routines, including special events and substitute teachers. Second, their behavior problems and self-stimulatory movements may interfere with effective teaching. The similar behavior of children with other disabilities may intrude on the teacher's efforts, but not with the same frequency and severity.

Third, it is particularly difficult to find reinforcers that motivate autistic children. Normal children are motivated to explore and control their surroundings but not children with autism. For reinforcers to be effective with autistic children, they must be explicit, concrete, or highly salient. A widely used method of increasing the range of reinforcers that autistic children respond to is to pair social reinforcement with primary reinforcers such as food.

A further problem that often interferes with the learning of autistic children is their overselectivity of attention. When the child's attention becomes focused on one particular aspect of a task or situation, other properties, including relevant ones, may not even be noticed. For example, in sign language training the instructor often says a word while making its sign in the presence of the referent object or its image. Students, it is assumed, will learn to associate the sign with the spoken word and the object. Children with autism are more likely to at-

tend to only one of the cues, however. An autistic child may appear to have learned to associate the sign with several spoken words and the object but has attended instead to the instructor's mouth movements. The child then will not select the correct object when he hears the word or sees the sign but only when he watches the instructor's lips move.

An additional concern, one which educators and therapists of autistic children share with educators of retarded children, is the youngsters' inability to generalize the learning. The overselective nature of autistic children's attention makes generalization especially difficult for them. For example, the child who learned several words by watching the instructor's lip movements may not comprehend the same words spoken by another person with less pronounced movements of the lips. In other words, the child's response may be contingent on a nonessential aspect of the situation, which is usually not present if the context is changed. In spite of all these problems, educational programs for students with autism have achieved some positive results.

Social-Learning Treatments

Child-centered approaches Mental health professionals agree that autistic children have been helped through modeling and operant conditioning. On the positive side, behavior therapists have helped autistic children talk (Hewett, 1965), modified their echolalic speech

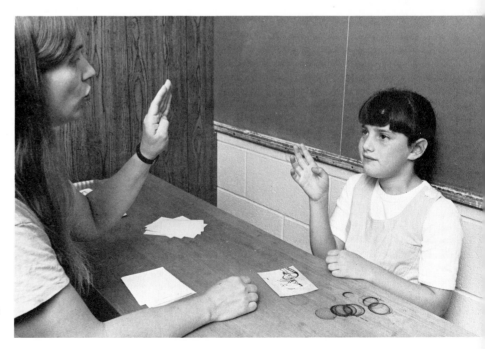

Autistic children may more readily learn to communicate with sign language than through spoken words.

(Carr, Schreibman, and Lovaas, 1975), encouraged them to play with other children (Romanczyk et al., 1975), and helped them become more generally responsive to adults (Davison, 1964).

In an early case report, which has served as an exemplar for over two decades of conditioning treatments for autism, Wolf, Risley, and Mees (1964) reduced the incidence of tantrums by regarding them as operant behavior maintained by adult attention. They isolated the boy in a room for short periods of time whenever he threw a temper tantrum. The acting out was soon eliminated. This _time-out_ procedure, whereby a person is temporarily excluded from situations in which positive reinforcement might be obtained, has proved effective with a number of behavioral problems and with children other than those diagnosed as autistic. For extreme and dangerous behavior, such as self-mutilation, brief but strong punishment may be necessary. Autistic children may bang their heads so hard against the wall that they have concussions, and they may bite their flesh to the bone. Ivar Lovaas, a leading clinical researcher in therapy for autistic children at the University of California at Los Angeles, demonstrated the effectiveness of spankings and brief electric shock in halting their self-destructive acts (Lovaas et al., 1965). Some therapists object to procedures in which children receive bodily punishment, but the investigators and the vast majority of other professionals feel that they are justified in extreme cases. Electric shock rapidly eliminates sometimes life-threatening behavior and enables therapists to proceed with more positive instruction and remediation (Lovaas, 1977). The Lovaas group has also found that therapeutic improvement can be sustained if the parents are trained to maintain the same reinforcement contingencies at home; when such children entered institutions where reinforcement contingencies were not sustained, they lost whatever gains they had made (Lovaas et al., 1973).

More recent work by Donnellan and her colleagues (1984) extends applied behavior analysis to the communicative aspects of some autistic children's aggressive behavior. According to these researchers, many of their tantrums and outbursts may be caused by their inability to communicate in a more positive, socially appropriate manner. They describe a twelve-year-old boy with autism and moderate mental retardation. The boy's parents wanted to be able to take him on shopping trips and other community outings. When in public he would vocalize loudly and repetitively, however, causing considerable disturbance.

The first step in treating the boy's outbursts was to search for consistencies in the conditions that brought them on. The researchers observed that the boy went into his vocal tantrums when confronted by noise and crowds. The next question the researchers asked was what the boy might be communicating with his inappropriate behavior. They thought that he might be trying to say, "I'm anxious and overwhelmed by the noise and crowds." With other autistic children in other situations, possible answers might be, "This task is too difficult." "I'm frustrated." "I'm bored." "I don't feel good." "I want some attention."

Donnellan and her co-workers decided to teach the autistic boy an alternate method of decreasing his overstimulation while in the community. They taught him to use a stereo headset with a cassette tape. Whenever he felt the need to reduce stimulation, he could put on the headset rather than have a verbal tantrum. Gradually, he needed the headset less and less as he learned to adapt to public places.

Family-centered approaches   Autism, like mental retardation, places considerable stress on a family. Because autistic children have few or no physical handicaps and some isolated normal and even superior abilities, their parents may even hope that the diagnosis is erroneous. One way to ease the parents' burden is to instruct them about the nature of infantile autism, especially the virtual certainty that it does not have a psychogenic cause. Relieved of the guilt associated with this pernicious belief, some parents will want to become involved in the education of their child. There is reason to expect the education provided by parents to be more beneficial to the child than clinic- or hospital-based treatment. Certainly Lovaas and his colleagues (1973) found reinforcement by parents necessary in maintaining gains.

Koegel and his colleagues (1982) have replicated and expanded the Lovaas research. After only 25 to 30 hours of parent training, autistic children's improvements on standardized tests and behavioral measures were similar to those after over 200 hours of direct clinic treatment. Koegel concluded that parent training is superior in generalizing learning because parents are present in many different situations, and, when training their children, they may actually spend more time with them in recreational and leisure activities.[7]

[7]At the same time, it must be clearly stated that some autistic and other severely disturbed children can be adequately looked after only in a group home staffed by mental health professionals. Moreover, the circumstances of some families preclude the home care of their seriously disturbed child. The fact that effective treatments can be implemented by parents should not be transformed into a must-do for those who are already living their lives and taking care of other normal children under trying circumstances.

Psychodynamic Treatment

A very different treatment of autism has been developed over many years by Bruno Bettelheim (1967, 1974) at the Orthogenic School of the University of Chicago. Bettelheim argues that a warm, loving atmosphere must be created to encourage the child to enter the world. Patience and what Rogerians would call unconditional positive regard are believed necessary for the child to begin to trust others and to take chances in establishing relationships. Bettelheim and his colleagues report many instances of success, but the uncontrolled nature of their observations makes it difficult to know what the active ingredients might be. Bettelheim's treatment may contain more direct instruction, systematic reinforcement, and extinction than comes through in the published reports. By the same token, of course, reports of behavior therapists usually underplay the rapport building that undoubtedly provides the context for their programs.

Drug Treatment

There is evidence that some autistic children have elevated blood levels of serotonin (Ritvo et al., 1970). Researchers at the University of California at Los Angeles have on this basis given them a drug known to lower serotonin levels in rats and monkeys, hoping to reduce their serotonin and to improve their behavior as well. Ritvo and his colleagues use an amphetamine derivative, fenfluramine, which is an appetite suppressor for adults sold under the trade name Pondimine.

After a preliminary study in which fenfluramine lowered the serotonin levels of three autistic preschoolers and improved their IQs and their behavior significantly (Geller et al., 1982), a more ambitious and better-controlled, double-blind experiment was conducted on fourteen children, outpatients at a child psychiatric clinic (Ritvo et al., 1983; Geller et al., 1984). Subjects ranged in age from two to eighteen, and all were enrolled in special-education programs throughout the study. Since the first study had shown that serotonin levels return to baseline, as does autistic behavior, when fenfluramine is withdrawn, similar reversals were expected to be uncovered by an ABAB experimental design. The study ran for seventeen months, divided as follows: month 1, placebo; months 2 through 5, fenfluramine; months 6 and 7, placebo; months 8 through 17, fenfluramine.

The children's behavior was observed both by parents, as they lived with the child at home, and by professional raters from the research project. Neither the parents nor the professional testers were told by the researchers when the crossover to drug or to placebo was taking place. The major improvements brought about by the drug were clearly noticeable, however. As had happened with the three preschoolers, fenfluramine markedly reduced the serotonin levels of these children and improved their IQs and behavioral ratings. When the children were on the drug, their fidgeting, arm flapping, and twirling decreased; their sleeping was better; bizarre behavior such as sniffing people lessened; they were more in tune with others, actually seeking eye contact; and they communicated better with language, using less echolalia. No serious weight losses were observed. For the most part behavior, along with serotonin levels, returned to baseline during the placebo months 6 and 7, but it improved again when the drug was reinstated in the last ten months of the study.

Not all children responded well, however, and the task of future research is to determine for whom the drug works best and for how long the child can be safely kept on the medication. It is promising, however, that such a drug does have measurable and positive effects. Parents can reasonably hope that the drug, combined with the kinds of educational procedures described earlier, will improve the lot of their autistic children.[8]

SUMMARY

The diagnostic criteria for mental retardation are subaverage intellectual functioning and deficits in adaptive behavior, with onset before the age of eighteen. Four levels of retardation are designated, ranging from the profound when IQ is less than 20, to mild when IQ is 50 to 70. Researchers have identified adaptive skills and general cognitive abilities that are wanting in retarded children. The more severe forms of mental retardation usually have a physiological basis, such as the chromosomal trisomy that causes Down's syndrome. Certain infectious diseases suffered by the pregnant mother, such as rubella and syphilis, or affecting the child directly, for example, encephalitis, can stunt cognitive and social development. So can malnutrition. So can severe falls and automobile accidents that injure the brain. For the mild range of retardation, which is by far the most prevalent, no identifiable brain damage is evident. Environmental factors are considered the principal causes. Among the specific findings are that these people come from lower-class homes in which deprivation is great.

[8]A large-scale collaborative study of fenfluramine, given to approximately 150 autistic children, is currently underway at eighteen medical centers across the United States.

Researchers try to prevent mild retardation by giving children at risk through impoverished circumstances special preschool training and social opportunities. Many retarded children who would have been institutionalized are now being educated in the public schools under the mainstreaming provisions of P.L. 94-142. In addition, using applied behavioral analysis, self-instructional training, and modeling, behavior therapists have been able to treat successfully many of the behavioral problems of retarded individuals as well as improving their intellectual functioning.

Infantile autism, one of the pervasive developmental disorders, begins before the age of thirty months. The major symptoms are extreme autistic aloneness, a complete failure to relate to other people; communication problems, either a failure to learn any language or speech irregularities such as echolalia and pronoun reversal; and preservation of sameness, an obsessive desire that daily routines and surroundings be kept exactly the same. On the basis of early clinical reports, some psychologically biased theorists had concluded that the coldness and aloofness of parents and their rejection of their children bring on autism. But recent research gives no credence to such notions. No certain physiological basis of autism has been found, but a number of points make such a cause plausible. Its onset is very early. Both family and twin studies give evidence of a genetic predisposition. The EEGs of some autistic children are abnormal, and neurological tests also reveal abnormalities. A syndrome similar to autism can develop after meningitis and encephalitis and through PKU. Many autistic children have the low intelligence associated with brain dysfunctions.

The most promising treatments of autism have often been by procedures that rely on modeling and operant conditioning. There is also recent evidence that the drug fenfluramine will reduce the serotonin blood level in autistic children and lessen many of their stereotypies and some of their aloofness. But even though specific aspects of their behavior can be abated, most autistic children still remain intellectually and socially handicapped.

Edvard Munch, *Self-Portrait Between the Clock and the Bed*, 1940–42. Munch Museet, Oslo

AGING AND PSYCHOLOGICAL DISORDERS

The more fortunate readers of this book will grow old one day. When and as you do, physiological changes are inevitable, and there may be many emotional and mental changes as well. The physiological processes are inexorable, although sensible health regimens have been shown to delay many of the ravages of aging. We are concerned here less with physical changes than with the psychological aspects of growing old. Is the ability to remember and to think rationally subject to unavoidable deterioration? Does society treat the elderly in ways that may set them on a downward slide to senescence and even death? Are the aged at higher risk for mental disorders than the young? Are earlier emotional problems of anxiety and depression likely to become worse in old age? Do these emotional problems develop in people who did not have them when younger? Is it reasonable to expect a satisfying sex life in old age? Finally, are some therapies especially appropriate to our elders, and does society devote suitable monetary and intellectual resources to the development of effective ways of helping our older citizens? As life expectancy extends further and further into the seventies and perhaps even beyond, what is the professional community doing *now* to acquire knowledge and techniques that can make old age more meaningful than it has been for past generations, in the United States and in many other countries?

The elderly in this country are treated badly. The process of growing old, although inevitable for us all, is abhorred, even resented. Perhaps the lack of regard for senior citizens stems from our own deep-seated fear of and misconceptions about growing old. The old person with serious infirmities is an unwelcome reminder that some of us may one day walk with a less steady gait, see less clearly, taste food less sharply, enjoy sex less frequently and with apparently less intensity, and fall victim to some of the many diseases and maladies that are the lot of most old people before they depart this world.

Growing old may be especially disagreeable for women. Even with all the consciousness raising carried out by the feminist movement in the past decade, women still have trouble accepting the wrinkles and sagging which become more and more prominent with advancing years. The cosmetics industry and plastic surgery make billions of dollars a year by exploiting the fear women have been taught to have about looking their age. Although gray hair at the temples and even a bald head are often considered distinguished in a man, a great many women who have the financial means to buy a few more years of youthful appearance do so. And so the psychological problems of aging may be especially severe for women.

In studies of aging, investigators need to be aware of cohort effects. A seventy-year-old born in 1860 can be quite different from a seventy-year-old born in 1915.

Mental health professionals have almost phobically ignored the behavioral and emotional problems of the elderly. Misinformation is rampant, such as the beliefs that intellectual deterioration is widespread and inevitable, that depression among old people is untreatable, that sex is a lost cause. Butler and Lewis (1982) have shown that such "ageism" abounds in the writings of academicians and in the treatment regimens of clinicians, often exacerbating the plight of many older adults.

The relative inattention to mental health problems of the aging is both a cause and an effect of the inattention to professional training. Little instruction in geriatrics has been given in medical schools, nursing schools, psychology departments, and schools of social work. For this reason, in June 1981, the American Psychological Association sponsored a conference on geriatric clinical training. Its purpose was to bring together experts from around the country to formulate guidelines for proper training of clinicians for the aging, as well as to encourage the development of such programs. In just the past few years research and training in gerontology have begun to be introduced into curricula of schools and universities preparing people for health professions.

CONCEPTS AND METHODS IN THE STUDY OF OLDER ADULTS

Diversity in Older Adults

Before we consider psychological disorders in late life, some basic concepts critical to the study of aging should be introduced. In any discussion of the differences between the elderly and those not yet old, the aged are usually defined as those over the age of sixty-five. The decision to use this age was set largely by social policies, not because age sixty-five is some detrimental point at which the physiological and psychological processes of aging suddenly begin. To have some rough demarcation points for better describing the diversity of the aged, gerontologists have divided those over sixty-five into two groups, the young-old, those sixty-five to seventy-four; and the old-old, those seventy-five and over. The health of these two groups differs in important ways. The word diversity is well applied to the older population. Not only are older people different from one another, but they are more different from one another than are individuals in any other age group! In essence, people tend to become less alike as they grow older.[1]

Age, Cohort, and Time-of-Measurement Effects

Chronological age is not as simple a variable in psychological research as we might expect, for being any age is associated with a host of other factors. For example, diet, medical care, and social habits all change with time; and each decade has its major political events. Being seventy in 1986 is different from having been seventy in 1956. We must be cautious when we attribute differences in age groups solely to the effects of aging, for other factors associated with age may be at work. In the field of aging, therefore, a distinction is made between the contributions of what are called *age effects*, *cohort effects*, and *time-of-measurement effects*. The two major research designs used to assess developmental change, the cross-sectional and the longitudinal, clarify these terms.

In cross-sectional studies the investigator compares different age groups at the same moment of time on the variable of interest. Suppose that in 1985 I take a poll and find that many of my interviewees who are over seventy speak with a European accent, whereas those in their thirties and forties do not. Can I conclude that as people grow older they develop European accents? Hardly! Because cross-sectional studies do not examine the same people over time, they allow us to make statements only about *age differences*, not about *age changes*, that is, changes over time. Cross-sectional research confounds the effects of aging with differences caused by another variable, *cohort*, which is a very important concept in the psychology of aging.

A cohort is a group of people who have a vital statistic in common, here being born within a certain time period. In the hypothetical study just mentioned, many in the older sample or cohort came to this country from abroad. A longitudinal study selects one cohort and

[1]That all old people are alike is a prejudice held by many younger adults. To know that a man is sixty-seven years old is, in itself, to know very little about him. And yet a moment's honest reflection may indicate to the reader that certain traits come to mind when we hear that a man is sixty-seven. The many *differences* in people who are sixty-five and older will become increasingly evident in the course of reading this chapter.

then periodically retests it, using the same measure over a number of years. Thus it allows us to trace individual patterns of consistency or change over time and to analyze how behavior in early life relates to behavior in old age.

Conclusions drawn from longitudinal studies are restricted to the particular cohort chosen, however, for each cohort is unique. For example, if a cohort is studied from 1940 to 1980 and its members are found to suffer a decline in intelligence as they enter their sixties, we cannot conclude that the intelligence of those in a cohort studied from 1980 to 2020 will decline when they reach the same age. Improvements in health and other variables might benefit the intelligence of the younger cohort. Longitudinal studies have another problem. Unfortunately, people often drop out of them as they proceed, creating a source of bias commonly called "selective mortality." The least able subjects are the most likely to drop from a study; the nonrepresentative people who remain are usually healthier than the general population. Thus, findings based on longitudinal studies may be too optimistic concerning the amount of decline over the life span.

Contrary to popular belief, longitudinal studies do not allow us to measure pure age changes. Time-of-measurement effects have to be considered. For example, because of a coronary risk scare in 1980, many in a cohort I am studying may give up drinking coffee between the time of my first measurement in 1970 and my next measurement in 1985. At the next evaluation their physical health—which usually declines—may actually have *improved* because fewer have drunk coffee since the 1980 scare, a time-of-measurement effect.

Diagnosing Psychopathology in Later Life
Throughout this text DSM-III has been our guide, but it refers little to aging and the aged. The nature and manifestation of mental disorders are apparently assumed to be the same in adulthood and old age, even though little research supports this assumption (LaRue, Dessonville, and Jarvik, 1985). We often do not know what certain symptoms of older adults mean because we have few specifics about psychopathology in the elderly (Zarit, Eiler, and Hassinger, 1985). For example, somatic symptoms are more prevalent in late life, but somatic symptoms are also evident in depression. Are the somatic symptoms of a depressed older adult necessarily a part of depression? Or might they reflect physical decline?

Range of Problems
We already know that mental health may be tied to the physical and social problems in a person's life. Although this can be true at any age, no other group of people have more of these problems than the aged. They have them all—physical decline and disabilities, sensory and neurological deficits, the cumulative effects of a lifetime of many unfortunate experiences and social stresses. To understand the psychopathology of older adults, we must take into account many physical, psychological, and social forces of later life.

SOME BASIC FACTS ABOUT OLDER ADULTS

Numbers of Older People
The proportion of older people in the population has increased greatly during the past century. This increase is attributable to many factors, in particular decreased infant, childhood, and maternal mortality, as well as improved sanitation and the effective control of infectious diseases. In 1900 only 4 percent of the United States population was over age sixty-five. As of the 1980 census, this percentage was 11.3 percent or 25.5 million persons. In fact, since 1970 the number of people sixty-five or over has increased by 5.5 million or 28 percent, to the point that today about one in every nine persons in the United States is age sixty-five or over. This steady growth in the older population is expected to continue: while the total United States population grows by one-third between 1982 and 2050, the fifty-five-plus age group is expected to increase at the rate of 115 percent! Thus, by the year 2000, older persons are predicted to represent 13.1 percent of the population, and, by the year 2030, the percentage may climb to 21.1 percent. No wonder the graying of the population has been considered one of the most significant trends of the century.

Although in the years to come all segments of the elderly population are expected to grow rapidly, the fastest-growing subgroup will be the old-old, those seventy-five and over. The older population is itself aging, which, as we shall see, is of great social, economic, and medical importance, for these people need more medical and mental health care (U.S. Bureau of the Census, 1982).

Characteristics of the Aged Population
This is the era of increasing numbers of older persons but of more older women in particular. Men and women have very different life expectancies. Men who had their sixty-fifth birthday in 1980 could expect to live another 14.02 years, women who had theirs another 18.35 years.

On the average, women in the United States live 7.8 years longer from birth and 4.4 years longer from age sixty-five than men. Thus the ratio of women to men increases with age, from 125 women to 100 men for the sixty-five to sixty-nine age group to a high of 229 women to 100 men for persons eighty-five and over. Because of this discrepancy in life expectancy, the health, social, and economic problems of the elderly, particularly of the old-old, are often the problems of women. As we might expect, given these figures, most older men are married and most older women are widowed. Approximately 80 percent of men in the sixty-five to seventy-four age group are married compared to 49 percent of the women. Of people over seventy-five, seven out of ten women are widowed, and seven out of ten men are married. Not only do women live longer than men, thus losing their spouses, but men tend to marry women younger than themselves, keeping theirs. In addition, elderly widowed men have a remarriage rate seven times that of widows (U.S. Bureau of the Census, 1982).

What is the racial or ethnic composition of our current older population? As of the last census, about 90 percent of persons sixty-five years of age and older were white, 8 percent were black, and about 2 percent were other races. Persons of Hispanic origin represented approximately 3 percent of the older population. These percentages for ethnic minorities are lower than they would be were their mortality rates not higher than those of whites.

Physical Decline

Many physical functions unquestionably decline with age. Although aging does not affect the entire body, it does all the major body systems—musculoskeletal, cardiovascular, respiratory, nervous, gastrointestinal, urinary, integumentary, reproductive, endocrine, and immune (Kenney, 1982). The capacity for homeostatic regulation is reduced. All five senses as well suffer a loss, thereby affecting perception. The lens of the eye yellows and becomes less accommodative, visual acuity decreases, and sensitivity to glare increases. Hearing is diminished, particularly the ability to perceive high-frequency sounds. Older people respond less quickly, taking longer to do many tasks and to recover from stress (Blazer and Siegler, 1984). The conservative driving habits of older adults are a wise adaptation to the slowdown in their reaction time and to diminished visual acuity.

The physical losses of aging are reflected in the health problems of older adults. The incidence of chronic illnesses increases with age. Over 80 percent of older persons have at least one chronic condition, and 50 percent have two or more (Jarvik and Perl, 1981). Arthritis, hypertension, heart problems, hearing and vis-

Old people, particularly older women, are becoming a steadily increasing percentage of the population.

Elderly people are too often considered to be on a steadily declining path. In reality, many continue to work, play, and participate in community activities.

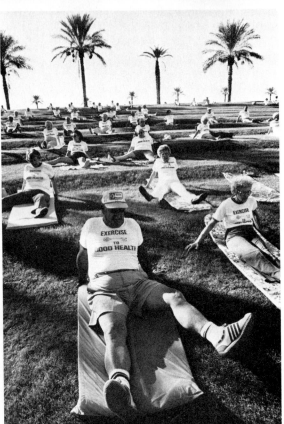

ual impairments, and diabetes are the most frequent debilities. In addition, although the incidence of acute illnesses and accidental injuries decreases with age, their impact is often more severe and protracted in the old (Hickey, 1980); for example, bones broken in a fall heal more slowly.

Yet in the face of these apparent losses in bodily performance, it has been estimated that at least 80 percent of people sixty-five and over are able to carry out major daily activities and otherwise function with a considerable degree of independence. Although the average older person may be afflicted with one or more chronic ailments, they are not necessarily limited severely by them. In fact, at any given time only about 10 percent are confined in hospitals, other long-term care facilities, or their homes by serious physical disabilities (U.S. Bureau of the Census, 1982). Significant health problems that may interfere with functioning do not usually develop until people pass the age of seventy-five.

IQ Changes

Does measured IQ decline with age? Methodological problems abound in research attempting to answer this question, but some patterns have been observed (Botwinick, 1977). Contrary to popular belief, there is no simple relation between age and intelligence. Findings suggest that some intellectual abilities do not decline with age, whereas others decline at different rates. In general, verbal abilities tend to be maintained with age, but psychomotor speed tends to decline. The achievement of better scores on verbal tests than on performance tests has been observed so universally that it is called the classic aging pattern (Botwinick, 1977). Even when declines in sensory functions and reaction time are accounted for, there remain age-related deficits on tests of intelligence (Storandt, 1977). After age eighty a decline in IQ is the rule for most people (Schaie, 1980).

There are some general problems in evaluating studies of intelligence, however, and they are relevant as well to studies of learning and memory difficulties. The age declines in IQ are neither as considerable as cross-sectional studies imply nor as minimal as longitudinal studies indicate, but rather are somewhere in the middle. Cross-sectional studies confuse age-related performance with the poorer health of the older cohort, whereas people studied longitudinally are usually healthier than the general population. When age and health are contrasted in the same study, health rather than age appears to account for declines in intellectual functioning (Siegler and Costa, 1985). Thus we do not know exactly what causes the declines in IQ that have been noted. Were we

Contrary to the prevalent belief, old people are able to learn effectively, especially if the pace of learning can be self-controlled.

able to improve the health of the older population, perhaps the age differences that have been reported would be reduced.

The IQ declines noted are usually statistically significant but are so small that their practical significance is questionable (Schaie, 1980).[2] Moreover, intelligence tests certainly do not measure important cognitive phenomena such as wisdom and creativity (Clayton and Birren, 1980), or the complex capacity to make good use of the experiences and knowledge of a lifetime.

Learning and Memory

The individual's ability to learn and remember is obviously important in IQ testing. Although older adults tend to perform more poorly than their younger counterparts in experiments, the differences can be reduced by altering certain aspects of the situation. For example, providing the aged more time to learn new material reduces age differences, often completely. And older people will abandon some of their cautiousness when given rewards for responding (Botwinick, 1984).

There is evidence that older people do less well than younger on memory tasks that demand considerable organization of the material to be memorized. They also perform less effectively tasks that require divided atten-

[2]Recall our earlier discussion of statistical versus clinical significance, page 100.

tion; older people apparently have a more limited cognitive capacity available to them at any one moment (Craik, 1977). Age differences in short-term memory are minimal. Older adults seem to be less proficient, however, at encoding material, transferring it into long-term memory, and eventually getting it back out again. Recognition declines less with age than recall (Perlmutter and Hall, 1985). "Who was the thirty-fifth president of the United States?" is an example of a free-recall question. A recognition question on the same topic gives cues and asks "Was the president assassinated in Dallas in November 1963 Kennedy or Johnson?" Older people answer this question about as well as younger people.

On a practical level, we might ask whether the decrements in the learning and memory abilities of older people, as measured in careful laboratory settings, reflect true functional deficits in their everyday lives. As people age, they adapt to all kinds of changes in their environment, and all this involves learning. The kinds of memory tasks used in experiments may uncover deficits that have no impact on day-to-day functioning.

Memory problems point up a general issue of attribution in thinking about aging. Older adults are "known" to be forgetful, and when they are, their failing memory is attributed to the inevitable processes of aging. Medications taken by the older individual and health problems, however, may account for the impairments. In fact, when health was held constant for a group of patients, performance on learning and memory tasks was not related to age (Hulicka, 1967). In another study half of a sample of people over sixty complained of memory problems, but their complaints were not reflected on objective tests of memory (Lowenthal et al., 1967). It may be that elderly people accept the cultural stereotype of forgetful old folks and then attach special significance to occasions when they have forgotten something (Kahn et al., 1975). This can create worry and anxiety which, in turn, can interfere with memory and other intellectual performance. Readers of this book under the age of sixty-five can confirm for themselves how often they forget another's name or how often they cannot remember why they have gotten up from studying and gone into another room. Younger people seemingly forget more easily that they have been forgetful, an interesting irony indeed!

Personality

Do people undergo predictable personality changes in old age or over the life span? It is widely assumed that old people are more rigid than young people. A number of experiments, however, have failed to confirm these assumptions (Botwinick, 1984; Zarit, 1980). Age per se appears to have little impact on personality (Neugarten, 1977). In fact, a series of longitudinal studies have found very few changes in the personalities of people as they age (Costa and McCrae, 1978; Leon et al., 1979; McCrae, Costa, and Arenberg, 1980; Siegler, George, and Okun, 1979). This conclusion, however, was drawn about survivors, the hardier individuals who remained part of the studies (Siegler and Costa, 1985). Those who drop out of such studies are reported to be more anxious than long-term survivors (Rusin and Siegler, 1975). Thus we cannot know whether the personality of these less stable individuals would have changed with time.

Medical Care

Medical expenses constitute a potential financial headache for the elderly. The Medicare program passed in 1965 as part of the Social Security law was intended to provide adequate medical care within the means of even the poor, but this has not happened. It has been estimated that in 1967 Medicare covered about 46 percent of medical expenses for the elderly; the latest data demonstrate that coverage has dropped to 38 percent (Butler and Lewis, 1982). The reasons for this failure are many and so complex that they are beyond the scope of this book. Suffice it to say that regulations keep changing so that older adults and even the professionals who try to help them are often confused about what is covered. Some treatments, such as physical rehabilitation after a stroke or fracture, are not consistently covered, nor is care for dementing disorders; moreover, Medicare coverage for psychiatric services is minimal, a situation which is believed by some to promote hospitalization rather than outpatient care (Butler and Lewis, 1982). Not surprisingly, many older people do without items that are excluded by Medicare, such as dentures, eyeglasses, physical examinations, and outpatient drugs. The increases in medical costs combined with the present limitations on length of hospital care may in fact deny many older individuals proper medical attention.

Assuming the elderly can obtain and pay for medical care, how good is it? The answer seems to be, not very. The chronic health problems of old people are not appealing to physicians because they seldom diminish. In fact, many maladies of old people—such as hearing loss, visual impairments, loss of mobility, aches and pains, especially in the feet (Pearson and Gatz, 1982), and a steadily declining cardiovascular system—are unlikely to get better and must somehow be adjusted to. The elderly come to rely heavily on their relationships with health care providers, but these providers may become impatient with them because they complain continually about not getting well or they become depressed.[3] Older people do not always take medication as instructed. Their relations with family members who must look after them are likely to suffer. The ailing elderly are sometimes torn both by feelings of guilt for needing so much from others, and by anger against these younger people whom they have spent so many of their "good years" looking after and sacrificing for. The sons and daughters also have feelings of guilt and anger (Zarit, 1980).

Income

The economic position of the aged is on the whole worse than that of the younger population. In 1981 three-fourths of the elderly had incomes below $10,000 compared to 42 percent of those ages twenty-five to sixty-four. About 25 percent of the younger group had incomes above $20,000, but only 7 percent of the elderly did (U.S. Bureau of the Census, 1982). The poverty rate for persons sixty-five and over was almost 15 percent in 1982, which was about the same as that for the general population. The official poverty level for an older-couple household is $4954, for an older individual living alone $3941. The elderly are more likely to be "near-poor," having an income between the poverty level and 125 percent of it: approximately one-quarter of the aged can be classified as near-poor compared to fewer than one-fifth of persons under age sixty-five. Although older people represent only 11.3 percent of the population, they constitute 20 percent of the poor in the United States. One group of the aged particularly hard-hit by poverty are older women, especially older women who live alone. In fact, elderly women are the largest single group with poverty-level incomes. Women in the current generation of older people are generally in a bad situation because the jobs they held seldom paid well or were infrequently covered by pension or Social Security plans. Thus elderly women are twice as likely as their male counterparts to be poor, 8.3 percent compared to 17.5 percent. At triple jeopardy are older, black women, 65.1 percent of whom are near-poor. The fixed, low incomes of some older people, even though there are adjustments for inflation, have reduced them to living in inadequate quarters and to subsisting on an inadequate diet. Our discussion of organic mental disorders will indicate the serious consequences for mental health.

[3]The situation may be even worse. As Zarit (1980) suggests, the illnesses of older people violate a "law" that the medical profession lives by, for these maladies are often incurable. Some of the impatience may therefore stem from the fact that older patients do not get well.

Health care for the elderly is not always good. One of the reasons may be that their chronic conditions, such as arthritis, are not appealing to physicians.

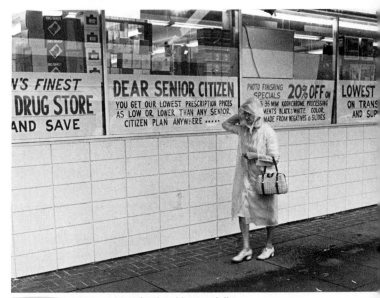

Poverty is a serious problem for the old, especially for older women who live alone.

Where the Elderly Live

One of the more prevalent myths regarding the aged is that the majority live in institutions. In fact, at any given time 95 percent of the aged reside in the community, living either by themselves or with a spouse, family, or friends. In 1980, 68 percent of the community elderly lived with their families. Again there are differences according to sex; 83 percent of older men and 57 percent of older women lived in "families," which usually means with a spouse. Nearly one-third of community older persons lived alone, 41 percent of older women and 15 percent of older men. As we would expect, the proportion of people living alone or not with their families increases as they grow older. Of course, the financial situation of older adults affects the quality of their housing. Up to 30 percent of older persons in the United States are estimated to live in substandard housing, largely because their incomes are marginal (American Association of Retired Persons, 1982).

Although only 5 percent of the elderly population live in institutions at any one time, this percentage increases dramatically with age. The National Nursing Home Survey conducted in 1977 showed that only one of every hundred persons in the sixty-five to seventy-four age group is in a nursing home on a given day (National Center for Health Statistics, 1979). This number climbs to seven out of every hundred persons in the seventy-four to eighty-four age group and to more than one out of five persons in the eighty-five and over population. The often-cited statistic that only 5 percent of older adults reside in nursing homes at any given time has been called the 5 percent fallacy (Kastenbaum and Candy, 1973), for this figure does not tell us the likelihood of spending some time in an institution at some period during late life. Vincente, Wiley, and Carrington (1979) found that of 455 individuals who were fifty-five and over at the start of a ten-year study, 38.9 percent had resided in a long-term care facility at least once before death.

Major Life Events

The effect of life events and stress (see page 168) on the aged is of particular interest. Many articles on aging begin by counting the losses of older people—retirement, widowhood, loss of friends, and so on. The studies done, however, do not indicate that old age is the period of life with the most stressful life events (Pearlin, 1983) or the greatest number of losses (McCrae, 1982).

But what of older adults' ability to *cope* with stress? What is crucial is that older adults may be more *vulnerable* to stress than at any other point in the life span. Declines in the immune system make them more likely to develop disease in response to a stressor that they might have coped with better when younger.

Societal Expectations

One final social factor to be considered concerns society's attitudes toward the aged and in particular the myths held about late life. A survey of Americans of all ages showed a wide gap between their view of the problems of old age and that of the old people actually experiencing them. The ten problems listed in Figure 17.1 were perceived as more common or serious for older adults than the aged actually found them to be. For example, only 13 percent of the aged actually reported loneliness to be a problem, whereas 65 percent of those under sixty-five and 45 percent of the aged *expected* it to be a problem. The gloomy expectations, which exceeded the reality of the problems, were held not only by those under sixty-five but by those over sixty-five as well. We are as yet unsure how these myths about late life may affect the mental health of older adults. But if someone believes that senility is an inevitable consequence of aging, which it is not, an older relative may be treated as though he or she were senile when in fact this may not be the case.

Ageism or discrimination against older adults, which is reported to be prevalent in our society (Butler and Lewis, 1982), can take several forms. The negative type of ageism casts all elderly people as sexless, senile, and feeble. In another, more subtle form of ageism, which is potentially as dangerous, we smile a special smile or shout a special hooray when a ninety-two year-old man crosses the finish line at a sporting event. Gatz and her colleagues (1983) have called negative ageism myth and positive ageism countermyth. Myths emphasize disadvantage and deterioration, the mistaken beliefs given in Figure 17.1. Countermyths find no problems in aging, such as there being no decline in intellectual capacity with age. As the truth probably lies somewhere between these two extremes, either form of ageism can be harmful to older adults.

BRAIN DISORDERS OF OLD AGE

Although the vast majority of older people, approximately 85 to 90 percent, do not have organic brain disorders, these problems account for more admissions and hospital inpatient days than any other condition of geriatric adults (Christie, 1982). Two principal types of brain disorders are distinguished, *dementia* and *delirium*.

Dementia

The prevalence of definite cases of dementia in the aged has been estimated at approximately 2 to 5 percent when noninstitutionalized adults are considered, and another 2 to 3 percent are added from the institutionalized aged

(Gurland and Cross, 1982). Only a small proportion of persons under sixty suffer from dementia, but approximately 20 percent of individuals over the age of eighty do (Bergmann et al., 1971; Gurland and Cross, 1982; LaRue, Dessonville, and Jarvik, 1985; Jarvik, Ruth, and Matsuyama, 1980).

Dementia is what laypeople call senility; it is a gradual deterioration of intellectual abilities over several years to the point that social and occupational functioning are impaired. Memory abilities decline as well as at least one other of the following realms of mental activity—abstract thinking, judgment, language, and personality. Generally, difficulty in remembering things is the most prominent symptom of dementia. People may leave tasks unfinished because they forget to return to them after an interruption. A person who had started to fill a teapot at the sink will leave the water running. Parents may become unable to remember the name of a daughter or son and later not even recall that they have children. Hygiene may become poor and appearance slovenly as the person loses awareness of when they last bathed and knowledge of how to dress adequately.

The loss of abstract thinking is frequently tested by asking the person the meaning of proverbs; he or she will give literal and concrete interpretations. A person with dementia is also unable to find similarities and differences in related words. Judgment may become faulty; people have difficulty in comprehending personal situations and making plans or decisions. They also lose their standards and control of their impulses; they may use coarse language, tell inappropriate jokes, shoplift, and make sexual advances to strangers. The course of dementia may be progressive, static, or remitting, depending on the cause. Eventually, many with progressive dementia are withdrawn and apathetic. In the terminal phase of the illness, the personality has lost its sparkle and integrity. Relatives and friends will say that the person is just not himself any more. Social involvement with others has kept on narrowing. The person is in the end oblivious to his surroundings.

Causes of Dementia

Surveys have shown that in 10 to 20 percent of older people who have dementia, the condition is reversible (Cummings and Benson, 1983; Gurland and Cross, 1982; Small, Liston, and Jarvik, 1981; Spar, 1982; Task Force Report, 1980; Wells, 1978). Alcohol and medication toxicities, malnutrition, metabolic disorders, and depression may all cause reversible dementia.

The remaining 80 percent of the cases of dementia are believed to be irreversible. Not long ago cerebrovas-

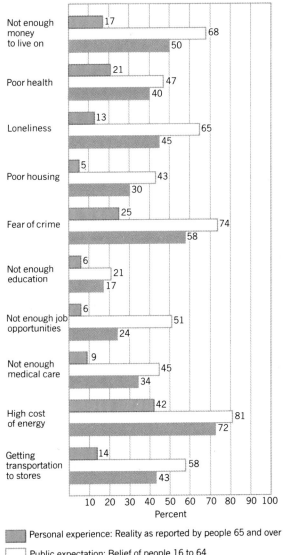

FIGURE 17.1 Myth versus the reality of aging. Elderly people experiencing problems never report them to be as serious as the general public expects them to be. After Harris, 1981.

cular diseases, often called "hardening of the arteries," were incorrectly regarded as the primary cause of dementia. More recent research has indicated that fewer than 25 percent of cases of dementia in the elderly are clearly traceable to heart and circulatory problems (Terry and Wisniewski, 1977). Dementia is never caused by hardening of the arteries per se. Indeed, it is estimated that approximately half of the cases of dementia are caused by Alzheimer's disease or dementia of the

BOX 17.1

PREVALENCE OF MENTAL DISORDERS IN LATE LIFE

Is age itself a contributing factor to emotional and mental malfunction? Do more old people than young people have mental disorders? Whether mental disorders become more prevalent with age is not clear, partly because of the methodological and conceptual difficulties that we have already discussed. Moreover, comprehensive and systematic research on the incidence and prevalence of various psychiatric disorders in late adulthood has yet to be done (LaRue, Dessonville, and Jarvik, 1985; Stenmark and Dunn, 1982). An extensive cross-sectional study conducted by the National Institute of Mental Health, using the DSM-III criteria for disorders, holds the potential of yielding valuable data on mental disorders in all age groups, including the elderly.

First some background. The Epidemiological Catchment Area program sponsored by the NIMH is a collaborative effort of five major United States cities to give the Diagnostic Interview Schedule (DIS) at six-month intervals to large general-population samples in order to estimate current and lifetime prevalences of psychiatric disorders. Current prevalence is the proportion of persons in the sample who at present have a given disorder; lifetime prevalence is the proportion of persons who have *ever* had the disorder up to the date of assessment, whether or not they have it at present. Assessed by the DIS are phobias, panic and obsessive-compulsive disorders, somatization disorder, affective disorders, antisocial personality disorder, substance abuse or dependence, schizophrenia, and an eighth, non-DSM-III category, cognitive impairment.

Although this large-scale, nationwide program is still in progress, initial results from three of the cities are in. The current prevalence rates for a sample of 9000 people indicated that persons over sixty-five had the lowest overall rates of all age groups when the disorders were grouped together. Indeed, schizophrenia and substance abuse are extremely rare in people in the upper age ranges. The primary

problem of old age was found to be *cognitive impairment*. In the NIMH study, rates for mild cognitive impairment were about 14 percent for elderly males and females, for severe impairment 5.5 percent for men and 4.7 percent for women (Myers et al., 1984). These rates tell us only the overall prevalence of cognitive impairment in the aged, not whether the causes were reversible or irreversible. As we shall see, this is an important issue.

What of lifetime prevalence? We would expect that because older adults have lived through a longer risk period in which disorders could develop, they would have the highest overall lifetime rates. Again, however, the lifetime rates of those sixty-five and older were the lowest.

What can explain these findings? Older people might have been absent from the community through mortality or institutionalization. Older adults may also have attributed their symptoms to physical illness or forgotten past episodes (Robins et al., 1984). Moreover, as we have said before, we do not really know whether we can measure disorders the same way in the old as we do in younger people. Some disorders, such as schizophrenia, have a maximum age for onset; DSM-III says that individuals do not become schizophrenic after age forty-five. Finally, perhaps there has been a true historical increase in psychiatric disorders in the last few generations, as compared to our current generation of older adults. Today's younger and middle-aged adults may have significantly higher rates of mental disorders than their parents and grandparents (Robins et al., 1984).

All in all, the majority of persons sixty-five years of age and older are free from serious psychopathology, but 10 to 20 percent do have psychological problems, either cognitive or mental, severe enough to warrant professional attention (Birren and Sloane, 1980; Gurland and Cross, 1982; LaRue, Dessonville, and Jarvik, 1985).

Alzheimer type (DAT), in which primary neuronal degeneration occurs. The degeneration consists of atrophy or wasting away of cortical cells, to the extent that sulci may widen and ventricles become larger (see Box A.1, page 601). Taking the place of the brain cells destroyed by Alzheimer's disease are senile or neuritic plaques, small structures consisting of the remnants of the nerve cells and amyloid, a waxy substance deposited when protein metabolism is disturbed. Neurofibrillary tangles, bundles of abnormal protein filaments, accumulate within the cell bodies of neurons.

Researchers have found at autopsy that the areas of the hippocampus for assembling memories coming in and going out look patchy and cell-poor. This degeneration isolates the hippocampus (Hyman et al., 1984). Neurons there also contain neurofibrillary tangles and vacuoles as well, which is called granulovacuolar degeneration. Acetylcholine-releasing neurons whose cell bodies lie in the basal forebrain selectively degenerate, depleting the supply of this neurotransmitter in the cortex and hippocampus (Coyle, Price, and Delong, 1983). In addition, little more than half the normal amounts of protein are synthesized in the Alzheimer brain, which may be one reason why neurons are lost (Sajdel-Sulkowska and Marotta, 1984). But no one knows yet for sure which of these conditions are causes and which effects.

Dementia of the Alzheimer type is believed to account for more cases of dementia than any other single disease. Next is multi-infarct dementia, which is held to account for 15 to 25 percent of the cases. In multi-infarct dementia small lesions, brought about by a series of small strokes or extended periods of diffuse cerebral insufficiency, accumulate throughout the cortex. Taken together, then, vascular and Alzheimer-type syndromes cause most irreversible dementias, although it is not uncommon to find mixed cases.

Diagnosis of Dementia

The diagnosis of dementia consists of two phases, identification of the syndrome and a systematic search for its causes. Dementia is usually identified by a clinical mental-status examination and psychological testing, with particular attention to orientation, memory, fund of information, language, ability for abstract thought, judgment, and ability to calculate. The second phase is to identify or rule out a specific organic cause, through a physical examination, laboratory tests, and taking the person's medical and psychiatric history. The physical examination should include a complete neurological workup and a minimum battery of laboratory screening tests. The history should be comprehensive, paying specific attention to onset of the symptoms and their progression, details of exposure to drugs and alcohol, recent stressors, and whether the person has symptoms suggestive of an affective disorder (Cummings and Benson, 1983; Spar, 1982).

Specific reversible causes of dementia, such as vitamin B-12 deficiency, are easily identified by laboratory tests, but many of the irreversible causes are not. CAT scans (see page 76), indicating small areas of infarction, and focal EEG abnormalities may help to confirm a diagnostic impression of multi-infarct dementia. The absence of such findings, however, cannot be used to rule out the diagnosis; a lesion has to be at least one millimeter thick in order to be visible on a CAT scan (LaRue, Dessonville, and Jarvik, 1985). Cortical atrophy as measured by CAT scans is correlated to some extent with degree of intellectual impairment in patients with DAT, but some degree of cortical atrophy is normal as people grow older. Thus cortical atrophy is insufficient to make a diagnosis of DAT (Wells and Duncan, 1977; Task Force Report, 1980). A positive diagnosis of Alzheimer's disease is generally believed possible only on autopsy.

Because current neurodiagnostic techniques are limited, once specific reversible causes of dementia have been ruled out, clinicians examine the pattern of behavioral impairment (Cummings and Benson, 1983). But the brain is a complex, little understood organ, and people can vary considerably in how they react psychologically to apparently similar deterioration of the brain. Some persons with extensive brain damage are able to compensate for it and have less behavioral and intellectual deterioration than might be expected, whereas others with minimal damage have considerable psychological loss (Tomlinson and Henderson, 1976). Prior education, occupation, and personality all play a role. In addition, other organic brain syndromes such as delirium may overlie dementia and, as noted, a particular case of dementia may have several causes. Moreover, as we shall see, the symptoms of many depressed elderly—memory lapses and complaints of forgetfulness, difficulties in concentration, and psychomotor changes—resemble those of dementia.

Because the diagnosis of DAT is usually accomplished by eliminating all other possible etiologies and by looking for poorly distinguished patterns of behavior, the probability of error is relatively large. Not only may potentially reversible causes of dementia go undetected, but the diagnosis of DAT may be given too often, by applying it to all cases of dementia with an unrecognized cause. In fact, surveys of the stability of diagnoses over time suggest that a sizable number are later changed. When examined five to fifteen years later, 25 to 57 percent of patients diagnosed as having probable Alzheimer's disease have failed to deteriorate in the expected manner. These surveys usually conclude that depression went unrecognized as the cause of intellecutual deterioration (Cummings and Benson, 1983).

In light of all the diagnostic problems, it is best to be conservative in diagnosing an irreversible cause of dementia and instead to explore temporary and reversible causes of the symptoms. It would seem better to fail to diagnose an irreversible dementia when it is present than to state that it is present when it is not. Further improvements in PET scanning and CAT scanning and more detailed behavioral and autopsy studies may eventually allow precise identification of the different causes of dementia.

Treatment of Dementia

If the dementia is found to have a reversible cause, appropriate medical treatment should begin immediately, for example, correcting a nutritional deficiency. To date, however, no clinically significant treatment has been found for Alzheimer's disease, although investigations are numerous. Certain drugs can bring mild improvements in learning and memory for short periods of time, particularly in mildly impaired people, but long-term treatments have not been found (Bartus et al., 1982). Zarit (1980) has succinctly summarized the interventions that make sense in these situations.

The treatment of persons with senile dementia is basically supportive both of affected individuals and of their social networks. At present there are no methods that can effectively restore intellectual function or prevent further deterioration in cases of senile brain disease. Treatment involves minimizing the disruption caused by the disorder. Goals for treatment include: maintaining the person in a community setting; allowing affected persons the opportunity of discussing their illness and its consequences; giving information to family members and other concerned persons about the nature of this disorder; supporting family members so that they can continue to provide assistance to the affected person; and using behavioral and problem-solving methods to deal with specific issues that arise as the result of the brain disorder (p. 356).

For every individual with a severely disabling dementia living in an institution, there are two living in the community (Gurland and Cross, 1982), usually supported by a spouse, daughter, or other family member. The burden of caring for the elderly with dementia usually falls on family members. Thus not only does the individual need to be considered in treatment but the family as well. Family caregivers and friends, faced with taxing demands on their time, energies, and emotions, can become depressed. One form of support is accurate information on the nature of the person's problems. For example, people with Alzheimer's have great difficulty placing new information into memory. This means that they can engage in a reasonable conversation but will forget a few minutes later what has been discussed. A caregiver may become impatient unless he or she understands that this impairment is to be expected because of the underlying brain damage. Making increased demands on the patient, perhaps in the belief that he or she is expressing hostility in a passive-aggressive manner, is likely to be aggravating for the person making them, and for other family members, and is not likely to help the elderly person's recollections. Homespun memory drills are also ill-advised, for there are no known techniques for improving the memories of persons with this disease.

Families can be taught, however, how to help their relatives cope with lost functions. Substituting recognition for recall in daily situations may help patients and families better manage their lives. Families can be taught to ask questions embedding the answer. It is much easier to respond to ''Was the person you just spoke to on the phone Harry or Tom?'' than to ''Who just called?'' Labels on drawers, appliances, and rooms help orient a person. If the individual has lost the ability to read, pictures can be used instead of verbal labels. Prominent calendars and clocks and strategic notes can also help, as can an automatic dialer on a telephone.

Caregivers should also be informed that patients do not always appreciate their limitations and may attempt to engage in activities beyond their abilities, sometimes in a dangerous manner. Although it is not advisable to coddle patients, it is important to set limits in light of their obliviousness to their own problems and impairments. Sometimes the caregiver's reactions to the patient's problems require attention. The daughter-in-law of a woman was offended by the woman's color combinations in clothing and wished to take over responsibility for coordinating her wardrobe, even though the woman was capable of dressing herself in an adequate, although not spiffy, fashion. The caregiver was urged not to impose her standards and taste on the woman, and to understand that her ability to dress herself and to take responsibility for her clothes was more important than adherence to conventional appearance (Zarit, 1980).

There are several other ways in which counselors and therapists can help those responsible for looking after people with dementia at home. Many caregivers are afraid to leave the infirm person alone, and as a consequence they exhaust themselves by paying constant attention to him or her. They may deny themselves simple diversions and pleasures because they view their leaving the house as neglect of the spouse or parent. In many instances their overattentiveness is inappropriate to the situation. If the infirm person's needs are really critical, outside help from a nurse or other professional should be sought. Sadly though, many families cannot afford such respite services, or such services are not available in their area.

The counselor must bear in mind that some of the tensions between caregiver and patient may well have their roots in aspects of the relationship that predate the onset of the dementia. There is a tendency to consider the most obvious facet of a situation, here the impairments of a sick person, as the cause of all difficulties. Counseling directed to long-standing problems may be called for.

The paranoid delusions sometimes found in dementia can be disruptive. As with paranoia generally, the beliefs should not be challenged directly. It is better to try to work around them, concentrating on aspects of the person's behavior that are more intact. The delusions in dementia diminish with time, as memory worsens with the progressive cerebral deterioration; the prognosis for this aspect of the illness is, in a sad sort of way, good.

Counseling the impaired person is difficult and, with the more severely deteriorated, of apparently little long-term benefit because of their cognitive losses. But some patients seem to enjoy and be reassured by occasional conversations with professionals and with others not directly involved in their lives. It would appear important not to discount entirely their ability to participate in their caregiver's discussions of ways to cope with the problems they face. Their inherent cognitive limitations must be appreciated, however; Zarit (1980) even suggests that no efforts be made to get them to admit to their problems, for their denial may be the most effective coping mechanism available.

The cognitive limitation of senile persons should always be treated with gentleness. Others should not consider them nonbeings, talking about their debilities in their presence, making fun of their occasional antics and forgetfulness, discounting their paranoid suspicions about others. Older people, even those with no organic disorder, are often infantilized or ignored by their juniors, a sign of disrepect that demeans not only the elderly person but the person showing the discourtesy.

Perhaps the most heart-rending decision is whether and when to institutionalize the impaired person. At some point the nursing needs may become so onerous and the mental state of the person so deteriorated that placement in a nursing home is the only realistic option, not only for the benefit of the person but of his or her family. The conflicts encountered in making this decision are not to be underestimated. The counselor can be a source of information about nearby facilities as well as a source of support for making and implementing the decision (Zarit, 1980).

People experiencing the memory loss associated with Alzheimer's disease can be helped by notes that spell out daily routines and provide instructions.

Delirium

The term delirium is derived from the Latin words *de* meaning from or out of and *lira* meaning furrow or track. The term thus implies being off track or deviating from the individual's usual state (Wells and Duncan, 1980). Although delirium is one of the most frequent organic mental disorders in older adults, it has been neglected in research and is, like dementia, often misdiagnosed. Progress in diagnosis has been impeded largely by terminological chaos. The literature reveals thirty or more synonyms signifying delirium (Liston, 1982), acute confusional state and acute brain syndrome being the two most common.

Delirium is described in DSM-III as a "clouded state of consciousness." The patient, sometimes rather suddenly, has great trouble concentrating and focusing attention, and he or she cannot maintain a coherent and directed stream of thought. The sleep-waking cycle is invariably disturbed, often reversed, and the person may shift abruptly from hyperactivity to lethargy.

T. H. is a fifty-six-year-old right-handed businessman who had entered the hospital for cervical disk surgery. Because of his busy schedule and his anxiety relating to surgery, he had canceled his admission on two previous occasions. The patient was a fairly heavy social drinker but not to the point of interfering in any way with his business performance. The surgery was uneventful and there were no immediate complications of the procedure. The patient was greatly relieved and seemed to be making a normal recovery until the third postoperative night. During that night he became quite restless and found it difficult to sleep. The next day he was visibly fatigued but otherwise normal. The following night his restlessness became more pronounced, and he became fearful and anxious. As the night progressed, he thought that he saw people hiding in his room, and shortly before dawn he reported to the nurse that he saw some strange little animals running over his bed and up the drapes. At the time of morning rounds, the patient was very anxious and frightened. He was lethargic, distractible, and quite incoherent when he tried to discuss the events of the night before. He knew who he was and where he was but did not know the date or when he had had his surgery. During that day his mental status fluctuated, but by nightfall he had become grossly disoriented and agitated. At this point, psychiatric consultation was obtained.

The consultant's diagnosis was acute postoperative confusional state. The cause was probably due to a combination of factors: withdrawal from alcohol, fear of surgery, use of strong analgesics, stress of the operation, pain, and the sleepless nights in an unfamiliar room. The treatment consisted of a reduction in medications for pain, partial illumination of the room at night, and a family member in attendance at all times. These simple changes in conjunction with 50 mg of chlorpromazine (Thorazine) three times daily and 500 mg of chloral hydrate at bedtime reversed his confusional state within two days, and he was able to return home in a week with no residual evidence of abnormal behavior. To date there has been no recurrence of these problems (Strub and Black, 1981, pp. 89–90).

In the early stages of delirium, the person is frequently restless, particularly at night. The sleep-waking cycle becomes disturbed so that he or she is drowsy during the day, and awake, restless, and agitated during the night. The individual is generally worse during sleepless nights and in the dark. Vivid dreams and nightmares are common.

Delirious patients may experience extreme difficulty in collecting their thoughts; they may be impossible to engage in conversation because of their wandering attention and fragmented thinking. Words are slurred, or they have difficulty finding them, and handwriting and spelling may become impaired. In severe delirium speech is sparse or pressured and incoherent. Bewildered and confused, delirious individuals may become disoriented for time, place, and sometimes for person. But very often they are so inattentive that they cannot be questioned about orientation. In the course of a twenty-four-hour period, however, they will have lucid intervals and become alert and coherent. These fluctuations help to distinguish delirium from other syndromes.

Perceptual disturbances are common; individuals mistake the unfamiliar for the familiar. For example, they state that they are in a hotel instead of a hospital, and see the attending nurse as a room clerk. Moreover, they may see objects as too small, too big, misshapen, or duplicated. Although illusions and hallucinations are common, particularly visual and mixed visual-auditory ones, they are not always present in delirium. Paranoid delusions have been noted in 40 to 70 percent of the delirious aged. These delusions tend to be poorly worked out, fleeting, changeable, and tied to the surroundings.

Accompanying their disordered thoughts and perceptions are swings in activity and mood. Delirious people can be erratic, ripping their clothes one moment and sitting lethargically the next. They are in great emotional turmoil and may shift rapidly from one emotion to another—depression, anxiety, and fright, anger, euphoria, and irritability. Fever, flushed face, dilated pupils, rapid tremors, rapid heartbeat, elevated blood pressure, and incontinence of urine and feces are also common. If the delirium proceeds, the person will completely lose touch with reality and may become stuperous (Lipowski, 1980, 1983; Strub and Black, 1981).

Although delirium usually develops swiftly, within a matter of hours or days, the exact mode of onset depends on the underlying cause. Delirium resulting from a toxic reaction or concussion will have an abrupt onset; when infection or metabolic disturbance underlies delirium, the onset of symptoms is gradual, over an extended period of time.

People of any age are subject to delirium, but it is more common in children and older adults. Investigators have reported that 10 to 15 percent of older general-surgery patients become delirious after their operations (Miller, 1981). And a review of the literature on delirium concluded that between one-third and one-half of all the hospitalized elderly are likely to be delirious at some point during their stay (Lipowski, 1983). Although the rates vary widely, even the lowest figures indicate that delirium is a serious health problem for older adults.

Why are the elderly especially vulnerable to delirium? Many explanations have been offered. There are the physical declines of aging, the increased general susceptibility to chronic diseases, the many medications prescribed for older patients, and vulnerability to stress. One other factor, brain damage, increases the risk of delirium. The elderly with dementing disorders appear to be the most susceptible of all. A retrospective review of 100 hospital admissions of people all ages who had a diagnosis of delirium revealed that 44 percent of them had a delirium superimposed on another organic brain condition (Purdie, Honigman, and Rosen, 1981).

Causes of Delirium

The causes of delirium in the aged can be grouped into several general classes: drug intoxications, metabolic and nutritional imbalances, infections or fevers, neurological disorders, and the stress of a change in the person's surroundings (Habot and Libow, 1980; Lipowski, 1980). Common physical illnesses causing delirium in this age group include congestive heart failure, pneumonia, urinary tract infection, cancer, uremia, malnutrition, dehydration, and cerebrovascular accidents or strokes. Probably the single most frequent cause of delirium in the aged is intoxication with prescription drugs (Besdine, 1980; Lipowski, 1983). In most cases, however, the delirium has more than one cause (Sloane, 1980).

Complete recovery is possible if the syndrome is correctly identified and the underlying cause promptly and effectively treated. Generally, the condition takes one to four weeks to clear, although it takes longer in the elderly than in the young. If the underlying causative condition is not treated, however, the brain can be permanently damaged and the patient may die. The mortality rate for delirium is extremely high; approximately 40 percent of the patients die, either from the underlying condition or from exhaustion (Rabins and Folstein, 1982). In fact, when fatality rates for dementia and delirium are compared over a one-year period of time, the rates are higher for delirium than for dementia, 37.5 compared to 16 percent. Thus delirium in an older adult is a very serious matter.

Diagnosis of Delirium

The accurate diagnosis of delirium and its differentiation from conditions that resemble it are obviously critical to the welfare of older persons. Recognition and differentiation, however, presuppose knowledge of the distinguishing clinical symptoms. An elderly woman, for example, was found in a filthy apartment with no food. Initially believed by a poorly informed physician to be demented, she was simply given routine custodial care in a nursing home. Fortunately, a professional knowledgeable about delirium learned that she had become depressed over the loss of a loved one and had neglected her diet. Once this was recognized, appropriate attention was given to her nutritional deficiencies, and her condition improved to the point that she was discharged back to her own home after one month (Zarit, 1980).

This case is not atypical. Older adults are often mistaken for "senile" and therefore beyond hope. A decision for long-term institutional care is all too often viewed as the only sound one, in spite of the fact that the person may have a reversible condition. The older adult who has cognitive impairment must be examined thoroughly for all possible reversible causes of the disorder, such as drug intoxications, infections, fever, malnutrition, and head trauma, and then treated accordingly.

Why are the diagnosis of delirium and its differentiation from dementia so difficult? First, the two syndromes as currently defined in DSM-III overlap (Lipowski, 1983). Moreover, the symptoms of delirium in people of different ages can be different, thus posing

BOX 17.2

CEREBROVASCULAR DISEASES—STROKE AND ITS AFTERMATH

The blood vessels supplying the brain are subject to several types of malfunction. In *atherosclerosis* deposits of fatty material narrow the lumen, or inner passageway, of the arteries of the body. When those in the brain are affected, some areas may not receive enough blood and hence insufficient oxygen and glucose. If the shortage is prolonged, the brain tissue, which is particularly dependent on receiving adequate supplies, softens, degenerates, and is even destroyed. The effects of cerebral atherosclerosis vary widely, depending on what area of the brain has clogged arteries and whether it is also supplied by nonaffected blood vessels. About three million Americans are incapacitated in some way by cerebral atherosclerosis.

In *cerebral thrombosis* a blood clot forms at a site narrowed by atherosclerosis and blocks circulation. Carbon dioxide builds up and damages the neural tissues. The loss of consciousness and control is referred to as apoplexy or *stroke*. The patient may die, suffer paralysis or decreased sensation from one side of the body or of an arm or leg, or lose other motor and sensory functions. The impairments of the patients who survive may disappear spontaneously, or they may be lessened through therapy and determined effort. Usually there is some residual damage. When only a small vessel is suddenly blocked, the patient suffers transient confusion and unsteadiness. A succession of these small strokes will bring cumulative damage, however.

A frequent impairment is *aphasia*, a disturbance of the ability to use words. The cause of this damage may be a clot in the middle cerebral artery supplying the parietotemporal region, usually of the dominant cerebral hemisphere. A right-handed person depends on the parietotemporal region in the left hemisphere for language skills; a left-handed person may depend on this region in the right hemisphere or in the left. Interestingly, damage to the right hemisphere in a right-handed person and to the left in a left-handed person disturbs the ability to use language to a lesser extent.

Aphasia is generally divided into two types, receptive or sensory and executive or motor. In sensory aphasias individuals have difficulty in understanding the meaning of words. They may have auditory aphasia and not understand the words spoken to them or visual aphasia and not understand the printed word. They will, however, be able to speak properly; and they may, for example, be able to read but not understand spoken speech, or they may understand spoken speech but not be able to read. With motor aphasia a person suffers no deficit in comprehension but has problems in speaking words and sentences. He or she may transpose syllables, utter words of a sentence out of order, or be unable to recall names of common objects.

In *cerebral hemorrhage* a blood vessel ruptures because of a weakness in its wall, damaging the brain tissue on which the blood spills. Cerebral hemorrhages are frequently associated with hypertension. The psychological disturbance produced depends on the size of the vessel that has ruptured and on the extent and the location of the damage. Often the person suffering a cerebral hemorrhage is overtaken suddenly and rapidly loses consciousness. When a large vessel ruptures, the person suffers a major stroke. All functions of the brain are generally disturbed—speech, memory, reasoning, orientation, and balance. The person usually lapses into a coma, sometimes with convulsions, and may die within two to fourteen days. If the person survives, he or she will probably have some paralysis and difficulties with speech and memory, although in some cases appropriate rehabilitation restores nearly normal functioning. Cerebral thromboses and hemorrhages together kill about 200,000 Americans each year (Terry and Wisniewski, 1974).

The following case illustrates the human impact of a stroke and efforts that can be made to restore some semblance of normalcy.

At age sixty-eight, Mr. H., a retired small businessman, was active in community affairs and with his hobby of woodworking. He had high blood pressure that was well controlled on medication and had had diabetes for several years, which was controlled with insulin. Mr. H. was accustomed to being independent and in charge of things, and this was acceptable to his wife of forty-five years. Mr. H. believed that any reduction of his independent status would be a sign of weakness. He was generally even tempered but would become angry when he was hindered from completing a task he had set out to do. . . .

Mrs. H. was active with her church group and had frequent visitors. She was in good health but had only moderate physical strength. She prepared well-balanced meals for both of them, including the special diet required for Mr. H. because of his diabetes and

---

further difficulties in diagnosis. Finally, as has been mentioned, delirium and dementia frequently occur together.

Treatment of Delirium

The treatment of delirium has two important aspects. The first is identification and correction of the underlying medical problem, the second, management of the problematic symptoms until the condition has lifted.

Adequate sensory stimulation and orientation should be provided for the individual. Having a radio or television set in the room may help to provide both of high blood pressure. They had two children, both of whom were married and living out of state, but who visited at holiday times.

One morning Mrs. H. entered her husband's workshop and found him sitting on a chair and unable to speak. The right side of his face drooped and he was unable to move his right arm or leg. He did not seem to see her when she approached him from his right but could see her when she moved to his left side. He made a few attempts to speak but was unsuccessful. Mrs. H. called their physician, who arranged for ambulance transportation to the hospital. Detailed examination and testing revealed that Mr. H. had sustained a stroke due to the occlusion of an artery supplying the left side of his brain. After receiving acute care including that necessary to prevent complications and reaching a stabilized condition, Mr. H. was transferred to a comprehensive medical rehabilitation center.

Mr. H.'s medical records were reviewed by the rehabilitation physician, he was examined, and his wife was informed of the results. She was also interviewed by a social worker who obtained further background information and answered questions about the facility. Mrs. H. found that she would be part of the rehabilitation process, that the staff would work closely with her, and that she would receive training necessary to help in her husband's care when he returned home. She would also receive counseling to aid her in coping skills and help her adapt to this change in their life situation. Mr. H. had a urinary catheter and had become constipated because of his illness and inactivity. These problems were attended to by the rehabilitation nursing staff, which also kept close watch on skin condition, both because of his impaired mobility and his diabetes. They monitored his blood pressure and regularly checked his urine for sugar. As Mr. H. progressed in the program, they taught him how to inject his insulin with his left hand and taught his wife how to draw up the proper amount in the syringe.

Mr. H. began to regain some communication ability, and his function was carefully evaluated by the speech pathologist, who aided him in improving general communication abilities. She informed Mrs. H. and the rehabilitation team members about how best to communicate with Mr. H. Speech therapy was also used to improve the volume and clarity of his speech.

As communication abilities improved, a psychologist evaluated Mr. H.'s mental status and cognitive skills and helped him to adapt to the frustrations of his disability and his feelings of [not] being in control. The psychologist also helped Mr. H. direct his anger in a more productive manner rather than diffusely taking out frustrations on the staff or on his wife. . . .

The physical therapist gradually helped Mr. H. improve his bed mobility and transfers, and eventually he progressed to the point where he was ambulating, first with a broad-based four-pointed cane and maximum assistance, and ultimately with a straight cane with his wife standing by. The occupational therapist worked on teaching Mr. H. to use his nondominant hand while he was also working to improve function in the weak right hand. He was taught to feed himself, to dress himself, and to perform the basic activities of daily living. He was also given exercises and training that would [allow him to pursue] his woodworking hobby, at least to a limited degree.

The recreational therapist helped Mr. H. to reach some self-fulfillment during his leisure time. His leisure activities were geared to those he had previously enjoyed, adapted to his disability. Transportation and financial status were discussed with Mrs. H. and also with her husband, and appropriate community agency referrals were made. An occupational therapist went out to the house to evaluate the existence of architectural barriers and to make recommendations for safety.

During this course of events, the rehabilitation team met weekly to discuss the problems that Mr. H. was experiencing, to compare ideas on solving these problems, and to plan the treatment approach for the forthcoming week. After about a month of this treatment Mr. H. was able to return home with his wife at a semi-independent level, with plans to return for outpatient treatment in order further to increase his strength, mobility, self-care, and communication skills (Zarit, 1980, pp. 179–180).

these. A relative or friend who stays with the person will give reassurance and reorientation. Leaving a light on at night can help delirious individuals comprehend their surroundings more quickly and decrease their confusion and agitation after dusk. It is important to protect the delirious patient from self-injury and injury to others.

Around-the-clock attendants may be needed, or the person can be placed near the nurse's station. Physical restraints should be avoided if at all possible, for they may actually increase agitation (Liston, 1982). Medication may be needed to treat the underlying problem, to sedate the person, or for both these reasons.

One often neglected aspect of the management of delirium is educating the family of a senile parent to recognize the symptoms of delirium and its reversible nature. They may interpret the onset of delirium as a new stage of a progressive dementing condition. For example, a father with Alzheimer's disease may run a high fever from an internal infection and begin to hallucinate and otherwise act bizarrely. These new symptoms, superimposed on the intellectual deterioration to which members of the family have become accustomed, may alarm them into concluding that he is losing ground fast and irreversibly. They may be rushed into a premature decision to institutionalize him. Proper diagnosis and treatment, however, can usually return the person to his earlier state, which, although problematic, was being coped with by those in the home.

PSYCHOLOGICAL DISORDERS OF OLD AGE

In an earlier discussion the point was made that transsexuals tend to attribute whatever personal unhappiness they experience to the discrepancy between their anatomy and their gender identity. A similar process operates with old people, at least as they are viewed by others. The most obvious characteristic of a seventy-five-year-old man is that he is old. If he is cranky, it is because he is old. If he is depressed, it is because he is old. Even when he is happy, it is assumed to be because of his age. Moreover, the "old-age explanation" is generally a somatic one, even if this is not made explicit. Some ill-defined physical deterioration is assumed to underlie not only the physical problems of old people but all their psychological problems as well.

Although a psychological disorder at any age may have a physical explanation, for the aged this explanation locates the cause of their problems within them and often blinds us to other factors that may have much to do with whatever mental or emotional distress they are suffering. The fact is that most psychopathology to be found in the aged has *not* been directly linked to the physiological processes of aging. Whether the person brings maladaptive personality traits and inadequate coping skills into old age plays a role, as do health, genetic predisposition, and life stressors.

Depression

Extent of the Problem
According to the recent NIMH data, affective disorders are less common in older adults than in younger (Myers et al., 1984), but they are estimated to account for nearly half the admissions of older adults to acute psychiatric care (Gurland and Cross, 1982; Redick and Taube, 1980). Unipolar depressions are much more common in the elderly than bipolar (Post, 1978). In fact, the onset of manic-depressive illness after the age of sixty-five is believed to be rare (Jamison, 1979). For this reason the following discussion will be of unipolar depression in older adults.

Depression is viewed as one of the most common and most treatable of the disorders affecting the elderly. Prevalence estimates of depression in the aged vary widely, however, depending on the population studied, community elderly versus those in hospitals; the method of assessment used, self-report or clinical evaluation; and perhaps most importantly, the diagnostic criteria. Past community surveys have reported that as many as 30 to 65 percent of older adults report some depressive symptoms, such as fatigue, dysphoric mood, and impaired sleep patterns (Dovenmuehle, Recklass, and Newman, 1970; Pfeiffer and Busse, 1973; Raymond, Michals, and Steer, 1980; Zung, 1967). Thus, if a survey concentrates on somatic complaints like fatigue and insomnia, persons over sixty-five appear more prone to depression than younger individuals. But when the full syndrome of major depression as defined in DSM-III is considered, only 2 to 6 percent of the elderly have depression (Blazer and Williams, 1980; Gurland and Cross, 1982; Weissman and Myers, 1978). In fact, the recent NIMH study noted a prevalence rate of less than one percent for major depression in older adults (Myers et al., 1984). Thus older persons in both community and patient populations are diagnosed as depressed less frequently than are younger persons. Increased age itself is not associated with depression (Liberman, 1983).

Women have more periods of depression than men for most of their lives, except possibly when they reach old-old age. In a study done in New York, more women than men under eighty had depression that needed to be treated, but for people over eighty, more men than women were seriously depressed, 24 versus 10 percent (Gurland and Cross, 1982). More than 30 percent of older individuals who have chronic health problems or are confined in hospitals are depressed (Blazer, 1982). Moreover, people with a dementing disorder such as Alzheimer's may simultaneously become depressed; 20 percent of those with dementia are estimated to have a superimposed depression (Reifler, Larson, and Hanley, 1982).

In general, depressions severe enough to warrant intervention are estimated to affect 10 to 15 percent of the geriatric population. The majority represent recurrences of similar episodes from earlier in life. We do not now have good incidence data, that is, statistics for how often people become depressed for the first time in old age.

Depression in Older versus Younger Adults

Is depression in older adults the same as or different from that in younger adults? Blazer (1982) states that worry, feelings of uselessness, sadness, pessimism, fatigue, inability to sleep, and volitional difficulties are common symptoms of depression in the elderly. These symptoms are of course similar to those of depression in other age groups. When Blazer (1982) compared the symptoms of depression in the aged to those of three younger adult populations being treated for depression, however, he noted some interesting differences. Feelings of guilt were found less often in the depressed elderly, whereas somatic complaints were more common. Thoughts of suicide were also less common in older patients, which contrasts with our knowledge that in older men actual suicide attempts and successes increase (see page 458).

Depression versus Dementia

A number of case histories and research studies document that symptoms of elderly individuals, seemingly of dementia, remit spontaneously or improve with treatment for depression (Kiloh, 1961; Post, 1975; Folstein and McHugh, 1978; McAllister and Price, 1982). And as we mentioned in our discussion of dementia, cases of depression are often misdiagnosed as a dementing disorder. Depressed patients may actually complain more of forgetfulness than patients with dementia, a distinction which may be clinically useful (Kahn et al., 1975; Raskin and Rae, 1981). Those with dementia may forget that they forget! In testing, depressed patients tend to underestimate their abilities and to be preoccupied with negative feedback (Miller, 1975; Weingartner and Silberman, 1982). The depressed also tend to have more errors of omission: they may not answer a question because it is just too much effort for them, or because they expect to make mistakes. Those with dementia, on the other hand, tend to make random or confabulatory errors (Whitehead, 1973).

Correlates of Depression in the Aged

Can a connection be drawn between the incidence of depressive symptoms in the aged and the theories and evidence that depression has a biochemical basis? Levels of norepinephrine are lower and levels of monoamine oxidase higher in older people than in younger (McGeer and McGeer, 1976; Lipton and Nemeroff, 1978). Since

Older people living in close and active contact with members of their family are less prone to depression than those living in institutions.

we know that depressed people have low levels of norepinephrine and serotonin and that MAO deactivates norepinephrine and serotonin, the combination of these age changes could contribute to the development of a depressive disorder in older people. Another contributor may be the diminishing output of the thyroid gland. Continued research may reveal other possible biochemical bases of depression in older people, but it would be a mistake to focus attention on them to the neglect of other factors.

As indicated earlier, many aged in poor physical health are depressed. In a survey of 900 elderly people living in the community, Blazer and Williams (1980) found that 44 percent of people with depressive symptoms were medically ill. Moreover, older men who have their first onset of depression in late life are likely to have undergone surgery before psychiatric admission, to have unusually high rates of chronic illness, and to have suffered from more medical conditions than other persons do (Roth and Kay, 1956).

Physical illness and depression are linked for reasons other than the disheartening aspects of an illness. Medications prescribed to treat a chronic condition can aggravate a depression that already exists, cause a depression to start, or produce symptoms that resemble the disorder but are not in fact a true depression (Klerman, 1983). The drugs that are the most likely to do this are antihypertensive medications, which cause depression in

20 percent of adults who take them: hormones and corticosteroids; and anti-Parkinsonian medications. Longitudinal and retrospective studies have pointed out that, on the other side of the coin, individuals who are originally depressed may be predisposed to develop physical illness (Vaillant, 1979; Wigdor and Morris, 1977).

As we grow older, we almost inevitably experience a number of life events that could cause depression. The elderly are commonly bereaved of their loved ones. Various studies have documented higher rates of illness and death among the widowed (Parkes and Brown, 1972; Clayton, 1973), and bereavement has been hypothesized to be a common precipitating factor for depressions that hospitalize elderly patients (Turner and Sternberg, 1978). And yet longitudinal studies have found relatively low rates of depression in the bereaved, and it has been concluded that the symptoms of depression in bereft individuals are generally less severe and fewer than those in individuals institutionalized for depression (Clayton et al., 1972; Bornstein et al., 1973; Gallagher et al., 1982). Few older people, then, appear to develop a disabling depressive illness following an expected loss of a loved one.

Retirement has also been assumed to have negative consequences for the person, but research does not generally support this assumption (Atchley, 1980; George, 1980). The ill effects of retirement found by studies may have had much to do with the poor health and low incomes of the retirees.

Each older person brings to late life a developmental history that makes his or her reactions to common problems unique. Their coping skills and personality determine how effectively they will respond to new life events (Butler and Lewis, 1982). We should not assume that depression rather than adaptation is the common reaction to losses and stress in late life.

Treatment of Depression

Although clinical lore commonly holds that depressions in the aged last longer and are more resistant to treatment, these claims are not substantiated (Small and Jarvik, 1982). Indeed, there is substantial evidence that depressed older adults can be helped by psychological interventions. Gallagher and Thompson (1982, 1983) compared cognitive, behavioral, and brief supportive psychotherapies for older depressed individuals. All three were found effective. At a one-year follow-up, however, people who had received the cognitive and behavioral therapies showed additional improvement, presumably because they were continuing to apply the skills that they had learned. The effects of cognitive and behavioral strategies have also been compared to psycho-

dynamic therapy for aged individuals (Jarvik et al., 1982; Steuer and Hammen, 1983). Both treatments significantly reduced depression and anxiety, according to self-report measures, with the cognitive and behavioral strategies favored. With the aged, as any population, we must consider the problems of the people treated. Behavioral strategies are more useful than cognitive for persons whose thinking is less intact (Steuer and Hammen, 1983), and medications may be more appropriate for those with long-standing depressive disorders.

Although clinical experience does suggest that antidepressant drugs are effective with the aged, their side effects need careful attention. A serious one is postural hypotension. Many older adults treated with tricyclic antidepressants become dizzy and fall and can even be at increased risk of myocardial infarction. And as we have seen in the discussion of delirium, the aged are also at high risk for toxic reactions to medications. The advantages and disadvantages of antidepressant drugs must be carefully weighed.

Paranoid Disorders

A sixty-six-year-old married woman reluctantly agreed to a clinical evaluation. She [had] a six-week history of bizarre delusions and hallucinations of her husband spraying the house with a fluid that smelled like "burned food." She complained that he sprayed the substance everywhere around the house, including draperies and furniture, although she had never seen him do it. She could smell the substance almost constantly, and it affected her head, chest, and rectum. She also complained that someone in the neighborhood had been throwing bricks and rocks at her house. In addition, she suspected her husband of having affairs with other women, whose footprints she claimed to have seen near home.

She gave a vague history of marital distress for about six years. Yet she had no history of a similar episode earlier in life, no history of previous psychiatric treatment, and no history of long-term suspiciousness or mistrust. The patient had been a domestic servant for thirty years and was still working. She was described as a loyal, active church member and as socially outgoing. Interviews revealed a sullen woman who was extremely hostile toward her husband. She focused on the delusion that he was spraying an unusual substance in an attempt to upset her; other issues in the relationship seemed secondary. No cognitive dysfunction could be determined in interviews, and her behavior with interviewers was otherwise socially appropriate. She denied vehemently that anything was wrong with her and insisted that her husband was the one with a problem. She looked very sad at times and would occasionally wipe away a tear; but her predominant affect was extreme hostility and consternation about her husband's alleged behavior. . . .

Medical evaluation revealed no abnormalities. The only suggestion of a precipitating event was the death of a son five years earlier. Though denying emotional problems of her own, she reluctantly agreed to come for weekly interviews with the clinic social worker and to take haloperidol, 1 mg three times per day. She began to suppress her delusional concerns after about three weeks, and the therapist was able to draw her into other topics during the interviews. She has been maintained on the same dosage of haloperidol for about seven months and has remained in remission (Varner and Gaitz, 1982, pp. 108–109).

As we can understand, given this case history, paranoia may have a disturbing and immediate impact on others, often bringing angry reactions and contributing to a decision to institutionalize the older adult (Berger and Zarit, 1978). Yet how common is paranoia in late life? As with depression, this depends on the diagnostic criteria used. When DSM-III criteria for paranoid disorders were applied consistently in 800 older patients at the Texas Research Institute of Mental Science for a period of five years, a 2 percent incidence for outpatients and a 4.6 percent incidence for inpatients were found (Varner and Gaitz, 1982). Yet paranoid symptomatology is held to be a general complaint of many elderly psychiatric patients (Pfeiffer, 1977). One study of geriatric inpatients found that 32 percent of them had paranoid symptoms associated with some other form of mental illness (Whanger, 1973). Because the term paranoia is loosely applied, the exact prevalence cannot be known.

Clinicians report an interesting and striking difference between the paranoid delusions of older people and those of younger individuals. The suspicions of older adults are more down to earth, concerned with persons in their immediate surroundings—such as neighbors, sons and daughters, people in stores, and the like. In contrast, the persecutors of younger paranoids are often located far away, in the C.I.A. or the F.B.I. or even outer space. Younger paranoids are given to more grandiosity than older ones. Moreover, older patients are more likely to be women who are in good health, except for problems with vision and, as we shall see, hearing.

Causes of Paranoia

Paranoia in the aged may be the continuation of a disorder that began earlier in life. It may also accompany organic brain conditions such as delirium and dementia. In fact, paranoia may serve a function for the demented, filling in the gaps caused by memory loss. Instead of admitting "I can't remember where I left my keys," they think "Someone must have come in and taken my keys" (Zarit, 1980). Paranoid ideation has also been linked to sensory losses, in particular hearing. Older people with severe paranoid disorders tend to have long-standing hearing loss in both ears, which makes them socially deaf (Post, 1980). An older woman who is deaf may believe that other people are whispering about her, so that she cannot hear what is being said. Her paranoid reactions may be an attempt to fill in the blanks caused by sensory loss (Pfeiffer, 1977; see Box 17.3), just as they fill the memory gaps of dementia. By explaining bewildering events, they are in a sense adaptive and understandable. Often the earlier social adjustment of paranoid patients has been poor; the onset of their symptoms may follow a period in which they have become increasingly isolated. And isolation itself limits a person's opportunities to check his or her suspicions about the world, making it easier for delusions to take hold. The individual builds a "pseudocommunity" rather than social relations based on good communication and mutual trust (Cameron, 1959).

Like other kinds of psychopathology, paranoia may be maintained, at least in part, by reinforcement from others. A lonely woman gets action from police and relatives if she complains of intruders. Sadly enough, sometimes such attention is the best the old person can manage, for as just stated, many of those who develop paranoia have been socially isolated throughout their lives. But it should not be supposed that the adoption of a paranoid belief is deliberate, nor does it seem plausible that reinforcement patterns can explain why a person began having delusions in the first place.

Older people are especially vulnerable to all kinds of abuse from others. They may be talked about behind their backs, or even to their faces, as though they were not present, and taken advantage of by others in many small and larger ways. There is thus a danger that a complaint of persecution from an older person will be quickly dismissed as "just" a sign of late-life paranoia. A client of one of the authors complained bitterly about being followed by a detective hired by her "evil" husband. Inquiry revealed that the husband was worried

BOX 17.3

PARTIAL DEAFNESS, GROWING OLD, AND PARANOIA

A relation between hearing problems in old age and the development of paranoid thinking was noted many years ago by Emil Kraepelin and has been verified since by careful laboratory studies (Cooper et al., 1974). The connection appears to be specific to paranoia, for the relation between difficulties in hearing and depression in older individuals is not as great. Since hearing losses appear to predate the onset of paranoid delusions, this may be a cause-effect relationship of some importance.

Stanford psychologist Philip Zimbardo and his associates conducted an experiment to study the relation of poor hearing to paranoia. They reasoned that loss of hearing acuity might set the stage for the development of paranoia if the person does not acknowledge, or is unaware of, the hearing problem (Zimbardo, Andersen, and Kabat, 1981). If I have trouble hearing people around me, which makes them seem to be whispering, I may conclude that they are whispering *about me*, and that what they say is unfavorable. I will think this way, however, only if I am unaware of my hearing problem. If I know that I am partially deaf, I will appreciate that I do not hear them well because of my deafness and will not think that they are whispering. A hard-of-hearing grandfather may eventually challenge the light-voiced, gesturing grandchildren he believes are whispering about him; and they will deny that they are. A tense cycle of allegations, denials, and further accusations will isolate the increasingly hostile and suspicious grandfather from the company of his grandchildren.

The experiment done by Zimbardo and his group examined the initial stage of this hypothesized development of paranoia. College students, previously determined to be easily hypnotized and capable of responding to a posthypnotic suggestion of partial deafness, participated in what they believed to be a study of the effects of various hypnotic procedures on creative problem solving. Each of the subjects sat in a room with two others who were actually confederates of the experimenter. The trio were provided a task to perform either cooperatively or by themselves; they were to make up a story concerning a TAT picture. The picture was shown on the screen, and projected first was the word ''FOCUS.'' The confederates, as planned, began to joke with each other as they made decisions about the story, inviting the subject to join them in the cooperative venture. After the story was completed, the subject was left alone to fill out the questionnaires, among them MMPI measures of paranoia and an adjective checklist to assess mood.

As described so far, there is nothing particularly interesting about the experiment. The actual manipulations took place earlier, *before* the TAT picture was presented. Each subject had been hypnotized and then given one of the three following hypnotic suggestions.

1. *Induced partial deafness without awareness.* Each member of the first group was told that when he saw the word ''FOCUS'' projected on a screen in the next room, he would have trouble hearing noises and whatever other people might be saying, that they would seem to be whispering, and that he would be concerned about not being able to hear. He was also instructed to forget this suggestion until

---

that she was having an affair and had indeed hired someone to follow her! It should always be determined whether suspicions have any bases in reality before they are attributed to paranoia.

Treatment of Paranoia

The treatment of paranoia in older adults is much the same as for younger adults. Clinical lore suggests that a patient, supportive approach is best; the therapist should provide empathic understanding of the person's concerns. Directly challenging the paranoid delusion or attempting to reason the person out of his or her beliefs is seldom effective. Rather, recognition of the distress caused by the paranoia is more likely to promote a therapeutic relationship with the person. Therapists should be mindful that, by the time the patient sees a health professional, many others—family, friends, the police— have probably tried, to no avail, to reason the person out of his or her delusional beliefs.

If the person has a hearing or a visual problem, a hearing aid or corrective lenses may alleviate some of the symptoms. When the individual is socially isolated, efforts can be made to increase his or her activities and contacts. Regular supportive therapy may help the patient in reestablishing relations with family members and friends. Attention should be provided for appropriate behavior. Even if these straightforward measures do not relieve paranoia, they may be beneficial in other areas of the person's life.

Studies of therapy outcomes indicate that delusions in the elderly can be treated successfully with major tranquilizers (Post, 1980). Unfortunately, paranoid individuals are generally suspicious of the motives of those who give them drugs. Toxicity from medications must also be considered, given the particular sensitivity of older people to drugs. Institutionalization, best considered as a last resort, may do little good. In practice, the decision depends more on how tolerant the person's so-an experimenter removed the amnesia by touching his shoulder.

2. *Induced partial deafness with awareness.* Subjects in the second group, the control group, were given the same partial-deafness suggestion, but they were instructed to remember that their hearing difficulty was by posthypnotic suggestion.

3. *Posthypnotic-suggestion control.* Subjects in the third group, controls for the effectiveness of posthypnotic suggestion, were instructed to react to the word "FOCUS" by experiencing an itchiness in the left earlobe, with amnesia for this suggestion until touched on the left shoulder by the experimenter.

After being given their posthypnotic suggestions, all subjects were awakened from the hypnotic state and ushered into the next room, where the experiment proceeded as already described. It can now be appreciated that participants who had deafness without awareness might perceive the joking of the confederates as directed toward them, for they would have trouble hearing what was being said and would be unlikely to attribute this difficulty to any hearing problem of their own. Subjects who had deafness with awareness would have the same problem hearing the joking, but they would know that they had a temporary decrement in hearing through hypnotic suggestion. The other control subjects would have no hearing problems, just itchy earlobes. At the completion of the study, all subjects were carefully informed about the purposes of the study, and steps were taken to ensure that the posthypnotic suggestions of partial deafness and itchy earlobes had been lifted.

The results are fascinating. The experience of being partially deaf without awareness showed up significantly on cognitive, emotional, and behavioral measures. As compared to members of the two control groups, these subjects scored more paranoid on the MMPI scales and described themselves as more irritated, agitated, and hostile. The two confederates who were in the same room with these subjects rated them as more hostile than the controls. (The confederates were of course not aware of which group a given subject was in.) When the confederates invited each subject to work with them in concocting the TAT story, only one of six experimental subjects accepted the overture, although most of the control subjects agreed. At the end of the study, just before the debriefing, all subjects were asked whether they would like to participate in a future experiment with the same partners; none of the deafness-without-awareness subjects said that he would, but most of the controls did.

The overall reaction of subjects who had trouble hearing and had no ready explanation for it, other than that others were whispering, was suspicion, hostility, agitation, and unwillingness to affiliate with these people. This pattern is similar to what Zimbardo hypothesizes to be the earliest stage of the development of some paranoid delusions. The creation of this "analogue incipient paranoia" in the laboratory by inducing deafness without awareness of the deafness is consistent with the view that when people's hearing becomes poor in old age, they are susceptible to paranoia *if*, for whatever reasons, they do not acknowledge their deafness.

cial environment is than on how severe and disruptive are the paranoid beliefs.

Schizophrenia

Does schizophrenia ever appear for the first time in old age? Debate on this question has raged for years; the answer depends on the definition of schizophrenia. According to DSM-III's narrower definition, first-time onset of schizophrenia after the age of sixty-five is very rare indeed.

Large-scale surveys have estimated the overall prevalence of schizophrenia at one percent or less in persons over the age of sixty (LaRue, Dessonville, and Jarvik, 1985; Myers et al., 1984). Ninety percent of the geriatric patients with schizophrenia acquired the disorder before the age of forty, which means that very few have late onset (Gurland and Cross, 1982; Bollerup, 1975). In these

cases paranoid symptoms are almost always present (Fish, 1960; Roth, 1955), and the schizophrenia of these people does not have the classical pattern (Post, 1980).

The next question of interest is what happens to schizophrenic symptomatology as people become older. Answers depend on what generation we are talking about. Now that the advent of neuroleptics, such as Thorazine, and political decisions to reduce the number of patients in mental hospitals have ushered in a veritable revolution in the treatment of schizophrenia, many more schizophrenics live at home or elsewhere in the community than was the case twenty or thirty years ago. They are less likely to have been institutionalized for long periods of time and have not suffered from the secondary problems of institutionalization. Mortality rates for this group are higher than those of age-matched controls, in part because their rates of suicide and traumatic death are higher (Post, 1980).

Given that many of the schizophrenics who do survive beyond the age of sixty-five are not in hospitals, and given that their symptoms are controlled somewhat by drugs, did the distortions of their thinking become less as they entered old age? Some researchers claim that schizophrenia sometimes "burns out" (Bridge, Cannon, and Wyatt, 1978), that symptoms become somewhat muted. Hallucinations and delusions decrease in intensity and frequency, and the capacity for social interactions improves. But, as Lawton (1972) cautions, these findings are based primarily on hospitalized patients who are taking drugs. As yet the course of schizophrenia in old age has not been adequately studied.

When schizophrenia does make an appearance in older adults, it is often called paraphrenia (Roth, 1955). These patients are reported to have a milder form of the disorder than patients with early onset. They also tend to be unmarried, live in isolation, have few surviving relatives, have hearing losses and a family history of schizophrenia, and belong to the lower socioeconomic classes (Post, 1980). In the United States the term paraphrenia, like paranoia, has been inconsistently used and the phenomenon little studied (Berger and Zarit, 1978; Bridge and Wyatt, 1980). Some researchers believe that the older patients diagnosed as having paraphrenia by Roth actually had an affective disorder (Cooper, Garside, and Kay, 1976; Cooper and Porter, 1976; Kay et al., 1976), for in many with prominent symptoms, cognition and overall functioning were preserved.

Substance Use Disorders

Alcohol Abuse and Dependence

Alcoholism, generally believed to be less prevalent in the aged than in younger cohorts, is estimated to range from 2 to 10 percent in the elderly. Problem drinkers, in fact, are not likely to survive to old age. The peak years for death from cirrhosis are between fifty-five and sixty-four years of age. Generational effects may also be at work, for younger cohorts did not grow up in an era that stressed temperance. Older people may also develop physiological intolerance for alcohol, counteracting its positive effects on mood (Gurland and Cross, 1982).

Older alcoholics fall into two groups, the two-thirds or more who began drinking in early or middle adulthood and who have continued their pattern into late life, and the small percentage who took to drink after age fifty (Rosin and Glatt, 1971). Alcoholics who started late either had intermittent drinking problems in

the past and now abuse alcohol regularly in late life or had no history of alcohol problems until their late years (Zimberg, 1978). The late-starting abuser is more likely to be separated or divorced, more likely to live alone, and more likely to have serious health difficulties (Schuckit and Moore, 1979). Age-related circumstances, such as retirement, may have provoked some of them to drink (Rosin and Glatt, 1971).

As people age, their tolerance for alcohol is reduced, for they metabolize it more slowly. Thus the drug may cause greater changes in their brain chemistry than in that of the young and may more readily bring on toxic effects such as delirium. A number of neuropsychological studies have shown that cognitive deficits associated with alcohol abuse are likely to be more pronounced in the aged alcoholic than in younger individuals with comparable drinking histories (Brandt et al., 1983). Although some intellectual functioning is recovered with abstinence, residual effects may remain long after the older person has stopped drinking.

Unfortunately, clinicians may be less likely to look for alcoholism in the aged and to attribute symptoms such as poor motor coordination and impaired memory to an organic problem or to late-life depression. If alcohol abuse goes unrecognized, treatment of the patient will be severely compromised and subject to errors.

Illegal Drug Abuse

The current older population abuses illegal drugs infrequently compared to other age groups. DuPont (1976) found that in the United States only 2 percent of those over fifty reported trying marijuana compared to 56 percent of individuals between eighteen and twenty-one. Studies of the few older narcotics abusers indicate that they began their habit early in life and reduced their drug intake as they grew older (Ball and Chambers, 1970). Contrary to earlier reports, only a very small number of these addicts discontinue drug use (Schuckit and Moore, 1979).

Medication Misuse

The misuse of prescription and over-the-counter medicines is a much greater problem in the aged population than drug or alcohol abuse (LaRue, Dessonville, and Jarvik, 1985). Since all phases of drug intake are altered in the elderly—absorption, distribution, metabolism, and excretion—they are more likely, as we have noted, to react adversely to medications in even normal doses and to experience more side effects to a wider range of drugs. Community surveys of the aged show that they have a higher overall rate of legal drug intake than any other group (Warheit, Arey, and Swanson, 1976); although they comprise only 11.3 percent of the population, they consume 25 percent of all prescribed medications.

Abuse of prescription or legal drugs can be deliberate or inadvertent. Some may seek out drugs to abuse, obtaining medications from a number of sources. Others may not take medications as they are prescribed, perhaps through misunderstanding, ignorance, or limited financial resources. One study showed that more than half of a group of aged could not afford to take their medications the way they were prescribed (Brand, Smith, and Brand, 1977). The chance for misuse is believed to increase the more medications are taken and the more complex are the instructions. Dependence on medications can develop, particularly in anxious, depressed, and hypochondriacal older adults (LaRue, Dessonville, and Jarvik, 1985). One side effect of medications, confusion, may be misdiagnosed as dementia, and the side effect of lethargy may be mistaken for depression.

The elderly with limited incomes should be provided the medication prescribed for them. Individuals of any age need to understand why they are taking a drug, what it is called, when and how often they should take it, and under what conditions, for example, before meals, on an empty stomach, and so on. Their comprehension of the instructions should be tested. An older woman who had been given an antibiotics prescription that cautioned against taking it before or after meals came to the attention of one of the authors. She believed that this warning meant she could not eat at all while taking the medication! Since visual acuity declines with age and susceptibility to glare increases, printing instructions in small type on a shiny label—a common practice of drug companies—is bad practice. A chart on which the forgetful person can check off when he or she has taken medication, taped in a prominent place, serves as a useful reminder.

Hypochondriasis

Older adults complain of a multitude of physical problems, among them sore feet and backs, poor digestion, constipation, labored breathing, and cold extremities. All are to be taken seriously by responsible health professionals. But some of the elderly only believe themselves to be ill, as do younger people, and complain unendingly about aches and pains for which there are no plausible physical causes. Indeed, it has been widely believed that hypochondriasis is especially common in the aged. Busse and Blazer (1979) estimated the prevalence in community-residing elderly to be between 10 and 20 percent. New cases of hypochondriasis in the elderly are found to peak between the ages of sixty and sixty-five, with a greater proportion of women affected than men (Busse, 1976).

Some new data, however, suggest that the proportion of hypochondriacs is *not* greater in old age than at any other age (Siegler and Costa, 1985). In fact, the aged as a whole tend to *under*report somatic symptoms rather than overreport them and often fail to seek help for serious illnesses (Besdine, 1980). We do not imply that there are no older hypochondriacs. Rather, as Siegler and Costa (1985) state, older persons who have many physical complaints have long-standing personality traits that predict such complaining. Their excessive somatic complaints appear to be associated with neuroticism or poor adjustment, which are *not* associated with age. In addition, the NIMH catchment area studies find no somatization disorder in the older adults surveyed (Myers et al., 1984). Thus one of our society's prevalent myths has been brought into serious question.

Causes of Hypochondriasis

It has been suggested that for older adults of this and previous generations, emotional concerns and distress are more difficult to talk about than physical ailments. The language they use to express unhappiness, then, is somatic. It is not that my feelings are hurt because my son never visits me. Rather, I can't keep my food down and my arms keep aching. Studies have indicated that somatizing is more frequent among lower-middle-class or semiskilled workers (Pilowsky, 1970) than among better-educated people, who presumably have greater psychological sophistication and are more accepting of nonmedical explanations for their psychological distress. Perhaps, then, hypochondriacal complaints in some older adults represent in part a cohort effect. The next generation of older people have lived in a social climate in which psychological problems are more openly discussed and in which seeing a "shrink" and taking medications for emotional disorders are more acceptable than they were to the previous generation. Future older adults may somatize less when they are unhappy.

Treatment of Hypochondriasis

No controlled studies of the treatment of hypochondriasis have been done. Clinicians generally agree, however, that reassuring the person that he or she is really healthy is generally useless, for these people are not swayed by negative laboratory tests or authoritative pronouncements from people in white coats. Some tentative evidence suggests that ignoring the somatic complaints and concentrating instead on more positive aspects of existence can be helpful (Goldstein and Birnbom, 1976). I know that you're feeling bad and that your feet really hurt, but let's take a walk in Palisades Park anyway. Diverting activities may allow these individuals at least to function in the face of their perceived medical ills and perhaps obtain some positive satisfactions from life.

Insomnia

Insomnia, a disturbance in the sleep process, is a frequent complaint of the elderly. In one community survey 23 percent of the respondents over sixty years of age reported frequent sleep problems as compared to 13 percent of the population in general (Karacan et al., 1976). The most common are awakening at night more often and for longer periods, frequent early-morning awakenings, greater difficulties in falling asleep, and greater daytime fatigue (Miles and Dement, 1980). These complaints have been found to parallel the physiological changes that occur normally in the sleep patterns of older adults (Bootzin, Engle-Friedman, and Hazelwood, 1983). For example, the total time that the elderly devote to sleep appears to be somewhat less or the same as that of younger age groups. But sleep is more often spontaneously interrupted as people grow older. Thus older people generally sleep less in relation to the total time they spend in bed. In addition, the aged spend less absolute time in a phase known as rapid eye movement (REM) sleep; and stage 4 sleep, the deepest, is virtually absent. In general, elderly men appear to have more disturbances of their sleep than do women, a difference found to a lesser extent in young adults (Dement, Laughton, and Carskadon, 1981).

Causes of Insomnia
Besides the changes in sleep associated with aging, various illnesses, medications, caffeine, stress, anxiety, depression, lack of activity, and poor sleep habits may make insomniacs of older adults. Pain, particularly that of arthritis, is a principal disrupter of their sleep (Prinz and Raskin, 1978). Sleep apnea, a respiratory disorder in which breathing ceases for a period of ten seconds or more repeatedly through the night, increases with age (Carskadon, Brown, and Dement, 1980). Whatever the cause of a particular person's insomnia, it is worsened by self-defeating actions like ruminating over it and counting the number of hours slept and those spent waiting to fall asleep.

Treatment of Insomnia
Over-the-counter medications and prescription drugs are taken by many older insomniacs. The little bottle of sleeping pills is a familiar companion to the many medications that sit on the night table. The elderly are major consumers of sleep aids, yet these rapidly lose their effectiveness and may in fact with continuous use make sleep light and fragmented. REM rebound sleep, an increase in REM sleep after prolonged reliance on drugs, is fitful (Bootzin, Engle-Friedman, and Hazelwood, 1983). In fact, medications can bring about what is called a drug-dependent insomnia. These so-called aids can also give people drug hangovers and increase respiratory difficulties, which in the aged is a great hazard, given the increased prevalence of sleep apnea. There is now considerable evidence that sleep medication is not the appropriate treatment for the chronic insomniac of any age, but particularly not for the elderly insomniac.

Explaining the nature of sleep, and the changes that take place as a normal part of the aging process, can reduce the worry that older persons have about their sleep pattern, concern which in itself can interefere with sleep. The therapist should also reassure them that it is not a calamity to go without sleep. It will not cause irreversible brain damage or insanity, fears that some people have. Some individuals are given relaxation training, to help them fall asleep, and instructions that will help them develop good sleep habits—rising at the same time every day; avoiding activities at bedtime that are inconsistent with falling asleep, such as watching television and reading; lying down only when sleepy; and if unable to go to sleep, getting up and going into another room. All these maneuvers can loosen the grip of insomnia.

Suicide

Several factors put people in general at especially high risk for suicide: serious physical illness, feelings of hopelessness, social isolation, loss of loved ones, dire financial circumstances, and depression. Because these problems are widespread among the elderly, we should not be surprised to learn that suicide rates for people over sixty-five are unusually high, perhaps three times greater than the rate for younger individuals (Pfeiffer, 1977).

Persons sixty years of age or older commit 23 percent of all suicides in the United States (Blazer, 1982). An examination of cross-sectional data indicates that the suicide rate for males rises from youth and increases in a linear fashion with age (Atchley, 1982). White older men are more likely to commit suicide than any other group; and their peak ages for taking their lives are from eighty to eighty-four. The rate for women peaks before they reach fifty and declines steadily thereafter. Thus rates of suicide in white men increase sharply during old age, and rates for women decline somewhat. Throughout the life span men have higher suicide rates than women, but the difference is most notable in the old-old.

Older persons communicate their intentions to commit suicide less often than the young and make fewer attempts. When they do make an attempt, however, they are more successful in killing themselves. Suicide attempts by people younger than thirty-five fail more often than they succeed, but those of people over fifty are more likely to be lethal. Once people are past sixty-five, their attempts rarely fail (Butler and Lewis, 1982). What is particularly distressing is that the statistics given are probably underestimates; older adults have many opportunities to "give up" on themselves by neglecting their diet or medications, thus killing themselves in a more passive fashion. Moreover, Butler and Lewis (1982) have argued that suicide of older adults may more often be a rational or philosophical decision than that of younger people. Consider, for example, the elderly man who faces the intractable pain of a terminal illness and knows that with each passing day his medical care is using up more and more of the money he might otherwise leave to his widow and his family.

Intervention to prevent the suicide of an older person is similar to that discussed earlier. In general, the therapist tries to persuade the person to regard his problems in less desperate terms. Mental health professionals, who are usually younger and healthier, may unwittingly try less hard to prevent an older person's suicide attempt. But even the older person, once the crisis has passed, is usually grateful that he or she has another chance at living.

Sexuality and Aging

Frequency of Sexual Activity

Biases against the expression of sexuality in old age and disbelief in older people's capacity for sex have abounded in our culture. Men and women alike have been expected to lose interest in and capacity for sex once they reach their senior years. Some believe that old people are unable to enjoy anything more passionate than an affectionate hug and a kiss on the cheek. An older male who shows sexual interest in much younger women is called a "dirty old man." And, after the strong sexual value placed on them when younger, older women are not considered especially sexual. Furthermore, their capacity for sexual arousal is confused with their inability to procreate.

The facts are that older people have considerable sexual interest and capacity. As we review them, it will be important to bear in mind that sexual interest and activity vary greatly in younger adults; disinterest or infrequent sex in an older person should not be blithely taken as evidence that older people are inherently asexual. The sixty-eight-year-old man who has no sex life may well have had little if any interest at age twenty-eight. Whether the person is twenty-eight or sixty-eight, one of the best predictors of continued sexual intercourse is past sexual enjoyment and frequency (Solnick and Corby, 1983).

The frequencies of sexual activity and interest in sex have been determined in several large-scale surveys, among them the famous Kinsey reports (Kinsey, Pome-

Contrary to popular belief, romance, intimacy, and sexual activity do not necessarily decline with advancing age.

roy, and Martin, 1948; Kinsey et al., 1953) and the Duke Longitudinal Studies (Pfeiffer, Verwoerdt, and Wang, 1968, 1969; George and Weiler, 1980). The picture that emerges from these surveys varies according to when the study was conducted.

The earlier studies, such as the Kinsey reports and the first Duke longitudinal study, noted a decline in heterosexual intercourse, masturbation, and homosexual intercourse beginning around age thirty and continuing across the life span. The belief that sex necessarily becomes less important to people in their middle years and in old age is not substantiated by the most recent research, however. The second Duke study (George and Weiler, 1980) covered the years 1968 through 1974 and indicated no decline in the sexual activity of people between ages forty-six and seventy-one, and in fact indicated that 15 percent of older persons increased their sexual activity as they aged. Another study showed that 47 percent of those between the ages of sixty and seventy-one still had regular and frequent intercourse (Comfort, 1980).

These facts can be interpreted in several ways. Clearly older people can be sexually active; even the earlier surveys indicated that. But it is noteworthy that the second Duke study did not reveal the decline of the first. The older people surveyed in the second study may have had less negative stereotyping to contend with, and they may have been healthier, both of which would be cohort effects. They may also have been more willing to discuss their sexual interests and activities with researchers because the cultural atmosphere has become more supportive, a time-of-measurement effect. Historical factors and sanctioning sexual attitudes may affect sexuality among older adults. In one study seventy- and eighty-year-olds reported rates of intercourse much like those that Kinsey found in forty-year-olds in the 1940s and 1950s (Starr and Weiner, 1981). Perhaps sexual activity in the aged will continue to rise as today's young grow older.

Physiological Changes in Sexual Response with Aging

Among the volunteer subjects studied by Masters and Johnson (1966) were a number of older adults. It is largely from this study that conclusions about older adults' sexual responding have been drawn. Two cautions in interpreting these data are warranted, however. First, the people were studied some time ago, the 1960s, thus bringing into question whether results would be the same today. Second, the sample was not a representative one. Given these provisos, physiological measurements showed the following differences in older adults as compared to younger.

Men   Older men take longer to have an erection, even when they are being stimulated in a way they like. They can maintain an erection longer before ejaculating than younger men, however, and the feeling that ejaculation is inevitable may disappear. It is not known whether physiological changes or control learned over the years explains this. During the orgasm phase, contractions are less intense and fewer in number, and the seminal fluid expelled is less in volume and under less pressure. Once orgasm has occurred, erection is lost more rapidly in older men, and the capacity for another erection cannot be regained as quickly as in younger men. In fact, the refractory period begins to lengthen in men in their twenties (Rosen and Hall, 1984).

Even allowing for the fact that men who agreed to be subjects were hardly a random sample of the population, it is clear that older men are capable of the same pattern of sexual activity as younger men, the major difference being that things take longer to happen, and when they do, there is less urgency. The way men and their partners view normal, age-related physiological changes may contribute to sexual dysfunction, however. If, for example, a man or his partner reacts with alarm to a slow buildup of sexual arousal, the stage is set for performance fears, which have been proclaimed a principal reason for psychosexual dysfunction. Unfortunately, changes that occur with aging are often misinterpreted as evidence that older men are becoming impotent. An important point to remember is that an older man does not lose his capacity for erection unless physical or emotional illness interferes.

Women   A number of age-related differences have been found in older women, but again none of them justifies the conclusion that they are incapable of a satisfactory sex life. Like men, older women need more time to become sexually aroused. Vaginal lubrication is slower and reduced because estrogen levels are lower, and there may be vaginal itching and burning. Steroid replacement can reduce many of these symptoms and be helpful against osteoporosis, a disease causing brittleness of the bones. There are risks, however, such as developing endometrial (uterine) cancer. Vaginal contractions during orgasm are fewer in number compared to those of younger women. Spastic contractions of the vagina and uterus, rather than the rhythmic ones of orgasm in younger women, can cause discomfort and even pain in the lower abdomen and legs. Direct stimulation of the clitoris may be painful in some older women. Like older men, older women return more quickly to a less-aroused state. There is some evidence that these physical changes are not as extensive in women who have been sexually stimulated on a regular basis once or twice a week throughout their sexual lives.

Age-related problems None of these changes, however, need have a significant negative impact on the enjoyment of sexual activity. Sexual relations of older people can be fulfilling, especially if the partners understand these age-related changes in physiological responding and do not view them as abnormal or in decline. Indeed, the ability of the older man to maintain an erection for longer periods of time may make intercourse more enjoyable for both him and his partner (Solnick and Corby, 1983). Nonetheless, physical illness can interfere, as it can in younger people. And because the aged suffer from many chronic ailments, the potential for interference from illness and medications is greater. This is particularly true for men; any disease that disrupts male hormone balance, the nerve pathways to the pelvic area, or blood supply to the penis can prevent erection. Tranquilizers and antihypertensive drugs can also bring about sexual dysfunctioning, as can fatigue and excessive drinking and eating.

Fears of resuming sexual activities after a heart attack have inhibited older men and their lovers, but for most of them the fears are exaggerated (Friedman, 1978). Regrettably, physicians often fail to provide accurate information to postcoronary patients; for example, heart rate is frequently higher during activities such as climbing stairs than it is during intercourse. The situation for patients with congestive heart failure, in which the heart is unable to maintain an adequate circulation of blood in the tissues of the body, or to pump out venous blood returned by the venous circulation, does create for some a risk in intercourse, but less strenuous sexual activity is not a problem.

Although women experience fewer physical problems than men, they are subject to all the myths about aging women's sexuality. In addition, a heterosexual woman's sexual activity typically centers on having a husband and on whether or not he is well and initiates sex. Thus sexual activity of older women is less than that of older men, perhaps because they lack a partner or because they tend to be married to men older than they who may have significant health problems.

Treatment of Sexual Dysfunction

Making the facts of sexuality in old age available to the general public and to the professionals who look after their medical and mental health needs is likely to benefit many older people. Physicians in particular have been guilty of telling the older patient to forget about sex or of not raising the issue when discussing the patient's adjustment, perhaps because of their own discomfort, lack of knowledge, or ageism. Nursing homes are often intolerant of sexuality among their residents; a married couple residing in the same nursing home may not be allowed to share a room. The authors have witnessed nurses in geriatric wards caution residents against stimulating themselves in public while at the same time not allowing for privacy.

Some older people will prefer not to be sexually active, but for older adults who are experiencing and are troubled by sexual dysfunctions, indications are that older people are good candidates for the type of sex therapy given by Masters and Johnson (Berman and Lief, 1976). Greater attention must be paid, however, to physical condition than is usual with younger adults.

GENERAL ISSUES IN TREATMENT AND CARE

Access to Services

Older adults apparently do not receive their just share of mental health services (Redick and Taube, 1980). It has been estimated that only 2.7 percent of clinical services provided by psychologists go to older adults (VandenBos, Stapp, and Kilburg, 1981). Nearly 70 percent of psychologists report never seeing an older client (Dye, 1978; VandenBos, Stapp, and Kilburg, 1981). Moreover, of persons diagnosed as having a psychiatric condition, younger adults are more likely to receive treatment than are older adults (Myers and Weissman, 1980). Why this apparent underservice to the mental health needs of older adults? Some feel that those who are currently elderly are reluctant to define their problems in psychological terms, and that this lack of psychological mindedness keeps them out of therapy (Lawton, 1979). The research that has been done, however, suggests that older adults are really not more reluctant to seek treatment (Knight, 1983; Zarit, 1980), nor are they more likely to drop out of treatment than other age groups (Knight, 1983).

The way services are provided may fail the elderly. Older adults often come to mental health centers through referrals. Yet research has shown that older people are less likely than younger adults to be referred (Ginsburg and Goldstein, 1974; Kucharski, White, and

Schratz, 1979). The reimbursement system may pose some problems, for it is biased toward inpatient care and pays less for outpatient therapy. Moreover, Medicare does not cover supportive care for persons with Alzheimer's disease.

Various studies have shown that clinicians do not expect to treat the aged with as much success as the young (Dye, 1978; Ford and Sbordonne, 1980; Settin, 1982). In one study patients who were older than the therapists were rated as having more severe psychopathology, less motivation for treatment, a poorer prognosis, and less insight than younger patients (Karasu, Stein, and Charles, 1979). Yet, in fact, research does not suggest that psychotherapy of the elderly is less successful (Garfield, 1978). If the aged are viewed as having limited possibilities for improvement, they may not be treated. But a therapist may also not have the knowledge necessary to give good treatment to older people, which will keep them from improving.

Provision of Services

Admissions of older adults to state and county mental hospitals and to psychiatric wards of city hospitals have substantially decreased in the past few years. Older people needing mental health treatment now live in nursing homes or receive community-based care.

Nursing Homes

The evidence indicates that nursing homes are becoming the major locus for institutional care for the aged with severe chronic illnesses and mental disorders (Kramer, 1977). According to forecasts based on current estimates, the number of older people residing in nursing homes is expected to increase from 1.2 million in 1980 to 2.2 million by the turn of the century, and by the year 2050 to triple to 5.4 million (U.S. Bureau of the Census, 1984). Given these projected future increases, it does not appear that enough people are being trained to provide mental health services within these nursing homes. This is a matter of concern, particularly since only 30 percent of nursing homes offer counseling as a routine service, and at least 50 percent of patients have diagnosed emotional disorders (National Center for Health Statistics, 1979).

A decade ago the news media were filled with exposés and lawsuits concerning ineptitude and brutality in some nursing homes. Violations of building codes, neglect, overmedication, intimidation, excessive billing, and other unethical and illegal practices have made people wary about the honesty of nursing home operators

and have occasioned considerable anxiety among families and old people themselves about the nursing home as the best place to spend final months or years.

But these flagrant abuses are probably less a problem than the more subtle disadvantages of nursing homes, which are found even in those with the best-intentioned staffs. A dramatic study by Blenker (1967) highlights the problem. Elderly people who came to a family service center were *randomly* assigned to one of three treatments, intensive, intermediate, and minimal. Intensive treatment involved the services of a nurse and a social worker, intermediate somewhat less professional attention. Minimal treatment consisted of information and referral to community-based services. We might expect intensive treatment to be the most effective, but quite the opposite was the case. After half a year the death rate of members of the intensive-care group was four times that of people in the minimal-care group! The intermediate-care group was less worse off than the intensive-care group; the death rate of its members was "only" twice that of the minimal-care group. What happened? It turned out that the major culprit was being placed in an institution such as a nursing home. A person was much more likely to be institutionalized if a nurse and social worker were intensively involved in planning his or her care, and the excessive death rates were found among the people so taken care of. Since people had been assigned randomly to the three treatments, it is unlikely that the death rates were related to differences existing before treatment began.

What is there about nursing homes that contributes to such decline? First, relocation to a new setting is in itself stressful and is believed to play a role in increased mortality (Aldrich and Mendkoff, 1963; Schulz and Brenner, 1977). Once in the nursing home, the extent and nature of care discourage rehabilitation and even maintenance of whatever self-care skills and autonomous activities the resident may be capable of. For example, a resident able to feed herself but only slowly and with occasional spills will be assisted at mealtime and even fed like a child to shorten the time devoted to serving meals, as well as to decrease the chances of messes on the floor and stains on the woman's clothing. The resident no longer thinks of herself as someone able to eat without help, which is likely to lead to still more loss of function and lowered morale. Muscles themselves weaken and deteriorate through disuse (DeVries, 1975). Relatives of the resident, anxious to know that they have made the right decision and that Mom is being well cared for, are pleased by the tidiness and orderliness that are the result of excessive staff involvement in all details of living.

Although nursing homes are often viewed negatively, in many instances a family's decision to institutionalize an older relative will benefit family relations and renew closeness.

Nursing homes are concerned as well with legal liability. If a resident can walk with a cane, but unsteadily, is it not better to have him pushed in a wheelchair than risk his falling? Falls are a common hazard to old people, and their bones heal slowly and imperfectly.

Custodial care may be excessive, but treatments to improve a patient's mental condition do not have priority. We know that depression is a prevalent psychological disorder of older people, especially of those in nursing homes. The type of psychoactive drug prescribed, however, is more likely to be a tranquilizer than an antidepressant; a less agitated, relatively inactive patient is easier to handle. Psychological interventions are virtually unheard of, for the staff either is untrained in their implementation or operates under the widely held assumption that such therapy is inappropriate for an old person.

In sum, all the problems of institutionalization are in bold and exaggerated relief in nursing homes. Independence is inadvertently, but with sad consequences, discouraged, and both physical and mental deteriorations, because unconsciously expected, are obtained (see Box 17.4).

The prevalent myth is that families dump their older relatives into institutions at the first sign of frailty. The data indicate, however, that families usually explore all their alternatives and exhaust their own resources before they institutionalize an older relative. Thus the decision to institutionalize comes as a last resort, not as a first choice. Institutionalization is also believed to have a negative impact on family relations. One research study, however, found that for a large number of families, moving the parent to a nursing home strengthened family ties and brought a renewed closeness between the parent and the child who was the primary caregiver. The care provided by the home alleviated the strain and pressure caused by the multiple physical or mental problems

Making decisions and caring for plants and pets have beneficial effects on the health of elderly people.

BOX 17.4

LOSS OF CONTROL AND MINDLESSNESS IN NURSING HOMES

Ellen Langer has advanced an argument relating lack of control over life circumstances to the deterioration in both physical and mental health often found in some of the elderly. The reasoning behind her research program is this. Since we know that a perceived or actual lack of control leads to deterioration in adaptive behavior, at least some of what we regard as senility—the inactivity of elderly people and their poor adjustment to changing circumstances—may be caused by loss of control rather than progressive brain disease (Langer, 1981).

Langer points out that our society actually *teaches* the elderly—and sometimes the nonelderly as well!—that older adults are incompetent, or at least far less competent than they were before they became old. In our eagerness to help them, we seem to protect old people from having to make decisions that they might, in fact, be able to make. In our concern to protect them from physical harm, we arrange environments that require little effort to control. And, of course, we set ages for compulsory retirement, overlooking the large individual differences of old people. These practices, especially in a society that values competence and activity, do much to destroy an elderly person's belief that he or she is still effective, that indeed life is worthwhile.

Langer and Rodin (1976b) argue that the crucial problem in nursing homes is loss of opportunity to exercise control and personal responsibility. In one study patients were assigned a particular fifteen-minute period during which the nurse would be on call specifically for them, thus increasing each individual's control over his or her own caretaking. The health of these patients improved more than that of the control group, and they were more sociable (Rodin, 1980).

In another study Langer and Rodin (1976a) told one group of residents that they would be given a variety of decisions to make, instead of the staff's making decisions for them; they were also given plants to take care of. A control group was told how eager the staff was to take care of them; the plants they were given would be looked after by the staff. Although initially matched on variables such as health, these two groups of elderly residents differed three weeks later on several measures of alertness, happiness, and general well-being. Members of the group given enhanced responsibility—and presumably a sense of greater control—tested superior on these measures. Even more impressive was the finding eighteen months later that only half as many of the experimental group, seven out of forty-seven, had died as had members of the control group, thirteen out of forty-four. Moreover, the group given responsibilities continued to show better psychological and physical health (Rodin and Langer, 1977).

Not only may our treatment of old people engender in them a sense of lost control, but their repetitious, unchallenging environments—especially the surroundings of those who are hospital patients or live in nursing homes—may encourage a mode of cognitive functioning Langer terms "mindlessness." Mindlessness is a kind of automatic information processing studied by cognitive psychologists, a mode of thinking that is adaptive when people are in situations that recur frequently, for example, remembering a familiar sequence such as tying one's shoes. In fact, attending to such overlearned activities—making the information processing conscious, not mindless—can actually *interfere* with performance!

Research indicates that people respond mindlessly when confronted by familiar situations. It is as though we operate with as little cognitive effort as we can get away with. When a situation is novel and requires our attention, however, we tend to operate *mindfully*.

What are the clinical implications of too much mindlessness, this mode of mental functioning that entails little cognitive effort? The nonelderly have ample opportunities to engage in thoughtful behavior, and it is reasonable to assume that we all need some minimum of thought and planning to feel good about ourselves and to maintain an alert state of mind. The elderly, in contrast, may be afforded too few opportunities to be thoughtful. Because of the restricted mobility of nursing home residents and hospital patients and because little is demanded of them, their experiences in particular tend to be repetitious and boring. The Langer and Rodin nursing home research may well demonstrate that conscious *thinking* per se as well as perceived control is essential in maintaining emotional and physical well-being. Lack of control and mindlessness are probably related, for what is there really to think about when people believe that they have lost control over the events in their lives? In addition to the undeniable losses that come with age, many elderly people develop a pronounced sense of incompetence and worthlessness because so little thinking and so few autonomous decisions are required of them.

of the parent. In only about 10 percent of the families were relations worsened by the move (Smith and Bengston, 1979).

Community-Based Care

Since 95 percent of the aged at any given time reside in the community, what in general can be said about community-based care for them? Traditional individual, family, and marital counseling, pet therapy,[4] and peer counseling have all been shown effective to some degree in relieving depression, anxiety, and loneliness; most of these therapies are described elsewhere. The frail elderly have an urgent need for help with their daily living arrangements. We discuss here some general principles that can foster the development of effective and comprehensive community care (Zarit, 1980).

Comprehensive community-based services Sound community care should provide a continuum of aid, ranging from information and referral to services that allow the frail elderly to remain in their homes. Some communities are organized to provide telephone reassurance, daily phone calls to old persons living alone, to check that they are all right; home services, such as Meals on Wheels, which brings a hot meal a day to the old person's door, visits from homemakers who cook meals and see to the household, shopping help from young people, light repair work by volunteers; a community day center for older people, which may also serve a hot lunch and provide help with state and federal forms; sheltered housing, apartments in which several old people may live together semi-independently; home visits by health professionals and social workers, who can assess the actual needs of old people and treat them; and regular social visits from community neighbors. Only by having a range of services available in the community can a true match be made with the needs of the older person. Otherwise he or she will either fail to have needs met or will be provided with more help than is necessary.

Working with the members of families who care for older relatives is especially important. They need information on how to handle problem situations and on how to keep the older relative in poor health as independent as possible. They also need support and encouragement, opportunities to vent their feelings of guilt and resentment. Some may need permission to take time off, or to feel that they will be able to, should the pressure become too great.

The vast majority of the aged reside in the community and therefore look to community-based services for assistance and recreation.

Coordination of services Mere availability of services is not enough, however. They must be coordinated, and regrettably they are not in most localities. All too often an older person and his or her family are shuffled from one agency to another, getting lost in a morass of bureaucratic niceties. In fact, even professionals who have experience with the system often have difficulties working through it to get needed services for their clients! Moreover, frustrating rules often interfere with the very goals for which programs were instituted. In California, for example, Medicare does not always pay for rehabilitation services, such as physical therapy after a broken hip has healed. As a consequence many older people do not regain the function that they might have and may suffer additional physical and emotional deterioration.[5]

[4]Pet therapy builds on age-old observations that people who have pets to take care of benefit from the companionship of their animals. The dependence of a domesticated animal on a human being can help the person physically and emotionally, by keeping him or her active and feeling useful. A pet's acceptance of us is usually more nearly unconditional than that given by people. Sheer physical contact with an animal is also beneficial. We do not argue that older adults, or anyone else, are better off taking care of household pets than having human companions. But the responsibility and pleasure of taking care of a cat, dog, or bird does enhance simple daily living and fosters healthful thoughts and actions (Brickel, 1984).

[5]Often these exacerbations require more expensive services.

Minimum intervention Sometimes less is better. Providing too much care for the older person can contribute to the phenomenon of "excess disability." He or she may have difficulties in functioning that exceed what would be expected on the basis of the person's physical condition alone (Kahn, 1975). The decreased ability to do many of the things that were part of the normal routine earlier in life may be perceived by the old person as good reason to rely physically on others. Often lost is the difference between necessary dependency and accepting help that is merely comforting or easier to accede to than reject. Younger and healthier caregivers tend to meet the older person's need and then some, providing physical help that is unnecessarily intrusive and restrictive. Of course, considerable judgment is needed, lest really serious problems be overlooked, but the principle of minimum intervention is advocated in order not to disable the elderly further.

Issues Specific to Therapy with Older Adults

As mentioned throughout this chapter, discussing a group of people who share only chronological age runs the risk of overlooking important differences in their backgrounds, developmental histories, and personalities. Although adults over sixty-five do have in common physical and psychological characteristics that make them different from younger adults, they are nonetheless *individuals*, each of whom has lived a long time and experienced unique joys and sorrows. In spite of this uniqueness, there are a few general issues important to consider in the conduct of therapy with older people. They can be divided into issues of content and issues of process.

Content

The incidence of organic brain syndromes does increase with age, but other mental health problems of older adults are not that different from those experienced earlier in life. Although the clinician should appreciate how physical incapacities and medications may intensify psychological problems, consistency and continuity from earlier decades of the older person's life should be noted too.

The clinician must also bear in mind that the emotional distress of older adults may be a realistic reaction to problems in living. Medical illnesses can create irreversible difficulties in walking, seeing, hearing. Fi-

nances may be a problem, particularly for the older woman who lives alone. To suggest that all psychological distress is pathological rather than an understandable response to real-life problems is unfair and inaccurate.

The older person's worries about impending death are another realistic source of stress. Much psychological turmoil about dying can be reduced by encouraging the client to attend to such concrete details as ensuring that estate and will are in order and that funeral or cremation plans are explicit and satisfactory. If clients deplore and dread the artificial life-support treatments sometimes applied in terminal illnesses, the therapist should suggest that they consider a Living Will to provide to those they choose to be responsible for them. Family members are wisely included in discussions, for their own concerns about death often influence their dealings with the old person.

Older clients may also be counseled to examine their lives from a philosophical or a religious perspective. Leo Tolstoy was but one of many people who became increasingly religious as they grow old. Philosophical and religious perspectives can help the client transcend the limitations aging imposes on human existence. When the person is finally dying, discussions of the meaning of the individual's life can facilitate self-disclosure and enhance his or her sense of well-being and personal growth. The loved ones, who will experience the inevitable loss, will also benefit from such discussions.

Process

Many clinicians have asked whether older adults require entirely different treatments from younger adults, or whether they can benefit from the same treatments. We have already indicated that traditional individual, family, and marital therapies are effective with the aged (Gatz et al., 1985). Some clinicians make adaptations and focus on here-and-now problems. They hold that therapy with the aged needs to be more active and directive, providing information, taking the initiative in seeking out agencies for necessary services, and helping the client and his or her family through the maze of federal and local laws and offices that are in place to help the aged.

In recent years several books have been published on therapy with older adults (Herr and Weakland, 1979; Hussian, 1981; Lewinsohn and Teri, 1983; Sherman, 1981; Storandt, 1983; Zarit, 1980). Establishing a good relationship with the older person; providing constructive contingencies in the surroundings; fostering a sense of control, self-efficacy, and hope; and elucidating a sense of meaning are believed to be the common mechanisms of change (Gatz et al., 1985).

SUMMARY

Until recently the psychological problems of older people have been neglected by mental health professionals. As the proportion of people who live beyond sixty-five continues to grow, it will become ever more important to learn about the disorders suffered by some older people and the most effective means of preventing or ameliorating them. Although physical deterioration is an obvious aspect of growing old, it appears that most of the emotional distress to which old people are prone is psychologically produced.

Serious brain disorders affect a very small minority of older people, fewer than 10 percent. Two principal ones have been distinguished, dementia and delirium. In dementia the person's intellectual functioning goes downhill; memory, abstract thinking, and judgment deteriorate. If the dementia is progressive, as most are, the individual seems another person altogether and is in the end oblivious of surroundings. A variety of diseases can cause this deterioration, the most important of which is an Alzheimer-type disease, in which cortical cells waste away. In delirium there is sudden clouding of consciousness and other problems in thinking, feeling, and behaving—fragmented and undirected thought, incoherent speech, inability to sustain attention, hallucinations, illusions, disorientation, lethargy or hyperactivity, and mood swings. The condition is reversible, provided the underlying cause is self-limiting or adequately treated. Brain cells malfunction but are not necessarily destroyed. Causes include overmedication, infection of brain tissue, high fevers, malnutrition, dehydration, endocrine disorders, head trauma, and cerebrovascular problems.

The treatments of these two disorders are quite different one from the other. If delirium is suspected, there should be a search for the cause so that the pathogenic situation can be rectified. Dementia, on the other hand, cannot usually be treated, but the person and the family affected by the disease can be counseled on how to make the remaining time reasonable and even rewarding. If adequate support is given to caregivers, many dementia patients can be looked after at home. There usually comes a time, however, when the burden of care impels most families to place the person in a nursing home or hospital.

Older people suffer from the entire spectrum of psychological disorders, in many instances brought with them into their senior years, particularly depression. The newer cognitive behavior therapies are being applied to depression of the elderly, and results so far are encouraging.

Although not as widespread as depression, paranoia is a problem for older people and for those who have a relationship with them. In contrast to the persecutors of young paranoids, distant agencies such as the F.B.I. and aliens from outer space, those of older individuals live closer to home—the neighbor who opens her mail, the ungrateful son who is conniving to steal his mother's money, the physician who prescribes drugs that pollute the mind. Paranoia is sometimes brought on by brain damage in dementia, but more often it is caused by psychological factors. Paranoia may be a reaction to hearing difficulties. If I cannot hear what they are saying—especially if I do not acknowledge my hearing problem—perhaps it is because they are whispering nasty things about me. Isolation as well can be a factor; when a person has little social intercourse, and indeed many old people have too little, it is difficult to verify impressions and suspicions, setting the stage for delusions to develop. Other psychological disorders discussed are schizophrenia; substance abuse, in particular the misuse of medication; hypochondriasis; and insomnia.

White males, as they enter old age, are at increasing risk of suicide. More of the suicide attempts of old people result in death than do those of younger people. Mental health professionals, most of them younger than sixty-five, may assume that, indeed, the old and debilitated have nothing to live for. This attitude may reflect their own fear of growing old.

Considerable mythology has surrounded sexuality and aging, the principal assumption being that at the age of sixty-five sex becomes improper, unsatisfying, and even impossible. Evidence indicates otherwise. Barring serious physical disability, older people, even those well into their eighties, are capable of deriving enjoyment from sexual intercourse and other kinds of lovemaking. There are differences as people age; it takes longer to become aroused and the orgasm is less intense. Dissemination of accurate information about sexual capacity in old age would probably prevent much unnecessary sexual dysfunction and disinterest.

Nursing homes and other extended-care facilities often do little to encourage residents to maintain or enhance whatever skills and capacities they still have; both physical and mental deteriorations are the rule. Nowadays care is provided in the community whenever possible. There should be comprehensive services, such as Meals on Wheels, regular home visits by health professionals, and support for caregivers. Such services should be coordinated so that people do not have to confront a bureaucratic maze. And intervention should be minimal so that old people remain as independent as their circumstances permit.

Many older people can benefit from psychotherapy, but several issues specific to treating the older adult should be borne in mind. The emotional distress of the elderly is sometimes realistic in content. They have often suffered irreplaceable losses and face real medical and financial problems; it is unwise always to attribute their complaints to a psychopathological condition. Death is a more immediate issue as well. As for the process of therapy, clinicians should sometimes be active and directive, providing information and seeking out the agencies that give the social services needed by their clients. Therapy should also foster a sense of control, self-efficacy, and hope and elucidate a sense of meaning for the older person.

PART SIX

Oskar Schlemmer, *Four Figures in a Room*, 1925

INTERVENTION

M. C. Escher, *Hand with Reflecting Sphere*, 1935 © M.C. Escher Heirs, c/o Cordon Art—Baarn, Holland

INSIGHT THERAPY

Throughout our account of the various psychopathologies, we have considered the ways in which therapists of varying persuasions attempt to prevent, lessen, and even eliminate mental and emotional suffering. The Chapter 2 descriptions of the several paradigms of treatment—physiological, psychoanalytic, learning, cognitive, and humanistic—laid the groundwork. Some forms of intervention are more appropriate than others for particular problems. Through our understanding of physiological processes, new parents now have means of halting or at least reducing certain forms of genetically transmitted mental retardation. And through better understanding of the process of learning, retarded children are now acquiring more cognitive, social, and self-care skills than was earlier thought possible. Psychoanalytic theory helps therapists in treating dissociative disorders, for it alerts them to the possibility that an amnesic patient, for example, cannot remember because the pain of certain past events forced them to be massively repressed. Humanistic treatment helps clients explore the depth and causes of their psychological pain and encourages them to take action, make choices, and assume responsibility for bettering their lives.

Now it is time to take a closer, more intensive look at therapy, to consider issues of general importance, to explore controversies, and to make comparisons. What we have studied so far of psychopathology and treatment should enable us to do so with some sophistication and perspective.

Shorn of its theoretical complexities, any psychotherapy ". . . is a situation in which one human being (the therapist) tries to act in such a way as to enable another human being to act and feel differently than he has . . ." (Wachtel, 1977, p. 271). The basic assumption, indeed article of faith, is that particular kinds of verbal and nonverbal exchanges in a trusting relationship can achieve goals such as reducing anxiety and eliminating self-defeating or dangerous behavior.

Simple as this definition may seem, there is little general agreement about what *really* constitutes psychotherapy. A person's next-door neighbor might utter the same words of comfort as would a clinical psychologist, but should we regard this as psychotherapy? In what way is psychotherapy different from such nonprofessional reassurance? Is the distinction made on the straightforward basis of whether the dispenser of reassurance has a particular academic degree or license? Does it relate to whether the giver of information has a theory that dictates or at least guides what he or she says? Does it depend on how sound the basic assumptions of the theory are? These are difficult questions,

and, as in other areas of abnormal psychology, there is less than perfect agreement among professionals.

The people who seek or are sent for *professional* help are usually those who have tried the nonprofessional avenues to feeling better and have failed to obtain relief. Before an individual goes to a therapist, he or she has probably confided in friends or in a spouse, perhaps spoken to the family doctor, has often consulted with a member of the clergy, and may have tried several of the vast number of self-help books and programs that are so

Many people talk over their problems with friends, teachers, clergy, and members of the family. How these solacements differ from the psychotherapy offered by professionals is an interesting question.

popular nowadays. For most people in psychological distress, one or more of these options provide enough relief, and they seek no further help (Bergin, 1971). But for others these attempts fall short, and individuals are left feeling helpless, often hopeless. These are the people who go to mental health clinics, university counseling centers, and the private offices of independent practitioners. Whatever the nature and efficacy of any form of psychotherapy, it should be borne in mind that professionals generally have as clients the especially trou-

bled people who have not been helped by other means.

Therapeutic activities and theories are very great in number. There are scores, perhaps hundreds, of schools of therapy, each with its band of enthusiastic adherents (both therapists and patients) proposing procedures ranging from screaming and writhing nude on the floor to forced inactivity and sleep for several weeks. One could almost say "You name it, someone thinks it's therapeutic." Because it would be impossible and unenlightening to examine every school, we have opted for a focused review of the field, presenting sufficient detail about the major approaches to allow a grasp of the basic issues and an overall perspective on the therapeutic enterprise.

London (1964) categorizes psychotherapies into *insight* and *action* (behavioral) therapies. Behavior therapy is the subject of Chapter 19. Insight therapy, which is discussed in this chapter, assumes that behavior, emotions, and thoughts become disordered because people do not adequately understand what motivates them, especially when their different needs and drives conflict. Insight therapy tries to help them discover the true reasons they behave, feel, and think as they do. The assumption is that greater awareness of motivations will yield greater control over and subsequent improvement in thought, emotion, and behavior. The emphasis is less on changing people directly than on uncovering the causes of their distress—both historical and current. To facilitate such insights, therapists of different theoretical persuasions have employed a variety of techniques, ranging from the free association of psychoanalysis to the reflection of feelings practiced in client-centered therapy.

Our principal concern in this chapter and the next is individual therapy, that is, therapy conducted by a clinician with one patient or client. But it should be noted that nearly everything said in these two chapters is relevant also for therapy in groups, a subject dealt with more completely as one of three principal topics in Chapter 20.

THE PLACEBO EFFECT

For reasons that will become clear, it is appropriate to begin our discussion of intervention with what has become known as the *placebo effect*. The term refers to improvement in physical or psychological condition that is attributable to a patient's expectations of help rather than to any specific active ingredient in a treatment. Although the word placebo generally refers to a pill or capsule that has no pharmacologically active substance—the familiar "sugar pill"—the term placebo effect need not be restricted to therapy with an inert pill. It can apply as well to therapeutic results, both psychological and physiological, brought about by any method that has no demonstrable specific action on the disorder being treated.

Frank (1973) relates placebo effects to faith healing in prescientific or nonscientific societies. For centuries, suffering human beings have derived benefit from making pilgrimages to sanctified places such as Lourdes and from ingesting sometimes foul-smelling concoctions.

Many people tend to dismiss placebo reactions as "not real" or second-best. After all, if a person has a tension headache, what possible benefit can he or she hope to get from a pill that is totally devoid of chemical action or direct physiological effect? The fact is, however, that such benefits can sometimes be significant and even long lasting. For example, Lasagna and his colleagues (1954) reported impressive relief from pain in surgical patients receiving saline injections. And Frank

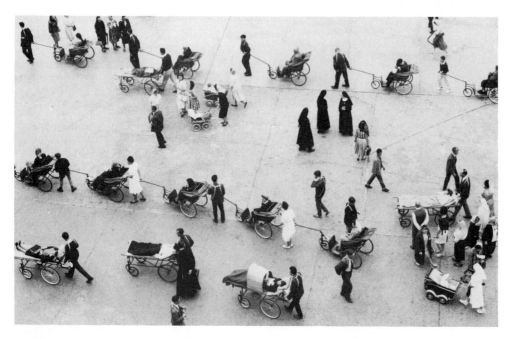

The steady procession of people to the shrine of Lourdes.

(1973) furnishes extensive evidence attesting to improvement in a variety of physical and mental problems after ingestion of pills and from exposure to other ministrations that, in themselves, could not possibly account for this relief. An appreciation of the placebo effect, however, is by no means an endorsement of quackery. A placebo, whether it be an inert pill or an impressive but worthless psychological intervention, will not deal directly with many potentially serious problems of humankind.

A psychotherapist who places great stock in a particular theory may not like to think that his or her professional activities derive much or even all their effectiveness from mobilizing a person's expectancies for help. But research on psychotherapy offers scant reassurance to the contrary. Many researchers agree that in psychotherapy, as in much of medicine, *the most reliable effect is the placebo effect.*

The place of placebo control groups in psychotherapy research is an often-debated and complex topic, the intricacies of which are beyond the scope of this book. Let it be noted, though, that a study that compares a particular therapy to no treatment at all and finds the therapy to bring more improvement indeed tells us something important, namely that being treated is better than receiving no treatment. But a given therapy usually tries to create improvement in a particular way, by removing the person's defenses, by easing the individual's way to self-actualization, by enhancing responsible choices, by counterconditioning fears, and so forth. To determine whether these processes are at work and are effective, a research study does need a control group of patients who are primarily instilled with expectancies of help, who believe that something worthwhile and beneficial is being done for them. *All* therapies derive at least some of their power from the faith that people have in the healer.

PSYCHOANALYTIC THERAPY

Despite the numerous critical attacks made on psychoanalytic theory and the claims that psychoanalytic therapy has limited effectiveness, psychoanalysis and its many offshoots remain the dominant force in American psychiatry and clinical psychology.

In this section we attempt to summarize the important elements both of classical—that is, traditional—psychoanalysis and of ego analysis.

Basic Techniques and Concepts in Psychoanalysis

The overall purpose of psychoanalysis derives from the Freudian assumption that psychopathology develops when people remain unaware of their true motivations and fears. They can be restored to healthy functioning only by becoming conscious of what has been repressed. When people can understand *what* is motivating their actions, they have a greater number of choices. Where id is, let there ego be, to paraphrase a maxim of psychoanalysis. The ego, being the primarily conscious, deliberating, choosing portion of the personality, can better guide the individual in rational, realistic directions if repressions are at a minimum.

Wachtel's (1977) woolly mammoth (see page 37) is an apt metaphor for the unresolved, buried conflicts from which psychoanalytic theory assumes neurotic problems arise. The proper focus of therapy then is not on the presenting problem, such as fears of being rejected, but on unconscious conflicts existing in the psyche from childhood. Only by lifting the repression can the person confront the underlying problem and reevaluate it in the context of his or her adult life.

Free Association

Psychoanalysts use a number of techniques to help the patient recover conflicts that have been repressed. Perhaps the best known and most important is free association: the patient, reclining on a couch, is encouraged to give free rein to thoughts and feelings, and to verbalize whatever comes to mind. The assumption is that with enough practice free association will facilitate the uncovering of unconscious material.[1] The analysand must follow the fundamental rule of reporting thoughts and feelings as accurately as possible, without screening out the elements he feels are unimportant or shameful. Freud assumed that thoughts and memories occurred in associative chains and that recent ones reported first would ultimately trace back to earlier crucial ones. In order to get to these earlier events, however, the therapist has to be very careful not to guide or direct the patient's thinking, and the patient must not monitor his thoughts. Ford and Urban (1963) have paraphrased the analyst's directions for free association.

[1]The adjective "free," however, does not mean uncaused, only free from conscious censorship and control. "As an avowed determinist, Freud believed that unconscious mechanisms governed by psychological laws produced the flow of free associations. Free associations are thus not truly free" (Morse, 1982, p.215).

A moment in a psychoanalytic session.

In ordinary conversation, you usually try to keep a connecting thread running through your remarks, excluding any intrusive ideas or side issues so as not to wander too far from the point, and rightly so. But in this case you must talk differently. As you talk various thoughts will occur to you which you like to ignore because of certain criticisms and objections. You will be tempted to think, "That is irrelevant or unimportant or nonsensical," and to avoid saying it. Do not give in to such criticism. Report such thoughts in spite of your wish not to do so. Later, the reason for this injunction, the only one you have to follow, will become clear. Report whatever goes through your mind. Pretend that you are a traveler, describing to someone beside you the changing views which you see outside the train window (p. 168).

Resistance

But blocks do arise, virtually thrusting themselves across the thoughts supposedly given free rein. Patients may suddenly change the subject or be unable to remember how a long-ago event ended. They will try any tactic to interrupt the session, remaining silent, getting up from the couch, looking out the window, making jokes and personal remarks to the analyst. Patients may even come late or "forget" sessions altogether. Such obstacles to free association—*resistances*—were noted by Freud and contributed to the development of the con-

cept of repression. He asserted that interference with free association can be traced to unconscious control over sensitive areas; it is precisely these areas that psychoanalytic therapists must thoroughly probe. Indeed, in some respects these resistances, these failures in free association, provide the analyst with the most critical information about the patient.

Analysis of Dreams

Akin to free association is dream analysis. Freud assumed that during sleep the ego defenses are lowered, allowing repressed material to come forth, usually in disguised form. Concerns of the patient are often expressed in symbols to help protect the conscious ego from the true significance of dream material. The manifest content of dreams—what is immediately apparent—may be regarded as a sort of compromise between repression of true meaning and a full expression of unconscious material. The content of dreams, then, is distorted by unconscious defensive structures which, never completely abandoned, even in sleep, continue their fight to protect the ego from repressed impulses.

Interpretation and Denial

As presumably unconscious material begins to appear, another technique comes into play, interpretation. According to Freud, this stage helps the person face the hitherto repressed and emotionally loaded conflict. At the "right time" the analyst begins to point out to the patient his defenses and the underlying meaning of his dreams. Great skill is required lest an interpretation be offered too early, for the patient may so totally reject it that he leaves treatment. To be effective, interpretations should reflect insights that the patient is on the verge of making himself; they can then be claimed by the patient as his own, rather then coming from the analyst. Presumably an interpretation that a patient attributes to himself will be more readily accepted and thereby have a stronger therapeutic effect.

Interpretation then is the analyst's principal weapon against the continued use of defense mechanisms. He points out how certain verbalizations of the patient relate to repressed unconscious material, and he suggests what the manifest content of dreams *truly* means. If the interpretation is timed correctly, the patient can start to examine the repressed impulse in the light of present-day reality. In other words, he begins to realize that he no longer has to fear the expression of the impulse.

Feeling safe under the undemanding conditions arranged by the analyst, the patient presumably uncovers more and more repressed material. Interpretations are held to be particularly helpful in establishing the mean-

"When Jud accuses Zack, here, of hostility toward his daughter, like he seems to every session, why, it's plain to me he's only rationalizing his own lack of gumption in standing up to a stepson who's usurping the loyalty of his second wife. The way he lit into him just now shows he's got this here guilt identification with Zack's present family constellation. Calling Zack egotistical ain't nothing but a disguise mechanism for concealing his secret envy of Zack's grit and all-around starch, and shows mighty poor ego boundaries of his own, it appears to me."

(Drawing by Whitney Darrow, Jr.; © 1976 The New Yorker Magazine, Inc.)

ing of the resistances that disturb the patient's free association. The therapist may, for example, point out how the patient manages to avoid a topic, and it is common for the analysand to deny the interpretation. Interestingly, this denial is sometimes interpreted as a sign that the therapist's interpretation is correct rather than incorrect. In the slow process of "working through" the disturbing conflicts, of confronting them again and again, the patient gradually faces up to the validity of the analyst's interpretations, often with great emotion.

Determining when an analysand's denial of an interpretation means that it is correct is, in our opinion, one of the thorniest problems in psychoanalysis. When, in truth, is it appropriate to consider that a No is really a Yes? Great abuse is possible here, and psychoanalysts are often satirized for these decisions. But the analyst, like any clinician, does not judge in a vacuum. He formulates hypotheses over time about the patient, noticing how one problem area relates to others. Like a detective, the therapist searches for clues in a slowly developing picture, and every statement, every gesture of the patient, is viewed within this scheme. A patient's No is considered a Yes only in the *context* of other ideas already formed by the analyst. And in part the analyst bases his judgment on how vigorously the patient denies an interpretation, generally regarding the denial expressed in an excessive manner as defensive. As Queen Gertrude in Shakespeare's *Hamlet* commented, "The lady doth protest too much, methinks" (Act III, Scene 2).

Transference

The core of psychoanalytic therapy is the *transference neurosis*. Being a good observer, Freud noted that some of his patients acted toward him in an emotion-charged and unrealistic way. For example, a patient much older than Freud would behave in a childish manner during a therapy session. Although these reactions were often positive and loving, many times they were quite negative and hostile. Since these feelings seemed out of character with the ongoing therapy relationship, Freud assumed that they were relics of attitudes *transferred* to him from those held in the past toward important people in the patient's history, primarily parents. That is, he felt that patients responded to him *as though* he were one of the important people in their past. Freud utilized this transference of attitudes, which he came to consider an inevitable aspect of psychoanalysis, as a means of explaining to patients the childhood origin of many of their concerns and fears. This revelation and explanation tended also to help lift repressions and allow the confrontation of hitherto buried impulses. In psychoanalysis transference is regarded as essential to a complete cure. Indeed, it is precisely when analysts notice transference developing that they take hope the important neurotic conflict from childhood is being approached.

Analysts encourage the development of transference by intentionally remaining shadowy figures, generally sitting behind the patient while the patient free-associates and serving as relatively blank screens on which the important persons in the neurotic conflicts can be projected. They take pains to reveal as little as possible of their own personal lives. Analysts are also caring persons, which may remind the patient of attributes, real or hoped for, in his or her parents. Because the therapy setting is so different from the childhood situation, analysts can readily point out to patients the irrational nature of their fears and concerns (see Box 18.1).

Countertransference

Related to transference is *countertransference*, the feelings of the analyst toward the patient. The analyst must take care lest she lay her own emotional vulnerabilities on the analysand. Her own needs and fears must be recognized for what they are; she should have enough understanding of her own motivations to be able to see the client clearly, without distortion. The problem has been well articulated in a discussion of therapy with depressed people, during which countertransference is a continuing challenge to a therapist.

Depressed patients bring their hopelessness and despair into therapy, and the therapist may be affected. If the depression improves slowly, or not at all, the therapist may feel guilty, angry, and/or helpless. After seeing several severely depressed patients in a day, the therapist may feel quite drained and eventually may become unwilling to work in the future with similar patients. Suicidal patients can evoke particularly difficult countertransferences. . . .

One safeguard against such difficulties is the therapist's continuing awareness of these feelings and their relation to his or her own psychodynamics. A suffering patient may mobilize the therapist's fantasy of being able to heal and earn gratitude, deftly and single-handedly; or may stir up the therapist's anger at the existence of suffering. An abiding awareness of these reactions will help the therapist maintain the patience and satisfaction with small gains that are necessary for conducting psychotherapy with severely depressed patients. At the same time, the therapist must avoid overstepping his/her role and trying to do all the work for an apparently weak patient (Jacobson and McKinney, 1982, p. 215).

For this reason a "training analysis," or *Lehranalyse*, is a formal part of the education of an analyst. Although many therapists of different theoretical persuasions consider it useful to have been in therapy themselves, a personal therapy is *required* in analytic training institutes. It is essential that analysts reduce to a minimum the frequency and intensity of countertransference toward their clients.

The Detachment of the Analyst

The analyst, moreover, must *not* become actively involved in helping the analysand deal with everyday problems. He assiduously avoids any intervention, such as a direct suggestion how to behave in a troublesome situation. Short-term relief might deflect the patient's efforts to uncover the repressed conflicts. Freud was emphatic on this point, writing in 1918 that the analyst must take care not to make the patient's life so comfortable that he or she is no longer motivated to delve into the unconscious. He put is this way in his criticism of nonanalytic helpers.

Their one aim is to make everything as pleasant as possible for the patient, so that he may feel well there and be glad to take refuge there again from the trials of life. In so doing, they make no attempt to give him more strength for facing life and more capacity for carrying out his actual tasks in it. In analytic treatment, all such spoiling must be avoided. As far as his relations with the physician are concerned, the patient must be left with unfulfilled wishes in abundance. It is expedient to deny him precisely those satisfactions which he desires most intensely and expresses most importunately (Freud, 1955, p. 164).

The detachment of the analyst has often been ridiculed or misinterpreted, which does an injustice both to analytic theory and to the people who apply it. When a person is in pain and need, the initial impulse is, figuratively, to take the sufferer into one's arms and comfort him or her, providing reassurance that all will be well,

BOX 18.1

EXCERPT FROM A PSYCHOANALYTIC SESSION, AN ILLUSTRATION OF TRANSFERENCE

Patient (a fifty-year-old male business executive): I really don't feel like talking today.

Analyst: (Remains silent for several minutes, then) Perhaps you'd like to talk about why you don't feel like talking.

Patient: There you go again, making demands on me, insisting I do what I just don't feel up to doing. (Pause) Do I always have to talk here, when I don't feel like it? (Voice becomes angry and petulant) Can't you just get off my back? You don't really give a damn how I feel, do you?

Analyst: I wonder why you feel I don't care.

Patient: Because you're always pressuring me to do what I feel I can't do.

Comments. This excerpt must be viewed in context. The patient had been in therapy for about a year, complaining of depression and anxiety. Although extremely successful in

the eyes of his family and associates, he himself felt weak and incompetent. Through many sessions of free association and dream analysis, the analyst had begun to suspect that the patient's feelings of failure stemmed from his childhood experiences with an extremely punitive and critical father, a man even more successful than the client, and a person who seemed never to be satisfied with his son's efforts. The exchange quoted was later interpreted by the analyst as an expression of resentment by the patient of his *father's* pressures on him and had little to do with the analyst himself. The patient's tone of voice (petulant), as well as his overreaction to the analyst's gentle suggestion that he talk about his feelings of not wanting to talk, indicated that the patient was angry not at his analyst but at his father. The expression of such feelings to the analyst, that is, transferring them from the father to the analyst, was regarded as significant by the therapist and was used in subsequent sessions in helping the patient to reevaluate his childhood fears of expressing aggression toward his father.

---

that the client will be taken care of. But the truth is that others have probably already tried to provide solace; if sympathy and support were going to help, they probably would already have done so. The analyst must work hard to *resist* showing concern through expressions of support and with concrete advice. Moreover, acting in a directive fashion will interfere with transference, for the therapist necessarily becomes less of a blank screen if he expresses opinions, voices objections, and gives advice and direction. The distance kept by the analyst from the analysand is intended for his or her betterment. This strategem is consistent with analytic theory and is rather rigidly applied by the more orthodox of psychoanalysts and by those who see utility in the theory.

Psychoanalysis is directly opposite in thrust to behavior therapy, for behavior therapists, unconcerned with factors that are presumed by analysts to be buried in the unconscious, concentrate precisely on what analysts ignore, namely helping patients change their attitudes, feelings, and overt behavior in concrete, current life situations. What the analyst, and to a large degree the ego analyst, terms "supportive therapy," the behavior therapist regards as the essence of therapy. By the same token, what the behavior therapist sees as unnecessary and even detrimental to the client—digging into the

repressed past and withholding advice on how to make specific changes in the here and now—is judged by the analyst to be essential to complete psychotherapeutic treatment.

Ego Analysis

The most important modifications in psychoanalytic theory come from a group generally referred to as ego analysts. Their views are often seen as constituting contemporary Freudian psychoanalysis. The major figures in this loosely formed movement include Karen Horney (1942), Anna Freud (1946), Erik Erikson (1950), David Rapaport (1951), and Heinz Hartmann (1958).[2] Al-

[2] In analytic circles distinctions are often drawn between ego analysts and Neo-Freudians. Horney and Harry Stack Sullivan, who is to be discussed, are often considered Neo-Freudians. Neo-Freudians regard Freud's model of humankind as too dependent on instinctual drives. The ego analysts introduced into Freudian circles a greater concern with adaptation to environmental demands; hence the "ego" in their name. A concern for adaptation, however, does seem at least implicitly to downplay the role of instinctual drives, thus blurring the distinction between ego analysis and Neo-Freudianism. The intricacies of these similarities and differences have provided grist for the mill of lively debates between theoreticians both loyal to and rebellious against Freud.

BOX 18.2

KOHUT AND THE NARCISSISTIC PERSONALITY

In recent years many psychoanalytically oriented clinicians have regarded as the prevalent disorder of our time the narcissistic personality, a person whose remarkable sense of self-importance, complete self-absorption, and fantasies of limitless success mask a very fragile self-esteem. Constantly seeking attention and adulation, narcissistic personalities are underneath extremely sensitive to criticism and deeply fearful of failure. Sometimes they seek out others whom they can idealize, because they are disappointed in themselves, but they generally do not allow anyone to be genuinely close to them. Their personal relationships are few and shallow; when people inevitably fall short of their unrealistic expectations, they become angry and rejecting. The inner lives of narcissists are similarly impoverished because, despite their self-aggrandizement, they actually think very little of themselves and are without resources.

At the center of this contemporary interest in narcissism is Heinz Kohut, whose two books *The Analysis of the Self* (1971) and *The Restoration of the Self* (1977) have established a variant of psychoanalysis known as self psychology. His basic idea is that parents must respond to their children with respect, warmth, and empathy if the children are to acquire a normal sense of self-worth. But a mother may further her own needs rather than being empathic with her child.

A little girl comes home from school, eager to tell her mother about some great successes. But this mother, instead of listening with pride, deflects the conversation from the child to herself [and] begins to talk about her own successes which overshadow those of her little daughter (Kohut and Wolf, 1978, p. 418).

A youngster neglected in this way has trouble accepting her own shortcomings. She may develop into a narcissistic personality, neurotically striving to bolster her sense of self

Heinz Kohut, the psychoanalytically oriented psychiatrist who founded self psychology and has written extensively about narcissism.

through unending quests for love and approval from others.

Kohutian analysts are far warmer and more empathic than the Freudian analyst, who intentionally remains a shadowy, detached figure. Indeed, they are much closer in attitude and behavior to the Rogerian therapist. By giving empathy, Kohutian analysts try to provide the thoroughgoing acceptance and respect that presumably were not given by parents. Through psychoanalytic techniques such as dream analysis, interpretation, and transference, the patient is helped to get in touch with unfilled childhood needs. In this way Kohutian analysts hope to restore the patient to a stronger and more positive sense of self.

though Freud by no means ignored the interactions of the organism with the environment, his view was essentially a "push model," one in which people are driven by intrapsychic urges. The ego analysts place greater emphasis on a person's ability to control the environment and to select the time and the means for satisfying certain instinctual drives. Their basic contention is that the individual is as much ego as id. The concept of control, first introduced in Chapter 6, is quite important to ego analysts. They also focus on current living conditions to a greater extent than Freud did, although they still advocate delving deeply into the historical causes of an individual's behavior.

The ego analysts do not view man as an automaton pushed hither and yon by imperative innate energies on the one hand and by situational events on the other, constantly seeking some compromise among these conflicting influences. When behavior develops in a healthy fashion, man controls both it and the influence of situational events, selectively responding to consequences he has thoughtfully selected. . . . Man is not at the mercy of either [innate energies or situational events]. He can impose delay and thought between innate energies and action, thus postponing the reduction of such energies indefinitely. Learned responses, primarily thought, make this possible, and although originally they may be learned as a consequence of their energy-reducing function, later they may become relatively independent of such influences (drives) and control them (Ford and Urban, 1963, pp. 187–188).

We have, then, a set of important ego functions which are primarily conscious, capable of controlling both id instincts and the external environment, and which, more significantly, do not depend on the id for their energy. Ego analysts assume that these functions and capabilities are present at birth and then develop through experience. Underemphasized by Freud, ego functions have energies and gratifications of their own, usually separate from the reduction of id impulses. And whereas society was, for Freud, essentially a negative inhibition against the unfettered gratification of libidinal impulses, the ego analysts hold that an individual's social interactions can provide their own special kind of gratification.

In spite of these changes, however, we cannot conclude that most ego analysts have entirely renounced Freud's repression theory. Consider this from Karen Horney (1885–1952).

The . . . task awaiting the patient is to change those factors within himself which interfere with his best development. This does not mean only a gross modification in action or behavior, such as gaining or regaining the capacity for public performance, for creative work . . . or losing phobias or tendencies toward depression. These changes will automatically take place in a successful analysis. They are not primary changes, however, but result from less visible changes within the personality . . . (1942, pp. 117–118).

The Interpersonal Views of Harry Stack Sullivan

The views on the development of normal and abnormal behavior held by the American psychiatrist Harry Stack Sullivan (1892–1949) are generally considered to be a variation of ego psychology, although some writers label him "interpersonal,"[3] others Neo-Freudian. His primary contributions derive from his emphasis on the interpersonal nature of emotional problems. The basic difficulty of patients, according to Sullivan (1953), is so-called *parataxic distortions*, which are misperceptions of reality stemming from some disorganization in the interpersonal relations of childhood, primarily those

[3]The interpersonal school holds that mental disorder stems from fear and inadequacy in one or more kinds of interpersonal situations.

between child and parents. The disturbed attitudes toward parents, siblings, and other people who were significant in the person's past are from that time forward projected unconsciously into all interpersonal relationships, including that between patient and therapist (Wolberg, 1954). The individual has never learned to behave properly in social situations and is therefore too anxious to bear the buffeting to the self of a close association. The principal goal of therapy is to bring these distortions in thinking to the patient's consciousness so that he or she can evaluate present reality and separate it from past conditioning and learning.

So far Sullivan appears traditionally Freudian, with his strong emphasis on the childhood sources of adult problems and the need to help the analysand achieve insight into the infantile origins of current difficulties. But he was also very directive and present-oriented, recommending that the therapist inform the patient of fairly predictable consequences of contemplated actions (Wachtel, 1977). Moreover, Sullivan is perhaps most noted for his conception of the analyst as a "participant observer" in the therapy process. In contrast to the classical or even ego-analytical view of the therapist as a blank screen for the transference neurosis, Sullivan argued that the therapist, like the scientist, is inevitably a part of the process he or she is studying. An analyst does not "see" patients without at the same time affecting them. What patients do and say—or do not do and say—is determined not only by what they bring to the therapy session but by how they interact with the therapist. Even a silent or "invisible" analyst will elicit a reaction from the patient (Box 18.3).

Sullivan provided relatively sparse descriptions of specific therapeutic techniques (Ford and Urban, 1963). He did, however, alert Freudians to the importance of using the interpersonal setting of therapy to help patients understand their maladaptive ways of dealing with the world.

Evaluation of Analytic Therapy

In clinical circles there are few issues more controversial than the question whether psychoanalysis and related therapies work. Some clinicians are uneasy with the psychoanalytic concepts themselves, especially those that seem wedded to a notion of *an* unconscious. As Levy puts it, ". . . nothing can be said by the canons of modern philosophy of science, of the existence of the unconscious as a substantive entity: the assertion of its existence is in principle untestable and hence meaningless" (1963, p. 22).

BOX 18.3

WHAT DOES THE THERAPIST SEE OF THE CLIENT IN TRANSFERENCE?

Sullivan suggested that the therapist can never be just a blank screen, that he becomes an important participant in the process of therapy. In a searching critique of transference, Wachtel (1977) goes even further. Opposing the orthodox psychoanalytic view that a shadowy therapist enables transference to develop, Wachtel hypothesizes that such unvarying behavior on the part of the therapist frustrates the client, who may be seeking some indication of how the therapist feels about what he or she is doing and saying. The sometimes childish reactions assumed to be part of the transference neurosis Wachtel regards, in part, as the normal reactions of an adult who is thwarted! The troubled client sees the analyst as a professional person who remains distant and noncommittal in the face of his or her increasing expression of emotion. Thus, rather than being exclusively an unfolding of the client's personality, "transference" may actually be in some measure his or her extreme frustration with minimal feedback. Moreover, because the analyst restricts his own behavior so severely in the consulting room, and intentionally limits the setting to which the client is exposed, he can sample only a limited range of the client's behavior, attitudes, and feelings. In contrast, behavior therapists and others who believe more than analysts do that behavior is in large part situationally determined often role-play someone in the person's life to see how the client reacts.

This harsh judgment points up one of the major themes of this textbook, namely the role of paradigms. Those who think in psychoanalytic terms might themselves take issue with "the canons of modern philosophy of science" on the grounds that a monolithic view of science is not tenable. That is, science itself, no less than psychopathology, is subject to different points of view. These paradigmatic differences bear on any evaluation of the effectiveness of psychoanalysis, in all its various forms. It is very difficult to evaluate scientifically. What, for example, are the criteria for improvement? A principal one is the lifting of repressions, making the unconscious conscious. But how is that to be demonstrated? How do we determine whether a repression has been lifted? Attempts to assess outcome have sometimes relied on projective tests like the Rorshach, which, in turn, rely on the concept of the unconscious. Clearly, if this very concept is rejected a priori, there is little common ground for discussion.

The central concept of insight is also questioned. Rather than accept insight as the recognition by the client of some important, externally valid historical connection or relationship, several writers (for example, Bandura, 1969; London, 1964) propose that the development of insight is better understood as a *social conversion process*, whereby the patient comes to accept the belief system of his or her therapist. Marmor (1962) has suggested that insight means different things depending on the school of therapy; a patient treated by a proponent of any one of the various schools develops insights along the lines of its particular theoretical predilections. Freudians tend to elicit insights regarding oedipal dilemmas, Sullivanians insights regarding interpersonal relationships. Indeed, Levy (1963) goes so far as to say that the concept of the unconscious is actually nothing more than a disagreement between what a psychoanalytically oriented therapist and the analysand believe to be the explanation of the client's predicament.

Should we be concerned whether an insight into the past is a true one? If an insight is in fact part of a social conversion process, is the truth of it necessarily an issue? When we examine cognitive behavior therapy in the next chapter, especially Ellis's rational-emotive therapy, we encounter this question again. Therapists who encourage clients to look at things differently—as do all the therapists discussed in this chapter and the cognitive behavior therapists of the next—believe that an insight may help the client to change his outlook, whether or not it is true. Because of the immense complexity of human lives, it is impossible to know with any degree of certainty whether an event really happened and, if it did, whether it caused the current problem.[4]

With all these cautions in mind, let us consider what efforts researchers have made to evaluate the power of psychoanalytic and ego-analytic therapy to effect desirable changes in people. Like all therapy research, psy-

---

[4]The issue has other ramifications. In our discussion of ethics in therapy in Chapter 21, we review suggestions that psychotherapy is inherently, ultimately, a moral enterprise. That is, therapists, sometimes unwittingly, convey to clients messages about how they *ought* to live their lives. They assume a "secular priest" role (London, 1964). In this framework the usefulness of a given insight would depend on whether it helps the client lead a life more consonant with a particular set of shoulds and oughts.

choanalytic research can be divided into studies concentrating on *outcome* and those concentrating on *process*. Outcome studies ask whether therapy works. Process studies focus on what happens *during* therapy that can be related to the outcome. For example, does transference have to occur for beneficial change to take place?

Outcome Research

The following generalizations about Freudian psychoanalysis were made by Luborsky and Spence (1978), who relied on outcome research conducted with some measure of controlled observation:

1. Patients with severe psychopathology (for example, schizophrenia) do not do as well as those with anxiety disorders. This is understandable in view of Freud's admitted emphasis on neurosis rather than psychosis and in view of the heavy reliance psychoanalysis places on rationality and verbal abilities.

2. The more education a patient has, the better he or she does in analysis, probably because of the heavy emphasis on verbal interaction.

3. The evidence is conflicting whether the outcome of psychoanalysis is any better than what would be achieved through the mere passage of time or by engaging other professional help, such as a family doctor (Bergin, 1971). This is *not* to say that psychoanalysis does no good, only that clear evidence is as yet lacking. Given the great diversity in the characteristics of both patients and therapists, and in the severity of patients' problems, the question being asked is probably too complex to yield a single, scientifically acceptable answer.

A widely cited study of Sloane and his colleagues (1975) is considered by some psychotherapy researchers (for example, Bergin and Lambert, 1978) the best comparative study of therapy yet carried out. At the Temple University Outpatient Clinic three behavior therapists and three analysts—all of them highly experienced and recognized leaders in their respective fields—treated a total of ninety adult patients for a period of four months. Most of the participants in this study can best be described as neurotic; they were the individuals typically seen in outpatient clinics or in private consulting rooms. For the most part they were troubled by anxiety and disturbed relationships. After being matched on age and sex, as well as severity of problems, they were assigned to behavior therapy or to short-term analytic therapy, meaning ego analysis, presumably. In addition to the ninety people treated, some who had gone

through the same comprehensive assessment were assigned to a wait-list control group. They were promised therapy later but were asked to wait while others were in treatment. The purpose of this control group was to judge the effects on patients of having taken steps to enter therapy.

Sloane and his colleagues drew up for their therapists a list of defining characteristics of the analytic and behavior therapy that they intended to compare (Table 18.1) and instructed the therapists to adhere to these definitions as closely as possible. Audiotape recordings of the fifth session of each treatment were analyzed to determine whether these rules were being followed. The judgment was made that they were.

Outcome measures, taken immediately after treatment and at an eight-month follow-up, included personality tests such as the MMPI, ratings of how much symptoms had improved, structured interviews to determine how well the clients were doing in their work and social adjustment, and a global rating of improvement. In addition to the psychiatrist or psychologist who had conducted the therapy, the client, a clinician who had not been involved in treatment and did not know which each participant had received, and a close friend or relative joined in the judgments.

Depending on how we look at the data, and there are many ways, given the complexity of the study and the several measures taken, the findings favor behavior therapy, analytic therapy, or no treatment at all! Immediately after termination of therapy it was determined that the problems of the clients in the two treatment groups had been relieved about equally and that their functioning was similarly improved. The independent clinicians rated 80 percent of the clients in each treatment group improved or cured and 48 percent of the wait-list control group improved or recovered. *But* at the eight-month follow-up the superiority of the two treated groups over the wait-list control group had vanished, for the subjects in the control group had improved markedly. The people waiting for treatment had received a fair amount of attention, for in addition to the initial and later assessments they were called regularly and given encouragement and support.[5]

This ambitious study is subject to several criticisms that are of general importance to the study of therapy.

---

[5]We can view negatively the fact that the wait-list control group "caught up with" the two therapy groups at the eight-month follow-up. But the same finding can be regarded as positive. The therapy, whether insight or behavioral, *speeded up* the rate of improvement, thus lessening overall the suffering of the clients and those close to them. In this way both types of therapy were helpful and could be judged superior to the attention given the wait-list group.

TABLE 18.1 Characteristics of Behavior Therapy and Psychoanalytically Oriented Psychotherapy in the Temple University Study   *(from Sloane et al., 1975)*

1. Specific advice
   b) Given frequently.*
   p) Given infrequently.

2. Transference interpretation
   b) Avoided.
   p) May be given.

3. Interpretation of resistance
   b) Not used.
   p) Used.

4. Dreams
   b) Polite lack of interest; not used in treatment.
   p) Interest in reported dreams which may be used in treatment.

5. Level of anxiety
   b) Diminished when possible except in implosive therapy.
   p) Maintain some anxiety as long as it does not disrupt behavior.

6. Training in relaxation
   b) Directly undertaken.
   p) Only an indirect consequence of sitting, and perhaps the example of the therapist.

7. Desensitization
   b) Directly undertaken.
   p) Only an indirect consequence of talking in comfortable circumstances with uncritical therapist.

8. Practical retraining
   b) Directly undertaken.
   p) Not emphasized.

9. Training in appropriately assertive action
   b) Directly undertaken and encouraged in everyday life.
   p) Only indirectly encouraged in everyday life. Assertive or aggressive speech which would be inappropriate in everyday life permitted in therapeutic session.

10. Symptoms
    b) Interest in the report of symptoms, may explain biologically.
    p) Report of symptoms discouraged, may interpret symbolically.

11. Childhood memories
    b) Usually history taking only.
    p) Usually further memories looked for.

12. Aversion, e.g., electric shock
    b) May be used.
    p) Not used.

13. Observers of treatment session
    b) May be permitted.
    p) Not usually permitted.

14. Deliberate attempts to stop behavior, such as thoughts, which makes the patient anxious
    b) May be used.
    p) Rarely directly attempted.

15. Role training
    b) May be used.
    p) Not used.

16. Repetition of motor habits
    b) May be used.
    p) Not used.

*The items preceded by b apply to behavior therapy, by p psychoanalysis.

First, did the use of multiple judges—the client, the therapist, an independent clinician, and a close friend or relative—make the information gathered about improvement especially valid? Unlikely. The ratings made by independent clinicians were based entirely on interviews with the clients. It is not surprising that their ratings correlated significantly with those of the clients. Yet these two ratings correlated much less strongly with those of the therapists, friends, and relatives. Which sets of ratings are valid?

Much of the information collected was obtained through interviews. Improvement was rated by what the client said and how he or she said it during treatment or evaluation interviews—except for the judgments of friends and relatives, who presumably observed the daily living of the client. No other observation of the cli-

ent in everyday surroundings or in contrived settings, such as the speech anxiety test employed by Paul (1966; see page 80) was attempted, however. By not arranging for such observations, Sloane and his colleagues made the assumption that we can know how a client is doing by sampling his or her behavior in the consulting room.

Prochaska (1984) was able to find eleven studies of the effectiveness of psychoanalysis or psychoanalytically oriented psychotherapy, one of them being the Temple University study just discussed. None of the studies justified concluding that psychoanalysis or its variations achieve therapeutic gains superior to a placebo treatment. Indeed, most of the studies failed to include a placebo treatment, and when a comparative treatment was included, analysis was no more effective. "To date no study has found either psychoanalysis or psychoanalytically oriented psychotherapy to be significantly more effective than either a placebo treatment or some alternative form of therapy'' (p. 55).

Process Research

It is difficult to draw general conclusions from process studies of analytic therapy, primarily because the variables are so complex and, as already stated, inextricably bound up with concepts referring to the unconscious. A number of projects, entailing intensive study of tape recordings and of analysts' notes for individual cases, have been underway for years. One of the factors studied is "associative freedom," or the extent to which the analysand can free-associate. If free association helps the analyst get to hitherto repressed material, great facility in free-associating should predict a good outcome. Unfortunately, the relationship is much more complex, for the patient's free association interacts with the analyst's interpretations, and the effectiveness of these, in turn, depends on their timing—not to mention their accuracy. Because of these difficulties, plus the problems of defining outcome criteria and of designing reliable measures, it is not surprising that process research in psychoanalysis and related therapies has thus far shed little light on how they work.

Perhaps the most sobering and thought-provoking statement about research in analytic therapy was made by Luborsky and Spence (1978), two leading psychotherapy researchers. Examined closely, it reveals the minor role that controlled research is expected to play in evaluating psychoanalytic therapy.

Quantitative research on psychoanalytic therapy presents itself, so far, as an unreliable support to clinical practice. Far more is known now through clinical wisdom than is known through quantitative, objective studies. Much of what is contributed by the quantitative literature represents a cumbersome, roundabout way of showing the clinician what he or she already "knows" . . . (p. 358).

HUMANISTIC AND EXISTENTIAL THERAPIES

Humanistic and existential therapies, like psychoanalytic therapies, are insight-oriented, being based on the assumption that disordered behavior can best be treated by increasing the individual's awareness of motivations and needs. But there is a useful contrast between psychoanalysis and its offshoots on the one hand and hu-

manistic-existential approaches on the other: humanistic-existential therapies place greater emphasis on the person's freedom of choice. Free will is regarded as the human being's most important characteristic. Free will is, however, a double-edged sword, for it not only offers fulfillment and pleasure but also threatens acute pain and suffering. It is an innately provided gift that *must* be used and that requires special courage to use. Not all of us can meet this challenge; those who cannot are regarded as candidates for client-centered, existential, and Gestalt therapies.

Carl Rogers's Client-Centered Therapy

Carl Rogers is an American psychologist whose theorizing about psychotherapy grew slowly out of years of intensive clinical experience. After teaching at the university level in the 1940s and 1950s, he helped organize the Center for Studies of the Person in La Jolla, California. Rogers makes several basic assumptions about human nature and the means by which we can try to understand it (Ford and Urban, 1963; Rogers, 1951, 1961).

1. We must adopt a phenomenological point of view (see page 49). People can be understood only from the vantage point of their own perceptions and feelings. It is the way people construe events rather than the events themselves that the investigator must attend to, for a person's phenomenological world is the major determinant of behavior and makes him or her unique.

2. Healthy people are aware of their behavior. In this sense Rogers's system is similar to psychoanalysis and ego analysis, for it emphasizes the desirability of being aware of motives.

3. People are innately good and effective; they become ineffective and disturbed only when faulty learning intervenes.

4. Behavior is purposive and goal-directed; people do not respond passively to the influence of their environment or to their inner drives. They are self-directive. In this assumption Rogers is closer to ego analysts than to orthodox Freudian psychoanalysts.

5. Therapists should not attempt to manipulate events for the individual; rather they should create conditions that will facilitate independent decision making by the client.

Personality Development

Rogers postulates an innate tendency to actualize, that is, to realize potentialities. This idea, drawn from Otto

Rank (1936), a Viennese psychoanalyst and a member of Freud's inner circle, is basic to Rogers's conception of human beings and therefore crucial to understanding his approach to therapy. In common with Freud and most learning theorists, Rogers holds that people try to reduce the physiological tensions of hunger, thirst, and pain. But Rogers proposes that people by nature seek also to learn new things and otherwise enhance their lives. In other words, people *seek out* pleasurable tension in addition to attempting to reduce unpleasurable tension. All behavior, for Rogers, originates in some way from this innate self-actualizing tendency. Furthermore, people evaluate behavior for its contribution to personal growth and tend to repeat activity that helps them approach this goal.

Rogers assumes that the most effective learning takes place when a person does not have to struggle for and concern herself with approval from others. The most important evaluations are to come from the person herself, for the self has its innate self-actualizing tendency. When a person receives *unconditional positive regard* from others, she is not distracted and is better able to evaluate how her own behavior is contributing to enhancement of self.

Faulty learning can interfere with the natural sequence of healthy development. A person may accept evaluations by others instead of paying heed to the internal evaluations provided by her own psyche and body. For example, she may apply the denigrating evaluations of others to her own intrinsically good behavior and actually begin to accept their judgment, as when a student regards herself as a worthless human being after being criticized by a teacher.

Therapeutic Intervention

Because a mature and well-adjusted person makes his own judgments based on what is intrinsically satisfying and actualizing, Rogers avoids imposing goals on the client during therapy. The client is to take the lead and direct the course of the conversation and of the session. The therapist's job is to create conditions so that during their hour together the client can return once again to his basic nature and judge for himself which course of life is intrinsically gratifying to him. Again, because of Rogers's very positive view of people, he assumes that their decisions will not only make them happy with themselves but also turn them into good, civilized people.

Rogers's thinking has evolved from a clear specification of techniques (Rogers, 1942) to an emphasis on the attitude and emotional style of the therapist and a deemphasis of specific procedures (Rogers, 1951). The therapist should have three core qualities. Genuineness, sometimes called congruence, encompasses spontaneity, openness, and authenticity. The therapist has no phoniness and no professional facade, self-disclosing himself, his feelings, and his thoughts informally and candidly to the client. In a sense the therapist through honest self-disclosure provides a model for what the client can become. He is in touch with his feelings and is able to express them and to accept responsibility for doing so. He has the courage to present himself to others as he really is. The second attribute of the successful therapist, according to Rogers, is being able to extend unconditional positive regard. Other people set what Rogers calls "conditions of worth"—I will love you if. . . . The client-centered therapist prizes clients as they are, and conveys unpossessive warmth for them, even if he does not approve of their behavior. People have value merely for being people, and the therapist must care deeply for and respect a client, for the simple reason that he or she is another human being, engaged in the struggle of growing and being alive. The third quality, accurate empathic understanding, is the ability to see the world through the eyes of clients from moment to moment, to understand the feelings of clients both from their own phenomenological vantage point, which is known to them, and from perspectives that they may be only dimly aware of.

Empathy

Let us examine empathy more closely. Empathizing—the acceptance, recognition, and clarification of feelings—is one of the few techniques of Rogerian therapy. Within the context of a warm therapeutic relationship, the therapist encourages the client to talk about his or her most deeply felt concerns and attempts to restate the emotional aspects, not just the content, of what the client says. This reflection of feelings to the client is meant to remove gradually the emotional conflicts that are blocking self-actualization. Because feelings are mirrored back without judgment or disapproval, the client can look at them, clarify them, and acknowledge and accept them. Feared thoughts and emotions that were previously too threatening to enter awareness can become part of the self-concept. The therapist, it should be noted, is not being truly nondirective, a term often applied to Rogers, for he selectively attends to evaluative statements and feelings expressed by the client. He believes that these are the matters the client should be helped to examine.

If therapeutic conditions allowing self-acceptance are established, clients begin to talk in a more honest and emotional way about themselves. Rogers assumes

BOX 18.4

EXCERPT FROM A CLIENT-CENTERED THERAPY SESSION

Client (an eighteen-year-old female college student): My parents really bug me. First it was Arthur they didn't like, now it's Peter. I'm just fed up with all their meddling.

Therapist: You really are angry at your folks.

Client: Well, how do you expect me to feel? Here I am with a 3.5 GPA, and providing all sorts of other goodies, and they claim the right to pass on how appropriate my boyfriend is. (Begins to sob.)

Therapist: It strikes me that you're not just angry with them. (Pause) Maybe you're worried about disappointing them.

Client: (Crying even more) I've tried all my life to please them. Sure their approval is important to me. They're really pleased when I get A's, but why do they have to pass judgment on my social life as well?

Comments. Although the emotion expressed initially was one of anger, the therapist believed that the client was really fearful of criticism from her parents. She therefore made an advanced empathic statement in an effort to explore with the client what was only implied but not expressed. Previous sessions had suggested that the client worked hard academically primarily to please her parents and to avoid their censure. She had always been able to win their approval by getting good grades, but more recently the critical eyes of her mother and father were directed at the young men she was dating. The client was beginning to realize that she had to arrange her social life to please her parents. Her fear of disapproval from her parents became the focus in therapy after the therapist had helped her see beyond her anger.

---

that such talk in itself is primarily responsible for changing behavior.

Rogers's application of empathy is sometimes mistakenly assumed to be an easy, straightforward matter, but it is not. In fact, it requires much subtlety and constitutes strong "medicine" indeed. The therapist does not always restrict herself to merely finding words for the emotional aspects of what the client says but, in what one writer calls "advanced accurate empathy" (Egan, 1975), she goes beyond to what she believes *lies behind* the client's observable behavior (see Box 18.4). The therapist makes an inference about what is troubling the client. She interprets what the client has told her in a way that seems different from the client's actual statements. In a sense, advanced empathy represents theory building on the part of the therapist: after considering over a number of sessions what the client has been saying and how he or she has been saying it, the therapist generates a hypothesis about what may be the true source of distress and yet remains hidden from the client.[6] The following is an example.

Client: I don't know what's going on. I study hard, but I just don't get good marks. I think I study as hard as anyone else, but all of my efforts seem to go down the drain. I don't know what else I can do.

[6]Whether an advanced empathy statement by the therapist should even be regarded as *accurate* is another interesting question. These interpretations by client-centered therapists can never be known for sure to be true. Rather, like scientific theories and insights into the past, they may be more or less *useful*.

Counselor A: You feel frustrated because even when you try hard you fail [primary empathy].

Counselor B: It's depressing to put in as much effort as those who pass and still fail. It gets you down and maybe even makes you feel a little sorry for yourself [advanced empathy] (Egan, 1975, p. 135).

In primary empathy the therapist tries to restate to clients their thoughts, feelings, and experiences *from their own point of view*. The work here is at the phenomenological level; the therapist views the client's world from the client's perspective and then communicates to the client that this frame of reference is understood and appreciated. In advanced empathy the therapist generates a view that takes the client's world into account but conceptualizes things differently and, it is hoped, in a more constructive way. The therapist presents to the client a way of considering himself or herself that may be quite different from the client's accustomed perspective.

To understand this important distinction, we must bear in mind that therapists operating within the client-centered framework assume that the client views things in an unproductive way, as evidenced by the psychological distress that has brought the client into therapy. At the primary empathic level the therapist accepts this view, understands it, and communicates to the client that it is appreciated. But at the advanced or interpretive level the therapist offers something new, a perspective she hopes is better and more productive and implies new modes of action. Advanced empathizing builds on the information made available over a number of sessions in which the therapist has concentrated on making primary-level empathic statements.

The client-centered therapist, operating within a phenomenological philosophy, *must* have as her goal the movement of a client from his or her present phenomenological world to another one; hence the importance of the advanced empathy stage. Since people's emotions and actions are determined by how they construe themselves and their surroundings, by their phenomenology, those who are dysfunctional or otherwise dissatisfied with their present mode of living are in need of a *new* phenomenology. From the very outset, then, client-centered therapy—and all other phenomenological therapies—have perforce been interested in clients' adopting frameworks different from what they had upon beginning treatment. Merely to reflect back to clients their current phenomenology cannot in itself bring therapeutic change. A new phenomenology must be acquired.

Evaluation

Largely because of Rogers's own insistence that the outcome and process of therapy be carefully scrutinized and empirically validated, numerous studies have attempted to evaluate client-centered therapy. Indeed, Rogers can be credited with originating the whole field of psychotherapy research. He and his students deserve the credit for removing the mystique and excessive privacy of the consulting room; for example, they pioneered the tape recording of therapy sessions for subsequent analysis by researchers.

Research on Rogerian therapy has focused principally on relating outcome to the personal qualities of therapists and has yielded inconsistent results, casting doubt on the widely held assumption that positive outcome is strongly related to the therapist's empathy, genuineness, and warmth (Parloff, Waskow, and Wolfe, 1978). It is probably useful to continue emphasizing such qualities in the training of young clinicians, however, for they would seem to help create for the client an atmosphere of trust and safety within which to reveal the deep inner workings of the self. But it is not justifiable, from a research perspective, to assert that these qualities, by themselves, are sufficient to help clients change.

In keeping with Rogers's phenomenological approach, self-reports by clients are the usual measures of the effectiveness of therapy. Research on Rogerian therapy has paid little attention to how patients actually *behave* following therapy. Rogers's basic datum is the individual's own phenomenological evaluation and reaction to himself and events in his world; the overt behavior, it is held, follows from these perceptions and is not the proper object of study by the client-centered therapy researcher.

The paradigmatic neglect of behavior outside the therapy session can conceivably create problems for clients. Even though feelings of inferiority are overcome during sessions, the client may very well be at a loss how to behave differently after leaving the consulting room. He may, for example, never have acquired an adequate repertoire of social skills. If he is truly to change his concept of himself, it would seem necessary, in our opinion, to do more than help the client understand himself better. He may very well need training in interpersonal skills.

Rogers's emphasis on subjective experience also raises epistemological problems, for the therapist must be able to make accurate and incisive inferences about what the client is feeling or thinking. Although the method seems to rely entirely on what the client says, Rogers asserts that clients can be unaware of their true feelings; indeed, it is this lack of awareness that brings most of them into therapy in the first place. As with psychoanalysis, we must ask how a therapist is to make an inference about internal processes of which a client is seemingly unaware, and then by what procedures the usefulness or validity of that inference is to be evaluated.

Rogers may also be criticized for assuming that self-actualization is the principal human motivation. Rogers infers the self-actualization motive from his observation that people seek out situations offering fulfillment. But then the self-actualization tendency is given in *explanation* of the search for these situations. Circular reasoning again!

Another point to consider is how faulty ideas are learned from the evaluation of others. Why does the master motive not always dominate the individual's learning? If the person is indeed always self-actualizing, under what circumstances does faulty learning take place, and what motives and needs are satisfied by such faulty learning?

Finally, Rogers assumes both that the psychologically healthy person makes choices to satisfy self-actualizing tendencies and that people are by their very natures good. But some social philosophers have taken a less optimistic view of human nature. Thomas Hobbes, for example, stated that life is "nasty, brutish, and short." How do we explain a person who behaves in a brutish fashion and yet asserts that this behavior is intrinsically gratifying and, indeed, self-actualizing?

It may be that the problem of extreme unreasonableness has not been adequately addressed by Rogers because he and his colleagues have concentrated on people who are only mildly disturbed. As a way to help unhappy but not severely disturbed people understand themselves better (and *perhaps* even to help them behave differently), client-centered therapy may very well be appropriate and effective. This humanistic approach remains popular in the encounter group movement (see page 529). Rogerian therapy may not, however, be appropriate for a severe psychological disorder, as Rogers himself has warned.

Existential Therapy

Those most commonly associated with existentialism are the Danish philosopher Sören Kierkegaard and the German philosophers Edmund Husserl and Martin Heidegger, with existential therapy the Swiss psychiatrists Ludwig Binswanger and Medard Boss and the Austrian psychiatrist Viktor Frankl, whose logotherapy and views on depression were discussed earlier (see page 216). In this country the principal proponents of existential therapy, or existential analysis as it is sometimes called, have been Rollo May and the late Abraham Maslow (1908–1970).

Basic Concepts of Existentialism
The following is a distillation of the existential position.

Man has the capacity for being aware of himself, of what he is doing, and what is happening to him. As a consequence, he is capable of making decisions about these things and of taking responsibility for himself. He can also become aware of a possibility of becoming completely isolated and alone, that is, nothing, symbolized by the ultimate nothingness of death. This is innately feared. He is not a static entity but in a constant state of transition. He does not exist; he is not a being; rather he is coming into being, emerging, becoming, evolving toward something. His ways of behaving toward himself and other events are changing constantly. His significance lies not in what he has been in the past, but in what he is now and the direction of his development, which is toward the fulfillment of his innate potentiality (Ford and Urban, 1963, p. 448).

Existential anxiety comes from several sources (Tillich, 1952). We are all aware that one day we shall die; when we with honesty confront this inescapable reality, we face up to existential anxiety. We are also aware of our helplessness against chance circumstances which can

Abraham Maslow, the humanistic therapist who made Carl Jung's term self-actualization central to his psychology.

forever change our lives, such as an automobile accident that cripples us. Third, we are aware that we must ultimately make decisions, act, and live with the consequences. Fourth, we must ourselves create the meaning of our lives; the ultimate responsibility for endowing our world and our lives with substance and purpose rests with each of us. And finally, we know that we are ultimately alone.

The existential point of view, like humanism, emphasizes personal growth. There are, though, some important distinctions. Humanism, as exemplified by Rogers's views, stresses the goodness of human nature. If unfettered by groundless fears and societal restrictions, human beings will develop normally, even exceptionally, much as a flower will sprout from a seed if only given enough light, air, and water. Existentialism is gloomier, having a strain of darkness within it. Although it embraces free will and responsibility, existentialism stresses the anxiety that is inevitable in making important choices, the existential choices on which existence depends, such as staying or not staying with a spouse, with a job, or even with this world. Hamlet's famous soliloquy beginning "To be, or not to be—that is the question" (Act III, Scene 1) is a classic existential statement. To be truly alive is to confront the anxiety that comes with existential choices. To avoid such choices, to pretend that they do not have to be made, may protect the individual from anxiety, but it also deprives him of living a life with meaning and is at the core of psychopathology. Thus whereas the humanistic message is upbeat, almost ecstatic, the existential is tinged with sadness and anxiety, but not despair, unless the exercise of free will and assumption of responsibility that accompanies it are avoided.

The Goals of Therapy

So oftentimes it happens that we live our lives in chains, and we never even know we have the key ("Already Gone," by Jack Tempchin and Robb Strandlund, 1973 and 1975).

A person is the sum of the choices he makes. Difficulties in making choices can be understood only by exploring experience. The existential therapist, by offering support and empathy through adoption of the individual's phenomenological frame of reference, helps him explore his behavior, feelings, relationships, and what his life means to him. But the therapist also encourages the client to confront and clarify past and present choices. Present choices are the most important.

In addition, existential therapy helps people relate *authentically* to others. People are assumed to define their identity and existence in terms of their personal relationships; a person is threatened with nonbeing—or alienation—if isolated from others. Even though he may be effective in dealing with people and his world (see page 49), he can become anxious if deprived of open and frank relationships. Hence, although the existential view is a highly subjective one, it strongly emphasizes *relating to others* in an open, honest, spontaneous, and loving manner.[7] The encounter group movement owes much to this existential tenet.

The therapeutic relationship should be an authentic encounter between two human beings so that the patient has some practice in relating to another individual in a straightforward fashion.[8] The therapist, through her own honesty and self-disclosure, helps the client learn authenticity. This can take the form of the therapist's openly expressing her strong disapproval of what the client is doing—but without rejecting the client as a worthwhile human being.

The principal goal of existential therapy is to make the patient more aware of his or her own potential for choice and growth. In the existential view people create their existence anew at each moment. The potential for disorder as well as growth is ever present. Individuals must be encouraged to accept the responsibility for their own existence and to realize that, within certain limits,

they can redefine themselves at any moment and behave and feel differently within their own social environment. But this freedom to choose and the responsibility that comes with it are not easy for humankind to accept and work with. Many people are afraid of this freedom, and as they begin to make choices, they realize that fulfillment is a *process,* that they must constantly choose and accept responsibility if they are to be truly human and fulfill their potential. Their prospects then are not cheery; with greater awareness of their freedom to choose comes more existential anxiety. One of the goals of therapy is to bolster their resolve and ability to cope with this inescapable anxiety and to continue growing.

The existential writers, however, are very vague about what therapeutic techniques will help the client grow. Indeed, a reliance on technique may be seen as an objectifying process, that is, a process in which the therapist acts upon the client as though he or she were a thing to be manipulated (Prochaska, 1984). The existential approach is a general *attitude* taken by certain therapists toward human nature, rather than a set of therapeutic techniques.

Evaluation

Research on existential therapy per se may be inherently impossible, for, as just mentioned, it represents not a set of definable techniques but an epistemological stance, whereby the therapist must do her utmost to view the world as the client perceives it, and a general commitment to certain goals of human conduct—authenticity, spontaneity, choice, growth, assumption of responsibility. Therapeutic change is achieved by helping the client to shift from his or her perceived reality and to develop the human qualities prized by existentialist philosophers. Existential therapy is without the definable, concrete operations on which scientific research can be conducted. Indeed, no research has been done, although existential therapists have published numerous case reports relating striking successes with a variety of clinical problems.

Moreover, contemporary science is seen as dehumanizing by existentialists, hence to be *avoided.* They believe that applying science to individuals denies their unique humanness. Several of the criticisms of client-centered therapy apply too to existential treatment. Since by definition a person's subjective experience is unique to himself, how can the therapist know that she is truly understanding a patient's world as it appears to him? Yet attention to subjective impressions is not necessarily unproductive. Paying heed to our freedom to choose and ability to change at any time may be an important means of improving behavior. Indeed, the mes-

---

[7]At the same time each of us is ultimately and basically *alone.* Although existentialism asserts that we must relate authentically to others, the paradox of life is that we are inherently separate from others, that we came into this world alone and must create our own existence in the world alone.

[8]It is interesting to note that this approach, which places so much emphasis on a person's perceptions, understanding, feelings, and other internal processes, is in a way very behavioristic. The person must at some point during therapy begin to behave differently, both toward the therapist and toward the outside world, in order for his or her own existential condition to be changed.

490 INTERVENTION

BOX 18.5

A GLIMPSE OF FRITZ PERLS

As Joe got on the elevator, he hardly noticed the short, gray-bearded man standing against the wall. Then recognition hit him. "Uh, Dr. Perls, I'm, uh, honored to meet you. I've read your work, and it's such—such an honor to meet—to be in your presence. . . . "Joe's stammering speech trailed away with no effect. The old man did not move.

The elevator slowed and Joe, realizing that an opportunity was slipping away, heard himself say, hopelessly, "I'm really nervous." Perls turned and smiled at him. As the doors opened, he took Joe's arm and said, "Now let us talk" (Gaines, 1974).

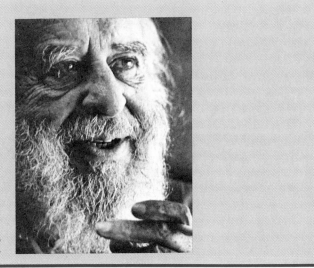

Frederich (Fritz) Perls (1893–1970), colorful founder of Gestalt therapy.

sage implicit in existentialism, that our existence is constantly being reaffirmed and that we are not prisoners of our past mistakes and misfortunes, might well be incorporated into *any* therapy.

Gestalt Therapy

Another humanistic therapy that has developed over the past thirty years is Gestalt therapy; its most important proponent was the late Frederich S. Perls (see Box 18.5). After receiving a medical degree in Germany in 1921, Perls became a psychoanalyst. But he was rejected by European analysts because he challenged some of the basic precepts of psychoanalytic theory, particularly the important place accorded to the libido and its various transformations in the development of neurosis (Perls, 1947). He emigrated to Holland in 1933, shortly after Hitler came to power, because he was opposed to totalitarianism, and to South Africa in 1934, as the country's first teaching analyst. There he developed the basics of Gestalt therapy. He took up residence in the United States in 1946 and eventually settled at Esalen, a center for humanistic therapy in Big Sur, California. Here his ideas and techniques of therapy underwent impressive growth, especially as applied in groups (Perls, Hefferline, and Goodman, 1951; Perls, 1970).

Basic Concepts of Gestalt Therapy

Like Rogers, Perls held that people have an innate goodness and that this basic nature should be allowed to ex-

press itself. Psychological problems originate in frustrations and denials of this innate goodness. Gestalt therapy, along with other humanistic approaches, tends to emphasize the creative and expressive aspects of people, rather than the negative and distorted features on which psychoanalysis seems to concentrate.

A basic assumption of Gestalt therapy is that all of us bring our needs and wants to any situation. We do not merely perceive situations "as they are"; instead we engage our social environment by projecting our needs, or fears, or desires onto what is "out there." Thus if I am talking to a stranger, I do not merely react to the person as that person exists; I react to the stranger in the context of my needs. Gestalt therapists working with groups sometimes have people pair off, close their eyes, and imagine the face of an individual to whom they have a strong emotional attachment. They are encouraged to concentrate on the feelings they have about that person. Then all open their eyes and look at their partner. After a few moments they are instructed to close their eyes again and think now of something neutral, such as an arithmetic problem. They then open their eyes again and look a second time at their partner. Finally, they are asked whether there was an important difference in the ways they felt about their partner in the two situations. This exercise is designed to exaggerate what is assumed to be inevitable in all our social interactions, namely the intrusion of our feelings into whatever is happening at any particular moment.

Perls and his followers have concentrated on the here and now and on the individual as an actor, as a being

This Gestalt group therapy exercise is designed to establish trust among the group members.

who is responsible for his or her own behavior and who is capable of playing a central role in bringing about beneficial changes.

The patient who comes for help, seeking to relate more adequately with other people and to be able to express his feelings more directly, is instructed to express what he is feeling at that moment to another person. The ways in which he stops, blocks, and frustrates himself quickly become apparent, and he can then be assisted in exploring and experiencing the blockings and encouraged to attempt other ways of expressing himself and of relating.

Thus, the general approach of Gestalt theory and therapy requires the patient to specify the changes in himself that he desires, assists him in increasing his awareness of how he defeats himself, and aids him in experimenting and changing. Blocks in awareness and behavior emerge [during the session] in the same way that they manifest themselves in a person's life; his increased awareness of his avoidances and his relief as he becomes able to expand his experience and behavior are felt immediately in increases in capacity for living (Fagan and Shepherd, 1970, p. 2).

The foregoing description of the theorizing behind Gestalt therapy does not distinguish it very well from what Rogers prescribes. But Gestalt therapy is supposedly related to Gestalt psychology, a branch of psychol-ogy concerned primarily with perception. Their closest similarity may be in their attention to *wholes*. Perls wanted to make individuals *whole* by increasing their awareness of unacknowledged feelings and having them reclaim the parts of the personality that have been denied or disowned.

The Gestalt therapist focuses on what a client is doing in the consulting room here and now, without delving into the past, for the most important event in the client's life is what is happening at this moment. In Gestalt therapy all that exists is the Now. If the past is bothersome, it is brought into the present. "Why" questions are discouraged, for searching after causes in the past is considered an attempt to escape responsibility for making choices in the present, a familiar existential theme. Clients are exhorted, cajoled, sometimes even coerced into awareness of what is happening now. Awareness is an immediate and direct thinking and sensing. Individuals must know what is going on about them, what they think and fantasize, want and feel, what they are doing at the moment, and they must also sense posture, facial expressions, muscular tensions, and gestures, the words they use, the sound of their voice. Perls believed that awareness is curative. People have only to be moved away from their ideas about themselves to an awareness of what they are feeling and doing at this exact moment.

Gestalt Therapy Techniques

Gestalt therapy is noted for its emphasis on techniques, in contrast to their paucity in the humanistic and existential therapies discussed so far.[9] The techniques described here are but a small sample of current Gestalt practices.

The Gestalt therapist insists that the client talk in the present tense. This is one way of directing his attention to current feelings and activities. To help him bear continuing responsibility for what he is and what he is to become, the therapist instructs him to change "it" language into "I" language.

Therapist: What do you hear in your voice?

Patient: My voice sounds like it is crying.

Therapist: Can you take responsibility for that by saying, I am crying? (Levitsky and Perls, 1970, p. 142).

This simple change in language, besides allowing the patient to assume responsibility for feelings and behavior, reduces his sense of being alienated from aspects of his very being. It helps the patient see himself as active rather than passive, as an open and searching person rather than as someone whose behavior is determined entirely by external events.

In one procedure of Gestalt therapy, the empty-chair technique, a client projects and then talks to his projection of a feeling, or of a person, object, or situation. Thus, seeing that a patient is crying, the Gestalt therapist might ask him to regard the tears as being in an empty chair opposite him and to speak *to* the tears. This tactic often seems to help people confront their feelings. Indeed, to ask a person to talk *about* his tears is assumed to encourage him to establish still greater distance between himself and his feelings—something Gestalt therapists assert interferes with psychological well-being.

Another technique is to have the person behave opposite to the way he feels. Someone who is excessively

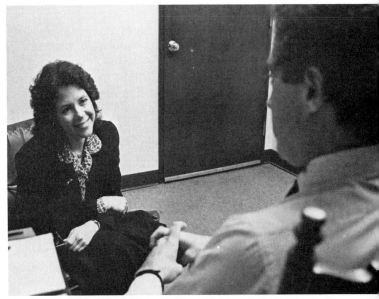

Therapists pay attention both to what their clients say and to the body language that is simultaneously expressed. Here the message that is being expressed facially seems in conflict with the woman's posture.

timid might be asked during the therapy session to behave like an outgoing person. Perls assumed that the opposite side of the coin actually lies within the being of the person and that acting out feelings not usually expressed allows the person to become aware of a part of himself that has thus far been submerged.

All therapists pay attention to nonverbal and paralinguistic cues given by the client. Nonverbal cues are body movements, facial expressions, gestures, and the like, paralinguistic the tone of voice, the rapidity with which words are spoken, and other audible components of speech beyond its content. People can negate with their hands or their eyes what they are saying with the larynx. Perls placed special emphasis on these nonlinguistic signals, closely observing them in order to determine what clients might really be feeling. "What we say is mostly lies or bullshit. But the voice is there, the gesture, the posture, the facial expression, the psychosomatic language" (Perls, 1969, p. 54).

At a Gestalt workshop we witnessed a man in his twenties who was bragging about his father's professional accomplishments. As he spoke, his right leg began to shake slightly. The therapist interrupted the story and asked the client to observe his leg. As he did so, he seemed about to cry. Sensing that the client was holding back his tears, the therapist asked him to shake his leg more. Soon the leg was jumping up and down in a violent fashion, and the man began to weep. The resent-

[9]Although Gestalt therapy over the years has tended to become identified with a set of techniques, many contemporary workers assert that it is not a set of defined procedures, or for that matter a particular theory of behavior and experience. Rather, Gestalt therapy entails a particular *attitude* toward the nature of humankind and toward treatment. A Gestalt therapist is constantly creative, is open to new experiences, and talks openly to the client on a person-to-person basis, the I-thou which is a tenet of existential philosophy. The core of therapy is to help the client be creative and open too. The Gestalt therapist is trained to "fine-tune" the person so that he or she can encounter the world on an immediate, nonjudgmental, nonreflective basis. We agree that equating Gestalt therapy with techniques does not tell the whole story. Gestalt therapy does indeed encourage both therapists and clients to be spontaneous and open to new experience in a general way. At the same time, though, Gestalt therapists employ a body of procedures on a rather consistent basis. Many of them have even been adopted by therapists of other persuasions.

ment toward his father, bottled up since childhood, was now expressed. The session continued, but its focus became the "unfinished business" the client had with his father. Perls believed that unresolved traumas of the past affect new relationships. They should be acted out in the present. By finishing this business, the individual becomes better able to confront the present, for it will not be contaminated by residues from a troubling past.

During the therapy session Gestalt therapists often create unusual episodes to externalize, to make more vivid and understandable, a problem they believe a client is having. In one session that we observed, a husband and wife sat together on a sofa, bickering about the woman's mother. The husband seemed very angry with his mother-in-law, and the therapist surmised that she was getting in the way of his relationship with his wife. The therapist wanted to demonstrate to the couple how frustrating this must be for both of them, and he also wished to goad both of them to do something about it. Without warning, he rose from his chair and wedged himself between the couple. Not a word was said. The husband looked puzzled, then hurt, and gradually became angry at the therapist. He asked him to move so that he could sit next to his wife again. The therapist shook his head. When the husband repeated his request, the therapist removed his jacket and placed it over the wife's head so that the husband could not even see her. A long silence followed, during which the husband grew more and more agitated. The wife meanwhile was sitting quietly, covered by the therapist's coat. Suddenly the husband stood up, walked past the therapist, and angrily removed the coat; then he pushed the therapist off the sofa. The therapist exploded in good-natured laughter. "I wondered how long it would take you to do something!" he roared.

This staged scene drove several points home in a way that mere words might not have. The husband—having been trained already by the therapist to get in better touch with his feelings and to express them without fear or embarrassment—reported tearfully that he had felt cut off from his wife by the therapist, in much the same way that he felt alienated from her by her mother. The mother was intruding, and he was not doing anything about it. He did not trust himself to assert his needs and to take action to satisfy them. The fact that he was able to remove the coat and the therapist as well made him wonder whether he might not behave similarly toward his mother-in-law. As he spoke, his wife began to sob; she confided to her husband that all along she had been wanting him to take charge of the problem with her mother. So far so good. But then the therapist turned to the woman and asked her why she had not removed the coat herself! The husband grinned as the therapist gently chided the wife for being unduly passive about her marital problems. By the end of the session, the clients, although emotionally drained, felt in better contact with each other and expressed resolve to work together actively to alter their relationship with her mother.

The interpretation of dreams is another important part of Gestalt therapy. Gestalt analysis of them is quite different from the psychoanalytic. The dream is not considered a rich source of symbolism relating to unconscious processes; rather,

Every image in the dream, whether human, animal, vegetable, or mineral, is taken to represent an alienated portion of the self. By reexperiencing and retelling the dream over and over again in the present tense, from the standpoint of each image, the patient can begin to reclaim these alienated fragments, and accept them, live with them and express them more appropriately (Enright, 1970, p. 121.).

For example, a woman in Gestalt therapy dreamed of walking down a crooked path among tall, straight trees. The therapist asked her to *become* one of the trees, and this made her feel serene and more deeply rooted. She then expressed her desire for such security. When she was asked to become the crooked path, tears welled as she confronted the deviousness of the way in which she lived. Once again the Gestalt therapist helped the client to externalize feelings customarily avoided, so that she could become aware of them, acknowledge them as her own, and then perhaps decide to change them.

Consistent with their phenomenological approach, Gestalt therapists encourage clients to recount, with emotion, the meaning that the dream has for them at that very moment. Even though the therapist may have a hypothesis about what a particular dream means to the client, care is taken not to impose that meaning on the dreamer, for it is the dreamer's dream. The only significance it has for the dreamer is the meaning it holds as it is discussed in the session. In this sense Gestalt therapy does not have a theory of dreams; rather it concerns itself with dream *work*, the analysis of dreams by the client with support from the therapist. Since only the phenomenal world has importance for each client, his or her immediate experience is the one thing worth focusing on.

Those who knew or met Fritz Perls are aware that he seemed to personify the ideals of his therapy. He was a very present-oriented, earthy, spontaneous individual, who placed great emphasis on satisfying his needs. This philosophy is well summed up in the following poetic statement by Perls.

I do my thing and you do your thing. I am not in this world to live up to your expectations. And you are not in this world to live up to mine. You are you and I am I. And if by chance we find each other, it's beautiful. If not, then not.

Evaluation

The literature suggests that Gestalt therapists spend much or most of their time urging clients to be more expressive, spontaneous, and responsive to their own needs. Perls describes this activity as making the person more attentive to emerging gestalts. Therapy also attempts to make the person whole by encouraging a reclamation of parts of the personality hitherto denied. The psychotherapy is therefore aligned with the experimental findings of Gestalt psychology. It is open to question, however, whether Perls's description is the most accurate or parsimonious way of talking about the techniques, and, more importantly, whether such concepts assist in the effective training of good therapists.

Gestalt therapy does forcefully convey the existential message that a person is not a prisoner of his past, that he can at any time make the existential choice to be different, and that the therapist will not tolerate stagnation. No doubt this optimistic view helps many people change. If the person does not know how to behave differently, however, considerable damage can be done to an already miserable individual.

Perls's emphasis on responsibility is not to be confused with commitment or obligation to others. Even as a therapist Perls did not present himself as a person who assumes responsibility for others, and he did not urge this on his patients either. The individual has the responsibility to take care of himself, to meet his *own* needs as they arise. This apparent egocentrism may be troubling for people with a social conscience and for those who have in the past made commitments to others. Indeed, Perls believed that commitments should never be made in the first place (Prochaska, 1984).

The same complaint voiced about Rogers's client-centered therapy applies to Gestalt therapy. Indeed, it may be common to all humanistic therapies. According to humanists, people are, by their very nature, good, purposive, and resourceful. If they are, it would be reasonable to trust this intrinsic good nature and to encourage direct expression of needs. But are people always good? Sometimes clients—especially those who are psychologically troubled—feel they must do something

that, in the judgment of the professional, is not in their own best interests. Suppose that a client feels the need to murder someone or to engage in other behavior that, to outside observers, is surely undesirable. What is the therapist's responsibility? At what point does the therapist intervene and impose his or her judgment?[10] We believe that Gestalt therapists do *not* abdicate all decisions to their clients and that they *do* exert considerable influence on them, if only by virtue of the models they themselves provide. We have already indicated that Perls was a very charismatic figure. It is likely that most people adopt the values of their therapists (Rosenthal, 1955; Pentony, 1966), and it seems preferable to us to admit this social influence so that it can be dealt with, rather than to deny that such influence exists and perhaps allow for even greater "tyranny" of therapists over patients. This issue is discussed at length in Chapter 21.

Several recent studies have attempted to examine aspects of Gestalt therapy, in particular the empty-chair technique. Conoley and his colleagues (1983) found, in an analogue study with college undergraduates, that self-rated anger was reduced after a twenty-minute empty-chair exercise. Greenberg and Rice (1981) report that the technique increases awareness and emotional expression. There is now a growing trend for those interested in Gestalt therapy to attempt to study parts of it in a reasonably controlled fashion. Indeed, in 1983, the Psychosocial Treatments Branch of the National Institute of Mental Health convened a group of distinguished Gestalt therapists and behavior therapists for the specific purpose of discussing ways in which the rigor of behavior therapists could be applied in experiments on the creative and clinical insights of Gestalt therapists. The federal agency plans to encourage such research, on the assumption that things Gestalt therapists do constitute powerful "medicine" and should be subjected to the kind of critical scrutiny that client-centered, behavioral, and analytic therapies have come under.

All therapies are subject to abuse; Gestalt is no exception. Indeed, it may present special problems. It is not difficult, even for trainees with a minimum of experience, to induce clients to express their feelings. Some Gestalt techniques may in themselves be so powerful in opening people up that clients can be harmed unintentionally. The forcefulness of Perls's personality and his confrontational style have led some therapists to mimic him without the thoughtfulness, skill, and caring he ap-

---

[10]As we shall see in Chapter 21, when we discuss the Tarasoff ruling, therapists now have no choice but to take drastic action in such circumstances, even against the client's wishes.

peared to possess in unusual abundance. The responsible Gestalt therapist is a professional who keeps the client's interests at the forefront, and who understands that the expression of strong emotion for its own sake is seldom enough to ease an individual's suffering. The nature of Gestalt therapy and the fact that a cult has grown up around the memory of Fritz Perls are reasons why practicing Gestalt therapists should strive for an extra measure of caution and humility.

SUMMARY

Insight therapies share the basic assumption that a person's behavior is disordered because he is not aware of what motivates his actions. Psychoanalysis and ego analysis tend to emphasize factors from the past, whereas most humanistic and existential approaches, such as those of Rogers and Perls, emphasize the current determinants of behavior.

Consistent with Freud's second theory of neurosis, psychoanalysis tries to uncover childhood repressions so that infantile fears of libidinal expression can be examined by the adult ego in the light of present-day realities. Ego analysis puts more emphasis on the need and ability of the patient to achieve greater control over the environment and over instinctual gratification.

Rogers trusts the basic goodness of the drive to self-actualize, and he proposes the creation of nonjudgmental conditions in therapy. Through empathy and unconditional positive regard for their clients, the therapists help them to view themselves more accurately and to trust their own instincts for self-actualization. Existential therapists, influenced primarily by European existential philosophy, similarly regard people as having the innate ability to realize their potential; they also have the freedom to decide at any given moment to become different. Both Rogers and the existentialists assume that the only reality is the one perceived by the individual; thus the therapist must try to view the world from the client's phenomenological frame of reference, rather than from his own.

The Gestalt therapy of Perls is usually regarded as humanistic, yet it is different in important ways from the therapies of Rogers and the existentialists. Perls stressed living in the now, and the many techniques he and his followers have introduced are designed to help clients experience their current needs and feel comfortable about satisfying them as they emerge. The emphasis is on changing behavior, and yet considerable attention is directed toward increasing the individual's awareness of what he or she is doing at the present moment and accepting responsibility for it.

In addition to the specific criticisms we have made of each of these insight therapies, all have a common problem which impedes progress and refinement. Carefully controlled studies to support the claims of efficacy and the assertions that changes do occur for the reasons expounded by the various theorists are scarce. Some theorists—especially the existentialists—dismiss a priori and paradigmatically the need for and even the possibility of the kind of controlled research that most social scientists deem important. The ultimate question, an important one in view of the large fees people pay to their therapists, is whether people are helped by the therapists. But even when patients do derive benefit, their improvement may be attributable at least in part to the ubiquitous placebo effect.

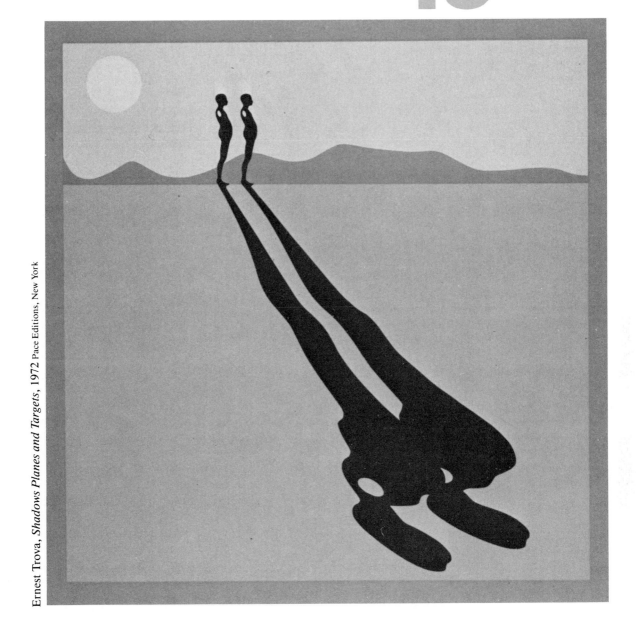

Ernest Trova, *Shadows Planes and Targets*, 1972 Pace Editions, New York

BEHAVIOR THERAPY

Over the past three decades a new way of treating psychopathology has been developed. Called *behavior therapy*, it was initially restricted to procedures based on classical and operant conditioning, but today it has a broader base, all of experimental psychology. Behavior therapy, as now conceived, is characterized more by its epistemological stance—its search for rigorous standards of proof—than by allegiance to any particular set of concepts (Davison and Goldfried, 1973). In brief, behavior therapy is an attempt to change abnormal behavior by drawing on the methods used and the discoveries made by experimental psychologists in their study of both normal and abnormal behavior.

That the most effective clinical procedures will be developed through science is an *assumption*. There is nothing inherent in the scientific method that guarantees victories for those studying human behavior by its principles. Because we have reached the moon and beyond by playing the science game does not mean that the same set of rules should be applied to human behavior. The existentialists, who emphasize free will, assume that the nature of man cannot be meaningfully probed by following the rules favored by the authors of this textbook. Although we are placing our bets on the scientific work described in this chapter, it nonetheless remains an article of faith that behavior therapy will prove the best means of treating disordered behavior.

Sometimes the term "behavior modification" has been used interchangeably with behavior therapy; therapists using operant conditioning as a means of treatment have often preferred this term. But we have argued elsewhere (Davison and Stuart, 1975) that the term behavior therapy should be employed in order to differentiate this approach from others. After all, every therapy—whether it be psychoanalysis or psychosurgery—has as its ultimate goal the modification of behavior. In the recent past, work done by clinicians of other bents, who do not adhere to the standards of evidence and procedure that are the essence of behavior therapy, has been confused with the efforts of behavior therapists.

Just when behavior therapy first began to be developed is difficult to date. It is, in any event, not the case that some social scientist woke up one morning and proclaimed that from this day forward people with psychological problems should be treated with techniques suggested by experimental findings. Rather, over a number of years people in the clinical field began to formulate a new set of assumptions about the best means of dealing with the problems that they encountered. We have found it helpful to distinguish four theoretical approaches applied in behavior therapy—counterconditioning, operant conditioning, modeling, and cognitive restructuring. After reviewing these, we discuss behavioral medicine, a new specialization which blends behavioral and biomedical knowledge to enhance physical health and lessen physical illness.

COUNTERCONDITIONING

In counterconditioning, illustrated in Figure 2.5 (page 44), a response (R_1) to a given stimulus (S) is eliminated by eliciting different behavior (R_2) in the presence of that stimulus. For example, if a man is afraid (R_1) of enclosed spaces (S), the therapist attempts to help him have a calm reaction (R_2) when he is in such situations. Experimental evidence suggests that unrealistic fears can be eliminated in this way. An early and now famous clinical demonstration of counterconditioning was a case reported by Mary Cover Jones (1924). She successfully eliminated a little boy's fear of rabbits by feeding him in the presence of a rabbit. The animal was at first kept several feet away and then gradually moved closer on successive occasions. In this fashion the fear (R_1) produced by the rabbit (S) was "crowded out" by the stronger positive feelings associated with eating (R_2).

Systematic Desensitization

Three decades later Joseph Wolpe (1958) employed similar techniques with fearful adults. He found that many of his clients, like the child treated by Jones, could be encouraged to expose themselves gradually to the situation or object they feared if they were at the same time engaging in behavior that inhibited anxiety. Rather than have his patients eat, however, Wolpe taught them deep muscle relaxation. His training procedures were adapted from earlier work by Edmund Jacobson (1929), who had shown that strong emotional states like anxiety could be markedly inhibited if a person is in a state of deep relaxation. In Jacobson's many experiments various autonomic indices as well as self-reports indicated that the anxiety of subjects was reduced after they had learned to let go of their muscles through a progressive program of contracting and relaxing muscle groups of the body.

Many of the fears felt by Wolpe's patients were so abstract—for example, fear of criticism and fear of failure—that it was impractical to confront them with *real-life* situations that would evoke these fears. Following earlier proposals by Salter (1949), Wolpe reasoned that he might have fearful patients *imagine* what they feared. Thus he formulated a new technique which he called *systematic desensitization*, a term originally applied to the medical procedure of administering increasing doses of allergens to hay fever and asthma sufferers. In systematic desensitization a deeply relaxed person is asked to imagine a graded series of anxiety-provoking situations; the relaxation tends to inhibit any anxiety that might otherwise be elicited by the imagined scenes. If relaxation does give way to anxiety, the client signals to the therapist by raising an index finger, stops imagining the situation in mind, rests, reestablishes relaxation, and then reimagines the situation. If anxiety drives out relaxation again, the client goes back to an earlier situation and tries later to handle the more difficult one. Over successive sessions a client is usually able to tolerate increasingly more difficult scenes as he or she climbs the hierarchy in imagination. As has been documented by Wolpe as well as by many other clinicians (for example, Goldfried and Davison, 1976), the ability to tolerate stressful imagery is generally followed by a reduction of anxiety in related real-life situations. The case study on page 45 illustrates the application of this technique.

Between therapy sessions clients are usually instructed to place themselves in progressively frightening real-life situations. These homework assignments help to move their adjustment from imagination to actuality (for example, Davison, 1968b; Sherman, 1972). As noted earlier in Chapter 6 (page 128), exposure to feared real-life situations has long been known to be an important means of reducing unwarranted anxieties.

Clinicians have treated a great variety of anxiety-related problems by systematic desensitization. The technique appears deceptively simple. But as with any therapy for people in emotional distress, its proper application is a complicated affair. First, the clinician must determine, by means of a comprehensive behavioral assessment, that the situations the client is reacting anxiously to do not warrant it. If a person is anxious because she lacks the skills to deal with a given set of circumstances, desensitization would not be appropriate; to be anxious, for example, about flying an airplane is logical when the individual does not know how to operate the aircraft! Desensitization, then, is an appropriate treatment if a client seems to be inhibited by anxiety from behaving in customary and known ways.

Sometimes the technique can be used when the client does not appear openly anxious. For example, a middle-aged construction worker complaining of depression sought help (Goldfried and Davison, 1976). He was having trouble getting out of bed in the morning and viewed

Joseph Wolpe, one of the pioneers in behavior therapy. He is known particularly for systematic desensitization, a widely applied behavioral technique.

his job and life in general with dread and foreboding. Careful assessment by the clinician revealed that the man was inordinately concerned whether the men working under him liked and approved of him. His depression had set in after he had been promoted to foreman, a position that required him to issue orders and monitor and criticize the activities of other workers. His men would occasionally object to his instructions and comments, and the client found their baleful stares and sullen silences very upsetting. He agreed with the therapist that a hierarchy of situations in which he was criticized and rejected by others would be appropriate. The reduction in job-related anxiety that followed treatment by desensitization succeeded in lifting his depression.

As with all the techniques described in this chapter, very rarely is only one procedure used exclusively. A person fearful of social interactions might well be given training in conversational and other social skills in addition to desensitization. In the most general sense, the treatments chosen and their applicability depend largely on the therapist's ingenuity in discovering the source of the anxiety underlying a client's problems.

Empirical Studies

Researchers became interested in studying desensitization because clinical reports indicated that the technique is effective. Initial steps in the experimental investigation of the procedure were taken by Lazovik and Lang

A small group of dog phobics being treated by systematic desensitization. While remaining deeply relaxed, they are shown a series of pictures of dogs.

(1960; Lang and Lazovik, 1963). They were concerned primarily with assessing the procedure under relatively controlled laboratory conditions. In the earlier clinical reports improvement had been judged by the clinicians who had given the treatment, and other therapeutic procedures were usually employed along with desensitization. Lang and Lazovik decided that for greater control in evaluating desensitization of the simple phobia chosen, fear of snakes, testers who were *not* treating the subjects should measure their pretreatment and post-treatment ability to approach snakes. They also restricted treatment to desensitization. Their experiments showed that, indeed, desensitization can measurably and significantly reduce avoidance of a phobic object.

One of the most widely known and highly regarded experiments in systematic desensitization, and in psychotherapy research as a whole, was conducted by Gordon Paul (1966). His purpose was to compare systematic desensitization, a placebo, and insight therapy for their effectiveness in reducing unrealistic fear. He recruited students who were taking a required public-speaking course and were all fearful of speaking in front of groups. Prior to treatment all students had to deliver a speech before an audience, and numerous measures of their anxiety were taken—self-reports, behavioral observations, and two physiological measures, of pulse rate and sweat (see page 79).

Students were then assigned to one of three treatments. The first was systematic desensitization. The second was an attention-placebo treatment. Subjects in this group met with a sympathetic therapist who led them to believe that a pill would reduce their overall sensitivity to stress. To convince them, the therapist had them listen to a tape which he said had been used in training astronauts to function under stress. They listened to this "stress tape" for several sessions after ingesting the "tranquilizer." In reality, the pill was a placebo, and the tape contained various nonverbal sounds that had been shown in other research to be quite boring. In this way Paul raised subjects' expectations that their social anxieties could be lessened by taking a pill.

The third treatment was insight therapy. Subjects met with skilled insight-oriented therapists to talk over their anxieties; the therapists were free to structure the sessions in any way they saw fit. All treatments were limited to five sessions, a number settled on by the insight therapists when they were asked how many sessions they would need to make a measurable impact on this kind of problem. An important feature of Paul's experimental design was training insight therapists to do systematic desensitization. In fact, insight therapists gave all three treatments. In this way Paul anticipated the criticism that any superiority of systematic desensitization could be attributed to greater enthusiasm shown by desensitization therapists. A fourth group of students did not receive any treatment; the anxiety of these students was measured as they gave two speeches along with the others, one before and one after the treatment sessions.

The results of this important study revealed that subjects who had received systematic desensitization improved much more than did the no-treatment group and more than did the attention-placebo and insight therapy subjects, who reacted about the same to their forms of therapy. Students receiving these two treatments did, however, show significant improvement. The results, then, indicated that systematic desensitization is superior both to insight therapy and to attention plus a placebo in lessening anxiety about making speeches. These results persisted in a two-year follow-up study (Paul, 1967). Subsequent research has attested to the effectiveness of desensitization in reducing a wide range of anxieties; it is doubtful that these gains are attributable to the placebo effect (Rachman and Wilson, 1980).

The Process Question

Behavioral researchers are interested not only in whether a given technique works—the outcome question—but also in *why*—the process question. Wolpe suggests that counterconditioning underlies the efficacy of desensitization; a state or response antagonistic to anxiety is substituted for anxiety as the person is exposed gradually to stronger and stronger doses of what he or she is afraid of. Many experiments (for example, Davison, 1968b) suggest that there may be a specific learning process underlying the technique and that, indeed, it may be counterconditioning. But a number of other explanations are possible. Some workers attach importance to exposure to what the person fears per se; relaxation is then considered merely a useful way to encourage a frightened individual to confront what he or she fears (Wilson and Davison, 1971). At this time many workers believe that the reasons the technique works are still not known (for example, Borkovec and O'Brien, 1976). Our knowledge of how people change is rudimentary; moreover, behavior therapy maintains skepticism about all aspects of treatment, which may be a particular strength of this approach.

Aversion Therapy

Aversion therapy attempts to attach negative feelings to stimuli that are considered inappropriately attractive. The literature on classical aversive conditioning of animals (that is, pairing a neutral or positive stimulus with an unpleasant unconditioned stimulus such as shock) led therapists to believe that negative reactions could be conditioned in human beings, and they formulated treatment programs along these lines. For example, a boot fetishist may wish to be less attracted to the sight or feel of boots. To reduce the attraction, a therapist gives the client repeated electric shocks when pictures of boots are presented. Instead of creating discomfort and shock, some therapists use emetics, drugs which make the client nauseous. The method is similar to desensitization but has the opposite goal, since a new response of anxiety or an aversion reaction is to be substituted for a positive response. In covert sensitization the attractive stimuli and negative states are imagined by the client. Among the problems treated with aversion therapy are excessive drinking, smoking, transvestism, exhibitionism, and overeating. Although some people have benefited from these procedures, the evidence does not indicate conclusively that these techniques are truly effective.

Aversion therapy is controversial for both ethical and scientific reasons. A great outcry has been raised about inflicting pain and discomfort on people, even when they ask for it. Perhaps the greatest ethical concern and anger have been voiced by the several gay liberation organizations. They hold that homosexuals who request painful treatment to help them shift sexual preference are actually seeking to punish themselves for be-

In this aversion therapy to discourage smoking, the client receives an electric shock each time she raises the cigarette to her lips.

BOX 19.1

FIGHTING FEAR WITH FEAR: FLOODING AND IMPLOSION THERAPIES

In systematic desensitization fearful clients expose themselves to fear in a gradual fashion by imagining a series of episodes, each more frightening than the preceding one. The therapist may also force the client to confront a very fearful episode immediately at full intensity in one of two related procedures, flooding and implosion. The principal difference between the two is the inclusion in implosion of cues that are psychodynamic in nature. Thomas Stampfl, the originator of implosion therapy, asserts that the kinds of fears people bring for treatment have been classically conditioned to what psychoanalytic theory holds are problem areas for people, primarily events relating to aggressive and sexual id impulses (Stampfl and Levis, 1967). Flooding procedures are not based on this kind of speculation. Confronting in imagination or in real life the situations bringing the greatest amount of fear is assumed the best way of reducing it. Whereas in desensitization a person first imagines the least fear-provoking episodes and is instructed to drop the image if it becomes the least bit bothersome, in both flooding and implosion the therapist urges the client to keep on imagining the most stressful situation for long periods, as long as an hour at a time! Clinical evidence suggests that by not allowing themselves the relief of escape, individuals are eventually able to decrease or extinguish their fears.

Unlike desensitization, which is a fairly benign procedure, both flooding and implosion are very difficult for clients. Stampfl's implosion therapy is particularly strenuous, and controversial, for the psychodynamic themes are introduced by constructing stories and scenes of sometimes unbelievable horror and degradation. Implosion therapy is of course applied only in imagination! For example, whereas in flooding a snake phobic may have to imagine at the very outset that she is holding a harmless snake as it crawls in her lap, in implosion she may be asked to envision the snake as a gigantic serpent which devours her eyes, crawls into her eye sockets, and systematically chews on her internal organs.

Important to both flooding and implosion is maintaining exposure until fear passes a peak and has substantially subsided, which accounts for the very long exposure times.

Rather than escaping from or avoiding altogether an aversive situation, the client confronts his or her worst fears until the fear extinguishes.

Not surprisingly, Stampfl's technique has been attacked by many therapists as inhumane, vulgar, and needlessly cruel. But it has also become clear over the years that many fearful people can overcome their anxieties by implosion (for example, Barrett, 1969). The efficacy of flooding is supported by research with animals. Their fear of a stimulus that has previously been paired with shock can sometimes be rapidly extinguished if they are prevented from escaping it (Baum, 1970; Wilson and Davison, 1971; Stampfl and Levis, 1967).

Controlled laboratory research that measures physiological signs of fear during implosion treatment sessions and compares them to the reduction of fear suggests that improvement is correlated to the amount of fear experienced: the greater amount of fear aroused and then extinguished, the more the patient improves. This finding is consistent with Stampfl's basic view that his treatment works by extinguishing fear of truly aversive situations (Orenstein and Carr, 1975). Careful analyses of various studies (for example Morganstern, 1973; Marshall, Gauthier, and Gordon, 1979) reveal some serious methodological errors, however; it is too early to accept Stampfl's reasons for why implosion therapy works. Research on flooding has similar methodological problems, but many reports of clinical treatments are encouraging, especially treatments of obsessive-compulsive disorders (for example, Meyer, Robertson, and Tatlow, 1975). Those who fear contamination are made to handle dirt; those who must keep checking whether they have locked the door are allowed to check only once.

Although investigators cannot agree whether flooding and implosion are as effective as other fear reduction methods, they do believe that a therapy fighting fear with fear exacts a high cost from the client. *Even if* such a treatment were as effective as a more benign method, they would seriously question whether it should be used except when all else fails.

havior that a prejudiced society has convinced them is dirty. They accuse behavior therapists of impeding the acceptance of homosexuality as a legitimate life style when they accede to such requests (Silverstein, 1972). The issue is a difficult one to resolve and has led several behavior therapists to question whether therapists should ever agree to help homosexuals change their sexual orientation (see Box 21.7, page 594.)

The scientific issue is whether the aversive reactions acquired by human beings through shock and nausea are stable. It is doubtful that a person will continue to react anxiously to an intrinsically harmless stimulus once he sees that he will no longer be shocked. Several experimental investigations of a wide range of aversion treatments (for example, Diament and Wilson, 1975) have failed to demonstrate their superiority over placebo control treatments. Many researchers therefore assert that any beneficial outcomes of this treatment cannot be attributed to conditioning.

Behavior therapists who choose aversive procedures, however, seldom use them alone. Instead, more positive techniques are instituted to teach new behavior to replace that eliminated. For example, a boot fetishist may also be given training in social skills to allow him more easily to initiate social contacts with women. The effects of aversion therapy may indeed be ephemeral, or short-lived, or the treatment may have only a placebo effect. The temporary reduction in undesirable behavior, however, creates some "space," which can be taken up by responses judged by the person or the culture to be more appropriate. When aversion therapy is the only treatment given, it is generally chosen as a last resort.

OPERANT CONDITIONING

In the 1950s a number of investigators suggested that therapists should try to shape overt behavior through rewards and punishments (Skinner, 1953). In the belief that they could through operant conditioning exercise some control over the complex, puzzling, often frenetic behavior of hospitalized patients, many experimentally minded psychologists determined to try to bring practical order into the chaos of institutions for the severely disturbed. Generally speaking, operant treatments work best with clients whose intellectual capacities are limited and in situations in which considerable control can be exercised by the therapist (Wilson and O'Leary, 1980).

The Token Economy

An early example of work within the operant tradition is the token economy of Ayllon and Azrin (1968). On the basis of research that Staats and Staats (1963) had done with children, they set aside an entire ward of a mental hospital for a series of experiments in which rewards were provided for activities such as making beds and combing hair and were not given when behavior was withdrawn or bizarre. The forty-five female patients, who averaged sixteen years of hospitalization, were systematically rewarded for their ward work and self-care by giving them plastic tokens which could later be exchanged for special privileges, such as listening to records and going to the movies, renting a private room, and extra visits to the canteen. The entire life of each patient was as far as possible controlled by this regime.

The rules of the token economy—the medium of exchange; the chores and self-care to be rewarded, and by

what number of tokens; the items and privileges that can be purchased, and for how many tokens—are carefully established and usually posted. These regimes have demonstrated how even markedly regressed adult hospital patients can be significantly affected by systematically manipulating reinforcement contingencies, that is, rewarding some behavior to increase its frequency, or ignoring other behavior to reduce its frequency. In order to show that a stimulus following behavior actually reinforces it, an experiment has to demonstrate not only that behavior increases when followed by a positive event, but also that behavior declines when nothing positive happens as a consequence. In Chapter 5 the ABAB design was presented as a method for studying the effect of contingencies. Ayllon and his associates demonstrated in this same way the effect of contingencies on the behavior of their ward patients. Figure 19.1 indicates that conduct such as brushing teeth and making beds markedly decreased when rewards were withdrawn, but became more frequent again when rewards were reinstated.

Since the publication of Ayllon's early studies of the token economy, many similar programs have been instituted throughout the country. The most impressive was

FIGURE 19.1 When receiving tokens was the contingency, patients on a ward spent more time grooming themselves and doing chores than when they were given no reward. Adapted from Ayllon and Azrin, 1965.

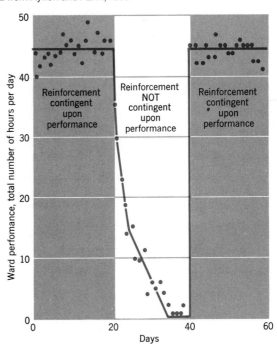

reported by Gordon Paul and Robert Lentz (1977) and has already been mentioned in Box 14.4 (page 362). The long-term, regressed, and chronic schizophrenic patients in their program are the most severely debilitated institutionalized adults ever studied systematically. Some of these patients screamed for long periods, some were mute; many were incontinent, a few assaultive. Most of them no longer used silverware, and some buried their faces in their food. The patients were matched for age, sex, socioeconomic background, symptoms, and length of hospitalization and then assigned to one of three wards, social learning, milieu therapy, and routine hospital management. Each ward had twenty-eight residents. The two treatment wards shared extensive objectives: to teach self-care, housekeeping, communication, and vocational skills; to reduce symptomatic behavior; and to release patients to the community.

1. **Social-learning ward.** Located in a new mental health center, the social-learning ward was operated on a token economy embracing all aspects of the residents' lives. Their appearance had to pass muster each morning, in eleven specific ways, in order to earn a token. Well-made beds, good behavior at mealtime, classroom participation, and socializing during free periods were other means of earning tokens. Residents learned to do as they should through modeling, shaping, prompting, and instructions. They were also trained to communicate better with one another and participated in problem-solving groups. Tokens were a necessity, for they purchased meals as well as small luxuries. In addition to living on the token economy, each individual received behavioral treatments tailored to his needs. Residents were kept busy 85 percent of their waking hours learning to behave better.

2. **Milieu therapy ward.** Another ward of the center operated on the principles of Jones's (1953) "therapeutic community." These residents too were kept busy 85 percent of their waking hours. Both individually and as a group, they were expected to act responsibly and to participate in decisions about how the ward was to function. In general, they were treated more as normal individuals than as incompetent mental patients. Staff members impressed on the residents their positive expectations of them and praised them for doing well. When they behaved symptomatically, staff members stayed with them, making clear their expectations that they would soon behave more appropriately.

3. **Routine hospital management.** The patients continued their accustomed hospital existence in an older state institution, receiving custodial care and heavy antipsychotic medication. Except for the 5 percent of their waking hours occupied by occasional activity, and recreational, occupational, and individual and group therapies, these individuals were on their own.

Before the program began, the staffs of the two treatment wards were carefully trained to adhere to detailed instructions in therapy manuals; regular observations confirmed that they were implementing the principles of a social-learning or a milieu therapy program. Over the four and a half years of hospitalization and the one and a half years of follow-up, the patients were carefully evaluated at regular six-month intervals by structured interviews and by meticulous, direct, behavioral observations.

The results? Both the social-learning and the milieu therapy reduced symptomatic behavior. The residents acquired self-care, housekeeping, social, and vocational skills. The behavior of members of these two groups within the institution was superior to that of the residents of the hospital ward. By the end of treatment, more of them had been discharged. In fact, over 10 percent of the social-learning patients left the center for independent existences; 7 percent of the milieu patients achieved this goal, and none of the hospital treatment patients did. Many more patients from all three groups were discharged to community placements such as boarding homes and halfway houses, where there was supervision, to be sure, but considerably less restraint than patients had been experiencing for an average of seventeen years. Members of the social-learning group were significantly better in remaining in these community residences than were patients in the other two groups.

Considering how poorly these patients had been functioning before this treatment project, these results are remarkable. And the fact that the social-learning program was superior to the milieu program is also significant, for milieu treatment is instituted in many mental hospitals. As implemented by Paul's team of clinicians, it provided more attention to patients than was given those on the social-learning ward. This greater amount of attention of the other treatment would appear to control well for the placebo effect of the social-learning therapy.

These results, though, should not be accepted as confirming the usefulness of token economies per se, for the social-learning therapy contained elements that went beyond operant conditioning of overt motor behavior.

Staff provided information to residents and attempted verbally to clarify misconceptions. Indeed, Paul (personal communication, 1981) relegates the token economy to a secondary, although not trivial, role. He sees it as a useful device for getting the attention of severely regressed patients in the initial stages of treatment. The token economy created the opportunity for his patients to acquire new information, or, in Paul's informal phrase, to "get good things into their heads."

Paul and Lentz have never claimed that any one of these patients was "cured." Although they were able to live outside the hospital, they continued to manifest many signs of mental disorder, and few of them had gainful employment or participated in the social activities most people take for granted. The outcome, though, is not to be underestimated; chronic mental patients, those typically shut away on back wards and forgotten by society, can be resocialized and taught self-care. They can learn to behave normally enough to be discharged from mental institutions. The marked superiority of the social-learning program argues strongly for reorganizing mental hospital care for severely disturbed patients along these lines (see Box 19.2).[1]

Operant Work with Children

Some of the best operant conditioning behavior therapy has been done with children, perhaps because much of their behavior is subject to the control of others. Children, after all, tend more than adults to be under continual supervision. At school their behavior is scrutinized by teachers, and when they come home parents frequently oversee their play and other social activities. In most instances the behavior therapist works with the parents and teachers in an effort to change the ways in which they reward and punish the children for whom they have responsibility. It is assumed that altering the reinforcement practices of the adults in a child's life will ultimately change the child's behavior.

The range of childhood problems dealt with through operant conditioning is very broad indeed, including bed-wetting, thumb-sucking, aggression, tantrums, hyperactivity, self-mutilation, disruptive classroom behavior, poor school performance, extreme social withdrawal, and asthmatic attacks. Even gender identity appears susceptible to operant procedures (see page 293). In general, rates of improvement are superior to those reported for traditional forms of therapy (Franks,

1984; O'Leary, Turkewitz, and Taffel, 1973; Ross, 1981). Operant behavior therapists must of course determine that the behavior being shaped or extinguished is in fact controllable through reward. A child who is crying because of physical pain should be attended to.

Encouraging results have been achieved by applying operant techniques to the training of retarded children. As indicated in Chapter 16, many operant conditioners have challenged assumptions about the limited trainability of retarded children, much to the benefit of some retarded youngsters and their families. Their work is arduous and consumes long stretches of time, but among other problems they have been able to improve table manners (Plummer, Baer, and LeBlanc, 1977), social skills (Williams et al., 1975), and hyperactive behavior (Doubros, 1966).

Generalization of Treatment Effects

As we have indicated, generalizing to real life whatever gains have been achieved in therapy is a problem common to all treatments. Insight therapists assume that therapeutic effects are made more general through restructuring of the personality. As environmentalists, behavior therapists wonder how changes brought about by their manipulations can be made to persist once clients return to their everyday situations, which are often assumed to have produced their problems in the first place! Behavior therapists have tried to meet this challenge in several ways.

Intermittent Reinforcement

Because laboratory findings indicate that intermittent reinforcement—rewarding a response only a portion of the times it appears—makes new behavior more enduring, many operant programs take care to move away from continuous schedules of reinforcement once desired behavior is occurring with satisfactory regularity. For example, if a teacher has succeeded in helping a disruptive boy spend more time in his seat by praising him generously for each arithmetic problem that he finishes there, he or she will gradually reward him for every other problem, and ultimately only infrequently. The hope is that the satisfactions of being a good pupil will make the child less dependent on the teacher's approval.

Another strategy is to move from artificial reinforcers to those that occur naturally in the social environment. A token program might be maintained only long enough to encourage certain desired behavior, after which the person is weaned to natural reinforcers such as praise from peers.

[1]The aftercare aspects of the Paul and Lentz project are discussed in detail in Chapter 20 (page 550).

BOX 19.2

TOKEN ECONOMIES, ASYLUMS, AND THE METRICS OF HUMAN EXISTENCE

Paul and Lentz's landmark study promises to establish the token economy as an important component of the institutional treatment of long-term mental patients. Nonetheless, questions will continue to be raised about token economies in institutional settings. Some of these concern the basic assumptions of these behavior control regimens (Gagnon and Davison, 1976).

David Rothman (1971), a historian, has traced the development of mental hospitals in this country during the nineteenth century. He shows that asylums of the time were instituted as they were because much of the madness of the day was assumed caused by the hurly-burly of a vigorous democratic and industrial society, which offered endless opportunities—and therefore possibilities for failure. Asylums were to be havens for those who could not keep up with the rapid economic and social expansion that had followed the industrial revolution.

Consider how different is this view of the mental hospital from the way token economies are organized. The disease, if you will, now becomes the doctor. The token economy is the nineteenth-century asylum on its head, for this innovation introduces into the hospital the very conditions that were assumed in the previous century to have caused mental disorders. Instead of protecting patients from the strains of an achievement-oriented, money-dominated society, the token economy introduces commercial relationships into the asylum.

Can we on these historical grounds claim that token economies are necessarily bad? Can we really say that commercialism is likely to cause or aggravate mental illness? After all, have we not made some progress in understanding mental disorder since the early nineteenth century? The reader may judge for himself by reflecting on the material presented in the preceding chapters of this book. It would seem that for the more serious disorders—schizophrenia, in particular—genetic factors and the biochemistry and pathology of the brain have provided and will provide the major clues to etiology. Economic failure may be a factor, but probably only as a stressor that activates a diathesis.

Other issues can be raised that are not tied to history. Token economies are effective in ward *management*. They do seem to introduce order where there has been only chaos; helping a regressed schizophrenic dress herself and arrive on time to a hospital dining hall is a significant accomplishment. And if the remarkable success of Paul and Lentz in returning chronic schizophrenics to the community, to live in sheltered residences, can be duplicated by other clinicians, the token economy will have proved of value in helping resocialize mental patients.

But what, in fact, do patients really learn on a token economy? Gagnon and Davison (1976) take an unusual position on this.

One thing that is learned is that producing certain kinds of behavior produces a stable response from the token-emitting behavioral engineer. . . . The value of any act is metrically stable, and its value can be compared to [that of] other acts [in] number of tokens. . . . [Is this a good thing for mental patients to learn if they are to be prepared for life outside the confines of the institution?] The exchanges that characterize most conventional social life [suggest] that things do not come out even. . . . [Sanity] is largely the capacity to tolerate interactions which have low predictability of outcome [and] to survive the fact that life is unjust: sometimes you get what you pay for, sometimes you get more than you pay for, sometimes you get less than you pay for. . . . Indeed, to stay "sane," you commonly have to doctor the books (pp. 532-534, emphasis added).

Finally, a token regimen may encourage people to view themselves and others in ways that are undesirable. Human relationships and human feelings run the risk of being cheapened when reduced to a monetary metric. If a patient, for example, has to have twenty tokens to see a clergyman, will this adversely affect how he feels about religion? If thirty tokens are required for a weekend pass, how will a patient feel about the people she sees while she is on leave?

We are unaware of attempts by behavior therapists to answer such questions. The failure to address these issues does *not* represent callousness to the human condition; such an allegation would be unfair and incorrect. Rather, apparently because of their professional training, psychologists and psychiatrists are not inclined to view their work in historical and sociological contexts. Perhaps the kind of critical analysis summarized here will goad token economy workers into such considerations.

Environmental Modification

Another strategy for bringing about generalization takes the therapist into the province of community psychology, which will be discussed in the next chapter. Behavior therapists manipulate surroundings, or attempt to do so, to support changes brought about in treatment. As one small example, Lovaas and his colleagues (1973) found that the gains painstakingly achieved in therapy for autistic children were sustained only when their parents continued to reinforce their good behavior.

Self-reinforcement

Generalization can also be effected by assigning the client a more active role, as done by Drabman, Spitalnik, and O'Leary (1973). In a three-month after-school program for disruptive young boys, the teacher rewarded nondisruptive classroom behavior and appropriate reading behavior. Later the boys were allowed to self-rate their behavior according to the teacher's criteria and reward their own good conduct. That is, the pupils were taught that they could earn special privileges not only by behaving well when the teacher dispensed rewards but through honest evaluation of their own good behavior. The findings for the first part of the study were similar to those of many other studies: disruptive behavior decreased and academic behavior improved when the teacher judged them and dispensed the tokens. This improvement then generalized to periods of each class during which the child *himself judged* how well he was doing and *reinforced himself* accordingly; in other words, improved performance was extended to periods of time when the pupils were not under direct external control (see Box 19.3).

The implications are clear. At least for disruptive children, self-evaluating and self-rewarding their own good behavior may be one effective way in which they can maintain it when the original controlling agent is absent.

Eliminating Secondary Gain

Most behavior therapists assign their clients homework, tasks to do between sessions. For example, clients may be asked to listen to audiotapes containing relaxation-training instructions. They sometimes fail to follow through in a consistent fashion, complaining of not having enough quiet time at home to listen to the tapes, or saying that they forgot about the assignment. Many patients are so resistant to doing on their own what they consciously and rationally agree is in their own best interests that therapists often invoke as an explanation the psychoanalytic concept of secondary gain, that the patient derives benefit from his problem. For complex and poorly understood reasons people sometimes act as though they unconsciously wish to keep their symptoms. Therapists, whatever their persuasion, may have to examine the client's interpersonal relationships for clues to why a person suffering directly from a problem seemingly prefers to hold on to it.

Attribution to Self

Attribution, a subject usually studied by social psychologists, may offer insight on how to maintain treatment gains once therapy is over. How a person explains to himself why he is behaving or has behaved in a particular way presumably helps to determine his subsequent actions. Might not a person who has been in therapy and attributes improvement in his behavior to an external cause, such as a reinforcer from the environment, lose ground once what he considers the external justification for change is gone? In an analogue study on attribution and maintaining a change in behavior (Davison and Valins, 1969), college undergraduates were shocked on their fingertips to determine how much they could bear. Then they took a "fast-acting vitamin compound" and were told that they would now be able to endure greater amounts of shock. And indeed they were, at least in their own minds. The experimenters had surreptitiously altered the voltage levels to ensure this belief. Half of the subjects were then told that the capsule ingested was only a placebo, the others that its effects would soon wear off. Those who believed that they had taken a placebo attributed to themselves the greater ability to withstand discomfort and endured higher levels of shock on the third test. Those who believed that they had been given a real drug which was no longer effective were in the third round able to endure only lesser amounts of shock.

In an experiment with a similar design, conducted with people who were having trouble falling asleep, Davison, Tsujimoto, and Glaros (1973) obtained similar results, indicating that "real" problems may be treated by helping patients to attribute improvements to themselves. A clinical report by Levendusky and Pankratz (1975) confirms the benefits to patients of feeling that they have improved through their own efforts. Individuals attempting to reduce their smoking (Chambliss and Murray, 1979) and lose weight (Jeffrey, 1974) have similarly benefited from believing that they have gained mastery over their bad habits.

What are the implications of attribution research? Since in behavior therapy most improvement seems to be controlled by environmental forces, especially therapy relying on operant manipulation, it might be wise for behavior therapists to help their clients to feel more responsibile. By encouraging an "I did it" attitude, perhaps by motivating them to practice new skills and to expose themselves to challenging situations, therapists may help their clients be less dependent on therapy and therapist and maintain better their treatment gains. Insight therapies have always emphasized the desirability of patients' assuming primary responsibility for their improvement. Behavior therapists have eventually realized that they must come to grips with the issue (Ban-

BOX 19.3

SELF-CONTROL—OUTSIDE A BEHAVIORAL PARADIGM?

One of the most exciting areas in behavior therapy concerns the exercise of self-control (Kanfer, 1979; Mahoney, 1972; Runck, 1982). Much of the research and theory reviewed in this chapter seems to assume that the human being is a relatively passive recipient of stimulation from the environment. Given this apparent dependence on the external world, how can we account for behavior that appears to be autonomous, willed, and often contrary to what might be expected in a particular situation? How, for example, do we account for the fact that a person on a diet refrains from eating a luscious piece of chocolate cake even when hungry?

Psychoanalytic writers, including the ego analysts, handle the issue by positing within the person some kind of internal agent. Thus many ego analysts assert that the ego can operate on its own power, making deliberate decisions for the entire psychic system—including decisions that go against the wishes of the id. Behaviorists, especially Skinner (1953), have objected to this ''explanation,'' regarding it as simply a relabeling of the phenomena.

Perhaps the most widely accepted behavioral view of self-control is Skinner's: an individual engages in self-control when he or she arranges the environment so that only certain controlling stimuli are present. A person wishing to lose weight rids his or her home of fattening foods and avoids passing restaurants when hungry. Behavior remains a function of the surroundings, but they are controlled by the individual.

A related behavioral conception of self-control is reflected in Bandura's (1969) explanation of aversive conditioning. Rather than being passively conditioned to feel distaste for stimuli that have been paired with shock, a person learns a skill of aversive self-stimulation which he or she deliberately applies in real life. According to this view, a person resists a temptation by *deliberately* recalling the earlier aversive experience of being shocked or nauseated during therapy. Here, then, the individual is said to create symbolic stimuli which, in turn, control behavior.

A familiar means of exercising self-control, also discussed in the behavior therapy literature, is setting standards for oneself and denying oneself reinforcement unless they are met (Bandura and Perloff, 1967). One example is a tactic often employed by the authors of this book: I will not leave this desk for a snack until I have finished writing this page. When a person sets goals, and makes a contract with himself about achieving them before enjoying a reward, and then keeps to the contract without obvious external constraints, he can be said to have exercised self-control.

Self-control can be applied with *any* therapy technique. The only stipulation is that the client implement the procedure on his own, after receiving instructions from the therapist. For example, a client who was being desensitized decided on his own to imagine some of the hierarchy scenes while relaxing in a warm tub. A sophisticated and intelligent man, he felt that he understood the rationale of desensitization well enough and had enough control over the processes of his imagination to meet the procedural requirements of the technique. Consequently, after achieving what he felt to be a state of deep relaxation in his bathtub, he closed his eyes and carried out the scene presentation and scene termination as he had learned to do from the behavior therapist. Later, when he was with the therapist, they were able to skip the items to which he had desensitized himself in the tub and proceed more rapidly through the

dura, 1977; Mischel, 1977). And on a more general level, the question of attributing improvement underscores the importance of cognitive processes in behavior therapy, to be discussed soon in this chapter.

MODELING

Modeling is the third theoretical approach employed by behavior therapists. The importance of modeling and imitation in behavior is self-evident, for children as well as adults are able to acquire complex responses and eliminate emotional inhibitions merely by watching how others handle themselves.

Problems Treated by Modeling

The effectiveness of modeling in clinical work was shown in an early study by Bandura, Blanchard, and Ritter (1969). They were attempting to help people overcome their snake phobias. The researchers had fearful adults view both live and filmed confrontations of people and snakes. In these confrontations the models gradually moved closer to the animals. The fears of the patients were decidedly reduced. Sex therapy researchers have found that inhibited adults can become more comfortable with their sexuality if shown tastefully designed explicit films of people touching themselves, masturbating, and having intercourse (Nemetz, Craig, and Reith, 1978; McMullen and Rosen, 1979). Other films have siganxiety hierarchy.

Implicit in all conceptions of self-control are three criteria: (1) there are *few external controls* that could explain the behavior; (2) control of self is difficult enough that the person has to *put forth some effort*; and (3) the behavior in question is engaged in with *conscious deliberation and choice*. The individual actively decides to exercise self-control either by performing some action or by keeping himself from doing something, such as overeating. He does not do it automatically, nor is he forced to by someone else.

Let us take the example of a male jogger. If an army sergeant is goading this man along, the first criterion is not met and his running would not be an instance of self-control, even though considerable effort is probably required to maintain the running. Physiological factors inside the body may also be regarded as "external" control, as paradoxical as this may seem. Behavior that is impelled, or driven forward, by some inner physical urgency—such as a man running through a crowded restaurant toward the men's room because he feels himself about to vomit—is not an instance of self-control.

If the jogger finds it pleasurable to run, so enjoyable that he would rather do so than engage in other activities, the running cannot be considered an instance of self-control. In the earliest stages of jogging, the man may indeed be exerting great effort. He groans as he dons his Nikes, looks at his watch after only a few minutes of running to see how long this torture has been going on, and collapses in relief after half a mile, glad that the ordeal is over. But with practice and conditioning—the physical, not the Pavlovian variety!—the man's attitude changes. Jogging becomes a virtual necessity; running through city streets each morning at 6:00 A.M. is an activity sought after and treasured to the exclusion of other competing activities.

The third criterion, acting with conscious deliberation and choice, distinguishes self-control from actions people perform in a mindless way. It is probably a good thing that much of our everyday behavior is mindless, for imagine how fatiguing (and boring!) it would be to mull over and make specific decisions to do such things as look out a window, tie our shoelaces, eat our breakfast, and so on. But these very acts would be categorized as instances of self-control if, on a given occasion, we have to decide whether to engage in them. Eating would require self-control if we were on a strict diet and had agreed, with our spouse, or doctor, or ourselves, to reduce caloric intake.

In our opinion, the concept of self-control places a strain on the behavioristic paradigm, for people are described as acting independently, putting forth effort, deliberating and choosing. Each of these verbs supposes the person to be an *initiator* of action, as the place where control *begins*. Ardent behaviorists, though, will counter by asserting with Skinner that our view of the person as an initiator only indicates our ignorance of the external forces that ultimately control behavior. Thus the person who denies himself an extra dessert is not really controlling himself; rather his self-denial is controlled by some subtle reward unappreciated by the observer, or by a distant reinforcer, such as being able later on to wear clothes of a smaller size. The flaw in this line of reasoning is that it is purely *post hoc* and irrefutable. We can *always* assert that, down the road, there will arrive the reinforcer that sustains the behavior. Such an "explanation" should be as unsatisfactory to the behaviorist as the psychoanalyst's invocation of an unconscious defense mechanism to account for an action.

nificantly reduced children's fears of dogs (Hill, Liebert, and Mott, 1968), of surgery (Melamed and Siegel, 1975), and of dental work (Melamed et al., 1975). Films prepared by Melamed show initially fearful children gradually coping with their anxieties about preparing for and undergoing medical and dental procedures. So helpful do such films appear to be that they have become a routine part of medical and dental practice in a number of hospitals and clinics. These modeling films for reducing children's fears of medical treatments are considered one of the new behavioral medicine or "health psychology" procedures.

Some of the clinical work of Arnold Lazarus, one of the leading behavior therapists, is also regarded as modeling treatment. As indicated in Chapter 2 (page 46), in *behavior rehearsal* Lazarus (1971) demonstrates for a client how to handle a difficult interpersonal problem in a better way. The client observes the therapist's exemplary performance and then attempts to imitate it during the therapy session. By continual practice and observation, the client can frequently acquire entire repertoires of more effective and more satisfying behavior. Often videotape equipment can be creatively used to facilitate such modeling and imitation.

In an attempt to expand the kinds of problems handled, some therapists and researchers have tried covert modeling (Cautela, 1971). The client imagines that he is watching a model, sometimes the client himself, coping with an object he fears or handling a situation requiring assertion. Research suggests that covert modeling can

Albert Bandura, pioneer in the study of modeling and the alleviation of neurotic fears through imitation.

reduce fears and promote more assertive behavior (Rimm and Masters, 1979; Kazdin, 1975). Covert procedures, in which the patient does nothing overt and has no real-life contact with what is feared or upsetting, are of course adopted when direct experience is not possible. Imagined substitutes are not expected to be as effective as actual exposure to threat and actual practice in confronting it (Bandura, 1977).

Behavior therapy programs for hospitalized patients also make use of modeling. Bellack, Hersen, and Turner (1976) contrived social situations for three chronic schizophrenic patients and then observed whether they behaved appropriately to the situation. For instance, a given patient would be told to pretend that he had just returned home from a weekend trip to find his lawn had been mowed. As he gets out of the car, his next-door neighbor approaches him and says that he has cut the patient's grass because he was already cutting his own. The patient must then respond to the situation. As expected, patients were initially not very good at making a socially appropriate response, which in this instance would have been some sort of thank-you. Training followed; the therapist encouraged the patient to respond, commenting helpfully on his efforts. If necessary, the therapist also modeled appropriate behavior so that the patient could observe and then try to imitate it. This combination of role playing, modeling, and positive reinforcement effected significant improvement in all

three patients. There was even generalization to social situations that had not been worked on during the training. This study, and others like it, indicate that many severely disturbed patients can be taught new social behavior which may help them function better both inside *and outside* the hospital.

The Role of Cognition

It is still unclear, however, *how* the observation of a model is translated into changes in overt behavior. In their original writings on modeling, Bandura and Walters (1963) asserted that an observer could, somehow, learn new behavior by watching others. Given the emphasis that much of experimental psychology places on learning through doing, this attention to learning without doing was important. But it left out the processes that could be operating. A moment's reflection on the typical modeling experiment suggests the direction theory and research have taken in recent years. The observer, a child, sits in a chair and watches a film of another child making a number of movements, such as hitting a Bobo doll in a highly stereotyped manner, and he hears the child uttering peculiar sounds. An hour later the youngster is given the opportunity to imitate what he saw and heard earlier. He is able to do so, as common sense and folk wisdom would predict. How shall we understand what happened? Since the observer did not *do* anything of interest in any motoric way while watching the film, except perhaps fidget in his chair, it would not be fruitful to look at overt behavior for a clue. Obviously, the child's cognitive processes were engaged, including his ability to remember later on what had happened.

Behavioral researchers are currently investigating what cognitive processes might account for the effects of modeling. For example, experimental cognitive research informs us that having a code by which to summarize information helps a person retain it better. Bandura, Jeffrey, and Bachicha (1974) found that the use of such a code helped observers pattern their actions on what they had seen modeled. Other theories about memory storage and retrieval may shed light on how people acquire new and complex patterns of behavior "simply" by watching others. The word "simply" is placed in quotation marks because, in fact, the process is not simple at all. The literature on modeling, which at first offered straightforward, commonsensical social-learning explanations, now regards modeling interventions as a type of cognitive behavior therapy.

COGNITIVE RESTRUCTURING

In the therapies discussed thus far, the emphasis has been on the direct manipulation of overt behavior and occasionally of covert behavior. Relatively little attention has been paid to direct alteration of the thinking and reasoning processes of the client. Perhaps it was in reaction to insight therapy that behavior therapists initially discounted the importance of cognition, regarding any appeal to thinking as a return to the "mentalism" that John Watson had vigorously objected to in the early part of the twentieth century (see page 40).

If behavior therapy is to be taken seriously as applied experimental psychology, however, it should incorporate theory and research on cognitive processes. Indeed, for a number of years behavior therapists have paid attention to "private events"—to thoughts, perceptions, judgments, and self-statements—and they have studied and manipulated these processes in their attempts to understand and modify overt and covert disturbed behavior (Mahoney, 1974). The cognitive-restructuring treatment of the man with "pressure points" described in Chapter 2 (page 47) is one early example. Cognitive restructuring is a general term for changing a pattern of thought that is presumed to be causing a disturbed emotion or behavior. It is carried out in several ways by cognitive behavior therapists.

Ellis's Rational-Emotive Therapy

For many years the work of a New York clinical psychologist, Albert Ellis, existed outside the mainstream of behavior therapy, but eventually it engaged the interest of behavior therapists. The principal thesis of Ellis's rational-emotive therapy is that sustained emotional reactions are caused by internal sentences that people repeat to themselves. The aim of therapy is to eliminate the wrongheaded sentences of disturbed people through a rational examination of them. As indicated earlier, anxious persons may create their own problems by adopting unrealistic expectations, such as "I must win the love of everyone." Or a depressed woman may say to herself, several times a day, "What a worthless person I am." Ellis proposes that people interpret what is happening around them, that sometimes these interpretations can cause emotional turmoil, and that a therapist's attention should be focused on these internal sentences, rather than on historical causes or, indeed, overt behavior (Ellis, 1962, 1984).

Ellis lists a number of irrational beliefs that people can harbor (see page 123); these beliefs underlie their

Albert Ellis's rational-emotive therapy helps patients to recognize the impossible "musts" they impose on themselves and to become more realistic in their expectations.

negative self-statements and cause their distress. One very common notion is that people must be thoroughly competent in everything they do. Ellis suggests that many people actually believe this untenable assumption, and that they evaluate every event within this context. Thus, if a person makes an error, it becomes a catastrophe since it violates his deeply held conviction that he must be perfect. It sometimes comes as a shock to clients to realize that they actually believe such strictures and as a consequence run their lives so that it becomes virtually impossible to live comfortably or productively.

After becoming familiar with the client's problems, the therapist presents the basic theory of rational-emotive therapy so that the client can understand and accept it.[2] The following transcript is from a session with a young man who had inordinate fears about speaking in front of groups. The therapist guides the client to view his "inferiority complex" in terms of the unreasonable things he may be telling himself. The therapist's thoughts during the interview are indicated in italics.

[2]We said in Chapter 18 that the usefulness of an insight into the past or of an empathy statement does not depend on whether it is true. Nor does the usefulness of rational-emotive therapy. Ellis's views may be only partially correct, or even entirely wrong, and yet it may be helpful for a client to act as though they are true.

Client: My primary difficulty is that I become very uptight when I have to speak in front of a group of people. I guess it's just my own inferiority complex.

Therapist: *[I don't want to get sidetracked at this point by talking about that conceptualization of his problem. I'll just try to finesse it and make a smooth transition to something else.]* I don't know if I would call it an inferiority complex but I do believe that people can, in a sense, bring on their own upset and anxiety in certain kinds of situations. When you're in a particular situation, your anxiety is often not the result of the situation itself, but rather the way in which you *interpret* the situation—what you tell yourself about the situation. For example, look at this pen. Does this pen make you nervous?

Client: No.

Therapist: Why not?

Client: It's just an object. It's just a pen.

Therapist: It can't hurt you?

Client: No. . . .

Therapist: It's really not the object that creates emotional upset in people, but rather what you think about the object. *[Hopefully, this Socratic-like dialogue will eventually bring him to the conclusion that self-statements can mediate emotional arousal.]* Now this holds true for . . . situations where emotional upset is caused by what a person tells himself about the situation. Take, for example, two people who are about to attend the same social gathering. Both of them may know exactly the same number of people at the party, but one person can be optimistic and relaxed about the situation, whereas the other one can be worried about how he will appear, and consequently be very anxious. *[I'll try to get him to verbalize the basic assumption that attitude or perception is most important here.]* So, when these two people walk into the place where the party is given, are their emotional reactions at all associated with the physical arrangements at the party?

Client: No, obviously not.

Therapist: What determines their reactions, then?

Client: They obviously have different attitudes toward the party.

Therapist: Exactly, and their attitudes—the ways in which they approach the situation—greatly influence their emotional reactions (Goldfried and Davison, 1976, pp. 163–165).

Having persuaded the client that his emotional problems will benefit from rational examination, the therapist proceeds to teach the person to substitute for irrational self-statements an internal dialogue meant to ease his emotional turmoil. At the present time therapists who implement Ellis's ideas differ greatly on how they persuade clients to change their self-talk. Some rational-emotive therapists, like Ellis himself, argue with clients, cajoling and teasing them, sometimes in very blunt language, to change their minds. Others, believing that social influence should be more subtle and that individuals should participate in changing themselves, encourage clients to discuss their own irrational thinking and then gently lead them to discover more rational ways of regarding the world.

One variation of rational-emotive therapy, *systematic rational restructuring* (Goldfried, Decenteceo, and Weinberg, 1974), is modeled after systematic desensitization. The therapist and client draw up a hierarchy of anxiety-provoking situations, but instead of having the client relax while imagining each, the therapist teaches the client to talk to himself differently about the situation. Anxiety, it is hoped, will be reduced during the visualization itself. Reasonably well-controlled studies attest to the effectiveness of systematic rational restructuring (for example, Goldfried, Linehan, and Smith, 1978). The following transcript is from a later session with the young man who was afraid of speaking in front of groups. Notice how the therapist shares the perspective of the client in an effort to direct his thinking in a more realistic direction. Once again, the therapist's own thoughts are shown in italics.

Therapist: I'm going to ask you to imagine yourself in a given situation, and to tell me how nervous you may feel. I'd then like you to think aloud about what you might be telling yourself that is creating this anxiety, and then [try] to put your expectations into a more realistic perspective. From time to time, I will make certain comments, and I'd like you to treat these comments as if they were your own thoughts, OK?

Client: All right.

Therapist: I'd like you to close your eyes now and imagine yourself in the following situation: You are sitting on stage in the auditorium, together with the other school board members. It's a few minutes before you have to get up and give your report to the people in the audience. Between 0 and 100 percent tension, tell me how nervous you feel?

Client: About 50.

Therapist: [*Now to get into his head.*] So I'm feeling fairly tense. Let me think. What might I be telling myself that's making me upset?

Client: I'm nervous about reading my report in front of all these people.

Therapist: But why does that bother me?

Client: Well, I don't know if I'm going to come across all right. . . .

Therapist: [*He seems to be having trouble. More prompting on my part may be needed than I originally anticipated.*] But why should that upset me? That upsets me because . . .

Client: . . . because I want to make a good impression.

Therapist: And if I don't . . .

Client: . . . well, I don't know. I don't want people to think that I'm incompetent. I guess I'm afraid that I'll lose the respect of the people who thought I knew what I was doing.

Therapist: [*He seems to be getting closer.*] But why should that make me so upset?

Client: I don't know. I guess it shouldn't. Maybe I'm being *overly* concerned about other people's reactions to me.

Therapist: How might I be overly concerned?

Client: I think this may be one of those situations where I have to please everybody, and there are an awful lot of people in the audience. Chances are I'm not going to get everybody's approval, and maybe that's upsetting me. I want everyone to think I'm doing a good job.

Therapist: Now let me think for a moment to see how rational that is.

Client: To begin with, I don't think it really is likely that I'm going to completely blow it. After all, I have prepared in advance, and have thought through what I want to say fairly clearly. I think I may be reacting as if I already have failed, even though it's very unlikely that I will.

Therapist: And even if I did mess up, how bad would that be?

Client: Well, I guess that really wouldn't be so terrible after all.

Therapist: [*I don't believe him for one moment. There is a definite hollow ring to his voice. He arrived at that conclusion much too quickly and presents it without much conviction.*] I say I don't think it'll upset me, but I don't really believe that.

Client: That's true. I would be upset if I failed. But actually, I really shouldn't be looking at this situation as [indicating] failure.

Therapist: What would be a better way for me to look at the situation?

Client: Well, it's certainly not a do-or-die kind of thing. It's only a ridiculous committee report. A lot of the people in the audience know who I am and what I'm capable of doing. And even if I don't give a sterling performance, I don't think they're going to change their opinion of me on the basis of a five-minute presentation.

Therapist: But what if some of them do?

Client: Even if some of them do think differently of me, that doesn't mean that I *would* be different. I would still be me no matter what they thought. It's ridiculous of me to base my self-worth on what other people think.

Therapist: [*I think he's come around as much as he can. We can terminate this scene now.*] With this new attitude toward the situation, how do you feel in percentage of anxiety?

Client: Oh, about 25 percent.

Therapist: OK, let's talk a little about some of the thoughts you had during that situation before trying it again (Goldfried and Davison, 1976, pp. 172–174).

Other techniques are used in rational-emotive therapy; the client is not left submerged in thought. Once a client verbalizes a different belief or self-statement during a therapy session, it must be made part of everyday thinking. In recent years, Ellis and his followers have paid particular attention to homework assignments designed to provide opportunities for the client to experiment with the new self-talk and to experience the positive consequences of viewing life in less catastrophic ways. There is also reason to believe that the therapy may be suitable for some childhood problems or even as a preventive measure (Ellis and Bernard, 1983).

It can be argued that Ellis is preaching an ethical system, for he suggests that a great deal of emotional suffering is engendered by goals that *he* asserts are wrong. He proposes that these goals are subject to modification, and that by altering them a person can reduce subjective discomfort. Indeed, the reduction of stress can

(Drawing by Geo. Price; © 1982, The New Yorker Magazine, Inc.)

often improve performance so that, ironically, it more closely approximates the goal previously viewed as a ''must'' or a ''should.'' Rational-emotive work appears at present to be one of the most promising and interesting areas in behavior therapy, but much remains to be done to evaluate the long-term efficacy of the therapy and to determine whether it is superior to other treatments.

Beck's Cognitive Therapy[3]

The reader will recall that Beck (see page 200) holds that numerous disorders, particularly depression, are caused by the negative patterns in which individuals think about themselves, the world, and the future. These negative patterns of thought, or negative schemata, are maintained by one or more errors in logic, such as arbitrary inference or selective abstraction. The overall goal of Beck's therapy is to provide the client with experiences, both within and without the consulting room, that will disconfirm the dark conclusions drawn through errors in logic and ultimately to alter the negative schemata in a favorable way. Thus if a client, through his ineptness schema, bemoans his witlessness because he burned the roast, he is encouraged to view the failure as regrettable but not to overgeneralize, one of the errors in

[3]Some of this section is based on Haaga and Davison (in press).

logic, and conclude, through his hopelessness schema, that he can do no good on future occasions. A negative schema fuels an illogicality, which in turns fuels another negative schema. The therapist tries to break into the vicious cycle of negative schemata fueling and being fueled by errors in logic.

Attempts to change negative thinking are made at both the behavioral and cognitive levels. One behavioral technique, useful for clients who are convinced that they are depressed all the time, and who become still more deeply depressed because of this belief, is to have them record their moods at regular intervals during the day. If it turns out that these reports show some variability, as indeed often happens even with very depressed people, this information can serve to challenge their general belief that life is always miserable. This change in thinking can then serve as the basis for a change in behavior, such as getting out of bed in the morning, doing a few chores, or even going to work.

Similarly, depressed clients often do very little because tasks seem insurmountable, and they believe they can accomplish nothing. To test this hypothesis or schema of insurmountableness, the therapist breaks down a particular task into small steps and encourages the client to focus on just one step at a time. If this tactic is skillfully handled, and a good therapeutic relationship is obviously important, the client finds that she can, in fact, accomplish *something*. Her accomplishments are then discussed with the therapist as inconsistent with her notion that tasks are beyond her efforts. As the client begins to change her view of herself, tasks of greater difficulty appear less forbidding, and success can build upon success, with still further beneficial changes in the client's beliefs about herself and her world.

''Collaborative empiricism'' is inherent to Beck's therapy. Therapist and client work as co-investigators to uncover and examine any maladaptive interpretations of the world that may be aggravating the client's depression and general life condition. They try to uncover both ''automatic thoughts'' and ''dysfunctional assumptions.'' Automatic thoughts are the things we tell or picture to ourselves as we go about our daily business, the running dialogue we have with ourselves as we drive to school, listen to a friend, watch others crossing the street. Clients usually need practice in taking note of such thoughts and images, especially the ones that are associated with their depressed mood. For example, a father hears his daughter tell him that she failed a test at school, and he thinks to himself, ''What a lousy parent I am.'' Thereafter he feels blue. The therapist helps the client monitor such thoughts, and together they examine their validity. Why should your daughter's problems at school mean that you are a bad parent? What else affects your youngster and determines whether she does well at school? In this fashion the therapist teaches the man to check his thoughts against the available information and to entertain hypotheses that might explain his daughter's failure on the test, other than his being a bad parent.

This phase of identifying and modifying automatic thoughts is followed by a more subtle phase, the identification of underlying dysfunctional assumptions. These can be likened to a *leitmotiv* in music, a dominant, recurring theme. The father may come to realize that he believes himself responsible for the happiness and welfare of his entire family, including how good a student his daughter is. The therapist can examine with the man the implications of the worst possible case, that the evidence does indeed indicate that he is a bad father. Is this something to be clinically depressed about? To be sure, his concern and desire to do something about his daughter's problems are understandable, but these reactions can energize a person to new action, not plunge him into despair.

How can the therapist help the individual to alter his or her dysfunctional assumptions? In addition to verbal persuasion, the therapist may encourage the client to behave in a way inconsistent with them. For example, a woman who believes that she must please everyone at her office can decline the next unreasonable request made of her and see whether, as she has been assuming, the sky will fall. If the situation has been properly analyzed ahead of time by client and therapist, clearly a necessary step, the woman can experience what happens when she acts against her absolutist belief.

Beck's therapy, like others that alter thinking, is *difficult!* Clients would probably not be depressed if they were readily convinced by mastery experiences that they are worthwhile individuals. Our brief account is only an outline; the implementation is invariably less systematic, less unidirectional, and certainly more arduous than the description implies.

The effectiveness of Beck's approach is under intensive study. A noteworthy effort was reported by Rush, Beck, and their colleagues (1977). Two groups of severely depressed men and women, outpatients with an average age of thirty-six, were treated, one group with a daily bedtime dose of imipramine or Tofranil, a psychoactive drug widely used for depression, the other with twenty sessions of Beck's therapy. The depression of these outpatients had been with them for about twelve months. The median number of therapists already seen by the patients, unsuccessfully, was two. Three-quarters of them had thought about suicide. After the twelve-week period of treatment, 79 percent of the cognitive-therapy group were very much improved or completely themselves, compared to 20 percent of those taking imipramine. There were also fewer dropouts from the cognitive-therapy group. Since people who terminate therapy prematurely are usually doing poorly, this was an early indication that these people were receiving more help than those who took the drug. Patients who had received cognitive therapy remained less depressed at six-month follow-up and for at least a year after termination of treatment (Kovacs et al., 1981).

In light of the demonstrated efficacy of imipramine in treating depression, these findings are praise indeed for Beck's treatment. Other research as well indicates that this cognitive-restructuring therapy is effective in relieving depression (Shaw, 1977; Wilson, Goldin, and Charbonneau-Powis, 1983). And as seen in Chapter 17, because older patients can be extremely sensitive to medications and can also suffer from medical problems that contraindicate prescribing psychoactive drugs, therapists often treat their depression cognitively.

The Therapies of Beck and Ellis— Some Comparisons

The views and techniques of Ellis and Beck are widely used by therapists nowadays. With the inevitable changes that inventive clinicians make as they apply the work of others, and with the evolution in the thinking of the theorists themselves, the differences between the two therapies can sometimes be difficult to discern. They do contrast, however, in interesting ways (Haaga and Davison, in press).

To the father who became depressed when he learned that his daughter had failed a test at school, Ellis, in essence, would say immediately, "So what if you are a bad father? It is irrational to be depressed about being a bad parent." Beck, in contrast, would first examine the evidence for the conclusion. His is a more scientific approach. "What evidence is there for thinking that you are a bad father?" If proof is lacking, this discovery in itself will be therapeutic. Ellis regards his own type of solution as more thoroughgoing. *Even if* the man is a bad father, the world will not end, for he does not have to be competent in everything he does. Beck may also eventually question with the man whether one has to be competent in everything to feel good about oneself, but not until the evidence that they accumulate suggests that the man is not a good father.

The Beckian therapist certainly has preconceptions, primarily about the forms that maladaptive, illogical thinking takes, such as overgeneralization. But working with a depressed individual is a collaborative, *inductive* procedure by which client and therapist attempt to discover the particular dysfunctional assumptions underlying the client's negative thoughts. Rational-emotive therapists, by contrast, are *deductive*. They are confident that a distressed person subscribes to one or more of a finite list of common irrational beliefs.

Beckian and standard rational-emotive practices differ in style on this inductive-deductive basis. Beck suggests that the therapist avoid being overly didactic, but Ellis often uses mini-lectures and didactic speeches. Beck proposes calling negative thoughts "unproductive ideas," to promote rapport with clients. He does not favor adjectives such as "irrational" or "nutty," which might be heard—with humor, it must be pointed out—from Ellis. Finally, Beck recommends that the therapist begin by acknowledging the client's frame of reference and asking for an elaboration of it. Having had a chance to present his or her case and feel understood, the client may be more willing to go through the collaborative process of undermining beliefs. Ellis, on the other hand, supposes that quite forceful interventions are necessary to disrupt a well-learned maladaptive pattern of thinking; he will therefore directly confront the client's irrational beliefs, sometimes within minutes in the first session.

Social Problem Solving

Some psychological distress can be regarded as a reaction to problems for which people have no solutions. I am late with a term paper and am upset about it. Shall I approach the professor, or is it better to deal at least initially with her teaching assistant? Should I request an Incomplete, or will it look bad on my record? My transcript is going to be sent out soon to the graduate programs I am applying to. But isn't an Incomplete better than a C? Students caught in such a predicament can be helped by knowing how to solve a problem in the most effective, efficient manner.

Therapists have devised what is called *social problem solving* (SPS) (D'Zurilla and Goldfried, 1971; Goldfried and D'Zurilla, 1969; Kanfer and Busenmeyer, 1982). Training clients in SPS consists of a number of steps, the

first being to regard their distress as a reaction to unsolved problems. They are taught to identify what the problems might be; to brainstorm—to generate as many alternative solutions as possible without evaluating their feasibility or possible effectiveness; to assess the likely consequences of each solution; and to implement a decision and evaluate its effectiveness for achieving their particular goals. Clients often have to cycle back to earlier stages, for their initial solution may not work out. People with serious problems often do have "second chances" to solve them.

Some clinical research finds SPS training to be useful. For example, depressed older adults in a nursing home shed more of their depression after such training than patients given a more behaviorally based treatment (Hussian and Lawrence, 1981). In another study school-aged children acquired problem-solving skills that generalized to situations different from those dealt with in the SPS training (Weissberg et al., 1981). In the best of all possible worlds, clients learn a general attitude and set of skills that they can apply to a wide range of future situations, thereby enhancing their general well-being.

"Metacognition," that is, what people know about knowing (Meichenbaum and Asarnow, 1979) is also applied in solving social problems. If I come to a new city, I am likely to get lost without a map. But once I obtain a street map, granted that I have earlier learned the general skill of map reading, I am well able to find my way around. At the metacognitive level I know that to locate streets and areas in a new city, I should get a city map and then read it.

Another example of metacognition is how we react to a problem that we find difficult to solve. We call it an interesting challenge; tell ourselves to go slow; think of as many solutions as possible, without committing ourselves to any particular one; and carefully and without rushing test out each of our alternatives.

SPS training, however, has been criticized for its overall approach to life. Goldfried (1980) points out that such training conveys the message that people *should* strive to take effective action against any frustration or problem, in order to gain or regain control over their situation. To view life as full of challenges to be overcome may encourage the development of a type A personality (Price, 1982). Furthermore, SPS training fosters a calculating attitude. Clients are taught, perhaps rather doggedly, to analyze all life's frustrations and difficulties in highly rational terms. Perhaps some problems are best left unexamined by our rational minds.

Some Reflections on Cognitive Behavior Therapy

As we have indicated, behavior therapy aligned itself initially with stimulus-response psychology—with the study of classical and operant conditioning—the assumption being that principles and procedures derived from conditioning experiments could be applied to lessen psychological suffering. The S–R orientation came from behaviorists like Watson and Skinner, who had become dissatisfied with the work done on the contents of the mind and consciousness in Wundt's and Titchener's laboratories and with their use of introspection in these studies. What has now developed and is called "cognitive behavior therapy" may appear to be a radical and novel departure, given the earlier focus of behavior therapists on classical and operant conditioning. But in a historical sense it actually represents a return to the cognitive foci of this earliest period of experimental psychology. And many experimental psychologists continued through the years to do research into cognition—into the mental processes of perceiving, recognizing, conceiving, judging, and reasoning, of problem solving, imagining, and other symbolizing activities.

Ellis and Beck try directly to change cognitive processes in order to relieve psychological distress. From the beginning, however, behavior therapists have relied heavily on the human being's capacity to symbolize, to process information, to represent the world in words and images. Wolpe's technique of systematic desensitization is a very clear example. This technique, believed by Wolpe to rest on conditioning principles, is inherently a cognitive procedure, for the client *imagines* what is fearful. Indeed, the most exciting overt behavioral event during a regimen of desensitization is the client's occasional signaling of anxiety by raising an index finger! If anything important is happening, it is surely going on "under the skin," and some of this activity is surely cognitive in nature.

As behavior therapy "goes cognitive," however, it is important to bear in mind that contemporary researchers continue to believe that behavioral *procedures* are more powerful than strictly verbal ones in affecting cognitive *processes* (Bandura, 1977). That is, they favor behavioral techniques while maintaining that it is important to alter a person's beliefs in order to effect an enduring change in behavior. Bandura suggests, in fact, that all therapeutic procedures, to the extent that they are effective, work their improvement by giving the person a sense of mastery, of "self-efficacy." At the same time he finds that the most effective way to gain a sense of self-efficacy, if one is lacking, is by changing behavior. Whether or not we believe self-efficacy to be as important as Bandura does, a distinction can be made between processes that underlie improvement and *procedures* that set these *processes* in motion. Cognitive behavior therapists continue to be behavioral in their use of performance-based procedures and in their commitment to behavioral change, but they are cognitive in the sense that they believe cognitive change to be an important mechanism that accounts for the effectiveness of at least some behavioral procedures.

All cognitive behavior therapists heed the mental processes of their clients in another way. They pay attention to the world as it is perceived by the client. It is not what impinges on us from the outside that controls our behavior, the assumption that has guided stimulus-response psychology for decades. Rather our feelings and behavior are determined by how we view the world. The Greek philosopher Epictetus stated it in the first century, "Men are disturbed not by things, but by the views they take of them." Thus behavior therapy is being brought closer to the humanistic and existential therapies reviewed in Chapter 18. A central thesis of therapists like Rogers and Perls is that the client must be understood from the client's own frame of reference, from his or her phenomenological world, for it is this perception of the world that controls life and behavior.

From the philosophical point of view, such assumptions on the part of those who would understand people and try to help them are profoundly important. Experimentally minded clinicians and researchers are intrigued by how much the new field of cognitive behavior therapy has in common with the humanists and their attention to the phenomenological world of their clients. To be sure, the *techniques* used by cognitive behavior therapists are usually quite different from those of the followers of Rogers and of Perls. But as students of psychotherapy and of human nature, these surface differences should not blind us to the links between the two approaches.

BEHAVIORAL MEDICINE

Behavioral medicine has two roots, the early work in psychosomatic medicine, done primarily by psychiatrists and other physicians; and the later work in behav-

BOX 19.4

ASSERTION TRAINING

"Children should be seen and not heard." "Keep a stiff upper lip." "He's the strong silent type." Our society does not generally value the open expression of beliefs and feelings. And yet people seem to pay an emotional price for concealing their thoughts and suppressing their feelings. Peoples' wants and needs may not be met if they shy away from stating them clearly. As we have seen, poor communication between sexual partners is one of the major factors contributing to an unsatisfying sexual relationship. Therapists of all persuasions spend a good deal of time encouraging clients to discover what their desires and needs are and then to take responsiblity for meeting them. If they have trouble expressing their feelings and wishes to others, assertion training may be able to help them.

Andrew Salter, in his book *Conditioned Reflex Therapy* (1949), was the first behavior therapist to set assertiveness as a positive goal for clients. Using Pavlovian, classical conditioning terms, Salter said that much human psychological suffering is caused by an excess of cortical inhibition; therefore greater excitation is called for. He encouraged socially inhibited people to express their feelings to others in an open, spontaneous way. They are to do so verbally, telling people when they are happy or sad, angry or resolute; and nonverbally with smiles and frowns, what Salter called facial talk. They are also to contradict people they disagree with, and with appropriate feeling; use the pronoun I as often as possible; express agreement with those who praise them; and improvise, that is, respond intuitively in the moment without ruminating. Although Salter's classical conditioning formulation of assertion has not been verified, assertiveness remains a goal for people in therapy, and his impact on therapeutic practice has been great and enduring.

How are we to define assertion? Is it not inconsiderate to put ourselves forward and express our beliefs and feelings to others? What if we hurt someone else's feelings in doing so? Much effort has gone into articulating the differences between assertive behavior and aggressive behavior. A useful distinction has been drawn by Lange and Jakubowski (1976); they consider assertion as

expressing thoughts, feelings, and beliefs in direct, honest, and appropriate ways which respect the rights of other people. In contrast, aggression involves self-expression which is characterized by violating others' rights and de-

meaning others in an attempt to achieve one's own objectives (pp. 38–39).

Arnold Lazarus regards the expression of positive and negative emotions as important for psychological well-being. He argues (1971) that "emotional freedom" in the most general sense of the term is important for many kinds of clients; they need to express affection and approval as well as dislikes and criticisms. In helping clients to assert themselves, behavior therapists, whether they acknowledge it or not, are doing therapeutic work with goals similar to those of humanistic therapists, who also regard expression of positive and negative feelings as a necessary component of effective living.

People may be unassertive for any number of reasons. The specific therapy procedures chosen will depend on the reasons believed to be causing the individual's unassertiveness. Assertion training, then, is actually a set of different techniques, having in common the goal of enhancing assertiveness. Goldfried and Davison (1976) have suggested several factors that can underlie unassertiveness, one or more of which may be found in an unassertive individual.

1. The client may not know what to say. Some unassertive people lack information on what to say in situations that call for expressiveness. The therapist should supply this information.

2. Clients may not know how to behave assertively. They may not assume the tone and loudness of voice, the fluency of speech, the facial expression and eye contact, and the body posture necessary for assertiveness. Modeling and role playing will help these people acquire the signals of firmness and directness.

3. Clients may fear that something terrible will happen if they assert themselves. Systematic desensitization may reduce this anticipatory anxiety. In others assertiveness seems to be blocked by negative self-statements, such as "If I assert myself and am rejected, that would be a catastrophe" (Schwartz and Gottman, 1976). They will profit from rational-emotive therapy.

4. The client may not feel that it is "proper" or "right" to be assertive. The value systems of some people preclude or discourage assertiveness. For example, some of the problems of a Catholic nun undergoing therapy seemed to relate

ior therapy, done primarily by psychologists (Brownell, 1982). The contributions of psychiatrists and physicians sensitized mental health workers to the role of psychological factors in both the etiology and the treatment of medical disorders. The contributions of the psycholo-

gists were primarily in the techniques of change, the tools by which psychological factors can be analyzed and manipulated to enhance our understanding of illness as well as to prevent it and treat it.

Many workers now favor a definition that is broader

to her unassertiveness, but through discussion it became clear that she would violate some of her vows were she more expressive and outspoken. By mutual agreement assertion training was not undertaken; instead, therapy focused on helping her work within her chosen profession in ways that were more personally satisfying and yet not more assertive.

Assertion training may begin with conversations in which the therapist tries to get the client to distinguish between assertiveness and aggression. For people who are submissive, even making a reasonable request or refusing a presumptuous one may make them feel that they are being hostile. Then therapists usually give clients sample situations which will leave them feeling put upon if they are unable to handle them. The situations usually require that they stand up for their rights, their time, and their energies.

You have been studying very hard for weeks, taking no time off at all for relaxation. But now a new film, which will play for only a few days, interests you and you have decided to take a few hours and go late this evening to see it. On the way to an afternoon class, your very good friend tells you that she has free tickets to a concert this evening and asks you to go with her. How do you say no?

Behavior rehearsal is a useful technique in assertion training. The therapist discusses and models appropriate assertiveness and then has the client role-play situations. Graded homework assignments, such as asking the garageman to explain the latest bill for repairs, then telling an uncle that his constant criticisms are resented, are given as soon as the client has acquired some degree of assertiveness through session work.

Assertion training raises several ethical issues. To encourage assertiveness in people who, like the nun mentioned earlier, believe that self-denial is a greater good than self-expression would violate the client's value system and could generate an unfavorable "ripple effect" in other areas of the person's life. Drawing a distinction between assertion and aggression is also an ethical issue. Behavior considered assertive by one person may be seen by another as aggressive. If we adopt the distinction made by Lange and Jakubowski, that assertion respects the rights of others whereas aggression does not, we still have to make a judgment about what the rights of others are. Thus assertion training touches on moral aspects of social living, namely the definition of other people's rights and the proper means of standing up for one's own.

In assertion training clients are taught to express their wants and needs more directly. Videotape can be a useful adjunct to the training.

than the one just implied, for to accord behavior therapy special status would, it is argued, discourage interdisciplinary cooperation with other behavioral and biomedical scientists (Brownell, 1982). We favor the definition offered by Gary Schwartz and Stephen Weiss (1978), two pioneers in behavioral medicine:

Behavioral medicine is the interdisciplinary field concerned with the development and integration of behavioral and biomedical science knowledge and techniques relevant to health and illness and the application of this knowledge and these techniques to prevention, diagnosis, treatment and rehabilitation (p. 250).

Behavioral medicine is truly a marriage of two disparate fields, but one which seems to be working very well indeed. A strong, institutional sign of its success is the recent establishment within the National Institutes of Health of a separate Behavioral Medicine Study Section. This department reviews its own grant proposals and dispenses federal moneys to researchers. Special journals on the subject and the Society for Behavioral Medicine, a professional organization, are other signs of its popularity.

Behavioral medicine is not restricted to a set of techniques or particular principles of changing behavior. Rather, workers in this field employ a wide variety of procedures—from contingency management through operant conditioning to desensitization through counterconditioning—all of which have in common the goal of altering bad living habits, distressed psychological states, and aberrant physiological processes, in order to have a beneficial impact on a person's physical condition. Behavioral medicine has already been mentioned several times in this book. Psychophysiological disorders (Chapter 8) and the problems of seriously ill children (Chapter 15) are treated by behavioral medicine, as are the addictive disorders that threaten health, such as cigarette smoking and alcoholism (Chapter 11). A sampling of some other activities will convey an even better sense of the scope of this emerging multidisciplinary field of research and treatment.

Chronic Pain and Activity

Eighty-six million Americans, it is estimated, suffer from chronic pain (Bonica, 1981). Defined as pain that persists beyond the healing time of the affected parts of the body, it accounts for millions of dollars of lost work time and disrupts family life, as well as keeping the sufferer in continuous and extreme discomfort. Behavioral medicine assumes that treatment can be psychological as well as medical.

After an attack of severe back muscle spasms, for example, a person may be reluctant to engage in physical activity more vigorous than getting into and out of bed. In the acute phase this is sensible behavior. As the spasms ease, and if no other damage has occurred, such as to the disks between the vertebrae, the patient should begin moving more normally, stretching, and eventually

attempting exercises to strengthen the very muscles that had gone into spasm. Behavioral medicine urges members of the patient's family to pay less attention to grimaces and complaints of pain and to encourage physical activity (Fordyce, 1973, 1976). This commonsense operant recommendation has achieved some success in reducing the frequency of expressions of distress and in increasing activity. These patients have also been given relaxation training and encouraged to relabel their pain as numbness or tickling (Rybstein-Blinchik, 1979), a cognitive-restructuring procedure.

Chronic Diseases and Life Style

Behavioral medicine is concerned not only with alleviation of illness and pain but with their prevention; when it has this purpose, it is often called "health psychology." At the beginning of this century, the leading causes of death were infectious diseases such as influenza and tuberculosis. With these illnesses largely under medical control, the 1980s see Americans succumbing most often to diseases of the heart, cancer, cerebrovascular diseases such as stroke, and accidents. For each of these the behavior of people over their lifetime—their life style—is implicated. We have already seen in Chapter 8 that, along with type A personality, a diet high in cholesterol, lack of exercise, and smoking contribute to heart disease.

Physicians have for years been dispensing sound advice about diet, exercise, and smoking, usually with little effect on life style. Getting people to do what is in the best interest of their health is a challenge! Merely telling a sedentary file clerk that she must exercise for at least fifteen minutes three times a week at 70 percent of her maximum heart rate will probably not rouse her to adhere to such a schedule.

In one study (Epstein et al., 1980) female college students agreed that they would run one to two miles a day for five weeks and made a five-dollar deposit, which was returned to them a dollar at a time as they complied. These young women ran more consistently than those in a control group who had no contingency. A number of similar programs for encouraging regular exercise have also been reported. Of particular interest was the posting of a cartoon at the base of a public stairway and escalator (Brownwell, Stunkard, and Albaum, 1980). It portrayed a glum, unhealthy-looking heart taking the escalator, next to a robust, happy heart bounding up a flight of stairs; the caption read, "Your heart needs exercise . . . here's your chance." Simple and inexpensive, the cartoon effected a dramatic change in people passing that way. Thereafter three times as many used the stairs as had been observed earlier. Stairs are of course far more available than aerobics exercise sessions and climbing them easier than instituting a jogging regimen. Regular stair use is known to be a very healthful cardiovascular exercise for people throughout their lives.

Many industries and corporations now maintain their own health and fitness programs, screening their employees for such illnesses as hypertension and providing facilities and incentives for taking regular exercise, even during work time hours. More than magnanimity is operating here; such programs are known to reduce absenteeism and improve health generally, making them cost-effective for the company.

Biofeedback

A visit to the commercial exhibit area of any psychological or psychiatric convention will reveal a plentiful display of complex biofeedback apparatus, touted as an efficient, even miraculous, means of helping people control one or another bodily-mental state. Basically, biofeedback gives a person prompt and exact information, otherwise unavailable, on muscle activity, brain waves, skin temperature, heart rate, blood pressure, and other bodily functions. It is assumed that a person can achieve greater voluntary control over these phenomena—most of which were once considered to be under involuntary control and completely unresponsive to will—if he or she knows immediately, through an auditory or visual signal, whether a bodily activity is increasing or decreasing. Because anxiety has generally been viewed as a state involving the autonomic ("involuntary") nervous system, and because psychophysiological disorders afflict organs innervated by this system, it is obvious why researchers and clinicians became intrigued with biofeedback. Indeed, biofeedback was for a time virtually synonymous with behavioral medicine.

In a series of studies at Harvard Medical School, Shapiro, Tursky, and Schwartz (1970; Schwartz, 1973) demonstrated that human volunteers could achieve significant short-term changes in blood pressure and in heart rate. They found that some subjects could even be trained to increase their heart rate while decreasing blood pressure. Achievement of this fine-grained control lent impetus to biofeedback work with human beings and awakened hope that certain clinical disorders might be alleviated in this new way.

In the move from analogue studies to the more challenging world of the clinic, at least three vital questions must be asked. First, can persons whose systems are *malfunctioning* achieve the same biofeedback control over bodily events that normal subjects can acquire? Second, if actual patients can achieve some degree of control, will it be enough to make a significant difference in their problems? And third, can the control achieved by patients hooked up to and receiving immediate feedback from a remarkable apparatus be carried over to real-life situations in which they will have no special devices to inform them of the state of the bodily functions that they have learned to control?

Research with patients suffering from essential hypertension has been somewhat encouraging, but results have not been certain enough to establish biofeedback as a standard treatment for the problem (Shapiro and Surwit, 1979). Moreover, some (Blanchard et al., 1979) believe that relaxation training, which is often given along with biofeedback, does more to reduce blood pressure than the biofeedback itself.

The control of various forms of epilepsy has been attempted with some success. Several patients have reduced the frequency of seizures through intensive biofeedback training to increase brain activity in the sensorimotor cortex, but this improvement did not invariably persist when training sessions were discontinued (Sterman, 1973).

Reports on the use of biofeedback for neuromuscular disorders—cerebral palsy, jaw clenching and teeth grinding, paralysis in the aftermath of stroke and of diseases such as poliomyelitis—have been especially heartening. The initial research was done by Basmajian (1977) in the early 1960s. Paralyzed patients proved able to activate single motor cells if informed of their firing by biofeedback. The Biofeedback Society of America is so enthusiastic about the effectiveness of biofeedback for hemiplegia, a paralysis on one side of the body usually caused by stroke, that it is regarded as the treatment of choice (Fernando and Basmajian, 1978). The fact that patients participating in these studies had not earlier been helped by conventional physical therapy lends credibility to the specific effectiveness of biofeedback in allowing them to make minute muscle movements. A 1980 report by the National Institute of Mental Health reasons that biofeedback should be especially useful for neuromuscular disorders because functions that have gone awry are normally under the voluntary control of the central nervous system. If the dysfunction is caused in part by the faintness of the signs of muscle movement in damaged tissue, amplifying these proprioceptive signals by feedback will make the patient aware of them and possibly allow control (Runck, 1980).

Even though biofeedback techniques bring about meaningful improvements in some patients, clinicians must remain mindful of the complexities of human problems. A man with high blood pressure, for example, might have to alter a tense, driven life style before he can significantly reduce blood pressure through biofeedback. It is unwise, and a sign of naive clinical practice, to assume that one technique focused on a specific malfunction or problem will invariably cure the patient.[4]

SOME BASIC ISSUES IN BEHAVIOR THERAPY

Behavior therapy is expanding each year; with such a proliferation of activity, everyone concerned should remain aware of problems and issues that transcend particular experimental findings. The following considerations, many of which have been alluded to earlier, need to be kept clearly in mind.

The Behavioral Focus on Current Maintaining Variables

An important defining characteristic of behavior therapy is its focus on current maintaining variables rather than on etiology. For example, a married woman is unhappy because she is unable to be assertive with her husband. Her problem might be traced to her inability as a child to deal effectively with her domineering father. A behavior therapist will, however, concentrate on helping her become more open with her husband rather than working on her past relationship with her father. Behavior therapists tend to concentrate their attention on maintaining variables regardless of what factors brought them into being.

Internal Behavior and Cognition

In Chapter 5, we demonstrated that the inference of intervening processes and other explanatory fictions is useful in interpreting data and generating fruitful hypotheses. Behavior therapists are often thought to hold the radical behavioristic positions of Watson and Skinner, that it is not useful or legitimate to make inferences about internal processes of the organism. Our intent is

to present a broader point of view as persuasively as we can, although not all contemporary behavior therapists (for example, Ullmann and Krasner, 1975; Bijou and Baer, 1961) agree on this issue.

The position we share with others (see Bandura, 1969; Kanfer and Phillips, 1970; Mahoney, 1974; MacCorquodale and Meehl, 1948; Meyer and Chesser, 1970; Mischel, 1968; O'Leary and Wilson, 1975) is that behavior therapy, as applied experimental psychology, is legitimately concerned with internal as well as external events, provided the internal mediators are securely anchored to observable stimuli or responses. Behaviorists do not have to ignore the internal life of human beings; but they do differ from psychologists with other views in the rigor of their inferences and in the care they take to ensure that the inferences are parsimonious as well as productive of good explanations and testable hypotheses.

Underlying Causes

A related misconception is that behavior therapy deals with symptoms whereas other therapies, particularly psychoanalytically oriented ones, are concerned with "root" or "underlying" causes. To many people a determinant of behavior that is assumed to lie in the unconscious or in the past is somehow more "underlying" or "basic" than a determinant that is anchored in the current environment. This conception fails to consider the fact that science searches for the most significant causes of behavior. If "underlying" is defined as "not immediately obvious," behavior therapists indeed search for underlying causes. If such causes are taken to be the most significant ones, that is, the controlling variables, the task of behavior therapists is the same as for all other therapists—to find the most significant causes (Bandura, 1969).

A clinical example will illustrate this point. A twenty-five-year-old man who had been discharged from a mental hospital was treated for problems that included occasional paranoid delusions. A careful behavioral assessment suggested to both client and therapist that these thoughts of persecution were triggered by considerable anxiety. Rather than working directly on the delusional episodes, then, the therapist desensitized the client to a number of social situations in which he might feel inadequate and be criticized by others. Such occasions seemed often to precede his paranoid "trips." As the client came gradually to be less upset about possible criticism, his paranoid thoughts dropped to near zero. Although there is of course no way of knowing whether desensitization to disturbing social situations was truly responsible for this outcome, the behavior

---

[4]Of course, medical consultation is always a part of responsible treatment of psychophysiological disorders such as hypertension.

therapist did search for and modify an underlying cause as the strongest controlling variable.

Broad-Spectrum Treatment

Our review of behavior therapy has necessarily been fragmented because we have dealt with separate techniques one at a time. In clinical practice, however, behavior therapists employ several procedures at once or sequentially in an attempt to deal with all the important controlling variables; this approach is generally referred to as *broad-spectrum behavior therapy* (Lazarus, 1971). For example, a woman fearful of leaving her home might well undergo in vivo desensitization by walking out of her door and gradually engaging in activities that take her farther and farther from her safe haven. Over the years, however, she may also have built up a dependent relationship with her husband. As she becomes bolder in venturing forth, this change in her behavior may disrupt the equilibrium of the relationship that she and her husband have worked out over the years (see page 127). To attend only to her fear of leaving home would be incomplete behavior therapy (Lazarus, 1965) and might even lead to replacement of the agoraphobia with another difficulty that would serve to keep the woman at home—a problem frequently called "symptom substitution."

In a related vein, it is often said that behavior therapists invariably focus only on the patient's complaint as it was stated during the first interview. The facts are otherwise. A clinical graduate student was desensitizing an undergraduate for test anxiety. The client made good progress up the hierarchy of imagined situations but was not improving at all in the real world of test taking. The supervisor of the graduate student suggested that the therapist find out whether the client was studying for his tests. It turned out that he was not; worry about the health of his mother was markedly interfering with his attempts to study. Thus the goal of making the client nonchalant about taking tests was inappropriate, for he was approaching the tests themselves without adequate preparation. On the basis of additional assessment, the therapy shifted away from desensitization to a discussion of how the client could deal with his realistic fears about his mother's possible death.

Relationship Factors

Because of the scientific language typically employed in the literature on behavior therapy, behavior therapists are considered little if at all concerned with the therapist-client relationship—whether, for example, the client trusts the therapist, believes that he or she can be of assistance, and the like. Although behaviorists have, in-

Arnold A. Lazarus, one of the principal figures in contemporary behavior therapy.

deed, tried to emphasize the learning mechanisms that are brought into play by the various techniques, they have never discounted the importance of the client's feelings about the therapist. Research in behavior therapy has, in fact, already documented the importance of sometimes vaguely defined relationship factors. In the Paul (1966) study of anxious public speakers, for example, considerable and long-lasting improvement was observed in subjects who were given the attention-placebo treatment. Thus, although desensitization subjects improved more than did the others, the significant improvement in the attention-placebo group demonstrates the substantial contribution of the warm, trusting relationship with a therapist.

A good therapeutic relationship is important for many reasons. As discussed in Chapter 4 (page 68), it seems doubtful that clients will reveal deeply personal information if they do not trust or respect their therapists. Furthermore, since behavior therapy cannot be imposed on an unwilling client, a therapist must obtain the cooperation of the client if there is to be any possibility that techniques will have their desired effect. In desensitization, for example, a client could readily sabotage the best efforts of the therapist by not imagining a particular scene, by not signaling anxiety appropriately, and by not practicing relaxation. And in virtually all other behavior therapy procedures clients are able to, and sometimes will, work against the therapist if relationship factors are neglected (Davison, 1973).

Flesh on the Theoretical Skeleton

Determining the most important controlling variables is related to another overlooked aspect of behavior therapy—indeed, of any therapy—namely moving from a general principle to a concrete clinical intervention.

To illustrate, let us consider a study in which undergraduates were trained to analyze the behavior of severely disturbed children in operant conditioning terms (Davison, 1964). The students were encouraged to *assume* that the important determinants of these children's behavior were the consequences of that behavior. Armed with M & M candies as reinforcers, these student-therapists attempted to bring the behavior of the severely disturbed children under their control. Eventually, one child appeared to be losing interest in earning the candies. Working within a framework that required an effective reinforcer, the therapist looked around for another incentive. Luckily, he noticed that each time the child passed a window, she would pause for a moment to look at her reflection. The therapist obtained a mirror and was subsequently able to make "peeking into the mirror" the reinforcer for desired behavior; the peeks into the mirror were used in the same *functional* way as the M & M candies. Thus, *although guided by a general principle, the therapist had to rely on improvisation and inventiveness as demanded by the clinical situation.*

An outsider can get the impression that devising therapy along behavioral lines is easy and straightforward, that the application of a general principle to a particular case is a simple matter. Those who have worked as behavioral clinicians, however, know otherwise. Although a given theoretical framework helps to guide the clinician's thinking, it is by no means sufficient.

. . . The clinician in fact approaches his work with a given set, a framework for ordering the complex data that are his domain. But frameworks are insufficient. The clinician, like any other applied scientist, must fill out the theoretical skeleton. Individual cases present problems that always call for knowledge beyond basic psychological principles (Lazarus and Davison, 1971, p. 203).

The preceding quotation from two behavior therapists is very similar to the following one from an article written by two experimental social psychologists.

In any experiment, the investigator chooses a procedure which he intuitively feels is an empirical realization of his conceptual variable. All experimental procedures are "contrived" in the sense that they are invented. Indeed, it can be said that the art of experimentation rests primarily on the skill of the investigator to judge the procedure which is the most accurate realization of his conceptual variable and has the greatest impact and the most credibility for the subject (Aronson and Carlsmith, 1968, p. 25).

Thus behavior therapists are faced with the same kinds of decision-making challenges that their experimental colleagues face. There are no easy solutions in dealing with human problems.

Psychoanalysis and Behavior Therapy— A Rapprochement?

Is contemporary psychoanalysis compatible with behavior therapy? This question has been discussed for many years, and few professionals are optimistic about a meaningful rapprochement, arguing that these two points of view are incompatible paradigms. But Paul Wachtel, in his book on just such an integration (1977), has offered a scheme that, in our view, holds considerable promise at least for establishing a dialogue between psychoanalytically oriented therapists and behavior therapists.

As indicated in Chapter 18, ego analysts place much more emphasis on current ego functioning than did Freud. Sullivan, for example, suggested that patients will feel better about themselves and function more effectively if they focus on problems in their current interpersonal behavior. But even Sullivan appears to have been ambivalent about the wisdom of working directly on how people act and feel in the present if this might mean they would not recover memories of repressed infantile conflicts. Wachtel, however, suggests that the therapist *should* help the client change his current behavior, not only so that he can feel better in the here and now but indeed so that he can *change* his childlike fears from the past.

Wachtel bases his principal position on Horney (1939), Sullivan (1953), and Erikson (1950) and calls it "cyclical psychodynamics" (1982). He believes that people maintain repressed problems by their current behavior and the feedback it brings from their social relations. Although their problems were set in motion by past repressed events, people keep acting in ways that continue them. Take, for example, a young man who has repressed his extreme rage at his mother for having mistreated his father years ago, when he was still a child. To control this rage, he as a youngster developed defenses which took the form of overpoliteness and deference to women. Today this solicitousness and unassertiveness encourage some women to take advantage of him, but he also misperceives situations in which women are genuinely nice to him. Misinterpreting their friendly overtures as condescending insults, he comes to resent women even more and retreats still further. In this fashion his submissiveness, originating in his "woolly mammoth," his buried problem of long ago, creates personal problems in the present and revives his repressed rage. It is as though his adult ego is saying, unconsciously, "You see, women, like my mother really are bitchy. They're not to be trusted. They're hurtful and sadistic." This present-day confirmation of his belief from childhood turns back upon the buried conflict and, as it were, keeps it alive. The cycle continues, with the young man's own behavior and misconceptions confirming the nastiness of women.

The implications for therapy are to alter current behavioral patterns both for their own sake, which is the behavior therapist's credo, and for the purpose of uncovering the underlying psychodynamics. By pointing out that a direct alteration of behavior may help clients attain a more realistic understanding of their past repressed conflicts, traditionally the goal of psychoanalysis, Wachtel hopes to interest his analytic colleagues in the techniques employed by behavior therapists. Wachtel would probably give the deferential young man some assertion training, in hopes of breaking into the vicious cycle by changing his here-and-now relations with women. With his belief that all women want to take advantage of him repeatedly disconfirmed, the young man can begin to understand the repressed conflict of love-hate with his mother.

Similarly, Wachtel holds that behavior therapists can learn much from their analytic colleagues, especially concerning the *kinds* of problems people tend to develop. For example, psychoanalytic theory tells us that children have strong and usually ambivalent feelings about their parents, and that, presumably, some of these are so unpleasant that they are repressed, or at least are difficult to focus on and talk about openly.

To a behavior therapist the deferential young man might initially appear fearful of heterosexual relationships. Taking these fears at face value, he or she would work to help him reduce them, perhaps by a combination of desensitization, rational-emotive therapy, and social-skills training. But the behavior therapist will fail to explore the possibility, suggested by the psychoanalytic literature, that the young man is basically *angry* at women. Wachtel advises that the behavior therapist sensitive to the childhood conflicts that analysts focus on will question the young man about his relationship with his mother. His reply or manner may give a hint of resentment. The therapist will then *see* the deferential young man differently and hypothesize that he is not just fearful of women but angry at them as well, because he associates them with a mother who has been the object of both hate and love from early childhood. This additional information will presumably suggest a different behavioral intervention, for the anger must be dealt with.

In a related vein, Wachtel argues that psychoanalysts are more likely than behavior therapists to consider the nonnormative or unusual concerns, wishes, and fears of their patients. Guided by the view that emotional problems derive from the repression of id conflicts, they consider them to reflect infantile wishes and fears, dark mysteries of primary process thinking. Behavior therapists tend to have a more straightforward, more prosaic, if you will, view of their patients' problems.

Wachtel would also have the behavior therapist appreciate that reinforcers can be *subtle* and that, furthermore, a client may deny that he or she really wants something. And the client may well be unaware of this denial. In other words, therapists should attune themselves to unconscious motivation, to the possibility that a person may be motivated or reinforced by a set of events that he or she, for psychodynamic reasons, is not conscious of.

Contemporary psychoanalytic thought may also help the behavior therapist become aware of the *meaning* that a particular intervention has for a client. Consider the case of a young woman with whom a behavior therapist decided to do assertion training. As role-playing procedures were described, the client stiffened in her chair and then began to sob. To proceed with the training without dealing with her reaction to the description of it would of course be insensitive and poor clinical practice. An awareness of psychoanalytic theories had sensitized the therapist to the possibility that assertion *symbolized* something to the client. The therapist gently encouraged the woman to talk freely, to free-associate, to the idea of assertion training. She recalled a series of incidents from childhood in which her parents had criticized the way she acted with her friends, without providing support and constructive suggestions about other ways to behave. Without initially being aware of it herself, the client was reminded of this pain from the past when the therapist suggested that she learn more assertive ways of dealing with others. The psychologist was able to distinguish the current enterprise, assertion training, from the unhelpful and negative criticisms made in the past and thereby persuaded the young woman to try role playing. The incident also pointed up the client's unresolved problems with her parents and with authority figures in general.

SUMMARY

In this chapter we have reviewed theory and research in behavior therapy, a branch of clinical psychology which attempts to apply the methodologies and principles of experimental psychology to the therapeutic modification of human behavior. Several areas of this field were surveyed. Via counterconditioning a substitute desirable response is elicited in the presence of a stimulus that has evoked an undesired response. Systematic desensitization is believed by some to be effective because of counterconditioning. In operant conditioning desired responses are taught and undesired ones discouraged by applying the contingencies of reward and punishment. The token economy is a prime example of the clinical application of operant conditioning. Modeling—helping the client to acquire new responses and unlearn old ones by observing models—is useful in eliminating fears and efficient in teaching new patterns of behavior. Cognitive-restructuring techniques, such as rational-emotive therapy, alter the thoughts that are believed to underlie emotional disorders. Self-control was examined and found to present some interesting challenges to the behavioral paradigm; an active and conscious human being by autonomous and deliberate choice acts independently of environmental influences. Behavioral medicine was reviewed as a specialty which attempts to alter bad living habits, distressed psychological states, and aberrant physiological processes by psychological procedures, in order to prevent and to treat medical illnesses. Finally, several important issues in behavior therapy— such as the role of underlying causes, relationship factors, and the possibilities of integrating some parts of psychoanalytic theorizing into behavior therapy—were discussed in the hope of providing the reader with a better and more sophisticated grasp of a field that is both promising and controversial.

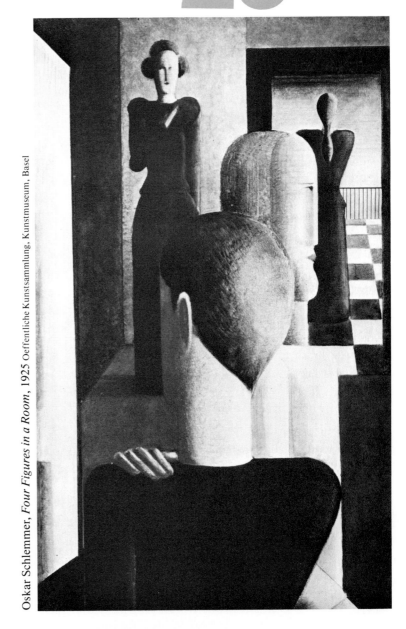

Oskar Schlemmer, *Four Figures in a Room*, 1925 Oeffentliche Kunstsammlung, Kunstmuseum, Basel

GROUP AND MARITAL THERAPY, COMMUNITY PSYCHOLOGY, AND SOMATIC TREATMENT

In this chapter we review three means of therapeutic intervention. Although different from one another in many important ways, they are similar in making far more efficient use of professional time than the one-to-one therapies reviewed in the preceding two chapters. In group and marital therapy a professional treats a number of patients simultaneously; community psychology is oriented toward prevention and treats the problems of patients without removing them from their customary surroundings; and somatic treatments—drugs, surgery, and electroconvulsive therapy—do not require much time to administer. All three, then, are more economical than individual therapy. As we shall soon see, however, economy is not the primary reason that any of the three is chosen. Rather, each treatment has developed from a particular rationale for providing effective help.

GROUP AND MARITAL THERAPY

A single therapist can obviously treat more people by seeing them in groups, and charge lower fees, than would be possible were he or she seeing them individually. But it would be a mistake to estimate the value of group therapy only in economic terms. Most group therapists regard their form of treatment as *uniquely* appropriate for accomplishing certain goals. For example, group members can learn vicariously (see page 42) when attention is focused on another participant. Social pressures, too, can be surprisingly strong in groups. If a therapist tells an individual client that his or her behavior seems hostile even when hostility is not intended, the message may be rejected; however, if three or four other people agree with the interpretation, the person may find it much more difficult to dismiss. In addition, many people derive comfort and support solely from the knowledge that others have problems similar to their own.

As we saw in the two preceding chapters, the literature on individual psychotherapy is confusing and extensive; so too is the information available on group therapy. Virtually every technique or theory employed in individual therapy has been, or can be, used for treating people in groups. Thus there are psychoanalytic groups (Slavson, 1950; Wolf, 1949), Gestalt groups (Perls, 1969), client-centered groups (Rogers, 1970), behavior therapy groups (Lazarus, 1968a; Paul and Shannon, 1966; Upper and Ross, 1980), and countless other kinds. Group therapies have also been used with children and their parents, with adolescents, with patients suffering from a host of medical illnesses, with the aged

and their caregivers; with drug and alcohol abusers, most notably Alcoholics Anonymous (see page 261), with abusive parents, with delinquents, with gays, with hospitalized mental patients (Lubin, 1983). We shall examine closely a few group psychotherapies, in hopes of imparting some idea of the range of prevailing theories and procedures, and then review the evidence bearing on their effectiveness.

Insight-Oriented Group Therapy

Moreno's Psychodrama

Jacob L. Moreno, a Viennese psychiatrist, is said to have coined the term "group psychotherapy" in 1931. He was unquestionably one of the most influential and colorful figures in the field. The essence of the form of group therapy he introduced—*psychodrama*—is to have participants take parts and act out their feelings as though they were in a play, with the therapist assuming the role of director of the psychic drama. A male patient might be asked to converse with another group member playing the role of his father. By this spontaneous, unrehearsed playacting the patient is apparently helped to express his feelings and perceptions about his father more effectively than were he to try to verbalize them. "We must stimulate the patients to be concrete, and bring forth their feelings and thoughts in a structured form" (Moreno and Kipper, 1968, p. 56). Like other forms of group therapy, psychodrama makes unique use of the group as a vehicle for changing people. Group members provide a company of potential actors with whom to stage the dramatic presentations.

To facilitate role taking and to give the proceedings the aspect of a true drama, Moreno advised using an actual stage. The presence of an audience also contributes to the theatrical atmosphere. Moreno suggested many kinds of role taking to promote the expression and confrontation of true feelings. For example, the *mirroring* technique is designed for patients who have difficulty expressing themselves in action or in words: another person, an "auxiliary ego," portrays the patient as best he can, thereby furnishing him concrete information on how others view him. In *role reversal* actors exchange roles; in *magic shop* the protagonist may "buy" a desired personal quality by temporarily giving up one already possessed. At all times the aim of the players is to express in dramatic form true feelings about certain situations. The therapist sometimes actively directs the "play" to ensure that therapeutic gain will be the maximum.

Should psychodrama be classified as insight or action-oriented therapy? Clearly, the therapist assumes responsibility for what happens during the session; furthermore, he or she goads the patients into specific behavior during treatment. On the other hand, the ultimate goal of the treatment was seen by Moreno as insight into motivation. Thus psychodrama appears to be an insight therapy that goes beyond reliance on the verbal interpretive methods of psychoanalysis but still tries to help patients achieve an understanding of their true motivations and needs.

Unfortunately, there is no body of controlled research on psychodrama, so it is not possible to assess the efficacy of Moreno's ideas.

Sensitivity Training and Encounter Groups

Without question, one of the most exciting developments in clinical psychology and psychiatry is the *sensitivity training group*, or T-group, movement. Aronson (1972) differentiates the T-group from the more radical "encounter group," which grew in popularity primarily on the West coast at such places as the Esalen Institute, where Perls was in residence in the 1960s. T-groups tend to rely more on verbal procedures and to avoid the physical contact, touching exercises, and unrestrained expressions of emotion employed by many encounter groups. Aronson's distinction is not accepted by all workers, however. Rogers (1970) traces the development of encounter groups to his training of counselors at the University of Chicago in 1946, in which he emphasized personal growth and improved interpersonal communication. We would agree with his judgment that T-groups and encounter groups are usually impossible to distinguish one from the other nowadays.

The T-group was originally conceived in 1947, and the National Training Laboratory was established through conferences on small-group dynamics held in Bethel, Maine. The impetus came from colleagues of Kurt Lewin, who was a famous social psychologist at MIT (Lubin, 1983). The original groups were made up of people in industry, and the goal was to increase efficiency in business practices at the highest levels of management by making executives more aware of their impact on other people and of their own feelings about others. Over the past thirty-five years millions of people have participated in such groups, including no doubt some readers of this book. Attention has shifted in these years from group dynamics to individual growth.

The T-group is best viewed as educational; it was not designed for those who are seriously disturbed. The T-group promotes personal growth and better understand-

A psychodrama session. The director-therapist (above) is guiding the patients in their roles.

A group of business people at a sensitivity training session. The T-group was originally devised to increase the efficiency of managers by making them more aware of their feelings and more sensitive to other people.

ing in people who are functioning reasonably well. Generally speaking, members are encouraged to focus on their "here and now" relationships with one another. Individuals are often drawn to T-groups because, even though their lives are not full of problems, they feel that they are missing something, that their days are lived through without intensity and intimacy. Aronson lists some general goals of T-groups.

1. To develop a willingness to examine one's behavior and to experiment with new ways of behaving.

2. To learn more about people in general.

3. To become more authentic and honest in interpersonal relations.

4. To work cooperatively with people rather than assuming an authoritarian or submissive manner.

5. To develop the ability to resolve conflicts through logical and rational thinking rather than through coercion and manipulation of others.

In the most general terms, T-groups and encounter groups provide a setting wherein people are encouraged to behave in an unguarded fashion. They are then helped to receive and give feedback, to see how they come across to and affect others, and to examine how they feel about their behavior and that of others. They are expected to become more aware and accepting of themselves and of other group members. Aronson (1972) provides the following description of a group session getting started.

He [the leader] . . . falls into silence. Minutes pass. They seem like hours. The group members may look at each other or out the window. Typically, participants may look at the trainer for guidance or direction. None is forthcoming. After several minutes, someone might express his discomfort. This may or may not be responded to. Eventually, in a typical group, someone will express annoyance at the leader: "I'm getting sick of this. This is a waste of time. How come you're not doing your job? What the hell are we paying you for? Why don't you tell us what we're supposed to do?" There may be a ripple of applause in the background. But

someone else might jump in and ask the first person why he is so bothered by a lack of direction—does he need someone to tell him what to do? And the T-group is off and running (p. 241).

Levels of communication. Figure 20.1 is Aronson's schematic representation of a dyadic or two-person interaction. In our everyday lives we usually operate at level P_3, namely behaving in some verbal or nonverbal way toward another person. Usually the recipient of our P_3 behavior eventually responds at level R_4, evaluating us. There are obviously many points at which misjudgments can occur. For example, at level R_3 the recipient may misinterpret P's intention. Even though the person, a man, may feel warmly (P_1) toward his friend the recipient, he may have difficulty expressing warmth and therefore show sarcasm at P_3. The recipient will then interpret P's intention as a wish to hurt him (R_3), rather than as a desire to express warm feelings toward him. Without the open discussion of feelings that is encouraged in a T-group, the recipient can reject (R_4) the person as a nasty individual and never come to understand that the person really feels warmly (P_1) but has just not learned to express his feelings (P_3) appropriately. A properly run T-group encourages the participants to break down their personal communications and reactions into all the various components so that they can examine their true feelings toward other persons and their perceptions of what they are receiving from them.

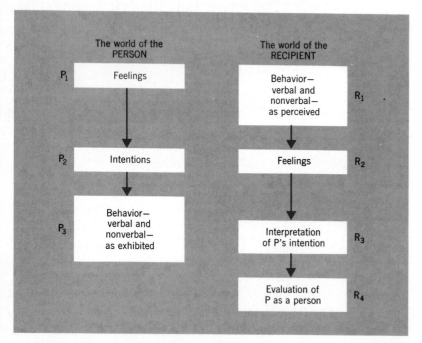

FIGURE 20.1 Schematic representation of a two-person interaction. The diagram illustrates the different levels of communication possible. After Aronson, 1972.

Within the T-group people talk frankly and listen to one another. Usually the group works on the ongoing interactions, rather than examining past histories, as would be the case in a psychoanalytically oriented group. The emphasis on openness is not necessarily a violation of a person's right to privacy, although there is little question that in some groups people feel pressured to reveal more about themselves than they might wish. Experienced and competent group leaders watch for undue coercion and direct the stream of conversation away from an individual when they sense excessive probing into the person's private feelings.

Role of T-group leader. Aronson has summarized the role and function of the group leader in a T-group.

1. The leader or trainer is a full member of the group. His or her own feelings, reactions, and effects on others are as legitimate a subject of discourse as are those of any other group member. Unlike some group therapists, T-group leaders do not hold themselves aloof from their clients.

2. Being professionals, however, leaders are busy performing other functions as well. They may occasionally comment on what is going on in the group, or they may step in to help people with difficult encounters and to make certain that participants discuss their feelings about others rather than judge them.

3. On the assumption that discoveries made by one's self are more meaningful and longer lasting than insights and observations doled out by experts, the group leader tries whenever possible not to intervene. At times, for example, he or she finds it best to remain silent.

4. Competent trainers will make every effort not to impose their will and ideas on the other participants, but they are of course aware of the very powerful position that they occupy in the group. It seems likely that some of the unfortunate abuses of encounter and T-groups can be attributed to the all-too-human tendency of some trainers to wield this power unwisely.

Variations. Particular sensitivity and encounter groups may vary in a number of ways. Rogers's (1970) groups tend to operate according to his individual client-centered therapy as outlined in Chapter 18; the leader tries to clarify the feelings of group members, on the assumption that growth can occur as people confront their emotions with honesty. The group leader—or "facilitator"—tends to be less active than in the T-groups Aronson describes. Some groups may meet for hours at a time, perhaps over a weekend, with little if any sleep allowed. Such *marathons* (Bach, 1966; Mintz, 1967; Stoller, 1968) rely on fatigue and extended exposure to a particular set of social conditions to weaken "defenses"

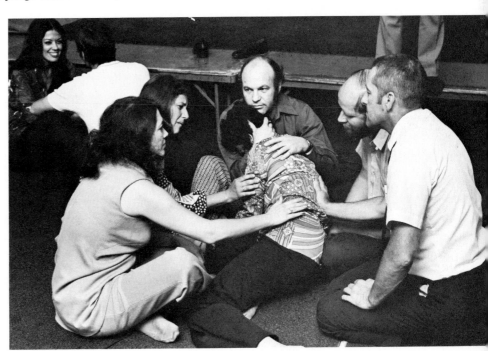

Encounter groups often encourage outpouring of intense emotion.

a   b

FIGURE 20.2 Distinction between (a) individualized group therapy and (b) group therapy in which interactions among all the members are regarded as important. Arrows indicate lines of communication and influences; T stands for therapist, P for patient.

and help the participants become more open and presumably more authentic. Many encounter group enthusiasts use exercises to break the ice (Schutz, 1967). For example, a man may be instructed to close his eyes and allow himself to be carried around by other group members, which is supposed to help him trust them. In another exercise two people stare into each other's eyes without speaking. Such maneuvers are meant to loosen people up, making clear to them that in this social setting feelings are to be expressed openly without censorship or fear of punishment. Bindrim (1968) introduced nudity as an aid to lowering defenses. Drug addict groups tend even to be brutal in the directness of their confrontations.

Behavior Therapy Groups

Individualized Behavior Therapy in Groups

Arnold Lazarus (1968a), a pioneer in group behavior therapy, has pointed out that a behavior therapist may, primarily for reasons of efficiency, choose to treat several people suffering from the same kind of problem by seeing them in a group rather than individually. The emphasis, as in one-to-one therapy, remains on interactions between the therapist and each individual patient or client (Figure 20.2a).[1]

Group desensitization (Lazarus, 1961) is a good example of this individualized approach. A single therapist can teach deep muscle relaxation and present a hierarchy to each member of the group simultaneously, thus

[1]Gestalt therapy groups generally operate in this fashion as well. The therapist works with one group member at a time; often this individual will sit in a particular chair, or on a particular pillow, referred to as "the hot seat."

saving therapist time. Fears handled in this manner include test anxiety (Nawas, Fishman, and Pucel, 1970), snake phobias (Ritter, 1968), anxiety about public speaking (Paul and Shannon, 1966), and social anxiety (Wright, 1976).

Therapies given to groups to help members lose weight (Wollersheim, 1970) and stop smoking (Koenig and Masters, 1965) have also been successful. Again, a particular technique was used on each member of the group. Whether this should be considered group therapy is open to question. The members of these special-purpose groups do seem to provide valuable encouragement and social support for one another, however.

Social-Skills Training Groups

Social skills are taught to groups of people who have similar deficits in relating to others. The members of these groups rehearse together the skills that they are learning and thus provide one another unique and appropriate help in changing behavior. Because members interact, the lines of communication are among all participants, not just between therapist and participant (Figure 20.2b). Groups of depressed people, for example, have learned social skills that are likely to bring them more reinforcement from others (Lewinsohn, Weinstein, and Alper, 1970).

Assertion Training Groups

Assertiveness is a social skill. Lazarus conducts assertion training groups composed of about ten people of the same sex. At the first meeting he describes the general goals of the therapy group, commenting particularly on the problems that unassertiveness can create for individuals in our society. He also suggests that the therapy group can provide a good setting for cooperative problem solving. Like Rogers, he calls for honesty and acceptance within the group and prescribes constructive criticism and the diligent practice of new skills. Then members introduce themselves briefly, and the others are encouraged to comment on the manner in which they presented themselves, especially if it was apologetic.

Members of the group are then given a situation that calls for an assertive response (see page 518). The therapist turns the situation into a skit and demonstrates being assertive. Then group members, in pairs or larger groupings, take turns playing out the skit. The therapist and other members tell the persons practicing assertiveness what they are doing right and doing wrong. Assertiveness is rehearsed again and again in each situation until members feel natural acting in this fashion. Of particular importance are assignments carried out by the members between sessions. People are encouraged to describe both successful and unsuccessful attempts at assertive behavior in their everyday activities, and they often role-play within the group to help them improve on their assertion in past or anticipated situations. The emphasis is at all times on the benefits to be derived from appropriate and effective expression of both positive and negative feelings. If the therapist is sensitive and skillful, he or she is able to create an atmosphere in which group members begin to trust themselves to express criticism without fearing that they are hurting other people's feelings. Assertion groups may even be effective in reducing the compliant, withdrawn behavior of chronic schizophrenics (Bloomfield, 1973).

There are some similarities between Lazarus's assertion training groups and the sensitivity training groups described earlier, but an important difference is the attention Lazarus pays to between-session activities; people are trained within the group to make specific changes later, outside the group therapy setting. Although T-groups are similarly concerned with helping people change their everyday lives, much less systematic attention is paid to what clients do between group sessions.

Evaluation of Group Therapy

Like other therapies, the T-group and encounter movement has its share of glowing testimonials.

I have known individuals for whom the encounter experience has meant almost miraculous change in the depth of their communication with spouse and children. Sometimes for the first time real feelings are shared. . . . I have seen teachers who have transformed their classroom . . . into a personal, caring, trusting, learning group, where students participate fully and openly in forming the curriculum and all the other aspects of their education. Tough business executives who described a particular business relationship as hopeless have gone home and changed it into a constructive one (Rogers, 1970, p. 71).

Such observations, especially by a highly skilled and innovative clinician, contribute to the faith many people have in encounter groups. Comments of this nature do not, however, satisfy most scientists of human behavior.

Some critics have suggested that those who participate in T-groups learn only how to participate in T-groups. They are not able to transfer to real-life situations the insights and skills that have been acquired in a group (Houts and Serber, 1972). Transfer of learning is a difficult problem for, whether we like it or not, the real world is not set up to encourage openness and frankness. Those who are not operating by the rules of a T-group may be offended by the open and honest expression of feelings. Indeed, as Aronson reminds us, if someone insists that others be totally open when they do not want to be, he or she is being insensitive to their feelings and so really has *not* learned some of the essentials from what might have seemed a good T-group experience. This is not to say that T-group experiences can never transfer to the real world. Knowledge of how a person feels about others and comes across to them may be extremely useful in everyday activities, even though the overt behavior encouraged in a T-group is not continued.

Because the independent variables are so complex and difficult to control, it is extraordinarily difficult to do good research with groups. As with all psychotherapy research, there is little agreement on what are the best means of measuring success. There is also wide disparity in how often groups meet and for how long, and the people assembled are quite diverse. Few studies have employed credible controls for the placebo effect. Most importantly, little attention is paid to what actually *happens* in the group. Mindful of these methodological shortcomings, Smith (1975) offered the following tentative conclusions about T-groups that met for at least twenty hours and were compared to no-treatment controls.

1. T-group participants tend to view themselves more favorably after a group experience, and this effect often persists for months afterward.

2. Some studies suggest that group members come to view themselves as more in control of their behavior, more responsible for themselves.

3. There is little if any good evidence that T-groups help participants become more open-minded and less prejudiced.

4. Some documentation suggests that participants are more willing to disclose personal information about themselves.

5. Since the purpose of a sensitivity training group is to foster understanding of others and their needs, it is surprising how little evidence shows participants becoming more empathic.

6. Some evidence suggests that participants improve more than controls in communication skills.

7. Some data indicate that associates of former group participants see them as functioning better in their everyday activities. For example, they seem more relaxed, more communicative. But in most instances the observers knew that their friends and colleagues had been in a group program, thus weakening the import of this observation.

Additional generalizations about other kinds of groups come from a careful review of studies that met certain methodological criteria, such as random assignment of subjects to different treatments; but ". . . these constraints have excluded the bulk of the potential literature" (Bednar and Kaul, 1978, p. 772), a sad commentary on the state of research in the complicated area of group therapy.

1. Dependent people appear to do better in a highly structured group, whereas independent, better-functioning individuals improve to a greater extent in groups that have less structure and offer more opportunity for self-expression.

2. Virtually no research has been directed at the factors generally assumed to be of principal therapeutic value in groups, such as learning by imitation, realizing that others have the same problems, and acquiring feelings of belongingness (Yalom, 1975).

3. Marathon groups may have no particular advantage over similarly constituted groups that meet for shorter periods of time; in fact, concentrating group hours in a few marathon sessions may accomplish less than spreading them over more sessions.

4. A variety of group therapies do initiate beneficial and lasting changes in the behavior of individual members, but seldom have there been appropriate attention-placebo controls for nonspecific factors.

(This complaint should by now be familiar to the reader.)

5. Casualties of therapy, people who become worse in the course of treatment, are very few, with most studies finding rates of less than 3 percent. Members who do become worse are usually particularly disturbed. Those responsible for selecting group members try to screen out people who might need more individual attention or for whom the stress of confrontation and open sharing of feelings with others might be too great. Particular *styles* of leadership, such as a challenging, authoritative attitude which pushes group members to deal with more feeling, especially anger, than they are ready for, may be harmful (Lieberman, Yalom, and Miles, 1973; see Box 20.1).

6. No body of evidence supports the superiority of one kind of group therapy over another. Although one theoretical approach may be more suitable than another for treating a particular problem, research has not yet addressed such questions.

7. Cohesive groups apparently produce better results for their members than do less cohesive groups, giving them comfort and courage.

8. It has long been assumed that progress in group therapy is facilitated by feedback, by candid comments made by one person to another about the feelings he or she arouses, the impressions made, "how you're comin' across." Evidence indicates that feedback is indeed useful, especially when negative feedback, "You sound imperious when you ask things of people," is followed by positive feedback, "I like the way you said that" (Jacobs et al., 1973).

Family and Marital Therapy

The Normality of Conflict

There is almost universal agreement among marital therapists and researchers, regardless of theoretical orientation, that conflict is *inevitable* in a marriage or in any other long-term relationship. The aura of the honeymoon passes when the couple makes unromantic decisions about where to live, where to seek employment, how to budget money, what kind of meals to prepare and who is to prepare them, when to visit in-laws, when to have children if they plan to do so, whether to experiment with novel sexual techniques to keep alive the spark of physical attraction. Now, in addition, they have the changed nature of gender roles to negotiate. For ex-

BOX 20.1

THERAPY, FOR BETTER OR FOR WORSE

In 1966 Allen Bergin applied the term *deterioration effect* to the harm that can come to someone from therapy. Several reviews of the literature since his initial report (Bergin, 1971; Bergin and Lambert, 1978; Lambert, Bergin, and Collins, 1977; Strupp, Hadley, and Gomes-Schwartz, 1977) indicate an unpleasant fact of life: although individual psychotherapy benefits many people, some are hurt by the experience. Group therapy (Yalom and Lieberman, 1971) and marital and family treatment (Gurman and Kniskern, 1978) also have casualties. Risk of being harmed is of course not peculiar to psychological intervention. Patients have been made worse by a wide range of medical procedures as well, including electroconvulsive therapy (Elmore and Sugerman, 1975) and the prescription of psychoactive drugs (Shader and DiMascio, 1970), both of which aim at psychological change.

Some people who do *not* seek treatment also deteriorate. Avoiding contact with a mental health professional is no guarantee against getting worse!*

What are the factors that might be responsible for the deterioration effect? Highly disturbed people and those with great expectations and a need to improve are among those often harmed. Moreover, therapies of all orientations are subject to the deterioration effect. Reports from the Menninger Foundation, a renowned center for research and training in psychoanalysis, suggest that Freudian therapy may be too stressful for people with little "ego strength," poor personal relationships, and little ability to tolerate anxiety and frustration (Kernberg, 1973; Horwitz, 1974).

The therapist will bear ultimate responsibility for harm to the client. Lieberman, Yalom, and Miles (1973) found casualties in encounter groups that were led by an "aggressive stimulator," by a challenging, authoritative person who insisted on self-disclosure and catharsis of group participants even when they were not willing or ready for it. Any therapy can be abused by a practitioner who follows it foolishly, without tailoring it to the needs of the client. Some clients, desperate for support, reassurance, and ad-

vice and lacking in interpersonal skills, may become worse if a client-centered therapist unflinchingly declines to provide some guidance. Other clients, already overly dependent on others, may not be able to make choices and grow if the behavior therapist does not recognize this as a need and, instead, takes total charge of their lives. Any therapist or community worker can err when assessing the patient's problem, thereby embarking on treatment that cannot possibly help him or her. In addition, therapists, it must be remembered, are only human beings! Their training and experience do not qualify them as Superpeople in Mental Health. Their own needs and personal problems, even though they know they should not allow them to intrude, can blind them to the needs of the client and can otherwise reduce their ability and willingness to work on the client's behalf. Sadly, some therapists are unethical as well. A few go so far as to claim that clients (always the more attractive ones) can profit from a sexual encounter with the therapist; these workers sometimes initiate or permit sexual intimacies. Licensing laws and codes of ethics do not themselves ensure that therapists will always act wisely and humanely. Most do, and the vast majority of clients are *not* hurt by them. But the deterioration effect has been observed too often to be disregarded or underestimated.

---

*Several noted behavior therapists have examined the studies on which Bergin and others base their claim of a deterioration effect. They (Mays and Franks 1980; Rachman and Wilson, 1980) suggest that the evidence is far weaker than assumed earlier. It is proving as difficult to show that therapy can sometimes harm as it has been to show that it can help. One problem is insufficient information on "spontaneous deterioration," that is, on the rate at which people who receive no therapy at all become worse. We know that some disturbed and untreated people do get worse. "If spontaneous deterioration did not take place, mental health workers would join the ranks of the unemployed . . ." (Rachman and Wilson, 1980, p. 99). But therapy outcome studies have thus far failed to assess this deterioration adequately. Thus certain people who deteriorate while in therapy may do so not because of the therapy itself, but because of factors outside the consulting room, beyond the control of the therapist. Even so, some patients clearly worsen during therapy, which raises serious empirical and ethical questions.

---

ample, if both spouses work, shall their place of residence be determined by the husband's employment or by the wife's? This list, some readers might term it litany, of sources of conflict must be handled by any two people living together, whether they are married or not, whether they are of the opposite sex or not.[2] Authorities

---

[2]Most of what is discussed under the rubric of marital therapy is relevant as well to unconventional relationships, such as those of gay people. For this reason the term couples therapy is becoming more common among mental health professionals.

agree that it is the way couples deal with such inherent conflicts that determines the quality and duration of their cohabitation relationship (for example, Schwartz and Schwartz, 1980).

A strategy some couples adopt, deliberately or unconsciously, is to avoid acknowledging disagreements and conflicts. Because they believe in the reality of the fairy tale ending, "And they lived happily ever after," any sign that their own marriage is not going smoothly is so threatening that it must be ignored. Unfortunately,

"I wouldn't call two 'Gesundheit's in seven years a sincere effort to communicate."

(Drawing by Geo. Price; copyright © 1971 The New Yorker Magazine, Inc.)

dissatisfactions and resentments usually develop and begin to take their toll as time goes by. Because the partners do not quarrel, they may appear ''a perfect couple'' to outside observers. But without discussing things openly, they drift apart emotionally.

From Individual to Conjoint Therapy

The terms family therapy and marital therapy do not denote a set procedure. Although the focus is on at least two members of a family, how the therapist views the problem, what techniques are chosen to alleviate them, how often family members are seen, and whether children and even grandparents are included are all variables of treatment.

Marital and family therapy share some of the same theoretical frameworks as individual therapy. Psychoanalytic marital therapists, for example, focus on the way a person seeks or avoids a partner who resembles, to his or her unconscious, the opposite-sexed parent. Frustrated and unsatisfied by his love-seeking attempts as a child, the adult man may unconsciously seek maternal nurturance from his wife and make excessive, even infantile, demands of her. Much of the discussion will center around the conflicts he is having with his wife and, presumably, the repressed strivings for maternal love that underlie his immature ways of relating to her. These unconscious forces will be plumbed, with the wife

assisting and possibly revealing some of her own unresolved yearnings for her father.

Ellis's rational-emotive therapy has also been applied to marital conflict. Again the perspective is individualistic or intrapsychic; the therapist assumes that something going on within one or both of the partners is causing the marital distress. The wife, for example, may harbor the irrational belief that her husband must constantly adore her, that his devotion must never falter. She is likely then to overreact when at a social gathering he enjoys himself away from her side, talking to other men and attractive women.

Early sex therapy treated a psychosexual problem of one or both partners directly, expecting that whatever other difficulties the couple might have—anger, resentment—would dissipate thereafter. This pattern undoubtedly holds for many sexually distressed couples. But, as already mentioned in Chapter 13, the increasing popularity of sex therapy since Masters and Johnson's *Human Sexual Inadequacy* was published in 1970 has brought to the attention of sex therapists many troubled couples for whom the sexual problem is but one aspect of a more complex *system*. Marital and family therapy looks for these systems. The following case history illustrates how a sexual dysfunction can serve a *useful* purpose in maintaining a couple's relationship and how its apparently successful treatment can actually worsen their overall connection and cut short their newfound sexual enjoyment.

A couple with a marriage of twenty years duration sought treatment for the male's problem of total inability to have an erection. This had been a problem for over nineteen of their twenty years of marriage. Successful intercourse had only taken place in the first few months of the marriage. The woman in this couple was also unable to reach an orgasm, and indeed had never had an orgasm from any form of stimulation, in her entire life. However, she reported that she greatly enjoyed sex and was extremely frustrated by her husband's inability to have an erection.

In treating this couple, through techniques [based on those of Masters and Johnson], very rapid progress was made. The husband very quickly began to have erections in response to his wife's manual stimulation of his genitals. She also learned to have orgasm, first through her own masturbation and then through her husband's manual and oral stimulation of her genitals. By session 10 of weekly therapy, the couple was able to engage in normal intercourse with both of them having orgasm. Thus, the case was essentially "cured" within ten sessions.

However, at this point, something rather peculiar happened. Rather than continuing intercourse after this success, the couple discontinued all sexual activity for the next several weeks. Upon careful exploration by the therapist a rather interesting picture emerged. First, it became clear that the husband had a great need to remain distant and aloof from his wife. He had great fears of being overwhelmed and controlled by her, and found closeness to be very uncomfortable. He himself had had a rather disturbed relationship with his mother, with her being extremely controlling, manipulating, and intrusive in his life, well into his adulthood. For him, the inability to have an erection served to keep his wife distant from him, and to maintain his need for privacy, separateness, and autonomy in the relationship.

In exploring the situation with the wife, [the therapist found] in contrast to her overt statements . . . an extremely ambivalent attitude toward sex. She had been raised in a very anti-sexual family. While she claimed to have rejected these anti-sexual teachings in her own late adolescence and adulthood, in point of fact this rejection had occurred only at a superficial intellectual level. Emotionally, she still had a great deal of difficulty in accepting her sexual

feelings. She had fears of being overwhelmed by uncontrollable sexual urges if she allowed herself to enjoy sex. Thus, her husband's erectile problems served to protect her from her own fears about sex. Furthermore, over the nineteen years of her husband being unable to attain an erection, she had come to have a very powerful position in the relationship. She very often reminded her husband that he owed her a lot because of her sexual frustration. Thus, she was essentially able to win all arguments with him, and to get him to do anything that she wanted.

For this couple, the rapid resolution of their sexual dysfunction threatened elements in both their own personalities, and in the way their relationship was structured. In exploring their inability to continue having intercourse, once they had succeeded, they came to realize the [link] between their sexual problems and the structure of their [marriage]. With several additional weeks of therapy focused on resolving these individual and relationship factors, they were able to resume sexual activity successfully (LoPiccolo and Friedman, 1985, pp. 465–466).

The Essentials of Conjoint Therapy

It has been noticed that many people who improve through individual therapy, usually in an institution, have a relapse when they return home (see Box 20.2). Theories blaming family relationships for schizophrenia were based on such observations. Sometimes forces work the other way around: improvement of the "identified patient" can be destructive to the family, as in the case description just given. Apparently the family unit and the relationships within it are sometimes distorted and need restructuring. As an overall approach, family therapy seems to have begun with the work of John Bell (1975), a psychologist working in the 1950s at the Mental Research Institute in Palo Alto, California. In the past forty years an increasing number of mental health professionals have devoted their professional lives to this kind of work. During the 1960s the efforts of Virginia Satir (1967), a psychiatric social worker, and of Donald Jackson (and Weakland, 1961), a psychiatrist, also at MRI, provided the field with fresh impetus.

The MRI people identify faulty communication patterns, uneasy relationships, and inflexibility. Members of the family come to realize how their behavior affects their relations with others. They then devote their energies to making specific changes. Few family therapists

Family therapy focuses on the whole family and how each member relates to each other member.

are concerned with past history, and none believes that working with only one member of the family can be fruitful. Whatever the clinical problem, the family therapist views it as that of a system, the family, and therefore treated to the best advantage within this group context.[3]

Most marital therapy is conjoint, that is, the partners are *together* in sessions with a therapist. Initially, distressed couples do not react very positively toward each other, which is not surprising! Jacobson and Margolin (1979), two behavioral marital therapists, recommend attending to this problem as an initial step in helping a couple improve their marriage. One strategy is the "caring days" idea of Richard Stuart (1976). The wife agrees to devote herself to doing nice things for her husband on a given day, without expecting anything in return. The husband will do the same for her on another day. If successful, this strategy accomplishes at least two important things: first, it breaks the cycle of distance, suspicion, and aversive control of each other; and second, it shows the giving partner that he or she is able to affect the spouse in a positive way. This enhanced sense of positive control is achieved simply by pleasing the partner. The giving can later be more reciprocal; each partner may agree to please the other in certain specific ways, in anticipation of the partner's reciprocating. For example, a husband may agree to prepare dinner on Tuesdays, and on that day the wife contracts to stop at the supermarket on her way home from work and do the weekly shopping. The improved atmosphere that de-

velops as a consequence of each partner's doing nice things for the other and having nice things done for him or her in return helps each become motivated to please the other person on future occasions.

Behavioral marital therapists generally adopt Thibaut and Kelley's (1959) exchange theory of interaction. According to this view of human relationships, people value others if they receive a high ratio of benefits to costs, that is, if they see themselves getting at least as much from the other person as they have to expend. Furthermore, people are assumed to be more disposed to continue a given relationship if other alternatives are less attractive to them, promising fewer benefits and costing more. Therapists therefore try to encourage a mutual dispensing of rewards by spouse A and spouse B.

A quid pro quo arrangement, however, carries with it the risk that one partner will perceive the other's kindness as expecting goodies in return. He's preparing the kind of meal he knows I like because he wants something from me. Would not a truly satisfactory, loving relationship be one in which partners do things for each other because they want to please them? Perhaps a strictly and explicitly stated policy of reciprocity takes the romance out of a long-term relationship! The reply to this criticism might be that, in a really distressed[4] relationship,

[3]An example of Salvador Minuchin's family systems therapy was given earlier in our discussion of anorexia nervosa (see page 396).

[4]"Distressed" is the term widely used in the marital therapy literature for relationships that need the help of a professional. But a close relationship can be dysfunctional without the active discomfort or suffering implied by the word distressed. A couple can, over the years, drift apart emotionally so that one or both of the partners no longer feel anything for the other (Christensen, 1983). But such emotional distance in a relationship may not make the partnership unstable. Some married couples stay together for years, for many reasons, without the intimacy and mutual facilitation of the earliest stages of their togetherness.

BOX 20.2

FAMILY THERAPY FOR SCHIZOPHRENIA

Research has recently attempted to help schizophrenics discharged from a mental hospital to remain at home. Since high levels of "expressed emotion" (see page 350) have been linked with relapse and reinstitutionalization, a family therapy team at the University of Southern California decided to try to lower, through cognitive and behavioral means, the emotional intensity of the households that schizophrenics returned to (Falloon et al., 1982). Their large-scale project was comparative.

The family therapy sessions, in which family members and the patient participated, took place in their own home. The importance of the patient's taking his or her medication regularly was stressed. The family was also instructed in ways to express both positive and negative feelings in a constructive, empathic manner and to defuse tense, personal conflicts through collaborative problem solving (see page 516). The patient's symptoms were explained, and ways of coping with them and of reducing emotional turmoil in the home were suggested. It was made clear to patient and family alike that schizophrenia is primarily a biochemical illness, but that proper medication and the kind of psychosocial treatment they were receiving can reduce stress on the patient and prevent relapses and deterioration. Treatment extended over the first nine months after the patient returned home, when the danger of relapse is especially great.

This family treatment, aimed at calming the home life of the family, was compared to an individual therapy in which the patient was seen alone at a clinic, with supportive discussions centering on problems in daily living and on developing a social network. Family members of patients in this control group were seldom seen, and when they were, it was not in conjoint home sessions with the patients. The control patients received in effect the individual, supportive management in widespread use in aftercare programs for schizophrenics.

Ongoing assessments were made of the patient's symptomatology, with special attention given to signs of relapse, such as delusions of control and hallucinations. Family members were also evaluated for their problem-solving skills and for the emotions they expressed toward the patient. All patients, including the controls, were maintained on antipsychotic medication, primarily Thorazine, which was monitored and adjusted throughout the project by a psychiatrist unaware of which patients were receiving family therapy and which individual.

In all, thirty-six patients were treated, eighteen in the family therapy group, eighteen in the individual therapy control group. Those receiving family therapy fared much better. Only one person in this group had a major clinical relapse, as compared to eight in the control group. Furthermore, patients receiving family therapy had significantly fewer schizophrenic symptoms.

In interpreting their results, the investigators were properly mindful of the possibility that the patients given family therapy may have improved more than the controls because they took their neuroleptic medications more faithfully; indeed, the family therapy subjects did comply better with their medication regimens. Other studies have shown, however, that deterioration in patients such as these is not adequately prevented by drugs alone. In other words, the family therapy seems to have been important.

merely breaking the cycle of recrimination and hostility is no mean achievement. Once the parties are at least being civil to each other, the stage is set for more constructive problem solving and communication.

Indeed, all forms of marital therapy try to improve communication. Each partner is trained to listen empathically to the other and to state clearly to the partner what he or she understands is being said and what the feelings behind the remarks are. One way to improve marital communication is to distinguish between the intent of a remark and its impact.[5] Partner A, for example, may wish to be helpful by asking partner B whether he can get her something from the store, but this question may have a negative impact if she would prefer him to stay home and help her with a project. The husband's intent, then, would be positive, but his question would affect his wife negatively. Research has shown that the communications of distressed and happy couples may not differ so much in intent as in impact. In one study Gottman and his colleagues (1976) found that both types of couples made the same number of positive statements to partners, but distressed spouses reported having *heard* fewer positive statements than satisfied spouses. Gottman proposed a technique for clarifying intent when two partners are in a heated argument going nowhere. The husband calls "Stop action" and asks his wife to tell him what she believes he is trying to say. Or the wife asks the same of her husband. The feedback indicates immediately whether remarks are having the intended impact.

[5]The reader will find the following similar to Aronson's analysis of a two-person exchange.

Marital and family therapy has made creative use of the good-quality videotape equipment now available. A couple can be given a problem to solve during part of a therapy session, such as where to go on vacation, and can be videotaped while they attempt to solve it. The ways in which they push forward their own wishes—or fail to—and the ways in which they accommodate to the other's wishes—or fail to—are but one aspect of their communication that a therapist can glean from later viewing of the tape, oftentimes with the couple themselves watching too. Patterns of communication and miscommunication can be more readily discerned. The husband and wife can agree to try out new ways of negotiating and new ways of dealing with conflictual issues (Margolin and Fernandez, in press).

Many operant behavior therapists follow Gerald Patterson's (1974a) practice of working with the parents to alter reinforcement of the child whose behavior is a problem. The child is involved little if at all in treatment. An improvement in the child's behavior often reduces much distress between husband and wife. But sometimes a child's aberrant behavior can be traced to the marital distress; although the child may be the "identified patient," his or her "problems" may better be regarded as reflecting marital conflict. In such instances family-marital therapists usually decide to intervene in the marital relationship, hoping that the child's difficulties will diminish if the parents learn to get along better. Unfortunately, there is little decisive information on where it it best to intervene. Some research done by a Stony Brook group suggests that altering the child's problematic behavior can improve the marital relationship (Oltmanns, Broderick, and O'Leary, 1976), but other research done by the same group indicates that successful marital treatment has a favorable impact on children's problems (Turkewitz and O'Leary, 1977).

Special Considerations

The marital dysfunction treated by therapists is not all the same, as Margolin and Fernandez (in press) remind us. One couple may seek professional assistance when there is only dissatisfaction in their relationship, but another may wait until the crisis is so great that one or both partners have already consulted a divorce lawyer. There are, then, different *stages* of marital distress (Weiss and Cerreto, 1980; Duck, 1984), and different therapeutic approaches may be called for, depending on where the therapist judges the couple to be.

Indeed, conjoint therapy may not even be the best tack, if, for example, one of the parties suffers from a psychological problem that disrupts the home but is itself related to issues outside the home. If a husband is depressed because of self-doubts about his job, there is little reason to alter the marital relationship. Such a strategy might lift his depression somewhat, but it will hardly address the source of the problem. Even so, married partners are usually the most significant people in each other's lives and thereby control many of the most powerful reinforcers that can be brought to bear on their partners. If the depressed man will benefit from being assertive at his job, his wife could encourage this by working with him first on becoming more assertive in the marriage (Jacobson and Margolin, 1979).

Divorce counseling is a new facet of marital therapy. Until recently marital-family therapists have regarded divorce as an evil to be avoided at all costs, but the advocacy of women's rights, the increasing acceptability of single-parent families, and the greater expectations people have of marriage have prompted mental health workers to explore ways of helping people leave a marriage that appears beyond repair (Kaslow, 1981). Therapists of this new specialty help the divorced or separated partner deal with the loss of the spouse, regain self-esteem—a person is likely to blame himself or herself for the "failure" of the marriage—and foster independence (Gurman and Kniskern, 1978). Sometimes divorce counseling or therapy begins while the couple are still living together; the participants might regard as successful a resolution of their ambivalence and fear about separating. Divorce counseling is still too new to have generated much in the way of research, but studies will probably be forthcoming in the near future.

Research in Family Therapy

Perhaps because the outcomes and processes of family and marital therapies are so complex and vague, controlled research on whether they work, with what kinds of problems, and how has only begun (Gottman et al., 1976; Weiss and Wider, 1982; Jacobson and Margolin, 1979; Jacobson et al., in press; Lieberman, Wheeler, and Kuehnel, 1983; O'Leary and Turkewitz, 1978; Stuart, 1980; Gurman and Kniskern, 1978). One important finding from the outcome literature is that conjoint therapy for marital problems appears to be much more successful than individual therapy with one spouse. Indeed, the state of about 10 percent of clients seen individually for marital problems worsens (Gurman and Kniskern, 1978). Conjoint therapy is apparently better for problems that are conjoint in nature.

A great virtue of most family therapists is their willingness to make their work public. It is commonplace to have therapy sessions videotaped, and several professional journals, such as *Family Process* and *Family Therapy*, publish detailed accounts of clinical work.

Some professionals view family therapy as a revolution in the treatment of human psychological suffering. Whether it will indeed prove this dramatically effective remains to be seen.

COMMUNITY PSYCHOLOGY

Prevention and Seeking

Community psychology's focus on prevention sets it apart from what we have studied so far. Gerald Caplan (1964), whose writings have had considerable impact, distinguishes three levels of prevention. _Tertiary prevention_ is in many respects equivalent to the treatment of disorders already discussed. It also seeks to reduce the long-term consequences of having a disorder; for example, mental health workers help those who have recovered from mental illness to participate fully in the occupational and social life of the community. _Secondary prevention_ consists of efforts to detect problems early, before they become serious, and to prevent their development into chronic disabilities. Quick and accurate assesssment by community people—physicians, teachers, clergymen, police officers, court officials, social workers—will allow remedial procedures to begin early. Crisis-intervention work and twenty-four-hour emergency services are examples of secondary prevention.

Primary prevention tries to reduce the incidence of new cases of social and emotional problems in a population. Altering stressful and depriving conditions in the environment and strengthening individuals so that they can resist stress and cope with adversity are two primary prevention means. Attention to overcrowding, poor housing, job discrimination, neighborhood recreation, and school curricula and neighborhood group work with children from broken homes are examples. Genetic counseling, prenatal care for ghetto mothers, school lunches, and Meals on Wheels are also primary prevention measures. Community psychologists concentrate their efforts on primary and secondary prevention.

Nearly all the therapies reviewed thus far are administered by professional persons with advanced degrees who make themselves available by appointment in offices, clinics, and hospitals. They provide assistance to individuals who initiate the contact themselves or are referred by the courts. Such delivery of services has been referred to as in the _waiting mode_ (Rappaport and Chinsky, 1974). In contrast, community psychology operates in the _seeking mode_, that is, those who are troubled or are likely one day to be so are sought out by

community workers, some of whom are paraprofessionals supervised by psychologists, psychiatrists, or social workers. Mental health services are often provided outside of offices and clinics, in the schools, businesses, and factories, and on the street corners of the person's own community.

Are the techniques employed by community psychologists different from those used in private practice so that a seeking mode makes especially good sense? The answer is complex.

Rappaport and Chinsky (1974) have proposed that every type of mental health care has two components, the delivery and the conceptual. The delivery component relates to the difference between seeking and waiting, to an _attitude_ about making services available. As noted, community psychology has a seeking orientation. The conceptual component, on the other hand, consists of the theoretical and data-based underpinnings of the services. Two examples are psychoanalytic and learning approaches. Table 20.1 illustrates how these two conceptual modes combine with either style of delivery. For example, a twenty-four-hour-a-day hot line in a suicide prevention center would be in the community psychology seeking mode. But what specifically the people answering the phones say and do when a call comes in depends on the conceptual mode. One worker might be psychoanalytic in approach; another might construe suicide threats in learning terms. Clearly, these two workers would answer the calls differently—but both would be delivering community psychology. The conceptual components section of Table 20.1 could, of course, be expanded almost indefinitely. Whether a particular conceptual orientation is more suited to one of the two delivery modes than to the other is a separate, and crucial, question, one which creates ongoing controversy among community psychologists and psychiatrists.

Values and the Question of Where To Intervene

In an effort to explain the essence of community psychology, Rappaport (1977) proposes that we view society as composed of four levels: the individual, the small group, the organization, and the institution. Therapists will intervene at a given level, depending on their values and goals for people. For example, if the therapist assumes that society itself is benign, human problems will be seen as failures to _adjust_ to this benign system. Treatment will therefore attempt to change the _individual_ so that he or she will fit into society. This tertiary preven-

Primary prevention includes activities such as providing more jobs and prenatal care, securing better housing, and improving nutrition.

tion is pursued in a number of ways—from behavior therapy to psychoanalysis to chemotherapy—but in all these modes of intervention society is considered good and people in need of adjustment to it.[6] In contrast, human problems may be assumed to derive from interpersonal difficulties such as conflicts within families, at work, and in other *small groups*. The therapist will ap-

ply family and encounter therapy to help members of the group communicate better. The therapist will *not* try to change just the individual because the problem is assumed to lie in group processes.

If the third level, that of *organizations*, is considered at fault, therapists have another view of human disorders. They "blame" the way units such as schools and

[6]Of course, a therapist can work with individuals and help them change so that they are better able to deal with a society that is not benign. In other words, therapists treating individuals may at the same time view society as exerting a negative, even evil, influence on people. They may decide that it is easier to help the individual client cope

with negative societal forces, rather than try to change the negative aspects of society. The community psychologist is concerned, however, that negative societal forces will be overlooked when all the attention is paid to the individual. Indeed, therapists are commonly accused of helping their troubled client *adjust* to an evil society.

TABLE 20.1 Some Possible Models for Mental Health Service
(adapted from Rappaport and Chinsky, 1974)

Conceptual Component*	Delivery Component	
	Waiting Mode	**Seeking Mode**
Psychoanalytic conception	Psychodynamic explanations of abnormal behavior. Therapist waits for patient to initiate contact and then uses insight therapy.	Psychodynamic explanations of abnormal behavior. Professional attempts to prevent illness through public education and extends traditional treatments into community settings.
Behavioral conception	Learning theory interpretation of emotional dysfunction. Therapist waits for client to initiate contact and then uses techniques such as systematic desensitization.	Learning theory interpretation of emotional dysfunction. Professional extends services into the community through public education; trains various nonprofessionals in behavior therapy techniques and social-learning principles.

*Listed here as examples are only two of a large number of possible conceptual components.

prisons operate. To help a child who is failing in her academic work, for example, therapists examine the school curriculum and how it is implemented by principals and teachers; they do *not* provide remedial tutoring for the pupil. Community psychology operates at this level and at the *institutional* level, which is closely related to it but is more abstract and all-inclusive. Institutions refer not to physical entities such as school buildings and prisons but to the basic values and ideologies that characterize a society, its religion, and its politics. For example, the community psychologist may assert that people are unhappy because of a lopsided distribution of wealth and power. Professional efforts would then be directed at political parties, the courts, legislatures, and the like, *not* to encourage them to function more efficiently but rather to change entirely their goals and basic assumptions so that they work toward a more equitable social distribution of wealth and power (see Box 20.3).

Rappaport's analysis makes it clear why some community workers tend to be impatient with individual and group therapy. They do not believe the problems lie with the individual or the group, and they even assert that by concentrating on these levels the therapist will "blame the victim" (Ryan, 1971) and overlook the real problems of organizations and institutions. For these reasons community psychologists work in the seeking mode and make no pretense, as some individual and group therapists frequently do, at being politically and ethically neutral.

Why was there a shift to community activism in the treatment of mental disorders? For many years it had been obvious how few people could avail themselves of psychotherapeutic services, which were usually very expensive, in short supply, and apparently geared to so-called YAVIS clients—individuals who are young, attractive, verbal, intelligent, and successful (Schofield, 1964). Eysenck (1952) had also questioned the effectiveness of most kinds of psychotherapy, finding treated patients' rates of improvement no better than the spontaneous remission rate. Although Eysenck's criticisms were compellingly rebutted by a number of scholars (for example, Bergin, 1971), the idea had taken hold among mental health professionals that psychotherapy aimed at changing the individual might not be the best way to alleviate the psychological problems of the majority of people. Focus began to shift from repressions, conflicts, and neurotic fears to large-scale social problems such as poverty, overcrowding, poor education, segregation, the alienation felt in large cities, and the impersonalism of many aspects of present-day living.

The shift from intrapsychic factors to social factors probably reflected the *Zeitgeist* or tenor of the times. The 1960s were a period of tremendous social upheaval and activism. Institutions of all kinds were being challenged. Cities and college campuses were erupting in riots, and a range of minority groups, from blacks in urban ghettoes to gays in the larger cities, charged racism and political repression. This social upheaval, which at times seemed to border on revolution, further encouraged a search for causes of individual suffering in social institutions. At the same time the Kennedy and Johnson administrations lent the monetary clout of the federal government to a progressive liberalism. Kennedy's New Frontier and Johnson's Great Society programs poured tens of millions of dollars into attempts at bettering the human condition.

Community Mental Health Centers

The greatest single impetus to the community psychology movement was a practical one. In 1955 Congress authorized the Joint Commission on Mental Illness and Health to examine the state mental hospitals. On the basis of its survey, which went on for six years, the commission concluded that the care offered was largely custodial and that steps must be taken to ensure that treatment is given. In its 1961 report it recommended that no additional large hospitals be built and that community mental health clinics be established. In 1963 President John F. Kennedy sent a message to Congress calling for a "bold new approach" and proposing the Community Mental Health Centers Act to provide comprehensive services in the community and to implement programs for the prevention and treatment of mental disturbances. The act was passed. For every 100,000 people a mental health center was to provide outpatient therapy, short-term inpatient care, day hospitalization for those able to go home at night, twenty-four-hour emergency services, and consultation and education to other agencies in the community.

The principal objective of a community mental health center is to provide outpatient mental health care in a person's own community and at a cost that is not beyond the means of most people. The increased availability of clinical services presumably means that fewer individuals need be committed to institutions. They can go across town and receive therapy several times a week without leaving their families, friends, and work. The community health center also provides short-term inpatient care, usually on a psychiatric ward of a community general hospital, again where relatives and friends of patients may conveniently visit them. Partial hospitalization, during the day or sometimes for the night, is usually also on a psychiatric ward. A twenty-four-hour walk-in crisis service offers emergency consultation around the clock and "rap sessions" for members of the community. In Chapter 12 (page 307) we discussed rape crisis work, a service often run by community mental health centers.

The centers are staffed by psychiatrists, psychologists, social workers, and nurses, and by paraprofessionals who live in the neighborhood and can help bridge the gap between the middle- and upper-middle-class professionals and community members to whom psychotherapy is sometimes an alien concept. Paraprofessionals and volunteers also of course provide needed numbers for staffing the centers within their limited budgets.

The first program involving paraprofessionals was probably that at Harvard University (Umbarger et al., 1962), in which students spent several hours per week as companions to patients in mental hospitals.[7] Community acceptance of these workers would seem to be a vital factor in community-based programs. They usually bring a fresh commitment to their work and sincere and warm interest in the patients. Yet a nonprofessional may not have all the qualities and talents necessary to make effective therapeutic interventions. Surely much depends on *what* the paraprofessional is supposed to do.

A wide range of services is included under the rubrics of "consultation" and "education." A principal one is to educate other community workers, the teachers, clergymen, and police, in the principles of preventive mental health and in how to extend help themselves (see Box 20.4). Consider the crisis-intervention effort made by the Westside Community Mental Health Center in 1971. The staff tried to help children adjust to enforced school busing in San Francisco.

We designed a program in which we placed a professional staff person on a school bus to ride to and from school with grade school children; in addition this staff person had streetcorner meetings with the parents about their busing concerns, and acted also as their advocate to the schools. Knowing the children would be experiencing separation anxiety in this [situation], we had our Hospital Art Department design coloring books with maps of the territory they would cover on the bus route; we attempted to introduce play materials and games that would be helpful to the children, would encourage the children to carry "transitional objects" from home . . . such as dolls, teddy bears, special favorite toys. Our staff member met with the children before they boarded

[7]See Guerney (1969) for numerous examples of other programs.

BOX 20.3

EMPOWERMENT, SMALL WINS, AND BROAD-SCALE SOCIAL CHANGE

Our earlier discussion of "hardiness" and physical health (see page 170) illustrates an approach that primary prevention can take. Studies by Kobasa and her colleagues (Kobasa, Maddi, and Kahn, 1982; Kobasa and Puccetti, 1983) indicate that people who have the three personality characteristics of commitment, control, and challenge—which make up hardiness—are less prone to medical problems than are those who are not hardy. Mindful that certain people are predisposed to certain illnesses—the diatheses spoken of so often in this book—perhaps the stresses that they encounter during the course of their lives can be reduced by encouraging them to be hardy. Encouraging hardiness is similar to Maddi's recommendation that children be urged to make independent decisions based on a system of values and to have an active internal life. Thus can they protect themselves from alienation, meaninglessness, and the inability to exert will that make up the existential neurosis (see page 49). We have repeatedly found that people need to feel in control of their lives, for if they do not, they are subject to anxiety, depression, and psychophysiological disorders. With all these converging lines of evidence, primary prevention workers are on fairly solid empirical ground in concentrating on what Rappaport (1981) calls empowerment.

Indeed, it has been argued by some distinguished community psychologists (Joffee and Albee, 1981) that powerlessness underlies the entire range of social problems and psychopathology.

It makes little sense to develop separate programs for the

prevention of child abuse, spouse abuse, elder abuse, the exploitation of women, minority group members, migrant farmworkers, the handicapped, the mentally ill, and the mentally retarded. If we see all these groups as powerless because of socioeconomic conditions, then a logical approach is to determine whether there might be an equitable redistribution of power. . . . Without meaning to be simplistic, we would like to suggest that we examine the arguments . . . for a redistribution of power through a redistribution of wealth in our society (p. 332).

These words counsel action on a grand scale—what could be wider-ranging than a redistribution of wealth? Other community psychologists define large social problems as made up of smaller, more manageable chunks (Weick, 1984). An example would be the increasing use of nonsexist language—he or she; plural pronouns like "they" rather than the singular ones; female pronouns where earlier only masculine pronouns would have been used, as in speaking of physicians; and conversely, male pronouns where earlier only female pronouns would have been heard, as in discussing elementary school teachers. This "small win" has been achieved in a relatively short time.

Weick argues that small, focused shifts are more readily accepted by opponents and attract resources—since everyone loves a winner—for the next effort at change. The failure of a too-ambitious attempt can be demoralizing, but small wins make more small wins possible, and in this stepwise fashion more sweeping changes can be achieved over time.

---

the bus, talked to them on the bus, again in their new schoolyard and on the way back home again (Heiman, 1973, p. 60).

Staff members at a mental health center might conceivably call a rent strike, should they decide that better housing would alleviate emotional suffering. Or suggestions might be made by a center's staff to change physical arrangements in a local factory in order to reduce the boredom or tension of performing particular kinds of work. Moreover, organized interventions such as these need not emanate solely from community mental health centers. Workers can operate from university departments, social welfare agencies, and even private offices and still undertake activities that would be best characterized as community psychology.

Suicide Prevention Centers and Telephone Crisis Services

Many suicide prevention centers are modeled after the Los Angeles Suicide Prevention Center, founded in 1958 by Farberow and Shneidman. There are at present more than 300 such centers in the United States. Staffed largely by nonprofessionals under the supervision of psychologists or psychiatrists, these centers attempt to provide twenty-four-hour consultation to people in suicidal crises. Usually the initial contact is made by telephone. The center's phone number is well publicized in the community. The worker tries to assess the likelihood that the caller will actually make a serious suicide attempt, and, most importantly, tries to establish personal contact and dissuade the caller from suicide. The sum-

BOX 20.4

COMMUNITY PSYCHOLOGY AND COMMUNITY MENTAL HEALTH—
RELATED BUT DIFFERENT

Although related, the community mental health movement and community psychology should be distinguished from each other. Community psychology is concerned primarily with primary prevention, with intervention where no dysfunctions are yet evident, often by attempting to change social systems at a broad, institutional level. Community mental health, by contrast, provides care for the needy, troubled people who have traditionally been underserved by the mental health professions. Because community mental health delivers mental health services for needy individuals, its orientation is often as individualistic as traditional consulting room therapy of the kind discussed in Chapters 18 and 19. On the staffs of mental health centers are psychiatrists, clinical psychologists, and social workers who conduct therapy in offices at the center. Community psychology, on the other hand, shows its concern for individ-

uals by trying to alter social systems and by creating different and, it is hoped, better environments for people to live in, both to reduce the forces that are thought to bring maladaptions and to promote opportunities for individuals to realize their potential. Community psychology requires intervention with the courts, police, schools, and city services and planning agencies. Political more than clinical skills are required for such work; in fact, relatively little time is spent dealing directly with the individuals affected by the larger social forces. The two movements are sometimes equated; the inclusion of community mental health in this discussion of community psychology reflects the relationship between these two forces in psychology today. Nonetheless, their differences are as important to appreciate as are their similarities.

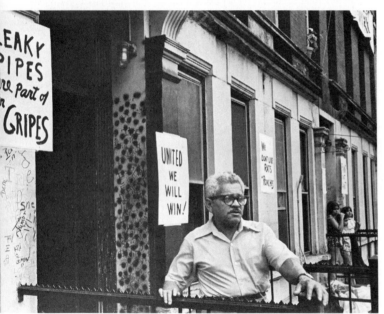

Community psychologists take a social-activist stance and may, for example, organize a rent strike to secure safer living conditions.

mary sheet on page 548, used by telephone workers at the Los Angeles center, speeds the recording of crucial bits of information.

Specialists hold that phone attendants in these centers should work toward the following goals (Speer, 1972).

1. "Tuning in," communicating empathy to the caller.

2. Conveying understanding of the problem.

3. Providing information regarding sources of help, for example, mental health clinics, psychologists, psychiatrists.

4. Obtaining an agreement from the caller to take some specific steps away from suicide, for example, making an appointment to come to the center itself.

5. Providing some degree of hope to the caller that the crisis will end and that life will not always appear so hopeless.

The potential value of such community facilities rests in the fact that most suicides give warnings—"cries for help"—before taking their lives (see page 221). Ambivalence about living or dying is the hallmark of the suicidal state (Shneidman, 1976). Usually their pleas are directed first to relatives and friends, but many potential suicides are isolated from these sources of emotional support; a hotline service may save the lives of such individuals.

It is exceedingly difficult to do controlled research on suicide. Evaluating the effectiveness of suicide prevention centers is similarly problematic, for a large proportion of those who call are not heard from again (Stein and Lambert, 1984). For example, Speer (1971) found that more than 95 percent of callers did not use the service repeatedly. Does this mean that the phone contact helped so much that no further consultation was needed? Perhaps so, but it is also possible that many callers killed themselves after the phone call. Some workers (for example, Jennings, Barraclough, and Moss, 1978; Weiner, 1969) found no difference in the suicide rates of cities with hot-line services and of those without. Although numerous factors might have masked real differences, we cannot conclude from these data that the centers have demonstrated their effectiveness.

Speer (1972) attempted to evaluate one crisis phone service. His study sheds light on the kind of research people in the field are doing and on the difficulties such research poses. The subjects were thirty-four callers to a suicide prevention center who subsequently appeared for individual counseling. Some were asked to rate their feelings after the phone call that had led them to the center; others were asked how they had felt after the preceding plea for help, the last one made to a personal acquaintance, friend, or relative before they called the center. In this way Speer hoped to learn whether potential suicides derive more comfort and benefit from a service or from a friend or relative, who is presumably not trained in handling a suicide threat.

The results are sobering: of the seven measures used, only one showed that calls to the center were significantly more helpful than calls to a friend. Speer concluded that, in this instance, the hot-line service gave no evidence of superiority in achieving the goals specified for it.

Can anything else be said about this study? One possible confound in the design was not considered by Speer. When a person calls a crisis service, he or she may be decidedly more desperate than when phoning a friend or relative. Those who rated phone calls to the service may therefore have been reporting reactions felt in a far more unhappy and more suicidal mood than were the individuals remembering their feelings after calls to friends. If so, there might very well be a significant difference in the efficacy of the two kinds of calls, a difference that would provide much-needed justification for the continuation or even the expansion of such centers.

Once again, we are left with little if any convincing evidence. Human lives are precious, however, and since many people who contact prevention centers weather a suicidal crisis successfully, there is at present no reason to discontinue these efforts.

Suicide hot lines, staffed twenty-four hours a day, are a service often provided by a community-health center.

The Use of Media To Change Harmful Life Styles

Cardiovascular diseases, such as high blood pressure and coronary heart disease, are responsible for more deaths in the United States than any other single group of illnesses. In many respects the life style of an affluent, industrialized society increases risk of premature cardiovascular diseases. A group of researchers at Stanford University, led by Nathan Maccoby, a psychologist noted for his work in communications, have for several years been studying ways to educate large numbers of people about the desirability of altering their life styles, in order to reduce their risk of cardiovascular diseases. For the Three Communities Project they chose a media campaign and a direct, intensive instructional program (Maccoby et al., 1977; Maccoby and Alexander, 1980).

Three towns in northern California were studied; Watsonville and Gilroy were the two experimental towns, Tracy was the control town. For two years both

LOS ANGELES SUICIDE PREVENTION CENTER - TELEPHONE SERVICE

Day Of The Week (1)

☐ 1. Sun. ☐ 2. Mon. ☐ 3. Tue. ☐ 4. Wed.

☐ 5. Thu. ☐ 6. Fri. ☐ 7. Sat.

Date (2-6)

Month | Date | Year

Time (7-10)

Hours | Minutes

Call Duration (11-12)

Minutes

Called Before (13)

☐ 1. Yes ☐ 2. No

NAMES

Client

Name_____

First   Last

Address_____

Phone_____ Work Phone_____

Third Party Caller (14)

☐ 1. Yes ☐ 2. No

Name_____

Address_____

Phone_____ Work Phone_____

Relationship To Client_____

CLIENT DATA

Age (15-16)

Sex (17)

☐ 1. M ☐ 2. F

Marital Status (18)

☐ 1. Single ☐ 2. Married ☐ 3. Divorced ☐ 4. Separated

☐ 5. Widowed ☐ 6. Living Together

Race (19)

☐ 1. White ☐ 2. Black ☐ 3. Spanish ☐ 4. Oriental

☐ 5. Other_____

Employment (20)

☐ 1. Full Time ☐ 2. Part Time ☐ 3. Unemployed

☐ 4. Retired ☐ 5. Disabled ☐ 6. Housewife ☐ 7. Student

CLIENT'S RESOURCES

Living Alone (21)

☐ 1. Yes ☐ 2. No

Social Contact (22)

☐ 0. None ☐ 1. Minimal ☐ 2. Moderate ☐ 3. Frequent

Friends/Relatives (23)   List on other side

☐ 1. Yes ☐ 2. No

Finances (24)

☐ 0 None ☐ 1 Cash

☐ 2 Medi-cal ☐ 3 Insurance

Insurance Co._____

SUBSTANCE ABUSE

Alcohol History (25)

☐ 0. None ☐ 1. Moderate ☐ 2. Severe

Current Alcohol Problem (26)

☐ 0. None ☐ 1. Moderate ☐ 2. Severe

Drinking At Time (27)

☐ 1. Yes ☐ 2. No ☐ 3. Can't Decide

Current Drug Problem (28)

☐ 0. None ☐ 1. Moderate ☐ 2. Severe

SUICIDAL HISTORY

How Long Since First Attempt (29)

☐ 0. None ☐ 1. 3 Mos or Less ☐ 2. 3 Mos - 1 Yr.

☐ 3. 1 - 5 Yrs. ☐ 4. Over 5 Yrs.

How Long Since Last Attempt (30)

☐ 0. None ☐ 1. 3 Mos or Less ☐ 2. 3 Mos. - 1 Yr.

☐ 3. 1 - 5 Yrs. ☐ 4. Over 5 Yrs.

Number Of Attempts (31)

☐ 0. None ☐ 1. One ☐ 2. Two

☐ 3. Three ☐ 4. Four or More

Current Behavior (32)

☐ 0. None ☐ 1. Thoughts ☐ 2. Threats

☐ 3. Preparation ☐ 4. Low Risk Attempt

☐ 5. High Risk Attempt

Plan (33)

☐ 0. None ☐ 1. Gun ☐ 2. Pills

☐ 3. Cutting ☐ 4. Jumping ☐ 5. Other_____

TREATMENT

Hospitalization (34)

☐ 1. Yes ☐ 2. No

Therapy (35)

☐ 0. None ☐ 1. Prior ☐ 2. Current

PRESENTING PROBLEMS

Presenting Problems (36-37)   Check One Only

☐ 1 Bizarre/Psychotic

☐ 2 Emotional/Psychological Long Term

☐ 3 Emotional/Psychological Short Term

☐ 4 Interpersonal Loss

☐ 5 Relationships

☐ 6 Depression

☐ 7 Medical

☐ 8 Lonely

☐ 9 Alcohol

☐ 10 Drugs

☐ 11 Marital/Family

☐ 12 Material Needs

☐ 13 Violence/Homicide

☐ 14 Multiple

☐ 15 Other_____

_____

RESOLUTION

Service Provided (38)

☐ 1. Support/Reinforce ☐ 2. Refer to Prof. Help

☐ 3. Refer to Emergency Help

☐ 4. Spc. Called Emergency Help

☐ 5. Service Rejected ☐ 6. No Service

RATES

Suicide Risk (39)

☐ 1. Low ☐ 2. Moderate ☐ 3. High

Emergency Risk (40)

☐ 1. Low ☐ 2. Moderate ☐ 3. High

experimental towns were bombarded by a mass media campaign to inform citizens about cardiovascular diseases. It consisted of television and radio spots, weekly newspaper columns, and newspaper advertisements and stories, all urging them to stop smoking, to exercise more, and to eat foods low in cholesterol. Posters in buses and in stores conveyed briefly and graphically such vital information as the desirability of eating fewer eggs, since the yolks are rich in cholesterol. In addition, a sample of Watsonville residents at high risk for heart disease received intensive instruction consisting of group sessions and individual home counseling over a ten-week period. The researchers wanted to examine whether information and exhortations to alter life style delivered face-to-face might add to whatever positive benefits derived from the mass media campaign.

The control town, Tracy, had media services that were quite different from those of the two experimental towns. Tracy is separated from Watsonville and Gilroy by a range of low mountains and therefore has entirely separate local television stations. The inhabitants of Tracy were of course not imprisoned in their hometown for the duration of the two-year study, but for the most part they did not receive through their media the messages conveyed to the citizens of the two experimental towns. Because all three towns had sizable numbers of Mexican and Chicano people, all media messages were in Spanish as well as in English.

The findings reveal that through the mass media campaign citizens of Watsonville and Gilroy did significantly increase their knowledge of cardiovascular risk factors; people in the control town did not gain in such knowledge. Egg consumption was reduced more in Watsonville and Gilroy than in Tracy, and clinically significant blood pressure decreases were observed in the two experimental towns, as contrasted with small increases in the control town. The high-risk people of Watsonville who participated in the special, intensive instruction program reaped even greater benefits in lower egg consumption and blood pressure. Finally, the researchers considered the townspeople's overall measure of risk, a weighted average of the several known physical risk factors—high blood levels of cholesterol, smoking cigarettes, and not exercising enough. Not suprisingly, they found highly significant drops in risk in the experimental townspeople, an important result since we know from previous research, the famous Framingham, Massachusetts, longitudinal study of risk factors in cardiovascular diseases (Truett, Cornfield, and Kannel, 1967), that elevated risk scores predict reasonably well the incidence of heart disease over a twelve-year period.

This work of Maccoby and his colleagues is important as a community psychology effort, for it demonstrates that laypeople can learn from the mass media what is known about cardiovascular diseases, and that they will also act in many ways on this knowledge to reduce their overall risk for such diseases. The two-year span of the study is a considerable length of time as far as experiments in psychology are concerned! But in terms of the serious health problems that develop through long-standing detrimental patterns of behavior, this is not a very long time at all. So far the researchers do not know whether cardiovascular diseases will, in fact, be reduced in the experimental towns as compared to the control town. Even so, they have determined that properly designed mass media efforts can significantly alter people's behavior and attitudes in ways that reduce their statistical risk for cardiovascular diseases. The mass media are far less expensive and far more encompassing than individual or group therapy. This demonstrated effectiveness of using the media is a definite plus for community psychology's mission of bringing the greatest good to the greatest number.

Halfway Houses and Aftercare

Some people function too well to remain in a mental hospital and yet do not function independently enough to live on their own or even within their own families. For such individuals there are halfway houses. These are protected living units, typically located in large, formerly private residences. Here patients discharged from a mental hospital live, take their meals, and gradually return to ordinary community life by taking a part-time job or going to school. Living arrangements may be relatively unstructured; some houses set up money-making enterprises that help to train and support the residents. Depending on how well funded the halfway house is, the staff may include psychiatrists or clinical psychologists. The most important staff members are paraprofessionals, often graduate students in clinical psychology or social work who live in the house and act both as administrators and as friends to the residents. Group meetings, at which residents talk out their frustrations and learn to relate to others in honest and constructive ways, are often part of the routine.

The nation's requirements for effective halfway houses for ex-mental patients cannot be underestimated. Properly run residences are scarce. In several states there has been pressure from governors and from legislators to discharge as many hospital patients as possible. Between 1955 and 1980 the population of state mental institutions shrank by more than three-fourths, from 559,000 to 138,000, even though the general population increased significantly during this period. But discharge has all too often been bad for the patients. Some local communities object to the presence of shabbily dressed, often inappropriately behaving ex-patients in their neighborhoods. They have sometimes been exploited by entrepreneurs who, for their federal disability money, house them in unsanitary, poorly administered hotels and motels. Many ex-patients reenter the hospital in what has been termed the "revolving door" syndrome. Clearly, it is not enough merely to discharge mental patients. They must have outpatient services and a protective place to live (see Box 21.4, page 582).

A model of what aftercare can be is provided by the Paul and Lentz (1977) comparative treatment study discussed in Chapter 19 (page 504). When patients were discharged from any of the three wards of the program, social-learning, milieu therapy, or routine hospital management, they usually went to live in nearby boarding homes. These homes, often converted motels, were staffed by workers who had been trained by the Paul-Lentz project to treat the ex-patients according to social-learning principles. These workers, some of whom had B.A. degrees, attended to the specific problems of the ex-patients, using rewards, including tokens for a time, to encourage more independence and normal functioning. They positively reinforced appropriate behavior of the residents and did not attend much to bizarre behavior, as they had done before their training.

The staff knew at all times how a particular patient was doing, because assessment was careful and ongoing. The mental health center project, and this is of paramount importance, acted as consultant to these community boarding homes in order to help their staff work with the ex-patients in as effective a manner as possible. Some boarding homes for ex-mental patients are supported financially by the state as part of the mental health system, but only rarely have the procedures followed in these homes been carefully planned and monitored by professional mental health staff.

In spite of many practical problems, such as staff layoffs, the results were as positive as had been the impact of the social-learning ward program. The ex-patients seemed to benefit from the aftercare; more than 90 percent of the patients discharged from the social-learning ward were able to remain continuously in the community residences during the year-and-a-half follow-up period. Some had been living in the community residences for over five years. The revolving-door

syndrome in this instance did not take hold. Finally, in a finding rather critical in these days of diminishing public funds, the social-learning program—the mental health center treatment combined with the aftercare—was much less expensive than the institutional care such patients usually receive.

Environmental Psychology

Do you recall the last time you entered an air-conditioned building after suffering the heat and humidity of a mercilessly steamy summer day? What was your mood after being inside the cool haven for half an hour, compared to how you felt while walking outside? Have you ever visited some of the Gothic cathedrals in France and Germany? As you gazed upward to the soaring heights of the vaults, did you feel uplifted, exhilarated?

Since its beginning American psychology has had a love affair with environmentalism. Over the past twenty years the study of how elements of the physical environment affect thoughts, feelings, and behavior has involved psychologists in the domain of designers, architects, and urban planners. Their attempts to control behavior through control of environmental stimuli is now called environmental design or environmental management (see Sommer, 1969; Proshanksy, Ittelson, and Rivlin, 1972). Given the community psychologists' appreciation of the importance of large social issues in behavior disorder, it is not surprising that they too want psychology applied in the planning of cities and mass transit systems, in the design of apartment and office buildings.

A fascinating example of research work in this field is a study done by Baum and Valins (1973). It investigated a proposal by Calhoun (1970) that within a given physical space there is a limit to the amount of social interaction that animals can tolerate before stress is created. Baum and Valins termed as "unwanted social interaction" any degree of social contact between people that exceeds some optimal level; any environment that provides unwanted social interaction is regarded as crowded.

In an initial field study they found that students living in older dormitories on a university campus complained more about overcrowding than those living in newer ones. Furthermore, when confronted with miniature bedroom and lounge areas and asked to place miniature figures in them until "you would feel crowded if you were there," the residents of the older dormitories placed far fewer figures than did those from the newer dormitories, indicating that they would feel crowded with fewer people than would those in the newer dormitories. The subjects in this research study were freshmen who had been *assigned* to their dormitories, thus controlling for self-selection factors that might render the analysis of the data more ambiguous.

In a subsequent study a subject coming either from the older dorms or from the newer residences was told to wait in a room in the laboratory with another subject. In reality, the other student was the experimenter's "stooge." The students from the older accommodations, being more sensitive to crowding, were expected to sit farther away from the stooge than those coming from newer dorms. This prediction was confirmed. Moreover, hidden observers counted the number of seconds within a five-minute period that each subject glanced in the direction of the stooge. Again significant differences emerged: "older-dorm" students looked at the stooge significantly less often than did "newer-dorm" students, and, moreover, reported being more uncomfortable after the enforced waiting period.

Valins and Baum examined why students would feel more crowded in the older dormitories. The first obvious question was whether, in fact, older dormitories were more crowded in absolute terms than the newer

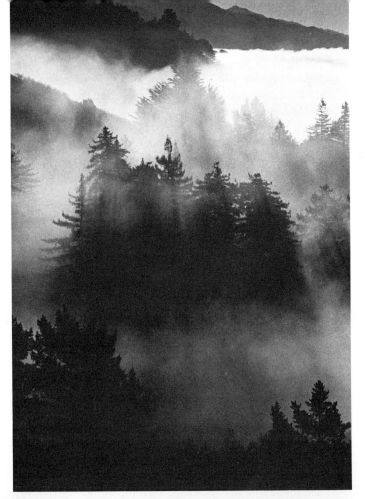

Environmental psychology is based on the idea that our environment has profound effects on our thoughts, feelings, and behavior.

Overcrowding in prisons increases the suicide and assault rates and causes more illness among inmates.

dormitories. This seemed not to be the case, for the numbers of people per square foot of living area were about the same. What differentiated the two sets of dormitories was the *configuration* of the space. The older dormitories were constructed along traditional lines; a typical floor contained a number of bedrooms, with two students to a bedroom, each of which opened out directly onto the hall. All three dozen students on a given floor shared one large bathroom and lounge. By contrast, the newer dormitories, with a comparable number of students per floor, were arranged in individual suites with separate living areas and bathrooms to accommodate small groups of four to six students, again two to a bedroom. The residents of the older dormitories apparently had to interact with more people than did the residents of newer ones. Privacy was simply more difficult to obtain, and Baum and Valins assumed that such forced interaction with larger numbers of students brought unwanted social contacts. It did not seem surprising that the students in the older dorms felt more crowded.

The negative effects of unwanted social interactions are striking indeed in prisons. Recent work by Cox, Paulus, and McCain (1984) found crowding in prisons to be associated with increased medical as well as psychological pathology. For example, between 1967 and 1977 the population in institutions in the Texas Department of Corrections doubled, but suicides of those over fifty years of age increased sixfold, as did disciplinary infractions. And in Mississippi inmate-inmate assaults dropped 60 percent when a court mandated a 30 percent drop in the prison population. Later, when the population was allowed to increase by 19 percent, assaults rose by 36 percent. The greater the density of the prison population, the higher the blood pressure of inmates and the more they complain of illnesses. There is little doubt that prison crowding increases fear, frustration, and violence. As Baum and Valins discovered about dormitories, in prisons the amount of space per se is not the problem. Rather, inmates have difficulties when their single cells become doubles, when their dormitories lack cubicles—circumstances that take away control of their meetings with others.

Overall Evaluation of Community Psychology Work

Primary Prevention
It has been suggested that the results of community psychology have not lived up to the rhetoric (Bernstein and Nietzel, 1980). Nowhere are successes more notably lacking than in primary prevention (Cowen, 1983), in keeping disorders from developing in the first place. Community psychologists often argue heatedly that the work of most clinicians in tertiary prevention, or therapy for already existing disorders, is effort in the wrong place and at the wrong time. They claim that too few people can be served at the tertiary level, because therapy requires highly skilled professional helpers, and that little success can be expected because the disorders have been allowed to develop fully and are for this reason very difficult, perhaps impossible, to treat.

Paraprofessionals and Ethnicity
Community psychology programs often rely on peers, on people who come from the same backgrounds as those receiving services; these paraprofessionals have some training but not the credentials for mental health work. The prevailing belief is that these individuals will better know the life circumstances of those in need, and, most importantly, will be more acceptable to them. Extensive research on modeling provides some justification for these assumptions. Subjects in studies of learning through observation are found to acquire information more readily from models who are perceived as credible and relevant to them; similarity of age and background are important determinants of credibility and relevance (Rosenthal and Bandura, 1978). We can therefore expect that individuals unaccustomed to the standard middle-class fare of a professional office and formal appointments will find the activities and advice of helpers similar to themselves more acceptable.

Few models seem as plausible or relevant as people who have shared but overcome clients' own problems. This is critical if a client rejects staff members as reference figures because they appear too remote in age, education, status, ethnicity, and so on, for suitable comparisons with self, or are perceived as outsiders, lacking vivid conversance with the client's burdens and viewpoint (Rosenthal and Bandura, 1978, p. 649).

Several studies have examined the effects of race on the counseling relationship. A review of them suggests that black clients prefer black counselors to white counselors, engage in more self-exploration with counselors of their own race, and in general feel more positively toward black helpers than toward white helpers (Jackson, 1973). At the same time the studies suggest that race differences are *not* insurmountable barriers to understanding between counselor and client. Counselors with considerable empathy are perceived as more helpful by clients, regardless of the racial mix. None of these studies investigated whether the therapy provided to black clients by white and black counselors differed in effectiveness.

What Is New in CMHCs?

Problems of community mental health centers were examined more than a decade ago in a rather controversial critique by Ralph Nader's Center for Study of Responsive Law (Holden, 1972). This report held that the centers are based on a good and commendable set of ideas but that the implementation has been rather poor. Often the problem is one of old wine in new bottles. Nader's group pointed out that centers are usually controlled by psychiatrists whose training and outlook are tied to one-to-one therapy, typically along psychoanalytic lines; the "fit" between treatment and the problems of lower-income people who are the centers' primary constituencies is often loose.

These are important criticisms. Evidence is being collected, however, to determine just what measures are effective with which of the disorders. But primary prevention procedures are more problematic. Social activism, "going out into the community" to change social systems and neighborhoods, rests on two assumptions: that the major causes of human psychological suffering are environmental, and that the community interventions now being undertaken are aimed at the correct environmental causes. The review of the major mental disorders in Chapters 6 through 17 gives scant assurance that we know this much about how mental and emotional problems develop. But what we do know strongly suggests an important role for physiological, often genetic, diatheses, which are not the usual targets of the primary prevention efforts of community psychologists (Lamb and Zusman, 1979). For this reason it can be argued that some community psychology efforts are premature and incomplete, that what is needed more than social action, or at least in addition to it, is continuing and vigorous research into the causes of the disorders, in particular the contributions of somatic factors.

Fewer than 800 of the 2000 community mental health centers envisioned by Congress and needed to provide care have been established. An examination of these centers by the President's Commission on Mental Health (1978) found that they are not serving severely disturbed children and adolescents, the aged, and discharged mental patients. Only about 7 percent of ex-patients ever go to a community mental health center.

Social Factors in Community Psychology

Enthusiasm for community psychology must unfortunately be tempered with awareness of social reality—the conditions of deprivation that community psychologists assume produce and maintain disordered behavior. To train a black youngster for a specific vocational slot can have a beneficial long-term outcome for the individual only to the extent that society at large provides the appropriate opportunity to use these skills. Those who work in community psychology are of course aware that racial and social prejudices play a central role in limiting the access of many minority groups to the rewards of the culture at large. Although efforts to improve the socio-cultural milieu must of course continue if our society has any commitment to fostering social and mental well-being, programs may raise expectations that will only be dashed by the realities of the larger culture. This is the quandary of any mental health professional who ventures forth from the consulting room into the community.

Community psychology has as its goal the change of large systems and groups of people rather than treating individual problems. And it is in the seeking mode; psychologists take the initiative in serving people, rather than waiting for individuals in need to come to them. On the face of it, this is a tall order. What do we know about the principles that operate to produce change in societal values and institutions? When a community psychologist organizes a rent strike, for example, what are the best ways of doing so, that is, of persuading the greatest number of tenants to work together in the joint effort? Will gentle persuasion be most effective, or does the situation call for harangues against the landlord? Further, if the community psychologist hopes to take actions that meet the wishes and needs of the community, how does he or she determine them? It will be recalled from Chapters 3 and 4 the difficulties the psychologist has in assessing the needs of an individual client with whom there is extensive direct contact. How much more difficult, then, to assess the needs of thousands of people! Does one talk primarily to their leaders? If so, how do certain people become leaders and spokespersons? And once chosen, how do these individuals stay abreast of what the needs of their constituents are?

Community psychologists necessarily become social activists to some degree, which raises the danger that these well-meaning professionals may *impose* values and goals on their clients. John Kennedy's launching of the community mental health movement proclaimed that the federal government is rightfully concerned about improving the mental health of Americans. But what is mental health? Who is to decide? To what extent do the people being served by community psychologists have a say in how they are to be helped?

These are but a few of the nettlesome questions that must continually be posed if community psychology is to act responsibly and effectively. The focus of this field is on large-scale factors. Many people are involved; many lives, then, will be affected by decisions and actions. Questions of values and questions of effectiveness are inherent in any effort to alter the human condition, but they are of special importance when the clients themselves do not seek the intervention.

Perhaps a major contribution of the community psychology movement is in sensitizing mental health professionals to the social, political, and ethical factors in human behavior. These "macro" variables are assumed to be critical in influencing behavior, and the attempt is made to manipulate them. The forces impinging on all of us exert their power in sometimes subtle fashion. If we do not look for these forces, we are unlikely, as suggested in our discussion of paradigms in Chapters 1 and 2, to find them.

SOMATIC TREATMENT

Many of the therapeutic procedures considered thus far are psychological in nature; improvements in behavior are sought through techniques that provide new learning experiences, raise expectations for help, and facilitate insight. But behavior can also be affected by direct manipulation of the body. The intimate relationship between mind and body was indicated in the discussion of psychophysiological disorders (see page 166). If psyche and soma are only two ways of talking about the same thing, it is reasonable to expect behavior to change when we intervene in certain bodily processes. Moreover, the many theories that blame psychopathology on physiological dysfunctions imply the efficacy of physiological treatments.

In the chapters on specific disorders, we have briefly discussed how some of them are treated by somatic means—by manipulations of physiological processes in order to relieve symptoms. Here we describe some of the most widely used somatic procedures in more detail.

There are three major types of somatic treatment for abnormal behavior—drugs, surgical procedures, and convulsion therapies. Evidence indicates that *some* methods are effective in treating *some* psychological problems. But, as we have cautioned many times before,

this evidence does not in turn provide support for a physiological explanation of any of these disorders. In fact, somatic therapies have *not* usually been discovered through investigation of the physiology behind a particular disorder. Rather, the majority of the current treatments were discovered by accident, a few, as we shall see, under somewhat astonishing circumstances.

Drug Therapies

Four major categories of drugs have been used for some time in the amelioration of psychological disorders: minor tranquilizers, neuroleptics, stimulants, and antidepressants. Table 20.2 gives examples of several widely used drugs in these categories, indicating the chemical groups that they belong to as well as both their generic and trade names. More recently lithium carbonate has become a preferred treatment for bipolar affective disorder.

Although we have reserved our extended discussion of therapeutic drugs for this chapter, the sad truth is that many of them could well have been mentioned in Chapter 11 on drug addiction and drug dependence. Even the minor tranquilizers can be abused, and some of them, like Miltown, are physically addictive over long periods of regular use. Both because of our psychological needs and because of the physiological realities of our bodies, human beings are all too prone to use psychoactive chemicals in self-defeating ways.

Minor Tranquilizers

As the name suggests, minor tranquilizers are used to reduce anxiety that is not of major proportions. They are usually prescribed for outpatients with anxiety and psychosomatic disorders, and sometimes for the depressed individual who is also anxious. Barbiturates, which have been used to relieve anxiety since the turn of the century, were the first drugs in this category to gain widespread acceptance. But because of hazards such as addiction and undesirable side effects (see page 266), they were supplanted in the 1950s by a number of newly developed minor tranquilizers. The first of these was patented in 1952 by Berger and called meprobamate. Its trade names are Miltown and Equanil. Meprobamate, which operates by reducing muscular tension, belongs to a group of drugs called the propanediols. At present the propanediols have fallen in popularity and have been replaced by another group of minor tranquilizers, the benzodiazepines. Librium and Valium are the most prominent. Tranquilizers have become an accepted part of American culture; anxious businesspeople and over-

TABLE 20.2 Several Psychoactive Drugs Categorized by Their Effects on Behavior

Effect Group	Chemical Group	Generic Name	Trade Name
Minor tranquilizers	propanediols	meprobamate	Miltown, Equanil
	benzodiazepines	chlordiazepoxide	Librium
		diazepam	Valium
Neuroleptics (antipsychotics)	phenothiazines	chlorpromazine	Thorazine
		trifluoperazine	Stelazine
		thioridazine	Mellaril
	butyrophenones	haloperidol	Haldol
	thioxanthenes	chlorprothixene	Taractan
Stimulants	amphetamines	dextroamphetamine	Dexedrine
	piperidyls	methylphenidate	Ritalin
Antidepressants	tricyclics	imipramine	Tofranil
		amitriptyline	Elavil
		nortriptyline	Aventyl
	monoamine oxidase inhibitors	phenelzine	Nardil
		tranylcypromine	Parnate
Antibipolar disorder	inorganic salts	lithium carbonate	Lithonate, Lithane

taxed parents are depicted as popping "happy" pills to get them through their trying days.

Because minor tranquilizers are usually prescribed for outpatients by general practitioners, arranging controlled research is very difficult. The few controlled evaluations of patients with anxiety disorders or anxious depression who take benzodiazepines find that these drugs generally produce greater improvement than a placebo (Greenblatt and Shader, 1978; Noyes et al., 1984). Many people who take benzodiazepines, however, complain of drowsiness and lethargy. Like meprobamate, these drugs too can be physically addictive if taken in heavy doses over a long period.

Neuroleptics[8]

Phenothiazine, the nucleus of the phenothiazine drugs, was first produced by a German chemist in the late nineteenth century and was used to treat parasitic worm infections of the digestive system of animals. The drug went largely unnoticed until the 1940s, when the antihistamines were discovered by Bovet. The drugs with antihistaminic properties also have a phenothiazine nucleus. Antihistamines were prescribed to treat a number of conditions ranging from the common cold and asthma to low blood pressure and shock. The French surgeon Laborit pioneered the use of antihistamines to reduce surgical shock. He noticed that they made his patients somewhat sleepy and less fearful about the impending operation. Laborit's work encouraged drug companies to reexamine antihistamines that had previously been rejected because they had stronger tranquilizing than antihistaminic effects. Shortly thereafter a French chemist, Charpentier, prepared a new phenothiazine derivative and called it chlorpromazine. It proved very effective in calming schizophrenics. As indicated earlier (see page 355), phenothiazines are now believed to block impulse transmission in the dopaminergic pathways of the brain, which gives them their therapeutic properties.

[8]Neuroleptics are sometimes referred to as antipsychotic drugs, a relatively accurate description of their effects, and as major tranquilizers, a misleading term. The implication of the term major tranquilizer is that drugs in this category are useful for anxiety of greater magnitude than that treated with minor tranquilizers. But this is not the case; neuroleptics are not an effective treatment for anxiety disorders.

Chlorpromazine was first used therapeutically in the United States in 1954 and rapidly became the preferred treatment for schizophrenics. By 1970 over 85 percent of all patients in state mental hospitals were receiving chlorpromazine or one of the other phenothiazines. In recent years two other neuroleptics have also been given to schizophrenics, the butyrophenones and the thioxanthenes. Both seem generally as effective as the phenothiazines. Each class of drug is able to reduce positive schizophrenic symptoms but not the negative ones (see page 356).

Is phenothiazine medication the preferred treatment when it is compared with other treatments a hospitalized schizophrenic patient might receive? In an attempt to answer this question, May (1968) assigned first-admission schizophrenic patients in a psychiatric hospital to one of five treatment groups.

1. Individual psychoanalytic psychotherapy conducted by psychiatric residents.

2. Phenothiazine drugs.

3. Individual psychoanalytic psychotherapy plus phenothiazine medication.

4. Electroconvulsive therapy (to be discussed later in this chapter).

5. Milieu therapy.

Two classes of dependent variables were analyzed: clinical ratings of the patient's progress made by nurses and therapists, and data on release rate and length of time spent in the hospital. Drugs alone and the psychotherapy-plus-drugs combination were the two best treatments according to all the clinical measures. These two treatments were also superior both in shortening stay and in increasing the number of releases. Indeed, phenothiazines alone were found to be as effective as phenothiazines plus an extensive course of psychotherapy. This pattern of results persisted at a five-year follow-up (May et al., 1976).

Although the phenothiazine regimen reduces the positive symptoms of schizophrenia, so that patients can be released from the hospital, it should not be viewed as a cure. Typically, patients are kept on so-called *maintenance doses* of the drug; they continue to take their medication and return to the hospital or clinic on occasion for adjustment of the dose level. But released patients being maintained on phenothiazine medication may make only marginal adjustment to the community. The phenothiazines keep the positive symptoms from returning but have little effect on negative symptoms, such as social incompetence. In addition, re-admissions are frequent. The advent of the "phenothiazine era" reduced long-term institutionalization significantly. But in its place evolved the revolving-door pattern of admission, discharge, and readmission already remarked on.

Some progress has been made in at least slowing down the revolutions per minute of the door. We know that applying social-learning principles in aftercare homes is one way of helping deinstitutionalized patients remain in the community. There is also some evidence that a maintenance program of drugs plus another form of psychotherapy is effective at preventing relapse (Hogarty et al., 1974). One group of released patients received drugs plus a treatment program called major role therapy. In this therapy ex-patients are helped to assume productive social roles in the community and to reestablish personal relationships through the active help of a counselor. Then gradually they make more and more of their own daily decisions. Members of this group were rated as more adjusted after eighteen months of treatment than three other groups of released patients who received only the drug, only a placebo, and a placebo plus major role therapy. The necessity for maintenance medication also depends on the homes to which the patients are discharged. We have indicated that the level of "expressed emotion" of family members, their criticism and hostility toward ex-schizophrenic patients, figures in whether they relapse. The relation of maintenance medication to the emotional atmosphere of the household and relapse is given in Table 20.3. Maintenance medication is valuable for ex-patients living in high-EE homes but does not affect the rate of relapse of those living in low-EE homes (Vaughn and Leff, 1976).

Finally, the potentially serious side effects of phenothiazines must be noted. Patients generally report that taking the drug is disagreeable, causing dryness of the mouth, blurred vision, grogginess, and constipation. Among the other common side effects are low blood pressure and jaundice. Perhaps this unpleasantness is one of the reasons maintenance programs have proved so difficult. It is a problem to get patients to take these drugs initially and to keep them on medication once they have left the hospital (Van Putten et al., 1981).

Even more disturbing are the extrapyramidal side effects; they stem from dysfunctions of the nerve tracts that descend from the brain to spinal motor neurons. Extrapyramidal side effects resemble symptoms of neurological diseases, which is the reason these drugs are called neuroleptics. These side effects most closely resemble the symptoms of Parkinson's disease. People taking phenothiazines have "pill-rolling" tremors of the fingers, a shuffling gait, muscular rigidity, and drool-

TABLE 20.3 Nine-Month Relapse Rates of Schizophrenics Discharged, with and without Maintenance Medication, to Low-EE Homes and to High-EE Homes with Little and Much Family Contact *(from Vaughn and Leff, 1976)*

Drug Status	Family Atmosphere and Contact		
	Low EE	High EE, Little Contact	High EE, Much Contact
Maintenance medication	12%	15%	53%
No drugs	15%	42%	92%

ing. Dystonia is disordered tonicity of tissues, dyskinesia abnormal motion of voluntary and involuntary muscles. They cause arching of the back and a twisted posture of the neck and body. Akasthesia is an inability to remain still; people pace constantly, fidget, and make chewing movements and other movements of the lips, fingers, and legs. These perturbing symptoms can be treated by drugs used with patients with Parkinson's disease. In a muscular disturbance of older patients, called tardive dyskinesia, the mouth muscles involuntarily make sucking, lip-smacking, and chin-wagging motions. This syndrome affects from 10 to 15 percent of patients treated with phenothiazines for a long period of time. Some improvement comes from treatment with benzodiazepines or phenobarbital (Borbruff et al., 1981).

In spite of the many difficulties, phenothiazines will undoubtedly continue to be the primary treatment for schizophrenics until something better is discovered. They are surely preferable to the straitjackets formerly used to restrain patients.

Stimulants

One form of amphetamine, dextroamphetamine, and a piperidyl derivative, methylphenidate, are currently prescribed for hyperactive children (see page 379). Their use for this purpose became controversial when a 1970 *Washington Post* article reported that between 5 to 10 percent of school children in Omaha, Nebraska, were receiving the stimulants (Maynard, 1970). The public became aroused and investigations followed. It became apparent that the use of stimulants for calming children was widespread, and that prescriptions were being written somewhat indiscriminately. Shortly thereafter the Food and Drug Administration tightened its regulations.

The available evidence indeed indicates that stimulants can be an effective treatment for hyperactivity (for example, Gittelman-Klein et al., 1976b). In one study 35 to 40 percent of the children showed dramatic improvement, and another 30 to 40 percent were moderately improved (Connors et al., 1972). The most frequent side effects of stimulants are decreased appetite and insomnia, but both are short-lived. Children taking stimulants do look different, however. Their cheeks are sunken, the skin is pale, and there are dark shadows beneath the eyes. People know that they are on medication, which can be upsetting to children. In the long term their growth may be somewhat stunted (Mattes and Gittelman, 1983).

A closer examination of the actual effects of stimulants reveals that they have differential impact on the many problems of the hyperactive child. Stimulants reduce impulsive and undercontrolled behavior, increase attention, and allow direction and control of motor activity. Yet they may not improve performance of cognitive tasks and ability to do schoolwork (Gittelman-Klein and Klein, 1976; Rie et al., 1976); as indicated earlier, they may even *interfere* with learning when administered in doses strong enough to reduce hyperactive behavior (Sprague and Sleator, 1977). For these reasons, as well as the possibility that undesirable side effects will appear with long-term use, other treatments for hyperactivity should be considered. A study by Gittelman-Klein and her co-workers (1976a) indicates that operant programs can be quite effective alone, and that a combination of stimulants and behavior therapy is the best available treatment. Three treatments were compared, behavior therapy plus a placebo, behavior therapy plus a stimulant, and behavior therapy alone. All brought significant improvement, but at the end of eight weeks, children receiving a combination of stimulants and behavior therapy were indistinguishable from their normal classmates.

Antidepressants

The *tricyclics* and *monoamine oxidase* (MAO) *inhibitors* are two subcategories of antidepressants. Both classes of drugs were discovered serendipitously. Imipramine, a tricyclic, has a three-ring molecular structure similar to that of the phenothiazines; hence it was hoped that it might also be an effective treatment for schizophrenics. Early clinical work with the drug showed that it was of little value with schizophrenics, but it did produce an unexpected elevation in mood; for this reason it was subsequently used as an antidepressant. Tricyclics are now assumed initially to interfere with the reuptake of norepinephrine and serotonin by the nerve cell after it has fired, thus keeping more of the neurotransmitter available at the synapse. Later the amounts of norepinephrine and serotonin return to what they had been earlier, but the postsynaptic receptors for these neurotransmitters seem to become more sensitive. The MAO inhibitor iproniazid was originally a treatment for tuberculosis. Because it improved the outlook of tubercular patients, it too was adopted as an antidepressant. The enzyme monoamine oxidase degrades monoamines of the central nervous system. Since a MAO inhibitor prevents this intracellular degradation, excess amounts of free norepinephrine and serotonin initially collect at the receptor sites (see Box 9.4, page 212). Again, the amounts of the transmitters later decrease, but their receptors appear to be more sensitive. Thus both classes of drugs are considered to produce their therapeutic effects by facilitating neural transmission. Like the phenothiazines, the tricyclics also produce some undesirable side effects. These include dry mouth, constipation, dizziness, palpitations, and blurred vision.

The available evidence suggests that the tricyclics are effective drugs in combatting depression (Davis, Klerman, and Schildkraut, 1967); they also reduce the risk of a relapse when taken after an acute episode is over (Prien et al., 1984). But it is also clear that tricyclics do not benefit *all* depressives. Thus research directed at determining which depressed patients are most likely to benefit from the drugs is important. Some of this research has been carried out on so-called endogenous and exogenous depressives, those who have a very deep depression as opposed to those with a less severe form. The tricyclic drugs were found more effective in relieving endogenous depression than exogenous (Stern, Rush, and Mendels, 1980). Of current interest is the evidence that we discussed in Chapter 9 concerning the specific biochemical effects of the several tricyclics. The data suggest that particular tricyclics may be differentially effective with particular unipolar depressives, but predicting which patient will do best on which is not yet possible.

Research has examined the combined effects of tricyclics and various forms of psychotherapy. In two stud-

ies the combination seemed to offer an optimal treatment (DiMascio et al., 1979; Weissman et al., 1981). The already reported study by Rush, Beck, and their colleagues (1977), comparing Beck's cognitive therapy with administration of imipramine, found the cognitive treatment superior. Murphy and his colleagues (1984), however, obtained different results in a comparison of four treatments: cognitive therapy plus tricyclics, cognitive therapy alone, tricyclics alone, and cognitive therapy plus a placebo drug. All treatments were effective and equally so. Clearly more research is needed to determine the most effective combination of antidepressant drugs and psychological treatments with different types of affective disorders.

Although MAO inhibitors are generally more effective than a placebo, they are decidedly less useful than the tricyclics (Klerman, 1975). They continue to be given to patients who do not respond to tricyclics, but interest in them has declined because of their severe side effects. MAO inhibitors have greater toxicity than any other drug used for the treatment of psychological disorders; they are harmful to the liver, brain, and cardiovascular system. Moreover, these drugs have even been found to interact with other drugs and foods to cause death. Patients taking MAO inhibitors should avoid foods and beverages high in tyramine. Aromatic cheeses, avocado, beer, broad beans, Chianti wine, chicken livers, cream, game, lox, pickled herring, snails, and yeast extracts (Honigfeld and Howard, 1978) cannot be ingested, even in moderate amounts.[9]

Lithium Carbonate

In this decade there has been great interest in the possibility of using lithium carbonate in the treatment of mania. The drug, a simple inorganic salt, was discovered in 1949 by Cade, who noted its sedative effect on guinea pigs. It was not widely used in the United States until more recently, however, for it had been judged dangerous after causing a few deaths. In these instances it had been ingested unrestrictedly as a salt substitute by patients with cardiac disease.

Although lithium carbonate is clearly an effective treatment for mania, whether it is the best somatic treatment available is unclear. For example, in double-blind studies in which lithium is compared with chlorpromazine, or other neuroleptics, the two treatments are about equally useful (for example, Shopsin et al., 1975).

[9]Antidepressant drugs, both the tricyclics and the MAO inhibitors, are also helpful in treating obsessive-compulsive disorder (Insell et al., 1983), bulimia (Walsh et al., 1984), and panic attacks (Zitrin et al., 1983).

Surgery performed in vertical plane
through side of skull

Surgery performed in vertical plane
through eye socket

FIGURE 20.3 Psychosurgeons attempt to eliminate especially troublesome behavior, such as violent psychotic episodes, by cutting the connections between the cortex of the frontal lobes and lower centers of the brain.

In addition to the claim that lithium subdues mania, it has also been proposed that the drug can lift depression and, when taken regularly, reduce the likelihood of subsequent manic and depressive episodes. Lithium can lift depression in some patients, particularly bipolars. Its greatest benefit, however, is as a prophylactic, forestalling subsequent episodes of mania and depression in bipolar patients (Gerbino, Oleshansky, and Gershon, 1978; Prien et al., 1984). Whenever lithium is used, it is important that blood levels be carefully monitored to avoid a potentially fatal overdose.

Psychosurgery

In the last decades of the nineteenth century, Gottlieb Burckhardt, a Swiss physician, reported removing parts of the brains of several very disturbed patients. The rudimentary practice of trephining in prehistoric times, which was occasionally taken up again during the medieval period and in a number of primitive societies, had already established breaching of the skull as a means of correcting behavior. The ''modern era'' of psychosurgery begins with the work of a Portugese neuropsychiatrist, Antonio de Egas Moniz. He had attended a scientific meeting in London in 1935 and was impressed by a report of Jacobsen and Fulton about brain surgery performed on two chimpanzees. The prefrontal areas of their cerebral cortexes had been removed. Before the operation the animals had been highly emotional and subject to violent temper tantrums when frustrated through experimentation. Afterward they were indifferent.

On the basis of this single case of two chimpanzees whose behavior was calmed through brain surgery,

Moniz later persuaded a colleague, Almeida Lima, to operate on the frontal lobes of human patients. Within a few years a hundred lobotomies had been performed, and in 1949 Moniz shared a Nobel prize in medicine for this work. Moniz himself retired in 1944, partly because he had been rendered a hemiplegic by a bullet lodged in his spine. One of his lobotomized patients had shot him (Valenstein, 1973).

Lobotomy was introduced in the United States by Walter Freeman and James Watts; by 1950 they had operated on over a thousand patients. The rate picked up in the early 1950s, and Freeman later claimed that he had performed or supervised over 3500 lobotomies.

The original lobotomy was a very crude surgical procedure. In one of the two methods usually applied, a hole was drilled in each side of the head, and a blunt instrument was then inserted and rotated in an arc, destroying considerable white matter. In the other procedure, the transorbital technique, a surgical needle inserted into the brain through the thin structure separating the eye and the brain was similarly rotated (Figure 20.3). It is estimated that each of these techniques destroys about 120 square centimeters of brain tissue (Shevitz, 1976). The rationale behind both procedures was that the frontal cortex exaggerates the emotional responses produced in lower regions of the brain, in particular the thalamus and hypothalamus. Cutting the tracts connecting these areas to the frontal cortex was assumed to have a calming effect.

As with most of the treatments we have discussed, there was an initial flurry of interest in psychosurgical procedures coupled with enthusiastic claims for their effectiveness. While the techniques were in relatively widespread use, they were applied to schizophrenics, to depressives, and less frequently to persons with personality and anxiety disorders. Persons plagued by obsessions were more frequently operated on than other neurotics. The results of studies attempting to assess the efficacy of the treatment were unimpressive. For example, Robbin (1958, 1959) compared changes in lobotomy patients and controls. Lobotomy was found to produce a slightly greater discharge rate, but more of these patients were subsequently readmitted. Similarly, Barahal (1958) did a five-to-ten year follow-up on 1000 lobotomy cases. His findings compelled him to publicize the high rate of undesirable side effects, such as seizures, extreme listlessness, stupor, and even death. In sum, these surgical procedures have little to recommend them; they lack demonstrated effectiveness and can have serious, *irreversible* consequences. With the advent of the phenothiazines in the mid-1950s, the popularity of lobotomy dropped off dramatically.

But newer surgical procedures have continued to be used in treating abnormal behavior. More precise techniques allow the frontal cortex to be separated from lower brain areas with a destruction of only 8 square centimeters of brain tissue (Shevitz, 1976). The procedure apparently has beneficial effects for some patients—notably those with severe depression, anxiety, and obsessive-compulsive disorders—and fewer undesirable side effects. Current thinking would limit these operations to patients with very severe, long-lasting problems that have not responded to any other treatment.

Convulsive Therapy

Several people became interested in the therapeutic induction of convulsions, all during the same decade. In 1932 in Vienna, the psychiatrist Manfred Sakel had been experimenting with insulin injections as a means of reducing withdrawal symptoms in morphine addicts. In one patient the low blood sugar level produced by the insulin accidentally elicited a coma, and Sakel observed that afterward the patient's mental state was less confused. He continued to experiment with insulin-produced coma and reported that it could even reduce psychotic symptoms. The technique was soon in rather widespread use, both in Europe and North America. But each treatment took four or five hours, and they went on for several months. Patients gained a great deal of weight through the disruption of their sugar metabolism. The procedure, which was very expensive because of the medical care required, declined in popularity as its health hazards and limited effectiveness came to be appreciated.

At about the same time that Sakel began his work, the clinical experience of a Hungarian physician, Von Meduna, led him to the opinion that an "antagonism" existed between epilepsy and schizophrenia. He leapt from this conclusion to propose that inducing a convulsion might cure schizophrenia. He chose the drug Metrazol for this purpose.

The originators of electroconvulsive shock therapy (ECT) were the Italian physicians Ugo Cerletti and Lucio Bini. Cerletti had been interested in epilepsy and was seeking a means by which its seizures could be experimentally induced. The "solution" became apparent during a visit to a slaughterhouse, where Cerletti saw animals rendered unconscious by electric shocks administered to the head. Shortly thereafter he found that by applying electric shocks he could produce full epileptic seizures, rigidity followed by spasms, in his laboratory. Not long after that, in 1938 in Rome, he used the technique on a schizophrenic patient.

The electrical means of inducing a convulsion became the preferred method. The technique has remained essentially the same since its introduction by Cerletti and Bini, at least until recently. Electrodes are placed on each side of the patient's forehead, and a current of between 70 and 130 volts is allowed to pass between them for a fraction of a second, inducing a grand mal seizure (see page 602n). A period of electrical silence in the patient's brain follows; then there is a gradual resumption of the preconvulsion pattern. Patients nowadays are usually given a sedative and a relaxant beforehand to reduce the incidence of bone fractures and bruises occasionally suffered during ECT. The usual ECT regimen entails about ten treatments given at a rate of about three per week.

Following ECT the patient is often very confused and shows loss of memory both for happenings before the treatments and for whatever transpired within one hour afterward. The confusion and loss of memory generally disappear within several weeks, but sometimes the individual has trouble remembering past events for months, even years.

An important development in ECT is unilateral shock, the application of shock to only one of the cerebral hemispheres, usually the nondominant one. Unilateral ECT causes less confusion and less impairment of memory. In most studies it has been found to be as therapeutically effective as the standard procedure (Inglis, 1969; Abrams, 1975).

Electroconvulsive therapy, although originally applied to both schizophrenics and depressed patients, is now used primarily for profoundly depressed people. As we saw previously when we reviewed the May (1968) study, phenothiazine medication is more effective for schizophrenics than is ECT. For severe depressives, though, ECT is a fast and sure treatment. Indeed, it is sometimes regarded as the optimal treatment for severe depression (for example, Klerman, 1972), even though the mechanism by which it works is unknown, and even though it does not prevent future episodes of depression.

In spite of the promise that carefully administered ECT holds for deeply depressed patients, many professionals object to its use; it is applied much less often than it once was. A major problem is the fear that many patients have of ECT. Even though they have amnesia for the episode, and even though muscle relaxants are given to prevent bone fractures, patients are often reluctant to undergo, or their families to sanction, such treatments, at least without considerable urging from the medical staff. The procedure is in truth violent in nature; ECT does entail the deliberate induction of a seizure and subsequent unconsciousness. Many people therefore consider the "cure" worse than the "disease." But it is difficult to dismiss ECT, since the evidence does indicate that it is effective in treating depression.

SUMMARY

Group therapy takes advantage of some special properties of the group itself. A group can exert especially strong social pressure for change. Members also benefit from sharing common concerns and aspirations. Sensitivity training and encounter groups enable people to learn how they affect others and are affected by them. Efforts are made to get behind the social facades that people present to the world, so that they may deal honestly and more effectively with one another. Controlled research on outcome and process in group therapy of all kinds is just beginning to be done.

In family therapy the problems of the "identified" patient are considered the manifestation of disturbances within the family unit. Family members learn how their behavior and attitudes affect one another, that flexibility and changing communication patterns can bring greater harmony. Marital therapy helps unhappy couples resolve the conflicts inevitable in any ongoing relationship of two adults living together. One technique consists of caring days; one partner at a time concen-

trates on giving pleasure to the other, breaking the cycle of bitterness and hostility plaguing them. Marital therapists of all theoretical allegiances try to improve partners' communication of needs and wants to each other. An act may be well intentioned but have a negative impact. Talking openly about this problem appears to ease the tensions of many couples.

In one research project schizophrenics discharged from the hospital to their homes managed to remain there because their families learned about schizophrenia, thus becoming less critical of their symptoms, and worked at reducing the emotional turmoil of the household. Continuing research in family and marital therapies promises to elucidate the problems for which they are the most appropriate and the processes by which they bring gratifying relief.

Community psychology and the related community mental health movement try to prevent mental disorders from developing, to seek out troubled people, and to find the social conditions that may be causing human problems. Community workers must make their values explicit, for they are often fostering social change rather than helping individuals adjust to what some consider untenable social conditions. Deinstitutionalization, the policy of having former mental patients live, if at all possible, at home or in small residences is part of this movement. Much work needs to be done, however, in designing and supplying adequate sheltered residences and care that will help them live in the community. Primary prevention is difficult to institute, a reflection of our inadequate knowledge of how disordered behavior develops. We know very little either about how to determine the needs of a community or how to mobilize large groups of people for change.

Somatic treatments attempt to alter abnormal functioning by intervening directly in bodily processes. A variety of psychoactive drugs have proved effective: minor tranquilizers for calming anxious but nonpsychotic people, neuroleptics for lessening the thought disorders and behavioral problems of schizophrenics, stimulants for reducing hyperactivity in children, antidepressants for lifting the mood of depressed individuals, and lithium for controlling the wide swings in affect of bipolar patients. As useful as these different drugs are, they all have side effects, sometimes serious ones, and psychological therapies are usually needed to treat aspects of the disorders that remain untouched by medication.

In earlier decades, more drastic treatments were also tried for seemingly intractable psychotic conditions: psychosurgery, in which connections between the cortex and lower regions of the brain are severed; and convulsive therapies, notably electroconvulsive shock treatment to induce a grand mal seizure by passing high-voltage shock through the cortex. Psychoactive drugs have virtually eliminated the need for these measures, although ECT remains an apparently effective treatment for profound depression.

Joseph Hirsch, *Interior with Figures*, 1962
Collection of The Whitney Museum of American Art, New York. Gift of Mr. and Mrs. Daniel Fraad, Jr.

LEGAL AND ETHICAL ISSUES

Amendment 1 Congress shall make no law respecting an establishment of religion, or prohibiting the free exercise thereof; or abridging the freedom of speech, or of the press; or the right of the people peaceably to assemble, and to petition the Government for a redress of grievances.

Amendment 4 The right of the people to be secure in their persons, houses, papers, and effects, against unreasonable searches and seizures, shall not be violated. . . .

Amendment 5 No person . . . shall be compelled in any criminal case to be a witness against himself, nor be deprived of life, liberty, or property, without due process of law. . . .

Amendment 6 In all criminal prosecutions, the accused shall enjoy the right to a speedy and public trial . . . ; to be confronted with the witnesses against him; to have compulsory process for obtaining witnesses in his favor, and to have the Assistance of Counsel for his defense.

Amendment 8 Excessive bail shall not be required, nor excessive fines imposed, nor cruel and unusual punishments inflicted.

Amendment 13 . . . Neither slavery nor involuntary servitude, except as a punishment for crime whereof the party shall have been duly convicted, shall exist within the United States, or any place subject to their jurisdiction. . . .

Amendment 14 . . . No State shall . . . deprive any person of life, liberty, or property, without due process of law; nor deny to any person within its jurisdiction the equal protection of the laws.

Amendment 15 . . . The right of citizens of the United States to vote shall not be denied or abridged by the United States or by any State on account of race, color, or previous condition of servitude.

These elegant statements describe and protect some of the rights of American citizens and others residing in this country. Against what are these rights being protected? Be mindful of the circumstances under which most of these statements were issued. After the Constitutional Convention delegates had delineated the powers of government in 1787, the first Congress saw fit in 1789 to amend what they had framed and to set specific limits on the federal government. Amendments beyond the original ten have been added since that time. The philosophical ideal of American government has always been to allow citizens the maximum degree of liberty consistent with preserving order in the community at large.

We open our final chapter in this way because the legal and mental health systems collaborate continually, although often subtly, to deny a substantial proportion of our population their basic civil rights. With the best of intentions, judges, governing boards of hospitals, bar associations, and professional mental health groups have worked over the years to protect society at large from the actions of people regarded as mentally ill or mentally defective and considered dangerous to themselves or to others. But in so doing they have abrogated the rights of thousands of people in both criminal and civil commitment proceedings. The mentally ill who have broken the law, or who are alleged to have done so, can be committed to a prison hospital through *criminal commitment* proceedings. *Civil commitment* is a set of procedures by which a person who has not broken a law can be deprived of his or her liberty and incarcerated in a mental hospital. In effect, both commitments remove individuals from the normal processes of the law.

CRIMINAL COMMITMENT

We shall examine first the role of psychiatry and psychology in the criminal justice system. Almost as early as the concept of *mens rea* or guilty mind and the rule "No crime without an evil intent" had begun to be accepted in English common law, insanity had to be taken into consideration, for a disordered mind may be regarded as unable to formulate and carry out a criminal purpose. At first insanity was not a trial defense, but the English crown sometimes granted pardons to people who had been convicted of homicide if they were judged completely and totally mad (A. A. Morris, 1968). By the reign of Edward I (1272—1307), the concept of insanity had begun to be argued in court and could lessen punishment. Then during the course of the fourteenth century it became the rule of law that a person proved to be wholly and continually mad could be defended against a criminal charge.

In modern times judges and lawyers have called on psychiatrists, and recently clinical psychologists as well, for assistance in dealing with criminal acts thought to result from the accused's disordered mental state, not from his free will. Are such emotionally disturbed perpetrators less criminally responsible than those who are not distraught but commit the same crimes? Should such individuals even be brought to trial for transgressions against society's laws? Although efforts to excuse or protect the accused through the insanity defense or by judging them incompetent to stand trial are undoubtedly well intentioned, invoking these doctrines can often subject the accused to a greater denial of his liberties than he would experience without them.

The Insanity Defense

A staggering amount of material has been written on the insanity defense, even though it is pled in only about 2 percent of all cases that reach trial and is rarely successful (N. Morris, 1968; Morse, 1982b; Steadman, 1979). Alan A. Stone (1975), a professor of law and psychiatry at Harvard, proposed an intriguing reason for this great interest. Criminal law rests on the assumption that people have free will and that, if they do wrong, they have *chosen* to do so and should therefore be punished. "Our jurisprudence . . . while not oblivious to deterministic components, ultimately rests on a premise of freedom of will" (*United States* v. *Brawner*[1]). Stone suggests that the insanity defense strengthens the concept of free will by pointing to the few people who constitute an exception because they do not have it, namely those judged to be insane. These individuals are assumed to have less responsibility for their actions because of a mental defect, an inability to distinguish between right and wrong, or both. They lack the degree of free will that would justify holding them legally accountable for criminal acts. By exclusion, everyone else *has* free will! "The insanity defense is in every sense the exception that proves the rule. It allows the courts to treat every other defendant as someone who chose 'between good and evil'" (Stone, 1975, p. 222).

Landmark Cases

Historically, in modern Anglo-American criminal law, there have been three important court rulings that bear on the problems of legal responsibility and mental illness. The so-called "irresistible impulse" concept was formulated in 1834 in a case in Ohio wherein it was decided that an insanity defense was legitimate if a pathological impulse or drive that the person could not control had compelled him to commit the criminal act. The irresistible impulse test was confirmed in two subsequent court cases, *Parsons* v. *State* and *Davis* v. *United States*.[2]

[1]United States v. Brawner, No. 22,714 (D.C. Cir. June 23, 1972).

[2]Parsons v. State, 2 So. 854, 866-67 (Ala. 1887); Davis v. United States, 175 U.S. 373, 378 (1897).

"BUT YOU JUST CAN'T PLEAD INSANITY DUE TO AN EXTRA Y-CHROMOSOME IN A CASE OF EMBEZZLING."

The second well-known concept, the M'Naghten rule, was announced in the aftermath of a murder trial in England in 1843. The defendant, Daniel M'Naghten, had meant to kill the British prime minister but had instead mistaken the secretary of Sir Robert Peel for his employer. M'Naghten claimed that he had been instructed to kill Lord Peel by the "voice of God." The judges ruled that

. . . to establish a defence of insanity, it must be clearly proved that, at the time of the committing of the act, the party accused was labouring under such a defect of reason, from disease of the mind, as not to know the nature and quality of the act he was doing; or if he did know it, that he did not know he was doing what was wrong.

This "right-wrong" concept has been applied in the United Sates for many years. It is the sole test in sixteen states; in five others it is applied in conjunction with irresistible impulse.

The third decision, made in the 1954 case of *Durham* v. *United States*,[3] says that the "accused is not criminally responsible if his unlawful act was the product of mental disease or mental defect." David Bazelon, the presiding justice, believed that by referring simply to mental illness he would leave the profession of psychiatry free to apply its full knowledge. It would no longer be limited to considering impulses or knowledge of right and wrong. Judge Bazelon purposely did not incorpo-

[3]Durham v. United States, 214 F. 2d 862, 876 (D.C. Cir. 1954).

rate in what would be called the Durham test any particular symptoms of mental disorder that might later become obsolete. The psychiatrist was accorded great liberty to convey to the court his or her own evaluation of the accused's mental condition. Forcing the jury to rely to this extent on expert testimony did not prove workable courtroom practice, however. The Durham test is currently used only in the state of New Hampshire.

In 1962 the American Law Institute (ALI) proposed its own guidelines, which were intended to be more specific and informative to lay jurors than other tests.

1. A person is not responsible for criminal conduct if at the time of such conduct as a result of mental disease or defect he lacks substantial capacity either to appreciate the criminality (wrongfulness) of his conduct or to conform his conduct to the requirements of law.

2. As used in the Article, the terms "mental disease or defect" do not include an abnormality manifested only by repeated criminal or otherwise antisocial conduct (The American Law Institute, 1962, p. 66).

The first of the ALI guidelines in a sense combines the M'Naghten rule and the irresistible-impulse concept. According to legal scholars, however, the phrases substantial capacity, appreciate criminality of conduct, and conform conduct to the law broaden these concepts and allow the jurors themselves to decide whether the defendant should be blamed for misconduct.[4] The questions whether there was irresistible impulse and whether there was knowledge of right and wrong are more exacting and require expert opinion. The second ALI guideline concerns those who are repeatedly in trouble with the law; they are not to be deemed mentally ill only because they keep committing crimes. The ALI test is currently used in twenty-four states and the District of Columbia and is the standard in all federal circuit courts of appeal.

Many issues are raised by the insanity defense, for in its application an abstract principle must be fit to specific life situations. As in all aspects of the law, terms can be defined in a number of ways—by the defendants, defense lawyers, prosecutors, judges, and of course, jurors—and testimony can be presented in diverse fashion, depending on the skill of the interrogators and the intelligence of the witnesses. Furthermore, only the de-

fendant's mental condition *at the time the crime was committed* is in question. Consequently, retrospective, often speculative, judgment on the part of attorneys, judges, jurors, and psychiatrists is required. And disagreement between defense and prosecution psychiatrists and psychologists is the rule.

The Case of *Jones* v. *United States*

Case description   To illustrate the predicament that a person can get into if he or she raises insanity as an excusing condition for a criminal act, we consider a recent Supreme Court case.[5] Michael Jones was arrested unarmed on September 19, 1975, for attempting to steal a jacket from a department store in Washington, D.C. He was charged the following day with attempted petit larceny, a misdemeanor punishable by a maximum prison sentence of one year. The court ordered that he be committed to St. Elizabeth's Hospital, a public mental hospital in Washington, D.C., for a determination of his competency to stand trial. On March 2, 1976, almost six months after the alleged crime, a hospital psychologist reported to the court that Jones was competent to stand trial, although he suffered from "schizophrenia, paranoid type." The psychologist also reported that the alleged crime itself was caused by Jones's condition, his paranoid schizophrenia. This is noteworthy because he was not asked to offer an opinion on the nature of the crime itself, only on whether Jones was competent to stand trial. Jones then decided to plead not guilty by reason of insanity—NGRI. Ten days later, on March 12, the court found him not guilty by reason of insanity and committed him to St. Elizabeth's Hospital for treatment of his mental disorder.

On May 25, 1976, a customary fifty-day hearing was held to determine whether Jones should remain in the hospital any longer. A psychologist from the hospital testified that, indeed, Jones still suffered from paranoid schizophrenia and was therefore still a danger to himself and to others. A second hearing was held on February 22, 1977, seventeen months after the commission of the crime and Jones' original commitment to St. Elizabeth's for determination of competency. The defendant demanded release since he had already been hospitalized longer than the one-year maximum sentence he would have served had he been found guilty of the theft of the jacket. The court denied the request and returned him to St. Elizabeth's.

---

[4]Strictly speaking, of course, jurors are always supposed to decide for themselves. A continuing issue in forensic psychiatry and psychology is the influence expert witnesses can have on jurors (Morse, 1978, 1982b).

[5]Jones v. United States, 463 U.S. _____, 103 S. Ct. _____, L. Ed. 2d _____, 51 U.S.L.W. 5041 (1983).

The District of Columbia Court of Appeals agreed with the original court. Ultimately, in November 1982, more than seven years after his hospitalization, Jones's appeal to the Supreme Court was heard. On June 29, 1983, by a five-to-four decision, the Court affirmed the earlier decision: Jones was to remain in St. Elizabeth's.

The decision of the Supreme Court The basic question that Jones took to the Supreme Court was whether someone ". . . who was committed to a mental hospital upon being acquitted of a criminal offense by reason of insanity, must be released because he has been hospitalized for a period longer than he might have served in prison had he been convicted" (*Jones v. United States*, p. 700). Having already been much longer in the prison hospital than he would have served in prison had he been convicted, Jones believed that he should be released.

The Supreme Court, however, saw matters differently.

An insanity acquittee is not entitled to his release merely because he has been hospitalized for a period longer than he could have been incarcerated if convicted. The length of a sentence for a particular criminal offense is based on a variety of considerations, including retribution, deterrence, and rehabilitation. However, because an insanity acquittee was not convicted, he may not be punished. *The purpose of his commitment is to treat his mental illness and protect him and society from his potential dangerousness. There simply is no necessary correlation between the length of the acquittee's hypothetical criminal sentence and the length of time necessary for his recovery (p. 700, emphasis added).*[6]

Where [the] accused has pleaded insanity as a defense to a crime, and the jury has found that the defendant was, in fact, insane at the time the crime was committed, it is just and reasonable . . . that the insanity, once established, should be presumed to continue and that the accused should automatically be confined for treatment until it can be shown that he has recovered (S Rep No. 1170, 84th Cong, 1st Sess 13 (1955), as cited in Jones v. United States, *p. 705).*

And because it is impossible to predict how long it will take for any given individual to recover—or indeed whether he ever will recover—Congress has chosen, as it has with respect to civil commitment, to leave the length

of commitment interdeterminate, subject to periodic review of the patient's suitability for release (p. 708).

The fact that Jones was acquitted means, said the Court, that he cannot be punished for the crime. For to be punished, the individual must be blameworthy. Jones's insanity left him legally blameless, for he could not possess *mens rea*, a guilty mind. His free will to have committed the theft was deemed to have been superseded by his disturbed mental state. This is the logic of the insanity defense. Furthermore, said the Court, since punishment cannot have any of its intended individual or societal effects on a mentally disturbed person—rehabilitation, deterrence, or retribution—it was irrelevant that Jones was being held longer than a normal prison sentence.

Critique of the Supreme Court decision The burden of proof was on Jones, the acquittee, to prove that he is no longer mentally ill or dangerous to society. This contrasts with the normal practice of justice in the United States, that a person's *accusers* have the burden to prove him or her guilty. It is different as well from civil commitment, in which the government, not the person, bears the burden of proof; Jones was denied this civil right.

The Court was concerned about Jones's illness-produced dangerousness. What the Court said about "dangerousness" is therefore interesting. Jones argued in his petition to the Supreme Court that his theft of the jacket was not dangerous because his was not a violent crime. The Court stated, however, that for there to be violence in a criminal act, the act itself need not be dangerous. It cited a previous decision that a nonviolent theft of an article such as a watch may frequently result in violence through the efforts of the criminal to escape, or of the victim to protect his property, or of the police to apprehend the fleeing thief.[7]

The dissenting justices of the Court commented that the longer someone like Jones had to remain in the hospital, the more difficult it would be for him to demonstrate that he is no longer a dangerous person and mentally ill. Extended institutionalization would likely make it more difficult for him to afford medical experts other than those associated with the hospital and to behave like someone who is not mentally ill.

The current [use of] psychotropic drugs . . . may render mental patients docile . . ., but it does not "cure" them or allow them to demonstrate that they would remain

---

[6]This absence of correlation between the criminal act and the length of incarceration can also work the other way, namely ". . . no matter how serious the act committed by the acquittee, he may be released within fifty days of his acquittal if he has recovered" (p. 708).

[7]Overholser v. O'Beorne, ____ App. D.C. ____, 302 F. 2d 852, 861 (1961).

non-violent if they were not drugged. . . . At petitioner's May 1976 hearing, the Government relied on testimony [from hospital mental health experts] that petitioner was "not always responsive in a positive way to what goes on" and was "not a very active participant in the informal activities on the Ward" to support its contention that he had not recovered (p. 716, fn 16).

Competency To Stand Trial

The insanity defense concerns the accused's mental state *at the time of the crime.* A second issue, whether the person is competent to stand trial, concerns the defendant's mental condition *at the time of his or her trial.* It is obviously possible for a person to be judged competent to stand trial yet be acquitted by reason of insanity. By the same token, it is possible for a person to be deemed incompetent to stand trial when no final courtroom consideration has yet been given to his criminal responsibility for the act in question.

Far greater numbers of people are committed to prison hospitals after being judged incompetent to stand trial than are tried and acquitted by reason of insanity. In fact, it has been estimated that as many as forty-five people are confined in prison hospitals because of incompetency to stand trial for every one ultimately sent there for having been found not guilty by reason of insanity (Steadman, 1979). Our criminal justice system is so organized that the fitness of individuals to stand trial must be decided before their responsibility for the crime of which they are accused can be determined (Schwitzgebel and Schwitzgebel, 1980). Once a trial is held, the defendant may be found guilty and sent to prison, be found not guilty of having performed the illegal act and consequently set free, or, like Michael Jones, be found not guilty by reason of insanity and therefore committed to a prison hospital.

With the Supreme Court case *Pate* v. *Robinson*[8] as precedent, the defense attorney, prosecutor, or judge may raise the question of mental illness whenever there is reason to believe that the accused's mental condition might interfere with the upcoming trial. Over the years most jurisdictions in this country have shown concern that the accused may be "presently insane and otherwise so mentally incompetent as to be unable to understand the proceedings against him or properly to assist in his own defense" (Pfeiffer, Eisenstein, and Dabbs, 1967, p. 322). Another way of stating this problem of competency is to say that the courts do not want a person to be brought to trial *in absentia*, which is a basic principle of English common law going back to the eighteenth century. A disturbed person can of course be physically present; what is referred to here is his or her mental state. If after examination the person is deemed too mentally ill to participate meaningfully in a trial, the trial is routinely delayed. The accused is incarcerated in a prison hospital with the hope that means of restoring adequate mental functioning can be found. This, too, happened to Jones, immediately after his arrest.

Being judged incompetent to stand trial can have severe consequences for the individual. Bail is automatically denied, even though it might be routinely granted if the question of incompetency had not been raised. The accused is kept in a facility for the criminally insane for the pretrial examination; these institutions are not the best of hospitals. The accused may well lose employment and undergo the trauma of being separated from family and friends and from familiar surroundings for months or even longer, perhaps making his emotional condition even worse and thereby delaying his fitness to stand trial. Some people have languished in a prison hospital for many years, waiting to be found competent to stand trial.

Many psychiatrists, when asked to render a competency judgment, assume that if they judge the person to be mentally disturbed in any way, it follows that he or she cannot stand trial; thus have many people been deprived of their day in court. Robey (1965) pointed out, however, that even a psychotic person may sufficiently understand his position in the legal proceedings to participate in them and to talk with his attorney rationally. Robey proposes that a person be allowed to come to trial *even though* he may behave in a bizarre manner before and during the proceedings. The accused may be at a severe disadvantage if, during the trial, he is confused, deluded, hallucinating, and so on, but a somewhat inequitable trial may be preferable to being incarcerated until behavior is judged normal once again. It should be kept in mind that some of the people we are talking about are proved, once they have been brought to trial, *not* to have committed the crimes of which they were accused.

A 1972 Supreme Court case, *Jackson* v. *Indiana*,[9] forced the states to a shorter-term determination of incompetency. The case concerned a mentally retarded deaf-mute man who was deemed not only incompetent to stand trial but unlikely ever to become competent. The Court ruled that the length of pretrial confinement

[8]Pate v. Robinson, 384 U.S. 375 (1966).

[9]Jackson v. Indiana, 406 U.S. 715 (1972).

must be limited to the time it takes to determine whether treatment during this detainment is likely to render the defendant competent to stand trial. If the defendant is unlikely ever to become competent, the state should after this period either institute civil commitment proceedings or release the defendant. It has been suggested that lawyers participate with mental health professionals in making the competency determination, for a knowledgeable lawyer understands exactly what the defendant must be able to do to participate in his own trial (Roesch and Golding, 1980). Legislation has been drafted in most states to define more precisely the minimal requirements for competency to stand trial, ending the latitude that has deprived thousands of people of their rights to due process (Amendment 14) and a speedy trial (Amendment 6).

The era of modern medicine has also had an impact on the competency issue. The concept of "synthetic sanity" (Schwitzgebel and Schwitzgebel, 1980) has been introduced: if a drug like Thorazine temporarily produces a modicum of rationality in an otherwise deranged defendant, the trial may proceed. The likelihood that the defendant will again become incompetent to stand trial if and when the drug is withdrawn will not disqualify him from having his day in court.[10] Furthermore, if the defendant wishes, the effects of the medication must be explained to the jury, lest—if the defendant is pleading NGRI—the jury conclude, from his relatively calm and rational drug-produced demeanor, that he could not have been insane at the time of the crime.[11]

Thomas S. Szasz and the Case Against Forensic Psychiatry and Psychology

His Polemic

By codifying acts of violence as expressions of mental illness, we neatly rid ourselves of the task of dealing with criminal offenses as more or less rational, goal-directed acts, no different in principle from other forms of conduct (Szasz, 1963, p. 141).

Thomas S. Szasz, noted psychiatrist who argues strongly against the use of the insanity defense.

This quotation from one of Thomas Szasz's most widely read books enunciates the basic theme of his argument against the weighty role that his own profession of psychiatry plays in the legal system. To understand the view of this outspoken critic of forensic psychiatry, we must first of all examine the distinction made between *descriptive* and *ascriptive responsibility*. As Szasz points out, a person may be judged descriptively responsible in the sense that all agree a particular act was, in fact, performed by him. Assigning ascriptive responsibility, however, is a social judgment that society should inflict consequences upon someone deemed descriptively responsible. The court verdict of "not guilty by reason of insanity" says, first, that John Doe was descriptively responsible for committing a crime, but second, that society will not ascribe legal responsibility to him and punish him for what he did. Killing in wartime is another example of this divergence between descriptive and ascriptive responsibilities. To murder the enemy as a member of a nation's armed forces is to be responsible for another person's death. Yet the soldier is not punished for his action and indeed may win honors for it.

To hold a person criminally responsible is to ascribe or attribute legal responsibility to him. A given social group makes the judgment that the person who is descriptively responsible for a criminal act will receive criminal punishment. As Szasz points out, being criminally responsible is not a trait that is inherent in a person and that society uncovers. Rather, society at a given time and for a given criminal act decides that it will hold the perpetrator legally responsible and will punish him.

[10]State of Louisiana v. Hamptom, 216 So. 2d 311 (1969); State of Tennessee v. Stacy, No. 446 (Crim. App., Knoxville, TN, August 4, 1977); United States v. Hayes, 589 F. 2d 811 (1979).

[11]State v. Jojola, 89 N.M. 489, 553 P. 2d 1296 (Ct. App. 1976). This ruling relates to our earlier comment about the difficulty of concluding, from retrospective evidence, what a defendant's mental state was at the time of committing his crime, perhaps years earlier than his trial. This legal principle would seem to acknowledge that juries form their judgment of legal responsibility or insanity at least in part on how the defendant appears during the trial. If he or she seems "too normal," they may be less likely to believe the crime to have been an act of a disturbed mental state than of free will.

Szasz argues that the insanity plea, commonly used in cases of attempted assassination such as that of Pope John Paul II, are attempts to cover up social ills.

Szasz goes on to suggest that mental illness began to be used as an explanation for criminal behavior when people acted in a way that was considered particularly irrational and threatening to society. According to Szasz, these exceptional cases all involved violence against people of high social rank. In shooting at a Lord Onslow in 1724, a man named Arnold was believed to have as little understanding of his murderous act as "a wild beast." Another man, James Hadfield, was deemed deranged for attempting to assassinate King George III in 1800 as he sat in a box at the Theatre Royal. And a third, Oxford by name, was regarded as insane for trying to kill Queen Victoria in 1840. The best-known case has already been mentioned, that of Daniel M'Naghten (1843), who killed Sir Robert Peel's private secretary after mistaking him for Peel. In all these cases from English law, which forms the basis for all American law, people of low social rank openly attacked their superiors. Szasz believes that ". . . the issue of insanity may have been raised in these trials in order to obscure the social problems which the crimes intended to dramatize" (1963, p. 128).

Other cases here and abroad, such as the assassinations of John and Robert Kennedy, the South African prime minister Hendrik Verwoerd, Martin Luther King, and John Lennon, and the attempted assassinations of Ronald Reagan and Pope John Paul II, may to a degree reflect the social ills of today. Moreover, events in the Soviet Union are ominous. In *A Question of Madness*,

the well-known Russian biochemist Zhores Medvedev (1972) told how Soviet psychiatrists collaborated with the state in attempting to muzzle his criticism of his government. They diagnosed him as suffering from paranoid delusions, split personality, and other mental ailments that would make it dangerous for him to be at large in society. In the years since, the confinement of political protesters for madness has, if anything, increased in the Soviet Union (Bloch and Reddaway, 1977; see Box 21.1).

But pleas of insanity are made in far more ordinary cases. And of course Szasz does not claim that all these pleas involve some sort of silent conspiracy of the establishment to cover up social problems. Szasz sets forth a polemic much broader in scope. His basic concern is with individual freedom, which includes the right to deviate from prevailing mores. Far from advocating that people be held *less* accountable for antisocial acts, he argues that legal responsibility be extended to *all*, even to those whose actions are so far beyond the limits of convention that some people explain their behavior in terms of mental illness. Szasz's overall lament is that

Instead of recognizing the deviant as an individual different from those who would judge him, but nonetheless worthy of their respect, he is first discredited as a self-responsible human being and then subjected to humiliating punishment defined and disguised as treatment (1963, p. 108).

Zhores Medvedev (left) and Vladimir Bukovsky (right), Soviet dissidents who were detained in mental hospitals for criticizing the government.

Evaluation of Szasz's Position

As might be expected, Szasz has been answered by many whom he has criticized and by others who sincerely believe that psychiatry and psychology should have an important role in deciding how to deal with people whose criminal acts seem attributable to mental illness. When society acts with great certainty on the basis of "expert scientific opinion," however, particularly when that opinion denies to an individual the rights and respect accorded others, it may be well to let Szasz remind us that Sir Thomas Browne, a distinguished British physician, in 1664 testified in a court of law that witches did indeed exist, "as everyone knew."

And yet the abuses documented by Szasz should not blind us to the fact that—for whatever combination of physiological and psychological reasons—some people are, at times, a danger to others and to themselves. Although Szasz and others object to mental illness as an explanation, it is difficult to deny that there is, indeed, madness in the world. People *do* occasionally imagine persecutors, whom they sometimes act against with force. Some people do hallucinate and on this basis may behave in a dangerous fashion. Our concern for the liberties of one individual has always been tempered with our concern for the rights of others.

But does it help a criminal acquitted by reason of insanity to place him in a prison mental hospital with an indeterminate sentence, pending his rehabilitation? The answer can surely not be an unqualified yes. Should such a person, then, be treated like any other convicted felon and be sent to a penitentiary? Considering the psychic damage that we know may occur in ordinary prisons, a yes to this question cannot be enthusiastic either. But a prison sentence is more often a finite term of incarceration. If we cannot demonstrate that people are rehabilitated in mental hospitals, perhaps it is just as well to rely on our prisons and on the efforts of penologists to improve these institutions and to find ways of helping inmates alter their behavior so that it will not be antisocial after release.[12]

The Szaszian point of view has recently been articulated by Stephen J. Morse, a University of Southern

[12]The treatment model, however, is being challenged by simple, old-fashioned, retributive justice (Monahan, 1977; Morse, 1979). Today punishment rather than rehabilitation is likely to be the primary purpose of imprisonment. Prisoners who were given treatment, whether job training or psychotherapy, have no different crime rates after release than inmates who simply sat out their terms in their cells and led a routine prison life. Prisoners themselves have been agitating for finite sentences, rather than the indeterminate sentence that promises early parole depending on "rehabilitation."

BOX 21.1

GENERAL SVETLICHNY: "WE WILL LET HIM ROT IN THE INSANE ASYLUM!"

. . . I was arrested in 1963 for preparing two photocopies of [Milovan] Djilas's book "The New Class" and was placed in solitary confinement at the Lubyanks Prison. I was . . . summoned by General Svetlichny, who was in charge of the Moscow K.G.B., and was offered [a chance] to repent and tell who gave me the book and who helped me make the photocopies. Then I would be released.

The obvious purpose of [this conversation] was to turn me into an informant and to make me cooperate with the authorities. But when nothing came of this, I was given a psychiatric examination, was declared mentally ill and was sent to Leningrad. I attribute my release to the fact that the Leningrad school [of psychiatry was disputing] with the Moscow school and [refuting] their diagnoses [of schizophrenia]. In February 1965 I was freed.

At the end of 1965, I was again arrested for organizing the first human rights demonstration, which took place on December 5 in defense of [Andrei] Sinyavsky and [Yuli] Daniel. . . . Up to that time, there had been no demonstrations since 1927 and the legislature forgot to foresee the proper measure of punishment for those who should take part in demonstrations. Consequently, there were no legal punitive means of punishment. I was simply dispatched to one of the Moscow psychiatric hospitals with the intention that my old diagnosis be confirmed and then, without a new court hearing or investigation, I would again be sent to

Leningrad as a person who had not as yet been fully "cured" from the previous time.

The K.G.B.'s calculations were undermined by honest young doctors at city hospital No. 13, who prepared an extensive report stating that I was not mentally ill. In spite of the doctors' conclusions, I was transferred to another city hospital, in accordance with the K.G.B.'s instructions. In this hospital, the doctors also did not find me to be ill and insisted that I be released. And once again—upon the instructions of the K.G.B.—I was transferred, but this time to the Serbsky Institute. In the face of the well-supported conclusion provided by two hospitals, even the Serbsky Institute did not [dare] to declare me insane. . . . [But at] that very time, when my mother went to see General Svetlichny, he stomped his feet and screamed: "He will never be released! We will let him rot in the insane aslyum!"

In the meantime, my case had attracted public attention and became well known in the West, thanks to the pronouncements made by Valery Tarsis and the activities of Amnesty International. Finally, the authorities were forced to appoint a neutral commission. But four professors who were specially summoned could not come to a unified conclusion. Two of them, representing Snezhnevsky's [Moscow] school, declared me to be mentally ill. The other two, opponents of his school, refuted their diagnosis.

I remained confined amid this situation for eight

California psychologist and law professor, who writes here on the need to treat mentally ill people as responsible individuals and on the associated need to improve the prison system.

If involuntary commitment is abolished, there may well be an increase in the processing of cases of relatively mild deviance through the criminal justice system and increased numbers of crazy persons may spend some time in unpleasant and often terrible jails. But, if crazy persons are almost always responsible for their behavior, and if incarceration in a jail is justified, there is no reason why they should not go to jail. This outcome is in fact more respectful of the dignity and autonomy of crazy persons than assuming that they are nonresponsible and must be "fixed." Jails and locked hospitals are both massive intrusions on liberty. The best response to the argument that jails are bad places, as they surely are for noncrazy and crazy inmates alike, is to clean them up. Using unjustified hospitalization—merely another

form of incarceration that offers little if any of the benefits it promises—to avoid jails is not a sensible solution to the problems of criminal justice: it merely allows us to avoid those problems (Morse, 1982a, p. 98).

CIVIL COMMITMENT

Civil commitment affects far greater numbers of people than criminal commitment. It is beyond the scope of this book to examine in detail the variety of state civil commitment laws and regulations. Each state has its own, and they are in almost constant flux. Our aim instead is to provide an overview that will give the reader a basic understanding of the issues and of the current directions of change.

In virtually all states of the union, a person can be committed to a mental hospital against his or her will if a judgment is made that he or she (1) is mentally ill and months, six of which were spent at the Serbsky Institute. You need not think that the dispute was strictly scientific: It was a matter of conformity or nonconformity of doctors, and the authorities could not find a sufficient number of conformists for a case which had attracted such publicity.

I was released after a representative of Amnesty International came to Moscow and went straight to Georgy Morozov, the director of the Serbsky Institute, and told him that if I were not immediately released, my case would be raised before the Bertrand Russell tribunal.

By the end of the 1960s, a well-established methodology of psychiatric repression had evolved . . . the K.G.B. provided the ideological direction, giving the instruction that opponents of the regime be declared insane and the psychiatrists worked out an entire system with a diagnostic basis. By this time the Snezhevsky school was in firm command of Soviet psychiatry.

The following categories of individuals were most liable to be declared "insane."

1. Prominent figures, whose trials would prove to be uncomfortable in the propagandistic sense.

2. So-called revisionists—that is, those who criticize the system from Marxist positions.

3. Persons who stood up for their convictions during the period of investigation, used legal means of defense and insisted on their right not to give any evidence whatsoever.

4. Believers, including those who faced purely political charges, without any "religious articles."

. . . In the 1970s political prisoners have been sent more and more often to psychiatric prison hospitals before the expiration of their camp sentences. This practice allows the authorities to lengthen their terms for an endless period of time.

Now another new method has emerged: the practice of giving psychiatric diagnosis to political prisoners prior to their release from camp. After being freed with such a diagnosis, a former prisoner always lives under the Damocles sword of compulsory hospitalization.

How do Soviet psychiatrists attempt to justify their complicity in such a widely developed system of psychiatric repression?

The main features of today's psychiatric prisons, of which psychiatrists can no longer claim to be unaware, include treatment (with no regard to harmful effects), indefinite periods of confinement, the necessity of showing repentance in order to be freed, the discreditation of the person and his ideas, constant blackmail after the person's release, and his complete lack of any rights (such tested means of resistance as hunger strikes and the lodging of complaints, which are widely used in camps and prisons, serve only to burden a psychiatric diagnosis).

Under these conditions, every person who is arrested is afraid of being declared insane, and the threat of being sent to a psychiatric prison is used as blackmail during the period of investigation and during the course of the psychiatric examination (Bukovsky, 1977).

---

(2) gravely disabled—unable to provide for his or her basic physical needs of food, clothing, and shelter; or a danger, to self or to others; or both (Warren, 1982). At present, dangerousness to others is more often the second criterion, and recent court rulings point to *imminent* dangerousness as the principal criterion.[13]

Historically, governments have had the duty to protect their citizens from harm. We take for granted the right and duty of government to set limits on our freedom for the sake of protecting us. Few drivers, for example, question the limits imposed on them by traffic signals. We usually go along with the Food and Drug Administration when it bans uncontrolled use of drugs that cause cancer in laboratory animals, although some people, to be sure, feel they have the right to decide for themselves what risks to take with their own bodies. Government, then, has a long-established right to protect us both from ourselves—the *parens patriae* power of the state; and from others—the police power of the state. Civil commitment is one further exercise of these powers.

Specific commitment procedures are generally of two types, formal and informal. Formal or judicial commitment is by order of a court. It can be requested by any responsible citizen; usually the police, a relative, or a friend seeks the commitment. If the judge believes that there is good reason to pursue the matter, he or she will order a mental health examination. The person has the right to object to these attempts to "certify" him, and a court hearing can be scheduled to allow him to present evidence against commitment.

Informal, emergency commitment can be accomplished without initially involving the courts. For example, a hospital administrative board may decide that a voluntary patient requesting discharge is too disturbed and dangerous to be released. They are able to detain the patient with a temporary, informal commitment order.

[13]Suzuki v. Yuen, 617 F. 2d 173 (1980).

Any person acting wildly may be taken immediately to the state hospital by the police. Perhaps the most common informal commitment procedure is the "2PC" or "two physicians' certificate." In most states two physicians, not necessarily psychiatrists, can sign a certificate that will allow a person to be incarcerated for some period of time, ranging from twenty-four hours to as long as twenty days.[14] Detainment beyond this period requires formal judicial commitment.

Dangerousness: Problems in Definition and Prediction

The likelihood of committing a dangerous act is central to civil commitment, but is "dangerousness" easily defined? Stone (1975) suggests that, like beauty, it is in the eye of the beholder. Society punishes physical violence in the streets, for example, far more harshly than it punishes a business executive who knowingly neglects to replace defective gasoline tanks in an airplane (Geis and Monahan, 1976). White-collar dangerousness receives much less attention and retribution, even though it hurts more people. Monahan (1981) does mention a ruling of a federal court that writing a bad check was an act sufficiently dangerous to justify commitment because the economy would collapse if everyone did it. This would seem to be an extreme interpretation of dangerousness! The court decision has not been widely applied.

Civil commitment is necessarily a form of preventive detention: the prediction is made that a person judged mentally ill may in the future behave in a dangerous manner and should therefore be detained. Ordinary prisoners, however, are released from penitentiaries, even though statistics show that most will commit additional crimes. Moreover, the imprisonment of a criminal and the conviction by a court of law that precedes it are carried out only after a person has done some harm to others. Some may say it is like closing the barn door after the horses have thundered out. But our entire legal and constitutional system is organized to protect people from preventive detention. Even if witnesses have seen a person commit a serious crime, he or she is assumed innocent until proved guilty by the courts. The person who openly threatens to inflict harm on others, such as a man who for an hour each day stands in the street and points a loaded machine gun at a nearby apartment

house, is another matter. Does the state have to wait until he fires a round? No. It is here that the civil commitment process can be brought into play, although the person must be deemed not only an imminent danger to others but mentally ill as well (Schwitzgebel and Schwitzgebel, 1980). Claiming mental illness turns out to be a minor problem. Most mental health professionals, in agreement with the lay public, will conclude that a person has to be insane to behave in this way.

Studies have examined how good mental health professionals are at predicting that a person will commit a dangerous act (for example, Kozol, Boucher, and Garofalo, 1972; Stone, 1975; Monahan, 1973, 1976); they were found to be poor at making this judgment. Some workers have even argued that civil commitment for the purposes of preventive detention should be abolished. Monahan (1978), however, carefully scrutinized these studies and concluded that the professional's ability to predict violence is still an open question. Most of the studies conformed to the following methodological pattern.

1. People were institutionalized for mental illness and for being a danger to the community.

2. While these people were in the hospital, some of them were again predicted to be violent should they be released into the community.

3. After a period of time, these people were released, thus putting together the conditions for "a natural experiment."

4. Checks on the behavior of the released patients over the next several years did not reveal much dangerous behavior.

What is wrong with such research? Monahan points out that little if any consideration was given to changes that institutionalization itself might have effected. In the studies reviewed, the period of incarceration ranged from several months to fifteen years. Prolonged periods of enforced hospitalization might very well make patients more docile, if for no other reason than that they become that much older. Furthermore, the conditions in the open community where the predicted violence would be done can vary widely. We should not expect this kind of prediction to have great validity.

These studies, which have occasioned such pessimism about predicting whether a patient is dangerous, are therefore flawed. Yet they have also been used in arguments against emergency commitment. The fact of the matter is that neither these studies nor any others have examined this specific issue! Monahan, however,

[14]Special issues are involved in the commitment, institutionalization, and treatment of the mentally retarded, juveniles, drug addicts, and the aged.

has theorized that prediction of dangerousness is probably far easier and surer in true emergency situations than after extended periods of hospitalization. When an emergency commitment is sought, the person may appear out of control and be threatening violence in his or her own living room or, like the man in the street with a machine gun, against people in the nearby apartment house. He or she may also have been violent in the past—a good predictor of future violence—and victims and weapons may be on hand. A dangerous outburst seems imminent. Thus, unlike the danger to society predicted in the studies previously examined, the violence requiring an emergency commitment is expected almost immediately and in a known situation. Common sense tells us that such predictions of violence are likely to be very accurate. To test the validity of these expectations, we would have to leave alone half the people predicted to be immediately violent and later compare their behavior to that of persons hospitalized in such emergency circumstances. Such an experiment would be ethically irresponsible. Mental health professionals must apply logic and make the most prudent judgments possible (see Box 21.2).[15]

Recent Trends for Greater Protection

The United States Constitution is a remarkable document. It lays down the basic duties of our elected federal officials and guarantees a set of civil rights. But there is often some distance between the abstract delineation of a civil right and its day-to-day implementation. Moreover, judges must *interpret* the Constitution as it bears on specific contemporary problems. Since nowhere in this cornerstone of our democracy is there specific mention of committed mental patients, lawyers and judges interpret various sections of the document to justify what they consider necessary changes in society's treatment of people whose mental health is in question.

In 1972 voluntary admissions to mental hospitals began to outnumber involuntary admissions. But it is still the case that great numbers of people admitted to a state or county mental hospital are there against their wishes. Moreover, it is impossible to know how many of those who admit themselves voluntarily do so under threat of civil commitment. One survey (Gilboy and Schmidt, 1971) revealed that 40 percent of patients who had "vol-

untarily" admitted themselves to a mental hospital in Chicago had actually been threatened with commitment by the police officers who had brought them there. The issue of enforced mental hospitalization is still very much with us. Even though psychiatrists, psychologists, the courts, and hospital staff are apparently growing more reluctant to commit, tens of thousands of mental patients are in hospitals against their will.

In a democratic society the most grievous wrong that can be suffered by a citizen is loss of liberty. The situation of mental patients is improving, however. The rights accorded to ordinary citizens, and even to criminals, are gradually being extended to those threatened with civil commitment and to those who have already been involuntarily hospitalized. No longer is it assumed that deprivation of liberty for purposes of mental health care is reason to deny to the individual all other rights. For example, a federal court decision in Wisconsin, *Lessard* v. *Schmidt*,[16] gives a person threatened with civil commitment the right to timely, written notice of the proceeding, opportunity for a hearing with counsel, the right to have the hearing decided by jury, Fifth Amendment protection against self-incrimination, and other similar procedural safeguards already accorded defendants in criminal actions. A Supreme Court decision, *Addington* v. *Texas*,[17] further provides that the state must produce "clear and convincing evidence" that a person is mentally ill and dangerous before he can be involuntarily committed to a mental hospital. And recently the Ninth Circuit Court of Appeals ruled that this danger must be "imminent."[18] Clearly the trend is to restrict the power of the state to curtail individual freedoms because of "mental illness." Although protection of the rights of the mentally ill will add tremendously to the burden of both civil courts and state and county mental hospital staffs, it is a price a free society will have to pay.

Given the record of past [criminal proceedings and] the tragic parody of legal commitment used to warehouse American citizens, it is . . . important that the individual feel sure that the [present] mental health system [in

---

[15]Indications are that what Monahan (1984) has termed a second generation of violence prediction is beginning to be more accurate (for example, Rofman, Askinazi, and Fant, 1980).

[16]Lessard v. Schmidt, 349 F. Supp. 1078 (E.D. Wisc. 1972), *vacated and remanded on other grounds*, 94 S. Ct. 712 (1974), *reinstated* 413 F. Supp, 1318 (E.D. Wisc. 1976).

[17]Addington v. Texas, 99 S. Ct. 1804 (1979). The "clear and convincing" standard of proof, however, still protects the person less than would application of the criminal standard of "beyond a reasonable doubt." The criminal standard—beyond a reasonable doubt—is referred to as the 90 percent standard. The clear and convincing standard is set at 75 percent certainty.

[18]Suzuki v. Yuen, 617 F. 2d 173 (1980).

BOX 21.2

VIOLENT BEHAVIOR OF FORMER MENTAL PATIENTS

The association between mental illness and proneness to violence is very strongly embedded in the public's mind. We *assume* that many psychotic people are violent, that violence is often a result of madness, and that therefore society should be very wary about allowing mentally ill people to remain in our midst (Morse, 1982a).

Is there really a cause-effect relationship or even a high correlation between mental disorder and dangerousness? First, it must be appreciated that only the violent ex-mental patient makes the six-o'clock news. Nonviolent, even positive and exemplary behavior on the part of former mental patients is not particularly newsworthy. Our impressions are therefore formed by extremely selective reporting.

Monahan (1981) reviewed the prevalence of mental disorder in prison populations and the violent crime rate of people released from mental hospitals. Granted that many violent people manage to avoid prison, and that many mentally ill people have never been in a mental hospital, he did not find a strong relationship between violence and mental disorder.

Mental Illness of Criminals

Several studies (for example, Bolton, 1976; Guze, 1976; Monahan, Caldeira, and Friedlander, 1979) have found the prevalence of psychiatric disorder in prisoners to be in the range of 25 percent. The estimate of emotional disorders in the general population is similar, according to the President's Commission on Mental Health (1978). But people designated as sociopaths by prison clinicians do represent a sizable proportion of the prison population. Is not this particular disorder then associated with crime and perhaps violent crime? Diamond (1974) does not believe so, for prisoners are usually judged to be sociopathic based on a large number of previous arrests, delinquency in schools, poor job records, and "wanderlust," with a history of prostitution added as a criterion for women. Such a broad defini-

tion makes most people in prison sociopaths! Prisoners then have not been shown to have higher rates of mental illness than people in the population at large.

Violent Behavior of Former Mental Patients

Almost all the studies published in the 1950s and earlier found that released mental patients had a *lower* arrest rate for violent behavior than the general population; studies published in the 1960s and 1970s found them to have a *higher* arrest rate. Does this mean that, somehow, mentally ill people have only in the past twenty years become especially violent? Cocozza, Melick, and Steadman (1978) have concluded rather that a different group of people are now confined for a time in mental hospitals. Figure 21.1 summarizes the arrest records of 1,938 patients released from mental hospitals in New York State in 1975. If we consider the total patient sample, their arrest rate for violent and potentially violent crimes is indeed significantly higher than in the general population. But if we divide the patients according to whether they had ever been arrested before their hospitalization, the statistics are more revealing. Released patients who had never been arrested before they entered the hospital had an arrest rate *lower* than in the general population, released patients with one earlier arrest had the same or slightly higher arrest rate, and released patients with two or more earlier arrests has a much higher arrest rate. Monahan concludes, ". . . compared with the general population, the higher rate of violent crime committed by released mental patients can be accounted for entirely by those patients with a record, particularly an extensive record, of criminal activity that predated their hospitalization" (1981, pp. 80–81).

A 1947 sample of patients indicated that 15 percent had a prior arrest record (Brill and Malzberg, 1954) as compared to 26 percent of the 1975 sample. The deinstitutionalization sweeps of the past decades released into the com-

---

particular] cannot be so used and abused . . . for while the average citizen may have some confidence that if called by the Grand Inquisitor in the middle of the night and charged with a given robbery, he may have an alibi or be able to prove his innocence, he may be far less certain of his capacity, under the press of fear, to instantly prove his sanity (Stone, 1975, p. 57).

Least Restrictive Alternative

Civil commitment rests on presumed dangerousness, but of late dangerousness is being considered not an unvarying trait of the individual but behavior occurring in a specific social context. Thus a person may be deemed

dangerous if allowed to live by himself in an apartment, but not dangerous if living in a boarding home and taking prescribed psychoactive drugs every day under medical supervision. The "least restrictive alternative" to freedom is to be provided when treating disturbed people and protecting them from harming themselves and others. A number of court rulings, for example, *Lake* v. *Cameron*[19] and *Lessard* v. *Schmidt*, require that only mental patients who cannot be adequately looked after in less restrictive homes be confined in hospitals. Thus

---

[19]Lake v. Cameron, 364 F. 2d 657 (D.C. Cir. 1966).

munity patients unlikely to cause trouble, but at the same time people who earlier might have been sent to jail or prison were being committed to mental hospitals. In just the past few years it has become more difficult to confine a person in a mental hospital against his or her will.

The President's Commission on Mental Health drew the following conclusion.

The sporadic violence of so-called "mentally ill killers" as depicted in stories and dramas is more a device of fiction than a fact of life. Patients with serious psychological disorders are more likely to be withdrawn, apathetic, and fearful. We do not deny that some mentally ill people are violent, but the image of the mentally ill person as essentially a violent person is erroneous (1978, p. 56).

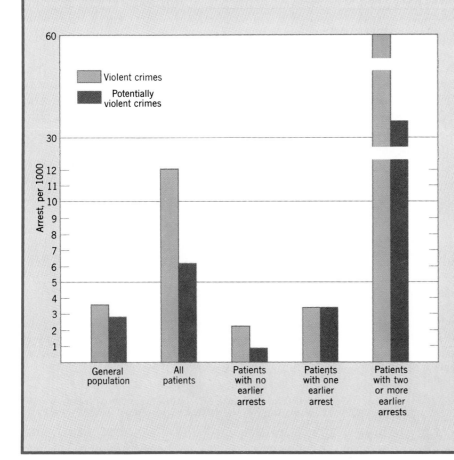

FIGURE 21.1 Annual arrest rates per 1000 for violent and potentially violent crimes for the general population, for all patients in a 1975 sample, and for patients with no earlier arrests and with one and two or more earlier arrests. After data reported by Cocozza, Melick, and Steadman, 1978.

commitment is no longer necessarily in an institution. Rather a patient might well be required to reside in a supervised boarding home or in other sheltered quarters (Schwitzgebel and Schwitzgebel, 1980). Of course, this principle will have meaning only if society provides suitable residences.

Right to Treatment

Another aspect of civil commitment that has come to the attention of the courts is the so-called right to treatment, a principle first articulated by Birnbaum (1960). If a person is deprived of liberty because he or she is mentally ill and is a danger to self or others, is not the state required to provide treatment to alleviate these problems? Is it not unconstitutional (and even indecent) to incarcerate someone without afterward providing the help he or she is supposed to need? This important question has been the subject of several court cases.

The right to treatment has gained in legal status since the 1960s and was extended to all civilly committed patients in a landmark decision involving the Partlow State School and Hospital for the mentally retarded of Tuscaloosa, Alabama, and two other institutions. In 1971 a class action suit was filed on behalf of a retarded boy, Ricky Wyatt, and all others similarly situated at the Partlow school, against Dr. Stickney, a new Commissioner of Mental Health. Dr. Stickney was a willing defendant, for he wanted very much to modernize the Alabama hospitals and the care they provided. In *Wyatt* v. *Stickney*[20] an Alabama federal court ruled in 1972 that the only justification for the civil commitment of patients to a state mental hospital is treatment. As stated by Judge Frank Johnson, "To deprive any citizen of his or her liberty upon the altruistic theory that the confinement is for humane and therapeutic reasons and then fail to provide adequate treatment violates the very fundamentals of due process." Rather, committed mental patients "have a constitutional right to receive such individual treatment as will give each of them a realistic opportunity to be cured or to improve his or her mental condition." This ruling, upheld on appeal, is frequently cited as ensuring protection of people confined by civil commitment, at least to this extent: the state cannot simply put them away without meeting minimal standards of care.

The *Wyatt* ruling, although applying only in Alabama, was significant, for in the past the courts had asserted that it was beyond their competence to pass judgment on the care given to mental patients. The courts had assumed that mental health professionals possess special and exclusive knowledge about psychopathology and its treatment. Repeated reports of abuses, however, gradually prodded the American judicial system to rule on what goes on within the walls of mental institutions (Schwitzgebel and Schwitzgebel, 1980). The *Wyatt* decision sets forth very specific requirements, such as dayrooms of at least forty square feet; curtains or screens for privacy in multi-patient bedrooms sleeping no more than five persons; a comfortable bed; one toilet per eight persons; the right to wear any clothing the patient wishes, provided it is not deemed dangerous; opportunities to interact with members of the opposite sex; and no physical restraints, except in emergency situations. And to provide care twenty-four hours a day, seven days a week, there should be, for every 250 patients, at least two psychiatrists, three additional physicians, twelve registered nurses, ninety attendants, four psychologists, and seven social workers. When the *Wyatt* action was taken, Alabama state mental facilities averaged one physician per 2000 patients, an extreme situation indeed.[21]

The trend of the *Wyatt* ruling, however, may have been weakened by a more recent 1982 Supreme Court decision, *Youngberg* v. *Romeo*,[22] regarding the treatment of a mentally retarded boy, Nicholas Romeo, who had been placed in physical restraints on occasion to keep him from hurting himself and others. Holding that the patient had a right to reasonable care and safety, the decision deferred to the professional judgment of the mental health professionals responsible for the boy: ". . . courts must show deference to the judgment exercised by a qualified professional. . . . the decision, if made by a professional, is presumptively valid" (pp. 322, 323).

In a more celebrated case,[23] which eventually found its way to the Supreme Court, a civilly committed mental patient sued two state hospital doctors for his release and for money damages, on the grounds that he had been incarcerated against his will for fourteen years without being treated and without being dangerous to himself or to others. In January 1957, at the age of forty-nine, Kenneth Donaldson had been committed to the Florida state hospital at Chattachoochee on petition by his father, who felt that his son was delusional. Donaldson was found at a brief court hearing before a county judge to be a paranoid schizophrenic and was committed for "care, maintenance, and treatment." The Florida statute then in effect allowed for such commitment on the usual grounds of mental illness and dangerousness. "Dangerousness" could then be defined as inability to manage property and to protect oneself from being taken advantage of by others.

In 1971 Donaldson sued Dr. O'Connor, the hospital superintendent, and Dr. Gumanis, a hospital psychiatrist, for release. Evidence presented at the trial in a United States district court in Florida indicated that the hospital staff could have released Donaldson at any time following a determination that he was not a dangerous person. Testimony made it clear that at no time during his hospitalization had Donaldson's conduct posed any real danger to others or to himself. In fact, just before his commitment in 1957, he had been earning a living and taking adequate care of himself (and immediately upon discharge he secured a job in hotel administration). Nonetheless, O'Connor had repeatedly refused the patient's requests for release, feeling it was his duty

[20]Wyatt v. Stickney, 325 F. Sup. 781 (M.D. Ala. 1971), *enforced in* 334 F. Supp. 1341 (M.D. Ala. 1971), 344 F. Supp. 373, 379 (M.D. Ala. 1972), *aff'd sub nom* Wyatt v. Anderholt, 503 F. 2d 1305 (5th Cir. 1974).

[21]Of course, the underlying assumption is that patients civilly committed to public mental hospitals will receive adequate care there. The evidence is weak, however. Even though the extremely negligent condi-

tions that the *Wyatt* decision remedied in Alabama seldom hold today, it is questionable, argues Morse (1982a), whether forced hospitalization benefits patients. But public mental hospitals can provide, at the very least, shelter, food, protection, and custodial care, which many deinstitutionalized patients are tragically without.

[22]Youngberg v. Romeo, 102 S. Ct. 2462 (1982).

[23]O'Connor v. Donaldson, 95 S. Ct. 2486 (1975).

to determine whether a committed patient could adapt successfully outside the institution. His judgment was that Donaldson could not. In deciding the question of dangerousness on the basis of "adjustment outside the institution," O'Connor continued to apply a more restrictive standard than that on which most current state laws for commitment rested.

Several responsible people had attempted to obtain Donaldson's release by guaranteeing that they would look after him. For example, in 1963 a halfway house formally requested that Donaldson be released to its care, and between 1964 and 1968 a former college classmate made four separate attempts to have the patient released to his care. O'Connor refused, saying that the patient could be released only to his parents, who by this time were quite old and infirm.

The evidence indicated that Donaldson received only custodial care during his hospitalization. No treatment that could conceivably alleviate or cure his assumed mental illness was undertaken.[24] The "milieu therapy" that O'Connor claimed Donaldson was undergoing consisted, in actuality, of being kept in a large room with sixty other patients, many of whom were under criminal commitment. Donaldson had been denied privileges to stroll around the hospital grounds or even to discuss his case with Dr. O'Connor.

The original trial and its appeal concluded that Donaldson was not dangerous and had been denied his constitutional right to treatment, a right based on the Fifth Amendment of the Constitution. O'Connor was found liable for a fine of $38,000. Throughout this litigation Donaldson declared that he was neither dangerous nor mentally ill. *But*, went his claim, *even if* he were mentally ill, he should be released because he was not receiving treatment.

On appeal to the Supreme Court, it was ruled, on June 26, 1975, that "a State cannot constitutionally confine . . . a nondangerous individual who is capable of surviving safely in freedom by himself or with the help of willing and responsible family members or friends." In 1977 Donaldson ultimately settled for $20,000 from the estate of O'Connor, who had died during the appeals process, and from Dr. Gumanis.

The Supreme Court decision on *O'Connor* v. *Donaldson* created a stir when it was issued, and is certain to

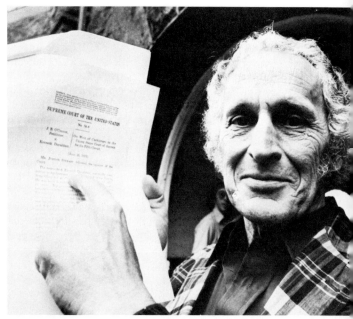

Kenneth Donaldson, displaying a copy of the Supreme Court opinion stating that nondangerous mental patients cannot be confined against their will under civil commitment.

give mental health professionals pause in detaining patients. At the same time, the decision says less than some have assumed. Donaldson earned his release by convincing the Court that he was not dangerous to himself or others, and that he could survive outside the hospital with support from family and friends. But most states already require that patients be, in fact, considered dangerous, in addition to being judged mentally ill, if they are to be detained under civil commitment. Moreover, although this decision is often cited as yet another affirmation of "right to treatment," the Supreme Court did not, in fact, rule on the constitutionality of this doctrine. Indeed, Chief Justice Warren E. Burger issued some warnings about the right to treatment.

Given the present state of medical knowledge regarding abnormal human behavior and its treatment, few things would be more fraught with peril than [for] a State's power to protect the mentally ill [to depend on its ability to provide] such treatment as will give them a realistic opportunity to be cured. Nor can I accept the theory that a State may lawfully confine an individual thought to need treatment and justify that deprivation of liberty solely by providing some treatment. Our concepts of due process would not tolerate such a "trade off" (pp. 588–589).

[24]Donaldson was prescribed psychotropic drugs, but he refused them because of his Christian Science beliefs, an action Dr. O'Connor considered evidence of Donaldson's mental illness. O'Connor also regarded as delusional Donaldson's expressed desire to write a book about his hospital experiences, which Donaldson did, in fact, do after his release.

OBTAINING PATIENTS' RIGHTS

One of the realities of life is the chasm that can exist between what is available in principle and what is available in actuality. Once there are laws, people often have to work to make these laws be of benefit to themselves. This may not be the way things should be, but it is indeed the way they are.

The American Civil Liberties Union maintains a compilation of the rights of mental patients which is constantly updated and is available from them (Ennis and Emery, 1978). Moreover, the ACLU informs mental patients of their rights and makes very practical suggestions on how to obtain these rights. Some of the advice may seem ruthless and conniving, but our adversarial legal system requires such an approach. The system may not always be pretty, but it does seem to work better than anything else in protecting innocent parties.

Ennis and Siegel (1973) recommended several techniques to attorneys representing committed patients who wish to be released. To begin with, a patient's lawyer may request a court hearing in the hope that the hospital will simply release the patient. Psychiatrists dislike court appearances; the mere threat of being hauled before a judge may persuade members of a hospital staff to release the patient. If the hearing is held, other strategies are in order, such as challenging the credibility and impartiality of the psychiatrist who has determined that the patient is dangerous. The following exchange is proposed.

Q: Do you think he might even be dangerous to you?

A: Well, possibly. (If he says no, you can ask why he would be dangerous to others but not to the psychiatrist who recommends deprivation of his liberty.)

Q: In other words, you would feel personally safer if he were hospitalized than if he were at liberty, isn't that correct?

A: Well, yes.

Q: Then you are not completely disinterested in the outcome of this proceeding, are you? (pp. 293–294)

The *Donaldson* decision did say that a committed patient's status must be periodically reviewed, for the grounds on which a patient was initially committed cannot be assumed to continue in effect forever. In other words, people can change while in a mental hospital and may no longer require confinement. This seems straightforward enough! The Court reminded mental hospital officials that they must not forget their patients. It is a sad commentary on the mental hospital system that the Supreme Court of the United States saw the need to caution it about the obvious and routine (See Box 21.4).

Right To Refuse Treatment

If a committed mental patient has the right to expect appropriate treatment, since he has lost his freedom because he needs help, does he have a right to *refuse* treatment, or a particular kind of treatment? The answer appears to be yes, for a right to obtain treatment does not oblige the patient to *accept* treatment (Schwitzgebel and Schwitzgebel, 1980). But there are qualifications. A state hospital may have adequate staff to provide up-to-date chemotherapy as well as group therapy but lack the professional resources to offer individual therapy. Suppose that patient X refuses the available modalities and insists on individual therapy. Would he later be able to sue the hospital for not offering the specific services requested? If the patient has the right to refuse certain forms of treatment, how far should the courts go in ensuring this right, remaining at the same time realistic about the state's ability to provide alternatives? When should the judgment of a professional staff override the wishes of a patient, especially one who is grossly psychotic? Are the patient's best interests always served if he or she can veto the plans of those responsible for care (Stone, 1975)?

Some recent court decisions illustrate the thorny issues that arise when the right to refuse treatment is debated. In a decision on some cases in which "unjustified polypharmacy" and "force or intimidation" had allegedly been applied, without due consideration for the serious negative side effects of drugs, the judge in a New Jersey federal district court concluded that drugs can actually inhibit recovery, that therefore, except in emergencies, even an involuntarily committed patient could refuse to take them, based on the rights of due process (Fifth Amendment) and privacy (Fourth Amendment).[25]

---

[25]Rennie v. Klein, Civil Action No. 77-2624, Federal District Court of New Jersey, 14 September 1979.

He ordered that there be advocates in each state mental hospital to help patients exercise the right to refuse treatment, and that there be posted in each hospital ward a listing of all the side effects of drugs that might be given to patients. A similar court ruling in Massachusetts[26] occasioned widespread medical refusals, with subsequent deterioration in the condition of many patients. In a reconsideration of the 1979 *Rennie* v. *Klein* decision,[27] however, the judge incorporated the *Youngberg* v. *Romeo* decision and stated that the judgment of the health professional must take precedence over the right to refuse treatment when patients are a danger to themselves or to others, in other words, in emergency situations.

Opponents of the right to refuse treatment are concerned that mental hospitals will revert to being warehouses of poorly treated patients. Psychiatrists fear that legal experts, unfamiliar with hospitals and with the people in them, will ". . . take at face value the verbal statements of such patients rather than also taking into account other communications which may convey a different message than those uttered" (McGarry and Chodoff, 1981, p. 217). In lay terms, they fear that lawyers and judges will not accept that some people are too mentally deranged to be believed, too mentally disturbed to be able to make sound judgments about their treatment.

Does civil commitment imply an incompetency that renders the patient incapable of forming reasonable opinions concerning therapies? The issue is similar to the problem in criminal commitment proceedings, when a judgment that the accused is mentally ill can deny him access to the courts. Stone believes that a civilly committed person may indeed be competent to refuse a given treatment. He proposes, though, that patients be given the right to refuse only certain treatments, those that are hazardous or very unpleasant, such as psychosurgery, ECT and any other convulsion therapy, aversion therapy, and chemotherapy with highly addictive drugs like methadone. Stone makes the point that these treatments are risky enough that patients should be allowed to refuse them—even patients under criminal commit-

ment—and that refusal should be overriden only under the special scrutiny of the courts. At the same time, however, administration of less risky treatments would remain the option of the professional staff, with the patient having little to say about their use.[28]

Rights to Treatment, To Refuse Treatment, and To Be Treated in the Least Restrictive Setting —Can They Be Reconciled?

Several legal principles developed over past years guide the courts and mental health professionals in meeting their constitutional obligations to civilly committed mental patients. Actions taken to implement one principle may conflict with another, however. The basic question is whether the right to be treated in the least restrictive residence can be reconciled with both the right to treatment and the right to refuse treatment. A creative proposal was put forth by Paul and Lentz (1977) in their report on social-learning and milieu therapies on wards at a mental health center. They argue that under certain conditions a committed mental patient can and should be coerced into a particular therapy program, even if the patient states that he or she does not wish to participate. And these conditions would not, as *Rennie* v. *Klein* requires, have to be emergencies.

They propose that some hospital treatments have minimal goals and others optimal, and that institutions should have the right and the duty to do whatever is reasonable to move patients toward minimal goals. Achievement of minimal goals—self-care, such as getting up in the morning, bathing, eating meals, and the like; being able to communicate with others on the most basic level; and not being violent or assaultive—will allow patients to move into a less restrictive residence. The elimination of symptomatic behavior would also be regarded as a minimal goal if the local community requires patients to conform, at least to some extent, to community standards.[29] Paul and Lentz go on to argue that if empirical evidence indicates that particular treatments do achieve minimal goals—as the social-learning programs did in their study—patients might justifiably be forced to participate in them, even if they or their le-

---

[26]Rogers v. Okin, 478 F. Supp. 1342 I.D. Mass. 1979.

[27]Rennie v. Klein, 720 F. 2d 266 (3d Cir. 1983).

[28]A resistant patient is able to ward off psychological therapies if he or she wishes, merely by refusing to participate. The high-risk techniques mentioned above are all somatic therapies, requiring little if any cooperation by the patient. What else in the armamentarium of clinical psychology and psychiatry could conceivably be *imposed* on an unwilling patient? The only answer seems to be various psychoactive drugs, such as Thorazine. When patients are given their "meds" in mental hospitals, the drugs are often dissolved in liquid and must be

drunk in the presence of a nurse or an aide, to ensure that they are being taken. Still, it is the common experience of those who have worked in mental hospitals that patients can manage to avoid taking their medication. Few treatments, then, can be forced on a patient. Unless staff members are able to enlist at least minimal cooperation, they can do little to help.

[29]Many therapists are accused of forcing patients to conform to community standards that are themselves open to question. But the basic issue here is not whether mental patients wear clean pants with a belt to hold them up, but whether they wear pants at all.

BOX 21.4

RELEASING MENTAL PATIENTS—TO THEIR BENEFIT?

The cumulative impact of court rulings such as *Wyatt* v. *Stickney* and *O'Connor* v. *Donaldson* is to put mental health professionals on notice that they must be more careful about keeping people in mental hospitals against their will, and that they must attend more to the specific treatment needs of committed patients. Pressure is being put on both of them and on state governments in particular to upgrade the quality of care in mental institutions. In view of the abuses that have been documented in hospital care, these are surely encouraging trends.

But the picture is not all that rosy. For judges to declare that patient care must meet certain minimal standards does not automatically translate into that praiseworthy goal. There is not an unlimited supply of money, and care of the mentally ill has never been one of government's high priorities. Nor is support of research in the social and behavioral sciences. Many states have instead embarked on deinstitutionalization, discharging as many patients as possible from mental hospitals and also discouraging admissions. The maxim has become "Treat them in the community," the assumption being that virtually anything is preferable to institutionalization.

But what is this community that former mental patients are supposed to find more helpful to them upon discharge? Facilities outside the hospitals are not prepared to cope with the influx of former mental patients. Some promising programs were described in Chapter 20, but these are very much the exception, not the rule. The state of affairs in many large metropolitan areas is an unrelenting social crisis, for hundreds of thousands of chronically ill mental patients have been released onto the street without sufficient job training and without community services to help them. Many are eligible for benefits from the Veterans Administration and for Social Security Disability Insurance, but they are not receiving them. Homeless persons do not have fixed addresses and need assistance in establishing eligibility and residency for the purpose of receiving benefits. An earlier study by the Community Service Society (Baxter and Hopper, 1981), an old and respected social agency in New York City, found them living in the streets, in train and bus terminals, in abandoned buildings, on subways, in cavernous steam tunnels running north from Grand Central Station in Manhattan, and some of them in shelters operated by public agencies, churches, and charitable organizations. The lives of these homeless are desperate.

[In a train station at 11:00 P.M.] . . . the attendant goes off duty and women rise from separate niches and head for the bathroom. There they disrobe, and wash their clothes and bodies. Depending on the length of [the] line at the hand dryers, they wait to dry their clothes, put them in their bags or wear them wet. One woman cleans and wraps her ulcerated legs with paper towels every night. The most assertive claim toilet cubicles, line them with newspapers for privacy and warmth and sleep curled around the basin. Once they are taken, the rest sleep along the walls, one on a box directly beneath the hand dryer which she pushes for warm air. One of the women regularly cleans up the floors, sinks and toilets so that no traces of their uncustomary use remain (p. 77).

In the last several years the ranks of all homeless have reached epidemic numbers in the United States and are still swelling. An estimated two and a half million people each year are involuntarily displaced from their low-income housing, and half a million units of low-rent dwellings are lost each year through conversion, inflation, abandonment, arson, and demolition. Federal funds for the construction of low-cost housing have been virtually eliminated. Another factor is the "deindustrialization of America." As the United States continues to move into the high-technology era, employees who had industrial jobs become unskilled workers in need of retraining and relocation, and many of them too are now homeless. Not since the Great Depression have so many people been without shelter.

---

gal guardians will not give consent voluntarily. Protection of their interests would be the responsibility of an institutional review board, a group of professionals and laypeople who would review all therapy and research activities for a given hospital. The board would decide *for* patients what therapy is likely to achieve minimal goals and allow them to leave the hospital.

If the patient is determined to be operating above minimal levels, he should have the right to refuse treatments that have optimal goals, such as acquiring vocational skills, obtaining a high school diploma, and other "luxury" items that can enhance the quality of a patient's life. According to Paul and Lentz, these goals should not be considered so vital that the patient is forced into working toward them.

ETHICAL DILEMMAS IN THERAPY AND RESEARCH

In this textbook we have examined a variety of theories and a multitude of data focusing on *what is* and *what is thought to be*. Ethics and values, often embodied in our

American society and governments at all levels have not responded commensurately to the problem of homelessness. Washington, D.C. has no publicly funded shelters. Phoenix has an uncovered, outdoor, fenced-in lot. New York and Los Angeles, because of suits filed by local organizations, are under court order to provide emergency shelter. New York City for the most part shelters the homeless in large numbers in such facilities as armories. In Los Angeles the county provides vouchers which are exchanged for beds in Skid Row flophouses, where conditions are unsanitary and degrading (Committee on Government Operations, 1985).

No one knows how many of the homeless are deinstitutionalized mental patients. They are a visible part of this population, but their proportions may be diminishing with so many people being dispossessed from their homes and apartments and losing their industrial jobs. The very state of homelessness undoubtedly exacerbates the emotional suffering of former mental patients. Whatever their numbers, the mentally ill remain an especially defenseless segment of the homeless population.

[Their] vulnerability . . . became clear in January 1982, when a sixty-one-year-old former psychiatric patient was found dead in a cardboard box on a New York City street. She had been living in the box for eight months after her entitlements were revoked for failure to appear for recertification. She had refused the efforts of various agencies to relocate her, and she died of hypothermia hours before a court order was obtained directing her removal to a hospital.

This case led to the creation of Project HELP, the Homeless Emergency Liaison Project, which is a mobile, psychiatric outreach team that identifies homeless people in need of psychiatric aid, and has authority under State and local laws to involuntarily remove homeless people in danger to themselves to a hospital for help and evaluation. Project HELP is the only organization of its kind in the United States (Committee on Government Operations, 1985, p. 5).

Deinstitutionalization has dumped many former mental patients onto metropolitan streets with no facilities to care for them.

laws, are a different order of discussion. They concern *what ought to be*, having sometimes little to do with what is. It is extremely important to recognize the difference. Within a given scientific paradigm we are able to examine what we believe is reality. As the study of philosophy and ethics reveals, however, the statements that people have made for thousands of years about what *should* be are another matter. The Ten Commandments are such statements. They are prescriptions and proscriptions about human conduct. For example, the eighth commandment, "Thou shalt not steal," in no way describes human conduct, for stealing is not uncommon. It is, instead, a pronouncement of an ideal that people *should* aspire to. The integrity of an ethical code that proscribes stealing does not depend on any evidence concerning the percentage of people who steal. Morals and data are two separate realms of discourse.

The legal trends reviewed thus far in this chapter place limits on the activities of mental health professionals. These legal constraints are important, for laws are one of society's strongest means of forcing all of us to behave in certain ways. Psychologists and psychiatrists also have professional and ethical constraints. All professional groups promulgate "shoulds" and "should nots," and by guidelines and mandates they limit to some degree what therapists and researchers may do with their patients, clients, and subjects. Courts as well have ruled on some of these questions. We examine now the ethics of making psychological inquiries and interventions into the lives of other human beings.

Ethical Restraints on Research

It is basic to science that what can be done is likely to be attempted. The most reprehensible ethical insensitivity is documented in the brutal experiments conducted by certain German physicians on concentration camp prisoners during the Third Reich. One experiment, for example, investigated how long people lived when their heads were bashed repeatedly with a heavy stick. Even if important information might be obtained from this kind of atrocity, which seems extremely doubtful, such actions cannot be allowed. The Nuremberg trials, conducted by the Allies following the war, brought these and other barbarisms to light and meted out severe punishment to soldiers, physicians, and other Nazi officials who had engaged in or contributed to such actions, even when they claimed that they had merely been following orders.

It would be reassuring to be able to say that such gross violations of human decency take place only during incredible and cruel epochs such as the Third Reich, but unfortunately this is not the case. Spurred on by a blind enthusiasm for their work, researchers in this country have sometimes dealt with human subjects in reproachable ways.[30]

Henry K. Beecher, a research professor at Harvard Medical School, surveyed medical research since 1945 and found that ". . . many of the patients [used as subjects in experiments] never had the risk satisfactorily explained to them, and . . . further hundreds have not known that they were the subjects of an experiment although grave consequences have been suffered as the direct result . . ." (1966, p. 1354). One experiment compared penicillin to a placebo as a treatment to prevent rheumatic fever. Even though penicillin had already been acknowledged as the drug of choice to give people with a streptococcal respiratory infection in order to protect them from later contracting rheumatic fever, placeboes were administered to 109 servicemen without

their knowledge or permission. More men received penicillin than the placebo, but three members of the control group contracted serious illnesses—two had rheumatic fever and one acute nephritis, a kidney disease—as compared to none of those who had received penicillin.

The training of scientists equips them splendidly to pose interesting questions, sometimes even important ones, and to design experiments that are as free as possible of confounds. They have no special qualifications, however, for deciding whether a particular line of inquiry that involves humankind *should* be followed. Society needs knowledge, and a scientist has a right in a democracy to seek that knowledge. The ordinary citizens employed as subjects in experiments must, however, be protected from unnecessary harm, risk, humiliation, and invasion of privacy.[31] There are several international codes of ethics for the conduct of scientific research—the Nuremberg Code formulated in the aftermath of the Nazi war crime trials, the Declaration of Helsinki, and statements from the British Medical Research Council. Closer to home, in the early 1970s the Department of Health, Education and Welfare began to issue guidelines and regulations governing scientific research that employs human subjects. In addition, a blue-ribbon panel, the National Commission for the Protection of Human Subjects of Biomedical and Behavioral Research, conducted hearings and inquiries into restrictions that the federal government might impose on research performed with mental patients, prisoners, and children. And already for several years the proposals of behavioral researchers, many of whom conduct experiments related to psychopathology and therapy, have been reviewed for safety and general ethical propriety by "human subjects committees" and "institutional review boards" in hospitals, universities, and research institutes. Such committees—and this is very significant— are composed not just of behavioral scientists but of citizens of the community, lawyers, students, and specialists in a variety of disciplines, such as professors of English, history, and comparative religion. They are able to block any research proposal or require questionable aspects to be modified if in their collective judgment the research will put participating subjects at too great risk.

Informed Consent

Participation in research brings up the all-important concept of *informed consent*. Just as committed mental patients are gaining some right to refuse treatment, so

---

[30]Researchers who use animals in their experiments have also occasionally dealt with their subjects in gratuitously harsh fashion. The American Psychological Association has guidelines for handling laboratory animals that are intended to minimize their discomfort and danger. More recently, strict standards have been promulgated by the National Institutes of Health.

[31]This very statement is an ethical, not an empirical, one.

may anyone refuse to be a subject in an experiment. The investigator must provide enough information to enable subjects to judge whether they want to take the risks inherent in being a participant (see also Box 21.5). The prospective subjects must be legally capable of giving consent, and there must be no deceit or coercion in obtaining it. For example, an experimental psychologist might wish to determine whether imagery helps college students associate one word with another. One group of subjects will be asked to associate pairs of words in their minds by generating a fanciful image connecting the two, such as "a CAT riding on a BICYCLE." The consent form will state that the experiment consists of sitting for half an hour in front of a screen, watching pairs of words being projected on it, and trying to learn the pairs by devising images that can connect them in memory. A prospective subject might decide, however, that such a session is likely to be boring and can, without penalty, decline to participate. In fact, review committees require that a subject be at liberty to withdraw from an experiment at any time, without penalty, although it is understandable that he or she would feel pressure not to do so.[32]

Paired-associates research is relatively innocuous, but what if the experiment poses real risks, such as ingesting a drug? Or the prospective subject may be a committed mental patient, or a retarded child, unable to understand fully what is being asked. Such a subject may not feel free or even be able to refuse participation. And what of the rights of the researcher, which often are not as carefully considered as those of subjects, and of the cost to society of important research left undone? Will scientists become reluctant to undertake certain types of work because review committees make the process of obtaining informed consent unduly onerous and time-consuming?

Davison and Stuart (1975) proposed a scheme (Table 21.1) that might protect subjects' rights when they participate in research, without hampering researchers in their quest for knowledge. In determining how careful the researchers must be when obtaining informed consent, Davison and Stuart would ask four questions.

---

[32]It is not easy to demonstrate that a researcher has in fact obtained informed consent. Epstein and Lasagna (1969) found that only one-third of subjects volunteering for an experiment really understood what the experiment entailed. In a more elaborate study Stuart (1978) discovered that most college students could not accurately describe a simple experiment, even though it had just been explained to them and they had agreed to participate. A signature on a consent form is no assurance that informed consent has really been obtained, which poses a real challenge to investigators and members of review panels who are committed to upholding codes of ethics governing participation of human subjects in research.

1. What is the level of risk? Little harm is likely in a memory experiment, but a study requiring subjects to withstand electric shock applied to the fingers poses some risk.

2. Is the research of potential benefit to the subject or client? A subject might stand to gain a great deal from being in the study or to gain nothing directly, except the satisfaction of having helped a scientist find out something new.

3. Is the technique an established one, whose risks and benefits are known, or is it new and experimental, so that the researcher is unable to indicate how beneficial, harmful, or discomfiting participation might be?

4. Is the subject realistically free to give consent or to refuse participation? A college student has great freedom to refuse, but a prisoner would probably feel considerable coercion to participate in an experiment if asked to do so.

These four questions are not the only ones that might be asked, and the numbered consent procedures in Table 21.1 are merely suggestions. Clearly, the judgment of many other people would be needed to establish meaningful values and to work out a set of procedures. The scheme, however, may help human subjects committees organize their thinking about the problem of obtaining informed consent in a variety of circumstances.

Treatment or Research?

What is the difference between treatment and research? This is a question that people attempting to replace old procedures with newer, possibly more effective methods must address. Martin (1975) considered the following example. In school district A a teacher who has read about some of the token economy research in classrooms (for example, O'Leary and O'Leary, 1977) has adopted token reinforcement as a means of persuading a group of underachieving and often disruptive students to attend to their lessons. The results have been quite encouraging: the classroom is quieter, the students are in their seats more often, and their academic performance has improved. Moreover, the students themselves like the program. Is this an experiment? Should the teacher have obtained informed consent from the parents? A few miles away in school district B another teacher is also applying a token economy. The project is funded by a federal grant, calls itself experimental, and routinely ob-

BOX 21.5

A CONTRACT TO IMPLEMENT INFORMED CONSENT FOR THERAPY

Informed consent is now an issue not just for research and for treatment in mental institutions but also for private therapy which individuals seek on their own initiative. Traditionally a person who consults a therapist, in essence hiring the therapist to perform expert services, consents to be treated in a certain way and for a certain purpose. In the past the client's informed consent to be treated was seldom obtained in any explicit or formal way, however.

The spirit of consumerism and a desire to be open and accountable, along with dramatic increases in malpractice suits, may prompt therapists to consider whether more explicit arrangements might not be in their own and in their clients' best interests. Richard Stuart, a leading behavior therapist, has suggested an intervention contract. The proposed contract would place great demands on the therapist and the fields of clinical psychology and psychiatry to provide evidence that particular techniques are effective, and on the client as well. Although not yet widely adopted, this kind of contract might become so should insurance companies require documentation on how and why a particular program of treatment was undertaken.

Name of Client: _____

Address: _____

Phone: _____

Name of Therapist: _____

Title: _____

Organization: _____

Highest academic degree: _____

License: _____

1. I, the above named therapist, certify that I am (circle one) duly licensed to offer the services described below *or* under the supervision of _____ who is so licensed.
(Address)

2. I have assessed the client's behavior change objective(s) in the following manner:

_____

_____

---

tained the informed consent that is commonplace for research. There is no doubt that *this* program is research, but does the similarity of district A's program to this one make it research as well?

Because of their relative newness, the application of behavioral procedures is likely to be construed as research, even though not so intended, and to be viewed with some apprehension. And yet we often take for granted—in fact, we applaud—an elementary school teacher who finds a novel way of exciting children about the learning process. "She's really a creative teacher. She doesn't content herself with the curriculum and the materials provided by the school board." To be sure, in many instances the difference between treatment and research is clear. For example, the drug Anectine, a paralytic agent often used to relax patients about to receive ECT, was imposed on a prisoner for a different purpose, to produce a frightening "unconditioned response"—inability to breathe—in an aversion therapy endeavor. Although the drug is in routine use to protect ECT patients from physical harm, a judge ruled that employing it in this way without obtaining informed consent appeared to be cruel and unusual punishment.[33]

[33]Mackey v. Procunier, 477 F. 2d 877 (9th Cir. 1973).

3. I propose to use the following intervention technique(s) in my effort to assist the client to achieve the above objective(s): _____

_____

a. This (these) technique(s) have been fully described in the following standard professional reference: _____

_____

b. The most recent comprehensive account of the clinical results achieved with this (these) technique(s) may be found in the following source(s):

4. It is expected that this (these) intervention technique(s) will have the following beneficial effects for the client by the dates specified: _____

5. It is also noted that this (these) intervention technique(s) may be associated with the following undesirable side effect(s): _____

_____

6. Both the progress toward achieving the specified objectives and the potential side effects will be monitored continuously in the following manner(s):

_____   _____
(Date)   (Signature of Therapist)

A. I, the above named client, assert that I have discussed the above named objectives for the change of my behavior and that I consent to work toward the achievement of those objectives.

B. I further assert that I have discussed the above named intervention technique(s) with the therapist and that I consent to apply these techniques.

C. I further assert that I shall provide the above named data in order to determine the effectiveness of the use of the intervention technique(s).

D. I further assert that I shall provide the therapist with the following compensation for his or her efforts in my behalf: _____

E. I further assert that I have freely entered into this contract knowing the therapeutic objectives and both the positive and negative potential effects of the intervention technique(s).

F. I further assert that I have been assured of my right to terminate my participation in treatment at any time, for any reason, and without the need to offer an explanation.

G. I further specifically limit the above named therapist's use of any information which can in any way identify me to others unless I have offered my specific, written permission.

_____   _____
(Date)   (Signature of Client)   (Signature of Witness)

Confidentiality and Privileged Communication

When an individual consults a physician, a psychiatrist, or a clinical psychologist, he or she expects all that goes on in the session to remain confidential. Nothing will be revealed to a third party, excepting only to other professionals and those intimately involved in the treatment, such as a nurse or medical secretary. The ethical codes of the various helping professions dictate this _confidentiality_.[34]

---

[34]Family and marital therapies introduce complexities of their own, discussed in Margolin (1982).

A _privileged communication_ is one between parties in a confidential relation that is protected by statute. The recipient cannot be compelled to disclose it as a witness. The right of privileged communication is a major exception to the access that courts have to evidence in judicial proceedings. Society believes that, in the long term, the interests of people are best served if communications to a spouse and to certain professionals remain off limits to the prying eyes and ears of the police, judges, and prosecutors. The husband-wife, doctor-patient, pastor-penitent, and attorney-client relationships are the traditional ones, but in recent years states have extended the right of privileged communication to the clients of licensed psychologists.

TABLE 21.1 Guidelines for Protecting Subjects' Right To Participate Only in Experiments of Own Choice   *(after Davison and Stuart, 1975)*

Level of Risk	Freedom To Give Consent	High Potential Benefit to Subject		Low Potential Benefit to Subject, High Potential Benefit to Society	
		Established Procedure	Experimental Procedure	Established Procedure	Experimental Procedure
Low risk	Great freedom	2–4*	4	2–4	4–5
	Feels some coercion	5	5	5–6	7
High risk	Great freedom	4	5	5–6	7
	Feels some coercion	6	6	7	8

*The numbers indicate the degree of care that should be exercised in obtaining consent.

1. *No consent by the subject is necessary.* The nonobtrusive observation of traffic flow in public places or other public behavior might fall into this category. This procedure and the next are permissible only when a review panel has determined that the potential risk of harm to the anonymously observed subjects is nil.

2. *Subject is simply asked to sign a consent form for participation in research as a subject of observations, with no explanation of the nature of the study.* One example would be observing the supermarket shopping of individuals; an explanation of the objectives of the study might change relevant behavior.

3. *Subject is asked to sign a consent form for participation in research, with "debriefing" following participation.* Such a study might examine interpersonal behavior in public places; prior disclosure of the hypotheses could change behavior. A panel of experts would have to determine that subjects risked little in participating, including minimal humiliation following debriefing.

4. *Subject is asked to sign a consent form for participation in a project, after full disclosure of the objectives and methods of the research.* This procedure would be applied in efforts to evaluate treatment by randomly assigning subjects to experimental, to placebo control, and to no-treatment control groups. A review panel must judge that risk of harm to control subjects is equal to or less than it would be were there no experiment.

5. *Subject is asked to sign a consent form for participation in a project, after full disclosure of the objectives and methods of the research and in the presence of at least one witness who is not involved in the research.* This procedure would be appropriate any time a review panel senses that subjects may feel obliged to participate. Research with adjudicated offenders could fall into this category.

6. *Subject is asked to sign a consent form for participation in a project, after full disclosure of the objectives and methods of the research and in the presence of witnesses. The consent is reviewed by an independent human subjects committee within the institution.* The procedure might be applied in the experimental evaluation of a program carrying out an institutional objective, for example, vocational training in prisons and mental hospitals.

7. *Subject is asked to sign a consent form for participation in a project, after full disclosure of the objectives and methods of the research and in the presence of witnesses. The consent is reviewed by an independent human subjects committee within the institution and by a similar committee outside the institution.* The procedure could be applied when the research concerns behavior changes that are not strictly related to institutional objectives, for example, a study of the role of repetition when mental patients are taught phrases in a foreign language.

8. *No consent is possible because the rights of the subjects cannot be protected.*

There are important limits to the client's right of privileged communication, however. According to the current California psychology licensing law, for example, this right is eliminated for any of the following reasons.

1. If the client is accused of a crime and has requested that a determination be made about his sanity.

2. If the client has accused the therapist of malpractice; the therapist, in other words, can divulge information about the therapy in order to defend himself in any legal action initiated by the client.

3. If the client is under sixteen, and the therapist has reason to believe that the child has been a victim of a crime, such as child abuse. In fact, the psychologist is *required* to report to the police within thirty-six hours any suspicion he or she has that the child client has been physically abused, including being sexually molested.

4. If the client initiated therapy in hopes of evading the law for having committed a crime or for planning to do so.

5. If the therapist judges that the client is a danger to himself or to others, and if disclosure of information is necessary to ward off such danger (see Box 21.6).

Who Is the Client?

Is it always clear to the clinician who the client is? In private therapy, when an adult pays a clinician a fee for help with a personal problem that has nothing to do with the legal system, the consulting individual is clearly the client. But an individual may be seen by a clinician for an evaluation of his or her competency to stand trial. Or the clinician may be hired by an individual's family to assist in civil commitment proceedings. Perhaps the clinician is employed by a state mental hospital as a regular staff member and sees a particular patient about problems in controlling aggressive impulses. It should be clear, although it is alarming how seldom it *is* clear, that in these instances the clinician is serving more than one client. In addition to the patient, he or she serves the family or the state, and it is incumbent on the mental health professional to inform the patient that this is so. This dual allegiance does not necessarily indicate that the patient's own interests will be sacrificed, but it does mean that discussions will not inevitably remain secret and that the clinician may act in a way that displeases the individual.

A United States Supreme Court ruling held that a psychiatrist who plans to testify for the prosecution must warn a defendant he or she is about to interview that what is said between them will not be held in confidence, that, in other words, the right of privileged communication has been suspended. This ruling—already part of the ethics codes of both the American Psychiatric and the American Psychological Associations—came in the aftermath of a dramatic series of twenty first-degree murder convictions in Texas.

The high court voted unanimously [on May 18, 1981] to throw out the death sentence imposed upon Ernest B. Smith, a convicted Texas murderer. Smith was condemned to die by a jury in Dallas after a psychiatrist who had examined Smith in jail testified for the state that Smith was a dangerous man who, if allowed to live, would commit future acts of violence. Before the prison examination, the psychiatrist told Smith only that he had come to determine whether Smith was mentally competent to stand trial. The justices ruled . . . that the psychiatrist should also have given Smith a "Miranda" warning, advising Smith that whatever he said in the interview might later be used against him in court. [In *Miranda* v. *Arizona*, the] landmark 1966 ruling, the high court held that police may not question a person in custody unless they first warn him he has a right to remain silent and talk with a lawyer, and that whatever he says may be used against him in court. . . .

Protection tightened. The ruling in the Texas case (*Estelle* v. *Smith*, 79-1127) will tighten up the legal protection granted to criminal defendants against being tricked into confessing crimes or making damaging statements to psychiatrists who examine them in jail. The decision will also overturn the death sentences of many other inmates who have been condemned on the basis of psychiatric testimony. The effect will be especially severe in Texas, where psychiatrists have routinely testified for the prosecution about the supposed "future dangerousness" of persons convicted of first-degree murder. The psychiatrist who testified against Smith . . . has also been a witness for the state against fifty persons sentenced to die in Texas. His presence in Texas death-penalty cases was so commonplace that he became known in the Dallas area as "the hanging psychiatrist."

Many cases threatened. Texas has 140 inmates on death row—more than any other state except Florida. Texas Assistant Attorney General Douglas Becker said . . . that the new court ruling "is going to invalidate so many of these cases. . . . It's frustrating." Becker said twenty is a "conservative estimate" of the number of death sentences that will be thrown out because of the Supreme Court decision. . . . Joe Berger, the attorney for the NAACP Legal Defense Fund who represented Smith, said he thinks the decision will void at least thirty death sentences in Texas and perhaps more. He said the ruling might also affect a few death-row inmates in Virginia and Oklahoma. . . .

In his decision for the court, [Chief Justice Warren E. Burger] wrote that by testifying for the prosecutors, [the] psychiatrist . . . became an "agent of the state, recounting unwarned statements (by Smith) made in a post-secret custodial setting." The high court carefully left open the possibility that a defendant could be forced to submit to an examination by a prosecution psychiatrist when defense lawyers are planning to introduce the testimony of a defense psychiatrist at this trial. In cases in which a defendant pleads innocent by reason of insanity, both prosecution and defense commonly call psychiatrists as witnesses to testify about the defendant's state of mind. The justices also emphasized that their ruling

BOX 21.6

THE TARASOFF CASE—THE DUTY TO WARN

The client's right to privileged communication—the legal right of a client to require that what goes on in therapy remain confidential—is an important protection, but as we have seen, it is not absolute. Society has long stipulated certain conditions in which confidentiality in a relationship should not be maintained because of the harm that can befall others. A famous California court ruling in 1974* described circumstances in which a therapist should breach the sanctity of a client's communication. First, what appear to be the facts of the case.

In the fall of 1968, Prosenjit Poddar, a graduate student from India studying at the University of California at Berkeley, met Tatiana (Tanya) Tarasoff at a folk dancing class. They saw each other weekly during the fall, and on New Year's Eve she kissed him. Poddar interpreted this act as a sign of formal engagement (as it might have been in India, where he was a member of the Harijam or "untouchable" caste). [But] Tanya told him that she was involved with other men, and indicated that she did not wish to have an intimate relationship with him.

Poddar became depressed as a result of the rebuff, but he saw Tanya a few times during the spring (occasionally tape recording their conversations in an effort to understand why she did not love him). Tanya left for Brazil in the summer, and Poddar at the urging of a friend went to the student health facility where a psychiatrist referred him to a psychologist for psychotherapy. When Tanya returned in October 1969, Poddar discontinued therapy. Based in part on Poddar's stated intention to purchase a gun, the psychologist notified the campus police, both orally and in writing, that

Poddar was dangerous and should be taken to a community mental health center for psychiatric commitment.

The campus police interviewed Poddar, who seemed rational and promised to stay away from Tanya. They released him and notified the health service. No further efforts at commitment were made because the supervising psychiatrist apparently decided that such was not needed and, as a matter of confidentiality, requested that the letter to the police as well as certain therapy records be destroyed.

On October 27, Poddar went to Tanya's home armed with a pellet gun and a kitchen knife. She refused to speak to him. He shot her with the pellet gun. She ran from the house, was pursued, caught, and repeatedly and fatally stabbed. Poddar was found guilty of voluntary manslaughter rather than first- or second-degree murder. The defense established, with the aid of the expert testimony of three psychiatrists, that Poddar's diminished mental capacity, paranoid schizophrenia, precluded the malice necessary for first-or second-degree murder. After his prison term, he returned to India where, according to his own report, he is happily married (Schwitzgebel and Schwitzgebel, 1980, p. 205).

Under the privileged-communication statute of California, the counseling center psychologist properly breached the confidentiality of the professional relationship and took steps to have Poddar civilly committed, for he judged him to be an imminent danger. Poddar had stated that he intended to purchase a gun, and by his other words and

Tatiana Tarasoff and Prosenjit Poddar, who was convicted of manslaughter in her death. The court ruled that his therapist, who had become convinced Prosenjit might harm Tatiana, should have warned her of the impending danger.

actions he had convinced the therapist that he was desperate enough to harm Tanya. What the psychologist did not do, and what the court decided he should have done, was to warn the likely victim, Tanya Tarasoff, that her former friend had bought a gun and might use it against her. Such a warning would have been consistent with previous court decisions that require physicians to warn the public when they are treating people with contagious diseases, and that require mental institutions to warn others when a dangerous patient has escaped (Knapp and Vandecreek, 1982). Or, as stated by the California Supreme Court in *Tarasoff*: "Once a therapist does in fact determine, or under applicable professional standards reasonably should have determined, that a patient poses a serious danger of violence to others, he bears a duty to exercise reasonable care to protect the foreseeable victims of that danger."

A subsequent California court ruling† held by a bare majority that foreseeable victims include those in close relationship to the identifiable victim, in this instance the son of a woman who was shot by a patient. The mother was hurt by a shotgun fired by the dangerous patient, and her seven-year-old son was present when this happened. The boy later sued the psychologists for damages brought on by emotional trauma. Since a young child is likely to be in the company of his mother, the court concluded that the *Tarasoff* ruling extended to him.

The duty-to-warn principle may be having a profound impact on psychotherapists, some claim a chilling effect, for it imposes on them a new obligation. They argue that if clients are informed of this limitation to the confidentiality of what they say to their therapists—and professional ethics require therapists to provide this information—clients may become reluctant to express feelings of anger to therapists, for fear therapists will notify the people at whom they are angry. Clients may become less open with their therapists, perhaps derive less benefit from therapy, and even become *more* likely to inflict harm on others for not having disclosed their anger as a first step toward controlling it. The welfare of the people whom the *Tarasoff* decision intends to protect may be endangered by the very ruling itself!

The *Tarasoff* ruling, now being applied in other states as well, requires clinicians, in deciding when to violate confidentiality, to use the very imperfect skill of predicting dangerousness. A survey of over 1200 psychologists and psychiatrists in California (Wise, 1978) indicates how the *Tarasoff* decision is affecting their thinking and practices; the effects are not necessarily positive. On the plus side, one-third reported consulting more often with colleagues concerning cases in which violence was an issue. This should have a good outcome, since input from other professionals may improve the solitary clinician's decision making, presumably to the benefit of the client. On the minus side, about 20 percent of the respondents indicated that

they now avoid asking their clients questions about violence, an ostrichlike stance which may keep the clinician from obtaining important information and yet, in a legal sense, reduces his or her legal liability should the client harm another person. And a substantial number of therapists keep less detailed records, again in an effort to reduce legal liability.

A 1983 decision of a federal circuit court in California‡ may alter some of these tactics of evasion. The court ruled that Veterans Administration psychiatrists should earlier have warned the murdered lover of an outpatient, Phillip Jablonski, that she was a foreseeable victim, even though the patient had never made an explicit threat against her to the therapists. The reasoning was that Jablonski, having previously raped and otherwise harmed his wife, would likely direct his continuing ". . . violence . . . against women very close to him" (p. 392).

The court also found the hospital psychiatrists negligent in not obtaining Jablonski's earlier medical records. These records showed a history of harmful violent behavior which, together with the present threats his lover was complaining about, should have moved the hospital to institute emergency civil commitment. The court ruled that the failure to warn was a proximate or immediate cause of the woman's murder. Proper consideration of the medical records, said the judge, would have convinced the psychiatrists that Jablonski was a real danger to others and should be committed.

This broadening of the duty to warn now places mental health professionals in California in an even more difficult predicament, for the potentially violent patient need not even mention whom specifically he may harm. It is up to the therapist to deduce who are possible victims, based on what he or she can learn of the patient's past and present circumstances. Ironically, Jablonski's lover realized that she was in danger, having recently moved out of the apartment she was sharing with him and having complained to her priest and to the Veterans Administration psychiatrists themselves that she feared for her safety. One of the psychiatrists had even advised her to leave Jablonski, at least while he was being evaluated at the medical center. But "when [the lover] responded 'I love him,' [the psychiatrist] did not warn her further because he believed she would not listen to him" (p. 393). The court found this warning "totally unspecific and inadequate under the circumstances" (p.398).

---

*Tarasoff v. Regents of the University of California, 529 P. 2d 553 (Cal. 1974), *vacated, reheard in bank, and affirmed* 131 Cal. Rptr. 14, 551 P. 2d 334 (1976). The 1976 California Supreme Court ruling was by a four-to-three majority.
†Hedlund v. Superior Court of Orange County, 194 Cal. Rptr. 805 (Cal. 1983).
‡Jablonski by Pahls v. United States, 712 F. 2d 391 (1983).

Choice of Goals

Ideally the client sets the goals for therapy, but in practice it is naive to assume that some are not imposed by the therapist and even go against the wishes of the client. School systems often want to institute programs that will teach children to "be still, be quiet, be docile" (Winett and Winkler, 1972, p. 499). Many behavior therapists have assumed that young children *should* be compliant, not only because the teacher can then run a

The open classroom (top) chooses to help youngsters acquire academic skills by encouraging curiosity and initiative, the traditional classroom (bottom) by maintaining orderliness and undivided attention.

more orderly class but because children are assumed to learn better when they are so. But do we really know that the most efficient and most enjoyable learning takes place when children are forced to remain quietly in their seats? Some advocates of "open classrooms" believe that curiosity and initiative, even in the youngest elementary school child, are at least as important as the acquisition of academic skills. As is generally the case in psychology, evidence is less plentiful than are strongly held and vehemently defended opinions. But the issue is clear: any professionals consulted by a school system should be mindful of their own personal biases with respect to goals and be prepared to work toward different ones if the parents and school personnel so wish. Any therapist of course retains the option of not working for a client whose goals and proposed means of attaining them are abhorrent in his or her view.

This question of goals is particularly complex in family and marital therapy (Margolin 1982). If several people are clients simultaneously—inevitable in family treatment!—an intervention that benefits one or more individuals may well work to the disadvantage of one or more of the others. This can happen if one partner in marital therapy really wants to end the relationship, but the other sees the therapy as a way to save it. People often do not openly express their real concerns and wishes at the very beginning of marital therapy; the therapist can already be deeply enmeshed in their lives before learning that the two partners have conflicting goals (Gurman and Kniskern, 1981).

Although the plight of people who voluntarily consult therapists is in no way as expressly confining as that of institutionalized patients, they do operate within constraints on their freedom. The issue has been stated by Seymour Halleck (1971), a psychiatrist, who asserts that the neutrality of the therapist is a myth. In his opinion therapists influence their clients in ways that are subtle yet powerful.

At first glance, a model of psychiatric [or psychological] practice based on the contention that people should just be helped to learn to do the things they want to do seems uncomplicated and desirable. But it is an unobtainable model. Unlike a technician, a psychiatrist [or psychologist] cannot avoid communicating and at times imposing his own values upon his patients. The patient usually has considerable difficulty in finding the way in which he would wish to change his behavior, but as he talks to the psychiatrist his wants and needs become clearer. In the very process of defining his needs in the presence of a figure who is viewed as wise and authoritarian, the pa-

tient is profoundly influenced. He ends up wanting some of the things the psychiatrist thinks he should want (p. 19).

Psychologists agree, and research (for example, Rosenthal, 1955) supports the contention that patients are profoundly influenced by the values of their therapists. A person not only seeks out a therapist who suits his taste and meets what he believes are his needs but also adopts some of the ideals, sometimes even the mannerisms, of the therapist. Most therapists are keenly aware of this modeling after themselves, which surely increases the already heavy responsibilities of their professional role. Perry London (1964), a leading writer on the ethics of therapeutic intervention, has even suggested that therapists are contemporary society's secular priests, purveyors of values and ethics to help clients live "the good life" (see Box 21.7).

Choice of Techniques

The end does not justify the means. Most of us take in this maxim with our mother's milk. It is said to be intrinsic to a free society. In recent years questions concerning behavioral techniques have been debated among professionals and have even been the subject of court rulings. Perhaps because the various insight therapies emphasize listening, they have seldom been scrutinized as behavior therapy has. The very concreteness, specificity, and directiveness of behavioral techniques have called attention to them, as has their alignment with experimental psychology. It is offensive to some to believe that our understanding of human beings could possibly be advanced by employing rats and pigeons as subject analogues.

Particular concern has been expressed about the ethics of inflicting pain for purposes of therapy. To some people the very term behavior therapy conjures up an image of the violent, Beethoven-loving protagonist in Kubrick's *Clockwork Orange*, eyes propped open with a torturous apparatus, being made nauseous by a drug while scenes of violence flashed on a screen and Beethoven's Ninth Symphony soared in his ears. Aversion therapy programs never really reach this level of coercion and drama, but certainly any such procedure entails making the patient uncomfortable, sometimes extremely so. Making patients vomit or cringe with pain from electric shock applied to the extremities are two aversive techniques worthy of their name. Can there be any circumstances that justify therapists inflicting pain on clients?

Before too glibly exclaiming "No!" consider the following report.

> The patient was a nine-month-old baby who had already been hospitalized three times for treatment of vomiting and chronic rumination (regurgitating food and rechewing it in the mouth). A number of diagnostic tests, including an EEG, plus surgery to remove a cyst on the right kidney, had revealed no organic basis for the problems, and several treatments, including a special diet, had been attempted without success. When referred to Lang and Melamed (1969), two behavior therapists, the child was in critical condition and was being fed by tubes leading from the nose directly into the stomach. The attending physician had stated that the infant's life was in imminent danger if the vomiting could not be halted.
>
> Treatment consisted of delivering a series of one-second-long electric shocks to the infant's calf each time he showed signs of beginning to vomit. Sessions followed feeding and lasted under an hour. After just two sessions, shock was rarely required, for the infant learned quickly to stop vomiting in order to avoid the shock. By the sixth session he was able to fall asleep after eating. Nurses reported that the in-session inhibition of vomiting generalized as the infant progressively reduced his vomiting during the rest of the day and night. About two weeks later the mother began to assume some care of the hospitalized child, and shortly thereafter the patient was discharged with virtually complete elimination of the life-threatening pattern of behavior. Throughout the three weeks of treatment and observation, the child gained weight steadily. One month after discharge the child weighed twenty-one pounds and was rated as fully recovered by the attending physician. Five months later he weighed twenty-six pounds and was regarded as completely normal, both physically and psychologically.

The use of aversion therapy has been subject to an understandably high degree of regulation. An additional reason for administrative and judicial concern is that aversion techniques smack more of research than of standard therapy. The more established a therapeutic procedure, whether it be medical or psychological, the less likely it is to attract the attention of the courts or other governmental agencies. Paul and Lentz (1977) had a few very assaultive patients. Their account of adminis-

BOX 21.7

NOT CAN BUT OUGHT: AN OPINION ON THE TREATMENT OF HOMOSEXUALITY

Several psychologists have argued that the social pressures on homosexuals to become heterosexual make it difficult to believe that the small minority of people who consult therapists for help in changing from same-sex to opposite-sex partners act with free choice (Silverstein, 1972; Davison, 1974, 1976; Begelman, 1975). Silverstein's statement about the pressures homosexuals are under to want to become heterosexual was given in Chapter 12 (page 309). It has further been suggested that the mere availability of change-of-orientation programs serves to condone the prejudice against homosexuality. Clinicians work to develop procedures and study their effects only if they are concerned about the problem to be dealt with by their techniques. The therapy literature contains scant material on helping homosexuals develop as individuals without changing their sexual orientation, in contrast to the many articles and books on how best to discourage homosexual behavior and substitute for it heterosexual patterns. Aversion therapy has been the most widely used behavioral technique (Davison and Wilson, 1973; Henkel and Lewis-Thomé, 1976). "What are we really saying to our clients when, on the one hand, we assure them that they are not abnormal and on the other hand, present them with an array of techniques, some of them painful, which are aimed at eliminating that set of feelings and behavior that we have just told them is okay?" (Davison, 1976, p. 161).

For these reasons it has been proposed that therapists not help homosexuals become heterosexual even when such treatment is requested. This is obviously a radical proposal, and it has evoked some strong reactions. Gay-activist groups are understandably pleased, considering the suggestion concrete support for the belief that homosexuality per se is not a mental disorder. But many psychologists and psychiatrists are concerned about limiting the choices available to people seeking therapy. Why should a therapist decide for potential clients which options are to be available? Do not therapists have a responsibility to satisfy the needs expressed by their clients (Sturgis and Adams, 1978)? A reply to this important criticism would be that therapists always decide what therapy they will offer when they refuse to take as clients people whose goals they disagree with. Court rulings can also put constraints on the treatments available to patients. In *Kaimowitz* v. *Michigan Department of Mental Health,* * for example, a state court held that a committed mental patient could not volunteer for psychosurgery, which he had hoped would eliminate fits of uncontrollable aggression and thereby gain him his release. The judge felt that, living in the coercive environment of a

state hospital, the patient could not give informed consent to such an untested procedure. The request of a patient for a certain kind of treatment has never been sufficient justification for providing it (see Davison, 1978).

It has been asserted that continued research will help develop sex reorientation programs that are even more effective than those already available (Sturgis and Adams, 1978). To discourage such work would deprive today's homosexuals of promising therapies and tomorrow's homosexuals of improved treatments. This objection, however, is not relevant. The fact that we *can* do something does not indicate that we *should.* The proposal to deny sexual reorientation therapy is philosophical-ethical in nature, not empirical. The decision whether we should change sexual orientation will have to be made on moral grounds.

Will numbers of people be hurt by eliminating the sex reorientation option? Some have raised the specter of an upsurge in suicides among homosexuals if therapists refuse to help them switch. These are very serious concerns, but they overlook the possibility, some would say the fact, that far greater numbers of people have been hurt over the years by the availability of sex reorientation programs. As already argued, the existence of these treatments is consistent with societal prejudices and discrimination against homosexuals.

The proponents who wish to terminate change-of-orientation programs believe that much good can come of their proposal. Homosexuals would be helped to think better of themselves, and greater efforts could be directed toward the problems homosexuals have, rather than to the problem of homosexuality.

It would be nice if an alcoholic homosexual, for example, could be helped to reduce his or her drinking without having his or her sexual orientation questioned. It would be nice if a homosexual fearful of interpersonal relationships, or incompetent in them, could be helped without the therapist assuming that homosexuality lies at the root of the problem. It would be nice if a nonorgasmic or impotent homosexual could be helped as a heterosexual would be rather than [being guided] to change-of-orientation regimens . . . the hope [is] that therapists will concentrate their efforts on such human problems rather than focusing on the most obvious "maladjustment"—loving members of one's own sex (Davison, 1978, p. 171).

*Kaimowitz v. Michigan Department of Mental Health, 42 U.S.L. Week 2063 (Mich. Cit. Ct., Wayne City, July 10, 1973).

trative problems demonstrates that patients might be subject to more extreme procedures because special attention is paid to new techniques.

Some consideration was given to the contingent use of mild electric shock. . . . However, early in the explorations of the necessary safeguards and review procedures to be followed before evaluating such methods, the department director telephoned to explain that aversion conditioning was a politically sensitive issue. Therefore, more than the usual proposal, preparation, documentation, and committee reviews would be required—to the extent that approval would probably take about eighteen months. Instead, it was suggested that convulsive shock (which can cause tissue damage) be employed since "ECT is an accepted medical treatment." With those alternatives, our choice was to abandon either use of shock . . .(p. 499).

Mindful that short-term application of electric shock can sometimes keep retarded and autistic children from their self-destructive acts, Martin (1975) proposed that

The test should be that aversive therapy might be used where other therapy has not worked, where it can be administered to save the individual from immediate and continuing self-injury, when it allows freedom from physical restraints which would otherwise be continued, when it can be administered for only a few short instances and when its goal is to make other nonaversive therapy possible. Such an aversive program certainly requires consent from a guardian and immediate review of the results of each separate administration (p. 77).[35]

Extra precautions such as these are necessary when treatment deliberately inflicts pain on a patient or client; they are especially necessary when the patient cannot realistically be expected to give informed consent. But should we be concerned only with physical pain? The anguish we suffer when a loved one dies is psychologically painful. It is perhaps more painful than an electric shock of 1500 microamperes. Who is to say? Since we allow that pain can be psychological, shall we permit a Gestalt therapist to make a patient cry by confronting him with feelings he has turned away from for years? Shall we forbid a psychoanalyst from guiding a

---

[35]In addition to being humane, Martin's suggestions are consistent with an established legal principle which holds that therapy should begin with the technique that intrudes least on the patient's freedom and exposes him or her to the least possible risk (Morris, 1966).

patient to an insight that will likely cause great anguish, all the more so for the conflict's having been repressed for years?

Concluding Comment

An underlying theme of this book concerns the nature of knowledge. How do we decide that we understand a phenomenon? The branch of philosophy concerned with the methods and grounds for knowledge is called epistemology. The rules of the science game that govern our definition of and search for knowledge require theories that can be tested, experiments that can be replicated, and data that are public. But given the complexity of abnormal behavior and given the vast areas of ignorance, far more extensive than the domains that have already been mapped by science as it is currently practiced, we have great respect for theoreticians and clinicians, those inventive souls who make suppositions, offer hypotheses, follow hunches—all based on rather flimsy data but holding some promise that scientific knowledge will be forthcoming.

This final chapter demonstrates again something emphasized at the very beginning of this book, namely that the behavioral scientists and the mental health professionals who conduct research and give treatment are only human beings. They suffer from the same foibles that sometimes plague nonspecialists. They occasionally act with a certainty their evidence does not justify, and they sometimes fail to anticipate the moral and legal consequences of the ways in which they conduct research and apply the tentative findings of their young discipline.

The authors of this textbook hope that they have communicated in some measure their love for the subject matter and, more importantly, their commitment to the kind of questioning, doubting stance that wrests useful knowledge from nature and will yield more as new generations of scholars build upon the achievements of their predecessors.

SUMMARY

This final chapter dealt with legal and ethical issues in treatment and research. Some of the civil liberties of people are rather routinely set aside when judgments are made by mental health professionals and the courts that mental illness has played a role in determining their behavior. Criminal commitment sends a person to a hospital, either before a trial for an alleged crime, because he is deemed incompetent to stand trial; or after an acquittal by reason of insanity, because a mental defect, the inability to know right from wrong, or both, are believed to have played a role in his committing a criminal act. A person who is considered ill and dangerous to himself and to others, though he has not broken a law, can be civilly committed to an institution. Recent court rulings have provided greater protection to all committed mental patients, particularly those under civil commitment: they have the right to written notification, to counsel, to a jury decision concerning their commitment, and to Fifth Amendment protection against self-incrimination; the right to the least restrictive treatment setting; the right to be treated; and, in most circumstances, the right to refuse treatment, particularly any procedure that entails considerable risk. A number of moral issues in therapy and research were reviewed: ethical restraints on research, the duty of scientists to obtain informed consent from prospective human subjects, the question whether a program is treatment or research, the right of clients to confidentiality, the setting of therapy goals, and the choice of techniques.

APPENDIX

BRAIN DYSFUNCTIONS
AND ABNORMAL BEHAVIOR

Organic Brain Syndromes
Organic Mental Disorders

When the brain becomes dysfunctional, a whole host of impairments, of sensory and motor functions as well as of emotional and psychological ones, are likely. The disorders to be considered here are psychological and behavioral abnormalities that are caused by transient or permanent brain dysfunctions; they are often similar to the psychopathologies considered in earlier chapters. For this reason it is always important for a clinician to be aware that an apparent psychological problem or symptom may have a clear physiological cause.

DSM-III distinguishes two major categories, *organic brain syndromes* and *organic mental disorders* (Table A.1). The several types of organic brain syndromes, for example, organic affective disorder and organic hallucinosis, each has specific groups of psychological and behavioral symptoms that can be produced by several different causes. Each of the organic mental disorders, in contrast, have a specific presumed cause. The symptoms for disorders in the two categories may be similar. For example, hallucinations are principal symptoms both of organic hallucinosis and of alcohol withdrawal delirium and alcohol hallucinosis, two of the alcohol organic mental disorders. The difference is that in organic mental disorders a presumed cause of the symptoms is part of the diagnosis itself.

ORGANIC BRAIN SYNDROMES

Delirium and Dementia

Delirium and its principal causes in the elderly were discussed in Chapter 17. Although more common in older people, delirium can occur at any age and can be traced to a wide range of conditions—systemic infections; metabolic disorders, such as kidney and liver disease and thiamine deficiency; substance intoxication and withdrawal; seizures; head traumas; and brain lesions in particular areas of the parietal and occipital lobes. As indicated in Chapter 17, in the elderly Alzheimer-type degeneration and vascular diseases are the most frequent causes of dementia. Infectious diseases of the central nervous system are another major cause of dementia.

Encephalitis is a generic term that refers to inflammation of brain tissue. A large number of living and nonliving agents can enter the body by various routes and inflame the brain. Most are living, and the most important are several viruses, usually carried by insects such as mosquitoes and ticks. In other cases, though, infection may have spread from another part of the body,

TABLE A.1 The Categories of Brain Disorders in DSM-III

I. *Organic Brain Syndromes* (symptoms presumed to be caused by a brain dysfunction but with no specific etiology indicated)
  A. Delirium.
  B. Dementia.
  C. Amnestic syndrome.
  D. Organic delusional syndrome.
  E. Organic hallucinosis.
  F. Organic affective syndrome.
  G. Organic personality syndrome.
  H. Intoxication.
  I. Withdrawal.
  J. Atypical or mixed organic brain syndrome.

II. *Organic Mental Disorders* (symptoms linked to specific known or presumed organic causes)
  A. Dementias Arising in the Senium and Presenium
    1. Primary degenerative dementia (for example, Alzheimer-type disease).
    2. Multi-infarct dementia.
  B. Substance-Induced Organic Mental Disorders (diagnosis usually made in conjunction with Substance Use Disorders)
    1. Alcohol organic mental disorders.
    2. Barbiturate or similarly acting sedative or hypnotic organic mental disorders.
    3. Opioid organic mental disorders.
    4. Cocaine organic mental disorder.
    5. Amphetamine or similarly acting sympathomimetic organic mental disorders.
    6. Phencyclidine (PCP) or similarly acting arylcyclohexylamine organic mental disorders.
    7. Hallucinogen organic mental disorders.
    8. Cannabis organic mental disorders.
    9. Tobacco organic mental disorder.
    10. Caffeine organic mental disorder.

for example, the sinuses and ears. Epidemics of one form, encephalitis lethargica, were widespread in the United States and Europe about the time of World War I. It was referred to as sleeping sickness because those infected were extremely lethargic and slept for prolonged periods, days and weeks at a time. They could, however, be roused from stupor for brief intervals. The epidemics are suspected of having an influenza virus as their cause, one which apparently vanished from the face of the earth, for the epidemics stopped occurring around 1926.

The major symptoms of encephalitis are vomiting, headache, drowsiness and lethargy, a stiff neck and back, fever, tremors, and sometimes convulsive seizures and coma. In the acute phase of the disease, patients are delirious and disoriented. Later they may remain depressed and irritable and have dementia. Recovery is usually complete, but some patients may have permanent paralysis of an arm or leg, uncontrollable tremors, seizures, deafness, speech disturbances, and dementia. If the disorder occurs in infants, they will often be mentally retarded; their developing brains are particularly susceptible to damage from infection.

The symptoms of meningitis, an inflammation of the meninges (see Box A.1), are quite similar to those of encephalitis. The causes are varied but usually bacterial. The principal epidemic form, meningococcal meningitis, occurs all over the world; epidemics of major proportions happen every eight to twelve years.

The syphilitic spirochete *Treponema pallidum* invades the body through mucous membranes after being contacted during either intercourse or oral-genital relations. The disorder may also be transmitted from an infected mother to her fetus. The first indication of the disorder is a small sore on the site of the infection—lips, genitals, or anus—which appears after ten to twenty days and then in a few weeks disappears. Before the sore disappears, a diffuse, copper-colored rash may cover the body. Fatigue, headache, and fever may accompany the rash, as well as sore throat, inflammation of the eyes, vague pains in bones and joints, and lesions in the mucous membranes of mouth and genitalia.[1] Thereafter no overt difficulties are evident for many years, but during this period spirochetes may be invading the lymph glands, the bone marrow, and the other tissues and organs of the body. Damage usually becomes observable when the individual is in his or her forties or fifties and the spirochetes have either invaded the walls of the heart, causing a heart attack, or penetrated the neural tissue. About 30 percent of those infected will ultimately have neurological impairment.

The clinical picture depends on the area of the nervous system affected. In some cases the meninges of the brain are infected, in others the motor nerves of the spinal cord. The most severe damage is done when the cerebral cortex, usually that of the frontal areas, is invaded, producing the syndrome called general paresis. The convolutions flatten through atrophy; on autopsy, the

shrinkage of the cerebral cortex is obvious. The first symptoms are irritability, fatigue, depression, loss of motivation at work, irresponsibility in personal affairs, and inattention to personal appearance. The individual becomes progressively more callous and forgetful and grossly lacking in judgment. Some become euphorically expansive and have absurd and grandiose delusions of position, power, wealth, and physical prowess. Others are depressed and hopeless.

Loss of tone in the facial muscles and failure of the pupils to contract to light are obvious signs. Tremors of the eyelids, lips, facial muscles, and fingers, mispronunciation and slurring of words, deterioration of handwriting, and a wobbly gait indicate loss of control of the voluntary musculature. Massive confusion gradually replaces psychosis. In the final stages the individual is paralyzed, inarticulate, and subject to convulsions, for the mind and body have all but ceased functioning.

With trauma, or injury to the brain, there is often some degree of hemorrhaging and destruction of brain tissue. If the damage is severe, dementia may result. One of the most frequent traumas causing dementia is the *subdural hematoma*. The skull is fractured and bone tears the arachnoid membrane (see Box A.1), causing blood to fill the subdural space between the dura mater and the arachnoid and to destroy much neural tissue.

Amnestic Syndrome

The principal symptom of *amnestic syndrome* is impairment in both short- and long-term memory when there is no delirium and dementia, no clouding of consciousness and no intellectual deterioration. The person is unable to recall information known in the past and cannot learn new material. The memory problems usually create some disorientation; sometimes the individual resists acknowledging memory difficulties through *confabulation*, filling in gaps with fictions.

Amnestic syndrome is brought on by damage to both sides of the brain, in certain diencephalic and temporal lobe structures. Although there are many possible causes—head trauma, infection, infarction of the posterior cerebral arteries—the most common are chronic alcohol use and thiamine deficiency.

One specific amnestic syndrome, *Wernicke's disease*, is frequent among alcoholics, who often do not eat properly. Symptoms include confusion and drowsiness, partial paralysis of the muscles that control eye movements, and an unsteady gait. Autopsy reveals lesions in the pons and cerebellum and in the mammillary bodies,

---

[1]Unfortunately, these early signs do not always appear, making detection of the disease difficult. For this reason blood tests are recommended if there is any suspicion of venereal disease after sexual contact with a highly experienced person or with a relative stranger.

STRUCTURE AND FUNCTION OF THE HUMAN BRAIN

The brain is located within the protective covering of the skull and is enveloped with three layers of nonneural tissue, membranes referred to as *meninges*. The three membranes are the outer, tough, *dura mater*, the intermediate, weblike *arachnoid*, and the inner, soft *pia mater*. Viewed from the top, the brain is divided by a midline fissure into two mirror-image *cerebral hemispheres*; together they constitute most of the cerebrum. The major connection between the two hemispheres is a band of nerve fibers called the *corpus callosum*. Figure A.1 shows the surface of one of the cerebral hemispheres. The upper, side, and some of the lower surfaces of the hemispheres constitute the *cerebral cortex*. The cortex consists of six layers of tightly packed neuron cell bodies with many short, unsheathed interconnecting processes. These neurons, estimated to be 10 to 15 billion in number, make up a thin outer covering, the so-called gray matter of the brain. The cortex is vastly convoluted; the ridges are called *gyri* and the depressions between them *sulci* or fissures. Deep fissures divide the cerebral hemispheres into several distinct areas, called lobes. The *frontal lobe* lies in front of the central sulcus; the *parietal lobe* is behind it and above the lateral sulcus; the *temporal lobe* is located below the lateral sulcus; and the *occipital lobe* lies behind the parietal and temporal lobes. Different functions tend to be localized in particular areas of the lobes—vision in the occipital; discrimination of sounds in the temporal; reasoning and other higher mental processes, plus the regulation of fine voluntary movement, in the frontal; initiation of movements of the skeletal musculature in a band in front of the central sulcus; in a band behind this sulcus, receipt of sensations of touch, pressure, pain, temperature, and body position from skin, muscles, tendons, and joints.

The two hemispheres of the brain are believed to have different functions. The left hemisphere, which generally controls the right half of the body by a crossing over of motor and sensory fibers, is usually dominant; it is responsible for speech and, according to some neuropsychologists, for analytical thinking in right-handed people and in a fair number of left-handed people as well. The right hemisphere controls the left side of the body and is believed to specialize in discerning spatial relations and patterns and in intuition. But analytical thinking cannot be located exclusively in the left hemisphere or intuitive and even creative thinking in the right; the two hemispheres communicate with each other constantly via the corpus callosum. Localization of apparently different modes of thought is probably not as clear-cut as some would have us believe.

If the brain is sliced in half, separating the two cerebral hemispheres (Figure A.2), additional important features can be seen. The gray matter of the cerebral cortex does not extend throughout the interior of the brain. Much of the interior is *white matter* and is made up of large tracts or bundles of myelinated (sheathed) fibers which connect cell bodies in the cortex with those in the spinal cord and in other centers lower in the brain. These centers are additional pockets of gray matter, referred to as *nuclei*. Some cortical cells project their long fibers or axons to motor neurons in the spinal cord, but others project them only as far as these clusters of interconnecting neuron cell bodies.

FIGURE A.1 Surface of the left cerebral hemisphere, indicating the lobes and the two principal fissues of the cortex.

Four masses are deep within each hemisphere, called collectively the *basal ganglia*; other important areas and structure of the brain also contain nuclei. The nuclei serve both as way stations, connecting tracts from the cortex with other ascending and descending tracts, and as integrating motor and sensory control centers. Deep within the brain too are cavities, called *ventricles*, which are continuous with the central canal of the spinal cord and which are filled with cerebrospinal fluid.

In Figure A.2 are shown four important functional areas or structures.

1. The *diencephalon*, connected in front with the hemispheres and behind with the midbrain, contains the *thalamus* and the *hypothalamus*, which consist of groups of nuclei. The thalamus is a relay station for all sensory pathways except the olfactory. The nuclei making up the thalamus receive nearly all impulses arriving from the different sensory areas of the body before passing them on to the cerebrum, where they are interpreted as conscious sensations. The hypothalamus is the highest center of integration for many visceral processes. Its nuclei regulate metabolism, temperature, water balance, sweating, blood pressure, sleeping, and appetite.

2. The *midbrain* is a mass of nerve fiber tracts connecting the cerebral cortex with the pons, the medulla oblongata, the cerebellum, and the spinal cord.

3. The *brainstem* is made up of the *pons* and *medulla oblongata* and functions primarily as a neural relay station. The pons contains tracts that connect the cerebellum with the spinal cord and the cerebellum with motor areas of the cerebrum. The medulla oblongata serves as the main line of traffic for tracts ascending from the spinal cord and descending from the higher centers of the brain. At the bottom of the medulla, many of the motor fibers cross to the opposite side. The medulla also contains nuclei that maintain the regular life rhythms of the heartbeat, of the rising and falling diaphragm, and of the constricting and dilating blood vessels. In the core of the brainstem is the *reticular formation*, sometimes called the reticular activating system because of the important role that it plays in arousal and in the maintenance of alertness. The tracts of the pons and medulla send in fibers to connect with the profusely interconnected cells of the reticular formation, which in turn send fibers to the cortex, the basal ganglia, the hypothalamus, the septal area, and the cerebellum.

4. The *cerebellum*, like the cerebrum, is made up for the most part of two deeply convoluted hemispheres with an exterior cortex of gray matter and an interior of white tracts. The cerebellum receives sensory nerves from the vestibular apparatus of the ear and from muscles, tendons, and joints. The information received and integrated relates to balance and posture and equilibrium and to the smooth coordination of the body when in motion.

A fifth important part of the brain, not shown in Figure A.2, is the *limbic system*, structures which are continuous with one another in the lower cerebrum, and which developed earlier than did the mammalian cerebral cortex. This system is made up of cortex that is phylogenetically older than the so-called neocortex, which covers most of the hemispheres. The *juxallocortex*, which consists of four or five layers of neurons, surrounds the corpus callosum and the underlying thalamus. The cingulate gyrus stretching about the corpus callosum is an important structure made up of this juxallocortex. The *allocortex*, with only three layers of neurons, makes up the cortex of the septal area, which is anterior to the thalamus; the long, tubelike hippocampus, which stretches from the septal area into the temporal lobe; and the part of the lower temporal lobe that surrounds the under portions of the hippocampus and the amygdala (one of the basal ganglia), which is embedded in its tip. The amygdala and the septal area itself, which also consists of nuclei, are sometimes considered part of the limbic system because of their anatomical and functional connections to its other structures. The limbic system controls the visceral and physical expression of emotion—quickened heartbeat and respiration, trembling, sweating, and alterations in facial expressions—and the expression of appetitive and other primary drives—hunger, thirst, mating, defense, attack, and flight.

Corpus callosum
Hypothalamus
Thalamus
Diencephalon
Midbrain
Pons
Medulla
Brain-stem
Cerebellum

FIGURE A.2 Slice of brain through the medial plane, showing the internal structures.

two small, rounded structures of the hypothalamus that contain nuclei. In addition, there is atrophy in the gray matter surrounding several of the ventricles.

A sizable number of patients with Wernicke's disease also develop _Korsakoff's psychosis_. The primary symptoms are anterograde amnesia, a loss of memory for events that have just occurred, and confabulation. Shortly after dinner a patient with Korsakoff's psychosis may be asked what he had for the evening meal. Unable to recall the details, he quickly provides a description of an imaginary meal. It often happens, however, that such descriptions are patently false and elaborate fabrications. A patient in a mental institution may state that he has just finished a meal of Beef Wellington with a delightful sauce containing truffles, apparently not recognizing the extreme improbability of being served such a dinner.

Patients with Korsakoff's psychosis are usually lucid and friendly, yet they lack judgment, being unaware of the implausibility of the stories they tell and only poorly planning other aspects of their lives. They may become apathetic and sometimes grossly confused and severely disoriented. On autopsy, these patients reveal a pattern of brain damage similar to that of Wernicke's disease. But in addition they also have lesions in the thalamus.

Organic Delusional Syndrome

The delusions in _organic delusional syndrome_ are caused by physiological factors that do not cloud consciousness or cause any significant loss of intellectual abilities. Mild impairments may be evident, however, and the person's speech may be somewhat incoherent and rambling. The patient may be either hyperactive, pacing and rocking back and forth, or apathetically immobile. Mood is anxious or depressed. Drugs such as amphetamines, marijuana, and hallucinogens and brain

lesions, particularly to the nondominant hemisphere, can cause the syndrome. Some individuals with Huntington's chorea have a paranoid delusional syndrome, as do some persons with general paresis. Finally, a number of people with temporal lobe epilepsy have delusions, even between seizures.

There are various forms of epilepsy, in all of which consciousness is altered by sudden disruption of the usual rhythmical electric discharge of brain cells.[2] In _temporal lobe epilepsy_ the focus of the abnormal and excessive electric discharge is in the temporal lobes of the brain. The seizures begin with an aura, a signal of the forthcoming attack, which may take the form of dizziness, fear, or unusual sensory experiences such as ringing in the ears or unusual odors. Then the person loses contact with the environment. But during the attack the epileptic appears conscious and engages in some sort of routine or organized activity. The act may be simple and repetitive, such as chewing or moving the limbs in a particular way, or the epileptic may engage in a complex and prolonged series of activities. These seizures may last only a few seconds or minutes but occasionally much longer. After the attack individuals have no memory for their actions. The behavior of these people is often psychotic, even between seizures (Glaser, Newman, and Schafer, 1963).

Organic Hallucinosis

In _organic hallucinosis_ the patient experiences persistent and recurrent hallucinations when alert, well oriented, and in a state of full wakefulness. The use of hallucinogens and prolonged heavy drinking of alcohol are the major causes. Hallucinogens generally bring visual hallucinations, long-term alcohol abuse auditory. In the course of the DTs, during withdrawal from alcohol, however, the hallucinations are visual. The sensory dep-

---

[2]The other major forms of epilepsy are grand mal, petit mal, and Jacksonian or focal epilepsy. _Grand mal_ begins with an aura. In the tonic phase the muscles of the body suddenly become rigid. The patient loses consciousness and falls heavily to the ground if he has not been able to prepare for the attack. The arms and trunk are flexed, the legs outstretched and breathing ceases. After about half a minute, in the clonic phase, which lasts another one or several minutes, the muscles alternately contract and relax, producing violent contortions and jerking movements of the limbs. Breathing resumes. The jaws also open and close, and saliva collects on the lips. Eventually, as the convulsive movements dissipate, the epileptic seizure passes from the clonic phase into coma. The individual remains unconscious and the muscles relax. Upon awakening, perhaps almost immediately or only after several hours, the individual has no memory of what happened after the beginning of the tonic phase. _Petit mal_, more frequent in children

and rare after twenty years of age, is only a short (15 to 50 seconds) disturbance or alteration of consciousness. The person stops what he is doing and his eyes roll up. There may be a few twitches of the eye and face muscles, but in most instances such seizures are difficult to recognize. The person may be aware only that his mind has gone blank for a few moments. _Jacksonian_ or _focal_ epilepsy muscle spasms are limited to particular areas of the body. There are several variants, depending on the area of the brain in which the neurons discharge abnormally. A motor seizure may begin with discharge near the lateral sulcus and be manifested as twitches of the thumb and index finger. A discharge beginning in the visual cortex may produce hallucinations. Sometimes these seizures remain localized and there is no loss of consciousness. But they may also spread, perhaps beginning with the thumb and index finger and then extending to the hand, arm, and shoulder, and sometimes ultimately throughout the entire body.

rivations of blindness and deafness may cause hallucinations. Those who are blind have visual ones, the deaf auditory hallucinations. Untreated cataracts and otosclerosis may cause chronic hallucinosis. Finally, seizures localized in the temporal or occipital lobes may also cause hallucinations.

Organic Affective Syndrome

The mood disturbances of *organic affective syndrome* resemble those of either mania or depression and are usually caused by toxic or metabolic factors. As with the other organic syndromes, these affective disturbances must occur without delirium or dementia to warrant the diagnosis. Depressive symptoms may be brought on by drugs such as reserpine, which is used to treat hypertension, and by methyldopa, used in the treatment of Parkinson's disease. Endocrine disturbances are another route to either mania or depression.

Endocrine glands secrete their hormones directly into the bloodstream. Thus these powerful substances are delivered to nearly every cell in the body, including the neurons of the brain. Either oversecretions or undersecretions of the thyroid gland may bring on affective problems. In hyperthyroidism or *Graves' disease*, described by an Irish physician, Robert Graves, in the first part of the nineteenth century, an oversecretion of the hormone thyroxin speeds up metabolic processes, causing weight loss, sweating, and motor agitation and inducing a state of apprehension, restlessness, and either elated mood or irritability. Thinking proceeds at a rapid pace; persons with Graves' disease may be misdiagnosed as suffering an episode of mania. About 20 percent of hyperthyroid patients may have transitory delusions and hallucinations. Hypothyroidism, which brings on a condition called *myxedema* in adults, is a deficiency in thyroid hormone. Metabolic processes are slowed down and so too are speech and thinking. The individual has poor emotional control, suffers from fatigue, and gains weight. He or she moves as little as possible and loses interest in activities and surroundings. As the disorder progresses, the skin becomes dry and brittle, and hair is lost from the eyebrows and the genital area. In severe cases depression may be deep enough to be considered psychotic. In children the disorder causes mental retardation. Fortunately, hypothyroidism is a very rare condition today, for the iodine of iodized salt prevents the thyroid deficiency.

The adrenal cortex is centrally involved in the activation of emergency physiological responses and the energy needs of the human organism. A chronic insufficiency of cortisone secretion by the adrenal cortex produces *Addison's disease*, first described by the English physician Thomas Addison. The patient loses weight, suffers from low blood pressure, and is irritable and easily fatigued; skin and mucuous membranes also darken. The person becomes depressed and less sociable. When abnormal growths on the cortices of the adrenal glands make them secrete too much cortisone, the condition produced is called *Cushing's syndrome*. Harvey Cushing, the American brain surgeon, described this rare disease, which usually affects young women. The afflicted individual has severe mood swings, none of them pleasant. She is most often depressed but may then become anxious, agitated, and irritable. Physical changes, some quite disfiguring ones—obesity, muscle wasting, changes in skin color and texture, and bone porosity which may bring spinal deformity—can also occur.

Organic Personality Syndrome

In *organic personality syndrome* the personality undergoes a great change, usually because of damage to the brain. The specific nature of the personality change, although very difficult to predict, depends to some extent on function and location of the brain structures that are altered. Some people become emotionally labile and unable to control themselves. They may have sudden bouts of crying and temper outbursts with little provocation. Or they may be sexually indiscrete, shoplift, and act otherwise inappropriately with little concern for consequences. Others may become apathetic, losing interest in their daily activities, friends, and hobbies. Still others may develop a paranoid suspiciousness.

One cause of these personality changes is a brain *tumor* or *neoplasm*, an abnormal growth which can produce a wide variety of psychological as well as physical symptoms. Tumors are either malignant or benign. Malignant growths interfere directly with neural functioning by destroying the original brain tissue from which they started to grow. Benign tumors do not destroy tissue but may, as they grow, increase intracranial pressure and thus disrupt the normal functioning of the brain. Brain tumors usually originate either in glial cells—which support and protect neurons, determine their supply of nutrients and enzymes, and remove dead cells—or in the dura, the outermost membrane covering the brain. Metastatic tumors, though, can invade the brain after being carried by the blood from another area of the body such as the lung.

In addition to causing persistent headaches, vomiting, and sensory and motor impairments—double vision, jerky reflexes and coordination, visual, olfactory, and auditory hallucinations, seizures, and paralysis—tumors in the frontal, temporal, and parietal lobes may first disturb the personality. The individual may be preoccupied and confused, depressed and irritable, and careless about dress, appearance and work. Very occasionally, the person explodes in a sudden and destructive outburst, totally out of character and completely incomprehensible to family, friends, and society at large. After the event it is usually realized, however, that the individual has had earlier warning symptoms and has even communicated them.

If either a benign or a malignant tumor continues to grow, the patient usually dies. Even if the tumor is removed, the functions that have been lost through the destruction of neural tissue do not return because brain cells do not regenerate.

The two lesser brain traumas—the *concussion*, a brief loss of consciousness caused by a jarring blow to the head; and the *contusion*, a bruise of neural tissue and coma when a blow shifts the brain and compresses it against the opposite side of the skull—are serious enough but will not usually change the personality.[3] But a *laceration*, a direct wound to the brain when a object enters the skull and pierces, ruptures, or tears tissue, may. A famous historical case, reported by Dr. J. M. Harlow (1896), illustrates vividly some personality changes following a severe laceration. The patient, Phineas Gage, was working on evacuation of rocks for the roadway of the Rutland and Burlington Railroad in Cavendish, Vermont, when a premature blast sent a tamping iron, three feet, seven inches in length and over an inch in diameter, through his left cheek, upward, and through the top of his skull. Although Gage recovered with no loss of motor or sensory functions, he was a changed person. Dr. Harlow described how the injury later affected Gage's behavior.

His physical health is good, and I am inclined to say that he has recovered. Has no pain in head, but says it has a queer feeling which he is not able to describe. Applied for his situation as foreman, but is undecided whether to work or travel. His contractors, who regarded him as the most efficient and capable foreman in their employ previous to his injury considered the change in his mind so marked that they could not give him his place again. The equilibrium or balance, so to speak, between his intellectual faculties and animal propensities, seems to have been destroyed. He is fitful, irreverent, indulging at times in the grossest profanity (which was not previously his custom), manifesting but little deference for his fellows, impatient of restraint or advice when it conflicts with his desires, at times pertinaciously obstinate, yet capricious and vascillating, devising many plans for future operations, which are no sooner arranged than they are abandoned in turn for others. . . . his mind is radically changed, so decidedly that his friends and acquaintances said he was "no longer Gage" (pp. 339–340).

ORGANIC MENTAL DISORDERS

Two major classes of organic mental disorders are distinguished, *Dementias Arising in the Senium and Presenium* and *Substance-Induced Mental Disorders*. Senile dementias have already been discussed in Chapter 17. The substance-induced disorders are the specific effects, such as intoxication, withdrawal, delirium, hallucinations, and memory dysfunctions, brought on by ingesting alcohol, narcotics, barbiturates, amphetamines, cocaine, and the other substances covered in Chapter 11. Therefore what remains to be presented here are the presenile dementias.

Presenile Dementias

Rare forms of mental deterioration that begin when the individual is in the forties or fifties are referred to as *presenile dementias*. Alzheimer's disease, Pick's disease, Huntington's chorea, and Parkinson's disease are such disorders.

Alzheimer's Disease
In *Alzheimer's disease* the brain tissue deteriorates rather rapidly, death usually occurring ten or twelve years after the onset of symptoms. The disorder is three times more prevalent among women than among men. The disease was first described by the German neurologist Alois Alzheimer in 1860. It commences with difficulties in concentration; the individual appears absent-

---

[3]A series of severe blows to the head, such as a boxer suffers, can eventually lead to a brain syndrome called "Punch-drunkenness." Areas of brain tissue become permanently damaged by the accumulation of injuries; the individual cannot pay attention or concentrate, and memory as well as motor functions are groggy and slow. A person speaks as though slightly drunk. Emotions are unstable and poorly controlled; intellectual impairment is sometimes profound.

minded and irritable, shortcomings which soon begin to interfere with the way she leads her life. She blames others for personal failings and has delusions of being persecuted. Memory continues to deteriorate, with the individual becoming increasingly disoriented and agitated.

The primary physiological change in the brain, evident at autopsy, is a general atrophy of the cerebral cortex as neurons are lost. The fissures widen and the ridges become narrower and flatter. Moreover, senile plaques—small round areas consisting of the remnants of the lost neurons and amyloid, a waxy substance deposited when protein synthesis is disturbed—are scattered throughout the cortex; tangled abnormal protein filaments, neurofibrillary tangles, accumulate within the cell bodies of neurons. (Alzheimer's disease is also discussed in Chapter 17, page 441.)

Pick's Disease

Another presenile disorder was first described by Arnold Pick, a Prague physician, in 1892. *Pick's disease* is a degenerative disorder of the central nervous system in which the frontal and temporal lobes atrophy. As the disease progresses, the deterioration becomes more and more pervasive. The total weight of the brain may be reduced to less than 1000 grams from the usual weight of about 1300 grams. As in Alzheimer's disease, the age of onset is generally in the forties and fifties, and symptoms of the two disorders are also similar. The patient has difficulties with memory and in abstract thinking; he or she is confused and unable to concentrate and has transitory speech impairment. But in Pick's disease affect may be blunted, and the patient is likely to become apathetic and inactive. Life expectancy after onset is usually four to seven years.

Huntington's Chorea

The degenerative disorder *Huntington's chorea* was first described by the American neurologist George Huntington in 1872, after his father and grandfather, both physicians, had observed the disease in several generations of a family. Symptoms usually begin when the individual is in the thirties, and thereafter deterioration is progressive. The early behavioral signs are slovenliness, disregard for social convention, violent outbursts, depression, irritability, poor memory, euphoria, poor judgment, delusions, suicidal ideas and attempts, and hallucinations. The term chorea was applied to the disorder because of the patient's choreiform movements—involuntary, spasmodic twitching and jerking of the limbs, trunk, and head. These signs of neurological disturbance do not appear until well after behavior has already started to deteriorate. Facial grimaces, a smacking of the lips and tongue, and explosive, often obscene

speech are other symptoms. The afflicted individual is likely to have severe problems in speaking, walking, and swallowing. Through the course of the disorder, the suicide rate becomes high, and eventually there is a total loss of bodily control. Death is inevitable, but it may be delayed for ten to twenty years after the onset of illness. The incidence is about 5 cases per 100,000 persons (Boll, Heaton, and Reitan, 1974). The following excerpts from the biography of the American folksinger Woody Guthrie illustrate the development of the disorder, some of the prominent clinical symptoms, and the personal tragedy of the illness.

[Describing the first signs, Woody's wife, Marjorie, commented] "What confused me, and Woody himself, in the early stage of the illness was that by nature he was a rather moody person. As early as 1948, we began to notice that he was more reflective, and often depressed by trivial things. . . . [Shortly thereafter] the symptoms of the disease had become more obvious. Woody developed a peculiar lopsided walk and his speech became explosive. He would take a deep sigh before breathing out the words. The moods and depressions became more exaggerated and more frequent. . . ." [In 1952 the first serious attack occurred. As his wife described it,] "Woody had a violent outburst and foamed at the mouth." [He was hospitalized for three weeks and diagnosed as an alcoholic. After his release he had another violent seizure which, this time, led to a three-month hospitalization. Later] "the disease was making rapid progress. Woody found it increasingly difficult to control his movements, appearing to be drunk even when he wasn't drinking. Friends watched with apprehension as he dived into traffic, oblivious of danger, Chaplinlike, warding off each car as it sped toward him."

[Finally, in 1956, it was recognized that Guthrie had Huntington's chorea, and he spent his remaining years in hospitals. One incident related by his wife, which occurred shortly after his hospitalization, is especially poignant.] "In the early years of his stay in hospitals, Woody would leave every now and then on his own. One day he took the wrong bus and landed in some town in New Jersey. Noticing his disheveled appearance, his distraught air and halting gait, a policeman picked him up, took him to the local police station, and booked him on a vagrancy charge.

"Woody told the police that he was not a homeless bum but a sick man. He explained that he was staying at a New York hospital and begged them to get him home. 'Well,' they said, 'if you're sick you can stay in our hospital.' Finally they let him call me and I went tearing out to New Jersey.

"When I arrived I was received by a staff doctor, a Viennese psychiatrist. 'Your husband is a very disturbed man,' he said imperiously, 'with many hallucinations. He says that he has written a thousand songs.'[4]

'It is true,' I said.
'He also says he has written a book.'
'That's also true.'
'He says that a record company has put out nine records of his songs!' The doctor's voice dripped disbelief.
'That is also the truth,' I said" (Yurchenco, 1970, pp. 139–148).

The disorder is a genetically determined one, passed on by a single dominant gene. The offspring of an individual with the disorder have a 50 percent chance of being afflicted. A postmortem examination of the brain of an individual with Huntington's chorea reveals widespread atrophy and scarring. The major pathological change is a loss of neurons in the caudate nucleus, one of the basal ganglia. The cerebral cortex also atrophies, especially the frontal areas. High levels of dopamine in the caudate nucleus appear to be primarily responsible for the choreiform movements.

Parkinson's Disease

In 1817 James Parkinson described a slowly progressive degeneration which begins later in life, between the ages of fifty and seventy. The primary symptoms of _Parkinson's disease_ are severe and continual muscular tremors, usually occurring at a rate of four to eight movements per second, which rhythmically agitate the limbs, hands, neck, and face. The tremor may begin in one hand or arm, spread to the leg of that side, then to neck, jaw, and face, and finally to the two other limbs. Only muscles that are at rest are subject to tremors, however, not those of the sleeping body or those that are engaged in a coordinated movement. But handwriting becomes small, and this and other manual skills may eventually be lost; speech, swallowing, and chewing are laborious. Other physiological effects include muscular rigidity, akinesia—an inability to initiate movements—and defects in balance. The face later becomes masklike and expressionless, the head shakes, the fingers make pill-rolling movements, and the gait is stiff and distinctive, with the upper part of the body moving forward ahead of the legs. The individual may have difficulty concentrating, become apathetic, and withdraw from social contact. About 90 percent of patients with Parkinson's disease are depressed, and in 30 percent intellectual deterioration is evident (DeJong and Sugar, 1971). About one and a half million Americans are afflicted with the disorder (Stang, 1970).

The etiology of Parkinson's disease varies. It is at times attributable to atherosclerosis; other cases are the aftereffects of encephalitis. The basic brain pathology is a loss of the deeply pigmented nerve cells in the substantia nigra, a nucleus within the midbrain which is an important motor relay station. The neurons in the substantia nigra that are destroyed are those that release dopamine. One by-product of dopamine metabolism is melanin, which gives the substantia nigra its characteristic color. A reduced number of these cells means not only that the substantia nigra loses color but that less dopamine is released in the corpus striatum, to which the axons of these neurons normally extend. The corpus striatum consists of the caudate and lenticular nuclei, two of the basal ganglia. Tracts of white matter between them give the mass a striped appearance. With reduced amounts of dopamine in the corpus striatum, the action of the neurotransmitter acetylcholine released by the cholinergic motor neurons in the caudate nucleus is insufficiently opposed. And because the neurotransmitter of the cholinergic tracts is not under the inhibitory control of dopamine, too many of the postsynaptic motor neurons fire, producing the uncontrollable muscular tremors and stiffness of Parkinson's disease. Parkinsonism can be treated either by administering anticholinergic drugs to reduce the action of the cholinergic neurons, or by giving the patient a precursor of dopamine, L-dopa. Encouraging as much movement as possible and speech therapy are also helpful.

---

[4]In addition to misdiagnosing Mr. Guthrie, the physician had confused the concepts of delusion and hallucination.

Acetylcholine. A *neurotransmitter*[1] of the central, somatomotor, and *parasympathetic* nervous systems and of the ganglia and the neuron–sweat gland junctions of the *sympathetic*.

Addiction. See *substance dependence*.

Addison's disease. An endocrine disorder produced by *cortisone* insufficiency and marked by weight loss, fatigue, and a darkening of the skin.

Adrenal glands. Two small areas of tissue, located just above the kidneys; the inner core of each gland, the medulla, secretes *epinephrine* and *norepinephrine*, the outer cortex secretes *cortisone* and other steroid hormones.

Adrenaline. A hormone that is secreted by the *adrenal glands*; also called *epinephrine*.

Adrenergic system. All the nerve cells for which *norepinephrine* and *epinephrine* (and more broadly, other *monoamines, dopamine* and *serotonin*) are the transmitter substances, as opposed to the *cholinergic*, which consists of the nerve cells activated by *acetylcholine*.

Advanced accurate empathy. A form of *empathy* in which the therapist infers concerns and feelings that lie behind what the client is saying; it represents an *interpretation*. Compare with *primary empathy*.

Affect. A subjective feeling or emotional tone often accompanied by bodily expressions noticeable to others.

Affective disorder. A disorder in which there are disabling mood disturbances.

Affirming the consequent. An error in logic by which, if A causes B on one occasion, it is assumed that A is the cause when B is observed on any other occasion.

Age effects. The consequences of being a given chronological age. Compare with *cohort effects*.

Ageism. Prejudicial attitudes toward old people.

Agoraphobia. A cluster of fears centering around being in open spaces and leaving the home.

Alcoholism. A behavioral disorder in which consumption of alcoholic beverages is continuous and excessive and impairs health and social and occupational functioning; a physiological dependence on alcohol. See *substance dependence*.

Alkaloid. An organic base found in seed plants, usually in mixture with a number of similar alkaloids. Alkaloids are the active chemicals that give many drugs their medicinal properties and other powerful physiologic effects.

Alogia. A *negative symptom* in *schizophrenia, marked by blocking and poverty of speech content*.

Alpha rhythm. A dominant pattern (8 to 13 cps) of the *brain waves* of a resting but awake adult.

Altruistic suicide. As defined by Durkheim, self-annihilation that the person feels will serve a social purpose, such as the self-immolations practiced by Buddhist monks during the Vietnam war.

Alzheimer's disease. A *dementia* involving a progressive atrophy of cortical tissue and marked by speech impairment, involuntary movements of limbs, occasional *convulsions*, intellectual deterioration, and psychotic behavior.

Ambivalence. The simultaneous holding of strong positive and negative emotional attitudes toward the same situation or person.

[1]Italicized words or variants of these terms are themselves defined elsewhere in the glossary.

American Law Institute Guidelines. Rules proposing insanity to be a legitimate defense plea if during criminal conduct an individual could not judge right from wrong or control his or her behavior as required by law. Repetitive criminal acts are disavowed as a sole criterion. Compare *M'Naghten rule* and *irresistible impulse*.

Amino acid. One of a large class of organic compounds, important as the building blocks of proteins.

Amnesia. Total or partial loss of memory that can be associated with a *dissociative disorder*, an *organic brain syndrome* or *hypnosis*. **Anterograde**, loss of memory for events that have just occurred. **Retrograde**, loss of memory for events immediately preceding a traumatic incident; and sometimes for events extending far back in time. See *psychogenic amnesia*.

Amphetamines. A group of stimulating drugs which produce heightened levels of energy and, in large doses, nervousness, sleeplessness, and paranoid *delusions*.

Anaclitic depression. The profound sadness of an infant when separated from its mother for a prolonged period.

Anal personality. An adult who, when anal retentive, is found by psychoanalytic theory to be stingy and sometimes obsessively clean; when anal expulsive, to be aggressive. Such traits are assumed to be caused by *fixation* through either excessive or inadequate gratification of *id* impulses during the *anal stage* of *psychosexual* development.

Anal stage. In psychoanalytic theory, the second *psychosexual stage*, occurring during the second year of life, during which the anus is considered to be the principal *erogenous zone*.

Analgesia. An insensitivity to pain without loss of consciousness; sometimes found in *conversion disorder*.

Analogue experiment. An experimental study of a phenomenon different from but related to the actual interests of the investigator.

Analysand. A person being psychoanalyzed.

Analyst. See *psychoanalyst*.

Anesthesia. An impairment or loss of sensation, usually of touch but sometimes of the other senses, that is often part of *conversion disorder*.

Anhedonia. A *negative symptom* in *schizophrenia*, in which the individual is unable to feel pleasure.

Animal phobias. The fear and avoidance of small animals.

Anomic suicide. As defined by Durkheim, self-annihilation triggered by the person's inability to cope with sudden and unfavorable change in a social situation.

Anorexia nervosa. A disorder in which a person is unable to eat or to retain any food or suffers a prolonged and severe diminution of appetite. The individual has an intense fear of becoming obese, feels fat even when emaciated, and, refusing to maintain a minimal body weight, loses at least 25 percent of original weight.

Anosmia. A *conversion disorder* marked by loss or impairment of the sense of smell.

Anoxia. A deficiency in oxygen reaching the tissues severe enough to damage the brain permanently.

Antabuse (*disulfiram*). A drug which makes the drinking of alcohol produce nausea and other unpleasant effects.

Anterograde amnesia. The inability to form new memories after the brain has been damaged.

Antidepressant. A drug which alleviates *depression*, usually by energizing the patient and thus elevating mood.

Antisocial personality. Also called a psychopath or a sociopath; this person is superficially charming and a habitual liar, has no regard for others, shows no remorse after hurting them, has no shame for behaving in an outrageously objectionable manner, is unable to form relationships and take responsibility, and does not learn from punishment.

Anxiety. An unpleasant feeling of fear and apprehension accompanied by increased physiological arousal. In learning theory it is considered a drive which mediates between a threatening situation and avoidance behavior. Anxiety can be assessed by self-report, by measuring physiological arousal, and by observing overt behavior.

Anxiety disorders. Disorders in which fear or tension is overriding and the primary disturbance: *phobic disorders*; the *anxiety states*, which are *panic disorder, generalized anxiety disorder,* and *obsessive-compulsive disorder*; and *posttraumatic stress disorder*. Major category of DSM-III covering most of what used to be referred to as the *neuroses*.

Anxiety neurosis. DSM-II term for what are now diagnosed as *panic disorder* and *generalized anxiety disorder*.

Aphasia. The loss or impairment of the ability to use language because of lesions in the brain. **Executive,** difficulties in speaking or writing the words intended. **Receptive,** difficulties in understanding written or spoken language.

Aphonia. A *conversion disorder* marked by a loss of voice.

Apnea. Cessation of breathing for short periods of time, sometimes occurring during sleep.

Arousal. A state of activation, either behavioral or physiological.

Ascriptive responsibility. The social judgment assigned to someone who has committed an illegal act and who, it is decided, should be punished for it. Contrast with *descriptive responsibility*.

Asociality. A *negative symptom in schizophrenia*, marked by inability to form close relationships and feel intimacy.

Assertion training. *Behavior therapy* procedures which attempt to help a person express more easily thoughts, wishes, and beliefs and legitimate feelings of resentment or approval.

Asthma. A *psychophysiological disorder* characterized by narrowing of the airways and increased secretion of mucus, which often cause breathing to be extremely labored and wheezy.

Asylum. A refuge established in western Europe in the fifteenth century as a place to confine and provide for the mentally ill; the forerunner of the mental hospital.

Attention. The maintenance of a readiness to respond, or focusing on relevant information.

Attention-deficit disorder with hyperactivity. A developmental disorder in children marked by difficulties in focusing adaptively on the task at hand and by inappropriate fidgeting and antisocial behavior.

Attribution. The explanation a person has for his or her behavior.

Aura. A signal or warning of an impending epileptic *convulsion*, taking the form of dizziness or an unusual sensory experience.

Autism. An absorption in self or fantasy as a means of avoiding communication and escaping objective reality. See also *infantile autism*.

Automatic thoughts. In Beck's theory, the things people picture or tell themselves as they make their way in life.

Autonomic nervous system. The division of the nervous system that regulates involuntary functions; innervates *endocrine glands, smooth muscle,* and heart muscle; and initiates the physiological changes that are part of expression of emotion. See *sympathetic* and *parasympathetic nervous system*.

Aversion therapy. A *behavior therapy* procedure which pairs a noxious stimulus, such as a shock, with situations that are undesirably attractive.

Aversive stimulus. A stimulus that elicits pain, fear, or avoidance.

Avoidance learning. An experimental procedure in which a neutral stimulus is paired with a noxious one so that the organism learns to avoid the previously neutral stimulus.

Avoidant disorder of childhood or adolescence. A persistent shrinking from strangers and from peers, despite a clear desire for affection, to the extent that social functioning is impaired; relations with family members are warm.

Avoidant personality. Thinking poorly of themselves, individuals with an avoidant personality are extremely sensitive to potential rejection and remain aloof from others, even though they very much desire affiliation and affection.

Avolition. A *negative symptom* in *schizophrenia*, in which the individual lacks interests and drive.

Barbiturate. A class of synthetic *sedative* drugs which are addictive and in large doses can cause death because the diaphragm relaxes almost completely.

Basal ganglia. Clusters of nerve cell bodies (*nuclei*) deep within the *cerebral hemispheres*. They are the lenticular nucleus, the caudate nucleus (collectively, the corpus striatum), the claustrum, and the amygdala.

Baseline. The state of a phenomenon before the *independent variable* is introduced, providing a standard against which the effects of the variable can be measured.

Behavior genetics. The study of individual differences in behavior that are attributable in part to differences in genetic makeup.

Behavior modification. A term sometimes used interchangeably with *behavior therapy*.

Behavior rehearsal. A *behavior therapy* technique in which a client practices new behavior in the consulting room, often aided by demonstrations of the therapist.

Behavior therapy. A branch of psychotherapy narrowly conceived as the application of *classical* and *operant conditioning* to the alteration of clinical problems, but more broadly conceived as applied experimental psychology in a clinical context.

Behavioral assessment. A sampling of ongoing cognitions, feelings, and overt behavior in their situational context. To be contrasted with the *projective test* and *personality inventory*.

Behavioral medicine. A new area of behavioral therapy procedures that apply to *psychophysiological disorders*.

Behavioral pediatrics. A branch of *behavioral medicine* concerned with psychological aspects of childhood medical problems.

Behaviorism. The school of psychology associated with John B. Watson, who proposed that observable behavior, not consciousness, is the proper subject matter of psychology. Currently, many who consider themselves behaviorists do use *mediational* concepts, provided they are firmly anchored to observables.

Bell and pad. A *behavior therapy* technique for eliminating nocturnal *enuresis*; if the child wets, an electric circuit is closed and a bell sounds, waking the child.

Beta rhythm. The dominant pattern (14 to 25 cps) of *brain waves* found in an alert adult responding to a stimulus. See also *alpha rhythm*.

Biofeedback. A term referring to procedures that provide an individual immediate information on even minute changes in muscle activity, skin temperature, heart rate, blood pressure, and other somatic functions. It is assumed that voluntary control over these bodily processes can be achieved through this knowledge, thereby ameliorating to some extent certain *psychophysiological disorders*.

Bioenergetics. The therapy based on Wilhelm Reich's unorthodox analytic theory that all psychological distress is caused by problems in achieving full sexual satisfaction.

Biophysical system. As applied by Masters and Johnson, the part of the sexual response system that includes the genitalia and hormones.

Bipolar disorder. A term applied to the disorder of people who have experienced episodes of both *mania* and *depression* or of mania alone.

Bisexual. One who engages in both *heterosexual* and *homosexual* relations.

Borderline personality. This impulsive and unpredictable person has an uncertain self-image, intense and unstable social relationships, and extreme swings of mood.

Brain wave. The rhythmic fluctuations in voltage between parts of the brain produced by the spontaneous firings of its *neurons*; recorded by the *electroencephalograph*.

Brainstem. The part of the brain connecting the spinal cord with the *cerebrum*. It contains the *pons* and *medulla oblongata* and functions as a neural relay station.

Brief reactive psychosis. A disorder in which the person has a sudden onset of *psychotic* symptoms—*incoherence, loosening of associations, delusions, hallucinations*—immediately after a severely disturbing event; the symptoms last more than a few hours but for no more than two weeks. New DSM-III diagnosis. See *schizophreniform disorder*.

Briquet's syndrome. See *somatization disorder*.

Bulimia. Episodic eating binge, often associated with induced vomiting.

Cardiovascular disorders. Medical problems involving the heart and blood circulation system, such as *hypertension* and *coronary heart disease*.

Case study. The collection of historical or biographical information on a single individual, often including experiences in therapy.

Castration. The surgical removal of the *testes*.

Castration anxiety. The fear of having the genitals removed or injured.

CAT scan. Computerized axial tomography, a new method of diagnosis employing X-rays taken from different angles and then analyzed by computer to produce a representation of the part of the body in cross section. It can be used on the brain.

Catatonic immobility (catatonia). A fixity of posture, sometimes grotesque, maintained for long periods with accompanying muscular rigidity, trancelike state of consciousness, and *waxy flexibility*.

Catatonic schizophrenic. A *psychotic* patient whose primary symptoms alternate between stuporous immobility and excited agitation.

Catecholamines. *Monoamine* compounds (NH$_2$), each having a catechol portion (C$_6$H$_6$). Catecholamines known to be *neurotransmitters* of the central nervous system are *norepinephrine* and *dopamine*; another, *epinephrine*, is principally a hormone.

Catechol-O-methyltransferase (COMT). An enzyme which deactivates *catecholamines* in the *synapse*.

Cathartic method. A therapeutic procedure introduced by Breuer in the late nineteenth century whereby a patient recalls and relives an earlier emotional catastrophe and reexperiences the tension and unhappiness.

Central nervous system. The part of the nervous system which in vertebrates consists of the brain and spinal cord and to which all sensory impulses are transmitted and from which motor impulses pass out; it also supervises and coordinates the activities of the entire nervous system.

Central sulcus. A major fissure transversing the middle of the top and lateral surfaces of each *cerebral hemisphere*, dividing the *frontal lobe* from the *parietal*.

Cerebellum. An area of the hindbrain concerned with balance, posture, and motor coordination.

Cerebral atherosclerosis. A chronic disease impairing intellectual and emotional life, caused by a reduction in the brain's blood supply through a buildup of fatty deposits in the arteries.

Cerebral contusion. A bruising of neural tissue marked by swelling and hemorrhage and resulting in coma; it may permanently impair intellectual functioning.

Cerebral cortex. The thin outer covering of each of the *cerebral hemispheres*, highly convoluted, and made up of nerve cell bodies, which constitute the *gray matter* of the brain.

Cerebral hemisphere. Either of the two halves which make up the *cerebrum*.

Cerebral hemmorrhage. Bleeding onto brain tissue from a ruptured blood vessel.

Cerebral thrombosis. The formation of a blood clot in a cerebral artery that blocks circulation in that area of brain tissue and produces paralysis, loss of sensory functions, and possibly death.

Cerebrovascular diseases. Illnesses that disrupt blood supply to the brain, as in *stroke*.

Cerebrum. The two-lobed structure extending from the *brainstem* and constituting the anterior part of brain. It is the largest and most recently developed portion of the human brain, which coordinates sensory and motor activities as well as being the seat of higher cognitive processes.

Character disorder. The old term for *personality disorder*.

Childhood onset pervasive developmental disorder. A disorder of children older than thirty months but younger than twelve who indicate little empathy or emotional responsiveness to their peers, cling to their parents, take peculiar postures or make stereotyped movements, resist any change, have sudden anxieties and unexplained rages, and may occasionally be self-injurious; it replaces the earlier diagnosis of *childhood schizophrenia*.

Childhood schizophrenia. DSM-II diagnosis replaced by *childhood onset pervasive developmental disorder*.

Chlorpromazine. The generic term for one of the most widely prescribed antipsychotic drugs, sold under the name *Thorazine*.

Cholinergic system. All the nerve cells for which *acetylcholine* is the transmitter substance, in contrast to the *adrenergic*, or more precisely the *monoaminergic*.

Choreiform. Pertaining to the involuntary, spasmodic, jerking movements of the limbs and head found in *Huntington's chorea* and other nervous disorders.

Chromosomes. The threadlike bodies within the nucleus of the cell, DNA being the principal constituent; regarded as carrying the genes.

Chronic. Of lengthy duration or recurring frequently, often with progressing seriousness.

Chronic brain syndrome. See *senile dementia*.

Chronic schizophrenic. A *psychotic* patient who had earlier deteriorated over a long period of time and who has usually been hospitalized for more than two years.

Civil commitment. A procedure whereby a person can be legally certified as mentally ill and hospitalized, even against his will.

Clang association. A stringing together of words because they are similar in sound, with no attention paid to their meaning, for example, "How are you Don, pawn, gone?"

Classical conditioning. A basic form of learning, sometimes referred to as Pavlovian conditioning, in which a neutral stimulus is repeatedly paired with another stimulus (called the *unconditioned stimulus*, UCS) that naturally elicits a certain desired response (UCR). After repeated trials the neutral stimulus becomes a *conditioned stimulus* (CS) and evokes the same or similar response, called now the *conditioned response* (CR).

Classificatory variables. The characteristics that subjects bring with them into scientific investigations, such as sex, age, and mental status; studied by *correlational* research and *mixed designs*.

Client-centered therapy. A *humanistic-existential insight therapy*, developed by Carl Rogers, which emphasizes the importance of the therapist's understanding the client's subjective experiences and assisting him or her to gain more awareness of the current motivations for behavior; the goal is not only to reduce anxieties but also to foster actualization of the client's potential.

Climacteric. The period in middle age when for the female menstruation ceases and for the male sexual activity and competence may be reduced.

Clinical psychologist. An individual who has earned a Ph.D. degree in psychology or a Psy.D. and whose training has included an internship in a mental hospital or clinic.

Clinical psychology. The special area of psychology concerned with the study of psychopathology, its causes, prevention, and treatment.

Clitoris. The small heavily innervated erectile structure located above the vaginal opening; the primary site of female responsiveness to sexual stimulation.

Clonic phase. The stage of violent contortions and jerking of limbs in a *grand mal epileptic* attack.

Cocaine. A pain-reducing and stimulating *alkaloid* obtained from coca leaves, which increases mental powers, produces euphoria, heightens sexual desire, and in large doses causes *paranoia* and *hallucinations*.

Cognition. The process of knowing; the thinking, judging, reasoning, and planning activities of the human mind. Behavior is now often explained as depending on the course these processes take.

Cognitive restructuring. Any *behavior therapy* procedure that attempts to alter the manner in which clients think about life so that they change their overt behavior and emotions.

Cohort effects. The consequences of having been born in a given year and having grown up during a particular time period with its own unique pressures, problems, challenges, and opportunities. To be distinguished from *age effects*.

Coitus. Sexual intercourse.

Colic. A condition found in infants in which gas collects in the stomach and produces distress.

Community mental health. The delivery of services to needy, underserved groups through centers that offer outpatient therapy, short-term in–patient care, day hospitalization, twenty-four-hour emergency services, and consultation and education to other community agencies such as the police.

Community psychology. An approach to therapy which emphasizes prevention and the seeking out of potential difficulties rather than waiting for troubled individuals to initiate consultation. The location for professional activities tends to be in the persons' natural surroundings rather than in the therapist's office. See *prevention*.

Competency to stand trial. A legal decision on whether a person can participate meaningfully in his or her own defense.

Compulsion. The irresistible impulse to repeat an irrational act over and over again.

Compulsive personality. Perfectionistic and work- rather than pleasure-oriented, people with a compulsive personality have inordinate difficulty making decisions, are overconcerned with details and efficiency, and relate poorly to others because they demand that things be done their way. They are unduly conventional, serious, formal, and stingy with their emotions.

Concordance. As applied in *behavior genetics*, the similarity in psychiatric diagnosis or in other traits in a pair of twins.

Concurrent validity. See *validity*.

Concussion. A jarring injury to the brain produced by a blow to the head that usually involves a momentary loss of consciousness followed by transient disorientation and memory loss.

Conditioned response (CR). The response elicited by a given neutral stimulus (CS), after it has become conditioned by repeated contingent pairings with another stimulus (UCS) that naturally elicits the same or a similar response.

Conditioned stimulus (CS). A neutral stimulus which, after repeated contingent pairings with another stimulus (UCS) that naturally elicits a certain response (UCR), comes to elicit the same or a similar response, called the *conditioned response* (CR).

Conduct disorders. Patterns of extreme disobedience in youngsters, including theft, vandalism, lying, and early drug use; may be precursors of *antisocial personality* disorder.

Confabulation. Filling in gaps in memory caused by brain dysfunction with made-up and often improbable stories that the subject accepts as true.

Confidentiality. A principle observed by lawyers, doctors, pastors, psychologists, and psychiatrists that the goings-on in a professional and private relationship are not divulged to anyone else. See *privileged communication*.

Conflict. A state of being torn between competing forces.

Confounds. Variables whose effects are so intermixed that they cannot be measured separately, making the design of the *experiment* internally invalid and its results impossible to interpret.

Congenital. Existing at or before birth but not acquired through heredity.

Construct. An entity inferred by a scientist to explain observed phenomena. See also *mediator*.

Contingency. A close relationship, especially of a causal nature, between two events, one of which regularly follows the other.

Control group. The subjects in an *experiment* for whom the *independent variable* is not manipulated, thus forming a *baseline* against which the effects of the manipulation can be evaluated.

Controlled drinking. A pattern of alcohol consumption that is moderate and avoids the extremes of total abstinence and of inebriation.

Conversion disorder. A *somatoform disorder* in which sensory or muscular functions are impaired, usually suggesting neurological disease, even though the bodily organs themselves are sound; *anesthesias* and paralyses of limbs are examples.

Convulsion. Violent and extensive twitching of the body caused by involuntary pathological muscle contractions.

Convulsive therapy. A biological therapy which induces *convulsions* by drugs or electric shock in hopes of effecting beneficial behavior change. See *electroconvulsive therapy*.

Coronary heart disease. Angina pectoris, chest pains caused by insufficient supply of blood and thus oxygen to the heart; and myocardial infarction, or heart attack, in which the blood and oxygen supply is reduced so much that heart muscles are damaged.

Corpus callosum. The large band of nerve fibers connecting the two *cerebral hemispheres*.

Correlational method. The research strategy used to establish whether two or more variables are related. Such relationships may be positive—as values for one variable increase, those for the other do also; or negative—as values for one variable increase, those for the other decrease.

Cortisone. A hormone secreted by the adrenal cortices.

Co-twin. In *behavior genetics* research using the *twin method*, the member of the pair who is tested later to determine whether he has the same diagnosis or trait discovered earlier in his birth partner, the *index case*.

Counterconditioning. Relearning achieved by eliciting a new response in the presence of a particular stimulus.

Countertransference. Feelings that the *analyst* unconsciously directs to the *analysand* but which come from his or her own emotional vulnerabilities and unresolved *conflicts*.

Covert sensitization. A form of *aversion therapy* in which the subject is told to imagine the undesirably attractive situations and activities at the same time that unpleasant feelings are also induced by imagery.

Cretinism. A condition beginning in prenatal or early life characterized by *mental retardation* and physical deformities, caused by severe deficiency in the output of the *thyroid gland*.

Criminal commitment. A procedure whereby a person is confined in a mental institution either for determination of *competency to stand trial* or after acquittal by reason of insanity.

Critical period. A stage of early development in which an organism needs certain inputs and during which important irreversible patterns of behavior are acquired. See *imprinting*.

Cross-sectional research. Studies in which different age groups are compared at the same time. Compare with *longitudinal research*.

Cultural-familial retardation. A mild backwardness in mental development with no indication of brain pathology but evidence of similar limitation in at least one of the parents or siblings.

Cunnilingus. The oral stimulation of female genitalia.

Cushing's syndrome. An endocrine disorder usually affecting young women, produced by oversecretion of *cortisone* and marked by mood swings, irritability, agitation, and physical disfigurement.

Cyclical psychodynamics. The reciprocal relations between current behavior and repressed conflicts, such that they mutually reinforce each other.

Defect theorist. In the study of *mental retardation*, a person who believes that the cognitive processes of retardates are qualitatively different from those of normal individuals; contrast with *developmental theorist*.

Defense mechanism. In psychoanalytic theory, a reality-distorting strategy unconsciously adopted to protect the ego from anxiety.

Delay of reward gradient. The learning theory term for the finding that rewards and punishments lose their effectiveness the farther in time they are removed from the response in question.

Delirium. A state of great mental confusion in which consciousness is clouded, attention cannot be sustained, and the stream of thought and speech is incoherent. The person is probably disoriented, emotionally erratic, restless or lethargic, and often has *illusions, delusions,* and *hallucinations*.

Delirium tremens (DTs). One of the *withdrawal* symptoms when a period of heavy alcohol consumption is terminated; marked by fever, sweating, trembling, cognitive impairment, and *hallucinations*.

Delta rhythm. See *slow brain waves*.

Delusion. A belief contrary to reality, firmly held in spite of evidence to the contrary; common in *paranoid disorders*. **Of control**, belief that one is being manipulated by some external force such as radar, TV, or a creature from outer space. **Of grandeur**, belief that one is an especially important or powerful person. **Of persecution**, belief that one is being plotted against or oppressed by others.

Delusional jealousy. The unfounded conviction that one's mate is unfaithful. The individual may collect small bits of "evidence" to justify the *delusion*.

Dementia. The deterioration of mental faculties—of memory, judgment, abstract thought, control of impulses, intellectual ability—that impairs social and occupational functioning and eventually changes the personality.

Dementia praecox. An older term for *schizophrenia*, chosen to describe what was believed to be an incurable and progressive deterioration of mental functioning beginning in adolescence.

Demographic variable. A varying characteristic that is a vital or social statistic of an individual, sample group, or population, for example, age, sex, *socioeconomic status*, racial origin, education, and the like.

Demonology. The doctrine that a person's abnormal behavior is caused by an autonomous evil spirit.

Dependent personality. Lacking in self-confidence, people with a dependent personality passively allow others to run their lives and make no demands on them, lest they endanger these protective relationships.

Dependent variable. In a psychological *experiment*, the behavior that is measured and is expected to change with manipulation of the *independent variable*.

Depersonalization. An alteration in perception of the self in which the individual loses a sense of reality and feels estranged from the self and perhaps separated from the body. It may be a temporary reaction to stress and fatigue or part of *panic disorder, depersonalization disorder,* or *schizophrenia*.

Depersonalization disorder. A *dissociative disorder* in which the individual feels unreal and estranged from the self and surroundings enough to disrupt functioning. The patient may feel that the extremities have changed in size or that he or she watches the self from a distance.

Depression. An emotional state marked by great sadness and apprehension, feelings of worthlessness and guilt, withdrawal from others, loss of sleep, appetite, and sexual desire, or interest and pleasure in usual activities; and either lethargy or agitation. Called *major depression* in DSM-III and *unipolar depression* by others. It can be an associated symptom of other disorders.

Derealization. Loss of the sense that the surroundings are real. It is present in several psychological disorders, such as *panic disorder, depersonalization disorder,* and *schizophrenia*.

Descriptive responsibility. In legal proceedings, the judgment that the accused performed an illegal act. Contrast with *ascriptive responsibility*.

Deterioration effect. In abnormal psychology, a harmful outcome from being in psychotherapy.

Detumescence. The flow of blood out of the genital area.

Developmental theorist. In the study of *mental retardation*, a person who believes that the cognitive development of retardates has simply been slower than that of normal individuals, and not qualitatively different. Contrast with *defect theorist*.

Diagnosis. The determination that the set of symptoms or problems of a patient indicates a particular disorder.

Diathesis. *Predisposition* toward a disease or abnormality.

Diathesis-stress paradigm. A view that, as applied in psychopathology, assumes that individuals predisposed toward a particular mental disorder will be particularly affected by stress and will then manifest abnormal behavior.

Dichotic listening. An experimental procedure in which a subject hears two taped messages simultaneously through earphones, one in each ear, usually with the instruction to attend to only one of the messages.

Diencephalon. The lower area of the forebrain containing the *thalamus* and *hypothalamus*.

Directionality problem. A difficulty in *correlational* research whereby it is known that two variables are related, but it is unclear which is causing the other.

Disease. The medical concept that distinguishes an impairment of the normal state of the organism by its particular group of symptoms and its specific cause.

Disease model. See *medical model*.

Disorganized schizophrenic. A person with *schizophrenia* who has rather diffuse and regressive symptoms; the individual is given to silliness, facial grimaces, and inconsequential rituals and has constantly changeable moods and poor hygiene. There are few significant remissions and eventually considerable deterioration. This form of schizophrenia was formerly called *hebephrenia*.

Disorientation. A state of mental confusion with respect to time, place, identity of self, other persons, and objects.

Displacement. A *defense mechanism* whereby an emotional response is unconsciously redirected from a perhaps dangerous object or concept to a substitute less threatening to the *ego*.

Dissociation. A process whereby a group of mental processes is split off from the mainstream of consciousness, or behavior loses its relationship with the rest of the personality.

Dissociative disorders. Disorders in which the normal integration of consciousness, memory, or identity is suddenly and temporarily altered: *psychogenic amnesia, psychogenic fugue, multiple personality,* and *depersonalization disorder* are examples.

Dizygotic (fraternal) twins. Birth partners who have developed from separate fertilized eggs and who are only 50 percent alike genetically, no more so than siblings born from different pregnancies.

Dominant gene. One of a pair of *genes* which predominates over the other and determines that the *trait* it fosters will prevail in the *phenotype*.

Dopamine. A *catecholamine* that is both a precursor of *norepinephrine* and itself a *neurotransmitter* of the central nervous system. Disturbances in certain of its tracts apparently figure in *schizophrenia* and *Parkinson's disease*.

Double bind. An interpersonal situation in which an individual is confronted, over long periods of time by mutually inconsistent messages to which she or he must respond, believed by some theorists to cause *schizophrenia*.

Double-blind procedure. A method for reducing the biasing effects of the expectations of subject and experimenter; neither is allowed to know whether the *independent variable* of the *experiment* is being applied to the particular subject.

Down's syndrome *(mongolism)*. A form of *mental retardation* generally caused by an extra *chromosome*. The child's IQ is usually less than 50, and his or her physical characteristics are distinctive, the one most often noted being slanted eyes.

Dream analysis. A key psychoanalytic technique in which the unconscious meanings of dream material are uncovered.

Drive. A *construct* explaining the motivation of behavior, or an internal physiological tension impelling an organism to activity.

Drug abuse. See *substance abuse*.

Drug addiction. See *substance dependence*.

DSM-III. The current diagnostic and statistical manual of the American Psychiatric Association.

Dualism. Philosophical doctrine that a human being is both mental and physical and that these two aspects are separate but interacting. It was advanced in its most definitive statement by Descartes. Contrast with *monism*.

Durham decision. A 1954 American court ruling that an accused person is not *ascriptively responsible* if his or her crime is judged attributable to mental disease or defect.

Dysfunction. An impairment or disturbance in the functioning of an organ, organ system, behavior, or cognition.

Dyslexia. A disturbance in the ability to read; one of the *learning disabilities* or *specific developmental disorders*.

Dyspareunia. Painful or difficult sexual intercourse, the pain or difficulty usually being caused by infection or a physical injury such as torn ligaments in the pelvic region.

Echolalia. The immediate and sometimes pathological repetition of the words of others; a speech problem often found in autistic children. In **delayed echolalia** this inappropriate echoing takes places hours or weeks later.

Eclecticism. In psychology, the view that more is to be gained by employing concepts from various theoretical systems than by restricting oneself to a single theory.

Ego. In psychoanalytic theory, the predominantly conscious part of the personality, responsible for decision making and for dealing with reality.

Ego-alien. Foreign to the self, such as a *compulsion*.

Ego analysis. An important set of modifications of classical *psychoanalysis*, based on a conception of the human being as having a stronger, more autonomous ego with gratifications independent of *id* satisfactions. Sometimes called ego psychology.

Ego-dystonic homosexuality. A disorder of people who are persistently dissatisfied with their *homosexuality* and wish instead to be attracted to members of the opposite sex.

Egoistic suicide. As defined by Durkheim, self-annihilation committed because the individual feels extreme alienation from others and from society.

Ejaculate. To expel semen, typically during male orgasm.

Elective mutism. A pattern of continuously refusing to speak in almost all social situations, including school, even though the child understands spoken language and is able to speak.

Electra complex. See *Oedipus complex*.

Electrocardiograph. A device for recording the electrical activity that occurs during the heartbeat.

Electroconvulsive therapy (ECT). A treatment which produces a *convulsion* by passing electric current through the brain. It can be useful in alleviating profound *depression*, although sometimes an unpleasant and occasionally dangerous procedure.

Electroencephalogram (EEG). A graphic recording of electrical activity of the brain, usually that of the *cerebral cortex,* but sometimes the electrical activity of lower areas.

Empathy. Awareness and understanding of another's feelings and thoughts. See *primary empathy* and *advanced accurate empathy*.

Empty-chair technique. A *Gestalt therapy* procedure for helping the client become more aware of denied feelings; the client talks to important people or to feelings as though they were present and seated in a nearby vacant chair.

Encephalitis. Inflammation of brain tissue caused by a number of agents, the most important being several viruses carried by insects.

Encephalitis lethargica. Known as sleeping sickness, a form of encephalitis which occurred earlier in this century and was characterized by lethargy and prolonged periods of sleeping.

Encopresis. A disorder in which, through faulty control of the sphincters, the person repeatedly defecates in his or her clothing after an age at which continence is expected.

Encounter group. See *sensitivity group*.

Endocrine gland. Any of a number of ductless glands which release *hormones* directly into the blood or lymph. The secretions of some endocrine glands increase during emotional arousal.

Endogenous. Attributable to internal causes.

Endogenous depression. A profound sadness assumed to be caused by a biochemical malfunction in contrast to an environmental event; more recently regarded descriptively as having a more severe set of *symptoms*. See melancholia.

Endorphins. *Opiates* produced within the body; they may have an important role in the processes by which the body builds up *tolerance* to drugs and is distressed by their withdrawal.

Enuresis. A disorder in which, through faulty control of the bladder, the person wets repeatedly during the night (nocturnal enuresis) or during the day after an age at which continence is expected.

Environmental psychology. A recent community-oriented psychology which assumes that people's feelings and behavior are an important function of their physical setting.

Enzyme. A complex protein produced by the cells to act as a catalyst in regulating metabolic activities.

Epilepsy. An altered state of consciousness accompanied by sudden changes in the usual rhythmical electrical activity of the brain. See also *grand mal, petit mal, Jacksonian,* and *psychomotor epilepsy*.

Epinephrine. A hormone (a *catecholamine*) secreted by the medulla of the *adrenal gland*; its effects are similar, but not identical, to those of stimulating the *sympathetic* nerves. It causes an increase in blood pressure, inhibits peristaltic movements, and liberates glucose from the liver. Also called *adrenalin.*

Ergot. See *LSD.*

Erogenous. Capable of giving sexual pleasure when stimulated.

Eros (libido). Freud's term for the life-integrating instinct or force of the *id,* sometimes equated with sexual drive. Compare *Thanatos.*

Essential hypertension. A *psychophysiologial disorder* characterized by high blood pressure that cannot be traced to an organic cause. Over the years it causes enlargement and degeneration of small arteries, enlargement of the heart, and kidney damage.

Estrogen. A female sex hormone produced especially in the ovaries that stimulates the development and maintains the secondary sex characteristics, such as breast enlargement.

Etiological validity. See *validity.*

Etiology. All the factors that contribute to the development of an illness or disorder.

Eugenics. The field concerned with improving the hereditary qualities of the human race through social control of mating and reproduction.

Ex post facto analysis. In *correlational research,* an attempt to reduce the *third-variable problem* by picking subjects who are matched on characteristics that may be *confounds.*

Excitement phase. As applied by Masters and Johnson, the first stage of sexual arousal which is initiated by any appropriate stimulus.

Executive functioning. The *cognitive* capacity to plan how to do a task, how to devise strategies, and how to monitor one's performance.

Exhibitionism. Marked preference for obtaining sexual gratification by exposing one's genitals to an unwilling observer.

Existential analysis. See *humanistic-existential therapy.*

Existential neurosis. A disorder in which the patient feels alienation, considers life meaningless, and finds no activity worth selecting and pursuing. See also *premorbid personality.*

Exogenous. Attributable to external causes.

Exogenous depression. A profound sadness assumed to be caused by an environmental event.

Exorcism. The casting out of evil spirits by ritualistic chanting or torture.

Experiment. The most powerful research technique for determining causal relationships, requiring the manipulation of an *independent variable,* the measurement of a *dependent variable,* and the *random assignment* of subjects to the several different conditions being investigated.

Experimental hypothesis. What the investigator assumes will happen in a scientific investigation if certain conditions are met or particular variables are manipulated.

Expressed emotion. In the literature on *schizophrenia,* the amount of hostility and criticism directed from other people to the patient, usually within a family.

External validity. See *validity.*

Extinction. The elimination of a classically *conditioned response* by the omission of the *unconditioned stimulus.* In *operant conditioning,* the elimination of the conditioned response by the omission of *reinforcement.*

Extradural hematoma. Hemorrhage and swelling between the skull and dura mater when a *meningeal* artery is ruptured by a fractured bone of the skull.

Extroversion. See *introversion-extroversion.*

Factitious disorder. A disorder in which the individual's physical or psychological symptoms appear under voluntary control and are adopted merely to assume the role of a sick person. This goal is not voluntary, however, and implies a severe disturbance. Compare with *malingering.*

Falsifiability. See *testability.*

Familiar. A supernatural spirit often embodied in an animal and at the service of a person.

Family interaction method. A procedure for studying family behavior by observing their interaction in a structured laboratory situation.

Family method. A research strategy in *behavior genetics* in which the frequency of a *trait* or of abnormal behavior is determined in relatives who have varying percentages of shared genetic background.

Family therapy. A form of *group therapy* in which members of a family are helped to relate better to one another.

Fear-drive. In the Mowrer-Miller theory, an unpleasant internal state which impels avoidance. The necessity to reduce a fear-drive can form the basis for new learning.

Fear-response. In the Mowrer-Miller theory, a response to a threatening or noxious situation which is covert and unobservable but which is assumed to function as a stimulus to produce measurable physiological changes in the body and observable overt behavior.

Fellatio. Oral stimulation of the *penis.*

Fetal alcohol syndrome. Retarded growth of the developing fetus and infant; cranial, facial, and limb anomalies, and *mental retardation* caused by heavy consumption of alcohol by the future mother during pregnancy.

Fetishism. A reliance on an inanimate object or a part of the body for sexual arousal.

First-rank symptoms. In *schizophrenia,* specific *delusions* and *hallucinations* proposed by Schneider as particularly important for its more exact diagnosis.

Fixation. In psychoanalytic theory, the arrest of *psychosexual* development at a particular stage through too much or too little gratification at that stage.

Flashback. An unpredictable recurrence of *psychedelic* experiences from an earlier drug trip.

Flat affect. A deviation in emotional response wherein virtually no emotion is expressed whatever the stimuli, emotional expressiveness is blunted, or a lack of expression and muscle tone is noted in the face.

Flight of ideas. A symptom of *mania* that involves a rapid shift from one subject to another in conversation with only superficial associative connections.

Flooding therapy. A *behavior therapy* procedure in which a fearful person exposes himself or herself to what is frightening, in reality or in the imagination, for extended periods of time and without opportunity for escape.

Follow-up study. A research procedure whereby individuals observed in an earlier investigation are contacted at a later time.

Forced-choice item. A format of a *personality inventory* in which the response alternatives for each item are equated for *social desirability.*

Forensic psychiatry or psychology. The branch of psychiatry or psychology that deals with the legal questions raised by disordered behavior.

Free association. A key psychoanalytic procedure, in which the *analysand* is encouraged to give free rein to his or her thoughts and feelings, verbalizing whatever comes into the mind without monitoring its content. The assumption is that, over time, hitherto *repressed* material will come forth for examination by the analysand and *analyst.*

Freebase. The most potent part of *cocaine,* obtained by heating the drug with ether.

Free-floating anxiety. Continual anxiety not attributable to any specific situation or reasonable danger. See *generalized anxiety disorder.*

Frontal lobe. The forward or upper half of each *cerebral hemisphere,* in front of the *central sulcus,* that is active in reasoning and other higher mental processes.

Fugue. See *psychogenic fugue.*

Functional psychosis. A condition in which thought, behavior, and emotion are disturbed without known pathological changes in tissues or the conditions of the brain.

Galvanic skin response (GSR). A change in electric conductivity of the skin caused by an increase in activity of sweat glands when the *sympathetic nervous system* is active, in particular when the organism is anxious.

Gay. A colloquial term for a homosexual, now often adopted by homosexuals who have openly announced their sexual orientation.

Gay liberation. The often militant movement seeking to achieve civil rights for homosexuals and recognition of the normality of *homosexuality*.

Gender identity. The deeply ingrained sense a person has of being either a man or a woman.

Gender identity disorders. Disorders in which there is a deeply felt incongruence between anatomic sex and the sensed gender: *transsexualism* and *gender identity disorder of childhood* are examples.

Gene. An ultramicroscopic area of the *chromosome*, the gene is the smallest physical unit of the DNA molecule that carries a piece of heredity information.

General paresis. See *neurosyphilis*.

Generalized anxiety disorder. One of the *anxiety disorders,* where anxiety is so chronic, persistent, and pervasive that it seems *free-floating*. The individual is jittery and strained, distractible and apprehensive that something bad is about to happen. A pounding heart, fast pulse and breathing, sweating, flushing, muscle aches, a lump in the throat, and an upset gastrointestinal tract are some of the bodily indications of this extreme anxiety.

Genetic disease. An abnormality determined at the moment of conception.

Genital stage. In psychoanalytic theory, the final *psychosexual stage* reached in adulthood, in which heterosexual interests predominate.

Genotype. An individual's unobservable, physiological genetic constitution; the totality of *genes* possessed by an individual. Compare *phenotype*.

Germ theory. The general view in medicine that disease is caused by infection of the body by minute organisms and viruses.

Gerontology. The interdisciplinary study of aging and of the special problems of the aged.

Gestalt therapy. A *humanistic therapy*, developed by Fritz Perls, that encourages clients to satisfy emerging needs so that their innate goodness can be expressed, to increase their awareness of unacknowledged feelings, and to reclaim parts of the personality that have been denied or disowned.

Gestation period. The length of time, normally nine months in human beings, during which a fertilized egg develops into an infant ready to be born.

Glans. The heavily innervated tip of the *penis*.

Glove anesthesia. A hysterical lack of sensation in the part of the hand that would usually be covered by a glove.

Going in drag. Dressing in female attire, usually with extensive makeup, by a male homosexual.

Grand mal epilepsy. The most severe form of *epilepsy*, involving loss of consciousness and violent *convulsions*.

Grandiosity. An inflated appraisal of one's worth, power, knowledge, importance, or identity.

Graves' disease. An endocrine disorder resulting from oversecretion of the hormone *thyroxin*, where metabolic processes are speeded up, producing apprehension, restlessness, and irritability.

Gray matter. The neural tissue made up largely of nerve cell bodies that constitutes the cortex covering the *cerebral hemisphere*, the *nuclei* in lower brain areas, columns of the spinal cord, and the ganglia of the *autonomic nervous system*.

Grimace. A distorted facial expression, often a symptom of *schizophrenia*.

Group therapy. Method of treating psychological disorders whereby several persons are seen simultaneously by a single therapist.

Gyrus. A ridge or convolution of the *cerebral cortex*.

Habituation. In physiology, a process whereby an organism's response to the same stimulus temporarily lessens with repeated presentations.

Halfway house. A homelike residence for people who are considered too disturbed to remain in their accustomed surroundings but do not require the total care of a mental institution.

Hallucination. A perception in any sensory modality without relevant and adequate external stimuli.

Hallucinogen. A drug or chemical whose effects include *hallucinations*. Hallucinogenic drugs such as *LSD, psyilocybin,* and *mescaline* are often called *psychedelic*.

Hardiness. A constellation of personality characteristics—commitment, control, and challenge—that has been linked to resistance to *stress*.

Hashish. The dried resin of the *Cannabis* plant, stronger in its effects than the dried leaves and stems which constitute *marijuana*.

Hebephrenia. See *disorganized schizophrenic*.

Helplessness. A *construct* referring to the sense of having no control over important events; considered by many theorists to play a central role in *anxiety* and *depression*. See *learned helplessness*.

Hermaphrodite. A person with parts of both male and female genitalia.

Heroin. An extremely addictive *narcotic* drug derived from *morphine*.

Heterosexual. One who desires or engages in sexual relations with members of the opposite sex.

Hidden observer. In hypnosis, the part of the self that is aware of things outside conscious awareness.

High-risk method. A research technique, used especially in the study of *schizophrenia*, involving the intensive examination of people who have a high probability of later becoming abnormal.

Histrionic personality. This person is overly dramatic and given to emotional excess, impatient with minor annoyances, immature, dependent on others, and often sexually seductive, without taking responsibility for flirtations. Formerly called hysterical personality.

Hives. A transient skin condition characterized by slightly raised, itching patches; often considered a *psychophysiological disorder*.

Homophobia. Fear of *homosexuality*.

Homosexuality. Sexual desire or activity directed toward a member of one's own sex.

Homovanillic avid. A major metabolite of *dopamine*.

Hormone. A chemical substance produced by an *endocrine gland* and released into the blood or lymph for the purpose of controlling the function of a distant organ or organ system. Metabolism, growth, and development of secondary sexual characteristics are among the functions so controlled.

Humanistic-existential therapy. *Insight* psychotherapy which emphasizes the individual's subjective experiences, free will, and ever-present ability to decide on a new life course.

Huntington's chorea. A fatal *presenile dementia*, passed on by a single *dominant gene*. The symptoms includes spasmodic jerking of the limbs, psychotic behavior, and mental deterioration.

5-Hydroxyindoleacetic acid (5-HIAA). The major metabolite of *serotonin* that is present in the cerebrospinal fluid.

Hyperactivity. A childhood disorder marked by an inability to inhibit movement and to concentrate in situations that call for it; problems in learning, in listening and finishing things, and in relating to others are also common. Called *attention-deficit disorder with hyperactivity* in DSM-III.

Hyperkinesis. See *hyperactivity.*

Hypertension. Abnormally high arterial blood pressure, with or without known organic causes. See *essential hypertension.*

Hyperventilation. Very rapid and deep breathing associated with high levels of anxiety that causes level of carbon dioxide in blood to be lowered with possible loss of consciousness.

Hypnosis. A trancelike state or behavior resembling sleep, characterized primarily by increased suggestibility and induced by suggestion.

Hypochondriasis. A *somatoform disorder* in which the person, misinterpreting rather ordinary physical sensations, is preoccupied with fears of having a serious disease and is not dissuaded by medical opinion. Difficult to distinguish from *somatization disorder.*

Hypomania. An above-normal elevation of mood, but not as extreme as *mania.*

Hypothalamus. A collection of *nuclei* and fibers in the lower part of the *diencephalon*, concerned with the regulation of many visceral processes, such as metabolism, temperature, water balance, and so on.

Hysteria (hysterical state). A disorder, known to the ancient Greeks, in which a physical incapacity, a paralysis, an anesthesia, or an analgesia, is not due to a physiological dysfunction, for example, *glove anesthesia*; an older term for *conversion disorder.* In the late nineteenth century *dissociative disorders* were identified as such and considered hysterical states.

Hysterical neurosis. The DSM-II category for *dissociative* and *somatoform disorders.*

Id. In psychoanalytic theory, that part of the personality present at birth, composed of all the energy of the *psyche* and expressed as biological urges which strive continually for gratification.

Ideas of reference. *Delusional* thinking which reads personal significance into seemingly trivial remarks and activities of others and completely unrelated events.

Idiographic. In psychology, relating to investigative procedures that consider the unique characteristics of a single person, studying them in depth, as in the *case study.* Contrast with *nomothetic.*

Idiot savant. An individual with a rare form of *mental retardation*, being extraordinarily talented in one or a few limited areas of intellectual achievement.

Illusion. A misperception of a real external stimulus, such as hearing the slapping of waves as footsteps.

Imipramine. An *antidepressant drug*, one of the *tricyclic* group.

Implosion therapy. A *behavior therapy* technique for reducing neurotic fears; the client is encouraged to imagine himself in the most frightening of situations and to visualize bizarre images, the assumption being that adult fears are traceable to *psychodynamic* themes of sex and aggression which must be confronted.

Impotence—primary. The physical or psychological condition of a male who has never had an erection sufficient for either heterosexual or homosexual intercourse. **Secondary**, inability of the male to have an erection sufficient for intercourse, although he has a history of at least one successful *intromission.* Replaced in DSM-III by *inhibited sexual excitement.*

Imprinting. The irreversible acquisition of behavior by a neonate of a social species during a *critical period* of development. The neonate is attracted to and mimics the first moving object seen, thereby acquiring specific patterns of behavior.

In absentia. Literally, "in one's absence." Courts are concerned that a person be able to participate personally and meaningfully in his or her own trial and not be tried *in absentia* because of a distracting mental disorder.

In vivo. As applied in psychology, taking place in a real-life situation.

Inappropriate affect. Emotional responses which are out of context, such as laughter when hearing sad news.

Incest. Sexual relations between close relatives for whom marriage is forbidden, most often between daughter and father or between brother and sister.

Incidence. In community studies of a particular disorder, the rate at which new cases occur in a given place at a given time; compare with *prevalence.*

Incoherence. In *schizophrenia*, an aspect of *thought disorder* wherein verbal expression is marked by disconnectedness, fragmented thoughts, jumbled phrases, and *neologisms.*

Independent variable. In a psychological *experiment*, the factor, experience, or treatment which is under the control of the experimenter and which is expected to have an effect on the subjects as assessed by changes in the *dependent variable.*

Index case. The person who in a genetic investigation bears the diagnosis or *trait* that the investigator is interested in: same as *proband.*

Indoleamines. *Monoamine* compounds (NH_2), each containing an indole portion (C_8H_7N); indoleamines believed to act in neurotransmission are *serotonin* and tryptamine.

Infantile autism. A childhood disorder marked by early and profound aloneless, a hedged inner world fended from all encroachments; *mutism* or *echolalic* speech; and intolerance of any change in routine or surroundings.

Infectious disease. An illness caused when a microorganism, such as a bacterium or a virus, invades the body, multiplies, and attacks a specific organ or organ system; pneumonia is an example.

Informed consent. The agreement of a person to serve as a research subject or to enter therapy after being told the possible outcomes, both benefits and risks.

Inhibited female orgasm. A recurrent and persistent delay or absence of orgasm in a woman during sexual activity adequate in focus, intensity, and duration; in many instances the woman may experience considerable sexual excitement nonetheless.

Inhibited male orgasm. A recurrent and persistent delay or absence of ejaculation after an adequate phase of sexual excitement.

Inhibited sexual desire. Sexual interest that is less than the individual, the partner, or both regard as sufficient.

Inhibited sexual excitement. A recurrent and persistent lack of sexual excitement during sexual activity. The new term for *impotence* in men, frigidity in women. See also *inhibited female orgasm.*

Insanity defense. The legal argument that a defendant should not be held *ascriptively responsible* for an illegal act if the conduct is attributable to mental illness.

Insight therapy. The general term for any *psychotherapy* that attempts to impart greater awareness to a patient of what motivates his or her behavior, the assumption being that disordered behavior is caused by *repression* or other unconscious *conflicts.*

Instrumental learning. See *operant conditioning.*

Intelligence quotient (IQ). A standardized measure indicating how far an individual's raw score on an *intelligence test* falls away from the average raw score of his or her chronological age group.

Intelligence test. A standardized means of assessing a person's current mental ability, for example, the Stanford-Binet test and the Wechsler Adult Intelligence Scale.

Internal validity. See *validity.*

Interpretation. In *psychoanalysis*, a key procedure in which the *ana-*

lyst points out to the *analysand* where *resistances* exist and what certain dreams and verbalizations reveal about impulses repressed in the *unconscious*; more generally, any statement by a therapist that construes the client's problem in a new way.

Introjection. In psychoanalytic theory, the unconscious incorporation of the values, attitudes, and qualities of another person into the individual's own ego structure.

Intromission. Insertion of *penis* into *vagina* or anus.

Introspective method. A procedure whereby trained subjects are asked to report on their conscious experiences. This was the principal method of study in early twentieth-century psychology.

Introversion-extroversion. In Eysenck's theory of personality, a dimension referring for the most part to conditionability. Extroverts are said to acquire *conditioned* responses slowly and lose them rapidly, while the reverse is true of introverts.

Involutional melancholia. An *affective disorder* characterized by profound sadness and occurring at a person's *climacteric* in late middle age; a DSM-II diagnosis that does not appear in DSM-III.

Irrational beliefs. Self-defeating assumptions which are assumed by *rational-emotive* therapists to underlie psychological distress.

Irresistible impulse. The term used in an 1834 Ohio court ruling on criminal responsibility in which it was decided that an *insanity defense* can be established by proving that the accused had an uncontrollable urge to perform the act.

Jacksonian epilepsy. A form of *epilepsy* in which muscle spasms are limited to a particular part of the body.

Juvenile paresis. A form of syphilis which is congenital and is similar to the adult disorder; the onset of deterioration is at twelve to fourteen years after a symptom-free childhood.

Klinefelter's syndrome. A disorder of males in which an extra X *chromosome* usually keeps the testes small at puberty. It may produce *mental retardation* and may cause secondary female sex characteristics to develop.

Korsakoff's psychosis. A chronic brain disorder associated with *Wernicke's disease* marked by loss of recent memories and associated *confabulation*, and by additional lesions in the *thalamus*.

La belle indifférence. The blasé attitude people with *conversion disorder* have toward their symptoms.

Labile. Easily moved or changed, quickly shifting from one emotion to another or easily aroused.

Laceration. A jagged wound; in the brain, a tearing of tissue by an object entering the skull, often causing paralysis, change in personality, intellectual impairment, and even death.

Latency period. In psychoanalytic theory, the years between ages six and twelve during which *id* impulses play a minor role in motivation.

Lateral sulcus. A major horizontal fissure along the side of each *cerebral hemisphere*, separating the *frontal* and *parietal lobes* from the *temporal lobe*.

Learned helplessness. An individual's passivity and sense of being unable to act and to control his or her life, acquired through unpleasant experiences and traumas in which efforts made were ineffective; according to Seligman, this brings on *depression*.

Learning disabilities. Problems in mastering reading, arithmetic, or speech that are not caused by *mental retardation*, impairment of visual or auditory functions, other psychological disorders, or cultural disadvantage. Called *specific developmental disorders* in DSM-III.

Learning paradigm. As applied in abnormal psychology, a set of assumptions that abnormal behavior is learned in the same way as other human behavior.

Least restrictive alternative. The legal principle according to which a committed mental patient must be treated in a setting that imposes as few restrictions as possible on his or her freedom.

Lesbian. Female homosexual.

Lesion. Any localized abnormal structural change in organ or tissue caused by disease or injury.

Libido. See *Eros*.

Life Change Unit (LCU) **score.** A score produced by totaling ratings of the stressfulness of recently experienced life events; high scores are found to be related to the contracting of a number of physical illnesses.

Limbic system. The lower parts of the *cerebrum* made up of primitive cortex that controls visceral and bodily changes associated with emotion and regulates drive-motivated behavior.

Lithium carbonate. A drug useful in treating both *mania* and *depression* in *bipolar disorder*.

Lobotomy. A brain operation in which the nerve pathways between the *frontal lobes* of the brain and the *thalamus* and *hypothalamus* are cut in hopes of effecting beneficial behavioral change.

Logotherapy. Existential *psychotherapy* developed by Viktor Frankl, aimed at helping the demoralized client restore meaning to life by placing his or her suffering in a larger spiritual and philosophical context. The individual assumes responsibility for his or her existence and for pursuing the values inherent in life.

Longitudinal research. Investigation which collects information on the same individuals repeatedly over time, perhaps many years, in an effort to determine how phenomena change. Compare with *cross-sectional research*.

Long-term memory. The part of our capacity to remember things that is virtually permanent and depends on coding and retrieval strategies.

Loose association. In *schizophrenia*, an aspect of *thought disorder* wherein the patient has difficulty sticking to one topic and drifts off on a train of associations evoked by an idea from the past.

LSD (*d*-lysergic acid diethylamide). A drug synthesized in 1938 and discovered to be a *hallucinogen* in 1943. It is derived from lysergic acid, the principal constituent of the *aklaloids* of ergot, a grain fungus which in earlier centuries brought on epidemics of spasmodic ergotism, a nervous disorder sometimes marked by *psychotic* symptoms.

Luria-Nebraska test. A battery of *neuropsychological* tests that can detect impairment in different parts of the brain.

Magical thinking. The conviction of the individual that his or her thoughts, words, and actions may in some manner cause or prevent outcomes in a way that defies the normal laws of cause and effect.

Mainstreaming. A policy of placing handicapped children in regular classrooms; special classes are provided for them as needed, but they share as much as possible in the opportunities and ambience afforded normal youngsters.

Major depression. A disorder of individuals who have experienced episodes of *depression* but not of *mania*; DSM-III term. Also called *unipolar depression*.

Malingering. Faking a physical or psychological incapacity in order to avoid a responsibility or gain an end; the goal is readily recognized from the individual's circumstances. To be distinguished from *conversion disorder*, in which the incapacity is assumed to be beyond voluntary control.

Malleus Maleficarum ("the witches' hammer"). A manual written by two Dominican monks in the fifteenth century to provide rules for identifying and trying witches.

Mammillary body. Either of two small rounded structures located in the *hypothalamus* and consisting of *nuclei*.

Mania. An emotional state of intense but unfounded elation evidenced in talkativeness, *flight of ideas* and distractibility, in grandiose plans, and spurts of purposeless activity. Called *bipolar disorder* in DSM-III.

Manic-depressive illness, manic-depressive psychosis. Originally described by Kraepelin, an *affective disorder* characterized by alternating moods of euphoria and profound sadness or by one of these moods. Called *bipolar disorder* in DSM-III.

Marathon group. A group session run continuously for a day or even longer, typically for *sensitivity training*, the assumption being that defenses can be worn down by the physical and psychological fatigue generated through intensive and continuous group interaction.

Marijuana. A drug derived from the dried and ground leaves and stems of the female hemp plant, *Cannabis sativa*.

Marital therapy. Any professional intervention which treats relationship problems of a couple.

Masochism. A marked preference for obtaining or increasing sexual gratification through subjection to pain.

Masturbation. Self-stimulation of the genitals, typically to *orgasm*.

M'Naghten rule. A British court decision of 1843 which stated that an *insanity defense* can be established by proving that the defendant did not know what he was doing or did not realize that it was wrong.

Mediation theory. In psychology, the general view that certain stimuli do not directly initiate an overt response but activate an intervening process, which in turn initiates the response. It explains thinking, drives, emotions, and beliefs in terms of stimulus and response.

Mediator. In psychology, an inferred state intervening between the observable stimulus and response, being activated by the stimulus and in turn initiating the response; in more general terms, a thought, drive, emotion, or belief. Also called a *construct*.

Medical model (disease model). As applied in abnormal psychology, a set of assumptions that conceptualizes abnormal behavior as being similar to physical diseases.

Medulla oblongata. An area in the *brainstem* through which nerve fiber tracts ascend to or descend from higher brain centers.

Megalomania. A paranoid *delusion* of *grandeur* in which an individual believes himself to be an important person or to be carrying out great plans.

Melancholia. A vernacular diagnosis of several millenniums' standing for profound sadness and depression. In *major depression* with melancholia the individual is unable to feel better even momentarily when something good happens, regularly feels worse in the morning and awakens early, and suffers a deepening of other symptoms of depression.

Meninges. The three layers of nonneural tissue that envelop the brain and spinal cord. They are the dura mater, the arachnoid, and the pia mater.

Meningitis. An inflammation of the *meninges* through infection, usually by a bacterium, or through irritation. **Meningococcal**, the epidemic form of the disease caused by *Neisseria meningitidis*, takes the life of 10 percent who contract it and causes cerebral palsy, hearing loss, speech defects, and other forms of permanent brain damage in one of four who recover.

Mental age. The numerical index of an individual's cognitive development determined by standardized *intelligence tests*.

Mental retardation. Subnormal intellectual functioning associated with impairment in social adjustment and beginning before age eighteen, usually long before.

Meprobamate. Generic term for *Miltown*, a minor *tranquilizer*, the first introduced and for a time one of the most widely used.

Mescaline. A *hallucinogen* and *alakloid* that is the active ingredient of *peyote*.

Mesmerize. The first term for hypnotize, after Franz Anton Mesmer, an Austrian physician who in the late eighteenth century treated, and cured, hysterical or *conversion disorders* by what he considered the animal magnetism emanating from his body and permeating the universe.

Metabolism. The sum of the intracellular processes by which large molecules are broken down into smaller ones, releasing energy and wastes, and by which small molecules are built up into new living matter by consuming energy.

Metacognition. The knowledge people have about the way they know their world, such as recognizing the usefulness of a map if one has to find one's way in a new city.

Methadone. A synthetic addictive *narcotic* for treating *heroin* addicts that acts as a substitute for heroin by eliminating its effects and the craving for it.

Methedrine. A very strong *amphetamine*, sometimes shot directly into the veins.

3-Methoxy-4-hydroxyphenylethylene glycol (MHPG). A major metabolite of *norepinephrine*.

Midbrain. The middle part of the brain which consists of a mass of nerve fiber tracts connecting the spinal cord and *pons, medulla,* and *cerebellum* to the *cerebral cortex*.

Migraine headache. Extremely debilitating headache caused by sustained dilation of the extracranial arteries, the temporal artery in particular; the dilated arteries trigger pain-sensitive nerve fibers in the scalp.

Mild mental retardation. A limitation in mental development measured on IQ tests at between 50 and 70; children with such a limitation are considered the educable mentally retarded and are placed in special classes.

Milieu therapy. A treatment procedure that attempts to make the total environment and all personnel and patients of the hospital a *therapeutic community*, conducive to psychological improvement; the staff conveys to the patients the expectation that they can and will behave more normally and responsibly.

Miltown. The trade name for *meprobamate*, one of the principal *minor tranquilizers*.

Minimal brain damage. The term sometimes applied to *hyperactive* children, reflecting the belief that at least some of these youngsters suffer from minor brain defects.

Minnesota Multiphasic Personality Inventory (MMPI). A lengthy *personality inventory* by which an individual is diagnosed through his true–false replies to groups of statements indicating states such as *anxiety, depression,* masculinity–femininity, and paranoia.

Minor tranquilizer. A drug which reduces moderate to low levels of *anxiety*; most often used with anxiety disorder.

Mirroring. A *psychodrama* technique in which an individual sees himself portrayed by another person, thereby acquiring a better idea of how he is viewed by others.

Mixed design. A research strategy in which both *classificatory* and *experimental* variables are used; assigning subjects from discrete populations to two experimental conditions is an example.

Model. A set of concepts from one domain applied to another by analogy. For example, in trying to understand the brain we may assume that it functions like a computer.

Modeling. Learning by observing and imitating the behavior of others.

Moderate mental retardation. A limitation in mental development measured on IQ tests between 35 and 49; children with this degree of retardation are often institutionalized, and their training is focused on self-care rather than development of intellectual skills.

Mongolism. See *Down's syndrome*.

Monism. Philosophical doctrine that ultimate reality is a unitary organic whole and that therefore mental and physical are one and the same. Contrast with *dualism*.

Monoamine. An organic compound containing nitrogen in one amino group (NH_2). Some of the known *neurotransmitters* of the central nervous system, called collectively brain amines, are *catecholamines* and *indoleamines*, which are monoamines.

Monoamine oxidase (MAO). An enzyme that deactivates *catecholamines* and *indoleamines* within the presynaptic *neuron*, indoleamines in the *synapse*.

Monoamine oxidase inhibitors. A group of *antidepressant* drugs that keep the enzyme *monoamine oxidase* from deactivating *neurotrans-*

mitters of the central nervous system. With more *norepinephrine* and *serotonin* available in the *synapse*, mood is elevated

Monozygotic twins. Genetically identical siblings who have developed from a single fertilized egg.

Moral anxiety. In psychoanalytic theory, the *ego's* fear of punishment for failure to adhere to the *superego's* standards of proper conduct.

Moral treatment. A therapeutic regimen, introduced by Philippe Pinel during the French Revolution, whereby mental patients were released from their restraints and were treated with compassion and dignity rather than with contempt and denigration . *Milieu therapy* gives patients similar encouraging attention.

Morbidity risk. The probability that an individual will develop a particular disorder.

Morphine. An addictive narcotic *alkaloid* extracted from *opium*, used primarily as an analgesic and as a *sedative*.

Mourning work. In Freud's theory of *depression*, the recall by a depressed person of memories associated with a lost one, serving to separate the individual from the deceased.

Multiaxial. Having several dimensions, each of which is employed in categorizing; the DSM-III is an example.

Multifactorial. Referring to the operation of several variables influencing in complex fashion the development or maintenance of a phenomenon.

Multiple-baseline design. An experimental design in which two behaviors of a single subject are selected for study and a treatment is applied to one of them. The behavior that is not treated serves as a baseline against which the effects of the treatment can be determined. This is a common design in operant research.

Multiple personality. A very rare *dissociative disorder* in which two or more fairly distinct and separate personalities are present within the same individual, each of them with its own memories, relationships, and behavior patterns and only one of them dominant at any given time.

Mutism. The inability or refusal to speak.

Myxedema. An endocrine disorder of adults produced by thyroid deficiency; metabolic processes are slowed, and the patient becomes lethargic, slow-thinking and depressed.

Narcissistic personality. Extremely selfish and self-centered, people with a narcissistic personality have a grandiose view of their uniqueness, achievements, and talents and an insatiable craving for admiration and approval from others. They are exploitative to achieve their own goals and expect much more from others than they themselves are willing to give.

Narcosynthesis. A psychiatric procedure originating during World War II in which a drug was employed to help stressed soldiers recall the battle trauma underlying their disorder.

Narcotic. One of the addictive *sedative* drugs, for example, *morphine* and *heroin*, that in moderate doses relieve pain and induce sleep.

Negative symptoms. In *schizophrenia*, these are behavioral deficits such as *flat affect* and *apathy*.

Negativism. A tendency to behave in a manner opposite to the desires of others or to what is expected or requested.

Neo-Freudian. A person who has contributed to the modification and extension of Freudian theory.

Neologism. A word made up by the speaker that is usually meaningless to a listener.

Neoplasm. See *tumor*.

Neurodermatitis. A chronic (*psychophysiological*) disorder in which patches of skin become inflamed.

Neuroleptic. A *psychoactive drug*, such as *Thorazine*, that reduces *psychotic* symptoms but has side effects resembling symptoms of neurological diseases.

Neurology. The scientific study of the nervous system, especially its structure, functions, and abnormalities.

Neuron. A single nerve cell.

Neuropsychology. A psychological specialty concerned with the relationships among cognition, affect, and behavior on the one hand, and brain function on the other.

Neurosis. One of a large group of nonpsychotic disorders characterized by unrealistic *anxiety* and other associated problems, for example, phobic avoidances, *obsessions*, and *compulsions*.

Neurosyphilis (general paresis). Infection of the central nervous system by the spirochete *Treponema pallidum*, that destroys brain tissue; marked by eye disturbances, tremors, and disordered speech as well as severe intellectual deterioration and *psychotic* symptoms.

Neurotic anxiety. In psychoanalytic theory, a fear of the consequences of expressing previously punished and repressed id impulses; more generally, unrealistic fear.

Neuroticism. In Eysenck's theory of personality, a dimension referring to the ease with which people can become autonomically aroused.

Neurotransmitter. A chemical substance important in transferring a nerve impulse from one *neuron* to another.

Niacin. One of the complex of B vitamins.

Nicotine. The principal *alkaloid* of tobacco and its addicting agent.

Niemann-Pick disease. An inherited disorder of lipid (fat) metabolism that produces *mental retardation*, paralysis and brings early death.

Nomothetic. Relating to the abstract, recurrent, universal, to the formulation of general laws that explain a range of phenomena. Contrast with *idiographic*.

Nomenclature. A system or set of names or designations used in a particular discipline, such as the DSM-III.

Norepinephrine. A *catecholamine* that is a *neurotransmitter* of the central nervous system. Disturbances in its tracts apparently figure in *depression* and *mania*. It is also a neurotransmitter secreted at the nerve endings of the *sympathetic nervous system*, a hormone, liberated with *epinephrine* in the adrenal medulla and similar to it in action, and a strong vasoconstrictor.

Normal curve. As applied in psychology, the bell-shaped distribution of a measurable *trait* depicting most people in the middle and few at the extremes.

Nosology. A systematic classification of diseases.

Nucleus. In anatomy, a mass of nerve cell bodies (*gray matter*) within the brain or spinal cord by which descending nerve fibers connect with ascending nerve fibers.

Object choice. In the psychology of sex, the type of person or thing selected as a focus for sexual activity.

Objective anxiety. In psychoanalytic theory, the *ego's* reaction to danger in the external world; the same as realistic fear.

Observer drift. The tendency of two raters of behavior to begin to agree with each other, achieving unusually high levels of *reliability*; their way of coding behavior differentiates their scores from those of another pair of raters. This is regarded as a threat to reliable and valid *behavioral assessment*.

Obsession. An intrusive and recurring thought that seems irrational and uncontrollable to the person experiencing it.

Obsessive-compulsive disorder. An *anxiety disorder* in which the mind is flooded with persistent and uncontrollable thoughts or the individual is compelled to repeat certain acts again and again, causing significant distress and interference with everyday functioning.

Occipital lobe. The posterior area of each *cerebral hemisphere*, situated behind the *parietal* and above the *temporal lobes* that is responsible for reception and analysis of visual information and for some visual memory.

Occupational drinking. The considerable consumption of alcohol that is associated with particular vocations, very often on the job, such as the uncommonly heavy drinking of bartenders.

Oedipus complex. In Freudian theory, the desire and conflict of the four-year-old male child who wants to possess his mother sexually and to eliminate the father rival. The threat of punishment from the father makes the boy *repress* these id impulses. Girls have a similar sexual desire for the father, which is repressed in analogous fashion and is called the **Electra complex.**

Operant behavior. A response that is supposedly voluntary and operates on the environment, modifying it so that a reward or goal is attained.

Operant conditioning. The acquisition or elimination of a response as a function of the environmental contingencies of *reward* and *punishment.*

Operational definition. A definition of a theoretical concept that equates it with a set of observable operations that can be measured.

Operationism. A school of thought in science that holds that a given concept must be defined in terms of a single set of identifiable and repeatable operations that can be measured.

Opium. The dried milky juice obtained from the immature fruit of the opium poppy. This addictive *narcotic* produces euphoria and drowsiness and reduces pain.

Oral stage. In psychoanalytic theory, the first *psychosexual stage* that extends into the second year, during which the mouth is the principal *erogenous zone.*

Organic brain syndrome. A mental disorder in which intellectual or emotional functioning or both are impaired through a *pathology* or dysfunction of the brain.

Organismic variable. The physiological or psychological factor assumed to be operating ''under the skin''; these variables are one of the foci of *behavioral assessment.*

Orgasm (climax). The involuntary, intensely pleasurable, climactic phase in sexual arousal that lasts a number of seconds and usually involves muscular contractions and *ejaculation* in the male and similar contractions in the genitalia of the female.

Orgasmic reorientation. A *behavior therapy* technique for altering classes of stimuli to which people are sexually attracted; individuals are confronted by a conventionally arousing stimulus while experiencing *orgasm* for another, undesirable reason.

Outcome research. Research on the effectiveness of *psychotherapy.* Contrast with *process research.*

Overcontrolled. In reference to childhood disorders, problems that create distress for the child, such as *anxiety* and *social withdrawal.*

Paired-associate learning. Memorizing words in pairs.

Panic disorder. An *anxiety disorder* in which the individual has sudden and inexplicable attacks of jarring symptoms, such as difficulty breathing, heart palpitations, dizziness, trembling, terror, and feelings of impending doom.

Paradigm. A set of basic assumptions that outline the universe of scientific inquiry, specifying both the concepts regarded as legitimate and the methods to be used in collecting and interpreting data.

Paradigm clash. The conflict created when a basically different set of assumptions threatens to replace a prevailing *paradigm,* for example, *behaviorism's* rejection of the *unconscious* as proposed by *psychoanalysis.*

Paralinguistic. Relating to audible components of speech, such as tone of voice, that communicate meaning beyond the content of the words spoken.

Paranoia. The general term for *delusions* of persecution, *grandiosity,* or both; found in several pathological conditions, *paranoid disorders, paranoid schizophrenia,* and *paranoid personality* disorder. Can be produced as well by large doses of certain drugs, such as *cocaine* and *alcohol.*

Paranoid disorder. A disorder in which the individual has persistent persecutory *delusions* or *delusional jealousy*—an unfounded conviction

that his or her mate is unfaithful—is very often contentious, but has no *thought disorder* and does not *hallucinate.*

Paranoid personality. This person, expecting to be mistreated by others, becomes suspicious, secretive, jealous, and argumentative. He or she will not accept blame and appears cold and unemotional.

Paranoid schizophrenic. A *psychotic* patient who has numerous systematized *delusions* as well as *hallucinations* and *ideas of reference.* He or she may also be agitated, angry, argumentative, and sometimes violent.

Paraphilias. Sexual attraction to unusual objects and sexual activities unusual in nature.

Paraphrenia. Term frequently used to refer to *schizophrenia* in an older adult.

Paraprofessional. In clinical psychology, an individual lacking a doctoral degree but trained to perform certain functions usually reserved for clinicians, for example, a college student trained and supervised by a behavioral therapist to shape the behavior of *autistic* children through contingent reinforcers.

Parasympathetic nervous system. The division of the *autonomic nervous system* that is involved with maintenance; it controls many of the internal organs and is active primarily when the organism is not aroused.

Parataxic distortion. According to Harry Stack Sullivan, an unconscious misperception of reality stemming from a childhood disorganization in interpersonal relationships and extended to all later relationships.

Paresthesia. *Conversion disorder* marked by a sensation of tingling or creeping on the skin.

Parietal lobe. The middle division of each *cerebral hemisphere,* situated behind the *central sulcus;* above the *lateral sulcus;* is the receiving center for sensations of the skin and of bodily positions.

Parkinson's disease. A *presenile dementia* characterized by uncontrollable and severe muscle tremors, a stiff gait, a masklike, expressionless face, and withdrawal.

Passive-aggressive personality. People with a passive-aggressive personality indirectly resist the demands of others by such exasperating behavior as being late, missing appointments, not answering calls, and making foolish mistakes; their dawdling is considered a hostile way to control others without assuming responsibility for their own anger.

Pathology. The anatomical, physiological, and psychological deviations of a disease or disorder, and the study of these abnormalities.

PCP. See *phencyclidine.*

Pearson product moment correlation coefficient (r). A statistic, ranging in value from -1.00 to $+1.00$; the most common means of denoting a correlational relationship. The sign indicates whether the relationship is positive or negative and the magnitude indicates the strength of the relationship.

Pedophilia. A preference for obtaining sexual gratification through contact with youngsters defined legally as underage; one of the *paraphilias.*

Penile plethysmograph. A device for detecting blood flow and thus for recording changes in size of the *penis.*

Penis. The male organ of copulation.

Pepsinogen. The substance secreted by the peptic cells of the gastric glands in the stomach; if amounts are excessive, it can contribute to the development of an *ulcer.*

Perseveration. The persistent repetition of words and ideas, often found in *schizophrenics.*

Personality disorders. A heterogeneous group of disorders, listed separately on axis II, that are regarded as long-standing, inflexible, and maladaptive traits which impair social and occupational functioning but not contact with reality.

Personality inventory. A self-report questionnaire by which an examinee indicates whether statements assessing habitual tendencies apply to him or her.

Personality structure. See *trait*.

PET Scan. Computer-assisted motion pictures of the living brain, created by analysis of radioactive particles from isotopes injected into the bloodstream.

Petit mal epilepsy. A form of *epilepsy* involving a momentary alteration in consciousness, more frequent in children than adults.

Peyote. A *hallucinogen* obtained from the root of the peyote cactus, the active ingredient being the *alkaloid mescaline*.

Phallic stage. In psychoanalytic theory, the third *psychosexual stage*, extending from ages three to six, during which maximal gratification is obtained from genital stimulation.

Phencyclidine. Also known as PCP, angel dust, PeaCE Pill, zombie, and other street names. This very powerful and hazardous drug causes profound disorientation, agitated and often violent behavior, and even seizures, coma, and death.

Phenomenology. As applied in psychology, the philosophical view that the phenomena of subjective experience should be studied because behavior is considered to be determined by how people perceive themselves and the world rather than by objectively described reality.

Phenothiazine. The class name for a group of nonaddictive drugs that relieve psychotic symptoms and are considered *neuroleptics*; their molecular structure, like that of the *tricyclic drugs*, consists of three fused rings.

Phenotype. The totality of observable characteristics of a person. Compare with *genotype*.

Phenylketonuria (PKU). A genetic disorder that, through a deficiency in a liver enzyme, phenylalanine hydroxylase, causes severe *mental retardation* unless phenylalanine can be largely restricted from diet until the age of six.

Phillips Scale. A series of questions that is filled out by the researcher from the case history of a schizophrenic and is used to assess his *premorbid adjustment*.

Phobic disorder. An *anxiety disorder* in which there is intense fear and avoidance of specific objects and situations, recognized as irrational by the individuals.

Physiological paradigm. A broad theoretical point of view holding that mental disorders are caused by aberrant *somatic* processes.

Physiology. The study of the functions and activities of living cells, tissues, and organs and of the physical and chemical phenomena involved.

Pick's disease. A *presenile dementia* involving diffuse atrophy of *frontal* and *temporal lobes*, which impairs memory, concentration, and ability to think abstractly and eventually results in *psychosis* and death.

Placebo. Any therapy or inactive chemical agent, or any attribute or component of such a therapy or chemical, that affects a person's behavior for reasons having to do with his or her expectation of change.

Placebo effect. The action of a drug or psychological treatment that is not attributable to any specific operations of the agent. For example, a tranquilizer can reduce anxiety both because of its special biochemical action and because the recipient expects relief. See *placebo*.

Plateau phase. According to Masters and Johnson, the second stage in sexual arousal during which excitement and tension have reached a stable high level before *orgasm*.

Play therapy. The use of play as a means of uncovering what is troubling a child and of establishing *rapport*.

Pleasure principle. In psychoanalytic theory, the demanding manner by which the *id* operates, seeking immediate gratification of its needs.

Plethysmograph. An instrument for determining and registering variations in the amount of blood present or passing through an organ.

Polydrug abuse. The misuse of more than one drug at a time, such as drinking heavily and taking heroin.

Pons. An area in the *brainstem* containing nerve fiber tracts connecting the *cerebellum* with the spinal cord and with motor areas of the *cerebrum*.

Positive spikes. An EEG pattern recorded from the *temporal lobe* of the brain, with frequencies of 6 to 8 cps and 14 to 16 cps that is often found in impulsive and aggressive people.

Positive symptoms. In *schizophrenia*, behavioral excesses such as *hallucinations* and bizarre behavior. Compare with *negative symptoms*.

Posttraumatic stress disorder. An *anxiety disorder* in which a particularly stressful event, such as military combat or a natural disaster, brings in its aftermath intrusive reexperiencings of the trauma, a numbing of responsiveness to the outside world, estrangement from others, a tendency to be easily startled, nightmares, recurrent dreams, and otherwise disturbed sleep.

Predictive validity. See *validity*.

Predisposition. An inclination or *diathesis* to respond in a certain way, either inborn or acquired; in abnormal psychology, a factor which lowers the ability to withstand stress and inclines the individual toward *pathology*.

Premature ejaculation. Inability of the male to inhibit his *orgasm* long enough for mutually satisfying sexual relations.

Premorbid adjustment. In research on *schizophrenia*, the social and sexual adjustment of the individual before the onset or diagnosis of his symptoms. Patients with good premorbid adjustment are those found to have been relatively normal earlier, but those with poor premorbid adjustment had inadequate interpersonal and sexual relations.

Premorbid personality. Maddi's term for a person who plays social roles well and satisfies his or her biological needs and yet has a feeling of emptiness and lack of fulfillment, thus regarded as a candidate for *existential neurosis*.

Preparedness. In *classical conditioning* theory, a biological *predisposition* to be especially sensitive to particular stimuli and to associate them readily with the *unconditioned stimulus*.

Presenile dementia. An often progressive mental deterioration occurring when the individual is in his or her forties or fifties.

Prevalence. In community studies of a disorder, the percent of a population that has it at a given time. Compare with *incidence*.

Prevention. **Primary**, efforts in *community psychology* to reduce the incidence of new cases of psychological disorder by such means as altering stressful living conditions and genetic counseling. **Secondary**, efforts to detect disorders early, so that they will not develop into full-blown, perhaps chronic disabilities. **Tertiary**, efforts to reduce the long-term consequences of having a disorder, equivalent in most respects to therapy.

Primary empathy. A form of *empathy* in which the therapist understands the content and feeling of what the client is saying and expressing from the client's *phenomenological* point of view. Compare with *advanced accurate empathy*.

Primary impotence. See *impotence*.

Primary narcissism. In psychoanalytic theory, the part of the *oral* stage of *psychosexual* development during which the ego has not yet differentiated from the *id*.

Primary process. In psychoanalytic theory, one of the *id's* means of reducing tension, by imagining what it desires.

Privileged communication. The communication between parties in a confidential relation that is protected by statute. A spouse, doctor, lawyer, pastor, psychologist, or psychiatrist cannot be forced, except under unusual cimcumstances, to disclose such information.

Proband. The person who in a genetic investigation bears the diagnosis or *trait* that the investigator is interested in; the same as *index case*.

Process-reactive. A dimension used to distinguish schizophrenics; process schizophrenics suffer long-term and gradual deterioration before the onset of their illness, whereas reactive schizophrenics have a better premorbid history prior to a more rapid onset of symptoms. See *premorbid adjustment.*

Process research. Research on the psychological mechanisms by which a therapy may bring improvement. Compare with *outcome research.*

Profound mental retardation. A limitation in mental development measured on IQ tests at less than 20; children with this degree of retardation require total supervision of all their activities.

Progestins. Steroid progestational hormones that are regarded as the biological precursors of androgens, the male sex hormones.

Prognosis. A prediction of the likely course and outcome of an illness.

Projection. A *defense mechanism* whereby characteristics or desires unacceptable to the *ego* are attributed to someone else.

Projective test. A psychological assessment device employing a set of standard but vague stimuli on the assumption that unstructured material will allow unconscious motivations and fears to be uncovered. The Rorschach series of inkblots is an example.

Pronoun reversal. A speech problem in which the child refers to himself as ''he'' or ''you'' and uses ''I'' or ''me'' in referring to others; often found in the speech of children with *infantile autism.*

Pseudocommunity. An illusory world built up by a *paranoid* person, dominated by false beliefs that are not properly verified and shared by others.

Psilocybin. A *psychedelic* drug extracted from the mushroom *Psilocybe mexicana.*

Psyche. The soul, spirit, or mind as distinguished from the body. In psychoanalytic theory, it is the totality of the *id, ego,* and *superego* including both conscious and unconscious components.

Psychedelic. A drug that expands consciousness. See also *hallucinogen.*

Psychiatrist. A physician (M.D. degree) who has taken specialized postdoctoral training, called a residency, in the diagnosis, treatment, and prevention of mental and emotional disorders.

Psychoactive drug. A chemical compound having a psychological effect that alters mood or thought process. A *tranquilizer* is an example.

Psychoanalysis. A term applied primarily to the therapy procedures pioneered by Freud, entailing *free association, dream interpretation*, and *working through* the *transference neurosis.* More recently the term has come to encompass the numerous variations on basic Freudian therapy.

Psychoanalyst (analyst). A therapist who has taken specialized postdoctoral training in psychoanalysis after earning either an M.D. or a Ph.D.

Psychodrama. A kind of group psychotherapy, introduced by Moreno, in which patients play out, in theatrical settings, their feelings toward important figures and situations in their lives.

Psychodynamic. In psychoanalytic theory, it relates to the mental and emotional forces and processes that develop in early childhood and their effects on behavior and mental states.

Psychogenesis. Development from psychological origins as distinguished from somatic origins. Contrast with *somatogenesis.*

Psychogenic amnesia. A *dissociative disorder* in which the person suddenly becomes unable to recall important personal information, to an extent that cannot be explained by ordinary forgetfulness.

Psychogenic fugue. A *dissociative disorder* in which the person, totally amnesic and unable to recall the past, suddenly moves to a new location and assumes a new identity.

Psychogenic pain disorder. A *somatoform disorder* in which the person complains of severe and prolonged pain that is not accounted for by organic pathology; it does follow stress or permits the patient to avoid a hated activity or to gain attention and sympathy.

Psychologial autopsy. The analysis of an individual's *suicide* through the examination of his letters and through interviews with friends and relatives in the hope of discovering why he or she committed suicide.

Psychological deficit. The term used to indicate that performance of a pertinent psychological process is below that expected of a normal person.

Psychological dependency. The term sometimes applied to the reason for *substance abuse*; the reliance on a drug because its effects make stressful situations more bearable, without physiological addiction to it.

Psychological test. A standardized procedure designed to measure a subject's performance of a particular task or to assess his or her personality.

Psychomotor epilepsy. A form of epileptic seizure in which the individual loses contact with the environment but appears conscious and performs some routine, repetitive act or engages in more complex activity.

Psychopath. See *antisocial personality.*

Psychopathologist. A mental health professional who conducts research into the nature and development of mental and emotional disorders; their academic backgrounds can differ, some having been trained as experimental psychologists, others as psychiatrists, and still others as biochemists.

Psychophysiological disorder. A disorder with physical symptoms that may involve actual tissue damage, usually in one organ system, and that are produced in part by continued mobilization of the *autonomic nervous system* under stress. *Hives* and *ulcers* are examples. No longer listed in DSM-III in a separate category, such disorders are now diagnosed on axis I as psychological factor influencing a physical condition; on axis III the specific physical condition is given.

Psychophysiology. The discipline concerned with the bodily changes that accompany psychological events.

Psychosexual disorders. Disorders of sexual functioning in which psychological factors are assumed to be of major etiological significance: *gender identity disorders, paraphilias,* and *psychosexual dysfunctions.*

Psychosexual dysfunctions. Dysfunctions in which the appetitive or psychophysiological changes of the normal sexual response cycle are inhibited.

Psychosexual stages. In psychoanalytic theory, critical developmental phases that the individual passes through, each stage characterized by the body area providing maximal erotic gratification. The adult personality is formed by the pattern and intensity of instinctual gratification at each stage.

Psychosexual trauma. As applied by Masters and Johnson, earlier frightening or degrading sexual experience that is related to a present *psychosexual dysfunction.*

Psychosis. A severe mental disorder in which thinking and emotion are so impaired that the individual is seriously out of contact with reality.

Psychosocial system. As applied by Masters and Johnson, the social, psychological, and cultural attitudes toward sexual responding.

Psychosomatic disorder. See *psychophysiological disorder.*

Psychosurgery. Any surgical technique in which neural pathways in the brain are cut in order to change behavior. See *lobotomy.*

Psychotherapy. A primarily verbal means of helping troubled individuals change their thoughts, feelings, and behavior to reduce distress and to achieve greater life satisfaction. See *insight therapy* and *behavior therapy.*

Psychotic depression. A profound sadness and unjustified feelings of unworthiness in which there are also *delusions.*

Psychoticism. In Eysenck's theory of personality, a dimension referring to the degree of contact with reality.

Punishment. In psychological experiments, any noxious stimulus imposed on the animal to reduce the probability that it will behave in the way deemed by the experimenter to be incorrect.

Q-sort. A personality test in which the respondent sorts a number of descriptive statements into categories ranging from "very characteristic" to "very uncharacteristic," depending on how they apply to him or her. It is often used in research on *client-centered therapy*.

Random assignment. A method of assigning subjects to groups in an *experiment* that gives each subject an equal chance of being in each group. The procedure helps to ensure that groups are comparable before the experimental manipulation begins.

Rape. To force sexual intercourse or other sexual activity on another person. **Forcible rape** is the legal term. **Statutory rape** is sexual intercourse between an adult male and someone who is under the age of consent.

Rapid-smoking treatment. A *behavior therapy* technique for reducing cigarette smoking in which the person is instructed to puff much more quickly than usual in an effort to make the whole experience an aversive one.

Rapport. A close, trusting relationship.

Rational-emotive therapy. A *cognitive-restructuring behavior therapy* introduced by Albert Ellis and based on the assumption that much disordered behavior is rooted in what people tell themselves. The therapy aims to alter the unrealistic goals individuals set for themselves, such as "I must be universally loved."

Rationalization. A *defense mechanism* in which a plausible reason is unconsciously invented by the *ego* to protect itself from confronting the real reason for an action, thought, or emotion.

Raynaud's disease. A *psychophysiological disorder* in which capillaries, especially of the fingers and toes, are subject to spasm. It is characterized by cold, moist hands, commonly accompanied by pain and may progress to local gangrene.

Reaction formation. A *defense mechanism* whereby an unconscious and unacceptable impulse or feeling that would cause anxiety is converted into its opposite so that it can become conscious and be expressed.

Reaction time test. A procedure for determining the interval between the application of a stimulus and the beginning of the subject's response.

Reactivity. The phenomenon whereby the object of observation is changed by the very fact that it is being observed.

Recessive gene. A *gene* that must be paired with one identical to it in order to determine a *trait* in the *phenotype*.

Recovery time. The period it takes for a physiological process to return to *baseline* after the body has responded to a stimulus.

Refractory phase. The brief period after stimulation of a nerve, muscle, or other irritable element during which it is unresponsive to a second stimulus; or the period after intercourse during which the male cannot have another orgasm.

Regression. A *defense mechanism* in which anxiety is avoided by retreating to the behavior patterns of an earlier *psychosexual stage*.

Reinforcement. In *operant conditioning*, increasing the probability that a response will recur either by presenting a contingent positive event or by removing a negative one.

Reliability. The extent to which a test, measurement, or classification system produces the same scientific observation each time it is applied.

Repression. A *defense mechanism* whereby impulses and thoughts unacceptable to the *ego* are pushed into the *unconscious*.

Resistance. During *psychoanalysis*, the defensive tendency of the unconscious part of the *ego* to ward off from consciousness particularly threatening *repressed* material.

Resistance to extinction. The tendency of a *conditioned response* to persist in the absence of any *reinforcement*.

Resolution phase. The last stage in the sexual arousal cycle during which sexual tensions abate.

Response acquiescence. A "yea"-saying *response set*, or agreeing with a question regardless of its content.

Response cost. An *operant conditioning* punishment procedure in which the misbehaving person is fined already earned reinforcers.

Response deviation. A tendency to answer questionnaire items in an uncommon way, regardless of their content.

Response hierarchy. The ordering of a series of responses according to the likelihood of their being elicited by a particular stimulus.

Response prevention. A *behavior therapy* technique in which the person is discouraged from making an accustomed response that is used primarily with *compulsive* rituals.

Response set. The tendency of an individual to respond n a particular way to questions or statements on a test—for example, with a "False"—regardless of the content of each query or statement.

Reticular formation. Network of *nuclei* and fibers in the central core of the *brainstem* that is important in arousing the cortex and maintaining alertness, in the processing of incoming sensory stimulation, and in adjusting spinal reflexes.

Retrograde amnesia. A loss of memory for events immediately preceding a traumatic incident; and sometimes, after brain damage, for events extending far back in time.

Retrospective report. A recollection by an individual of a past event.

Revealed-differences technique. A procedure for studying family behavior by observing its members in a laboratory as they try to agree on an answer to a particular question.

Reversal design (ABAB design). An experimental design in which behavior is measured during a baseline period (A), during a period when a treatment is introduced (B), during the reinstatement of the conditions that prevailed in the baseline period (A), and finally during a reintroduction of the treatment (B). It is common in operant research to isolate cause-effect relationships.

Reward. In psychological experiments, any satisfying event or stimulus that, by being contingent upon a response, reinforces this response which it follows and increases the probability that the subject will so respond again.

Rh factor. Substances present in the red blood cells of most people. If Rh factors are present in the blood of a fetus but not in that of the mother, her system produces antibodies that may enter the bloodstream of the fetus and indirectly damage the brain.

Right to refuse treatment. A legal principle according to which a committed mental patient may decline to participate in unconventional or risky treatments.

Right to treatment. A legal principle according to which a committed mental patient must be provided some minimal amount and quality of professional intervention, enough to provide a realistic opportunity for meaningful improvement.

Rorschach test. A *projective test* in which the examinee is instructed to interpret a series of ten inkblots reproduced on cards.

Role playing. See *behavioral rehearsal*.

Rosenthal effect. The tendency for results to conform to experimenters' expectations unless stringent safeguards are instituted to minimize human bias; named after Robert Rosenthal, who performed many of the original experiments revealing the problem.

Rubella (German measles). An infectious disease that if contracted by the mother during the first three months of pregnancy has a high risk of causing *mental retardation* and physical deformity in the child.

Sadism. A marked preference for obtaining or increasing sexual gratification by inflicting pain on another person.

Schema. A mental structure for organizing information about the world. Pl. schemata.

Schizoaffective disorder. Diagnosis to be applied when it is difficult to determine whether a patient has an *affective disorder* or either *schizophreniform disorder* or *schizophrenia*. First suggested as a type of schizophrenia, it is retained in DSM-III without diagnostic criteria.

Schizoid personality. This person, emotionally aloof and indifferent to the praise, criticism, and feelings of others, is usually a "loner" with few, if any, close friends and with solitary interests.

Schizophrenia. A group of *psychotic* disorders characterized by major disturbances in thought, emotion, and behavior—disordered thinking in which ideas are not logically related; faulty perception and attention; bizarre disturbances in motor activity; flat or inappropriate emotion; reduced tolerance for stress of interpersonal relations. It causes a patient to withdraw from people and reality, often into a fantasy life of *delusions* and *hallucinations*. The problems must last at least six months at some time during the person's life. See *schizoaffective disorder, schizophreniform disorder,* and *brief reactive psychosis.*

Schizophreniform disorder. Diagnosis for people who have all the symptoms of *schizophrenia*, except that the disorder lasts more than two weeks and less than six months. Emotional turmoil, fear, and confusion are evident, and *hallucinations* are particularly vivid, but the disorder does not appear to be precipitated by stress. See *brief reactive psychosis.*

Schizophrenogenic. Causing or contributing to the development of *schizophrenia*; often applied to the cold, conflict-inducing mother who is alleged to make her children schizophrenic.

Schizotypal personality. This eccentric individual has oddities of thought and perception—*magical thinking, illusions, depersonalization, derealization*—speaks digressively and with overelaborations, and is usually socially isolated. Under stress he or she may appear *psychotic.*

School phobia. An acute, irrational dread of attending school, usually accompanied by somatic complaints. It is the most common *phobia* of childhood.

Secondary gain. Benefits that a person unconsciously obtains from a disability.

Secondary impotence. See *impotence.*

Secondary process. The reality-based decision-making and problem-solving activities of the *ego*. Compare with *primary process.*

Sedative. A drug that slows bodily activities, especially those of the central nervous system; it is used to reduce pain and tension and to induce relaxation and sleep.

Selective mortality. A possible confound in *longitudinal research*, whereby the less healthy people in a sample are more likely to drop out.

Self-actualization. Fulfilling one's potential as an always growing human being; believed by *client-centered therapists* to be the master motive.

Self-monitoring. In *behavioral assessment*, a procedure whereby the individual observes and reports certain aspects of his or her own behavior, thoughts, or emotions.

Self psychology. Kohut's variant of psychoanalysis, in which the focus is on the development of the person's self-worth from acceptance and nurturance by key figures in childhood.

Semantic Differential. A self-report inventory requiring the respondent to rate each concept, such as mother, in one–seven positions between a number of polar adjectives, such as clean–dirty, strong–weak.

Senile dementia. A disorder which can be brought on by progressive deterioration of the brain caused in part by aging; marked by memory impairment, inability to think abstractly, loss of standards and control of impulses, poor personal hygiene, great *disorientation*, and eventually obliviousness.

Senile placques. Small areas of tissue degeneration in the brain, made up of granular material and filaments.

Sensate focus. A term applied to exercises prescribed at the beginning of the Masters and Johnson sex therapy program; partners are instructed to fondle each other to give pleasure but to refrain from intercourse, thus reducing anxiety about sexual performance.

Sensitivity (encounter) group. A small group of people who spend a period of time together both for therapy and for educational purposes; participants are encouraged or forced to examine their interpersonal functioning and their often-overlooked feelings about themselves and others.

Sensory-awareness procedures. Techniques that help clients tune into their feelings and sensations, as in *sensate-focus* exercises, and to be open to new ways of experiencing and feeling.

Separation anxiety disorder. A disorder in which the child feels intense fear and distress when away from someone on whom he or she is very dependent; it is said to be an important cause of *school phobia.*

Serotonin. An *indoleamine* that is a *neurotransmitter* of the central nervous system. Disturbances in its tracts apparently figure in *depression* and *mania.*

Severe mental retardation. A limitation in mental development measured in IQ tests at between 20 and 34. Individuals so afflicted often cannot care for themselves, communicate only briefly, and are listless and inactive.

Sex-change surgery. An operation removing existing genitalia of a *transsexual* and constructing a substitute for the genitals of the opposite sex.

Sexual orientation disturbance. An earlier term for DSM-III's *ego-dystonic homosexuality.*

Sexual response cycle. The general pattern of sexual physical processes and feelings, building to an orgasm by stimulation, as proposed by Masters and Johnson and made up of four phases: *excitement, plateau, orgasm* and *resolution.*

Sexual script. Rules people have for guiding their actions in sexual situations.

Sexual value system. As applied by Masters and Johnson, the activities that an individual holds to be acceptable and necessary in a sexual relationship.

Shaping. In *operant conditioning*, reinforcing responses that are successively closer approximations of the desired behavior.

Shell shock. A term from World War I for what is now referred to as *posttraumatic stress disorder*; it was believed to be due to sudden atmospheric changes from nearby explosions.

Short-term memory. The part of our capacity to remember things that is limited to about 7 items and decays rapidly if the items are not rehearsed.

Sibling. One of two or more persons having the same parents.

Sidestream smoke. The smoke from the burning end of a cigarette, that contains higher concentrations of ammonia, carbon monoxide, nicotine, and tar than that inhaled by the smoker.

Significant difference. See *statistical significance.*

Single-subject experimental designs. Designs for experiments conducted with a single subject; these procedures include the *reversal* and *multiple-baseline* designs in operant research.

Situational determinants. The environmental conditions that precede and follow a particular piece of behavior, being a primary focus of *behavioral assessment.*

Situational orgasmic dysfunction. Inability of a woman to have an *orgasm* in particular situations.

Skeletal (voluntary) muscle. One of the muscles that clothe the skeleton of the vertebrate, that is attached to bone, and is under voluntary control.

Skinner box. A laboratory apparatus in which an animal is placed for an *operant conditioning* experiment. It contains a lever or other device that the animal must manipulate to obtain a reward or avoid punishment.

Sleeping sickness. See *encephalitis lethargica.*

Slow brain waves. The theta rhythm (4 to 7 cps) usually recorded by an EEG from subcortical parts of the brain and the delta rhythm (less than 4 cps) normally recorded during deep sleep; sometimes recorded in awake sociopaths.

Smooth (involuntary) muscle. Thin sheets of muscle cells associated with *viscera* and walls of blood vessels that perform functions not usually under direct voluntary control.

Social desirability. In completion of *personality inventories*, the tendency of the responder to give what he or she considers the socially acceptable answer, whether or not it is accurate.

Social phobia. A collection of fears linked to the presence of other people.

Social-skills training. *Behavior therapy* procedures for teaching socially unknowledgeable individuals how to meet others, to talk to them and maintain eye contact, to give and receive criticism, offer and accept compliments, to make requests and express feelings, and how otherwise to improve their relations with other people. *Modeling* and *behavior rehearsal* are two such procedures.

Social-withdrawal disorder. A disorder of extremely shy children who never "warm up" to new people both young and old, even after prolonged exposure to them. They have loving relations within the family; but they do not join in group play, and in crowded rooms they cling to their parents or hide.

Socioeconomic status. A relative position in the community as determined by occupation, income, and amount of education.

Sociopath. See *antisocial personality.*

Sodomy. Originally, penetration of the male organ into the anus of another male, it was later broadened in English law to include heterosexual anal intercourse and by some state statutes to cover unconventional sex generally.

Soma. The totality of an organism's physical makeup.

Somatic weakness. The vulnerability of a particular organ or organ system to psychological stress and thereby to a particular *psychophysiological disorder.*

Somatization disorder. A *somatoform disorder* in which the person continually seeks medical help for recurrent and multiple physical symptoms that have no discoverable physical cause. The medical history is complicated and dramatically presented. It is also called Briquet's syndrome. Compare with *hypochondriasis.*

Somatoform disorders. Disorders in which physical symptoms suggest a physical problem but have no known physiological cause; they are therefore believed to be linked to psychological conflicts and needs but not voluntarily assumed; *somatization disorder* (Briquet's syndrome), *conversion disorder, psychogenic pain disorder, hypochondriasis.*

Somatogenesis. Development from bodily origins as distinguished from psychological origins. Compare with *psychogenesis.*

SORC. An acronym for the four sets of variables that are the focus of *behavioral assessment; situational determinants, organismic variables,* overt responses, and *reinforcement* contingencies.

Specific attitudes theory. The hypothesis that certain attitudes are associated with certain *psychophysiological disorders,* for example, that a person who feels mistreated may develop *hives.*

Specific developmental disorders. Delays in the development of language and articulation, in being able to read and do arithmetic, skills that are related to maturation. Some signs of the disturbances are often evident in adulthood. Also called *learning disabilities;* listed on axis II.

Specific-reaction theory. The hypothesis that an individual develops a given *physschophysiological disorder* because of the innate tendency of the autonomic system to respond in a particular way to stress, for example, by increasing heart rate or developing tension in the forehead.

Spectator role. As applied by Masters and Johnson, a pattern of behavior in which the individual's focus on and concern for sexual performance impedes his or her natural sexual responses.

Stability-lability. A dimension of classifying the responsiveness of the *autonomic nervous system.* Labile individuals are those in whom a wide range of stimuli can elicit autonomic *arousal.* Stable individuals are not so easily aroused.

State-dependent learning. The phenomenon whereby an organism shows the effects of learning that took place in a special condition, such as intoxication, better than in the ordinary state.

State-dependent memory. The phenomenon whereby people are more able to remember an event if they are in the same state as when it happened. If they are in a greatly different state when they try to remember—happy now, and sad then, for example—memory is poor.

Statistical significance. A magnitude of difference that has a low probability of having occurred by chance alone and is by convention regarded as important.

Statutory rape. Sexual intercourse, whether forced or not, with someone who is below an age fixed by local statute as that of consent.

Steppingstone theory. The belief that the use of one kind of drug, such as *marijuana,* leads to the use of a more dangerous one, such as *cocaine.*

Stimulant. A drug which increases alertness and motor activity and at the same time reduces fatigue, allowing an individual to remain awake for an extended period of time.

Strategic processing. The use of *cognitive* strategies to solve problems; it is said to be defective in the *mentally retarded.*

Stress. A stimulus that strains the physiological or psychological capacities of an organism.

Stroke. A sudden loss of consciousness and control followed by paralysis; caused by sudden anemia of a portion of the brain when a blood clot obstructs an artery or by hemorrhage into the brain when an artery ruptures.

Subdural hematoma. Hemorrhage and swelling of the arachnoid torn by a fractured bone of the skull.

Subintentioned death. A death that is believed to have been caused in some measure by the person's unconscious intentions.

Substance abuse. The use of a drug for at least a month to such an extent that the person is often intoxicated throughout the day and fails in important obligations and in attempts to abstain, but where there is no physiological dependence. See *psychological dependency.*

Substance dependence. The abuse of a drug accompanied by a physiological dependence on it, made evident by *tolerance* and *withdrawal symptoms;* also called *addiction.*

Substance use disorders. Disorders in which drugs like *alcohol* and *cocaine* are abused to such an extent that behavior becomes maladaptive; social and occupational functioning is impaired, and control or abstinence becomes impossible. Reliance on the drug may be either psychological, as in *substance abuse,* or physiological, as in *substance dependence* or *addiction.*

Successive approximations. Responses that closer and closer resemble the desired response in *operant conditioning.* See *shaping.*

Suicide. The taking of one's own life intentionally.

Sulcus (fissure). A shallow furrow in the *cerebral cortex* separating adjacent convolutions or *gyri.*

Superego. In psychoanalytic theory, the part of the personality that acts as the conscience and reflects society's moral standards as they have been learned from parents and teachers.

Symbiotic psychosis. A disorder of childhood marked by extreme reluctance of the child to be separated from his or her mother and by agitated panic attacks.

Symbolic loss. In psychoanalytic theory, the unconscious interpretation by the *ego* of an event like rejection as a total loss such as suffered in the death of a loved one.

Sympathetic nervous system. The division of the *autonomic nervous system* that acts on bodily systems—for example, speeding up the contractions of the blood vessels, slowing those of the intestines, and increasing the heartbeat—to prepare the organism for exertion, emotional stress, and extreme cold.

Symptom. An observable physiological or psychological manifestation of a disease, often occurring in a patterned group of symptoms to constitute a *syndrome*.

Synapse. A small gap between two *neurons* where the nerve impulse passes from the axon of the first to the dendrites or cell body of the second.

Syndrome. A group or pattern of *symptoms* that tend to occur together in a particular *disease*.

Systematic desensitization. A major *behavior therapy* procedure that has a fearful person, while deeply relaxed, imagine a series of progressively more fearsome situations. The two responses of relaxation and fear are incompatible and fear is dispelled. It is useful for treating psychological problems in which *anxiety* is the principal difficulty.

Systematic rational restructing. A variant of *rational-emotive therapy* in which the client imagines a series of increasingly anxiety-provoking situations while attempting to reduce distress by talking about them to the self in a more realistic, defusing fashion.

Systematized delusion. A highly organized set of mistaken beliefs that has become the dominant focus of the paranoid patient's life.

Tachycardia. A racing of the heart, often associated with high levels of anxiety.

Tarantism. Wild dancing *mania*, prevalent in the thirteenth century in western Europe, supposedly incited by the bite of a tarantula.

Taraxein. A protein (a gamma globulin) in the blood serum of schizophrenics, asserted by Heath to be responsible for their *psychosis*.

Tardive dyskinesia. A muscular disturbance of older patients who have taken *phenothiazines* for a very long time, that is marked by involuntary lip-smacking and chin-wagging.

Tay-Sachs disease. A disorder of lipid (fat) metabolism causing severe *mental retardation*, muscular weakness, eventual blindness, and death in about the third year.

Taylor Manifest Anxiety Scale. Fifty items drawn from the MMPI as a self-report questionnaire to assess anxiety.

Temporal lobe. A large area of each *cerebral hemisphere* situated below the *lateral sulcus* and in front of the *occipital lobe* that contains primary auditory projection and association areas and general association areas.

Testability. The extent to which a scientific assertion is amenable to systematic probes, any one of which could negate the scientist's expectations.

Testes. Male reproductive glands or gonads; the site where sperm develop and are stored.

Testoterone. Male sex hormone secreted by the *testes* that is responsible for the development of sex characteristics such as enlargement of the testes and growth of facial hair.

Tetrahydrocannabinol (THC). The major active chemical in *marijuana* and *hashish*.

Thalamus. A major brain relay station consisting of two egg-shaped lobes located in the *diencephalon* that receives impulses from all sensory areas except for the olfactory and transmits them to the *cerebrum*.

Thanatos. In psychoanalytic theory, the death instinct that is the second of the two basic instincts within the *id*, the other being *Eros*.

Thematic Apperception Test (TAT). A *projective test* consisting of a set of black and white pictures reproduced on cards, each depicting a potentially emotion-laden situation. The examinee, presented with the cards one at a time, is instructed to make up a story about each situation.

Theory. A formally stated and coherent set of propositions that purport to explain a range of phenomena, order them in a logical way, and suggest what additional information might be gleaned under certain conditions.

Therapeutic community. A concept in mental health care that views the total environment as contributing to prevention or treatment.

Theta rhythm. See *slow brain waves*.

Thiamine. One of the complex of B vitamins.

Third-variable problem. The difficulty in *correlational research* on two variables whereby their relationship may be attributable to a third factor.

Thorazine. Trade name for *chlorpromazine*, one of the *neuroleptics* and a member of the *phenothiazine* group of drugs.

Thought disorder. A symptom of *schizophrenia*, evidenced by problems such as *incoherence, loose associations,* and *concrete reasoning* and speech marked by *neologisms* and *clang associations*.

Thyroid gland. An endocrine structure whose two lobes are located on either side of the windpipe; it secretes *thyroxin*.

Thyroxin. An iodine-containing hormone secreted by the *thyroid gland* that participates in regulation of carbohydrate *metabolism*, thus determining the level of activity and in infants' growth, development, and intelligence.

Time-of-measurement effects. A possible confound in *longitudinal research*, whereby events at a particular point in time can have a specific effect on a variable one is studying over time.

Time-out. An *operant conditioning* punishment procedure in which for bad behavior the person is temporarily removed from a setting where reinforcers can be obtained and placed, for example, in a boring room.

Token economy. A *behavior therapy* procedure, based on *operant conditioning* principles, in which institutionalized patients are given scrip rewards such as poker chips for socially constructive behavior. The tokens themselves can be exchanged for desirable items and activities such as cigarettes and extra time away from the ward.

Tolerance. A physiological process in which greater and greater amounts of an addictive drug are required to produce the same effect. See *substance dependence*.

Tonic phase. The state of rigid muscular tension and suspended breathing in a *grand mal epileptic* attack.

Trait. A somatic characteristic or an enduring *predisposition* to respond in a particular way, distinguishing one individual from another.

Trance logic. A way of thinking during *hyponosis* that allows a person to entertain as real phenomena notions and images that are inherently contradictory, such as seeing two people in place of one.

Tranquilizer. A drug that reduces anxiety and agitation, such as *Valium*.

Transference. The venting of the *analysand's* emotions, either positive or negative, by treating the *analyst* as the symbolic representative of someone important in the past. An example is the analysand's becoming angry with the analyst to release emotions actually felt toward his or her father.

Transference neurosis. A crucial phase of *psychoanalysis* during which *analysand* reacts emotionally toward the *analyst*, treating him as a parent and reliving childhood experiences in his presence. It enables both analyst and analysand to examine hitherto *repressed* conflicts in the light of present-day reality.

Transsexual. A person who believes he is opposite in sex to his biological endowment and often desires *sex-change surgery*.

Transvestism. The practice of dressing in the clothing of the opposite sex, usually for the purpose of sexual arousal.

Trauma. A severe physical injury or wound to the body caused by an external force, or a psychological shock having a lasting effect on mental life.

Traumatic disease. An illness produced by external assault such as poison, a blow, or stress, for example, a broken leg.

Tremor. An involuntary quivering of voluntary muscle, usually limited to small musculature of particular areas.

Trephining. A crude surgical practice of the Stone Age, whereby a hole was chipped in the skull of a person who was behaving peculiarly, presumably to allow the escape of evil spirits.

Tricyclic drug. One of a group of *antidepressants* so-called because the molecular structure of each is characterized by three fused rings. Tricyclics are assumed to interfere with the reuptake of *norepinephrine* and *serotonin* by a *neuron* after it has fired.

Trisomy. A condition wherein there are three rather than the usual pair of *chromosomes* within the cell nucleus.

Tumescence. The flow of blood into the genitals.

Tumor (neoplasm). Abnormal growth that when located in the brain can be either malignant and directly destroy brain tissue, or benign and disrupt functioning by increasing intracranial pressure.

Twin method. Research strategy in *behavior genetics* in which *concordance* rates of *monozygotic* and *dizygotic* twins are compared.

Two-factor theory. Mowrer's theory of avoidance learning according to which (1) fear is attached to a neutral stimulus by pairing it with a noxious *unconditioned stimulus*, and (2) a person learns to escape the fear elicited by the *conditioned stimulus*, thereby avoiding the UCS. See *fear-drive*.

Type A and type B. Two contrasting behavior patterns revealed through studies seeking the cause of *coronary heart disease*. Type A people are competitive, rushed, aggressive, and overcommitted to their work, type Bs more relaxed and relatively free of pressure. Type As are at heightened risk for heart disease.

Ulcer. A break in skin or mucous membrane accompanied by tissue disintegration; in the stomach or duodenum, a lesion in the lining caused by excessive secretion of hydrochloric acid, and generally regarded as a *psychophysiological disorder*.

Ultrasound. The use of controlled sound waves to visualize internal organs without having to use X-rays.

Unconditional positive regard. According to Rogers, a crucial attitude for the *client-centered* therapist to adopt toward the client, who needs to feel accepted totally as a person in order to evaluate the extent to which his current behavior contributes to his self-actualization.

Unconditioned stimulus (UCS). A stimulus which elicits an instinctual, unconditional response; meat powder producing salivation is an example.

Unconscious. A state of unawareness without sensation or thought. In psychoanalytic theory, it is the part of the personality, in particular the *id* impulses, or *id* energy, of which the *ego* is unaware.

Undercontrolled. In reference to childhood disorders, problem behavior of the child that creates trouble for others, such as his or her disobedience and aggressiveness.

Unipolar depression. A term applied to the disorder of individuals who have experienced episodes of *depression* but not of *mania*; referred to as major depression in DSM-III.

Vagina. The sheathlike female genital organ that leads from the uterus to the external opening.

Vaginal barrel. The passageway of the vaginal canal leading from the external opening to the uterus.

Vaginal orgasm. The sexual climax experienced through stimulation of the *vagina*.

Vaginal plethysmorgraph. A device for recording the amount of blood in the walls of the *vagina* and thus for measuring arousal.

Vaginismus. Painful, spasmodic contractions of the outer third of the *vaginal barrel*, that make insertion of the *penis* impossible or extremely difficult.

Validity—internal. The extent to which experimental results can be confidently attributed to the manipulation of the *independent variable*. **External**, the extent to which research results may be generalized to other populations and settings. As applied to psychiatric diagnoses, **concurrent**, the extent to which previous undiscovered features are found among patients with the same diagnosis; **predictive**, the extent to which predictions can be made about the future behavior of patients with the same diagnosis; **etiological**, the extent to which a disorder in a number of patients is found to have the same cause or causes.

Valium. A *minor tranquilizer*, believed to be the most widely prescribed drug of those available to physicians.

Variable. A characteristic or aspect in which people, objects, events, or conditions vary.

Vasoconstriction. A narrowing of the lumen of a blood vessel, implicated in diseases such as *hypertension*.

Vicarious conditioning. Learning by observing the reactions of others to stimuli or through listening to what they say.

Vineland Adaptive Behavior Scale. An instrument for assessing how many age-appropriate, socially adaptive behaviors a child engages in.

Viscera. The internal organs of the body located in the great cavity of the trunk proper.

Vitamin. Any of various organic substances that are, as far as is known, essential to the nutrition of many animals, acting usually in minute quantities to regulate various metabolic processes.

Voodoo death. The demise of a member of a primitive culture after breaking a tribal law or being cursed by the witch doctor.

Voyeurism (peeping). Marked preference for obtaining sexual gratification by watching others in a state of undress or having sexual relations.

Waxy flexibility. An aspect of *catatonia* in which the patient's limbs can be moved into a variety of positions and thereafter maintained for unusually long periods of time.

Wernicke's disease. A chronic brain disorder produced by a deficiency of B-complex vitamins that is marked by confusion, drowsiness, partial paralysis of eye muscles, and unsteady gait and by lesions in the *pons*, *cerebellum* and *mammillary bodies*. Chronic alcoholics are especially susceptible.

White matter. The neural tissue, particularly of the brain and spinal cord, consisting of tracts or bundles of myelinated (sheathed) nerve fibers.

Withdrawal symptoms. Negative physiological and psychological reactions evidenced when a person suddenly stops taking an addictive drug; cramps, restlessness, and even death are examples. See *substance dependence*.

Wooly mammoth. A metaphor for the way the repressed conflicts of psychoanalytic theory are encapsulated in the *unconscious*, making them inaccessible to examination and alteration; thus maintained they cause disorders in adulthood.

Working through. In *psychoanalysis*, the arduous, time-consuming process through which the *analysand* confronts repressed conflicts again and again and faces up to the validity of the analyst's *interpretations* until problems are satisfactorily solved.

Zeitgeist. The German word for the trends of thought and feeling of culture and taste of a particular time period.

Zygote. The fertilized egg cell formed when the male sperm and female ovum unite.

REFERENCES

Abel, C. C., Barlow, D. H., Blanchard, E. B., & Guild, D. (1977). The components of rapists' sexual arousal. *Archives of General Psychiatry*, **34**, 895–903.

Abraham, K. (1911). Notes on the psychoanalytical investigation and treatment of manic-depressive insanity and allied conditions. In E. Jones (Ed.), *Selected papers of Karl Abraham, M.D.* London: Hogarth Press. 1927.

Abrams, R. (1975). What's new in convulsive therapy? In S. Arieti & G. Chrzanowski (Eds.), *New dimensions in psychiatry*. New York: Wiley.

Abramson, L. Y., Garber, J., Edwards, N. B., & Seligman, M. E. P. (1978). Expectancy changes in depression and schizophrenia. *Journal of Abnormal Psychology*, **87**, 102–109.

Abramson, L. Y., Seligman, M. E. P., & Teasdale, J. D. (1978). Learned helplessness in humans. Critique and reformulation. *Journal of Abnormal Psychology*, **87**, 49–74.

Achenbach, T. M. (1982). *Developmental psychopathology*. (2nd ed.). New York: Wiley.

Achenbach, T. M., & Edelbrock, C. S. (1978). The classification of child psychopathology: A review of empirical efforts. *Psychological Bulletin*, **85**, 1275–1301.

Achenbach, T. M., & Edelbrock, C. S. (1981). Behavioral problems and competencies reported by parents of normal and disturbed children aged 4 through 16. *Monographs of the Society for Research in Child Development*, **46**, Serial No. 188.

Adams, E. H., & Durell, J. (1984). Cocaine: A growing public health problem. In J. Grabowski (Ed.), *Cocaine: Pharmacology, effects, and treatment of abuse*. Rockville, Md.: NIDA.

Adams, K. M. (1980). In search of Luria's battery: A false start. *Journal of Consulting and Clinical Psychology*, **48**, 511–516.

Adler, A. (1964). Compulsion neurosis, 1931. In H. L. Ansbacher & R. R. Ansbacher (Eds.), *Superiority and social interest*. Evanston, Ill.: Northwestern University Press.

Agras, S., Sylvester, D., & Oliveau, D. (1969). The epidemiology of common fears and phobias. Unpublished manuscript, 1969.

Akhter, S., Wig, N. N., Varma, V. K., Pershad, D., & Verma, S. K. (1975). A phenomenological analysis of symptoms in obsessive-compulsive neurosis. *British Journal of Psychiatry*, **127**, 342–348.

Albee, G. W., Lane, E. A., & Reuter, J. M. (1964). Childhood intelligence of future schizophrenics and neighborhood peers. *Journal of Psychology*, **58**, 141–144.

Aldrich, C. K., & Mendkoff, E. (1963). Relocation of the aged and disabled: A mortality study. *Journal of the American Geriatrics Society*, **11**, 185–194.

Alexander, F. (1950). *Psychosomatic medicine*. New York: Norton.

Alexander, F., & French, T. M. (1946). *Psychoanalytic therapy*. New York: Ronald Press.

Allderidge, P. (1979). Hospitals, mad houses, and asylums: Cycles in the care of the insane. *British Journal of Psychiatry*, **134**, 321–324.

Allen, M. G. (1976). Twin studies of affective illness. *Archives of General Psychiatry*, **33**, 1476–1478.

Alloy, L. B., & Abramson, L. Y. (1979). Judgment of contingency in depressed and nondepressed students: Sadder but wiser? *Journal of Experimental Psychology: General*, **108**, 441–485.

Allport, G. W. (1961). *Pattern and growth in personality*. New York: Holt, Rinehart and Winston.

American Cancer Society. (1976). *Task force on tobacco and cancer—Target 5*. Report to the Board of Directors, American Cancer Society.

American Heart Association Heart Facts 1982. (1981). Dallas, Texas: American Heart Association.

American Law Institute. (1962). *Model penal code: Proposed official draft*. Philadelphia: The American Law Institute.

American Psychiatric Association. (1980). *Diagnostic and statistical manual of mental disorders*. First edition, 1952; second edition, 1968; third edition, 1980. Washington, D.C.: American Psychiatric Association.

Andersen, B. L. (1983). Primary orgasmic dysfunction: Diagnostic considerations and review of treatment. *Psychological Bulletin*, **93**, 105–136.

Andreasen, N. C. (1979). Thought, language, and communication disorders: II. Diagnostic significance. *Archives of General Psychiatry*, **36**, 1325–1330.

Andreasen, N. C. (1982). Negative symptoms in schizophrenia. Definition and reliability. *Archives of General Psychiatry*, **39**, 784–787.

Andreasen, N. C., & Olsen, S. A. (1982). Negative versus positive schizophrenia. Definition and validation. *Archives of General Psychiatry*, **39**, 789–794.

Andreasen, N. C., Olsen, S. A., Dennert, J. W., & Smith, M. R. (1982). Ventricular enlargement in schizophrenia: Relationship to positive and negative symptoms. *American Journal of Psychiatry*, **139**, 297–302.

Angrist, B., Lee, H. K., & Gershon, S. (1974). The antagonism of amphetamine-induced symptomatology by a neuroleptic. *American Journal of Psychiatry*, **131**, 817–819.

Aragone, J., Cassady, J., & Drabman, R. S. (1975). Treating overweight children through parental training and contingency contracting. *Journal of Applied Behavior Analysis*, **8**, 269–278.

Arieti, S. (1955). *Interpretation of schizophrenia*. New York: Basic Books.

Arieti, S. (1979). New views on the psychodynamics of phobias. *American Journal of Psychotherapy*, **33**, 82–95.

Arkonac, O., & Guze, S. B. (1963). A family study of hysteria. *New England Journal of Medicine*, **268**, 239–242.

Armor, D. J., Polich, J. M., & Stambul, H. B. (1978). *Alcoholism and treatment*. New York: Wiley.

Aronson, E. (1972). *The social animal*. San Francisco: Freeman.

Aronson, E., & Carlsmith, J. R. (1968). Experimentation in social psychology. In G. Lindzey & E. Aronson (Eds.). *The handbook of social psychology: Vol 2. Research methods*. Menlo Park, Calif.: Addison-Wesley.

Ashcroft, G., Crawford, T., & Eccleston, E. S. (1966). 5-Hydroxyindole compounds in the cerebrospinal fluid of patients with psychiatric or neurological disease. *Lancet*, **2**, 1049–1052.

Atchley, R. (1980). Aging and suicide: Reflection of the quality of life. In S. Haynes & M. Feinleib (Eds.), *Proceedings of the Second Conference on the Epidemiology of Aging*. National Institute of Health. Washington, D.C.: U.S. Government Printing Office.

Atthowe, J. M. (1976). Treating the hospitalized person. In W. E. Craighead, A. E. Kazdin, & M. J. Mahoney (Eds.), *Behavior modification: Principles, issues, and applications*. Boston: Houghton Mifflin.

Ausubel, D. P. (1961). Causes and types of narcotic addictions: A psychosocial view. *Psychiatric Quarterly*, **35**, 523–531. (a)

Ausubel, D. P. (1961). Personality disorder is disease. *American Psychologist*, **16**, 69–74. (b)

Ax, A. F. (1953). The physiological differentiation between fear and anger in humans. *Psychosomatic Medicine*, **15**, 433–442.

Ayllon, T., & Azrin, N. H. (1968). *The token economy: A motivational system for therapy and rehabilitation*. New York: Appleton-Century-Crofts.

Bach, G. R. (1966). The marathon group: Intensive practice of intimate interactions. *Psychological Reports*, **181**, 995–1002.

Bagby, E. (1922). The etiology of phobias. *Journal of Abnormal Psychology*, **17**, 16–18.

Bahm, A. K., Chandler, C., & Eisenberg, L. (1961). *Diagnostic characteristics related to service on psychiatric clinics for children*. Paper presented at the 38th Annual Convention of Orthopsychiatry, Munich.

Bakwin, H. (1973). The genetics of enuresis. In J. Kolvin, R. C. MacKeith, & S. R. Meadow (Eds.), *Enuresis and encopresis*. Philadelphia: Lippincott.

Ball, J. C., & Chambers, C. D. (Eds.), (1970). *The epidemiology of opiate addiction in the United States*. Springfield, Ill.: Charles C. Thomas.

Baller, W. R. (1975). *Bed-wetting: Origin and treatment*. Elmsford, N.Y.: Pergamon Press.

Bancroft, J. H., Jones, G. H., & Pullan, B. R. (1966). A simple transducer for measuring penile erections, with comments on its use in the treatment of sexual disorders. *Behaviour Research and Therapy*, **4**, 239–241.

Bandura, A. (1969). *Principles of behavior modification*. New York: Holt, Rinehart and Winston.

Bandura, A. (1973). *Aggression: A social learning analysis*. Englewood Cliffs, N.J.: Prentice-Hall.

Bandura, A. (1977). Self-efficacy: Toward a unifying theory of behavioral change. *Psychological Review*, **84**, 191–215.

Bandura, A., Blanchard, E. B., & Ritter, B. (1969). Relative efficacy of desensitization and modelling approaches for inducing behavioral, affective, and attitudinal changes. *Journal of Personality and Social Psychology*, **13**, 173–199.

Bandura, A., Grusec, J. E., & Menlove, F. L. (1967). Vicarious extinction of avoidance behavior. *Journal of Personality and Social Psychology*, **5**, 16–23.

Bandura, A., Jeffrey, R. W. & Bachicha, D. L. (1974). Analysis of memory codes and cumulative rehearsal in observational learning. *Journal of Research in Personality*, **7**, 295–305.

Bandura, A., & Menlove, F. L. (1968). Factors determining vicarious extinction of avoidance behavior through symbolic modeling. *Journal of Personality and Social Psychology*, **8**, 99–108.

Bandura, A., & Perloff, B. (1967). Relative efficacy of self-monitored and externally imposed reinforcement systems. *Journal of Personality and Social Psychology*, **7**, 111–116.

Bandura, A., & Rosenthal, T. L. (1966). Vicarious classical conditioning as a function of arousal level. *Journal of Personality and Social Psychology*, **3**, 54–62.

Bandura, A., & Walters, R. H. (1959). *Adolescent aggression*. New York: Ronald Press.

Bandura, A., & Walters, R. H. (1963). *Social learning and personality development*. New York: Holt, Rinehart and Winston.

Barahal, H. S. (1958). 1000 prefrontal lobotomies: Five-to-ten-year follow-up study. *Psychiatric Quarterly*, **32**, 653–678.

Barbach, L. G. (1975). *For yourself*. New York: Doubleday.

Barber, T. X. (1969). *Hypnosis: A scientific approach*. New York: Van Nostrand Reinhold.

Barber, T. X., & Silver, M. J. (1968). Fact, fiction, and the experimenter bias effect. *Psychological Bulletin, Monograph Supplement*, **70**, 1–29.

Barefoot, J. C., Dahlstrom, G., & Williams, R. B. (1983). Hostility, CHD incidence, and total mortality: A 25-year follow-up study of 255 physicians. *Psychosomatic Medicine*, **45**, 59–63.

Barkley, R. A., & Cunningham, C. E. (1979). The effects of methylphenidate on the mother-child interactions of hyperactive children. *Archives of General Psychiatry*, **36**, 201–208.

Barkley, R. A., Hasting, J. E., Tousel, R. E., & Tousel, S. E. (1976). Evaluation of a token system for juvenile delinquents in a residential setting. *Journal of Behavior Therapy and Experimental Psychiatry*, **7**, 227–230.

Barlow, D. H., Abel, G. G., & Blanchard, E. B. (1979). Gender identity change in transsexuals. *Archives of General Psychiatry*, **36**, 1001–1007.

Barlow, D. H., Becker, R., Leitenberg, H., & Agras, W. S. (1970). A mechanical strain gauge for recording penile circumference. *Journal of Applied Behavior Analysis*, **3**, 73–76.

Barlow, D. H., Reynolds, E. J., & Agras, W. S. (1973). Gender identity change in a transsexual. *Archives of General Psychiatry*, **29**, 569–576.

Barlow, D. H., Vermilyea, J., Blanchard, E. B., Vermilyea, B. B., Di Nardo, P. A., & Carny, J. A. (in press). The phenomenon of panic. *Journal of Abnormal Psychology*.

Baron, R. A., & Byrne, D. (1977). *Social psychology: Understanding human interaction* (2nd ed.). Boston: Allyn and Bacon.

Barrett, C. L. (1969) Systematic desensitization versus implosive therapy. *Journal of Abnormal Psychology*, **74**, 587–592.

Barrett, C. L., Hampe, E., & Miller, L. (1978). Research on psychotherapy with children. In S. L. Garfield & A. E. Bergin (Eds.), *Handbook of psychotherapy and behavior change: An empirical analysis* (2nd ed.). New York: Wiley.

Bartlett, F. (1932). *Remembering*. Cambridge, England: Cambridge University Press.

Bartus, R. T., Dean, R. L., Beer, B., & Lippa, A. S. (1982). The cholinergic hypothesis of geriatric memory dysfunction. *Science*, **217**, 408–417.

Basedow, H. (1925). *The Australian aboriginal*. London: Adelaide.

Basmajian, J. V. (1977). Learned control of single motor units. In G. E. Schwartz & J. Beatty (Eds.), *Biofeedback: Theory and Research*. New York: Academic Press.

Bateson, G., Jackson, D. D., Haley, J., & Weakland, J. (1956). Toward a theory of schizophrenia. *Behavioral Science*, **1**, 251–264.

Battle, E. S., & Lacey, B. A. (1972). Context for hyperactivity in children, over time. *Child Development*, **43**, 757–773.

Bauer, D. H. (1976). An exploratory study of developmental changes in children's fears. *Journal of Child Psychology and Psychiatry.*, **17**, 69–74.

Baum, A., & Valins, S. (1973). Residential environments, group size and crowding. *Proceedings of the 81st Annual Convention of the American Psychological Association*. Washington, D.C.: American Psychological Association.

Baum, M. (1970). Extinction of avoidance responding through response prevention (flooding). *Psychological Bulletin*, **74**, 276–284.

Baumeister, A. A., & Berkson, G. (1980). FY 1981 Appropriations Statement on Appropriations to the National Institute of Child Health and Human Development.

Baumeister, A. A., & Maclean, W. E., Jr. (1979). Brain damage and mental retardation. In N. R. Ellis (Ed.), *Handbook of mental deficiency, psychological theory and research* (2nd ed.). Hillsdale, N.J.: Lawrence Erlbaum Associates.

Baxter, E., & Hopper, K. (1981). *Private lives/public places: Homeless adults on the streets of New York City.* New York: Community Service Society.

Beck, A. T. (1967). *Depression: Clinical, experimental and theoretical aspects.* New York: Harper and Row.

Beck, A. T. (1976). *Cognitive therapy and the emotional disorders.* New York: International Universities Press.

Beck, A. T., Kovacs, M., & Weissman, A. (1979). Assessment of suicidal ideation: The Scale for Suicide Ideation. *Journal of Consulting and Clinical Psychology, 47,* 343–352.

Beck, A. T., Kovacs, M., & Weissman, A. (1975). Hopelessness and suicidal behavior: An overview. *Journal of the American Medical Association., 234,* 1146–1149.

Beck, A. T., Rush, A. J., Shaw, B. F., & Emery, G. (1979). *Cognitive therapy of depression.* New York: Guilford Press.

Beck, A. T., Schuyler, D., & Herman, I. (1974). Development of suicidal intent scales. In A. T. Beck, H. L. P. Resnik, & D. J. Lettieri (Eds.), *The prediction of suicide.* Bowie, M.D.: Charles Press.

Beck, A. T., & Ward, C. H. (1961). Dreams of depressed patients: Characteristic themes in manifest content. *Archives of General Psychiatry, 5,* 462–467.

Beck, A. T., Ward, C. H., Mendelson, M., Mock, J. E., & Erbaugh, J. K. (1962). Reliability of psychiatric diagnosis: II. A study of consistency of clinical judgments and ratings. *American Journal of Psychiatry., 119,* 351–357.

Beck, J. G., Sakheim, D. K., & Barlow, D. H. (1983). Operating characteristics of the vaginal photoplethysmograph: Some implications for its use. *Archives of Sexual Behavior, 12,* 43–58.

Beck, M. (1979, November 12). Viet vets fight back. *Newsweek,* 44–49.

Becker, C., & Kronus, S. (1977). Sex and drinking patterns: An old relationship revisited in a new way. *Social Problems, 24,* 482–497.

Bednar, R. L., & Kaul, T. J. (1978). Experiential group research: Current perspectives. In S. L. Garfield & A. E. Bergin (Eds.), *Handbook of psychotherapy and behavior change: An empirical analysis* (2nd ed.). New York: Wiley.

Beecher, H. K. (1966). Ethics and clinical research. *New England Journal of Medicine., 274,* 1354–1360.

Begab, M. J. (1974). The major dilemma of mental retardation: Shall we prevent it? (Some implications of research in mental retardation). *American Journal of Mental Deficiency, 78,* 519–529.

Begelman, D. A. (1975). Ethical and legal issues of behavior modification. In M. Hersen, R. Eisler, & P. M. Miller (Eds.). *Progress in behavior modification.* New York: Academic Press.

Bell, J. E. (1975). *Family therapy.* New York: Jason Aronson.

Bellack, A. S., Hersen, M., & Turner, S. M. (1976). Generalization effects of social skills training in chronic schizophrenics: An experimental analysis. *Behavior Research and Therapy, 14,* 391–398.

Belliveau, E., & Richter, L. (1970). *Understanding "Human Sexual Inadequacy."* New York: Bantam.

Belmont, J. M., & Butterfield, E. C. (1969). The relations of short-term memory to development and intelligence. In L. P. Lipsitt & H. W. Reese (Eds.), *Advances in Child Development and Behavior,* Vol. 4. New York: Academic Press.

Belmont, J. M., & Butterfield, E. C. (1971). Learning strategies as determinants of memory deficiencies. *Cognitive Psychology, 2,* 411–420.

Bem, D. J., & Allen, A. (1974). On predicting some of the people some of the time: The search for cross-situational consistencies in behavior. *Psychological Review, 81,* 506–520.

Bem, S. L.(1974). The measurement of psychological androgeny. *Journal of Consulting and Clinical Psychology, 42,* 155–162.

Bem, S. L. (1984). Gender schema theory and its implications for child development: Raising gender-aschematic children in a gender-schematic society. *Signs: Journal of Women in Culture and Society, 8,* 598–616.

Bemis, K. M. (1978). Current approaches to the etiology and treatment of anorexia nervosa. *Psychological Bulletin, 85,* 593–617.

Bender, L., & Blau, A. (1937). The reactions of children to sexual relations with adults. *American Journal of Orthopsychiatry, 7,* 500–518.

Bennett, I. (1960). *Delinquent and neurotic children.* London: Tavistock Publications.

Bennett, W. (1980). The nicotine fix. *Harvard Magazine, 82,* 10–14.

Benson, H. (1975). *The relaxation response.* New York: Morrow.

Ben-Tovim, Marilov, V., & Crisp, A. H. (1979). Personality and mental state within anorexia nervosa. *Journal of Psychosomatic Research, 23,* 321–325.

Benton, A. (1978). Some conclusions about dyslexia. In A. L. Benton & D. Pearl (Eds.), *Dyslexia.* New York: Oxford University Press.

Berger, P. A., & Dunn, M. J. (1982). Substance induced and substance use disorders (opioids, cocaine, amphetamines and similarly acting sympathomimetics, phencyclidine (PCP), inhalants, hallucinogens, and cannabis, tobacco, caffeine). In J. H. Greist, J. W. Jefferson, & R. L. Spitzer (Eds.), *Treatment of mental disorders.* New York: Oxford University Press.

Berger, K. S., & Zarit, S. H. (1978). Late life paranoid states: Assessment and treatment. *American Journal of Orthopsychiatry, 48,* 528–537.

Bergin, A. E. (1966). Some implications of psychotherapy research for therapeutic practice. *Journal of Abnormal Psychology, 71,* 235–246.

Bergin, A. E. (1971). The evaluation of therapeutic outcomes. In A. E. Bergin & S. L. Garfield (Eds.), *Handbook of psychotherapy and behavior change: An empirical analysis.* New York: Wiley.

Bergin, A. E., & Lambert, M. J. (1978). The evaluation of therapeutic outcomes. In S. L. Garfield & A. E. Bergin (Eds.), *Handbook of psychotherapy and behavior change: An empirical analysis* (2nd ed.). New York: Wiley.

Bergler, E. (1946). Personality traits of alcohol addicts. *Quarterly Journal of Studies on Alcohol, 7,* 356–361.

Bergmann, K., Kay, D. W. K., Foster, E. M., McKechnie, A. A., & Roth, M. (1971). A follow-up study of randomly selected community residents to assess the effects of chronic organic brain syndrome and cerebrovascular disease. *Psychiatry,* Part II, Proceedings of the Fifth World Congress of Psychiatry, Mexico.

Berman, E. M., & Lief, H. I. (1976). Sex and the aging process. In W. W. Oaks, G. A. Melchiode, & I. Ficher (Eds.), *Sex and the life cycle.* New York: Grune and Stratton.

Bernard, J. (1973). *The future of marriage.* New York: Bantam.

Bernstein, D. A., & Nietzel, M. T. (1980). *Introduction to clinical psychology.* New York: McGraw-Hill.

Berry, J. C. (1967). Antecedents of schizophrenia, impulsive character and alcoholism in males. Paper presented at the 75th Annual Convention of the American Psychological Association, Washington, D.C.

Besdine, R. W. (1980). Geriatric medicine: An overview. In C. Eisodorfer (Ed.), *Annual review of gerontology and geriatrics.* New York: Springer.

Bettelheim, B. (1960). *The informed heart.* New York: The Free Press.

Bettelheim, B. (1967). *The empty fortress.* New York: The Free Press.

Bettelheim, B. (1969). *Children of the dream.* London: Collier-Macmillan.

Bettelheim, B. (1973). Bringing up children. *Ladies Homes Journal,* **90,** 28.

Bettelheim, B. (1974). *A home for the heart.* New York: Knopf.

Bibring, E. (1953). The mechanism of depression. In P. Greenacre (Ed.), *Affective disorders.* New York: International Universities Press.

Bieber, I., Dain, H. J., Dince, P. R., Drellich, M. G., Grand, H. C., Gundlach, R. H., Kremer, M. W., Rifkin, A. H., Wilbur, C. B., & Bieber, T. B. (1962). *Homosexuality: A psychoanalytical study.* New York: Random House.

Bijou, S. W., & Baer, D. M. (1961). *Child development: Vol. 1. A systematic and empirical theory.* New York: Appleton-Century-Crofts.

Billings, A. G., Cronkite, R. C., & Moos, R. H. (1983). Social-environmental factors in unipolar depression: Comparisons of depressed patients and nondepressed controls. *Journal of Abnormal Psychology,* **92,** 119–133.

Bindrim, P. (1968). A report on a nude marathon: The effect of physical nudity upon the practice interaction in the marathon group. *Psychotherapy: Theory, Research and Practice,* **5,** 180–188.

Birnbaum, M. (1960). The right to treatment. *American Bar Association Journal,* **46,** 499–505.

Birren, J. E., & Sloane, R. B. (Eds.). (1980). *Handbook of mental health and aging.* Englewood Cliffs, N.J.: Prentice-Hall.

Bitterman, M. E. (1975). Issues in the comparative psychology of learning. In R. B. Masterson, M. E. Bitterman, C. B. G. Campbell, & N. Hotten (Eds.), *The evolution of brain and behavior in vertebrates.* Hillsdale, N.J.: Lawrence Erlbaum Associates.

Blanchard, E. B., & Miller, S. T. (1977). Psychological treatment of cardiovascular disease. *Archives of General Psychiatry,* **34,** 1402–1413.

Blanchard, E. B., Miller, S. T., Abel, G. G., Haynes, M. R., & Wicker, R. (1979). Evaluation of biofeedback in the treatment of borderline essential hypertension. *Journal of Applied Behavior Analysis,* **12,** 99–109.

Bland, K., & Hallam, R. (1981). Relationship between response to graded exposure and marital satisfaction in agoraphobics. *Behaviour Research and Therapy,* **19,** 335–338.

Blanken, A. J., Adams, E. H., & Durell, J. (in press). Drug abuse: Implications and current trends. *Psychiatric Medicine.*

Blatt, B. (1966). The preparation of special educational personnel. *Review of Educational Research,* **36,** 151–161.

Blazer, D. (1982). *Depression in late life.* St. Louis, Mo.: Mosby.

Blazer, D., & Siegler, I. C. (1984). *A family approach to health care of the elderly.* Menlo Park, Calif.: Addison-Wesley.

Blazer, D., & Williams, C. D. (1980). Epidemiology of dysphoria and depression in the elderly population. *American Journal of Psychiatry,* **137,** 439–444.

Blenker, M. (1967). Environmental change and the aging individual. *Gerontologist,* **7,** 101–105.

Bleuler, E. (1923). *Lehrbuch der psychiatrie* (4th ed.). Berlin: Springer.

Bliss, E. L. (1980). Multiple personalities: A report of 14 cases with implications for schizophrenia and hysteria. *Archives of General Psychiatry,* **37,** 1388–1397.

Bloch, S., and Reddaway, P. (1977). *Psychiatric terror: How Soviet psychiatry is used to suppress dissent.* New York: Basic Books.

Block, J. (1971). *Lives through time.* Berkeley, Calif.: Bancroft Books.

Bloomfield, H. H. (1973). Assertive training in an outpatient group of chronic schizophrenics: A preliminary report. *Behavior Therapy,* **4,** 277–281.

Blumenthal, J. A., Williams, R. B., Kong, Y., Schanberg, S. M., & Thompson, I. W. (1978). Type A behavior and angiographically documented coronary disease. *Circulation,* **58,** 634–639.

Bobruff, A., Gardos, G., Tarsy, D., Rapkin, R. M., Cole, J. O., & Moore, P. (1981). Clonazepan and phenobarbital in tardive dyskinesia. *American Journal of Psychiatry,* **138,** 189–193.

Bockhoven, J. (1963). *Moral treatment in American psychiatry.* New York: Springer.

Bohman, M., Cloninger, R. C., Sigvardsson, S., & Knorring, A. von. (1982). Predisposition to criminality in Swedish adoptees: I. Genetic and environmental heterogeneity. *Archives of General Psychology,* **39,** 1233–1241.

Bohman, M., Sigvardsson, S., & Cloninger, C. R (1981). Maternal inheritance of alcohol abuse. *Archives of General Psychiatry,* **38,** 965–969.

Boll, T. J., Heaton, R., & Reitan, R. M. (1974). Neuropsychological and emotional correlates of Huntington's chorea. *Journal of Nervous and Mental Disease,* **158,** 61–69.

Bollerup, T. (1975). Prevalence of mental illness among 70 year olds domiciled in nine Copenhagen suburbs. *Acta Psychiatrica Scandinavica,* **51,** 327–339.

Bolton, A. (1976). A study of the need for and availability of mental health services for mentally retarded jail inmates and juveniles in detention facilities. Unpublished report, Arthur Bolton Associates, Boston. Cited in J. Monahan (1981). *The clinical prediction of violent behavior.* Rockville, Md.: National Institute of Mental Health.

Bond, I. K., & Hutchison, H. C. (1960). Application of reciprocal inhibition therapy to exhibitionism. *Canadian Medical Association Journal,* **83,** 23–25.

Bonica, J. J. (1981). Pain research and therapy: Past and current status and future needs. In L. Ng & J. J. Bonica (Eds.), *Pain, discomfort, and humanitarian care.* New York: Elsevier.

Bootzin, R. R., Engle-Friedman, M., & Hazelwood, L. (1983). Sleep disorders and the elderly. In P. M. Lewinsohn & L. Teri (Eds.), *Clinical geropsychology: New directions in assessment and treatment.* New York: Pergamon Press.

Borkovec, T. D., & O'Brien, G. T. (1976). Methodological and target behavior issues in analogue outcome research. In M. Hersen, R. M. Eisler, & P. M. Miller (Eds.), *Progress in behavior modification,* Vol. 3. New York: Academic Press.

Borkowski, Peck, & Danbery (1983). See Keri Weed letter for Mender, 9/19/85

Bornstein, P. E., Clayton, P. J., Halikas, J. A., & Robins, E. (1973). The depression of widowhood after thirteen months. *British Journal of Psychiatry,* **122,** 561–566.

Bornstein, P. H., Hamilton, P., Miller, D., Quevillon, C., & Spitzform, R. (1977). Reliability and validity enhancement: A treatment package for increasing fidelity of self-report. *Journal of Clinical Psychology,* **33,** 861–866.

Bosch, G. (1970). *Infanile autism.* New York: Springer-Verlag.

Boskind-Lodahl, M., & White, W. C. (1978). The definition and treatment of bulimarexia in college women—A pilot study. *Journal of American College Health Association,* **27,** 84–97.

Botwinick, J. (1977). Intellectual abilities. In J. E. Birren & K. W.

Schaie (Eds.), *Handbook of the psychology of aging.* New York: Van Nostrand Reinhold.

Botwinick, J. (1984). *Aging and Behavior,* (3rd ed.). New York: Springer.

Bourne, P. G. (1970). *Men, stress, and Vietnam.* Boston: Little, Brown.

Bourne, P. G., Alford, J. A., & Bowcock, J. Z. (1966). Treatment of skid row alcoholics with disulfiram. *Quarterly Journal of Studies on Alcohol,* **27,** 42–48.

Bower, G. H. (1981). Mood and memory. *American Psychologist,* **36,** 129–148.

Bower, G. H., Black, J. B., & Turner, T. J. (1979). Scripts in memory for text. *Cognitive Psychology,* **11,** 177–220.

Bowers, M. B., Jr. (1974). Central dopamine turnover in schizophrenic syndromes. *Archives of General Psychiatry,* **31,** 50–54.

Bowlby, J. (1973). *Attachment and loss: Vol. 2. Separation.* New York: Basic Books.

Brand, F. N., Smith, R. T., & Brand, P. A. (1977). Effect of economic barriers to medical care on patients' noncompliance. *Public Health Reports,* **92,** 72–78.

Brand, R. J., Rosenman, R. H., Jenkins, C. D., Sholtz, R. L. & Zyzanski, S. J. (in press). Comparison of coronary heart disease prediction in the Western Collaborative Group Study using the structured interview and the Jenkins Activity Survey assessments of coronary-prone Type A behavior pattern. *Journal of Chronic Diseases.*

Brandt, J., Butters, N., Ryan, C., & Bayog, R. (1983). Cognitive loss and recovery in chronic alcohol abusers. *Archives of General Psychiatry,* **40,** 435–442.

Bransford, J. D., & Johnson, M. K. (1973). Considerations of some problems of comprehension. In W. G. Chase (Ed.), *Visual information processing.* New York: Academic Press.

Brecher, E. M., & the Editors of *Consumer Reports* (1972). *Licit and illicit drugs.* Mount Vernon, N.Y.: Consumers Union.

Brehony, K. A., & Geller, E. S. (1981). Agoraphobia: Appraisal of research and a proposal for an integrative model. In M. Hersen, R. M. Eisler, & P. M. Miller (Eds.), *Progress in behavior modification,* Vol. 12. New York: Academic Press.

Breuer, J., & Freud, S. (1895). *Studies in hysteria.* Translated and edited by J. Strachey, with the collaboration of A. Freud. New York: Basic Books, 1982.

Brickel, C. M. (1984). The clinical use of pets with the aged. *Clinical Gerontologist,* **2,** 72–75.

Bridge, T. B., & Wyatt, R. J. (1980). Paraphrenia: Paranoid states of late life. II. American research. *Journal of the American Geriatrics Society,* **28,** 210–205.

Bridge, T. P., Cannon, H. E., & Wyatt, R. J. (1978). Burned-out schizophrenia: Evidence for age effects on schizophrenic symptomatology. *Journal of Gerontology,* **33,** 835–839.

Bridger, W. H., & Mandel, I. J. (1965). Abolition of the PRE by instructions in GSR conditioning. *Journal of Experimental Psychology,* **69,** 476–482.

Brill, H., & Malzberg, B. (1954). Statistical report on the arrest record of male ex-patients, age 16 and over, released from New York State mental hospitals during the period 1946–48. Unpublished manuscript, New York State Department of Mental Hygiene. As cited in J. Monahan (1981). *The clinical prediction of violent behavior.* Rockville, Md.: National Institute of Mental Health.

Brodie, H. K. H., & Leff, M. J. (1971). Bipolar depression: A comparative study of patient characteristics. *American Journal of Psychiatry,* **127,** 1086–1090.

Broverman, J. K., Broverman, D. M., & Clarkson, F. E. (1970). Sexual stereotypes and clinical judgments of mental health. *Journal of Consulting and Clinical Psychology,* **34,** 1–7.

Brown, A. L. (1974). The role of strategic behavior in retardate memory. In N. R. Ellis (Ed.), *International review of research in mental retardation,* Vol. 7. New York: Academic Press.

Brown, G. W., & Birley, J. L. T. (1968). Crises and life changes and the onset of schizophrenia. *Journal of Health and Social Behavior,* **9,** 203–214.

Brown, G. W., Bone, M., Dalison, B., & Wing, J. K. (1966). *Schizophrenia and social care.* London: Oxford University Press.

Brown, G. W., & Harris, T. O. (1978). *Social origins of depression.* London: Tavistock.

Brown, W. F. (1942). Heredity in the psychoneuroses. *Proceedings of the Royal Society of Medicine,* **35,** 785–790.

Brownell, K. D. (1982). Behavioral medicine. In C. M. Franks, G. T. Wilson, P. C. Kendall, & K. D. Brownell (Eds.), *Annual review of behavior therapy: Theory and practice,* Vol. 8. New York: Guilford Press.

Brownell, K. D., Stunkard, A. J., & Albaum, J. M. (1980). Evaluation and modification of exercise patterns in the natural environment. *American Journal of Psychiatry,* **137,** 1540–1545.

Brownmiller, S. (1975). *Against our will: Men, women and rape.* New York: Simon and Schuster.

Bruch, H. (1980). Preconditions for the development of anorexia nervosa. *American Journal of Psychoanalysis,* **40,** 169–172.

Bruch, H. (1981). Developmental considerations of anorexia nervosa and obesity. *Canadian Journal of Psychiatry,* **26,** 212–217.

Budzynski, T. H., Stoyva, J. M., Adler, C. S., & Mullaney, D. M. (1973). EMG biofeedback and tension headache: A controlled outcome study. *Psychosomatic Medicine,* **35,** 484–496.

Buell, J., Stoddard, P., Harris, F. R., & Baer, D. M. (1968). Collateral social development accompanying reinforcement of outdoor play in a preschool child. *Journal of Applied Behavior Analysis,* **1,** 167–173.

Buglass, D., Clarke, J., Henderson, A. S., Kreitman, N., & Presley, A. S. (1977). A study of agoraphobic housewives. *Psychological Medicine,* **7,** 73–86.

Bukovsky, V. (1977, May 3). General Svetlichny: "We will let him rot in the insane asylum!" *The New York Times.*

Bulman, R. J., & Wortman, C. B. (1977). Attributions of blame and coping in the "real world": Severe accident victims react to their lot. *Journal of Personality and Social Psychology,* **35,** 351–363.

Bunney, W. E., Goodwin, F. K., & Murphy, D. L. (1972). The "Switch Process" in manic-depressive illness. *Archives of General Psychiatry,* **27,** 312–317.

Bunney, W. E., Murphy, D. L., Goodwin, F. K., & Borge, G. F. (1970). The switch process from depression to mania: Relationship to drugs which alter brain amines. *Lancet,* **1,** 1022.

Burgess, A. W., & Holmstrom, L. L. (1974). *Rape: Victims of crisis.* Bowie, Md.: Robert J. Brady Company.

Burwen, L. S., & Campbell, D. T. (1957). The generality of attitudes toward authority and nonauthority figures. *Journal of Abnormal and Social Psychology,* **54,** 24–31.

Buss, A. H. (1966). *Psychopathology.* New York: Wiley.

Busse, E. W. (1976). Hypochondriasis in the elderly: A reaction to social stress. *Journal of the American Geriatrics Society,* **24,** 145–149.

Busse, E. W., & Blazer, D. G. (1979). Disorders related to biological functioning. In E. W. Busse & D. Blazer (Eds.), *Handbook of geriatric psychiatry.* New York: Van Nostrand Reinhold.

Butler, R. N., & Lewis, M. I. (1982). *Aging and mental health: Positive psychosocial approaches* (3d ed.). St. Louis: Mosby.

Butterfield, E. C., & Belmont, J. M. (1977). Assessing and improving the cognitive functions of mentally retarded people. In I. Bialer and M. Sternlicht (Eds.), *The psychology of mental retardation: Issues and approaches.* New York: Psychological Dimensions.

Caddy, G. R. (1983). Alcohol use and abuse. In B. Tabakoff, P. B. Sutker, C. L. Randell (Eds.), *Medical and social aspects of alcohol use.* New York: Plenum Press.

Cadoret, R. J. (1978). Evidence for genetic inheritance of primary affective disorder in adoptees. *American Journal of Psychiatry*, **135**, 463–466. (a)

Cadoret, R. J. (1978). Psychopathology in adopted-away offspring of biologic parents with antisocial behavior. *Archives of General Psychiatry*, **35**, 176–184. (b)

Cadoret, R. J., Cain, C. A., & Grove, W. M. (1980). Development of alcoholism in adoptees raised apart from alcoholic biologic relatives. *Archives of General Psychiatry*, **37**, 561–563.

Calhoun, J. B. (1970). Space and the strategy of life. *Ekistics*, **29**, 425–437.

Cameron, N. (1959). The paranoid pseudo-community revisited. *American Journal of Sociology*, **65**, 52–58.

Cameron, N. (1963). *Personality development and psychopathology: A dynamic approach.* Boston: Houghton Mifflin.

Cameron, N., & Magaret, A. (1951). *Behavior pathology.* Boston: Houghton Mifflin.

Cannon, W. E. (1942). "Voodoo" death. *American Anthropologist*, **44**, 169–182.

Cantwell, D. P. (1975). Genetic studies of hyperactive children. In R. Fieve, D. Rosenthal, & H. Brill (Eds.), *Genetic research in psychiatry.* Baltimore: Johns Hopkins University Press.

Cantwell, D. P., Baker, L., & Rutter, M. (1978). Family factors. In M. Rutter & E. Schopler (Eds.), *Autism: A reappraisal of concepts and treatment.* New York: Plenum Press.

Cantwell, D. P., & Carlson, G. A. (1978). Stimulants. In J. S. Werry (Ed.), *Pediatric psychopharmacology: The use of behavior modifying drugs on children.* New York: Brunner/Mazel.

Cantwell, D. P., Russell, A. T., Mattison, R., & Will, L. (1979). A comparison of DSM-II and DSM-III in the diagnosis of childhood psychiatric disorders. *Archives of General Psychiatry*, **36**, 1208–1228.

Caplan, G. (1964). *Principles of preventive psychiatry.* New York: Basic Books.

Caporael, L. (1976). Ergotism: The satan loosed in Salem? *Science*, **192**, 21–26.

Carpenter, W. T., Murphy, D. L., & Wyatt, R. J. (1975). Platelet monoamine oxidase activity in acute schizophrenia. *American Journal of Psychiatry*, **132**, 438–441.

Carr, A. T. (1971). Compulsive neurosis: Two psychophysiological studies. *Bulletin of the British Psychological Society*, **24**, 256–257.

Carr, A. T. (1974). Compulsive neurosis: A review of the literature. *Psychological Bulletin*, **81**, 311–319.

Carr, E. G., Schreibman, L., & Lovaas, O. I. (1975). Control of echolalic speech in psychotic children. *Journal of Abnormal Child Psychology*, **3**, 331–351.

Carskadon, M. A., Brown, E., & Dement, W. C. (1980). Respiration during sleep in the elderly. *Sleep Research*, **9**, 99.

Cashman, J. A. (1966). *The LSD story:* Greenwich, Conn.: Fawcett Publications.

Casper, R. C., Eckert, E. O., Halmi, K. A., Goldberg, S. C., & Davis, J. M. (1980). Bulimia: Its incidence and clinical importance in patients with anorexia nervosa. *Archives of General Psychiatry*, **37**, 1030–1035.

Cautela, J. R. (1966). Treatment of compulsive behavior by covert sensitization. *Psychological Record*, **16**, 33–41.

Cautela, J. R. (1971). Covert extinction. *Behavior Therapy*, **2**, 192–200.

Chambliss, C. A., & Murray, E. J. (1979). Efficacy attribution, locus of control, and weight loss. *Cognitive Therapy and Research*, **3**, 349–353.

Chao, R. C., Green, D. E., Forrest, J. S., Kaplan, J. N., Winship-Ball, A., & Braude, M. (1976). The passage of ^{14}C-delta^9-tetrahydrocannabinol into the milk of lactating squirrel monkeys. *Research Communications in Chemical Pathology and Pharmacology*, **15**, 303–317.

Chapman, L. J., & Chapman, J. P. (1969). Illusory correlation as an obstacle to the use of valid psychodiagnostic signs. *Journal of Abnormal Psychology*, **74**, 271–287.

Charlesworth, W. B. (1976). Human intelligence as adaptation. An ethological approach. In L. E. Resnick (Ed.), *The nature of intelligence.* Hillsdale, N.J.: Lawrence Erlbaum Associates.

Charney, D. S., Heninger, G. R., & Sternberg, D. E. (1984). Serotonin function and the mechanism of action of antidepressant treatment. *Archives of General Psychiatry*, **41**, 359–365.

Chein, I., Gerard, D. L., Lee, R. S., & Rosenfield, E. (1964). *The road to H: Narcotics, delinquency, and social policy.* New York: Basic Books.

Chester, P. (1972). *Women and madness.* Garden City, N.Y.: Doubleday.

Chesney, M. A., Eagleston, J. R., & Rosenman, R. H. (1980). The Type A Structured Interview: A behavioral assessment in the rough. *Journal of Behavioral Assessment*, **2**, 255–272.

Chesno, F. A., & Kilmann, P. R. (1975). Effects of stimulation intensity on sociopathic avoidance learning. *Journal of Abnormal Psychology*, **84**, 144–151.

Christensen, A. (1983). Intervention. In H. H. Kelley, E. Berscheid, A. Christensen, J. H. Harvey, T. L. Huston, G. Levinger, E. McClintock, L. A. Peplau, & D. R. Peterson (Eds.), *Close relationships.* San Francisco: Freeman.

Christie, A. B. (1982). Changing patterns in mental illness in the elderly. *British Journal of Psychiatry*, **140**, 154–159.

Churchill, D. W. (1969). Psychotic children and behavior modification. *American Journal of Psychiatry*, **125**, 1585–1590.

Churchill, W. (1967). *Homosexual behavior among males: A cross-cultural and cross-species investigation.* Englewood Cliffs, N.J.: Prentice-Hall.

Clark, R. (1970). *Crime in America.* New York: Simon and Schuster.

Clark, W. B., & Cahalan, D. (1976). Changes in drinking behavior over a four-year span. *Addictive Behaviors*, **1**, 251–259.

Clausen, J. A., & Kohn, M. L. (1959). Relation of schizophrenia to the social structure of a small city. In B. Pasamanick (Ed.), *Epidemiology of mental disorder.* Washington, D.C.: American Association for the Advancement of Science.

Clayton, P. J. (1973). The clinical morbidity of the first year of bereavement: A review. *Comparative Psychiatry*, **14**, 151–157.

Clayton, P. J., Halikas, J. A., & Maurice, W. L. (1972). The depression of widowhood. *British Journal of Psychiatry*, **129**, 532–538.

Clayton, V. P., & Birren, J. E. (1980). The development of wisdom across the life span: A reexamination of an ancient topic. In P. B. Baltes & O. G. Brim (Eds.), *Life-span development and behavior,* Vol. 3. New York: Academic Press.

Cleckley, J. (1976). *The mask of sanity* (5th ed.). St. Louis: Mosby.

Cloninger, C. R., Reich, T., & Guze, S. B. (1975). The multifactorial model of disease transmission: II. Sex differences in the familial transmission of sociopathy (antisocial personality). *British Journal of Psychiatry*, **127**, 11–22.

Cloninger, R. C., Sigvardsson, S., Bohman, M., & Knorring, A. von (1982). Predisposition to petty criminality in Swedish adoptees: II. Cross-fostering analysis of gene-environment interaction. *Archives of General Psychiatry*, **39**, 1242–1247.

Cobb, S., & Rose, R. M. (1973). Hypertension, peptic ulcer, and diabetes in air traffic controllers. *Journal of the American Medical Association*, **224**, 489–493.

Cocozza, J., Melick, M., & Steadman, H. (1978). Trends in violent crime among ex-mental patients. *Criminology*, **16**, 317–334.

Cohen, H. L., & Filipczak, J. (1971). *A New learning environment*. San Francisco: Jossey-Bass.

Cohen, S. (1980). Therapeutic aspects. In *Marijuana research findings: 1980*. Washington, D.C.: U.S. Government Printing Office.

Cohen, S. (1981). Adverse effects of marijuana: Selected issues. *Annals of the New York Academy of Science*, **362**, 119–124.

Collaborative study of children treated for phenylketonuria, preliminary report 8 (February 1975). Principal investigator: R. Koch. Presented at the Eleventh General Medicine Conference, Stateline, Nevada.

Combs, G., Jr., & Ludwig, A. M. (1982). Dissociative disorders. In J. H. Greist, J. W. Jefferson, & R. L. Spitzer (Eds.), *Treatment of mental disorders*. New York: Oxford University Press.

Comfort, A. (1980). Sexuality in later life. In J. E. Birren & R. B. Sloane (Eds.), *Handbook of mental health and aging*. Englewood Cliffs, N.J.: Prentice-Hall.

Committee on Government Operations (1985). *The federal response to the homeless crisis*. Washington, D.C.: U.S. Government Printing Office.

Conger, J. J. (1951). The effects of alcohol on conflict behavior in the albino rat. *Quarterly Journal of Studies on Alcohol*, **12**, 1–29.

Conger, J. J., Sawrey, W. L., & Turrell, E. S. (1958). The role of social experience in the production of gastric ulcers in hooded rats in a conflict situation. *Journal of Abnormal and Social Psychology*, **57**, 214–220.

Conners, C. K. (1969). A teacher rating scale for use in drug studies with children. *American Journal of Psychiatry*, **126**, 884–888.

Conners, C. K., Taylor, E., Meo, G., Kurtz, M., & Fournier, M. (1972). Magnesium pemoline and dextroamphetamine: A controlled study in children with minimal brain dysfunction. *Psychopharmacologia*, **26**, 321–336.

Conoley, C. W., Conoley, J. C., McConnell, J. A., & Kimzey, C. E. (1983). The effect of the ABCs of rational emotive therapy and the empty-chair technique of Gestalt therapy on anger reduction. *Psychotherapy: Theory, Research, and Practice*, **20**, 112–117.

Cooper, A. F., Garside, R. F., & Kay, D. W. K. (1976). A comparison of deaf and non-deaf patients with paranoid and affective psychoses. *British Journal of Psychiatry*, **129**, 532–538.

Cooper, A. F., Kay, D. W. K., Curry, A. R., Garside, R. F., & Roth, M. (1974). Hearing loss in paranoid and affective psychoses of the elderly. *Lancet*, **2**, 851–854.

Cooper, A. F., & Porter, R. (1976). Visual acuity and ocular pathology in the paranoid and affective psychoses of later life. *Journal Psychosomatic Research*, **20**, 107–114.

Cooper, J. E., Kendell, R. E., Guland, B. J., Sharpe, L., Copeland, J. R. M., & Simon, R. (1972). *Psychiatric diagnosis in New York and London*. London: Oxford University Press.

Coppen, A., Prange, A. J., Whybrow, P. C., & Noguera, R. (1972). Abnormalities in indoleamines in affective disorders. *Archives of General Psychiatry*, **26**, 474–478.

Corey, G. (1977). *Theory and practice of counseling and psychotherapy*. Belmont, Calif.: Wadsworth.

Costa, P. T., Jr., & McCrae, R. R. (1978). Objective personality assessment. In M. Storandt, I. E. Siegler, & M. R. Elias, (Eds.), *The clinical psychology of aging*. New York: Plenum Press.

Covi, L., Lipman, R. S., Derogatis, L. R., Smith, J. E., & Pattison, J. H. (1974). Drugs and group psychotherapy in neurotic depression. *American Journal of Psychiatry*, **131**, 191–197.

Cowan, P. A., Hoddinott, B. A., & Wright, B. A. (1965). Compliance and resistance in the conditioning of autistic children: An exploratory study. *Child Development*, **36**, 913–923.

Cowen, E. L. (1983). Primary prevention in mental health: Past, present, and future. In R. D. Felner, L. A. Jason, J. N. Moritsugu, & S. S. Farber (Eds.), *Preventive psychology: Theory, research and practice*. New York: Pergamon Press.

Cox, A., Rutter, M., Newman, S., & Bartak, L. (1975). A comparative study of infantile autism and specific developmental language disorders: II. Parental characteristics. *British Journal of Psychiatry*, **126**, 146–159.

Cox, V. C., Paulus, P. B., & McCain, G. (1984). Prison crowding research: The relevance for prison housing standards and a general approach regarding crowding phenomena. *American Psychologist*, **39**, 1148–1160.

Coyne, J. C. (1976). Depression and the response of others. *Journal of Abnormal Psychology*, **85**, 186–193.

Coyle, J. T., Price, D. L., & Delong, M. R. (1983). Alzheimer's disease: A disorder of cortical cholinergic innervation. *Science*, **219**, 1184–1190.

Craft, M. J. (1969). The natural history of psychopathic disorder. *British Journal of Psychiatry*, **115**, 39–44.

Craig, M. M., & Glick, S. J. (1963). Ten years' experience with the Glueck social prediction table. *Crime and Delinquency*, **9**, 249–261.

Craik, F. I. M. (1977). Age differences in human memory. In J. E. Birren & K. W. Schaie (Eds.), *Handbook of the psychology of aging*. New York: Van Nostrand Reinhold.

Creer, T. L. (1982). Asthma. *Journal of Consulting and Clinical Psychology*, **50**, 912–921.

Creer, T. L., Renna, C. M., & Chai, H. (1982). The application of behavioral techniques to childhood asthma. In D. C. Russo & J. W. Varni (Eds.), *Behavioral pediatrics: Research and practice*. New York: Plenum Press.

Creer, T. L., Weinberg, E., & Molk, L. (1974). Managing a hospital behavior problem: Malingering. *Journal of Behavior Therapy and Experimental Psychiatry*, **5**, 259–262.

Crisp, A. H. (1967). The possible significance of some behavioral correlates of weight and carbohydrate intake. *Journal of Psychosomatic Research*, **11**, 117–131.

Crisp, A. H., Palmer, R. L., & Klucy, R. S. (1976). How common is anorexia nervosa? A prevalence study. *British Journal of Psychiatry*, **128**, 529–554.

Crissey, M. S. (1975). Mental retardation. Past, present, and future. *American Psychologist*, **30**, 800–808.

Crowe, R. R. (1974). An adoption study of antisocial personality. *Archives of General Psychiatry*, **31**, 785–791.

Crowe, R. R., Noyes, R., Pauls, D. L., & Slymen, D. J. (1983). A family study of panic disorder. *Archives of General Psychiatry*, **40**, 1065–1069.

Crowe, R. R., Pauls, D. L., Slymen, D. J., & Noyes, R. (1980). A family study of anxiety neurosis: Morbidity risk in families of patients with and without mitral valve prolapse. *Archives of General Psychiatry*, **37**, 77–79.

Crtryn, L., & McKnew, D. H. (1979). Affective disorders. In J. Noshpitz (Ed.), *Basic handbook of child psychiatry,* Vol. 2. New York: Basic Books.

Cruickshank, W. M. (1977). Myths and realities in learning disabilities. *Journal of Learning Disabilities*, **10**, 51–63.

Cummings, J. L., & Benson, D. F. (1983). *Dementia: A clinical approach.* Woburn, Mass.: Butterworth.

Cunningham, C. E., & Barkley, R. A. (1979). The interactions of normal and hyperactive children with their mothers in free play and structured tasks. *Child Development*, **50**, 217–224.

Curran, J. P. (1977). Skills training as an approach to the treatment of heterosexual social anxiety. *Psychological Bulletin*, **89**, 140–157.

Daneman, E. A. (1961). Imipramine in office management of depressive reactions (a double-blind study). *Diseases of the Nervous System*, **22**, 213–217.

Davidson, P. R., Malcolm, P. B., Lanthier, R. D., Barbaree, H. E., & Ho, T. P. (1981). Penile response measurement: Operating characteristics of the Parks plethysmograph. *Behavioral Assessment*, **3**, 137–143.

Davis, J. M. (1976). Overview: Maintenance therapy in psychiatry: II. Affective disorders. *American Journal of Psychiatry*, **133**, 1–13.

Davis, J. M. (1978). Dopamine theory of schizophrenia: A two-factor theory. In L. C. Wynne, R. L. Cromwell, & S. Matthysse (Eds.), *The nature of schizophrenia.* New York: Wiley.

Davis, J. M., Klerman, G., & Schildkraut, J. (1967). Drugs used in the treatment of depression. In L. Efron, J. O. Cole, D. Levine, & J. R. Wittenborn (Eds.), *Psychopharmacology, A review of progress.* Washington, D.C.: U.S. Clearinghouse of Mental Health Information.

Davison, G. C. (1964). A social learning therapy programme with an autistic child. *Behaviour Research and Therapy*, **2**, 146–159.

Davison, G. C. (1966). Differential relaxation and cognitive restructuring in therapy with a "paranoid schizophrenic" or "paranoid state." *Proceedings of the 74th Annual Convention of the American Psychological Association.* Washington, D.C.: American Psychological Association.

Davison, G. C. (1968). Elimination of a sadistic fantasy by a client-controlled counterconditioning technique. *Journal of Abnormal Psychology*, **73**, 84–90. (a)

Davison, G. C. (1968). Systematic desensitization as a counterconditioning process. *Journal of Abnormal Psychology*, **73**, 91–99. (b)

Davison, G. C. (1973). Counter control in behavior modification. In L. A. Hamerlynck, L. C. Handy, & E. J. Mash (Eds.), *Behavior change: Methodology, concepts and practice.* Champaign, Ill.: Research Press.

Davison, G. C. (1974). Homosexuality: The ethical challenge. Presidential address to the Eighth Annual Convention of the Association for Advancement of Behavior Therapy, Chicago.

Davison, G. C. (1976). Homosexuality: The ethical challenge. *Journal of Consulting and Clinical Psychology*, **44**, 157–162.

Davison, G. C. (1978). Not can but ought: The treatment of homosexuality. *Journal of Consulting and Clinical Psychology*, **46**, 170–172.

Davison, G. C. (1980). And now for something completely different: Cognition and little r. In M. J. Mahoney (Ed.), *Psychotherapy process: Current issues and future directions.* New York: Plenum Press.

Davison, G. C., Feldman, P. M., & Osborn, C. E. (1984). Articulated thoughts, irrational beliefs, and fear of negative evaluation. *Cognitive Therapy and Research*, **8**, 349–362.

Davison, G. C., & Goldfried, M. R. (1973). Postdoctoral training in clinical behavior therapy. *Menninger Clinic Bulletin* 17.

Davison, G. C., Robins, C., & Johnson, M. K. (1983). Articulated thoughts during simulated situations: A paradigm for studying cognition in emotion and behavior. *Cognitive Therapy and Research*, **7**, 17–40.

Davison, G. C., & Stuart, R. B. (1975). Behavior therapy and civil liberties. *American Psychologist*, **30**, 755–763.

Davison, G. C., Tsujimoto, R. N., & Glaros, A. G. (1973). Attribution and the maintenance of behavior change in falling asleep. *Journal of Abnormal Psychology*, **82**, 124–133.

Davison, G. C., & Valins, S. (1969). Maintenance of self-attributed and drug-attributed behavior change. *Journal of Personality and Social Psychology*, **11**, 25–33.

Davison, G. C., & Wilson, G. T. (1973). Attitudes of behavior therapists toward homosexuality. *Behavior Therapy*, **4**, 686–696.

Davison, G. C., & Zighelboim, V. (1985). Irrational beliefs in the articulated thoughts of socially anxious college students. Unpublished manuscript, University of Southern California.

deCharms, R. (1968). *Personal causation: The internal affective determinants of behavior.* New York: Academic Press.

DeJong, R. N., & Sugar, O. (1971). *The yearbook of neurology and neurosurgery.* Chicago: Year Book Medical Publishers.

DeJonge, G. A. (1973). Epidemiology of enuresis: A survey of literature. In I. Kolvin, R. C. Mackeith, & S. R. Meadow (Ed.), *Enuresis and encopresis.* Philadelphia: Lippincott.

Dekker, E., & Groen, J. (1956). Reproducible psychogenic attacks of asthma. *Journal of Psychosomatic Research*, **1**, 58–67.

Dekker, E., Pelser, H. E., & Groen, J. (1957). Conditioning as a cause of asthmatic attacks. *Journal of Psychosomatic Research*, **2**, 97–108.

Dement, W. C., Laughton, E., & Carskadon, M. A. (1981). "White paper" on sleep and aging. *Journal of the American Geriatrics Society*, **30**, 25–50.

DeMyer, M. (1975). The nature of the neuropsychological disability of autistic children. *Journal of Autism and Childhood Schizophrenia.*, **5**, 109–127.

DeMyer, M., Barton, S., DeMyer, W. E., Norton, J. A., Allen, J., & Steele, R. (1973). Prognosis in autism: A follow-up study. *Journal of Autism and Childhood Schizophrenia*, **3**, 199–246.

DeMyer, M., Pontius, W., Norton, J. A., Barton, S., Allen, J., & Steele, R. (1972). Parental practices and innate activity in autistic and brain-damaged infants. *Journal of Autism and Childhood Schizophrenia*, **2**, 49–66.

Denhoff, E. (1973). The natural history of children with minimal brain dysfunction. *Annals of the New York Academy of Sciences*, **205**, 188–205.

Depue, R. A., & Monroe, S. M. (1978). Learned helplessness in the perspective of the depressive disorders: Conceptual and definitional issues. *Journal of Abnormal Psychology*, **87**, 3–20.

Detterman, D. K. (1979). Memory in the mentally retarded. In N. R. Ellis (Ed.), *Handbook of mental deficiency, psychological theory and research* (2nd ed.). Hillsdale, N.J.: Lawrence Erlbaum Associates.

Deutsch, A. (1949). *The mentally ill in America.* New York: Columbia University Press.

DeVries, H. A. (1975). Physiology of exercise and aging. In D. S. Woodruff & J. E. Birren (Eds.), *Aging: Scientific perspectives and social issues.* New York: Van Nostrand Reinhold.

Dewys, W. D., Begg, C., & Lavin, P. T. (1980). Prognostic effect of weight loss prior to chemotherapy in cancer patients. *American Journal of Medicine*, **69**, 491–497.

Diament, C., & Wilson, G. T. (1975). An experimental investigation of the effects of covert sensitization in an analogue eating situation. *Behavior Therapy*, **6**, 499–509.

Diamond, B. (1974). The psychiatric prediction of dangerousness. *University of Pennsylvania Law Review*, **123**, 439–452.

Diamond, M. (1982). Sexual identity, monozygotic twins reared in discordant sex roles and a BBC follow-up. *Archives of Sexual Behavior*, **11**, 181–186.

Diamond, S., Baldwin, R., & Diamond, R. (1963). *Inhibition and choice*. New York: Harper and Row.

Didion, J. (1979). *The white album*. New York: Simon and Schuster.

DiMascio, A., Weissman, M. M., Prusoff, B. A., Neu, C., & Zwilling, M. (1979). Differential symptom reduction by drugs and psychotherapy in acute depression. *Archives of General Psychiatry*, **36**, 1450–1456.

Dodson, B. (1974). *Liberating masturbation*. New York: Bodysex Designs.

Dogoloff, L. I. (1980). Prospect of the 1980s: Challenge and response. *Drug Enforcement*, **7**, 2–3.

Dohrenwend, B. S., Krasnoff, L., Askenasy, A. R., & Dohrenwend, B. P. (1978). Exemplification of a method for scaling life events: The PERI life events scale. *Journal of Health and Social Behavior*, **19**, 205–229.

Dole, V., & Nyswander, M. (1966). Methadone maintenance: A report of two years' experience. In *Problems of drug dependence*. Washington, D.C.: National Academy of Science. National Research Council.

Doleys, D. M. (1977). Behavioral treatments for nocturnal enuresis in children: A review of the recent literature. *Psychological Bulletin*, **8**, 30–54.

Dollard, J., & Miller, N. E. (1950). *Personality and psychotherapy*. New York: McGraw-Hill.

Domino, E. F., Krause, R. R., & Bowers, J. (1973). Various enzymes involved with putative transmitters. *Archives of General Psychiatry*, **29**, 195–201.

Donnellan, A. M., Mirenda, P. L., Mesaros, R. A., & Fassbender, L. L. (1984). Analyzing the communicative functions of aberrant behavior. *The Journal of the Association for Persons with Severe Handicaps*, **9**, 201–212.

Doris, J., & Sarason, S. B. (1955). Test anxiety and blame assignment in a failure situation. *Journal of Abnormal Psychology*, **50**, 335–338.

Doubros, S. G. (1966). Behavior therapy with high level, institutionalized, retarded adolescents. *Exceptional Children*, **33**, 229–233.

Douglas, J. D. (1967). *The social meanings of suicide*. Princeton, N.J.: Princeton University Press.

Dovenmuehle, R. H., Recklass, J. B., & Newman, G. (1970). Depressive reactions in the elderly. In *Normal aging*. Durham, N.C.: Duke University Press.

Drabman, R. S., Cordue, G. D., Hammer, D., Jarvie, G. I., & Horton, W. (1979). Developmental trends in eating rates of normal and overweight preschool children. *Child Development*, **50**, 211–216.

Drabman, R. S., Spitalnik, R., & O'Leary, K. D. (1973). Teaching self-control to disruptive children. *Journal of Abnormal Psychology*, **82**, 10–16.

Duck, S. (1984). A perspective on the repair of personal relationships. In S. Duck (Ed.), *Personal relationships 5: Repairing personal relationships*. New York: Academic Press.

Dunham, H. W. (1965). *Community and schizophrenia: An epidemiological analysis*. Detroit: Wayne State University Press.

DuPont, R. W. (1976). Testimony before the subcommittee on aging and subcommittee on alcoholism and narcotics of the U.S. Senate Committee on Labor and Public Welfare, Washington, D.C. Cited in

D. M. Peterson, F. I. Whittington, & E. T. Beer (1979). Drug use and misuse among the elderly. *Journal of Drug Issues*, **9** (1), 5–26.

Durkheim, E. (1897). *Suicide* (2nd ed., 1930, in French). English translation by J. A. Spaulding & G. Simpson, (1951). New York: The Free Press.

Dworkin, B. R., Filewich, R. J., Miller, N. E., & Craigmyle, N. (1979). Baroreceptor activation reduces reactivity to noxious stimulation: Implications for hypertension. *Science*, **205**, 1299–1301.

Dye, C. J. (1978). Psychologist's role in the provision of mental health care for the elderly. *Professional Psychology*, **9**, 38–49.

Dysken, M. W. (1979). Clinical usefulness of sodium amobarbital interviewing. *Archives of General Psychiatry*, **36**, 789–794.

D'Zurilla, T. J., & Goldfried, M. R. (1971). Problem-solving and behavior modification. *Journal of Abnormal Psychology*, **78**, 107–126.

Eastman, C. (1976). Behavioral formulations of depression. *Psychological Review*, **83**, 277–291.

Eckert, E. D., Goldberg, S. C., Halmi, K. A., Casper, R. C., & Davis, J. M. (1982). Depression in anorexia nervosa. *Psychological Medicine*, **12**, 115–122.

Edwards, A. L. (1957). *The social desirability variable in personality research*. New York: Dryden Press.

Edwards, G., Gross, M. M., Keller, J., Moser, J., & Room, R. (1977). *Alcohol related disabilities*. Geneva, Switzerland: World Health Organization.

Edwards, G., Hensman, C., Hawker, A., & Williamson, V. (1967). Alcoholics Anonymous: The anatomy of a self-help group. *Social Psychiatry*, **1**, 195–204.

Egan, G. (1975). *The skilled helper*. Monterey, Calif.: Brooks/Cole.

Ehrhardt, A., & Money, J. (1967). Progestin-induced hermaphroditism: IQ and psychosexual identity in a study of ten girls. *Journal of Sex Research*, **3**, 83–100.

Ellenberger, H. F. (1972). The story of "Anna O": A critical review with new data. *Journal of the History of the Behavior Sciences*, **8**, 267–279.

Ellingson, R. J. (1954). Incidence of EEG abnormality among patients with mental disorders of apparently nonorganic origin: A criminal review. *American Journal of Psychiatry*, **111**, 263–275.

Ellis, A. (1961). *The folklore of sex*. New York: Grove Press.

Ellis, A. (1962). *Reason and emotion in psychotherapy*. New York: Lyle Stuart.

Ellis, A. (1971). Rational-emotive treatment of impotence, frigidity, and other sexual problems. *Professional Psychology*, **2**, 346–349.

Ellis, A. (1984). Rational-emotive therapy. In R. J. Corsini (Ed.), *Current psychotherapies* (3rd. ed.). Itasca, Ill.: Peacock Press.

Ellis, A., & Bernard, M. E. (1983). An overview of rational-emotive approaches to the problems of childhood. In A. Ellis & M. E. Bernard (Eds.), *Rational-emotive approaches to the problems of childhood*. New York: Plenum Press.

Ellis, H. (1906). *Studies in the psychology of sex*. New York: Random House.

Ellis, N. R. (1963). The stimulus trace and behavioral inadequacy. In N. R. Ellis (Ed.), *Handbook of mental deficiency*. New York: McGraw-Hill.

Ellis, N. R. (1970). Memory processes in retardates and normals. In N. R. Ellis (Ed.), *International review of research in mental retardation*, Vol. 4. New York: Academic Press.

Elmore, A. M. (1979). A comparison of the psychophysiological and clinical response to biofeedback for temporal pulse amplitude reduction and biofeedback for increases in hand temperature in the treatment of migraine. Unpublished doctoral dissertation. State University of New York at Stony Brook.

Elmore, A. M., & Tursky, B. (1978). The biofeedback hypothesis: An idea in search of a theory and method. In A. A. Sugerman & R. E. Tarter (Eds.), *Expanding dimensions of consciousness*. New York: Springer.

Elmore, A. M., & Tursky, B. (1981). A comparison of two psychophysiological approaches to the treatment of migraine. *Headache*, **21**, 93–101.

Elmore, J. L., & Sugerman, A. A. (1975). Precipitation of psychosis during electroshock therapy. *Diseases of the Nervous System*, **3**, 115–117.

Endicott, J., Nea, J., Fleiss, J., Cohen, J., Williams, J. B., & Simon, R. (1982). Diagnostic criteria for schizophrenia. Reliability and agreement between systems. *Archives of General Psychiatry*, **39**, 884–889.

Engel, B. T., & Bickford, A. F. (1961). Response specificity: Stimulus response and individual response specificity in essential hypertension. *Archives of General Psychiatry*, **5**, 478–489.

Emery, R. E., & O'Leary, K. D. (1979). Children's perceptions of marital discord and behavior problems of boys and girls. Paper presented at the annual meeting of the Association for Advancement of Behavior Therapy, San Francisco.

Endicott, J., & Spitzer, R. L. (1978). A diagnostic interview: The Schedule for Affective Disorders and Schizophrenia. *Archives of General Psychiatry*, **35**, 837–844.

Englemann, S. (1969). *Conceptual learning*. San Rafael, Calif.: Dimensions Publishing Company.

English, H. B. (1929). Three cases of the "conditioned fear response." *Journal of Abnormal and Social Psychology*, **34**, 221–225.

Ennis, B., & Emery, R. (1978). *The rights of mental patients—An American Civil Liberties Union Handbook*. New York: Avon.

Ennis, B., & Siegel, L. (1973). *The rights of mental patients*. American Civil Liberties Union Handbook Series. New York: Avon.

Enright, J. B. (1970). An introduction to Gestalt techniques. In J. Fagan & I. L. Shepherd (Eds.), *Gestalt therapy now: Theory, techniques, applications*. Palo Alto, Calif.: Science and Behavior Books.

Epstein, L. C., & Lasagna, L. (1969). Obtaining informed consent. *Achives of Internal Medicine*, **123**, 682–688.

Epstein, L. H., Beck, S., Figueroa, J., Farkas, G., Kazdin, A. E., Danema, D., & Becker, D. (1981). The effects of point economy and parent management on urine glucose and metabolic control in children with insulin dependent diabetes. *Journal of Applied Behavior Analysis*, **14**, 365–375.

Epstein, L. H., Masek, B. J., & Marshall, W. R. (1978). A nutritionally based school program for control of eating in obese children. *Behavior Therapy*, **9**, 766–788.

Epstein, L. H., Wing, R. R., Thompson, J. K., & Griffen, W. (1980). Attendance and fitness in aerobics exercise: The effects of contract and lottery procedures. *Behavior Modification*, **4**, 465–479.

Epstein, S. (1979). The stability of behavior: On predicting most of the people much of the time. *Journal of Personality and Social Psychology*, **37**, 1097–1126.

Erikson, E. H. (1950). *Childhood and society*. New York: Norton.

Evans, I. M. (1976). Classical conditioning. In M. P. Feldman & A. Broadhurst (Eds.), *Theoretical and experimental bases of the behaviour therapies*. New York: Wiley.

Evans, R. B. (1969). Childhood parental relationships of homosexual men. *Journal of Consulting and Clinical Psychology*, **33**, 129–135.

Evans, R. I., Rozelle, R. M., Maxwell, S. E., Raines, B. E., Dill, C. A., Guthrie, T. J., Henderson, A. H., & Hill, P. C. (1981). Social modelling films to deter smoking in adolescents: Results of a three-year field investigation. *Journal of Applied Psychology*, **66**, 399–414.

Exner, J. E. (1978). *The Rorschach: A comprehensive system. Vol. 2. Current research and advanced interpretation*. New York: Wiley.

Eysenck, H. J. (1952). The effects of psychotherapy: An evaluation. *Journal of Consulting Psychology*, **16**, 319–324.

Eysenck, H. J. (1957). *Dynamics of anxiety and hysteria*. London: Routledge and Kegan Paul.

Eysenck, H. J. (1975). Crime as destiny. *New Behaviour*, **9**, 46–49.

Fagan, J., & Shepherd, I. L. (Eds.). (1970). *Gestalt therapy now: Theory, techniques, applications*. Palo Alto, Calif.: Science and Behavior Books.

Fagerstrom, K-O. (1978). Measuring degree of physical dependence to tobacco smoking with reference to individualization of treatment. *Addictive Behaviors*, **3**, 235–241.

Fagerstrom, K-O. (1982). A comparison of psychological and pharmacological treatment in smoking cessation. *Journal of Behavioral Medicine*, **5**, 343–351.

Fairburn, C. G. (1980). Self-induced vomiting. *Journal of Psychosomatic Research*, **24**, 193–197.

Fairweather, G. W., Ed. (1964). *Social psychology in treating mental illness: An experimental approach*. New York: Wiley.

Falloon, I. R. H., Boyd, J. L., McGill, C. W., Razani, J., Moss, H. B., & Gilderman, A. N. (1982). Family management in the prevention of exacerbation of schizophrenia: A controlled study. *New England Journal of Medicine*, **306**, 1437–1440.

Farina, A. (1976). *Abnormal psychology*. Englewood Cliffs, N.J.: Prentice-Hall.

Farkas, G., & Rosen, R. C. (1976). The effects of alcohol on elicited male sexual response. *Studies in Alcohol*, **37**, 265–272.

Farris, E. J., Yeakel, E. H., & Medoff, H. (1945). Development of hypertension in emotional gray Norway rats after air blasting. *American Journal of Physiology*, **144**, 331–333.

Feingold, B. F. (1973). *Introduction to clinical allergy*. Springield, Ill.: Charles C. Thomas.

Feingold, B. F. (1975). *Why your child is hyperactive*. New York: Random House.

Feinsilver, D. B., & Gunderson, J. G. (1972). Psychotherapy for schizophrenics—Is it indicated? *Schizophrenia Bulletin*, **1**, 11–23.

Felner, R. D., Stolberg, A., Cowen, E. L. (1975). Crisis events and school mental health referral patterns of young children. *Journal of Consulting and Clinical Psychology*, **43**, 305–310.

Fenichel, O. (1945). *The psychoanalytic theory of neurosis*. New York: Norton.

Fernando, C. K., & Basmajian, J. V. (1978). Biofeedback in physical medicine and rehabilitation. *Biofeedback and Self-regulation*, **3**, 435–455.

Ferster, C. B. (1961). Positive reinforcement and behavioral deficits of autistic children. *Child Development*, **32**, 437–456.

Ferster, C. B. (1965). Classification of behavioral pathology. In L. Krasner & L. P. Ullman (Eds.), *Research in behavior modification*. New York: Holt, Rinehart and Winston.

Feuerstein, R. (1980). *Instrumental enrichment: An intervention program for cognitive modifiability*. Baltimore: University Park Press.

Field, T., Goldberg, S., Stern, D., & Sostek, A. (Eds.). (1980). *High-risk infants and children: Adult and peer interactions*. New York: Academic Press.

Field, T., Sostek, A., Goldberg, J., & Shuman, M. (Eds.). (1979). *Infants born at risk*. New York: Spectrum Books.

Figley, C. R. (1978). Introduction. In C. R. Figley (Ed.), *Stress disorders among Vietnam veterans*. New York: Brunner/Mazel. (a)

Figley, C. R. (1978). Psychosocial adjustment among Vietnam veterans: An overview of the research. In C. R. Figley (Ed.), *Stress disorders among Vietnam veterans.* New York: Brunner/Mazel. (b)

Figley, C. R., & Leventman, S. (1980). Introduction: Estrangement and victimization. In C. R. Figley & S. Leventman (Eds.), *Strangers at home: Vietnam veterans since the war.* New York: Praeger.

Fillmore, K. M., & Caetano, R. (1980). Epidemiology of occupational alcoholism. Paper presented at the National Institute on Alcohol Abuse and Alcoholism's Workshop on Alcoholism in the Workplace. Reston, Va., May 22, 1980.

Finkelhor, D. (1979). *Sexually victimized children.* New York: Free Press.

Finn, S. E. (1982). Base rates, utilities, and DSM-III: Shortcomings of fixed-rule systems of psychodiagnosis. *Journal of Abnormal Psychology*, **91**, 294–302.

Fischer, M. (1971). Psychoses in the offspring of schizophrenic monozygotic twins and their normal co-twins. *British Journal of Psychiatry*, **118**, 43–52.

Fish, F. (1960). Senile schizophrenia. *Journal of Mental Science*, **106**, 938–946.

Fleming, M., Steinman, C., & Bocknek, G. (1980). Methodological problems in assessing sex-reassignment surgery. A reply to Meyer and Reter. *Archives of Sexual Behavior*, **9**, 451–456.

Fletcher, C., & Doll, R. (1969). A survey of doctors' attitudes to smoking. *British Journal of Prevention and Social Medicine*, **23**, 145–153.

Fodor, I. (1978). Phobias in women: Therapeutic approaches. In *Helping women change: A guide for professional counseling.* New York: BMA Audio Cassette Program.

Folstein, M. F., & McHugh, P. R. (1978). Dementia syndrome of depression. In R. Katzman, R. D. Terry, & K. L. Bick (Eds.), *Alzheimer's disease: Senile dementia and related disorders*, Vol. 7. *Aging* New York: Raven Press.

Folstein, S., & Rutter, M. (1978). A twin study of individuals with infantile autism. In M. Rutter & E. Schopler (Eds.), *Autism: A reappraisal of concepts and treatment.* New York: Plenum Press.

Fontana, A. (1966). Familial etiology of schizophrenia: Is a scientific methodology possible? *Psychological Bulletin*, **66**, 214–228.

Ford, C., & Neale, J. M. (1985). Effects of a helplessness induction on judgments of control. *Journal of Personality and Social Psychology.*

Ford, C. S., & Beach, F. A. (1951). *Patterns of sexual behavior.* New York: Harper.

Ford, C. V., & Sbordone, R. J. (1980). Attitudes of psychiatrists towards elderly patients. *American Journal of Psychiatry*, **137**, 571–575.

Ford, D. H., & Urban, H. B. (1963). *Systems of psychotherapy: A comparative study.* New York: Wiley.

Fordney-Settlage, D. S. (1975). Heterosexual dysfunction: Evaluation of treatment procedures. *Archives of Sexual Behavior*, **4**, 367–388.

Fordyce, W. E. (1973). An operant conditioning method for managing chronic pain. *Postgraduate Medicine*, **53**, 123–128.

Fordyce, W. E. (1976). *Behavioral methods for chronic pain and illness.* St. Louis: Mosby.

Frances, A. (1980). The DSM-III personality disorders section: A commentary. *American Journal of Psychiatry*, **137**, 1050–1054.

Frank, J. D. (1973). *Persuasion and healing* (2nd ed.). Balitmore: Johns Hopkins University Press.

Frankel, B. G., & Whitehead, P. C. (1981). *Drinking and damage: Theoretical advantages and implications for prevention.* Monograph 14. New Brunswick, N.J.: Rutgers Center of Alcohol Studies.

Frankl, V. (1959). *From death camp to existentialism.* Boston: Beacon Press.

Frankl, V. (1963). *Man's search for meaning.* New York: Washington Square Press.

Franks, C. M. (1984). Behavior therapy with children and adolescents. In G. T. Wilson, C. M. Franks, K. D. Brownell, & P. C. Kendall (Eds.), *Annual review of behavior therapy: Theory and practice,* Vol. 9. New York: Guilford Press.

Freed, E. X. (1971). Anxiety and conflict: Role of drug-dependent learning in the rat. *Quarterly Journal of Studies on Alcohol*, **32**, 13–29.

Freud, A. (1946). *The ego and mechanisms of defense.* New York: International Universities Press.

Freud, A. (1946). *The psychoanalytic treatment of children: Lectures and essays.* London: Imago.

Freud, S. (1905). Three contributions to the theory of sex. In A. A. Brill (Ed.), *The basic writings of Sigmund Freud.* New York: Modern Library, 1938.

Freud, S. (1909). Analysis of a phobia in a five-year-old boy. In *Collected works of Sigmund Freud,* Vol. 10. London: Hogarth Press.

Freud, S. (1915). A case of paranoia running counter to the psychoanalytical theory of the disease. In *Collected papers*, Vol. 2. London: Hogarth Press, 1956.

Freud, S. (1917). Mourning and melancholia. In *Collected papers,* Vol. 4. London: Hogarth Press and the Institute of Psychoanalysis, 1950.

Freud, S. (1918). Lines of advance in psychoanalytic therapy. In *The complete psychological works of Sigmund Freud.* Translated by J. Strachey. London: The Hogarth Press, and the Institute of Psychoanalysis, 1955.

Freud, S. (1936). *The problem of anxiety.* New York: Norton, 1926.

Freud, S. (1937). Analysis terminable and interminable. *International Journal of Psychoanalysis*, **18**, 373–391.

Freud, S. (1949). *A general introduction to psychoanalysis.* New York: Garden City Publishing Company.

Freund, K. (1963). A laboratory method for diagnosing predominance of homo- and hetero-erotic interest in the male. *Behaviour Research and Therapy*, **1**, 85–93.

Friar, L. R., & Beatty, J. (1976). Migraine: Management by trained control of vasoconstriction. *Journal of Consulting and Clinical Psychology*, **44**, 46–53.

Friedberg, C. K. (1966). *Diseases of the heart* (3rd ed.). Philadelphia: Saunders.

Friedman, E., Shopsin, B., Sathananthan, G., & Gershon, S. (1974). Blood platelet monoamine oxidase activity in psychiatric patients. *American Journal of Psychiatry*, **131**, 1392–1394.

Friedman, J. M. (1978). Sexual adjustment of the postcoronary male. In J. LoPiccolo & L. LoPiccolo (Eds.), *Handbook of sex therapy.* New York: Plenum Press.

Friedman, M. (1969). *Pathogenesis of coronary artery disease.* New York: McGraw-Hill.

Friedman, M., Thoresen, C. E., Gill, J. J., Ulmer, D., Thompson, L., Powell, L., Price, A., Elek, S. R., Rabin, D. D., Breall, W. S., Piaget, G., Dixon, T., Bourg, E., Levy, R., & Tasto, D. I. (1982). Feasibility of altering Type A behavior pattern after myocardial infarction. *Circulation*, **66**, 83–92.

Friedman, R., & Dahl, L. K. (1975). The effect of chronic conflict on the blood pressure of rats with a genetic susceptibility to experimental hypertension. *Psychosomatic Medicine*, **37**, 402–416.

Fristoe, M., & Lloyd, L. L. (1979). Nonspeech communication. In N. R. Ellis (Ed.), *Handbook of mental deficiency, psychological the-*

ory and research (2nd ed.). Hillsdale, N.J.: Lawrence Erlbaum Associates.

Fromm-Reichmann, F. (1948). Notes on the development of treatment of schizophrenics by psychoanalytic psychotherapy. *Psychiatry*, **11**, 263–273.

Fromm-Reichmann, F. (1952). Some aspects of psychoanalytic therapy with schizophrenics. In E. Brady & F. C. Redlich (Eds.), *Psychotherapy with schizophrenics*. New York: International Universities Press.

Frude, N. (1982). The sexual nature of sexual abuse: A review of the literature. *Child Abuse and Neglect*, **6**, 211–223.

Furinan, Stolberg, & Coner (1975). xxxxxxxx ?????????? xxxxxx

Gagnon, J. H. (1977). *Human sexualities*. Chicago: Scott, Foresman.

Furman, W., Rahe, D., & Hartup, W. (1979). Rehabilitation of socially withdrawn preschool children through mixed-age and same-age socialization. *Child Development,*, **50**, 915–922.

Gagnon, J. H., & Davison, G. C. (1974). Enhancement of sexual responsiveness in behavior therapy. Paper presented at the 82nd Annual Convention of the American Psychological Association, New Orleans.

Gagnon, J. H., & Davison, G. C. (1976). Asylums, the token economy, and the metrics of mental life. *Behavior Therapy*, **7**, 528–534.

Gagnon, J. H., & Simon, W. (1973). *Sexual conduct: The social origins of human sexuality*. Chicago: Aldine.

Gaines, J. (1974). The founder of Gestalt therapy: A sketch of Fritz Perls. *Psychology Today*, **8**, 117–118.

Galin, D., Diamond, R., & Braff, D. (1977). Lateralization of conversion symptoms: More frequent on the left. *American Journal of Psychiatry*, **134**, 578–580.

Gallagher, D., Breckenridge, J. N., Thompson, L. W., Dessonville, C., & Amaral, P. (1982). Similarities and differences between normal grief and depression in older adults. *Essence*, **5**, 127–140.

Gallagher, D., & Thompson, L. W. (1982). Elders' maintenance of treatment benefits following individual psychotherapy for depression: Results of a pilot study and preliminary data from an ongoing replication study. Paper presented at the annual meeting of the American Psychological Association, Washington, D.C.

Gallagher, D., & Thompson, L. W. (1983). Cognitive therapy for depression in the elderly. A promising model for treatment and research. In L. D. Breslau & M. R. Haug (Eds.), *Depression and Aging: Causes, care and consequences*. New York: Springer.

Garcia, J., McGowan, B. K., & Green, K. F. (1972). Biological constraints on conditioning. In A. H. Black & W. F. Prokasy (Eds.), *Classical conditioning II: Current research and theory*. New York: Appleton-Century-Crofts.

Garfield, S., & Kurtz, R. (1974). A survey of clinical psychologists: Characteristics, activities, and orientations. *The Clinical Psychologist*, **28**, 7–10.

Garfinkel, P. E., Moldofsky, H., & Garner, D. M. (1980). The heterogeneity of anorexia nervosa. *Archives of General Psychiatry*, **37**, 1036–1040.

Garmezy, N. (1977). DSM-III: Never mind the psychologists—Is it good for the children? *The Clinical Psychologist*, **31**, 3–4.

Gauthier, Y., Fortin, C., Drapeau, P., Breton, J., Gosselin, J., Quintal, L., Weisnagel, J. & Lamarre, A. (1978). Follow-up study of 35 asthmatic preschool children. *Journal of the American Academy of Child Psychiatry*, **17**, 679–694.

Gauthier, Y., Fortin, C., Drapeau, P., Breton, J., Gosselin, J., Quintal, L., Weisnagel, J., Tetreault, L., & Pinard, G. (1977). The mother-child relationship and the development of autonomy and self-assertion in young (14–30 months) asthmatic children. *Journal of the American Academy of Child Psychiatry*, **16**, 109–131.

Gebhard, P. H., Gagnon, J. H., Pomeroy, W. B., & Christenson, C. V. (1965). *Sex offenders*. New York: Harper and Row.

Geer, J. H., Heiman, J., & Leitenberg, H. (1984). *Human sexuality*. Englewood Cliffs, N.J.: Prentice-Hall.

Geer, J. H., Davison, G. C., & Gatchel, R. I. (1970). Reduction of stress in humans through nonveridical perceived control of aversive stimulation. *Journal of Personality and Social Psychology*, **16**, 731–738.

Geer, J. H., Morokoff, P., & Greenwood, P. (1974). Sexual arousal in women. The development of a measuring device for vaginal blood volume. *Archives of Sexual Behavior*, **3**, 559–566.

Geis, G. (1977). Forcible rape: An introduction. In D. Chappell, R. Geis, & G. Geis (Eds.), *Forcible rape: The crime, the victim, and the offender*. New York: Columbia University Press.

Geis, G., & Monahan, J. (1976). The social ecology of violence. In T. Lickona (Ed.), *Moral development and behavior*. New York: Holt, Rinehart and Winston.

Geller, E., Ritvo, E. R., Freeman, B. J., & Yuwiler, A. (1982). Preliminary observations on the effect of fenfluramine on blood serotonin and symptoms in three autistic boys. *New England Journal of Medicine*, **307**, 165–169.

Geller, E., Yokota, A., Schroth, P., & Novak, P. (1984). Study of fenfluramine in outpatients with the syndrome of autism. *Journal of Pediatrics*, **105**, 823–828.

General Register Office (1968). *A glossary of mental disorders*. Studies on Medical and Population Subjects 22. London: General Register Office.

Gentry, W. D., Chesney, A. P., Gary, H. G., Hall, R. P., & Harburg, E. (1982). Habitual anger-coping styles: I. Effect of mean blood pressure and risk for essential hypertension. *Psychosomatic Medicine*, **44**, 195–202.

Gentry, W. D., Chesney, A. P., Hall, R. P., & Harburg, E. (1981). Effect of habitual anger-coping pattern on blood pressure in black/white, high/low stress area respondents. *Psychosomatic Medicine*, **43**, 88.

George, L. K. (1980). *Role transitions in later life*. Monterey, Calif.: Brooks Cole.

George, L. K., & Weiler, S. J. (1981). Sexuality in middle and late life: The effects of age, cohort, and gender. *Archives of General Psychiatry*, **38**, 919–923

Gerald, P. S. (1980). X-Linked mental retardation and an X-chromosome marker. *New England Journal of Medicine*, **303**, 696–697.

Gerbino, L., Oleshansky, M., & Gershon, S. (1978). Clinical use and mode of action of lithium. In M. A. Lipton, A. DiMascio, & F. K. Killam (Eds.), *Psychopharmacology: A generation of progress*. New York: Raven Press.

Gibbons, D. C. (1975). *Delinquent behavior*. Englewood Cliffs, N.J.: Prentice-Hall.

Gibbs, J. (Ed.). (1968). *Suicide*. New York: Harper and Row.

Gilboy, J. A., & Schmidt, J. R. (1971). "Voluntary" hospitalization of the mentally ill. *Northwestern University Law Review*, **66**, 429–439.

Ginsburg, A. B., & Goldstein, S. G. (1974). Age bias in referral to psychological consultation. *Journal of Gerontology*, **29**, 410–415.

Gittelman-Klein, R., & Klein, D. F. (1976). Methylphenidate effects in learning disabilities. *Archives of General Psychiatry*, **33**, 655–664.

Gittelman-Klein R., Klein, D. F., Abikoff, H., Katz, S., Gloisten, A. C., & Kates, W. (1976). Relative efficacy of methylphenidate and behavior modification in hyperkinetic children: An interim report. *Journal of Abnormal Child Psychology*, **4**, 361–379. (a)

Gittelman-Klein, R., Klein, D. F., Katz, S., Saraf, K., & Pollack, E. (1976). Comparative effects of methylphenidate and thioridazine in hyperkinetic children. *Archives of General Psychiatry*, **33**, 1217–1231. (b)

Glaser, G. H., Newman, R. J., & Schafer, R. (1963). Interictal psychosis in psychomotor-temporal lobe epilepsy: An EEG psychological study. In G. H. Glaser (Ed.), *EEG and behavior.* New York: Basic Books.

Glass, C. R., & Merluzzi, T. V. (1981). Cognitive assessment of social-evaluative anxiety. In T. W. Merluzzi, C. R. Glass, & M. Genest (Eds.), *Cognitive assessment.* New York: Guilford.

Glass, D. C. (1977). *Behavior patterns, stress, and coronary disease.* Hillsdale, N.J.: Lawrence Erlbaum Associates.

Glassman, A. H., & Roose, S. P. (1981). Delusional depression. *Archives of General Psychiatry*, **38**, 424–427.

Glover, E. (1956). *On the early development of mind.* New York: International Universities Press.

Glueck, S., & Glueck, E. (1959). *Predicting delinquency and crime.* Cambridge, Mass.: Harvard University Press.

Goetzl, U., Green, R., Whybrow, P., & Jackson, R. (1974). X-linkage revisited. *Archives of General Psychiatry*, **31**, 665–671.

Goffman, E. (1961). *Asylums: Essays on the social situation of mental patients and other inmates.* Chicago: Aldine.

Goldberg, E. M., & Morrison, S. L. (1963). Schizophrenia and social class. *British Journal of Psychiatry*, **109**, 785–802.

Golden, C. J. (1981). A standardized version of Luria's neuropsychological tests: A quantitative and qualitative approach to neuropsychological evaluation. In S. B. Filskov & T. J. Boll (Eds.), *Handbook of clinical neuropsychology.* New York: Wiley.

Golden, C. J., Hammeke, T., & Purisch, A. (1978). Diagnostic validity of a standardized neuropsychological battery derived from Luria's neuropsychological test. *Journal of Consulting and Clinical Psychology*, **46**, 1258–1265.

Goldfried, M. R. (1980). Psychotherapy as coping skills training. In M. J. Mahoney (Ed.), *Psychotherapy process: Current issues and future directions.* New York: Plenum Press.

Goldfried, M. R., & Davison, G. C. (1976). *Clinical behavior therapy.* New York: Holt, Rinehart and Winston.

Goldfried, M. R., Decenteceo, E. T., & Weinberg, L. (1974). Systematic rational restructuring as a self-control technique. *Behavior Therapy*, **5**, 247–254.

Goldfried, M. R., & D'Zurilla, T. J. (1969). A behavioral-analytic model for assessing competence. In C. D. Speilberger (Ed.), *Current topics in clinical and community psychology,* Vol. 1. New York: Academic Press.

Goldfried, M. R., Linehan, M., & Smith, J. L. (1978). Reduction of text anxiety through cognitive restructuring. *Journal of Consulting and Clinical Psychology*, **46**, 32–39.

Goldfried, M. R., & Sobocinski, D. (1975). Effects of irrational beliefs on emotional arousal. *Journal of Consulting and Clinical Psychology*, **43**, 504–510.

Goldfried, M. R., Stricker, G., & Weiner, I. B. (1971). *Rorschach handbook of clinical and research applications.* Englewood Cliffs, N.J.: Prentice-Hall.

Goldstein, A. (1976). Opioid peptides (endorphins) in pituitary and brain. *Science*, **193**, 1081–1086.

Goldstein, M., & Rodnick, E. (1975). The family's contribution to the etiology of schizophrenia: Current status. *Schizophrenia Bulletin*, **14**, 48–63.

Goldstein, S. E., & Birnbom, F. (1976). Hypochondriasis and the elderly. *Journal of the American Geriatrics Society*, **24**, 150–154.

Goodwin, D. W. (1979). Alcoholism and heredity: A review and hypothesis. *Archives of General Psychiatry*, **36**, 57–61.

Goodwin, D. W. (1982). Substance induced and substance use disorders: Alcohol. In J. H. Griest, J. W. Jefferson, & R. L. Spitzer (Eds.), *Treatment of mental disorders.* New York: Oxford University Press.

Goodwin, D. W., Crane, J. B., & Guze, S. B. (1969). Alcoholic "blackouts": A review and clinical study of 100 alcoholics. *American Journal of Psychiatry*, **26**, 191–198.

Goodwin, D. W., & Guze, S. B. (1984). *Psychiatric diagnosis* (3rd ed.). New York: Oxford University Press.

Goodwin, D. W., Schulsinger, F., Hermansen, L., Guze, S. B., & Winokur, G. A. (1973). Alcohol problems in adoptees raised apart from alcoholic biological parents. *Archives of General Psychiatry*, **128**, 239–243.

Goodwin, D. W., Schulsinger, F., Knop, J., Mednick, S. A., & Guze, S. B. (1977). Psychopathology in adopted and nonadopted daughters of alcoholics. *Archives of General Psychiatry*, **34**, 1005–1009.

Gorenstein, E. E. (1982). Frontal lobe functions in psychopaths. *Journal of Abnormal Psychology*, **91**, 368–379.

Gorman, J. M., Levy, G. F., Liebowitz, M. R., McGrath, P., Appleby, I. L., Dillon, D. J., Davies, S. O., & Klein, D. F. (1983). Effect of acute beta-adrenergic blockade on lactate-induced panic. *Archives of General Psychiatry*, **40**, 1079–1082.

Gotlib, I. H., & Robinson, L. A. (1982). Responses to depressed individuals: Discrepancies between self-report and observer-rated behavior. *Journal of Abnormal Psychology*, **91**, 231–240.

Gottesman, I. (1962). Differential inheritance of the psychoneuroses. *Eugenics Quarterly*, **9**, 223–227.

Gottesman, I., & Shields, J. (1972). *Schizophrenia and genetics: A twin study vantage point.* New York: Academic Press.

Gottlieb, J., Gottlieb, B. W., Schmelkin, L. P., & Curci, R. (1983). Low- and high-IQ learning disabled children in the mainstream. *Analysis and Intervention in Developmental Disabilities*, **3**, 59–69.

Gottman, J., Notarius, C., Gonso, J., & Markman, H. (1976). *A couple's guide to communication.* Champaign, Ill.: Research Press.

Gove, W. R. (1970). Societal reaction as an explanation of mental illness: An evaluation. *American Sociological Review*, **35**, 873–884.

Gove, W. R., & Fain, T. (1973). The stigma of mental hospitalization. *Archives of General Psychiatry*, **28**, 494–500.

Gove, W. R., & Tudor, J. (1973). Adult sex roles and mental illness. *American Journal of Sociology*, **78**, 812–835.

Goyette, C. H., & Conners, C. K. (1977) Food additives and hyperkinesis. Paper presented at the 85th Annual Convention of the American Psychological Association.

Grabowski, J. (Ed.). (1984). *Cocaine: Pharmacology, effects, and treatment of abuse.* Rockville, Md.: National Institute on Drug Abuse.

Graham, D. T. (1967). Health, disease and the mind-body problem: Linguistic parallelism. *Psychosomatic Medicine*, **29**, 52–71.

Graham, J. R., & Wolff, H. G. (1938). Mechanisms of migraine headache and action of ergotamine tartrate. *Archives of Neurology and Psychiatry*, **18**, 23–45.

Graham, P. J., Rutter, M. L., Yule, W., & Pless, I. B. (1967). Childhood asthma: A psychosomatic disorder? Some epidemiological considerations. *British Journal of Preventive Medicine*, **21**, 78–85.

Gray, J. (1971). *The psychology of fear and stress.* New York: McGraw-Hill.

Green, R. (1974). *Sexual identity conflict in children and adults.* New York: Basic Books.

Green, R. (1976). One hundred ten feminine and masculine boys: Behavioral contrasts and demographic similarities. *Archives of Sexual Behavior*, **5**, 425–446.

Green, R., & Money, J. (1969). *Transsexualism and sex reassignment.* Baltimore: Johns Hopkins University Press.

Greenberg, L. S., & Rice, L. N. (1981). The specific effects of a gestalt intervention. *Psychotherapy: Theory, Research, and Practice,* **18,** 31–37.

Greenblatt, D. J., & Shader, R. I. (1978). Pharmacotherapy of anxiety with benzodiazepines and β-adrenergic blockers. In M. A. Lipton, A. DiMascio, & K. F. Killiam (Eds.), *Psychopharmacology: A generation of progress.* New York: Raven Press.

Greenblatt, M., Solomon, M. H., Evans, A. S., & Brooks, G. W., (Eds.), (1965). *Drugs and social therapy in chronic schizophrenia.* Springfield, Ill.: Charles C. Thomas.

Grings, W. W., & Dawson, M. E. (1978). *Emotions and bodily responses: A psychophysiological approach.* New York: Academic Press.

Grinker, R. R., & Spiegel, J. P. (1945). *War neuroses.* New York: Arno Press, 1979.

Gross, M. B., & Wilson, W. C. (1974). *Minimal brain dysfunction.* New York: Brunner/Mazel.

Grossman, H. J. (Ed.). (1983). *Classification in mental retardation.* Washington, D.C.: American Association of Mental Deficiency.

Grosz, H. J., & Zimmerman, J. (1970). A second detailed case study of functional blindness: Further demonstration of the contribution of objective psychological laboratory data. *Behavior Therapy,* **1,** 115–123.

Groth, N. A., & Burgess, A. W. (1977). Sexual dysfunction during rape. *New England Journal of Medicine,* **297,** 764–766.

Group for Advancement of Psychiatry. (1966). *Psychopathological disorders in childhood: Theoretical considerations and a proposed classification.* Report 62. New York: Mental Health Memorials Center.

Gubbay, S., Lobascher, M., & Kingerlee, P. (1970). A neurological appraisal of autistic children: Results of a Western Australia survey. *Developmental Medicine and Child Neurology,* **12,** 422–429.

Guerney, B. G. (Ed.). (1969) *Psychotherapeutic agents: New roles for nonprofessionals, parents and teachers.* New York: Holt, Rinehart and Winston.

Gunderson, J. G., Kolb, J. E., & Austin, V. (1981). The diagnostic interview for borderline patients. *American Journal of Psychiatry,* **138,** 896–903.

Gurland, B. J., & Cross, P. S. (1982). Epidemiology of psychopathology in old age. In L. F. Jarvik & G. W. Small (Eds.), *Psychiatric Clinics of North America.* Philadelphia: Saunders.

Gurman, A. S., & Kniskern, D. P. (1978). Research on marital and family therapy: Progress, perspective, and prospect. In S. L. Garfield & A. E. Bergin (Eds.), *Handbook of psychotherapy and behavior change: An empirical analysis* (2nd ed.). New York: Wiley.

Gurman, A. S., & Kniskern, D. P. (1981). Family therapy outcome research: Knowns and unknowns. In A. S. Gurman & D. P. Kniskern (Eds.), *Handbook of family therapy.* New York: Brunner/Mazel.

Guze, S. B. (1967). The diagnosis of hysteria: What are we trying to do? *American Journal of Psychiatry,* **124,** 491–498.

Guze, S. B. (1976). *Criminality and psychiatric disorders.* New York: Oxford University Press.

Haaga, D. A., & Davison, G. C. (in press). Cognitive change methods. In A. P. Goldstein & F. H. Kanfer (Eds.), *Helping people change* (3rd ed.). Elmsford, N.Y.: Pergamon Press.

Habot, B., & Libow, L. S. (1980). The interrelationship of mental and physical status and its assessment in the older adult: Mind-body interaction. In J. E. Birren & R. B. Sloane (Eds.), *Handbook of mental health and aging.* Englewood Cliffs, N.J.: Prentice-Hall.

Hafner, R. J. (1982). Marital interaction in persisting obsessive-compulsive disorders. *Australian and New Zealand Journal of Psychiatry,* **16,** 171–178.

Hafner, R. J., Gilchrist, P., Bowling, J., & Kalucy, R. (1981). The treatment of obsessional neurosis in a family setting. *Australian and New Zealand Journal of Psychiatry,* **15,** 145–151.

Haggard, E. (1943). Some conditions determining adjustment during and readjustment following experimentally induced stress. In S. Tomkins (Ed.), *Contemporary psychopathology.* Cambridge, Mass.: Harvard University Press.

Haley, S. A. (1978). Treatment implications of post-combat stress response syndromes for mental health professionals. In C. R. Figley (Ed.), *Stress disorders among Vietnam veterans.* New York: Brunner/Mazel.

Hall, C. S. (1954). *A primer of Freudian psychology.* New York: New American Library.

Halleck, S. L. (1971). *The politics of therapy.* New York: Science House.

Hamilton, E. W., & Abramson, L. Y. (1983). Cognitive patterns and major depressive disorder: A longitudinal study in a hospital setting. *Journal of Abnormal Psychology,* **92,** 173–184.

Hammen, C. L. (1980). Depression in college students: Beyond the Beck Depression Inventory. *Journal of Consulting and Clinical Psychology,* **48,** 126–128.

Hammen, C. L., & Cochran, S. D. (1981). Cognitive correlates of life stress and depression in college students. *Journal of Abnormal Psychology,* **90,** 23–27.

Hanusa, B. H., & Schulz, R. (1977). Attributional mediators of learned helplessness. *Journal of Personality and Social Psychology,* **35,** 602–611.

Haracz, J. L. (1982). The dopamine hypothesis: An overview of studies with schizophrenic patients. *Schizophrenia Bulletin,* **8,** 438–469.

Harburg, E., Erfurt, J. C., Hauenstein, L. S., Chape, C., Schull, W. J., & Schork, M. A. (1973). Socioecological stress, suppressed hostility, skin color, and black-white male blood pressure: Detroit. *Psychosomatic Medicine,* **35,** 276–296.

Hare, R. D. (1970). *Psychopathy: Theory and research.* New York: Wiley.

Hare, R. D. (1978). Electrodermal and cardiovascular correlates of sociopathy. In R. D. Hare & D. Schalling (Eds.), *Psychopathic behaviour: Approaches to research.* New York: Wiley.

Hare, R. D. (1980). A research scale for the assessment of psychopathy in criminal populations. *Personality and Individual Differences,* **1,** 111–119.

Hare, R. D. (in press). Psychopathy and physiological activity during anticipation of an aversive stimulus in a distraction paradigm. *Psychophysiology.*

Hare, R. D., & Jutai, J. W. (in preparation). Psychopathy and electrocortical indices of perceptual processing during selective attention.

Harlow, J. M. (1868). Recovery from the passage of an iron bar through the head. *Publication of the Massachusetts Medical Society,* **2,** 327ff.

Harrington, A., & Sutton-Simon, K. (1977). Rape. In A. P. Goldstein, P. J. Monti, T. J. Sardino, & D. J. Green (Eds.), *Police crisis intervention.* Kalamazoo, Mich.: Behaviordelia.

Harris, E. L., Noyes, R., Crowe, R. R., & Chaudhry, D. R. (1983). Family study of agoraphobia: Report of a pilot study. *Archives of General Psychiatry,* **40,** 1061–1064.

Hart, B. M., Reynolds, N. J., Baer, D. M., Brawley, E. R., & Harris, F. R. (1968). Effect of contingent and noncontingent social reinforcement on the cooperative play of a preschool child. *Journal of Applied Behavior Analysis, 1*, 73-76.

Hartmann, H. (1958). *Ego psychology and the problem of adaptation.* New York: International Universities Press.

Harvey, J., Judge, C., & Wiener, S. (1977). Familial X-linked mental retardation with an X chromosome abnormality. *Journal of Medical Genetics, 14*, 45-50.

Hawley, C., & Buckley, R. (1974). Food dyes and hyperkinetic children. *Academic Therapy, 10*, 27-32.

Haynes, S. N., & Horn, W. F. (1982). Reactivity in behavioral observation: A review. *Behavioral Assessment, 4*, 369-385.

Hays, P. (1976). Etiological factors in manic-depressive psychoses. *Archives of General Psychiatry, 33*, 1187-1188.

Haywood, H. C., Filler, J. W., Jr., Shiffman, M. A., & Chatelanat, G. (1975). Behavioral assessment in mental retardation. In P. McReynolds (Ed.), *Advances in psychological assessment,* Vol. 3. Palo Alto, Calif.: Science and Behavior Books.

Heaton, R. K. (1975). Subject expectancy and environmental factors as determinants of psychedelic flashbacks. *Journal of Nervous and Mental Disease, 161*, 157-165.

Heaton, R. K., & Victor, R. G. (1976). Personality characteristics associated with psychedelic flashbacks in natural and experimental settings. *Journal of Abnormal Psychology, 85*, 83-90.

Heiman, J. R., & LoPiccolo, J. (1983). Effectiveness of daily versus weekly therapy in the treatment of sexual dysfunction. Unpublished manuscript, State University of New York at Stony Brook.

Heiman, N. M. (1973). Postdoctoral training in community mental health. *Menninger Clinical Bulletin 17.*

Heller, J. (1974). *Something happened.* New York: Knopf.

Hembree, W. C., Nahas, G. G., & Huang, H. F. S. (1979). Changes in human spermatozoa associated with high dose marihuana-smoking. In G. G. Nahas & W. D. M. Paton (Eds.), *Marihuana: Biological effects.* Elmsford, N.Y.: Pergamon Press.

Hempel, C. (1958). The theoretician's dilemma. In H. Feigl, M. Scriven, & G. Maxwell (Eds.), *Minnesota studies in the philosophy of science,* Vol. 2. Minneapolis: University of Minnesota Press.

Heninger, G. R., Charney, D. S., & Menkes, D. B. (1983). Receptor sensitivity and the mechanism of action of antidepressant treatment. In P. J. Clayton & J. E. Barrett (Eds.), *Treatment of depression: Old controversies and new approaches.* New York: Raven Press.

Henkel, H., & Lewis-Thomé, J. (1976). *Verhaltenstherapie bei männlichen Homosexuellen.* Diplomarbeit der Studierenden der Psychologie. University of Marburg.

Henker, B., & Whalen, C. K. (1980). The changing face of hyperactivity. In C. K. Whalen & B. Henker (Eds.), *Hyperactive children.* New York: Academic Press.

Henry, J. P., Ely, D. L., & Stephens, P. M. (1972). Changes in catecholamine-controlling enzymes in response to psychosocial activation of defense and alarm reactions. In *Physiology, emotion, and psychosomatic illness.* Ciba Symposium 8. Amsterdam Netherlands: Associated Scientific Publishers.

Hepler, R. S., & Frank, I. M. (1971). Marijuana smoking and intraocular pressure. *Journal of the American Medical Association, 217*, 1392.

Herbert, J. (1965). Personality factors and bronchial asthma. A study of South African Indian children. *Journal of Psychosomatic Research, 8*, 353-364.

Herbert, M. (1978). *Conduct disorders of childhood and adolescence.* New York: Wiley.

Herbert, M. (1982). Conduct disorders. In B. B. Lahey & A. E. Kaz-

din (Eds.), *Advances in clinical child psychology,* Vol. 5. New York: Plenum.

Herman, C. P., & Mack, D. (1975). Restrained and unrestrained eating. *Journal of Personality, 43*, 647-660.

Herman, C. P., & Polivy, J. (1980). Restrained eating. In A. Stunkard (Ed.), *Obesity.* Philadelphia: Saunders.

Hernández-Peón, R., Chávez-Ibarra, G., & Aguilar-Figueroa, E. (1963). Somatic evoked potentials in one case of hysterical anesthesia. *EEG and Clinical Neurophysiology, 15*, 889-892.

Herr, J. J., & Weakland, J. H. (1979). *Counseling elders and their families: Practical techniques to applied gerontology.* New York: Springer.

Hersen, M., & Bellack, A. S. (Eds.). (1981) *Behavioral assessment: A practical handbook.* 2nd ed. New York: Pergamon Press.

Heston, L. L. (1966). Psychiatric disorders in foster home reared children of schizophrenic mothers. *British Journal of Psychiatry, 112*, 819-825.

Hetherington, E. M., & Martin B. (1979). Family interaction. In H. C. Quay & J. S. Werry (Eds.), *Psychopathological disorders of childhood* (2nd ed.). New York: Wiley.

Hewett, F. M. (1965). Teaching speech to an autistic child through operant conditioning. *American Journal of Orthopsychiatry, 33*, 927-936.

Heyd, D., & Bloch, S. (1981). The ethics of suicide. In S. Bloch & P. Chodoff (Eds.), *Psychiatric ethics.* New York: Oxford University Press.

Hibbert, G. A. (1984). Hyperventilation as a cause of panic attacks. *British Medical Journal, 288*, 263-264.

Hickey, T. (1980). *Health and aging.* Belmont, Calif.: Wadsworth.

Higgins, G. F. (1978). Sexuality and the spinal cord injured patient. In J. LoPiccolo & L. LoPiccolo (Eds.), *Handbook of sex therapy.* New York: Plenum Press.

Hilgard, E. R. (1979). The Stanford hypnotic susceptibility scales as related to other measures of hypnotic responsiveness. *American Journal of Clinical Hypnosis, 21*, 68-83.

Hilgard, E. R., Morgan, A. H., & MacDonald, H. (1975). Pain and dissociation in the cold pressor test: A study of hypnotic analgesia with "hidden reports" through automatic keypressing and automatic talking. *Journal of Abnormal Psychology, 84*, 280-289.

Hill, D. (1952). EEG in episodic psychotic and psychopathic behavior: A classification of data. *EEG and Clinical Neurophysiology, 4*, 419-442.

Hill, J. H., Liebert, R. M., & Mott, D. E. W. (1968). Vicarious extinction of avoidance behavior through films: An initial test. *Psychological Reports, 12*, 192.

Hill, S. Y. (1980). Introduction: The biological consequences. In *Alcoholism and alcohol abuse among women: Research issues.* Rockville, Md.: National Institute on Alcohol Abuse and Alcoholism.

Hilterbrand, K. (1983). Depression in anorexia nervosa. Unpublished manuscript, University of Southern California.

Hiroto, D. S., & Seligman, M. E. P. (1975). Generality of learned helplessness in man. *Journal of Personality and Social Psychology, 31*, 311-327.

Hirschfeld, R. A., & Cross, C. K. (1982). Epidemiology of affective disorders. *Archives of General Psychiatry, 39*, 35-46.

Hite, S. (1976). *The Hite report.* New York: Macmillan.

Hobbs, S. A., Beck, S. J., & Wansley, R. A. (1984). Pediatric behavioral medicine: Directions in treatment and prevention. In M. Hersen, R. M. Eisler, & P. M. Miller (Eds.), *Progress in behavior modification,* Vol. 16. New York: Academic Press.

Hoch, P. H., & Dunaif, S. L. (1955). Pseudopsychopathic schizophrenia. In P. H. Hoch & J. Zubin (Eds.), *Psychiatry and the law.* New York: Grune and Stratton.

Hoch, P. H., & Polatin, P. (1949). Pseudoneurotic forms of schizophrenia. *Psychiatric Quarterly,* 23, 248–276.

Hodapp, V., Weyer, G., & Becker, J. (1975). Situational stereotypy in essential hypertension patients. *Journal of Psychosomatic Research,* 19, 113–121.

Hodgson, R. J., & Rachman, S. J. (1972). The effects of contamination and washing on obsessional patients. *Behaviour Research and Therapy,* 10, 111–117.

Hodgson, R., & Rachman, S. J. (1972). The treatment of chronic obsessive-compulsive neurosis. *Behaviour Research and Therapy,* 10, 181–189.

Hoffman, M. L. (1970). Moral development. In P. H. Mussen (Ed.),. *Carmichael's manual of child psychology.* London: Wiley.

Hogan, D. (1978). The effectiveness of sex therapy: A review of the literature. In J. LoPiccolo & L. LoPiccolo (Eds.), *Handbook of sex therapy.* New York: Plenum Press.

Hogarty, G. E., Goldberg, S. C., Schooler, N. R., Ulrich, R. F., & The Collaborative Study Group (1974). Drug and socio-therapy in the aftercare of schizophrenic paitents: II. Two-year relapse rates. *Archives of General Psychiatry,* 31, 603–608.

Hokanson, J. E., & Burgess, M. (1962). The effects of three types of aggression on vascular processes. *Journal of Abnormal and Social Psychology,* 65, 446–449.

Hokanson, J. E., Burgess, M., & Cohen, M. F. (1963). Effects of displaced aggression on systolic blood pressure. *Journal of Abnormal and Social Psychology,* 67, 214–218.

Hokanson, J. E., Willers, K. R., & Koropsak, E. (1968). Modification of autonomic responses during aggressive interchange. *Journal of Personality,* 36, 386–404.

Holden, C. (1972). Nader on mental health centers: A movement that got bogged down. *Science,* 177, 413–415.

Holinger, P. C. (1979). Violent deaths among the young: Recent trends in suicide, homicides, and accidents. *American Journal of Psychiatry,* 136, 1144–1147.

Hollingshead, A. B., & Redlich, F. C. (1958). *Social class and mental illness: A community study.* New York: Wiley.

Hollon, S. D., & Beck, A. T. (1979). Cognitive therapy of depression. In P. C. Kendall & S. D. Hollon (Eds.), *Cognitive-behavioral interventions: Theory, research, and procedures.* New York: Academic Press.

Hollon, S. D., & Kendall, P. C. (1980). Cognitive self-statements in depression: Development of an automatic thoughts questionnaire. *Cognitive Therapy and Research,* 4, 383–395.

Holmes, T. H., & Rahe, R. H. (1967). The social readjustment rating scale. *Journal of Psychosomatic Research,* 11, 213–218.

Holmes, T. S., & Holmes, T. H. (1970). Short-term intrusions into the life style routine. *Journal of Psychosomatic Research,* 14, 121–132.

Holmstrom, L. L., & Burgess, A. W. (1980). Sexual behavior during reported rapes. *Archives of Sexual Behavior,* 9, 427–439.

Honigfeld, G., & Howard, A. (1978). *Psychiatric drugs: A desk reference* (2nd ed.). New York: Academic Press.

Hoon, E. F., & Hoon, P. W. (1978). Styles of sexual expression in women: Clinical implications of multivariate analyses. *Archives of Sexual Behavior,* 7, 105–116.

Horan, J. J., Linberg, S. E., & Hackett, G. (1977). Nicotine poisoning and rapid smoking. *Journal of Consulting and Clinical Psychology,* 45, 344–347.

Horn, A. S., & Snyder, S. H. (1971). Chlorpromazine and dopamine: Conformational similarities that correlate with the anti-schizophrenic activity of phenothiazine drugs. *Proceedings of the National Academy of Sciences,* 68, 2325–2328.

Horney, K. (1939). *New ways in psychoanalysis.* New York: International Universities Press.

Horney, K. (1942). *Self-analysis.* New York: Norton.

Horowitz, M., (1975). Intrusive and repetitive thoughts after experimental stress. *Archives of General Psychiatry,* 32, 223–228.

Horwitz, L. (1974). *Clinical prediction in psychotherapy.* New York: Jason Aronson.

Houts, P. S., & Serber, M. (Eds.). (1972). *After the turn-on, what? Learning perspectives on humanistic groups.* Champaign, Ill.: Research Press.

Hsu, L. K. G. (1980). Outcome of anorexia nervosa: A review of the literature (1954 to 1978). *Archives of General Psychiatry,* 37, 1041–1046.

Hugdahl, K., Fredrikson, M., & Öhman, A. (1977). Preparedness and arousability as determinants of electrodermal conditioning. *Behaviour Research and Therapy,* 15, 345–353.

Hulicka, I. M. (1967). Short-term learning and memory efficiency as a function of age and health. *Journal of the American Geriatrics Society,* 15, 285–294.

Hull, J. G. (1981). A self-awareness model of the causes and effects of alcohol consumption. *Journal of Abnormal Psychology,* 90, 586–600.

Hunt, D. D., Carr, J. E., & Hampson, J. L. (1981). Cognitive correlates of biologic sex and gender identity in transsexualism. *Archives of Sexual Behavior,* 10, 65–77.

Hunt, W. A., & Bespalec, D. A. (1974). An evaluation of current methods of modifying smoking behavior. *Journal of Clinical Psychology,* 30, 431–438.

Hussian, R. A. (1981). *Geriatric psychology: A behavioral perspective.* New York: Van Nostrand Reinhold.

Hussian, R. A., & Lawrence, P. S. (1980). Social reinforcement of activity and problem-solving training in the treatment of depressed institutionalized elderly patients. *Cognitive Therapy and Research,* 5, 57–69.

Husted, J. R. (1975). Desensitization procedures in dealing with female sexual dysfunction. *The Counseling Psychologist,* 5, 30–37.

Hutchings, B., & Mednick, S. A. (1974). Registered criminality in the adoptive and biological parents of registered male adoptees. In S. A. Mednick, F. Schulsinger, J. Higgins, & B. Bell (Eds.), *Genetics, environment and psychopathology.* New York: Elsevier.

Hutt, C., Hutt, S. J., Lee, D., & Ounsted, C. (1964). Arousal and childhood autism. *Nature,* 204, 908–909.

Huttenlocher, P. R. (1974). Dendritic development in neocortex of children with mental defect and infantile spasms. *Neurology,* 24, 203–210.

Hyman, B. T., Van Hoesen, G. W., Damasio, A. R., & Barnes, C. L. (1984). Alzheimer's disease: Cell-specific pathology isolates the hippocampal formation. *Science,* 225, 1168–1170.

Inglis, J. (1969). Electrode placement and the effect of ECT on mood and memory in depression. *Canadian Psychiatric Association Journal,* 14, 463–471.

Innes, G., Millar, W. M., & Valentine, M. (1959). Emotion and blood pressure. *Journal of Mental Sciences,* 105, 840–851.

Insell, T. R., Murphy, D. L., Cohen, R. M., Alterman, I., Itts, C., & Linnoila, M. (1983). Obsessive-compulsive disorder. A double-blind trial of clomipramine and clorgyline. *Archives of General Psychiatry,* 40, 605–612.

Insull, W. (Ed.). (1973). *Coronary risk handbook.* New York: American Heart Association, 1973.

Isen, A. M., Shaiken, T. F., Clark, M., & Karp, L. (1978). Affect, accessibility of material in memory, and behavior: A cognitive loop? *Journal of Personality and Social Psychology*, **36**, 1–12.

Issidorides, M. R. (1979). Observations in chronic hashish users: Nuclear aberrations in blood and sperm and abnormal acrosomes in spermatozoa. In G. G. Nahas & W. D. M. Paton (Eds.), *Marihuana: Biological effects*. Elmsford, N.Y.: Pergamon Press.

Jackson, A. M. (1973). Psychotherapy: Factors associated with the race of the therapist. *Psychotherapy: Theory, Research, and Practice*, **10**, 273–277.

Jackson, D. D., & Weakland, J. (1961). Conjoint family therapy: Some considerations on theory, technique and results. *Psychiatry*, **24**, 30–45.

Jacobs, M., Jacobs, A., Gatz, M., & Schaible, T. (1973). Credibility and desirability of positive and negative structured feedback in groups. *Journal of Consulting and Clinical Psychology*, **40**, 244–252.

Jacobson, A., & McKinney, W. T. (1982). Affective disorders. In J. H. Greist, J. W. Jefferson, & R. L. Spitzer (Eds.), *Treatment of mental disorders*. New York: Oxford University Press.

Jacobson, E. (1929). *Progressive relaxation*. Chicago: University of Chicago Press.

Jacobson, N. S., Follette, W. C., Baucom, D. H., Hahlweg, K., & Margolin, G. (in press). Variability in outcome and clinical significance of behavioral marital therapy: A reanalysis of outcome data. *Journal of Consulting and Clinical Psychology*.

Jacobson, N. S., & Margolin, G. (1979). *Marital therapy: Strategies based on social learning*. New York: Brunner/Mazel.

James, N., & Chapman, J. (1975). A genetic study of bipolar affective disorder. *British Journal of Psychiatry*, **126**, 449–456.

Jamison, K. R. (1979). Manic-depressive illness in the elderly. In O. J. Kaplan (Ed.), *Psychopathology of aging*. New York: Academic Press, 79–95.

Jarvik, L. F., Mintz, J., Steuer, J., & Gerner, R. (1982). Treating geriatric depression: A 26-week interim analysis. *Journal of the American Geriatrics Society*, **30**, 713–717.

Jarvik, L. F., & Perl, M. (1981). Overview of physiologic dysfunction related to psychiatric problems in the elderly. *Aging: Neuropsychiatric Manifestations of Physical Disease in the Elderly*, **14**, 1–15.

Jarvik, L. F., Ruth, V., & Matsuyama, S. (1980). Organic brain syndrome and aging: A six-year follow-up of surviving twins. *Archives of General Psychiatry*, **37**, 280–286.

Jarvik, M. E. (1979). Biological influences on cigarette smoking. In N. A. Krasnegor (Ed.), *The behavioral aspects of smoking*. Washington, D.C.: National Institute on Drug Abuse.

Jarvik, M. E., & Schneider, N. G. (1984). Degree of addiction and effectiveness of nicotine gum therapy for smoking. *American Journal of Psychiatry*, **141**, 790–791.

Jarvis, M. J., Raw, M., Russell, M. A. H., & Feyerabend, C. (1982). Randomised controlled trial of nicotine chewing-gum. *British Medical Journal*, **285**, 537–540.

Jay, S. M., Elliott, C. H., Ozolins, M., & Olson, R. A. (1982). Behavioral management of children's distress during painful medical procedures. Paper presented at the annual meeting of the American Psychological Association, Washington, D.C.

Jeans, R. F. I. (1976). An independently validated case of multiple personality. *Journal of Abnormal Psychology*, **85**, 249–255.

Jeffrey, D. B. (1974). A comparison of the effects of external control and self-control on the modification and maintenance of weight. *Journal of Abnormal Psychology*, **83**, 404–410.

Jellinek, E. M. (1952). Phases of alcohol addiction. *Quarterly Journal of Studies on Alcohol*, **13**, 673–684.

Jemmott, J. B., III, Borysenko, J. Z., Borysenko, M., McClelland, D. C., Chapman, R., Meyer, D., & Benson, H. (1983). Academic stress, power motivation, and decrease in salivary secretory immunoglobulin A secretion. *Lancet*, **1**, 1400–1402.

Jemmott, J. B., III, & Locke, S. E. (1984). Psychosocial factors, immunologic mediation, and human susceptibility to infectious disease: How much do we know? *Psychological Bulletin*, **95**, 79–108.

Jenkins, C. D. (1971). Psychologic and social precursors of coronary disease. *New England Journal of Medicine*, **284**, 244–255, 307–317.

Jenkins, C. D. (1976). Recent evidence supporting psychologic and social risk factors for coronary disease. *New England Journal of Medicine*, **294**, 987–994, 1033–1038.

Jenkins, C. D., Rosenman, R. H., & Zyzanski, S. J. (1974). Prediction of clinical coronary heart disease by a test for the coronary-prone behavior pattern. *New England Journal of Medicine*, **290**, 1271–1275.

Jenkins, C. D., Zyzanski, S. J., & Rosenman, R. H. (1978). Coronary-prone behavior: One pattern or several? *Psychosomatic Medicine*, **40**, 25–43.

Jenkins, R. L., & Glickman, S. (1947). Patterns of personality organization among delinquents. *Nervous Child*, **6**, 329–339.

Jennings, C., Barraclough, B. M., & Moss, J. R. (1978). Have the Samaritans lowered the suicide rate? A controlled study. *Psychological Medicine*, **8**, 413–422.

Jersild, A. T., & Holmes, F. B. (1935). *Children's fears*. New York: Teachers College Press, Columbia University.

Jersild, A. T., Markey, F. V., & Jersild, C. L. (1933). Children's fears, dreams, wishes, daydreams, likes, dislikes, pleasant and unpleasant memories. In A. T. Jersild (Ed.), *Child psychology*. Englewood Cliffs, N.J.: Prentice-Hall, 1960.

Joffee, J. M., & Albee, G. W. (1981). Powerlessness and psychopathology. In J. M. Joffee & G. W. Albee (Eds.), *Prevention through political action and social change: Primary prevention of psychopathology*, Vol. 5. Hanover, N.H.: University Press of New England.

Johnson, A. M., Falstein, E. I., Szurek, S. A., & Svendson, M. (1941). School phobia. *American Journal of Orthopsychiatry*, **11**, 701–702.

Johnson, E. H. (1984). Anger and anxiety as determinants of elevated blood pressure in adolescents. Unpublished doctoral dissertation, University of South Florida.

Johnston, M. B., Whitman, T. L., & Johnson, M. (1980). Teaching addition and subtraction to mentally retarded children: A self-instructional program. *Applied Research in Mental Retardation*, **1**, 141–160.

Jones, B. M. (1973). Memory impairment on the ascending and descending limbs of the blood alcohol curve. *Journal of Abnormal Psychology*, **82**, 24–32.

Jones, B. M., & Parsons, O. A. (1971). Impaired abstracting ability in chronic alcoholics. *Archives of General Psychiatry*, **24**, 71–75.

Jones, B. M., & Parsons, O. A. (1975). Alcohol and consciousness: Getting high, coming down. *Psychology Today*, **8**, 53–58.

Jones, E. (1955). *The life and work of Sigmund Freud*, Vol. 2. New York: Basic Books.

Jones, M. (1953). *The therapeutic community*. New York: Basic Books.

Jones, M. C. (1924). A laboratory study of fear: The case of Peter. *Pedagogical Seminary*, **31**, 308–315.

Jones, R. T. (1977). Human effects. In R. C. Peterson (Ed.), *Marijuana research findings: 1976*. NIDA Research Monograph 14. Washington, D. C.: U.S. Government Printing Office.

Jones, R. T. (1980). Human effects: An overview. In *Marijuana research findings: 1980*. Washington, D.C.: U.S. Government Printing Office.

Jones, R. T. (1984). The pharmacology of cocaine. In J. Grabowski (Ed.), *Cocaine: Pharmacology, effects, and treatment of abuse*. Rockville, Md: National Institute on Drug Abuse.

Jones, R. T., & Benowitz, N. (1976). The 30-day trip—Clinical studies of cannabis tolerance and dependence. In M. C. Braude & S. Szara (Eds.), *Pharmacology of marijuana*. New York: Raven Press.

Justice, B., & Justice, R. (1979). *The broken taboo: Sex in the family*. New York: Human Sciences Press.

Jutai, J. W., & Hare, R. D. (1983). Psychopathy and selective attention during performance of a complex perceptual-motor task. *Psychophysiology*, **20**, 140–151.

Kagan, J. (1965). Reflection-impulsivity and reading ability in primary grade children. *Child Development*, **36**, 609–628.

Kahn, R. L. (1975). The mental health system and the future aged. *The Gerontologist*, **15**, Part II, 24–31.

Kahn, R. L., Zarit, S. H., Hilbert, N. M., & Niederehe, G. (1975). Memory complaint and impairment in the aged. *Archives of General Psychiatry*, **32**, 1569–1573.

Kammen, D. P. van, Bunney, W. E., Docherty, J. P., Jimerson, D. C., Post, R. M., Sivis, S., Ebart, M., & Gillin, J. C. (1977). Amphetamine-induced catecholamine activation in schizophrenia and depression. *Advances in Biochemical Psychopharmacology*, **16**, 655–659.

Kanfer, F.H. (1979). Self-management: Strategies and tactics. In A. P. Goldstein & F. H. Kanfer (Eds.), *Maximizing treatment gains: Transfer enhancement in psychotherapy*. New York: Academic Press.

Kanfer, F. H., & Busemeyer, J. R. (1982). The use of problem-solving and decision making in behavior therapy. *Clinical Psychology Review*, **2**, 239–266.

Kanfer, F. H., & Nay, W. R. (1982). Behavioral assessment. In G. T. Wilson & C. R. Franks (Eds.), *Contemporary behavior therapy: Conceptual and empirical foundations*. New York: Guilford Press.

Kanfer, F. H., & Phillips, J. S. (1970). *Learning foundations of behavior therapy*. New York: Wiley.

Kanner, L. (1943). Autistic disturbances of affective contact. *Nervous Child*, **2**, 217–250.

Kanner, L. (1973). Follow-up of eleven autistic children originally reported in 1943. In L. Kanner (Ed.), *Childhood psychosis: Initial studies and new insights*. Washington, D.C.: Winston-Wiley.

Kanner, L., & Eisenberg, L. (1955). Notes on the follow-up studies of autistic children. In P. Hoch & J. Zubin (Eds.), *Psychopathology of childhood*. New York: Grune and Stratton.

Kantor, J. S., Zitrin, C. M., & Zeldis, S. M. (1980). Mitral valve prolapse syndrome in agoraphobic patients. *American Journal of Psychiatry*, **137**, 467–469.

Kantorovich, N. V. (1930). An attempt at associative-reflex therapy in alcoholism. *Psychological Abstracts*, **4**, 493.

Kaplan, H. S. (1974). *The new sex therapy*. New York: Brunner/Mazel.

Karacan, I., Thornby, J., Holzer, C. E., Warheit, G. J., Schwab, J. J., & Williams, R. L. (1976). Prevalence of sleep disturbance in a primarily urban Florida county. *Social Science Medicine*, **10**, 239–244.

Karasu, T. B., Stein, S. P., & Charles, E. S. (1979). Age factors in patient-therapist relationship. *Journal of Nervous and Mental Disease*, 167, 100–104.

Karrer, R., Nelson, M., & Galbraith, G. C. (1979). Psychophysiological research with the mentally retarded. In N. R. Ellis (Ed.), *Handbook of mental deficiency, psychological theory and research* (2nd ed.). Hillsdale, N.J.: Lawrence Erlbaum Associates.

Kasl, S. V., & Cobb, S. (1970). Blood pressure changes in men undergoing job loss: A preliminary report. *Psychosomatic Medicine*, **32**, 19–38.

Kaslow, F. W. (1981). Divorce and divorce therapy. In A. S. Gurman & D. P. Kniskern (Eds.), *Handbook of family therapy*. New York: Brunner/Mazel.

Kastenbaum, R., & Candy, S. E. (1973). The 4% fallacy: A methodological and empirical critique of extended care facility population statistics. *International Journal of Aging and Human Development*, **4**, 15–21.

Katchadourian, H. A., & Lunde, D. T. (1972). *Fundamentals of human sexuality*. New York: Holt, Rinehart and Winston.

Katz, E. R. (1980). Illness impact and social reintegration. In J. Kellerman (Ed.), *Psychological aspects of childhood cancer*. Springfield, Ill.: Charles C. Thomas.

Katz, E. R., Kellerman, J., & Siegel, S. E. (1980). Behavioral distress in children with leukemia undergoing bone marrow aspirations. *Journal of Consulting and Clinical Psychology*, **48**, 356–365.

Katzman, R. (1976). The prevalence and malignancy of Alzheimer's disease. *Archives of Neurology*, **33**, 217–218.

Kay, D. W. K., Cooper, A. F., Garside, R. F., & Roth, M. (1976). The differentiation of paranoid from affective psychoses by patient's premorbid characteristics. *British Journal of Psychiatry*, **129**, 207–215.

Kazdin, A. E. (1975). Covert modelling, imagery assessment, and assertive behavior. *Journal of Consulting and Clinical Psychology*, **43**, 716–724.

Kazdin, A. E., & Wilson, G. T. (1978). *Evaluation of behavior therapy: Issues, evidence, and research strategies*. Cambridge, Mass.: Ballinger.

Keen, S. (1979). Some ludicrous theses about sexuality. *Journal of Humanistic Psychology*, **19**, 15–22.

Kegel, A. H. (1957). Sexual function of the pubococcygeus muscle. *Western Journal of Surgery*, **60**, 521–524.

Keith, S. J., Gunderson, J. G., Reifman, A., Buchsbaum, S., & Mosher, L. R. (1976). Special report: Schizophrenia 1976. *Schizophrenia Bulletin*, **2**, 509–565.

Keller, M. B., Shapiro, R. W., Lavori, P. W., & Wolfe, N. (1982). Relapse in major depressive disorder. *Archives of General Psychiatry*, **39**, 911–915.

Kellerman, J., & Varni, J. W. (1982). Pediatric hematology/oncology. In D. C. Russo & J. W. Varni (Eds.), *Behavioral pediatrics: Research and practice*. New York: Plenum Press.

Kellner, R. (1982). Disorders of impulse control (not elsewhere classified). In J. H. Greist, J. W. Jefferson, & R. L. Spitzer (Eds.), *Treatment of Mental Disorders*. New York: Oxford University Press.

Kelly, E., & Zeller, B. (1969). Asthma and the psychiatrist. *Journal of Psychosomatic Research*, **13**, 377–395.

Kendall, P. C., & Hollon, S. D. (Eds.). (1981) *Assessment strategies for cognitive-behavioral interventions*. New York: Academic Press.

Kendell, R. E. (1975). *The role of diagnosis in psychiatry*. London: Blackwell.

Kennedy, W. A. (1965). School phobia: Rapid treatment of 50 cases. *Journal of Abnormal Psychology*, **70**, 285–289.

Kenney, R. A. (1982). *Physiology of aging*. Chicago, Ill.: Year Book Medical Publishers.

Kent, R. N., O'Leary, K. D., Diament, C., & Dietz, A. (1974). Expectation biases in observational evaluation of therapeutic change. *Journal of Consulting and Clinical Psychology*, **42**, 774–780.

Kernberg, O.F. (1970). A psychoanalytic classification of character pathology. *Journal of the American Psychoanalytic Association*, **18**, 800–822.

Kernberg, O. F. (1973). Summary and conclusion of "Psychotherapy and psychoanalysis: Final report of the Menninger Foundation's Psychotherapy Research Project.'' *International Journal of Psychiatry*, **11**, 62–77.

Kessler, J. (1966). *Psychopathology of childhood*. Englewood Cliffs, N.J.: Prentice-Hall.

Kety, S. S. (1974). From rationalization to reason. *American Journal of Psychiatry*, **131**, 957-963.

Kety, S. S., Rosenthal, D., Wender, P. H., & Schulsinger, F. (1968). The types and prevalence of mental illness in the biological and adoptive families of adopted schizophrenics. In D. Rosenthal & S. S. Kety (Eds.), *The transmission of schizophrenia*. Elmsford, N.Y.: Pergamon Press.

Kety, S. S., Rosenthal, D., Wender, P. H., Schulsinger, F., & Jacobson, B. (1975). Mental illness in the biological and adoptive families of adopted individuals who have become schizophrenic: A preliminary report based on psychiatric interviews. In R. R. Fieve, D. Rosenthal, & H. Brill (Eds.), *Genetic Research in Psychiatry*. Baltimore: Johns Hopkins University Press.

Keuthen, N. (1980). Subjective probability estimation and somatic structures in phobic individuals. Unpublished manuscript, State University of New York at Stony Brook.

Kidder, T. (1978). Soldiers of misfortune. *The Atlantic Monthly*, **241**, 41–52.

Kiloh, L. G. (1961). Pseudo-dementia. *Acta Psychiatrica Scandinavia*, **37**, 336–351.

Kinsey, A. C., Pomeroy, W. B., & Martin, C. E. (1948). *Sexual behavior in the human male*. Philadelphia: Saunders.

Kinsey, A. C., Pomeroy, W. B., Martin, C. E., & Gebhard, P. H. (1953). *Sexual behavior in the human female*. Philadelphia: Saunders.

Kinsman, R. A., Spector, S. L., Shucard, D. W., & Luparello, T. J. (1974). Observations on patterns of subjective symptomatology of acute asthma. *Psychosomatic Medicine*, **36**, 129–43.

Klee, G. D., Bertino, J., Weintraub, W., & Calaway, E. (1961). The influence of varying dosage on the effects of lysergic acid diethylamide (LSD-25). *Journal of Nervous and Mental Disease*, **132**, 404–409.

Klee, G. D., & Weintraub, W. (1959). Paranoid reactions following lysergic acid diethylamide (LSD-25). In P. B. Bradley, P. Demicker, & C. Radonco-Thomas (Eds.), *Neuropsychopharmacology*. Amsterdam, Netherlands: Elsevier.

Kleeman, S. T. (1967). Psychiatric contributions in the treatment of asthma. *Annals of Allergy*, **25**, 611–619.

Klein, D. C., & Seligman, M. E. P. (1976). Reversal of performance deficits and perceptual deficits in learned helplessness and depression. *Journal of Abnormal Psychology*, **85**, 11–26.

Klein, D. F., & Davis, J. M. (1969). *Diagnosis and drug treatment of psychiatric disorders*. Baltimore: Williams and Wilkins.

Klein, M. (1932). *The psychoanalysis of children*. London: Hogarth Press.

Kleinmuntz, B. (1967). *Personality measurement: An introduction*. Homewood, Ill.: Dorsey Press.

Klerman, G. L. (1972). Drug therapy of clinical depressions. *Journal of Psychiatric Research*, **9**, 253–270.

Klerman, G. L. (1975). Drug therapy of clinical depressions— Current status and implications for research on neuropharmacology of the affective disorders. In D. F. Klein & R. Gittelman-Klein (Eds.), *Progress in psychiatric drug treatment*. New York: Brunner/Mazel.

Klerman, G. L. (1983). Problems in the definition and diagnosis of depression in the elderly. In M. Hauge & L. Breslau (Eds.), *Depression in the elderly: Causes, care, consequences*. New York: Springer.

Kluger, J. M. (1969). Childhood asthma and the social milieu. *American Academy of Child Psychiatry*, **8**, 353–366.

Knapp, P. H. (1969). The asthmatic and his environment. *Journal of Nervous and Mental Disease*, **149**, 133–151.

Knapp, S., & Vandecreek, L. (1982). Tarasoff: Five years later. *Professional Psychology*, **13**, 511–516.

Knight, B. (1983). An evolution of a mobile geriatric team. In M. A. Smyer & M. Gatz (Eds.), *Mental health and aging: Programs and evaluations*. Beverly Hills, Calif.: Sage Publications.

Knight, R. P. (1937). The dynamics of chronic alcoholism. *Journal of Nervous and Mental Disease*, **86**, 538–548.

Kobasa, S. C. (1979). Stressful life events, personality and health: An inquiry into hardiness. *Journal of Personality and Social Psychology*, **37**, 1–11.

Kobasa, S. C., Maddi, S. R., & Kahn, S. (1982). Hardiness and health: A prospective study. *Journal of Personality and Social Psychology*, **42**, 168–177.

Kobasa, S. C., & Puccetti, M. C. (1983). Personality and social resources in stress resistance. *Journal of Personality and Social Psychology*, **45**, 839–850.

Koegel, R. L., Schreibman, L., Britten, K. R., Burke, J. C., & O'Neill, R. E. (1982). A comparison of parent training to direct child treatment. In R. L. Koegel, A. Rincover, & A. L. Egel (Eds.), *Educating and understanding autistic children*. San Diego, Calif.: College-Hill.

Koenig, K., & Masters, J. (1965). Experimental treatment of habitual smoking. *Behaviour Research and Therapy*, **3**, 235–243.

Kohn, M. L. (1968). Social class and schizophrenia: A critical review. In D. Rosenthal & S. S. Kety (Eds.), *The transmission of schizophrenia*. Elmsford, N.Y.: Pergamon Press.

Kohut, H. (1966). Forms and transformations of narcissism. *Journal of the American Psychoanalytic Association*, **14**, 243–272.

Kohut, H. (1971). *The analysis of the self*. New York: International Universities Press.

Kohut, H. (1977). *The restoration of the self*. New York: International Universities Press.

Kohut, H., & Wolf, E. S. (1978). The disorders of the self and their treatment: An outline. *International Journal of Psychoanalysis*, **59**, 413–425.

Kolb, L. C. (1968). *Noyes' modern clinical psychiatry* (7th ed.). Philadelphia: Saunders.

Kolvin, I., MacKeith, R. C., & Meadows, S. R. (1973). *Bladder control and enuresis*. Philadelphia: Lippincott.

Konig, P., & Godfrey, S. (1973). Prevalence of exercise-induced bronchial lability in families of children with asthma. *Archives of Diseases of Childhood*, **48**, 518.

Kopfstein, J. M., & Neale, J. M. (1972). A multivariate study of attention dysfunction in schizophrenia. *Journal of Abnormal Psychology*, **80**, 294–299.

Kornetsky, C. (1976). Hyporesponsivity of chronic schizophrenic patients to dextroamphetamine. *Archives of General Psychiatry*, **33**, 1425–1428.

Kovacs, M., & Beck, A. T. (1977). The wish to live and the wish to die in attempted suicides. *Journal of Clinical Psychology*, **33**, 361–365.

Kovacs, M., Rush, A. J., Beck, A. T., & Hollon, S.D. (1981). Depressed outpatients treated with cognitive therapy or pharmacotherapy: A one-year follow-up. *Archives of General Psychiatry*, **38**, 33–39.

Kozel, N. J., Grider, R. A., & Adams, E. H. (1982). National surveillance of cocaine use and related health consequences. *Morbidity and Mortality Weekly Report 31*, **20**, 265–273.

Kozol, H., Boucher, R., & Garofalo, R. (1972). The diagnosis and treatment of dangerousness. *Crime and Delinquency*, **18**, 371–392.

Kraepelin, E. (1883). *Lehrbuch der Psychiatrie* (1st ed., 1883; 8th ed., 1915). *Clinical psychiatry.* Translated from the 7th German edition by A. R. Diefendorf. Delmar, N.Y.: Scholars' Facsimiles and Reprints, 1981.

Kramer, M. (1977). *Psychiatric services and the changing institutional scene 1950–1985.* Washington, D.C.: National Institute of Mental Health.

Krantz, S., & Hammen, C. L. (1979). Assessment of cognitive bias in depression. *Journal of Abnormal Psychology, 88,* 611–619.

Kranz, H. (1936). Lebenschicksale krimineller Zwillinge. Berlin: Springer-Verlag, 1936.

Krech, D., Rosenzweig, M., & Bennett, E. (1966). Environmental impoverishment, social isolation, and changes in brain chemistry and anatomy. *Physiology and Behavior,, 1,* 99–104.

Kringlen, E. (1970). Natural history of obsessional neurosis. *Seminars in Psychiatry, 2,* 403–419.

Kroll, P., Chamberlain, P., Halpern, D. (1979). The diagnosis of Briquet's syndrome in a male population. *Journal of Nervous and Mental Disease, 169,* 171–174.

Kucharski, L. T., White, R. M., & Schratz, M. (1979). Age bias, referral for psychological assistance and the private physician. *Journal of Gerontology, 34,* 423–428.

Kuhn, T. S. (1962). *The structure of scientific revolutions.* Chicago: University of Chicago Press.

Kunst-Wilson, W. R., & Zajonc, R. B. (1980). Affective discrimination of stimuli that cannot be recognized. *Science, 207,* 557–558.

Kuriansky, J. B., Deming, W. E., & Gurland, B. J. (1974). On trends in the diagnosis of schizophrenia. *American Journal of Psychiatry, 131,* 402–407.

Kutchinsky, B. (1970). *Studies on pornography and sex crimes in Denmark.* Copenhagen: New Social Science Monographs.

Lacey, J. I. (1967). Somatic response patterning and stress: Some revisons of activation theory. In M. H. Appley & R. Trumball (Eds.), *Psychological stress.* New York: McGraw-Hill.

Lachman, S. J. (1972). *Psychosomatic disorders: A behavioristic interpretation.* New York: Wiley.

Laing, R. D. (1964). Is schizophrenia a disease? *International Journal of Social Psychiatry, 10,* 184–193.

Lamb, H. R., & Zusman, J. (1979). Primary prevention in perspective. *American Journal of Psychiatry, 36,* 12–17.

Lambert, M. J., Bergin, A. E., & Collins, J. L. (1977). Therapist-induced deterioration in psychotherapy. In A. S. Gurman & A. M. Razin (Eds.), *Effective psychotherapy: A handbook of research.* Elmsford, N.Y.: Pergamon Press.

Lando, H. A. (1977). Successful treatment of smokers with a broad-spectrum behavioral approach. *Journal of Consulting and Clinical Psychology, 45,* 361–366.

Lane, E. A., & Albee, G. W. (1965). Childhood intellectual differences between schizophrenic adults and their siblings. *American Journal of Orthopsychiatry, 35,* 747–753.

Lang, A. R., Goeckner, D. J., Adessor, V. J., & Marlatt, G. A. (1975). Effects of alcohol on aggression in male social drinkers. *Journal of Abnormal Psychology, 84,* 508–518.

Lang, A. R., & Marlatt, G. A. (1982). Problem drinking: A social learning perspective. In R. J. Gatchel, A. Baum, & J. E. Singer (Eds.), *Handbook of psychology and health.* Hillsdale, N.J.: Lawrence Erlbaum Associates.

Lang, P. J. (1969). The mechanics of desensitization and the laboratory study of fear. In C. M. Franks (Ed.), *Behavior therapy: Appraisal and status.* New York: McGraw-Hill.

Lang, P. J., & Lazovik, A. D. (1963). Experimental desensitization of a phobia. *Journal of Abnormal and Social Psychology, 66,* 519–525.

Lang, P. J., & Melamed, B. G. (1969). Case report: Avoidance conditioning therapy of an infant with chronic ruminative vomiting. *Journal of Abnormal Psychology, 74,* 1–8.

Lange, A. J., & Jakubowski, P. (1976). *Responsible assertive behavior.* Champaign, Ill.: Research Press.

Lange, J. (1929). *Verbrechen als Schicksal.* Leipzig: Georg Thieme Verlag.

Langer, E. J. (1981). Old age: An artifact? In J. McGaugh & S. Kiesler (Eds.), *Aging: Biology and behavior.* New York: Academic Press.

Langer, E. J., & Albelson, R. P. (1974). A patient by any other name . . . : Clinician group difference in labelling bias. *Journal of Consulting and Clinical Psychology, 42,* 4–9.

Langer, E. J., & Rodin, J. (1976). The effects of choice and enhanced personal responsibility for the aged. *Journal of Personality and Social Psychology, 34,* 191–198.

Langevin, R., Paitich, D., Ramsay, G., Anderson, C., Kamrad, J., Pope, S., Geller, G., Pearl, L., & Newman, S. (1979). Experimental studies of the etiology of genital exhibitionism. *Archives of Sexual Behavior, 8,* 307–331.

Langevin, R., Paitich, D., & Steiner, B. (1977). The clinical profile of male transsexuals living as females versus those living as males. *Archives of Sexual Behavior, 6,* 143–154.

LaRue, A., Dessonville, C., & Jarvik, L. F. (1985). Aging and mental disorders. In J. E. Birren & K. W. Schaie (Eds.), *Handbook of psychology of aging* (2nd ed.). New York: Van Nostrand Reinhold.

Lasagna, L., Mosteller, F., Von Felsinger, J. M., & Beecher, H. K. (1954). A study of the placebo response. *American Journal of Medicine, 16,* 770–779.

Lavelle, T. L., Metalsky, G. I., & Coyne, J. C. (1979). Learned helplessness, test anxiety, and acknowledgment of contingencies. *Journal of Abnormal Psychology, 88,* 381–387.

Lawton, M. P. (1972). Schizophrenia forty-five years later. *Journal of Genetic Psychology, 121,* 133–143.

Lawton, M. P. (1979). Clinical geropsychology: Problems and prospects. In *Master lecture series on the psychology of aging.* Washington, D.C.: American Psychological Association.

Lazarus, A. A. (1961). Group therapy of phobic disorders by systematic desensitization. *Journal of Abnormal and Social Psychology, 63,* 504–510.

Lazarus, A. A. (1965). Behavior therapy, incomplete treatment, and symptom substitution. *Journal of Nervous and Mental Disease, 140,* 80–86.

Lazarus, A. A. (1968). Behavior therapy in groups. In G. M. Gazda (Ed.), *Basic approaches to group psychotherapy and counseling.* Springfield, Ill.: Charles C. Thomas. (a)

Lazarus, A. A. (1968). Learning theory and the treatment of depression. *Behavior Research and Therapy, 6,* 83–89. (b)

Lazarus, A. A. (1971). *Behavior therapy and beyond.* New York: McGraw-Hill.

Lazarus, A. A., & Davison, G. C. (1971). Clinical innovation in research and practice. In A. E. Bergin & S. L. Garfield (Eds.), *Handbook of psychotherapy and behavior change: An empirical analysis.* New York: Wiley.

Lazarus, A. A., Davison, G. C., & Polefka, D. (1965). Classical and operant factors in the treatment of school phobia. *Journal of Abnormal Psychology, 70,* 225–229.

Lazarus, R. S. (1974). Psychological stress and coping in adaptation and illness. *International Journal of Psychiatry in Medicine*, **5**, 321–333.

Lazarus, R. S., & Cohen, J. B. (1977). Environmental stress. In I. Altman & J. F. Wohlwill (Eds.), *Human behavior and environment*, Vol. 2. New York: Plenum Press.

Lazovik, A. D., & Lang, P. J. (1960). A laboratory demonstration of systematic desensitization psychotherapy. *Journal of Psychological Studies*, **11**, 238–247.

Lee, T., & Seeman, P. (1977). Dopamine receptors in normal and schizophrenic human brains. *Proceedings of the Society of Neurosciences*, **3**, 443.

Leff, J. P. (1976). Schizophrenia and sensitivity to the family environment. *Schizophrenia Bulletin*, **2**, 566–574.

Lefkowitz, M. M., & Burton, N. (1978). Childhood depression: A critique of the concept. *Psychological Bulletin*, **85**, 716–726.

Lehrer, P. M., & Woolfolk, R. L. (1982). Self-report assessment of anxiety: Somatic, cognitive, and behavioral modalities. *Behavioral Assessment*, **4**, 167–177.

Leibtag, D. (1980, July 11). Potent new heroin smoked and snorted. *ADAMHA News*.

Leland, H., & Smith, D. (1965). *Play therapy with mentally subnormal children*. New York: Grune and Stratton.

Lemieux, G., Davignon, A., & Genest, J. (1956). Depressive states during rauwolfia therapy for arterial hypertension. *Canadian Medical Association Journal*, **74**, 522–526.

Leon, G. R., Gillum, B., Gillum, R., & Gouze, M. (1979). Personality stability and change over a 30-year period—Middle age to old age. *Journal of Consulting and Clinical Psychology*, **47**, 517–524.

Levendusky, P., & Pankratz, L. (1975). Self-control technique as an alternative pain medication. *Journal of Abnormal Psychology*, **84**, 165–168.

Levenson, M. (1972). Cognitive and perceptual factors in suicidal individuals. Unpublished doctoral dissertation, University of Kansas.

Levitsky, A., & Perls, F. S. (1970). The rules and games of Gestalt therapy. In J. Fagan & I. L. Shepherd (Eds.), *Gestalt therapy now: Theory, techniques, applications*. Palo Alto, Calif.: Science and Behavior Books.

Levitt, E. E. (1971). Research on psychotherapy with children. In A. E. Bergin & S. L. Garfield (Eds.), *Handbook of psychotherapy and behavior change: An empirical analysis*. New York: Wiley.

Levy, L. H. (1963). *Psychological interpretation*. New York: Holt, Rinehart and Winston.

Levy, R., & Muskin, J. (1973). Somatosensory evoked response in patients with hysterical anesthesia. *Journal of Psychosomatic Research*, **17**, 81–84.

Lewinsohn, P. H. (1974). A behavioral approach to depression. In R. J. Friedman & M. M. Katz (Eds.), *The psychology of depression: Contemporary theory and research*. Washington, D.C.: Winston: Wiley.

Lewinsohn, P. H., & Libet, J. M. (1972). Pleasant events, activity schedules and depression. *Journal of Abnormal Psychology*, **79**, 291–295.

Lewinsohn, P. M., Steinmetz, J. L., Larsen, D. W., & Franklin, J. (1981). Depression-related cognitions: Antecedent or consequences? *Journal of Abnormal Psychology*, **90**, 213–219.

Lewinsohn, P. M., & Teri, L. (1983). *Clinical geropsychology: New directions in assessment and treatment*. New York: Pergamon Press.

Lewinsohn, P. H., Weinstein, M., & Alper, T. (1970). A behavioral approach to the group treatment of depressed persons: A methodological contribution. *Journal of Clinical Psychology*, **26**, 525–532.

Lichtenstein, E., & Danaher, B. G. (1977). Modification of smoking behavior: A critical analysis of theory, research, and practice. In M. Hersen, R. M. Eisler, & P. M. Miller (Eds.), *Progress in behavior modification*, Vol. 4. New York: Academic Press.

Liberman, M. A. (1983). Social contexts of depression. In L. D. Breslau & M. R. Haug (Eds.), *Depression and aging: Causes, care and consequences*. New York: Springer.

Liberman, R. P., Wheeler, E. G., & Kuehnel, J. M. (1983). Failures in behavioral marital therapy. In E. B. Foa & P. M. G. Emmelkamp (Eds.), *Failures in behavior therapy*. New York: Wiley.

Lieberman, M. A., Yalom, J. D., & Miles, M. B. (1973). *Encounter groups: First facts*. New York: Basic Books.

Liebert, R. M., & Baron, R. A. (1972). Short-term effects of televised aggression on children's aggressive behavior. In J. P. Murray, E. A. Rubinstein, & G. A. Comstock (Eds.), *Television and social behavior*. Vol. 2. Washington, D.C.: U.S. Government Printing Office.

Liebert, R. M., Neale, J. M., & Davidson, E. S. (1973). *The early window: The effects of television on children and youth*. Elmsford, N.Y.: Pergamon Press.

Liebowitz, M. R., Fyer, A. J., Gorman, J. M., Dillon, D. J., Appleby, I. L., Levy, G. F., Anderson, S., Levitt, M., Palij, M., Davies, S. O., & Klein, D. F. (1984). Lactate provocation of panic attacks. *Archives of General Psychiatry*, **41**, 764–770.

Liebson, I. (1967). Conversion reaction: A learning theory approach. *Behaviour Research and Therapy*, **7**, 217–218.

Liem, J. H. (1974). Effects of verbal communications of parents and children: A comparison of normal and schizophrenic families. *Journal of Consulting and Clinical Psychology*, **42**, 438–450.

Lifton, R. J. (1976). Advocacy and corruption in the healing profession. In N. L. Goldman & D. R. Segal (Eds.), *The social psychology of military service*. Beverly Hills, Calif.: Sage Publications.

Linton, H. B., & Langs, R. J. (1964). Empirical dimensions of LSD-25 reactions. *Archives of General Psychiatry*, **10**, 469–485.

Lion, J. R. (1978). Outpatient treatment of psychopaths. In W. H. Reid (Ed.), *The psychopath: A comprehensive study of antisocial disorders and behaviors*. New York: Brunner/Mazel.

Lipinski, D. P., Black, J. L., Nelson, R. O., & Ciminero, A. R. (1975). The influence of motivational vairables on the reactivity and reliability of self-recording. *Journal of Consulting and Clinical Psychology*, **43**, 637–646.

Lipowski, Z. J. (1980). *Delirium: Acute brain failure in man*. Springfield, Ill.: Charles C. Thomas.

Lipowski, Z. J. (1983). Transient cognitive disorders (delirium and acute confusional states) in the elderly. *American Journal of Psychiatry*, **140**, 1426–1436.

Lipton, M. A., & Nemeroff, C. B. (1978). The biology of aging and its role in depression. In G. Usdin & C. K. Hofling (Eds.), *Aging: The process and the people*. New York: Brunner/Mazel.

Liskow, B. (1982). Substance induced and substance use disorders: Barbiturates and similarly acting sedative hypnotics. In J. H. Greist, J. W. Jefferson, & R. L. Spitzer (Eds.), *Treatment of mental disorders*. New York: Oxford University Press.

Liston, E. H. (1982). Delirium in the aged. In L. F. Jarvik & G. W. Small (Eds.), *Psychiatric clinics of North America*. Philadelphia, Penn.: Saunders.

Lockyer, L., & Rutter, M. (1969). A five-to-fifteen-year follow-up of infantile psychosis: III. Psychological characteristics. *British Journal of Psychiatry*, **115**, 865–882.

London, P. (1964). *The modes and morals of psychotherapy*. New York: Holt, Rinehart and Winston.

Loney, J., Langborne, J. E., Jr., & Paternite, C. E. (1978). An empirical basis for subgrouping the hyperkinetic-minimal brain dysfunction syndrome. *Journal of Abnormal Psychology*, **87**, 431–441.

LoPiccolo, J. (1977). Direct treatment of sexual dysfunction in the couple. In J. Money & H. Musaph (Eds.), *Handbook of sexology*. New York: Elsevier/North Holland.

LoPiccolo, J., & Friedman, J. M. (1985). Sex therapy: An integrated model. In S. J. Lynn & J. P. Garskee (Eds.), *Contemporary psychotherapies: Models and methods*. New York: Charles E. Merrill.

LoPiccolo, J., & Hogan, D. R. (1979). Multidimensional treatment of sexual dysfunction. In O. F. Pomerleau & J. P. Brady (Eds.), *Behavioral medicine: Theory and practice*. Baltimore: Williams and Wilkins.

Loranger, A. W., Oldham, J. M., & Tulis, E. H. (1983). Familial transmission of DSM-III borderline personality disorder. *Archives of General Psychiatry*, **40**, 795–799.

Lothstein, L. M. (1980). The postsurgical transsexual: Empirical and theoretical considerations. *Archives of Sexual Behavior*, **9**, 547–564.

Lothstein, L. M. (1983). *Female-to-male transsexualism: Historical, clinical, and theoretical issues*. Boston: Routledge and Kegan Paul.

Lotter, V. (1966). Epidemiology of autistic conditions in young children: I. Prevalence. *Social Psychiatry*, **1**, 124–137.

Lotter, V. (1974). Factors related to outcome in autistic children. *Journal of Autism and Childhood Schizophrenia.*, **4**, 263–277.

Lotter, V. (1978). Follow-up studies. In M. Rutter & E. Schopler (Eds.), *Autism: A reappraisal of concepts and treatment*. New York: Plenum Press.

Lovaas, O. I. (1977). *The autistic child: Language development through behavior modification*. New York: Irvington.

Lovaas, O. I., Freitag, G., Gold, V. J., & Kassorla, I. C. (1965). Experimental studies in childhood schizophrenia: Analysis of self-destructive behavior. *Journal of Experimental Child Psychology*, **2**, 67–84.

Lovaas, O. I., Koegel, R., Simmons, J. Q., & Long, J. S. (1973). Some generalization and follow-up measures on autistic children in behavior therapy. *Journal of Applied Behavior Analysis*, **6**, 131–166.

Lovaas, O. I., Schreibman, L., Koegel, R., & Rehm, R. (1971). Selective responding by autistic children to multiple sensory input. *Journal of Abnormal Psychology*, **77**, 211–222.

Lovibond, S. H. (1964). *Conditioning and enuresis*. Oxford, England: Pergamon Press.

Lovibond, S. H., & Caddy, G. (1970). Discriminated aversive control in the moderation of alcoholics' drinking. *Behavior Therapy*, **1**, 437–444.

Lowen, A. (1958). *The physical dynamics of character structure*. New York: Grune and Stratton.

Lowenthal, M. F., Berkman, P., & Associates (1967). *Aging and mental disorder in San Francisco*. San Francisco: Jossey-Bass.

Lubin, B. (1983). Group therapy. In I. B. Weiner (Ed.), *Clinical methods in psychology* (2nd ed.). New York: Wiley.

Lubin, R. A. (1977). Influences of alcohol upon performance and performance awareness. *Perceptual and Motor Skills*, **45**, 303–310.

Luborsky, L., & Spence, D. P. (1978). Quantitative research on psychoanalytic therapy. In S. L. Garfield & A. E. Bergin (Eds.), *Handbook of psychotherapy and behavior change: An empirical analysis* (2nd ed.). New York: Wiley.

Luparello, T. J., McFadden, E. R., Lyons, H. A., & Bleecker, E. R. (1971). Psychologic factors and bronchial asthma. *New York State Journal of Medicine*, **71**, 2161–2165.

Luria, A. R. (1961). *The role of speech in the regulation of normal and abnormal behavior*. New York: Pergamon Press.

Luria, D. B. (1970). *Overcoming drugs: Program of action*. New York: McGraw-Hill.

Luthe, W., & Schultz, J. H. (1969). *Autogenic therapy*, Vol. 1. *Autogenic methods*. New York: Grune and Stratton.

Lyght, C. E. (Ed.). (1966). *The Merck manual of diagnosis and therapy* (11th ed.). Rahway, N.J.: Merck Sharp and Dohme Research Laboratories.

Lykken, D.T. (1957). A study of anxiety in the sociopathic personality. *Journal of Abnormal and Social Psychology*, **55**, 6–10.

Lystad, M. M. (1957). Social mobility among selected groups of schizophrenics. *American Sociological Review*, **22**, 288–292.

Maccoby, N., & Alexander, J. (1980). Use of media in lifestyle programs. In P. O. Davidson & S. M. Davidson (Eds.), *Behavioral medicine: Changing health lifestyles*. New York: Brunner/Mazel.

Maccoby, N., Farquhar, J. W., Wood, P. D., & Alexander J. (1977). Reducing the risk of cardiovascular disease: Effects of a community-based campaign on knowledge and behavior. *Journal of Community Health*, **3**, 100–114.

MacCorquodale, K., & Meehl, P. (1948). On the distinction between hypothetical constructs and intervening variables. *Psychological Review*, **5**, 95–107.

MacFarlane, J. W., Allen, L., & Honzik, M. R. (1954). *A developmental study of the behavior problems of normal children between 21 months and 14 years*. Berkeley, Calif.: University of California Press.

Mackay, A. V. P., Iversen, L. L., Rossor, M., Spokes, E., Arregio, A., Crease, I., & Snyder, S. H. (1982). Increased brain dopamine and dopamine receptors in schizophrenia. *Archives of General Psychiatry*, **39**, 991–997.

MacPhillamy, D. J., & Lewinsohn, P. M. (1973). A scale for the measurement of positive reinforcement. Unpublished manuscript, University of Oregon.

MacPhillamy, D. J., & Lewinsohn, P. M. (1974). Depression as a function of levels of desired and obtained pleasure. *Journal of Abnormal Psychology*, **83**, 651–657.

Maddi, S. R. (1967). The existential neurosis. *Journal of Abnormal Psychology*, **72**, 311–325.

Magenis, R. E., Overton, K. M., Chamberlin, J., Brady, T., & Lovrien, E. (1977). Paternal origin of the extra chromosome in Down's syndrome. *Human Genetics*, **37**, 7–16.

Maher, B. A. (1966). *Principles of psychopathology: An experimental approach*. New York: McGraw-Hill.

Maher, B. A. (1974). *Journal of Consulting and Clinical Psychology*, **42**, 1–3 (editorial).

Mahoney, M. J. (1972). Research issues in self-management. *Behavior Therapy*, **3**, 45–63.

Mahoney, M. J. (1974). *Cognition and behavior modification*. Cambridge, Mass.: Ballinger.

Mahoney, M. J. (1980). *Abnormal psychology: Perspectives on human variance*. New York: Harper and Row.

Main, T. F. (1958). Perception and ego-function. *British Journal of Medical Psychology*, **31**, 1–7.

Malin, H., Coakley, J., Kaelber, C., Munch, N., & Holland, W. (1982). An epidemiologic perspective on alcohol abuse in the United States. In *Alcohol consumption and related problems*. National Institute of Alcohol Abuse and Alcoholism. Washington, D.C.: U.S. Government Printing Office.

Malloy, T. R., Wein, A. J., & Carpiniello, V. L. (1980). Comparison of the inflatable penile and the small carrion prostheses in the surgical treatment of erectile impotence. *Journal of Urology*, **123**, 678–679.

Mandler, G. (1966). Anxiety. In D. L. Sills (Ed.), *International encyclopedia of the social sciences*. New York: Macmillan.

Mannello, T. A., & Seaman, F. J. (1979). *Prevalence, costs and handling of drinking problems on seven railroads*. Washington, D.C.: University Research Corporation.

Margolin, G. (1982). Ethical and legal considerations in marital and family therapy. *American Psychologist, 37,* 788–801.

Margolin, G. (1978). The relationship among marital assessment procedures: A correlational study. *Journal of Consulting and Clinical Psychology, 46,* 1556–1558.

Margolin, G., & Fernandez, V. (in press). Marital dysfunction. In M. Hersen & A. S. Bellack (Eds.), *Handbook of clinical behavior therapy with adults*. New York: Plenum Press.

Margolin, G., & Weiss, R. L. (1978). Comparative evaluation of therapeutic components associated with behavioral marital treatment. *Journal of Consulting and Clinical Psychology, 46,* 1476–1486.

Marijuana research findings. (1980). Washington, D.C.: U.S. Government Printing Office.

Marks, I. M. (1969). *Fears and phobias*. New York: Academic Press.

Marks, I. M. (1981). *Care and cure of neuroses: Theory and practice of behavioral psychotherapy*. New York: Wiley. (a)

Marks, I. M. (1981). Review of behavioral psychotherapy: I. Obsessive-compulsive disorders. *American Journal of Psychiatry, 138,* 584–592. (b)

Marks, I. M., & Gelder, M. G. (1966). Different onset ages in varieties of phobia. *American Journal of Psychiatry, 123,* 218, 221.

Marks, I. M., & Gelder, M. G. (1967). Transvestism and fetishism: Clinical and psychological changes during faradic aversion. *British Journal of Psychiatry, 113,* 711–729.

Marks, I. M., Gelder, M. G., & Bancroft, J. (1970). Sexual deviants two years after electrical aversion. *British Journal of Psychiatry, 117,* 73–85.

Marlatt, G. A. (1983). The controlled drinking controversy: A commentary. *American Psychologist, 38,* 1097–1110.

Marlatt, G. A., Demming, B., & Reid, J. B. (1973). Loss of control drinking in alcoholics: An experimental analogue. *Journal of Abnormal Psychology, 81,* 233–241.

Marmor, J. (1962). Psychoanalytic therapy as an educational process: Common denominators in the therapeutic approaches of different psychoanalytic schools. In J. H. Masserman (Ed.), *Science and psychoanalysis,* Vol. 5. *Psychoanalytic education*. New York: Grune and Stratton.

Marshall, W. L., Gauthier, J., & Gordon, A. (1979). The current status of flooding therapy. In M. Hersen, R. M. Eisler, & P. M. Miller (Eds.), *Progress in behavior modification,* Vol. 7. New York: Academic Press.

Marston, A., & Marston, M. (1980). *Comprehensive weight control*. New York: BMA cassettes.

Martin, B. (1961). The assessment of anxiety by physiological behavioral measures. *Psychological Bulletin, 58,* 234–255.

Martin, D., & Lyon, P. (1972). *Lesbian/woman*. New York: Bantam.

Martin, R. (1975). *Legal challenges to behavior modification: Trends in schools, corrections, and mental health*. Champaign, Ill.: Research Press.

Maslow, A. H. (1968). *Toward a psychology of being*. New York: Van Nostrand Reinhold.

Massie, H. N., & Beels, C. C. (1972). The outcome of family treatment of schizophrenia. *Schizophrenia Bulletin, 1,* 24–36.

Masters, W. H., & Johnson, V. E. (1966). *Human sexual response*. Boston: Little, Brown.

Masters, W. H., & Johnson, V. E. (1970). *Human sexual inadequacy*. Boston: Little, Brown.

Mathe, A., & Knapp, P. (1971). Emotional and adrenal reactions of stress in bronchial asthma. *Psychosomatic medicine, 33,* 323–329.

Mattes, J. A., & Gittelman, R. (1983). Growth of hyperactive children on maintenance regimen of methylphenidate. *Archives of General Psychiatry, 40,* 317–321.

Matthews, K. A. (1978). Assessment and developmental antecedents of pattern A behavior in children. In T. M. Dembroski, S. M. Weiss, J. L. Shields, S. G. Haynes, & M. Feinleib (Eds.), *Coronary-prone behavior*. New York: Springer-Verlag.

Matthews, K. A. (1982). Psychological perspectives on the Type A behavior pattern. *Psychological Bulletin, 91,* 293–323.

Matthews, K. A., Glass, D. C., Rosenman, R. H., & Bortner, R. W. (1977). Competitive drive, Pattern A, and coronary heart disease: A further analysis of some data from the Western Collaborative Group Study. *Journal of Chronic Diseases, 30,* 489–498.

Matthews, K. A., Krantz, D. S., Dembroski, T. M., & McDongal, J. M. (1982). Unique and common variance in Structured Interview and Jenkins Activity Survey measures of the Type A behavior pattern. *Journal of Personality and Social Psychology, 42,* 303–313.

Mausner, B. (1973). An ecological view of cigarette smoking. *Journal of Abnormal Psychology, 81,* 115–126.

May, P. R. A. (1968). *Treatment of schizophrenia: A comparative study of five treatment methods*. New York: Science House.

May, P. R. A. (1974). Psychotherapy research in schizophrenia—Another view of present reality. *Schizophrenia Bulletin, 1,* 126–132.

May, P. R. A., Tuma, A. H., Yale, C., Potepan, P., & Dixon, W. J. (1976). Schizophrenia—A follow-up study of results of treatment: II. Hospital stay over two to five years. *Psychiatry, 33,* 481–486.

Maynard, R. (1970, June 29). Omaha pupils given "behavior" drugs. *Washington Post*.

Mays, D. T., & Franks, C. M. (1980). Getting worse: Psychotherapy or no treatment—The jury should still be out. *Professional Psychology, 11,* 78–92.

McAdoo, W. G., & DeMyer, M. K. (1978). Personality characteristics of parents. In M. Rutter & E. Schopler (Eds.), *Autism: A reappraisal of concepts and treatment*. New York: Plenum Press.

McAllister, T. W., & Price, T. R. P. (1982). Severe depressive pseudo-dementia with and without dementia. *American Journal of Psychiatry, 139,* 626–629.

McCary, J. L. (1973). *Human sexuality* (2nd ed.). New York: Van Nostrand Reinhold.

McCord, J., McCord, W., & Thurber, S. (1962). Some effects of paternal absence on male children. *Journal of Abnormal and Social Psychology, 64,* 361–369.

McCord, W., & McCord, J. (1964). *The psychopath: An essay on the criminal mind*. New York: Van Nostrand Reinhold.

McCord, W., McCord, J., & Gudeman, J. (1959). Some current theories of alcoholism. *Quarterly Journal of Studies on Alcohol, 20,* 727–749.

McCord, W., McCord, J., & Gudeman, J. (1960). *Origins of alcoholism*. Stanford, Calif.: Stanford University Press.

McCrae, R. R. (1982). Age differences in the use of coping mechanisms. *Journal of Gerontology, 37,* 454–460.

McCrae, R. R., Costa, P. T., Jr., & Arenberg, D. (1980). Constancy of adult personality structure in males: Longitudinal, cross-sectional and times-of-measurement analysis. *Journal of Gerontology, 35,* 877–883.

McFall, R. M., & Hammen, C. L. (1971). Motivation, structure, and self-monitoring: Role of nonspecific factors in smoking reduction. *Journal of Consulting and Clinical Psychology, 37,* 80–86.

McFall, R. M., & Lillesand, D. B. (1971). Behavior rehearsal with modeling and coaching in assertion training. *Journal of Abnormal Psychology*, **77**, 313–323.

McGarry, L., & Chodoff, P. (1981). The ethics of involuntary hospitalization. In S. Bloch & P. Chodoff (Eds.), *Psychiatric ethics*. New York: Oxford University Press.

McGeer, E., & McGeer, P. L. (1976). Neurotransmitter metabolism in the aging brain. In R. D. Terry & S. Gershon (Eds.), *Aging,* Vol. 3. New York: Raven Press.

McGhie, A., & Chapman, J. S. (1961). Disorders of attention and perception in early schizophrenia. *British Journal of Medical Psychology*, **34**, 103–116.

McGlashan, T. M. (1983). The borderline syndrome: I. Testing three diagnostic systems. *Archives of General Psychiatry*, **40**, 1311–1318.

McGuire, R. J., Carlisle, J. M., & Young, B. G. (1965). Sexual deviations as conditioned behaviour: A hypothesis. *Behaviour Research and Therapy*, **2**, 185–190.

McMullen, S., & Rosen, R. C. (1979). Self-administered masturbation training in the treatment of primary orgasmic dysfunction. *Journal of Consulting and Clinical Psychology*, **47**, 912–918.

McNally, R. J., & Reiss, S. (1982). The preparedness theory of phobias and human safety-signal conditioning. *Behaviour Research and Therapy*, **20**, 153–159.

McNeill, E. (1967). *The quiet furies.* Englewood Cliffs, N.J.: Prentice-Hall, 1967.

Mednick, S. A., Gabrielli, W. F., & Hutchings, B. (1984). Genetic influences in criminal convictions: Evidence from an adoption cohort. *Science*, **224**, 891–894.

Mednick, S. A., & Hutchings, B. (1978). Genetic and psychophysiological factors in psychopathic behaviour. In R. D. Hare & D. Schalling (Eds.), *Psychopathic behavior: Approaches to research.* New York: Wiley.

Mednick, S. A., & Schulsinger, F. (1968). Some premorbid characteristics related to breakdown in children with schizophrenic mothers. In D. Rosenthal & S. S. Kety (Eds.), *The transmission of schizophrenia.* Elmsford, N.Y.: Pergamon Press.

Mednick, S. A., Schulsinger, F., & Griffith, J. (1981). Children of schizophrenic mothers: The Danish high-risk study. In F. Schulsinger, S. A. Mednick, & J. Knop (Eds.), *Longitudinal research: Methods and uses in behavioral science.* Hingham, Mass.: Martinus Niggoff.

Medvedev, Z. (1972). *A question of madness.* New York: Knopf.

Meehl, P. E. (1962). Schizotaxia, schizotypy, schizophrenia. *American Psychologist*, **17**, 827–838.

Meichenbaum, D. H., & Asarnow, J. (1979). Cognitive-behavioral modification and metacognitive development: Implications for the classroom. In P. C. Kendall & S. D. Hollon (Eds.), *Cognitive-behavioral interventions: Theory, research, and procedures.* New York: Academic Press.

Meichenbaum, D. H., & Goodman, J. (1969). Reflection-impulsivity and verbal control of motor behavior. *Child Development*, **40**, 785–797.

Meichenbaum, D. H., & Goodman, J. (1971). Training impulsive children to talk to themselves. A means of developing self-control. *Journal of Abnormal Psychology*, **77**, 115–126.

Meiselman, K. C. (1978). *Incest: A psychological study of causes and effects with treatment considerations.* San Francisco, Calif.: Jossey-Bass.

Melamed, B. G., Hawes, R. R., Heiby, E., & Glick, J. (1975). Use of filmed modeling to reduce uncooperative behavior of children during dental treatment. *Journal of Dental Research*, **54**, 797–801.

Melamed, B. G., & Siegel, L. J. (1975). Reduction of anxiety in children facing hospitalization and surgery by use of filmed modeling. *Journal of Consulting and Clinical Psychology*, **43**, 511–521.

Mello, N. K., & Mendelson, J. H. (1970). Experimentally induced intoxication in alcoholics: A comparison between programmed and spontaneous drinking. *Journal of Pharmacology and Experimental Therapy*, **173**, 101.

Mellor, C. S. (1970). First rank symptoms of schizophrenia. *British Journal of Psychiatry*, **117**, 15–23.

Meltzer, H. Y., Sachar, E. J., & Frantz, A. G. (1974). Serum prolactin levels in acutely psychotic patients: An indirect measurement of central dopaminergic acitivity. In E. Usdin (Ed.), *Neuropsychopharmacology of monoamines and their regulatory enzymes.* New York: Raven Press.

Mendels, J. (1970). *Concepts of depression.* New York: Wiley.

Mendels, J., & Cochrane, C. (1968). The nosology of depression. The endogenous-receptive concept. *American Journal of Psychiatry*, **124**, 1–11.

Mendels, J., Fieve, A., Fitzgerand, R. G., Ramsey, T. A., & Stokes. J. W. (1972). Biogenic amine metabolites in cerebrospinal fluid of depressed and manic patients. *Science*, **175**, 1380–1382.

Mendels, J., Stinnett, J. L., Burns, D., & Frazer, A. (1975). Amine precursors and depression. *Archives of General Psychiatry*, **32**, 22–30.

Mendelson, J. H. (1964). Experimentally induced chronic intoxication and withdrawal in alcoholics. *Quarterly Journal of Studies on Alcohol,* Supplement 2.

Mendelson, J. H., Rossi, A. M., & Meyer, R. E. (Eds.). (1974). *The use of marijuana, A psychological and physiological inquiry.* New York: Plenum Press.

Mendlewicz, J., & Rainer, J. D. (1977). Adoption study supporting genetic transmission in manic-depressive illness. *Nature*, **268**, 327–329.

Merskey, H. (1979). *The analysis of hysteria.* London: Bailliere Tindall.

Metalsky, G. I., Abramson, L. V., Seligman, M. E. P., Semmel, A., & Peterson, C. (1982). Attributional styles and life events in the classroom: Vulnerability and invulnerability to depressive mood reactions. *Journal of Personality and Social Psychology*, **43**, 612–617.

Metzner, R., Litwin, G., & Weil, G. M. (1965). The relation of expectation and mood to psilocybin reactions. *Psychedelic Review*, **5**, 3–39.

Mey, B. J. V., & Neff, R. L. (1982). Adult-child incest: A review of research and treatment. *Adolescence*, **17**, 717–735.

Meyer, A. (1917). The aims and meaning of psychiatric diagnosis. *American Journal of Insanity*, **74**, 163–168.

Meyer, J., & Reter, D. J. (1979). Sex reassignment follow-up. *Archives of General Psychiatry*, **36**, 1010–1015.

Meyer, V. (1966). Modification of expectations in cases with obsessional rituals. *Behaviour Research and Therapy*, **4**, 273–280.

Meyer, V., & Chesser, E. S. (1970). *Behavior therapy in clinical psychiatry.* Baltimore: Penguin.

Meyer, V., Robertson, J., & Tatlow, A. (1975). Home treatment of an obsessive-compulsive disorder by response prevention. *Journal of Behavior Therapy and Experimental Psychiatry*, **6**, 37–38.

Meyer-Bahlburg, H. (1979). Sex hormones and female homosexuality: A critical examination. *Archives of Sexual Behavior*, **8**, 101–119.

Miklich, D. R., Rewey, H. H., Weiss, J. H., & Kolton, S. (1973). A preliminary investigation of psychophysiological responses to stress among different subgroups of asthmatic children. *Journal of Psychosomatic Research*, **17**, 1–8.

Miles, L. E., & Dement, W. C. (1980). Sleep and aging. *Sleep*, **3**, 119–220.

Milgram, N. A. (1973). Cognition and language in mental retardation: Directions and implications. In D. K. Routh (Ed.), *The experimental psychology of mental retardation.* Chicago: Aldine.

Miller, E. (1975). Impaired recall and the memory disturbance in presenile dementia. *British Journal of Social and Clinical Psychology*, **14**, 73–79.

Miller, H. R. (1981). Psychiatric morbidity in elderly surgical patients. *British Journal of Psychiatry*, **138**, 17–20.

Miller, I. W., & Norman, W. H. (1979). Learned helplessness in humans: A review and attribution theory model. *Psychological Bulletin*, **86**, 93–118.

Miller, N. E. (1948). Studies of fear as an acquirable drive. I. Fear as motivation and fear-reduction as reinforcement in the learning of new responses. *Journal of Experimental Psychology*, **38**, 89–101.

Miller, N. E. (1959). Liberalization of basic S-R concepts: Extensions to conflict behavior, motivation, and social learning. In S. Koch (Ed.), *Psychology: A study of a science,* Vol. 2. New York: McGraw-Hill.

Miller, R. G., Palkes, H. S., & Stewart, M. A. (1973). Hyperactive children in suburban elementary schools. *Child Psychiatry and Human Development*, **4**, 121–127.

Miller, S. M. (1979). Controllability and human stress: Method, evidence and theory. *Behaviour Research and Therapy*, **17**, 287–304.

Miller, W. R., Seligman, M. E. P., & Kurlander, H. M. (1975). Learned helplessness, depression, and anxiety. *Journal of Nervous and Mental Disease*, **161**, 347–357.

Milton, F., & Hafner, J. (1979). The outcome of behavior therapy for agoraphobia in relation to marital adjustment. *Archives of General Psychiatry*, **36**, 807–811.

Milton, O., & Wahler, R. G. (Eds.). (1969). *Behavior disorders: Perspectives and trends* (2nd ed.). Philadelphia: Lippincott.

Mintz, E. (1967). Time-extended marathon groups. *Psychotherapy*, **4**, 65–70.

Mintz, R. S. (1968). Psychotherapy of the suicidal patient. In H. L. P. Resnik (Ed.), *Suicidal behaviors*. Boston: Little, Brown.

Minuchin, S., Baker, L., Rosman, B. L., Liebman, R., Milman, L., & Todd, T. C. (1975). A conceptual model of psychosomatic illness in children: Family organization and family therapy. *Archives of General Psychiatry*, **32**, 1031–1038.

Mirenda, P. L., Donnellan, A. M., & Yoder, D. E. (1983). Gaze behavior: A new look at an old problem. *Journal of Autism and Developmental Disorders*, **13**, 397–409.

Mirsky, I. A. (1958). Physiologic, psychologic, and social determinants in the etiology of duodenal ulcer. *American Journal of Digestive Diseases*, **3**, 285–314.

Mischel, W. (1968). *Personality and assessment*. New York: Wiley.

Mischel, W. (1973). Toward a cognitive social learning reconceptualizaton of personality. *Psychological Review*, **80**, 252–283.

Mischel, W. (1977). On the future of personality assessment. *American Psychologist*, **32**, 246–254.

Mischel, W., & Peake, P. K. (1982). Beyond déjà vu in the search for cross-situational consistency. *Psychological Review*, **89**, 730–755.

Mohr, J. W., Turner, R. E., & Jerry, M. B. (1964). *Pedophilia and exhibitionism*. Toronto: University of Toronto Press.

Monahan, J. (1973). The psychiatrization of criminal behavior. *Hospital and Community Psychiatry*, **24**, 105–107.

Monahan, J. (1976). The prevention of violence. In J. Monahan (Ed.), *Community mental health and the criminal justice system*. Elmsford, N.Y.: Pergamon Press.

Monahan, J. (1977, April 30). Prisons: A wary verdict on rehabilitation. *Washington Post*, A13.

Monahan, J. (1978). Prediction research and the emergency commitment of dangerous mentally ill persons: A reconsideration. *American Journal of Psychiatry*, **135**, 198–201.

Monahan, J. (1981). *The clinical prediction of violent behavior*. Rockville, Md: National Institute of Mental Health.

Monahan, J. (1984). The prediction of violent behavior: Toward a second generation of theory and policy. *American Journal of Psychiatry*, **141**, 10–15.

Monahan, J., Caldeira, C., & Friedlander, H. (1979). The police and the mentally ill: A comparison of arrested and committed persons. *International Journal of Law and Psychiatry*, **2**, 509–518.

Money, J., & Ehrhardt, A. (1972). *Man and woman, boy and girl*. Baltimore: Johns Hopkins University Press.

Money, J., Hampson, J. G., & Hampson, J. L. (1955). An examination of some basic sexual concepts: The evidence of human hermaphroditism. *Johns Hopkins Hospital Bulletin*, **97**, 301–319.

Moniz, E. (1936). *Tentatives opératories dans le traitement de certaines psychoses*. Paris: Masson.

Moos, R. H. (1974). *Evaluating treatment environments*. New York: Wiley.

Moreno, J. L., & Kipper, D. A. (1968). Group psychodrama and community-centered counseling in G. M. Gazda (Ed.), *Basic approaches to group psychotherapy and group counseling*. Springfield, Ill.: Charles C. Thomas.

Morganstern, K. P. (1973). Implosive therapy and flooding procedures: A critical review. *Psychological Bulletin*, **79**, 318–334.

Morris, A. A. (1968). Criminal insanity. *Washington Review*, **43**, 583–622.

Morris, J. (1974). *Conundrum*. New York: Harcourt Brace Jovanovitch.

Morris, J. B., & Beck, A. T. (1974). The efficacy of antidepressant drugs. *Archives of General Psychiatry*, **30**, 667–674.

Morris, N. (1966). Impediments to legal reform. *University of Chicago Law Review*, **33**, 627–656.

Morris, N. (1968). Psychiatry and the dangerous criminal. *Southern California Law Review*, **41**, 514–547.

Morrison, J. R., & Stewart, M. A. (1971). A family study of the hyperactive child syndrome. *Biological Psychiatry*, **3**, 189–195.

Morrison, J. R., & Stewart, M. A. (1973). The psychiatric status of the legal families of adopted hyperactive children. *Archives of General Psychiatry*, **28**, 888–891.

Morse, S. J. (1978). Crazy behavior, morals, and science: An analysis of mental health law. *Southern California Law Review*, **51**, 527–654.

Morse, S. J. (1979). Diminished capacity: A moral and legal conundrum. *International Journal of Law and Psychiatry*, **2**, 271–298.

Morse, S. J. (1982). A preference for liberty: The case against involuntary commitment of the mentally disordered. *California Law Review*, **70**, 54–106. (a)

Morse, S. J. (1982). Failed explanation and criminal responsibility: Experts and the unconscious. *Virginia Law Review*, **68**, 971–1084. (b)

Morse, S. J. (1982, June 23). In defense of the insanity defense. *Los Angeles Times*. (c)

Mowrer, O. H. (1939). A stimulus-response analysis of anxiety and its role as a reinforcing agent. *Psychological Review*, **46**, 553–565.

Mowrer, O. H. (1947). On the dual nature of learning—a reinterpretation of "conditioning" and "problem-solving." *Harvard Educational Review*, **17**, 102–148.

Mowrer, O. H. (1950). *Learning theory and personality dynamics*. New York: Ronald Press.

Mowrer, O. H., & Mowrer, W. M. (1938). Enuresis: A method for its study and treatment. *American Journal of Orthopsychiatry*, **8**, 436–459.

Mowrer, O. H., & Viek, P. (1948). An experimental analogue of fear from a sense of helplessness. *Journal of Abnormal and Social Psychology*, **43**, 193–200.

Munby, M., & Johnston, D. W. (1980). Agoraphobia: The long-term follow-up of behavioural treatment. *British Journal of Psychiatry*, **137**, 418–427.

Munjack, D. J., & Kanno, P. H. (1979). Retarded ejaculation: A review. *Archives of Sexual Behavior*, **8**, 139–150.

Murphy, D. L., & Wyatt, R. J. (1972). Reduced MAO activity in blood platelets from schizophrenic patients. *Nature*, **238**, 225–226.

Murphy, G. E., Simons, A. D., Wetzel, R. D., & Lustman, P. J. (1984). Cognitive therapy and pharmacotherapy: Singling out together in the treatment of depression. *Archives of General Psychiatry*, **41**, 33–41.

Muscettola, G., Potter, W. Z., Pickar, D., & Goodwin, F. K. (1984). Urinary 3-methoxy-4-hydroxyphenylglycol and major affective disorders. *Archives of General Psychiatry*, **41**, 337–342.

Myers, J. K., & Weissman, M. M. (1980). Psychiatric disorders and their treatment. *Medical Care*, **18**, 117–123.

Myers, J. K., Weissman, M. M., Tischler, G. L., Holzer, C. E., Leaf, P. J., Orvaschel, H. A., Anthony, J. C., Boyd, J. H., Burke, J. D., Kramer, M., & Stoltzman, R. (1984). Six-month prevalence of psychiatric disorders in three communities: 1980–1982. *Archives of General Psychiatry*, **41**, 959–967.

Nathan, P. E., & Goldman, M. S. (1979). Problem drinking and alcoholism. In O. F. Pomerleau & J. P. Brady (Eds.), *Behavioral medicine: Therapy and practice*. Baltimore: Williams and Wilkins.

Nathan, P. E., & Harris, S. L. (1980). *Psychopathology and society* (2nd ed.). New York: McGraw-Hill.

Nathan, P. E., Titler, N. A., Lowenstein, L. W., Solomon, P., & Rossi, A. M. (1970). Behavioral analysis of chronic alcoholism. *Archives of General Psychiatry*, **22**, 419–430.

National Cancer Institute (1977). *The smoking digest: Progress report on a nation kicking the habit*. Washington, D.C.: U.S. Department of Health, Education and Welfare.

National Center for Health Statistics (1979). *The National Nursing Home Survey: 1977 Summary for the United States*. Department of Health, Education and Welfare Publication (PHS) 79-1794.

National Institute on Alcohol Abuse and Alcoholism. (1983). *Special Report to the U.S. Congress on Alcohol and Health*. Washington, D.C.: U.S. Government Printing Office.

National Institute on Drug Abuse. (1983). *Population projections, based on the National Survey on Drug Abuse, 1982*. Rockville, Md.

National Survey on Drug Abuse. (1979). Washington, D.C.: National Institute on Drug Abuse.

National Survey on Drug Abuse. (1982). Washington, D.C.: Department of Health and Human Services, National Institute on Drug Abuse.

Nawas, M. M., Fishman, S. T., & Pucel, J. C. (1970). The standardized desensitization program applicable to group and individual treatment. *Behaviour Research and Therapy*, **6**, 63–68.

Neale, J. M. (1971). Perceptual span in schizophrenia. *Journal of Abnormal Psychology*, **77**, 196–204.

Neale, J. M., & Katahn, M. (1968). Anxiety, choice and stimulus uncertainty. *Journal of Personality*, **36**, 238–245.

Neale, J. M., & Liebert, R. M. (1980). *Science and behavior: An introduction to methods of research* (2nd ed.). Englewood Cliffs, N.J.: Prentice-Hall.

Neisser, U. (1976). *Cognition and reality*. San Francisco: Freeman.

Nelson, J. C., & Bowers, M. B. (1978). Delusional unipolar depression. *Archives of General Psychiatry*, **35**, 1321–1328.

Nelson, R. E., & Craighead, W. E. (1977). Selective recall of positive and negative feedback, self-control behaviors, and depression. *Journal of Abnormal Psychology*, **86**, 379–388.

Nelson, R. O. (1977). Assessment and therapeutic functions of self-monitoring. In M. Hersen, R. M. Eisler, & P. M. Miller (Eds.), *Progress in behavior modification*. New York: Academic Press.

Nelson, R. O., Lipinski, D. P., & Black, J. L. (1975). The effects of expectancy on the reactivity of self-recording. *Behavior Therapy*, **6**, 337–349.

Nelson, R. O., Lipinski, D. P., & Black, J. L. (1976). The reactivity of adult retardates' self-monitoring: A comparison among behaviors of different valences, and a comparison with token reinforcement. *Psychological Record*, **26**, 189–201.

Nelson, R. O., Lipinski, D. P., & Boykin, R. A. (1978). The effects of self-recorders' training and the obtrusiveness of the self-recording device on the accuracy and reactivity of self-monitoring. *Behavior Therapy*, **9**, 200–208.

Nemetz, G. H., Craig, K. D., & Reith, G. (1978). Treatment of female sexual dysfunction through symbolic modeling. *Journal of Consulting and Clinical Psychology*, **46**, 62–73.

Neugarten, B. L. (1977). Personality and aging. In J. E. Birren & K. W. Schaie (Eds.), *Handbook of the psychology of aging*. New York: Van Nostrand Reinhold.

Neugebauer, R. (1979). Mediaeval and early modern theories of mental illness. *Archives of General Psychiatry*, **36**, 477–484.

Neuhaus, E. C. (1958). A personality study of asthmatic and cardiac children. *Psychosomatic Medicine*, **20**, 181–186.

Neuringer, C. (1964). Rigid thinking in suicidal individuals. *Journal of Consulting Psychology*, **28**, 54–58.

Newmark, C. S., Frerking, R. A., Cook, L., & Newmark, L. (1973). Endorsement of Ellis' irrational beliefs as a function of psychopathology. *Journal of Clinical Psychology*, **29**, 300–302.

Nihira, K., Foster, R., Shellhaas, M., & Leland, H. (1975). *AAMD-Adaptive Behavior Scale*. Washington, D.C. American Association on Mental Deficiency.

Nisbett, R. E., & Wilson, T. D. (1977). Telling more than we can know: Verbal reports on mental processes. *Psychological Review*, **84**, 231–259.

Nogrady, H., McConkey, K. M., Laurence, J. R., & Perry, C. (1983). Dissociation, duality, and demand characteristics in hypnosis. *Journal of Abnormal Psychology*, **92**, 223–235.

Norton, G. R., Harrison, B., Hauch, J., & Rhodes, L. (1985). Characteristics of people with infrequent panic attacks. *Journal of Abnormal Psychology*, **94**, 216–221.

Norton, J. P. (1982). Expressed emotion, affective style, voice tone and communication deviance as predictors of offspring schizophrenia spectrum disorders. Unpublished doctoral dissertation, University of California at Los Angeles.

Nowlan, R., & Cohen, S. (1977). Tolerance to marijuana: Heart rate and subjective "high." *Clinical Pharmacology Therapeutics*, **22**, 550–556.

Noyes, R., Anderson, D. J., Clancy, J., Crowe, R. R., Slyman, D. J., Ghoneim, M. M., & Hinrichs, J. V. (1984). Diazepam and propanolol in panic disorder and agoraphobia. *Archives of General Psychiatry*, **41**, 287–292.

Noyes, R., Clancy, J., Crowe, R., Hoenk, P. R., & Slymen, D. J. (1978). The familial prevalence of anxiety neurosis. *Archives of General Psychiatry*, **35**, 1057–1059.

Nunnally, J. C. (1967). *Psychometric theory*. New York: McGraw-Hill.

Obler, M. (1973). Systematic desensitization in sexual disorders. *Journal of Behavior Therapy and Experimental Psychiatry*, **4**, 93–101.

Ochitil, H. (1982). Conversion disorder. In J. H. Greist, J. W. Jefferson, & R. L. Spitzer (Eds.), *Treatment of mental disorders*. New York: Oxford University Press.

O'Connor, R. D. (1969). Modification of social withdrawal through symbolic modeling. *Journal of Applied Behavior Analysis*, **2**, 15–22.

O'Donnell, J. A., & Clayton, R. R. (in press). The steppingstone hypothesis: A reappraisal. *Chemical Dependencies*.

Öhman, A., Erixon, G., & Löfberg, I. (1975). Phobias and preparedness: Phobic versus neutral pictures as conditional stimuli for human autonomic responses. *Journal of Abnormal Psychology*, **84**, 41–45.

O'Leary, K. D. (1980). Pills or skills for hyperactive children. *Journal of Applied Behavior Analysis*, **13**, 191–204.

O'Leary, K. D., & O'Leary, S. G. (Eds.). (1977). *Classroom management* (2nd ed.). Elmsford, N.Y.: Pergamon Press.

O'Leary, K. D., Pelham, W. E., Rosenbaum, A., & Price, G. H. (1976). Behavioral treatment of hyperkinetic children: An experimental evaluation of its usefulness. *Clinical Pediatrics*, **15**, 510–515.

O'Leary, K. D., & Turkewitz, H. (1978). Marital therapy from a behavioral perspective. In T. J. Paolino, Jr., & B. S. McCrady (Eds.), *Marriage and marital therapy*. New York: Brunner/Mazel.

O'Leary, K. D., Turkewitz, H., & Taffel, S. J. (1973). Parent and therapist evaluation of behavior therapy in a child psychological clinic. *Journal of Consulting and Clinical Psychology*, **41**, 289–293.

O'Leary, K. D., & Wilson, G. T. (1975). *Behavior therapy: Application and outcome*. Englewood Cliffs, N.J.: Prentice-Hall.

Oltmanns, T. F., Broderick, J. E., & O'Leary, K. D. (1976). Marital adjustment and the efficacy of behavior therapy with children. Paper presented at the Association for the Advancement of Behavior Therapy. New York City.

O'Neal, J. M. (1984). First person account: Finding myself and loving it. *Schizophrenia Bulletin*, **10**, 109–110.

Orenstein, H., & Carr, J. (1975). Implosive therapy by tape-recording. *Behaviour Research and Therapy*, **13**, 177–182.

Orne, M. T. (1959). The nature of hypnosis: Artifact and essence. *Journal of Abnormal and Social Psychology*, **58**, 277–299.

Orne, M. T., Dinges, D. F., & Orne, E. C. (1984). The differential diagnosis of multiple personality in the forensic court. *International Journal of Clinical and Experimental Hypnosis*, **32**, 118–169.

Orris, J. B. (1967). Visual monitoring performance in three subgroups of male delinquents. Unpublished M.A. thesis, University of Illinois.

Pahnke, W. N. (1963). Drugs and mysticism. Unpublished doctoral dissertation, Harvard University.

Parfitt, D. N., & Gall, C. (1944). Psychogenic amnesia: The refusal to remember. *Journal of Mental Science*, **90**, 511–531.

Parkes, C. M., & Brown, R. J. (1972). Health after bereavement: A controlled study of young Boston widowers. *Psychosomatic Medicine*, **34**, 49–461.

Parloff, M. B., Waskow, I. E., & Wolfe, B. E. (1978). Research on therapist variables in relation to process and outcome. In S. L. Garfield & A. E. Bergin (Eds.), *Handbook of psychotherapy and behavior change: An empirical analysis* (2nd ed.). New York: Wiley.

Parsons, O. A. (1975). Brain damage in alcoholics: Altered states of consciousness. In M. M. Gross (Ed.), *Alcohol intoxication and withdrawal*. New York: Plenum Press.

Pasamanick, B., Rogers, M., & Lilienfeld, M.A. (1956). Pregnancy experience and the development of behavior disorder in children. *American Journal of Psychiatry*, **112**, 613–617.

Paternite, C. E., & Loney, J. (1980). Childhood hyperkinesis: Relationships between symptomatology and home environment. In C. K.

Whalen & B. Henker (Eds.), *Hyperactive children*. New York: Academic Press.

Patsiokas, A. T., Clum, G. A., & Luscomb, R. L. (1979). Cognitive characteristics of suicide attempters. *Journal of Consulting and Clinical Psychology*, **47**, 478–484.

Patterson, G. R. (1974). A basis for identifying stimuli which control behaviors in natural settings. *Child Development*, **45**, 900–911. (a)

Patterson, G. R. (1974). Interventions for boys with conduct problems: Multiple settings, treatments, and criteria. *Journal of Consulting and Clinical Psychology*, **42**, 471–481. (b)

Patterson, G. R., Cobb, J. A., & Ray, R.S. (1973). A social engineering technology for retraining families of aggressive boys. In H. E. Adams & I. P. Unikel (Eds.), *Issues and trends in behavior therapy*. Springfield, Ill.: Charles C. Thomas.

Patterson, G. R., Ray, R. S., Shaw, D. A., & Cobb, J. A. (1969). *Manual for coding of family interactions*. New York: ASIS/NAPS, Microfiche Publications.

Patterson, G. R., & Reid, J. B. (1970). Reciprocity and coercion: Two facets of social systems. In C. Neuringer & J. Michael (Eds.), *Behavior modification in clinical pyschology*. New York: Appleton-Century-Crofts.

Paul, G. L. (1966). *Insight vs. desensitization in psychotherapy*. Stanford, Calif.: Stanford University Press.

Paul, G. L. (1967). Insight versus desensitization in psychotherapy two years after termination. *Journal of Consulting Psychology*, **31**, 333–348.

Paul, G. L. (1969). Chronic mental patient: Current status—future directions. *Psychological Bulletin*, **71**, 81–94.

Paul, G. L., & Lentz, R. J. (1977). *Psychosocial treatment of chronic mental patients: Milieu versus social learning programs*. Cambridge, Mass.: Harvard University Press.

Paul, G. L., & Shannon, D. T. (1966). Treatment of anxiety through systematic desensitization in therapy groups. *Journal of Abnormal Psychology*, **71**, 124–135.

Paulauskas, S.L., & Campbell, S. B. G. (1979). Social perspective-taking and teacher ratings of peer interaction in hyperactive boys. *Journal of Abnormal Child Psychology*, **7**, 483–493.

Pavlov, I. P. (1928). *Lectures on conditioned reflexes*. New York: International Publishers.

Paykel, E. S. (1979). Recent life events in the development of the depressive disorders. In R. A. Depue (Ed.), *The psychobiology of the depressive disorders*. New York: Academic Press.

Pearlin, L. I. (1983). Role strains and personal stress. In H. B. Kaplan (Ed.), *Psychosocial stress: Trends, theory and research*. New York: Academic Press.

Pearson, C., & Gatz, M. (1982). Health and mental health in older adults: First steps in the study of a pedestrian complaint. *Rehabilitation Psychology*, **27**, 37–50.

Pechacek, T. F. (1979). Modification of smoking behavior. In N. A. Krasnegor (Ed.), *The behavioral aspects of smoking*. Washington, D.C.: National Institute on Drug Abuse.

Pendery, M. L., Maltzman, I. M., & West, L. J. (1982). Controlled drinking by alcoholics? New findings and a reevaluation of a major affirmative study. *Science*, **217**, 169–175.

Penk, W. E., Robinowitz, R., Roberts, W. R., Patterson, E. T., Dolan, M. P., & Atkins, H. G. (1981). Adjustment differences among male substance abusers varying in degree of combat experience in Vietnam. *Journal of Consulting and Clinical Psychology*, **49**, 426–437.

Pentoney, P. (1966). Value change in psychotherapy. *Human Relations*, **19**, 39–46.

Perley, M. J., & Guze, S. B. (1962). Hysteria—the stability and usefulness of clinical criteria. *New England Journal of Medicine*, **266**, 421–426.

Perlmutter, M. (1978). What is memory aging the aging of? *Developmental Psychology*, **14**, 330–345.

Perlmutter, M., & Hall, E. (1985). *Adult development and aging.* New York: Wiley.

Perls, F. S. (1947). *Ego, hunger, and aggression.* New York: Vintage.

Perls, F. S. (1969). *Gestalt therapy verbatim.* Moab, Utah: Real People Press.

Perls, F. S. (1970). Four lectures. In J. Fagan & I. L. Shepherd (Eds.), *Gestalt therapy now: Therapy, techniques, applications.* Palo Alto, Calif.: Science and Behavior Books.

Perls, F. S., Hefferline, R. F., & Goodman, P. (1951). *Gestalt therapy: Excitement and growth in the human personality.* New York: Julian Press.

Perris, L. (1969). The separation of bipolar (manic-depressive) from unipolar recurrent depressive psychoses. *Behavioral Neuropsychiatry*, **1**, 17–25.

Pervin, L. A. (1963). The need to predict and control under conditions of threat. *Journal of Personality*, **31**, 570–585.

Peters, J. J. (1977). The Philadelphia rape victim project. In D. Chappell, R. Geis, & G. Geis. (Eds.), *Forcible rape: The crime, the victim, and the offender.* New York: Columbia University Press.

Peterson, C., & Seligman, M. E. P. (1984). Causal explanations as a risk factor for depression: Theory and evidence. *Psychological Review*, **91**, 347–374.

Pfeiffer, E. (1977). Psychopathology and social pathology. In J. E. Birren & K. W. Schaie (Eds.), *Handbook of psychology and aging.* New York: Van Nostrand Reinhold.

Pfeiffer, E., & Busse, E. W. (1973). Mental disorders in later life—Affective disorders: Paranoid, neurotic and situational reactions. In E. W. Busse & E. Pfeiffer (Eds.), *Mental illness in later life.* Washington, D. C.: American Psychiatric Association.

Pfeiffer, E., Eisenstein, R. B., & Dabbs, G. E. (1967). Mental competency evaluation for the federal courts: I. Methods and results. *Journal of Nervous and Mental Disease*, **144**, 320–328.

Pfeiffer, E., Verwoerdt, A., & Wang, H. S. (1968). Sexual behavior in aged men and women: I. Observations on 254 community volunteers. *Archives of General Psychiatry*, **19**, 753–758.

Pfeiffer, E., Verwoerdt, A., & Wang, H. S. (1969). The natural history of sexual behavior in a biologically advantaged group of aged individuals. *Journal of Gerontology*, **24**, 193–198.

Phares, J. (1979). *Clinical psychology: Concepts, methods, and professions.* Homewood, Ill.: Dorsey Press.

Phillips, E. I. (1968). Achievement Place: Token reinforcement procedures in a home style rehabilitation setting for predelinquent boys. *Journal of Applied Behavior Analysis*, **1**, 213–223.

Phillips, L. (1953). Case history data and prognosis in schizophrenia. *Journal of Nervous and Mental Disease*, **117**, 515–525.

Pilowsky, I. (1970). Primary and secondary hypochondriasis. *Acta Psychiatrica Scandinavica*, **46**, 273–285.

Pinel, P. (1962). *A treatise on insanity, 1801.* English translation by D. D. Davis. New York: Hafner.

Pirsig R. M. (1974). *Zen and the art of motorcycle maintenance: An inquiry into values.* New York: Morrow.

Plummer, S., Baer, D. M., & LeBlanc, J. M. (1977). Functional consideration in the use of time out and an effective alternative. *Journal of Applied Behavior Analysis*, **10**, 689–706.

Pokorny, A. D.(1968). Myths about suicide. In H. L. P. Resnik (Ed.), *Suicidal behaviors.* Boston: Little, Brown.

Polivy, J. (1976). Perception of calories and regulation of intake in restrained and unrestrained eaters. *Addictive Behavior*, **1**, 237–243.

Pope, H. G., & Hudson, J. I. (1984). *New hope for binge eaters: Advances in the understanding and treatment of bulimia.* New York: Harper and Row.

Pope, H. G., Jonas, J. M., Hudson, J. I., Cohen, B. M., & Gunderson, J. G. (1983). The validity of DSM-III borderline personality disorder. *Archives of General Psychiatry*, **40**, 23–30.

Post, F. (1975). Dementia, depression, and pseudodementia. In D. F. Benson & D. Blumer (Eds.), *Psychiatric aspects of neurologic disease.* New York: Grune and Stratton.

Post, F. (1978). The functional psychosis. In A. D. Isaacs & F. Post (Eds.), *Studies in Geriatric Psychiatry.* Chichester, England: Wiley.

Post, F. (1980). Paranoid, schizophrenia-like and schizophrenic states in the aged. In J. E. Birren & R. B. Sloane (Eds.), *Handbook of mental health and aging.* Englewood Cliffs, N.J.: Prentice-Hall.

Post, R. M., Fink, E., Carpenter, W. T., & Goodwin, F. K. (1975). Cerebrospinal fluid amine metabolites in acute schizophrenia. *Archives of General Psychiatry*, **32**, 1063–1069.

President's Commission on Mental Health (1978). Report to the President. Washington, D.C.: Superintendent of Documents, U.S. Government Printing Office.

Price, R. H. (1972). *Abnormal behavior. Perspectives in conflict.* New York: Holt, Rinehart and Winston.

Price, V. A. (1982). *Type A behavior pattern: A model for research and practice.* New York: Academic Press.

Prien, R.F., Kupfer, D. J., Mansky, P. A., Small, J. G., Tuason, V. B., Voss, C. B., & Johnson, W. E. (1984). Drug therapy in the prevention of recurrences in unipolar and bipolar affective disorders. *Archives of General Psychiatry*, **41**, 1096–1104.

Prinz, P., & Raskind, M. (1978). Aging and sleep disorders. In R. Williams & R. Karacan (Eds.), *Sleep disorders: Diagnosis and Treatment.* New York: John Wiley & Sons.

Prizant, E. M. (1983). Echolalia in autism: Assessment and intervention. *Seminars in Speech and Language*, **4**, 63–77.

Prochaska, J. O. (1984). *Systems of psychotherapy* (2nd ed.). Homewood, Ill. Dorsey Press.

Proctor, J. T. (1958). Hysteria in childhood. *American Journal of Orthopsychiatry*, **28**, 394–407.

Proshansky, H. M., Ittelson,W. M., & Rivlin, L. (Eds.). (1972). *Theory and research in environmental psychology.* New York: Holt, Rinehart and Winston.

Purcell, K., Brady, K., Chai, H., Muser, J., Molk, L., Gordon, N., & Means, J. (1969). The effect on asthma in children of experimental separation from the family. *Psychosomatic Medicine*, **31**, 144–164.

Purcell, K., & Weiss, J. H. (1970). Asthma. In C. G. Costello (Ed.), *Symptoms of psychopathology: A handbook.* New York: Wiley.

Purdie, F. R., Honigman, T. B., & Rosen, P. (1981). Acute organic brain syndrome: A view of 100 cases. *Annals of Emergency Medicine*, **10**, 455–461.

Purpura, D. P. (1976). Discussants' comments. In T. D. Tjossem (Ed.), *Intervention strategies for high risk infants and young children.* Baltimore: University Park Press.

Quay, H. C. (1964). Personality dimensions in delinquent males as inferred from the factor analysis of behavior ratings. *Journal of Research in Crime and Delinquency*, **1**, 33–37.

Quay, H. C. (1965). Psychopathic personality as pathological stimulus seeking. *American Journal of Psychiatry*, **122**, 180–183.

Quay, H. C. (1979). Classification. In H. C. Quay & J. S. Werry (Eds.), *Psychopathological disorders of childhood* (2nd ed.). New York: Wiley.

Rabavilas, A., & Boulougouris, J. (1974). Physiological accompaniments of ruminations, flooding and thought-stopping in obsessional patients. *Behaviour Research and Therapy*, **12**, 239–244.

Rabins, P. V., & Folstein, M. F. (1982). Delirium and dementia: Diagnostic criteria and fatality rates. *British Journal of Psychiatry*, **140**, 149–153.

Rachman, S. J. (1966). Sexual fetishism: An experimental analogue. *Psychological Record*, **16**, 293–296.

Rachman, S. J., & Hodgson, R. J. (1980). *Obsessions and compulsions*. Englewood Cliffs, N.J.: Prentice-Hall.

Rachman, S. J., & Wilson, G. T. (1980). *The effects of psychological therapy* (2nd ed.). Elmsford, N.Y.: Pergamon Press.

Radloff, L. (1975). Sex differences in depression: The effects of occupation and marital status. *Sex Roles*, **1**, 249–265.

Rahe, R. H., & Holmes, T. H. Life crises and disease onset: A prospective study of life crises and health changes. Unpublished manuscript.

Rahe, R. H., & Lind, E. (1971). Psychosocial factors and sudden cardiac death: A pilot study. *Journal of Psychomatic Research*, **15**, 19–24.

Ramey, C. T., MacPhee, D., & Yeates, K. O. (1982). Preventing developmental retardation. A general systems model. In L. Bond & J. Joffee (Eds.), *Facilitating infant and early childhood development*. Hanover, N.H.: University Press of New England.

Rank, O. (1936). *Will therapy*. New York: Knopf.

Rapaport, D. (1951). *The organization and pathology of thought*. New York: Columbia University Press.

Rapaport, K., & Burkhart, B. R. (1985). Personality and attitudinal characteristics of sexually coercive college males. *Journal of Abnormal Psychology*.

Rapoport, J. L., Buchsbaum, M. S., Zahn, T. P., Weingartner, H., Ludlow, D., & Mikkelson, E. J. (1978). Dextroamphetamine: Cognitive and behavioral effects in normal prepubertal boys. *Science*, **199**, 560–563.

Rappaport, J. (1977). *Community psychology: Values, research, and action*. New York: Holt, Rinehart and Winston.

Rappaport, J. (1981). In praise of paradox: A social policy of empowerment over prevention. *American Journal of Community Psychology*, **9**, 1–25.

Rappaport, J., & Chinsky, J. M. (1974). Models for delivery of service from a historical and conceptual perspective. *Professional Psychology*, **5**, 42–50.

Raskin, F., & Rae, D. S. (1981). Psychiatric symptoms in the elderly. *Psychopharmacology Bulletin*, **17**, 96–99.

Raymond, E. F., Michaels, T. J., & Steer, R. A. (1980). Prevalence and correlates of depression in elderly persons. *Psychological Reports*, **47**, 1055–1061.

Raymond, J. G. (1979). *The transsexual empire: The making of the she-male*. Boston: Beacon Press.

Redfield, J., & Stone, A. (1979). Individual viewpoints of stressful life events. *Journal of Consulting and Clinical Psychology*, **47**, 147–154.

Redick, R. W., & Taube, C. A. (1980). Demography and mental health care of the aged. In J. E. Birren & R. B. Sloane (Eds.), *Handbook of mental health and aging*. Englewood Cliffs, N.J.: Prentice-Hall.

Rees, L. (1963). The significance of parental attitudes in childhood asthma. *Journal of Psychosomatic Research*, **7**, 181–190.

Rees, L. (1964). The importance of psychological, allergic and infective factors in childhood asthma. *Journal of Psychosomatic Research*, **7**, 253–262.

Reeve, V. C. (1979). Incidence of marijuana in a California impaired driver population. Sacramento: State of California, Department of Justice, Division of Law Enforcement Investigative Service.

Reich, W. (1942). *The function of the orgasm*. New York: Noonday Press.

Reid, E. C. (1910). Autopsychology of the manic-depressive. *Journal of Nervous and Mental Disease*, **37**, 606–620.

Reifler, B. V., Larson, E., & Hanley, R. (1982). Co-existence of cognitive impairment and depression in geriatric outpatients. *American Journal of Psychiatry*, **139**, 623–626.

Rekers, G. A., & Lovaas, O. I. (1974). Behavioral treatment of deviant sex role behaviors in a male child. *Journal of Applied Behavioral Analysis*, **7**, 173–190.

Rescorla, R. A., & Solomon, R. L. (1967). Two-process learning theory: Relationships betwen Pavlovian conditioning and instrumental learning. *Psychological Review*, **74**, 151–182.

Resnik, H. L. P. (Ed.). (1968). *Suicidal behaviors*. Boston: Little, Brown.

Review Panel on Coronary-Prone Behavior and Coronary Heart Disease. (1981). A critical review. *Circulation*, **63**, 1199–1215.

Richards, P., Berk, R. A., & Forster, B. (1979). *Crime as play: Delinquency in a middle class suburb*. Cambridge, Mass.: Ballinger.

Richter, C. P. (1957). On the phenomenon of sudden death in animals and man. *Psychosomatic Medicine*, **19**, 191–198.

Ricks, D. M. (1972). The beginning of vocal communication in infants and autistic children. Unpublished dissertation, University of London.

Rie, H. E., Rie, E. D., Stewart, S., Ambuel, F. P. (1976). The effects of methylphenidate on underachieving children. *Journal of Consulting and Clinical Psychology*, **44**, 250–260.

Rieder, R. O., Mann, L. S., Weinberger, D. R., Kammen, D. P. van, & Post, R. M. (1983). Computer tomographic scans in patients with schizophrenia, schizoaffective, and bipolar affective disorder. *Archives of General Psychiatry*, **40**, 735–739.

Rimland, B. (1964). *Infantile autism*. New York: Appleton-Century-Crofts.

Rimland, B. (1969). Psychogenesis versus biogenesis: The issues and the evidence. In S. C. Plog & R. B. Edgerton (Eds.), *Changing perspectives in mental illness*. New York: Holt, Rinehart and Winston.

Rimm, D. C., & Masters, J. C. (1979). *Behavior therapy: Techniques and empirical findings* (2nd ed.). New York: Academic Press.

Ritter, B. (1968). The group treatment of children's snake phobias, using vicarious and contact desensitization procedures. *Behaviour Research and Therapy*, **6**, 1–6.

Ritvo, E. R., Freeman, B. J., Geller, E., & Yuwiler, A. (1983). Effects of fenfluramine on 14 outpatients with the syndrome of autism. *Journal of the American Academy of Child Psychiatry*, **22**, 549–558.

Ritvo, E. R., Yuwiler, A., Geller, E., Ornitz, E. M., Saeger, K., & Plotkin, S. (1970). Increased blood serotonin and platelets in early infantile autism. *Archives of General Psychiatry*, **23**, 556–572.

Robbin, A. A. (1958). A controlled study of the effects of leucotomy. *Journal of Neurology, Neurosurgery, and Psychiatry*, **21**, 262–269.

Robbin, A. A. (1959). The value of leucotomy in relation to diagnosis. *Journal of Neurology, Neurosurgery, and Psychiatry*, **22**, 132–136.

Roberto, L. G. (1983). Issues in diagnosis and treatment of transsexualism. *Archives of Sexual Behavior*, **12**, 445–473.

Robey, A. (1965). Criteria for competency to stand trial: A checklist for psychiatrists. *American Journal of Psychiatry*, **122**, 616–622.

Robins, E., & Guze, S. B. (1970). Establishment of diagnostic validity in psychiatric illness: Its application to schizophrenia. *American Journal of Psychiatry*, **126**, 983–987.

Robins, L. N. (1966). *Deviant children grown up*. Baltimore, Md.: Williams and Wilkins.

Robins, L. N. (1972). Follow-up studies of behavior disorders in children. In H. C. Quay & J. S. Werry (Eds.), *Psychopathological disorders of childhood*. New York: Wiley.

Robins, L. N., Helzer, J. E., Weissman, M. M., Orvaschel, H., Gruenberg, E., Burke, J. D., & Regier, D. A. (1984). Lifetime prevalence of specific psychiatric disorders in three sites. *Archives of General Psychiatry*, 41, 949–958.

Robinson, N. M., & Robinson, H. B. (1976). *The mentally retarded child*. 2nd ed. New York: McGraw-Hill.

Rodin, J. (1980). Managing the stress of aging: The control of control and coping. In H. Ursin & S. Levine (Eds.), *Coping and health*. New York: Academic Press.

Rodin, J., & Langer, E. J. (1977). Long-term effects of a control-relevant intervention with the institutionalized aged. *Journal of Personality and Social Psychology*, 35, 897–902.

Roesch, R., & Golding, S.L. (1980). *Competency to stand trial*. Urbana, Ill.: University of Illinois Press.

Rofman, E. S., Askinazi, C., & Fant, E. (1980). The prediction of dangerous behavior in emergency commitment. *American Journal of Psychiatry*, 137, 1061–1064.

Rogers, C. R. (1942). *Counseling and psychotherapy: New concepts in practice*. Boston: Houghton Mifflin.

Rogers, C. R. (1951). *Client-centered therapy*. Boston: Houghton Mifflin.

Rogers, C. R. (1961). *On becoming a person: A therapist's view of psychotherapy*. Boston: Houghton Mifflin.

Rogers, C. R. (1970). *Carl Rogers on encounter groups*. New York: Harper and Row.

Rogers, C. R., Gendlin, G. T., Kiesler, D. V., & Truax, C. B. (1967). *The therapeutic relationship and its impact: A study of psychotherapy with schizophrenics*. Madison: University of Wisconsin Press.

Romanczyk, R. G., Diament, C., Goren, E. R., Trunell, G., & Harris, S. L. (1975). Increasing isolate and social play in severely disturbed children: Intervention and postintervention effectiveness. *Journal of Autism and Childhood Schizophrenia*, 43, 730–739.

Romanczyk, R. G., Kent, R. N., Diament, C., & O'Leary, K. D. (1973). Measuring the reliability of observational data: A reactive process. *Journal of Applied Behavior Analysis*, 6, 175–184.

Rooth, F. G. (1973). Exhibitionism, sexual violence, and pedophilia. *British Journal of Psychiatry*, 122, 705–710.

Rorschach, H. (1921). *Psychodiagnostics: A diagnostic test based on perception*. Translation and English edition by P. Lemkau & B. Kronenberg (9th ed.). New York: Grune and Stratton, 1981.

Rose, R. M., Jenkins, C. D., & Hurst, M. W. (1978). *Air traffic controller health change study*. Report to the Federal Aviation Administration.

Rosen, E., Fox, R., & Gregory, I. (1972). *Abnormal psychology* (2nd ed.). Phildelphia: Saunders.

Rosen, J. C., & Leitenberg, H. (1982). Bulimia nervosa: Treatment with exposure and response prevention. *Behavior Therapy*, 13, 117–124.

Rosen, J. N. (1946). A method of resolving acute catatonic excitement. *Psychiatric Quarterly*, 20, 183–198.

Rosen, R. C., & Hall, E. (1984). *Sexuality*. New York: Random House.

Rosen, R. C., & Rosen, L. (1981). *Human sexuality*. New York: Knopf.

Rosenbaum, M. (1980). The role of the term schizophrenia in the decline of diagnoses of multiple personality. *Archives of General Psychiatry*, 37, 1383–1385.

Rosenhan, D. L. (1973). On being sane in insane places. *Science*, 179, 250–258.

Rosenman, R. H., Brand, R. J., Jenkins, C. D., Friedman, M., Straus, R., & Wurm, M. (1975). Coronary heart disease in the Western Collaborative Group Study: Final follow-up experience of 8½ years. *Journal of the American Medical Association*, 233, 872–877.

Rosenman, R. H., Friedman, M., Straus, R., Wurm, M., Kositichek, R., Hahn, W., & Werthessen, N. T. (1964). A predictive study of coronary heart disease. *Journal of the American Medical Association*, 189, 103–110.

Rosenthal, D. (1955). Changes in some moral values following psychotherapy. *Journal of Consulting Psychology*, 19, 431–436.

Rosenthal, D. (1970). *Genetic theory and abnormal behavior*. New York: McGraw-Hill.

Rosenthal, R. (1966). *Experimenter bias in behavioral research*. New York:Appleton-Century-Crofts.

Rosenthal, T. L., & Bandura, A. (1978). Psychological modeling: Theory and practice. In S. L. Garfield & A. E. Bergin (Eds.), *Handbook of psychotherapy and behavior change: An empirical analysis* 2nd ed. New York: Wiley.

Rosin, A. J., & Glatt, M. M. (1971). Alcohol excess in the elderly. *Quarterly Journal of Studies on Alcoholism*, 32, 53–59.

Rosman, B. L., Minuchin, S., & Liebman, R. (1975). Family lunch session: An introduction to family therapy in anorexia nervosa. *American Journal of Orthopsychiatry*, 45, 846–852.

Rosman, B. L., Minuchin, S., & Liebman, R. (1976). Input and outcome of family therapy of anorexia nervosa. In J. L. Claghorn (Ed.), *Successful psychotherapy*. New York: Brunner/Mazel.

Ross, A. O. (1981). *Psychological disorders of childhood: A behavioral approach to theory, research, and practice* (2nd ed.). New York: McGraw-Hill.

Ross, D. M., & Ross, S. A. (1973). Storage and utilization of previously formulated mediators in educable mentally retarded children. *Journal of Educational Psychology*, 65, 205–210.

Ross, D. M., & Ross, S. A. (1976). *Hyperactivity: Research, theory, and action*. New York: Wiley.

Ross, J. L. (1977). Anorexia nervosa: An overview. *Bulletin of the Menninger Clinic*, 41, 418–436.

Roth, D., & Rehm, L. P. (1980). Relationships among self-monitoring processes, memory, and depression. *Cognitive Therapy and Research*, 4, 149–157.

Roth, M. (1955). The natural history of mental disorder in old age. *Journal of Mental Science*, 99, 439–450.

Roth, M., & Kay, D. W. K. (1956). Affective disorder arising in the senium: II. Physical disability as an etiological factor. *Journal of Mental Science*, 102, 141–150.

Roth, S., & Kubal, L. (1975). The effects of noncontingent reinforcement on tasks of differing importance: Facilitation and learned helplessness effects. *Journal of Personality and Social Psychology*, 32, 680–691.

Rothman, D. (1971). *The discovery of the asylum*. New York: Harper and Row.

Runck, B. (1980). *Biofeedback—Issues in treatment assessment*. Rockville, Md.: National Institute of Mental Health.

Runck, B. (1982). *Behavioral self-control: Issues in treatment assessment*. Rockville, Md.: National Institute of Mental Health.

Rush, A. J., Beck, A. T., Kovacs, M., & Hollon, S. D. (1977). Comparative efficacy of cognitive therapy and pharmacotherapy in the treatment of depressed outpatients. *Cognitive Therapy and Research*, **1**, 17-39.

Rusin, M., & Siegler, I. C. (1975). Personality differences betwen participants and dropouts in a longitudinal study. Paper presented at the Gerontological Society, Louisville, Ky.

Ruskin, A., Board, O. W., & Schaffer, R. L. (1948). Blast hypertension: Elevated arterial pressure in victims of the Texas City disaster. *American Journal of Medicine*, **4**, 228-236.

Russell, D. E. H. (1982). *Rape in marriage*. New York: Macmillan.

Russo, D. C., & Varni, J. W. (1982). Behavioral pediatrics. In D. C. Russo, & J. W. Varni (Eds.), *Behavioral pediatrics: Research and practice*. New York: Plenum Press, 1982.

Rutter, M. (1966). Prognosis: Psychotic children in adolescence and early adult life. In J. K. Wing (Ed.), *Childhood autism: Clinical, educational, and social aspects*. Elmsford, N.Y.: Pergamon Press.

Rutter, M. (1967). Psychotic disorders in early childhood. In A. J. Cooper (Ed.), *Recent developments in schizophrenia. British Journal of Psychiatry*, Special Publication.

Rutter, M. (1971). Parent-child separation: Psychological effects on the children. *Journal of Child Psychology and Psychiatry*, **12**, 233-260.

Rutter, M. (1978). Diagnosis and definition. In M. Rutter & E. Schopler (Eds.), *Autism: A reappraisal of concepts and treatment*. New York: Plenum Press.

Rutter, M. (1979). Maternal deprivation. 1972-1978: New findings, new concepts, new approaches. *Child Development*, **50**, 283-305.

Rutter, M., & Lockyer, L. (1967). A five to fifteen year follow-up of infantile psychosis: I. Description of sample. *British Journal of Psychiatry*, **113**, 1169-1182.

Rutter, M., Tizard, J., & Whitmore, K. (1970). *Education, health, and behavior*. London: Longmans.

Ryall, R. (1974). Delinquency: The problem for treatment. *Social Work Today*, **15**, 98-104.

Ryan, W. (1971). *Blaming the victim*. New York: Random House.

Rybstein-Blinchik, E. (1979). Effects of different cognitive strategies on chronic pain experience. *Journal of Behavioral Medicine*, **2**, 93-101.

Sackeim, H. A., Nordlie, J. W., & Gur, R. C. (1979). A model of hysterical and hypnotic blindness: Cognition, motivation and awareness. *Journal of Abnormal Psychology*, **88**, 474-489.

Safer, D. J., & Allen, R. P. (1976). *Hyperactive children: Diagnosis and management*. Baltimore: University Park Press.

Sajdel-Sulkowska, E. M., & Marotta, C. A. (1984). Alzheimer's disease brain: Alterations in RNA levels and in ribonuclease-inhibitor complex. *Science*, **225**, 947-949.

Sakel, M. (1938). The pharmacological shock treatment of schizophrenia. *Nervous and Mental Disease Monograph 62*.

Sallan, S. E., Zinberg, N. E., & Frei, E. (1975). Antiemetic effect of delta-9-THC in patients receiving cancer chemotherapy. *New England Journal of Medicine*, **293**, 795-797.

Salter, A. (1949). *Conditioned reflex therapy*. New York: Farrar, Straus.

Salzman, L. (1980). *Psychotherapy of the obsessive personality*. New York: Jason Aronson.

Salzman, L., & Thaler, F. H. (1981). Obsessive-compulsive disorders: A review of the literature. *American Journal of Psychiatry*, **138**, 286-296.

Sargent, J. D., Green, E. E., & Walters, E. D. (1972). Preliminary report on the use of autogenic feedback techniques in the treatment of migraine headaches. *Headache*, **12**, 120-124.

Sargent, J. D., Green, E. E., & Walters, E. D. (1973). The use of autogenic feedback training in a pilot study of migraine and tension headaches. *Psychosomatic Medicine*, **35**, 129-135.

Sartorius, N., Shapiro, R., & Jablonsky, A. (1974). The international pilot study of schizophrenia. *Schizophrenia Bulletin*, **2**, 21-35.

Sassenrath, E. N., Chapman, L. F., & Goo, G. P. (1979). Reproduction in rhesus monkeys chronically exposed to moderate amounts of delta-9-tetrahydrocannabinol. In G. G. Nahas & W. D. M. Paton (Eds.), *Marihuana: Biological effects*. Elmsford, N.Y.: Pergamon Press.

Satterfield, J. H., Cantwell, D. P., Lesser, L. I., & Podosin, R. L. (1972). Physiological studies of the hyperactive child. *American Journal of Psychiatry*, **128**, 1418-1424.

Sawrey, W. L., & Weisz, J. D. (1956). An experimental method of producing gastric ulcers: Role of psychological factors in the production of gastric ulcers in the rat. *Journal of Comparative and Physiological Psychology*, **49**, 457-461.

Scarlett, W. (1980). Social isolation from agemates among nursery school children. *Journal of Child Psychology and Psychiatry*, **21**, 231-240.

Schachter, S. (1977). Nicotine regulation in heavy and light smokers. *Journal of Experimental Psychology: General*, **106**, 5-12.

Schachter, S. (1978). Pharmacological and psychological determinants of smoking. *Annals of Internal Medicine*, **88**, 104-114.

Schachter, S., Kozlowski, L. T., & Silverstein, B. (1977). Effects of urinary pH on cigarette smoking. *Journal of Experimental Psychology: General*, **106**, 13-19.

Schachter, S., & Latané, B. (1964). Crime, cognition, and the autonomic nervous system. In D. Levine (Ed.),. *Nebraska symposium on motivation*, Vol. 12. Lincoln: University of Nebraska Press.

Schachter, S., Silverstein, B., Kozlowski, L. T., Herman, C. P. & Liebling, B. (1977). Effects of stress on cigarette smoking and urinary pH. *Journal of Experimental Psychology: General*, **106**, 24-30.

Schachter, S., Silverstein, B., & Perlik, O. (1977). Psychological and pharmacological explanations of smoking under stress. *Journal of Experimental Psychology: General*, **106**, 31-40.

Schaie, K. W. (1980). Intelligence and problem solving. In J. E. Birren & R. B. Sloane (Eds.), *Handbook of mental health and aging*. Englewood Cliffs, N.J.: Prentice-Hall.

Schain, R. J., & Reynard, C. J. (1975). Effects of a central stimulant drug (methylphenidate) in children with hyperactive behavior. *Pediatrics*, **55**, 709-716.

Schank, R., &Abelson, R. (1977). *Scripts, plans, goals, and understanding*. Hillsdale, N.J.: Lawrence Erlbaum Associates.

Schatzberg, A. F., Orsulak, P. J., Rosenbaum, A. H., Cole, J. O., & Scheerenberger, R. C. (1983). *A history of mental retardation*. Baltimore, Md.: P. H. Brookes.

Scheerer, M., Rothman, E., & Goldstein, K. (1945). A case of "idiot savant": An experimental study of personality organization. *Psychological Monographs*, **58** (whole No. 269).

Scheff, T. J. (1966). *Being mentally ill: A sociological theory*. Chicago: Aldine.

Schildkraut, J. J. (1965). The catecholamine hypothesis of affective disorders. *American Journal of Psychiatry*, **122**, 509-522.

Schildkraut, J. J. (1983). Biochemical subtypes of unipolar depressions. In P. J. Clayton & J. E. Barrett (Eds.), *Treatment of depression: Old controversies and new approaches*. New York: Raven Press.

Schlesier-Stropp, B. (1984). Bulimia: A review of the literature. *Psychological Bulletin*, **95**, 247-257.

Schmauk, F. J. (1970). Punishment, arousal, and avoidance learning in sociopaths. *Journal of Abnormal Psychology*, **76**, 443-453.

Schneider, K. (1959). *Clinical psychopathology.* New York: Grune and Stratton.

Schneider, N. G., Jarvik, M. E., & Forsythe, A. B. (1984). Nicotine vs. placebo gum in the alleviation of withdrawal during smoking cessation. *Addictive Behaviors*, 9, 149–156.

Schneider, N. G., Jarvik, M. E., Forsythe, A. B., Read, L. L., Elliott, M. L., & Schweiger, A. (1983). Nicotine gum in smoking cessation: A placebo-controlled, double-blind trial. *Addictive Behaviors*, 8, 253–261.

Schoeneman, T. J. (1977). The role of mental illness in the European witchhunts of the sixteenth and seventeenth centuries: An assessment. *Journal of the History of the Behavioral Sciences*, 13, 337–351.

Schofield, W. (1964). *Psychotherapy: The purchase of friendship.* Englewood Cliffs, N.J.: Prentice-Hall.

Schuckit, M. A. (1983). The genetics of alcoholism. In B. Tabakoff, P. B. Sutker, & C. L. Randall (Eds.), *Medical and social aspects of alcohol use.* New York: Plenum Press.

Schuckit, M. A., & Moore, M. A. (1979). Drug problems in the elderly. In O. J. Kaplan (Ed.), *Psychopathology of aging.* New York: Academic Press.

Schuckit, M. A., & Rayses, V. (1979). Ethanol ingestion: Differrences in blood acetaldehyde concentrations in relatives of alcoholics and controls. *Science*, 203, 54–55.

Schulsinger, F. (1972). Psychopathy: Heredity and environment. *International Journal of Mental Health*, 1, 190–206.

Schultz, R., & Brenner, G. (1977). Relocation of the aged: A review and theoretical analysis. *Journal of Gerontology*, 32, 323–333.

Schutz, W. C. (1967). *Joy.* New York: Grove Press.

Schwab, J. J., Fennell, E. B., & Warheit, G. J. (1974). The epidemiology of psychosomatic disorders. *Psychosomatics*, 15, 88–93.

Schwarz, J. R. (1981). *The Hillside strangler: A murderer's mind.* New York: New American Library.

Schwartz, G. E. (1973). Biofeedback as therapy: Some theoretical and practical issues. *American Psychologist*, 28, 666–673.

Schwartz, G. E., & Weiss, S. M. (1978). Behavioral medicine revisited: An amended definition. *Journal of Behavioral Medicine*, 1, 249–252.

Schwartz, G. J. (1977). College students as contingency managers for adolescents in a program to develop reading skills. *Journal of Applied Behavior Analysis*, 10, 645–655.

Schwartz, M. A., Wyatt, R. J., Yang, H., & Neff, N. (1974). Multiple forms of monamine oxidase in brain: A comparison of enzymatic activity in mentally normal and chronic schizophrenic individuals. *Archives of General Psychiatry*, 31, 557–560.

Schwartz, M. S. (1946). The economic and spatial mobility of paranoid schizophrenics. Unpublished M.A. thesis. University of Chicago.

Schwartz, R., & Schwartz, L. J. (1980). *Becoming a couple.* Englewood Cliffs, N.J.: Prentice-Hall.

Schwartz, R. M., & Gottman, J. M. (1976). Toward a task analysis of assertive behavior. *Journal of Consulting and Clinical Psychology*, 44, 910–920.

Schwitzgebel, R. L., & Schwitzgebel, R. K. (1980). *Law and psychological practice.* New York: Wiley.

Segovia-Riquelma, N., Varela, A., & Mardones, J. (1971). Appetite for alcohol. In Y. Israel & J. Mardones (Eds.), *Biological basis of alcoholism.* New York: Wiley.

Seidman, L. J. (1983). Schizophrenia and brain dysfunction: An integration of recent neurodiagnostic findings. *Psychological Bulletin*, 94, 195–238.

Seiden, R. H. (1974). Suicide: Preventable death. *Public Affairs Report*, 15, 1–5.

Seligman, M. E. P. (1971). Phobias and preparedness. *Behavior Therapy*, 2, 307–320.

Seligman, M. E. P. (1973). Fall into helplessness. *Psychology Today*, 7, 43–48.

Seligman, M. E. P. (1974). Depression and learned helplessness. In R. J. Friedman & M. M. Katz (Eds.), *The psychology of depression: Contemporary theory and research.* Washington, D.C.: Winston-Wiley.

Seligman, M. E. P. (1978). Comment and integration. *Journal of Abnormal Psychology*, 87, 165–179.

Seligman, M. E. P. (1975). *Helplessness: On depression, development, and death.* San Francisco: Freeman.

Seligman, M. E. P., Abramson, L. V., Semmel, A., & Von Baeyer, C. (1979). Depressive attributional style. *Journal of Abnormal Psychology*, 88, 242–247.

Seligman, M. E. P., & Hager, M. (Eds.). (1972). *Biological boundaries of learning.* New York: Appleton-Century-Crofts.

Selling, L. S. (1940). *Men against madness.* New York: Greenberg, Publishing.

Selye, H. (1936). A syndrome produced by diverse nocuous agents. *Nature*, 138, 32.

Settin, J. M. (1982). Clinical judgment in geropsychology practice. *Psychotherapy: Theory, Research and Practice*, 19, 397–404.

Shader, R. I., Caine, E. D., & Meyer, R. E. (1975). Treatment of dependence on barbiturates and sedative hypnotics. In R. I. Shader (Ed.), *Manual of psychiatric therapeutics: Practical psychopharmacology and psychiatry.* Boston, Mass.: Little, Brown.

Shader, R. I., & DiMascio, A. (1970). *Psychotropic drug side-effects: Clinical and theoretical perspectives.* Baltimore, Md.: Williams and Wilkins.

Shapiro, A. P. (1961). An experimental study of comparative responses of blood pressure to different noxious stimuli. *Journal of Chronic Diseases*, 13, 293–311.

Shapiro, D., & Surwit, R.S. (1979). Biofeedback. In O. F. Pomerleau & J. P. Brady (Eds.), *Behavioral medicine: Theory and practice.* Baltimore, Md.: Williams and Wilkins.

Shapiro, D., Tursky, B., & Schwartz, G. E. (1970). Control of blood pressure in man by operant conditionong. *Circulation Research*, 26, 127–132.

Shatan, C. F. (1978). Stress disorders among Vietnam veterans: The emotional content of combat continues. In C. R. Figley (Ed.), *Stress disorders among Vietnam veterans.* New York: Brunner/Mazel.

Shaw, B. F. (1977). Comparison of cognitive therapy and behavior therapy in the treatment of depression. *Journal of Consulting and Clinical Psychology*, 45, 543–551.

Shaywitz, S.E., Cohen, D. J., & Shaywitz, B. A. (1978). The biochemical basis of minimal brain dysfunction. *The Journal of Pediatrics*, 92, 179–187.

Sher, K. J., & Levenson, R. W. (1982). Risk for alcoholism and individual differences in the stress-response-dampening effects of alcohol. *Journal of Abnormal Psychology*, 91, 350–367.

Sherman, A. R. (1972). Real-life exposures as a primary therapeutic factor in the desensitization treatment of fear. *Journal of Abnormal Psychology*, 79, 19–28.

Sherman, E. (1981). *Counseling the aging: An integrative approach.* New York: The Free Press.

Shevitz, S. A. (1976). Psychosurgery: Some current observations. *American Journal of Psychiatry*, 133, 266–270.

Shilling, L. E. (1984). *Perspectives on counseling therapies.* Englewood Cliffs: N.J.: Prentice-Hall.

Shneidman, E. S. (1976). A psychological theory of suicide. *Psychiatric Annals*, **6**, 51–66.

Shneidman, E. S. (1973). Suicide. In *Encyclopedia Britannica*. Chicago: Encyclopedia Britannica.

Shneidman, E. S., & Farberow, N. L. (1970). A psychological approach to the study of suicide notes. In E. S. Shneidman, N. L. Farberow, & R. E. Litman (Eds.), *The psychology of suicide*. New York: Jason Aronson.

Schneidman, E. S., Farberow, N. L., & Litman, R. E. (Eds.), (1970). *The psychology of suicide*. New York: Jason Aronson.

Shopsin, B., Friedman, E., & Gershon, S. (1976). Parachlorophenylalanine reversal of tranylcypromine effects in depressed patients. *Archives of General Psychiatry*, **33**, 811–819.

Shopsin, B., Gershon, S., Thompson, H., & Collins, P. (1975). Psychoactive drugs in mania. *Archives of General Psychiatry*, **32**, 34–42.

Short, J. F., & Nye, F. I. (1958). Extent of unrecorded juvenile delinquency: Tentative conclusions. *Journal of Criminal Law, Criminology, and Police Science*, **29**, 296–302.

Siegel, R. A. (1978). Probability of punishment and suppression of behavior in psychopathic and nonpsychopathic offenders. *Journal of Abnormal Psychology*, **87**, 514–522.

Seigel, R. K. (1982). Cocaine smoking. *Journal of Psychoactive Drugs*, **14**, 277–359.

Siegler, I. C., & Costa, P. T., Jr. (1985). Health behavior relationships. In J. E. Birren & K. W. Schaie (Eds.), *Handbook of the psychology of aging*. 2nd ed. New York: Van Nostrand Reinhold.

Siegler, I. C., George, L. K., & Okun, M. A. (1979). A cross sequential analysis of adult personality. *Developmental Psychology*, **15**, 350–351.

Siemens, A. J. (1980). Effects of cannabis in combinations with ethanol and other drugs. In *Marijuana research findings: 1980*. Washington, D.C.: U.S. Government Printing Office.

Silverstein, B., Kozlowski, L. T., & Schachter, S. (1977). Social life, cigarette smoking, and urinary pH. *Journal of Experimental Psychology: General*, **106**, 20–23.

Silverstein, C. (1972). Behavior modification and the gay community. Paper presented at the annual convention of the Association for Advancement of Behavior Therapy, New York City.

Silverstein, C. (1977). *A family matter: A parent's guide to homosexuality*. New York: McGraw-Hill.

Simeons, A. T. W. (1961). *Man's presumptuous brain: An evolutionary interpretation of psychosomatic disease*. New York: Dutton.

Simpson, G. M., & May, P. R. A. (1982). Schizophrenic disorders. In J. H. Greist, J. W. Jefferson, & R. L. Spitzer (Eds.), *Treatment of mental disorders*. New York: Oxford University Press.

Simpson, M. T., Olewine, D. A., Jenkins, F. H., Ramsey, S. J., Zyzanski, S. J., Thomas, G., & Hames, C. G. (1974). Exercise-induced catecholamines and platelet aggregation in the coronary-prone behavior pattern. *Psychosomatic Medicine*, **36**, 476–487.

Sines, J. O. (1963). Physiological and behavioral characteristics of rats selectively bred for susceptibility to stomach ulcer development. *Journal of Neuropsychiatry*, **4**, 396–398.

Singer, M., & Wynne, L. C. (1963). Differentiating characteristics of the parents of childhood schizophrenics. *American Journal of Psychiatry*, **120**, 234–243.

Sintchak, G. H., & Geer, J. H. (1975). A vaginal plethysmograph system. *Psychophysiology*, **12**, 113–115.

Sizemore, C. C., & Pittillo, E. S. (1977). *I'm Eve*. Garden City, N.Y.: Doubleday.

Skinner, B. F. (1948). ''Superstition'' in the pigeon. *Journal of Experimental Psychology*, **38**, 168–172.

Skinner, B. F. (1953). *Science and human behavior*. New York: Macmillan.

Skinner, H. A., & Allen, B. A. (1982). Alcohol dependence syndrome: Measurement and validation. *Journal of Abnormal Psychology*, **91**, 199–209.

Sklar, L. A., & Anisman, H. (1979). Stress and coping factors influence tumor growth. *Science*, **205**, 513–515.

Skrzypek, G. J. (1969). The effects of perceptual isolation and arousal on anxiety, complexity preference and novelty preference in psychopathic and neurotic delinquents. *Journal of Abnormal Psychology*, **74**, 321–329.

Slater, E. (1938). Erbpathologie des manisch-depressiven Irreseins. Die Eltern und Kinder von Manisch-Depressiven. *Zeitschrift für die gesarnte Neurologie und Psychiatrie*, **163**, 1–17.

Slater, E. (1961). The thirty-fifth Maudsley lecture: Hysteria 311. *Journal of Mental Science*, **107**, 358–381.

Slater, E., & Glithero, E. (1965). A follow-up of patients diagnosed as suffering from hysteria. *Journal of Psychosomatic Research*, **9**, 9–13.

Slater, E., & Shields, J. (1969). Genetic aspects of anxiety. In M. H. Lader (Ed.), *Studies of anxiety*. Ashford, England: Headley Brothers.

Slavson, S. R. (1950). *Analytic group psychotherapy with children, adolescents and adults*. New York: Columbia University Press.

Sloane, R. B. (1980). Organic brain syndrome. In J. E. Birren & R. B. Sloane (Eds.), *Handbook of mental health and aging*. Englewood Cliffs, N.J.: Prentice-Hall.

Sloane, R. B., Staples, F. R., Cristol, A. H., Yorkston, N. J., & Whipple, K. (1975). *Psychoanalysis versus behavior therapy*. Cambridge, Mass.: Harvard Universtiy Press.

Small, G. W., & Jarvik, L. F. (1982). The dementia syndrome. *Lancet*, 1443–1446.

Small, G. W., Liston, E. H., & Jarvik, L. F. (1981). Diagnosis and treatment of dementia in the aged. *The Western Journal of Medicine*, **135**, 469–481.

Smith, D. W., Bierman, E. L., & Robinson, N. M. (1978). *The biologic ages of man: From conception through old age*. Philadelphia, Penn.: Saunders.

Smith, K. F., & Bengston, V. L. (1979). Positive consequences of institutionalization: Solidarity between elderly parents and their middle aged children. *The Gerontologist*, **5**, 438–447.

Smith, P. B. (1975). Controlled studies of the outcome of sensitivity training. *Psychological Bulletin*, **82**, 597–622.

Snyder, S. H. (1974). *Madness and the brain*. New York: McGraw-Hill.

Snyder, S. H., Banerjee, S. P., Yamamura, H. I., & Greenberg, D. (1974). Drugs, neurotransmitters, and schizophrenia. *Science*, **184**, 1243–1253.

Sobell, M. B., & Sobell, L. C. (1978). *Behavioral treatment of alcohol problems: Individualized therapy and controlled drinking*. New York: Plenum Press.

Sobell, M. B., & Sobell, L.C. (1976). Second-year treatment outcome of alcoholics treated by individualized behavior therapy: Results. *Behaviour Research and Therapy*, **14**, 195–215.

Solnick, R. L., & Corby, N. (1983). Human sexuality and aging. In D. S. Woodruff & J. E. Birren (Eds.), *Aging: Scientific perspectives and social issues*. 2nd ed. Monterey, Calif.: Brooks/Cole.

Sommer, R. (1969). *Personal space: The behavioral basis of design*. Englewood Cliffs, N.J.: Prentice-Hall.

Soueif, M. I. (1976). Some determinants of psychological deficits associated with chronic cannabis consumption. *Bulletin of Narcotics*, **28**, 25–42.

Spadoni, A. J., & Smith, J. A. (1969). Milieu therapy in schizophrenia. *Archives of General Psychiatry*, **20**, 547–557.

Spanos, N. P. (1978). Witchcraft in histories of psychiatry: A critical appraisal and an alternative conceptualization. *Psychological Bulletin*, **35**, 417–439.

Spanos, N. P. (1982). Hypnotic behavior: A cognitive, social psychological perspective. *Research Communications in Psychology, Psychiatry, and Behavior*, **7**, 199–213.

Spanos, N. P., Gwynn, M. I., & Stam, H. J. (1983). Instructional demands and ratings of overt and hidden pain during hypnotic analgesia. *Journal of Abnormal Psychology*, **92**, 479–488.

Spanos, N. P., Weekes, J. R., & Bertrand, L. D. (in press). Multiple personality: A social psychological perspective. *Journal of Abnormal Psychology*.

Spar, J. E. (1982). Dementia in the aged. In L. F. Jarvik & G. W. Small (Eds.), *Psychiatric clinics of North America*. Philadelphia, Penn.: Saunders.

Sparrow, S. S., Ballo, D.A., & Cicchetti, D. V. (1984). Vineland Adaptive Behavior Scales. Circle Pines, Minn.: American Guidance Service.

Special Report to the U.S. Congress on Alcohol and Health (1983). Washington, D.C.: NIAA.

Speer, D. C. (1971). Rate of caller re-use of a telephone crisis service. *Crisis Intervention*, **3**, 83–86.

Speer, D. C. (1972). An evaluation of a telephone crisis service. Paper presented at the Midwestern Psychological Association meeting, Cleveland, Ohio.

Sperling, M. (1973). Conversion hysteria and conversion symptoms: A revision of classification and concepts. *Journal of the American Psychoanalytic Association*, **21**, 745–771.

Spielberger, C. D., Johnson, E. H., Russell, S. F., Crane, R. J. & Worden, T. J. (1985). The experience and expression of anger. In M. A. Chesney, & R. H. Rosenman (Eds.), *Anger and hostility in cardiovascular and behavioral disorders*. New York: Hemisphere.

Spiers, P. A. (1982). The Luria-Nebraska Neuropsychological Battery revisited: A theory in practice or just practicing? *Journal of Consulting and Clinical Psychology*, **50**, 301–306.

Spinetta, J. J. (1980). Disease-related communication: How to tell. In J. Kellerman (Ed.), *Psychological aspects of childhood cancer*. Springfield, Ill.: Charles C. Thomas.

Spitzer, R. L., & Endicott, J. (1978). *Schedule for Affective Disorders and Schizophrenia*. New York: Biometrics Research, New York State Psychiatric Institute.

Spitzer, R. L., Endicott, J., & Gibbon, M. (1979). Crossing the border into borderline personality and borderline schizophrenia. *Archives of General Psychiatry*, **36**, 17–24.

Sprague, R. L., & Gadow, K. D. (1976). The role of the teacher in drug treatment. *School Review*, **85**, 109–140.

Sprague, R. L., & Sleator, E. K. (1977). Methylphenidate in hyperkinetic children: Differences in dose effects on learning and social behavior. *Science*, **198**, 1274–1276.

Srole, L., Langner, T. S., Michael, S. T., Opler, M. K., & Rennie, T. A. C. (1962). *Mental health in the metropolis: The midtown Manhattan study*. New York: McGraw-Hill.

Sroufe, L. A. (1975). Drug treatment of children with behavior problems. In F. Horowitz (Ed.), *Review of child development research*. Chicago: University of Chicago Press.

Staats, A. W., & Butterfield, W. H. (1965). Treatment of nonreading in a culturally deprived juvenile delinquent: An application of learning principles. *Child Development*, **36**, 925–942.

Staats, A. W., & Staats, C. K. (1963). *Complex human behavior*. New York: Holt, Rinehart and Winston.

Stampfl, T. C., & Levis, D. J. (1967). Essentials of implosive therapy: A learning-therapy-based psychodynamic behavior therapy. *Journal of Abnormal Psychology*, **72**, 496–503.

Stang, R. R. (1970). The etiology of Parkinson's desease. *Diseases of the Nervous System*, **31**, 381–390.

Stanton, A. H., & Schwartz, M. S. (1954). *The mental hospital*. New York: Basic Books.

Stanton, M. D., & Bardoni, A. (1972). Drug flashbacks: Reported frequency in a military population. *American Journal of Psychiatry*, **129**, 751–755.

Stanton, M. D., & Figley, C. R. (1978). Treating the Vietnam veteran within the family system. In C. R. Figley (Ed.), *Stress disorders among Vietnam veterans*. New York: Brunner/Mazel.

Starfield, B. (1972). Enuresis: Its pathogenesis and management. *Clinical Pediatrics*, **11**, 343–350.

Starr, B. D., & Weiner, M. B. (1981). *The Starr-Weiner report on sex and sexuality in the mature years*. New York: Stein and Day.

Staub, E., Tursky, B., & Schwartz, G. E. (1971). Self-control and predictability: Their effects on reactions to aversive stimulation. *Journal of Personality and Social Psychology*, **18**, 157–162.

Steadman, H. J. (1979). *Beating a rap: Defendants found incompetent to stand trial*. Chicago: University of Chicago Press.

Stein, D. M., & Lambert, M. I. (1984). Telephone counseling and crisis intervention: A review. *American Journal of Community Psychology*, **12**, 101–126.

Stein, Z., & Susser, M. A. (1971). Changes over time in the incidence and prevalence of mental retardation. In J. Hellmuth (Ed.), *Exceptional infant*. New York: Brunner/Mazel.

Stenmark, D. E., & Dunn, V. K. (1982). Issues related to the training of geropsychologists. In J. F. Santos & G. R. VandenBos (Eds.), *Psychology and the older adult*. Washington, D.C.: American Psychological Association.

Stephens, J. H., & Kamp, M. (1962). On some aspects of hysteria: A clinical study. *Journal of Nervous and Mental Disease*, **134**, 305–315.

Sterman, H. B. (1973). Neurophysiologic and clinical studies of sensorimotor EEG biofeedback training: Some effects on epilepsy. *Seminars in Psychiatry*, **5**, 507–525.

Stern, D. B. (1977). Handedness and the lateral distribution of conversion reactions. *Journal of Nervous and Mental Disease*, **164**, 122–128.

Stern, R. S., & Cobb, J. P. (1978). Phenomenology of obsessive-compulsive neurosis. *British Journal of Psychiatry*, **132**, 233–234.

Stern, S. L., Rush, J., & Mendels, J. (1980). Toward a rational pharmacotherapy of depression. *American Journal of Psychiatry*, **137**, 545–552.

Sternbach, R. A. (1966). *Principles of psychophysiology*: New York: Academic Press.

Steuer, J. L., & Hammen, C. L. (1983). Cognitive-behavioral group therapy for the depressed elderly: Issues and adaptations. *Cognitive Theory and Research*, **7**, 285–296.

Stevenson, J., & Jones, I. H. (1972). Behavior therapy technique for exhibitionism: A preliminary report. *Archives of General Psychiatry*, **27**, 839–841.

Stewart, M. A., Pitts, F. N., Craig, A. G., & Dieruf, W. (1966). The hyperactive child syndrome. *American Journal of Orthopsychiatry*, **36**, 861–867.

Stoller, F. H. (1968). Accelerated interaction: A time-limited approach based on the brief intensive group. *International Journal of Group Psychotherapy*, **18**, 220–235.

Stone, A. A. (1975). *Mental health and law: A system in transition*. Rockville, Md.: National Institute of Mental Health.

Stone, A. A., & Neale, J. M. (1984). New measure of daily coping: Development and preliminary results. *Journal of Personality and Social Psychology, 46,* 892–906.

Stone, L. J., & Hokanson, J. E. (1967). Arousal reduction via self-punitive behavior. *Journal of Personality and Social Psychology, 12,* 72–79.

Storandt, M. (1977). Age, ability level and methods of administering and scoring the WAIS. *Journal of Gerontology, 32,* 175–178.

Storandt, M. (1983). *Counseling and therapy with older adults.* Boston: Little, Brown.

Strub, R. L., & Black, F. W. (1981). *Organic brain syndromes: An introduction to neurobehavioral disorders.* Philadelphia, Penn.: F. A. Davis Company.

Strupp, H. H., Hadley, S. W., & Gomes-Schwartz, B. (1977). *Psychotherapy for better or worse: An analysis of the problem of negative effects.* New York: Jason Aronson.

Stuart, R. B. (1976). An operant interpersonal program for couples. In D. H. L. Olson (Ed.), *Treating relationships.* Lake Mills, Iowa: Graphic Publishing Company.

Stuart, R. B. (1978). Protection of the right to informed consent to participate in research. *Behavior Therapy, 9,* 73–82.

Stuart, R. B. (1980). *Helping couples change: A social learning approach to marital therapy.* New York: Cuilford Press.

Sturgis, E. T., & Adams, H. E. (1978). The right to treatment: Issues in the treatment of homosexuality. *Journal of Consulting and Clinical Psychology, 46,* 165–169.

Sullivan, H. S. (1929). Research in schizophrenia. *American Journal of Psychiatry, 9,* 553–567.

Sullivan, H. S. (1953). *The interpersonal theory of psychiatry.* New York: Norton.

Sutherland, S., & Scheri, D. J. (1977). Crisis intervention with victims in rape. In D. Chappell, R. Geis, & G. Geis (Eds.), *Forcible rape: The crime, the victim and the offender.* New York: Columbia University Press.

Syndulko, K. (1978). Electrocortical investigations of sociopathy. In R. D. Hare & D. Schalling (Eds.), *Psychopathic behaviour: Approaches to research.* New York: Wiley.

Szasz, T. S. (1960). The myth of mental illness. *American Psychologist, 15,* 113–118.

Szasz, T. S. (1963). *Law, liberty, and psychiatry.* New York: Macmillan.

Szasz, T. S. (Ed.), (1974). *The age of madness: The history of involuntary hospitalization.* New York: Jason Aronson.

Tashkin, D. P., Calvarese, B., & Simmons, M. (1978). Respiratory status of 75 chronic marijuana smokers: Comparison with matched controls. University of California at Los Angeles School of Medicine. Abstract in *American Review of Respiratory Diseases, 117,* 261.

Tate, B. G., & Baroff, G. S. (1966). Aversive control of self-injurious behavior in a psychotic boy. *Behaviour Research and Therapy, 4,* 281–287.

Taylor, C. B. (1983). DSM-III and behavioral assessment. *Behavioral Assessment, 5,* 5–14.

Taylor, J. A. (1953). A personality scale of manifest anxiety. *Journal of Abnormal and Social Psychology, 48,* 285–290.

Terry, R. D., & Wisniewski, H. M. (1974). Sans teeth, sans eyes, sans taste, sans everything. *Behavior Today, 5,* 84.

Terry, R. D., & Wisniewski, H. M. (1977). Structural aspects of aging of the brain. In C. Eisdorfer & R. O. Friedel (Eds.), *Cognitive and emotional disturbances in the elderly.* Chicago: Year Book Medical Publishers.

Theodor, L. H., & Mandelcorn, M. S. (1973). Hysterical blindness: A case report and study using a modern psychophysical technique. *Journal of Abnormal Psychology, 82,* 552–553.

Thibaut, J. W., & Kelley, H. H. (1959). *The social psychology of groups.* New York: Wiley.

Thigpen, C. H., & Cleckley, H. (1954). *The three faces of Eve.* Kingsport, Tenn.: Kingsport Press.

Thoits, P. A. (1982). Conceptual, methodological, and theoretical problems in studying social support as a buffer against life stress. *Journal of Health and Social Behavior, 23,* 145–159.

Thompson, S. C. (1981). Will it hurt less if I can control it? A complex answer to a simple question. *Psychological Bulletin, 90,* 89–101.

Thorndike, E. L. (1935). *The psychology of wants, interests and attitudes.* New York: Appleton, Century.

Tillich, P. (1952). *The courage to be.* New Haven, Conn.: Yale University Press.

Tollefson, D. J. (1972). The relationship between the occurrence of fractures and life crisis events. Unpublished master of nursing thesis, University of Washington, Seattle.

Tomlinson, B. E., & Henderson, G. (1976). Some quantitative findings in normal and demented old people. In R. D. Terry & S. Gershon (Eds.), *Neurobiology of aging.* New York: Raven Press.

Torgersen, S. (1983). Genetic factors in anxiety disorders. *Archives of General Psychiatry, 40,* 1085–1089.

Tramontana, J., & Stimbert, V. (1970). Some techniques of behavior modification with an autistic child. *Psychological Reports, 27,* 498.

Treffert, D. A., McAndrew, J. B., & Dreifuerst, P. (1973). An inpatient treatment program and outcome for 57 autistic and schizophrenic children. *Journal of Autism and Childhood Schizophrenia, 3,* 138–153.

Truett, J., Cornfield, J., & Kannel, W. (1967). Multivariate analysis of the risk of coronary heart disease in Framingham. *Journal of Chronic Disease, 20,* 511–524.

Tuckman, J., Kleiner, R. J., & Lavell, M. (1959). Emotional content of suicide notes. *American Journal of Psychiatry, 116,* 59–63.

Turkewitz, H., & O'Leary, K. D. (1977). A comparison of communication and behavioral marital therapy. Paper presented at the Eleventh Annual Convention of the Association for Advancement of Behavior Therapy, Atlanta.

Turner, R. J., & Sternberg, M. P. (1978). Psychosocial factors in elderly patients admitted to a psychiatric hosptial. *Age and aging, 7,* 171–177.

Turner, R. J., & Wagonfeld, M. O. (1967). Occupational mobility and schizophrenia. *American Sociological Review, 32,* 104–113.

Ullmann, L., & Krasner, L. (1975). *A psychological approach to abnormal behavior.* 2nd ed. Englewood Cliffs, N.J.: Prentice-Hall.

Umbarger, C. C., Dalsimer, J. S., Morrison, A. P., & Breggin, P. R. (1962). *College students in a mental hospital.* New York: Grune and Stratton.

Upper, D., & Ross, S. M. (Eds.), (1980). *Behavioral group therapy 1980: An annual review.* Champaign, Ill.: Research Press.

U.S. Department of Health and Human Services (1982). *Prevention in adulthood: Self-motivated quitting.* In *Cancer: The health consequences of smoking, a report of the Surgeon General.* Washington, D.C.: U.S. Government Printing Office.

Vaillant, G. E. (1979). Natural history of male psychologic health: Effects of mental health on physical health. *New England Journal of Medicine, 301,* 1249–1254.

Valenstein, E. S. (1973). *Brain control.* New York: Wiley.

Van Praag, H., Korf, J., & Schut, D. (1973). Cerebral monamines and depression: An investigation with the probenecid technique. *Archives of General Psychiatry, 28,* 827–831.

Van Putten, T., May, P. R. A., Marder, S. R., & Wittman, L. A. (1981). Subjective response to antipsychotic drugs. *Archives of General Psychiatry*, **38**, 187–190.

VandenBos, G. R., Stapp, J., & Kilburg, R. R. (1981). Health service providers in psychology: Results of the 1978 APA Human Resources Survey. *American Psychologist*, **36**, 1395–1418.

Vardaris, R. M., Weisz, D. J., Fazel, A., & Rawitch, A. B. (1976). Chronic administration of delta-9-tetrahydrocannabinol to pregnant rats: Studies of pup behavior and placental transfer. *Pharmacology and Biochemistry of Behavior*, **4**, 249–254.

Varner, R. V., & Gaitz, C. M. (1982). Schizophrenic and paranoid disorders in the aged. In L. F. Jarvik & G. W. Small (Eds.), *Psychiatric clinics of North America*. Philadelphia, Penn.: Saunders.

Varni, J. W., & Dietrich, S. L. (1981). Behavioral pediatrics: Towards a reconceptualization. *Behavioral Medicine Update*, **3**, 5–7.

Varni, J. W., & Wallander, J. L. (in press). Adherence to health-related regimens in pediatric chronic disorders. *Clinical Psychology Review*.

Varni, J. W. (1981). Self-regulation techniques in the management of chronic arthritic pain in hemophilia. *Behavior Therapy*, **12**, 185–194.

Vaughn, C. E., & Leff, J. P. (1976). The influence of family and social factors on the course of psychiatric illness. A comparison of schizophrenic and depressed neurotic patients. *British Journal of Psychiatry*, **129**, 125–137.

Vincente, K., Wiley, J. A., & Carrington, R. A. (1979). The risk of institutionalization before death. *Gerontologist*, **19**, 361–367.

Voeltz, L. M. (1977). Syntactic rule mediation and echolalia in autistic children. Unpublished manuscript, University of Hawaii.

Voeltz, L. M. (1980). Children's attitudes toward handicapped peers. *American Journal of Mental Deficiency*, **84**, 455–464.

Voeltz, L. M. (1982). Effects of structured interactions with severely handicapped peers on children's attitudes. *American Journal of Mental Deficiency*, **86**, 380-390.

Von Felsinger, J. M., Lasagna, L., & Beecher, H. K. (1956). The response of normal men to lysergic acid derivatives. *Journal of Clinical and Experimental Psychopathology*, **17**, 414–428.

Von Wright, J. M., Pekanmaki, L., & Malin, S. (1971). Effects of conflict and stress on alcohol intake in rats. *Quarterly Journal of Studies on Alcohol*, **32**, 420–441.

Vygotsky, L. S. (1978). *Mind in society: The development of higher psychological processes*. Edited and translated by M. Cole, V. John-Steiner, S. Scribner, & E. Souberman. Cambridge, Mass.: Harvard University Press.

Wachtel, P. (1977). *Psychoanalysis and behavior therapy: Toward an integration*. New York: Basic Books.

Wachtel, P. L. (1982). Vicious circles: The self and the rhetoric of emerging and unfolding. *Contemporary Psychoanalysis*, **18**, 259–273.

Waldron, I. (1978). The coronary-prone behavior pattern, blood pressure, employment and socio-economic status in women. *Journal of Psychosomatic Research*, **22**, 79–87.

Walen, S., Hauserman, N. M., & Lavin, P. J. (1977). *Clinical guide to behavior therapy*. Baltimore, Md.: William and Wilkins.

Walker, E., Bettes, B. A., Kain, E., & Harvey, P. (1985). Relationship of gender and marital status with symptomatology in psychotic patients. *Journal of Abnormal Psychology*, **94**, 42–50.

Wallander, J. L., & Hubert, N. C. (1985). Long-term prognosis for children with attention deficit disorder with hyperactivity (ADD/H). In B. B. Lahey & A. E. Kazdin (Eds.), *Advances in child clinical psychology*. Vol. 8. New York: Plenum Press.

Walsh, B. T., Stewart, J. W., Roose, S. P., Gladis, M., & Glassman, A. H. (1984). Treatment of bulimia with phenelzine. *Archives of General Psychiatry*, **41**, 1105–1109.

Walton, D. (1961). The application of learning theory to the treatment of a case of somnambulism. *Journal of Clinical Psychology*, **37**, 96–99.

Ward, C. H., Beck, A. T., Mendelson, M., Mock, J. E., & Erbaugh, J. K. (1962). The psychiatric nomenclature: Reasons for diagnostic disagreement. *Archives of General Psychiatry*, **7**, 198–205.

Warheit, G. J., Arey, S. A., & Swanson, E. (1976). Patterns of drug use: An epidemiologic overview. *Journal of Drug Issues*, **6**, 223–237.

Warner, K. E. (1977). The effects of the antismoking campaign on cigarette consumption. *American Journal of Public Health*, **67**, 645–650.

Warren, C. A. B. (1982). *The court as last resort: Mental illness and the law*. Chicago: University of Chicago Press.

Watson, G. C., & Buranen, C. (1979). The frequency and identification of false positive conversion reactions. *Journal of Nervous and Mental Disease*, **167**, 243–247.

Watson, J. B. (1913). Psychology as the behaviorist views it. *Psychological Review*, **20**, 158–177.

Watson, J. B., & Rayner, R. (1920). Conditioned emotional reactions. *Journal of Experimental Psychology*, **3**, 1–14.

Watt, N. F. (1974). Childhood and adolescent roots of schizophrenia. In D. Ricks, A. Thomas, & M. Roff (Eds.), *Life history research in psychopathology*. Vol. 3. Minneapolis, Minn.: University of Minnesota Press.

Watt, N. F., Stolorow, R. D., Lubensky, A. W., & McClelland, D. C. (1970). School adjustment and behavior of children hospitalized for schizophrenia as adults. *American Journal of Orthopsychiatry*, **40**, 637–657.

Weick, K. E. (1984). Small wins: Redefining the scale of social problems. *American Psychologist*, **39**, 40–49.

Weinberg, G. (1972). *Society and the healthy homosexual*. New York: St. Martin's Press, 1972.

Weinberger, D. R., Cannon-Spoor, H. E., Potkin, S. G., & Wyatt, R. J. (1980). Poor premorbid adjustment and CT scan abnormalities in chronic schizophrenia. *American Journal of Psychiatry*, **137**, 1410–1413.

Weinberger, D. R., Wagner, R. L., & Wyatt, R. J. (1983). Neuropathological studies of schizophrenia: A selective review. *Schizophrenia Bulletin*, **9**, 193–212.

Weiner, B., Frieze, L., Kukla, A., Reed, L., Rest, S., & Rosenbaum, R. M. (1971). *Perceiving the causes of success and failure*. New York: General Learning Press.

Weiner, H. (1977). *Psychobiology and human disease*. New York: Elsevier.

Weiner, H., Thaler, M., Reiser, M. F., & Mirsky, I. A. (1957). Etiology of duodenal ulcer: I. Relation of specific psychological characteristics to rate of gastric secretion. *Psychosomatic Medicine*, **17**, 1–10.

Weiner, J. W. (1969). The effectiveness of a suicide prevention program. *Mental Hygiene*, **53**, 357–363.

Weingartner, H., & Silberman, E. (1982). Models of cognitive impairment: Cognitive changes in depression. *Psychopharmacology Bulletin*, **18**, 27–42.

Weiss, J. M. (1968). Effects of coping responses on stress. *Journal of Comparative and Physiological Psychology*, **24**, 409–414.

Weiss, J. M. (1970). Somatic effects of predictable and unpredictable shock. *Psychosomatic Medicine*, **32**, 397–408.

Weiss, J. M. (1977). Psychological and behavioral influences on gastrointestinal lesions in animal models. In J. D. Maser & M. E. P. Seligman (Eds.), *Psychopathology: Experimental models.* San Francisco: Freeman.

Weiss, R. L., & Cerreto, M. C. (1980). The Marital Status Inventory: Development of a measure of dissolution potential. *American Journal of Family Therapy*, **8**, 80–85.

Weiss, R. L., & Wieder, G. B. (1982). Marital and family distress. In A. S. Bellack, M. Hersen, & A. E. Kazdin (Eds.), *International handbook of behavior modification.* New York: Plenum Press, 1982.

Weiss, R. L., Hops, H., & Patterson, G. R. (1973). A framework for conceptualizing marital conflict, a technology for altering it, some data for evaluating it. In L. A. Hamerlynck, L. C. Handy, & E. J. Mash (Eds.), *Behavior change: Methodology, concepts, and practice.* Champaign, Ill.: Research Press.

Weissberg, R. P., Gesten, E. L., Rapkin, B. D., Cowen, E. L., Davidson, E., deApodaca, R. F., & McKim, B. J. (1981). Evaluation of a social-problem-solving training program for suburban and inner-city third-grade children. *Journal of Consulting and Clinical Psychology*, **49**, 251–261.

Weissman, M. M., Kidd, K. K., & Prusoff, B. A. (1982). Variability in rates of affective disorders in relatives of depressed and normal probands. *Archives of General Psychiatry*, **39**, 1397–1403.

Weissman, M. M., & Myers, J. K. (1978). Affective disorders in a U.S. urban community. *Archives of General Psychiatry*, **35**, 1304–1310.

Weissman, M. M., Klerman, G. L., & Paykel, E. S. (1971). Clinical evaluation of hostility in depression. *American Journal of Psychiatry*, **128**, 261–266.

Weissman, M. M., Klerman, G. L., Prusoff, B. A., Sholomskas, D., & Padian, N. (1981). Depressed outpatients. Results one year after treatment with drugs and/or interpersonal psychotherapy. *Archives of General Psychiatry*, **38**, 51–56.

Weitzenhoffer, A. M., & Hilgard, E. R. (1959). *Stanford hypnotic susceptibility scale, Forms A and B.* Palo Alto, Calif: Consulting Psychologists Press.

Wells, C. C. (1978). Chronic brain disease: An overview. *American Journal of Psychiatry*, **135**, 1–12.

Wells, C. E., & Duncan, G. W. (1980). *Neurology for psychiatrists.* Philadelphia, Pa.: F. A. Davis Company.

Werry, J. S., Methven, R. J., Fitzpatrick, J., & Dixon, H. (1983). The interrater reliability of DSM-III in children. *Journal of Abnormal Child Psychology*, **11**, 341–354.

Wertsch, J. (1979). From social interactions to higher psychological processes: A clarification and application of Vygotsky's theory. *Human Development*, **22**, 1–22.

Whalen, C. K. (1983). Hyperactivity, learning problems, and the attention deficit disorders. In T. H. Ollendick & M. Hersen (Eds.), *Handbook of child psychopathology.* New York: Plenum Press.

Whanger, A. D. (1973). Paranoid syndrome of the senium. In E. Eisdorfer & W. E. Fann (Eds.), *Psychopharmacology—Aging.* New York: Plenum Press.

White, W. A. (1932). *Outlines of psychiatry.* 13th ed. New York: Nervous and Mental Disease Publishing Company.

White, W. C., & Boskind-White, M. (1981). An experiential-behavioral approach to the treatment of bulimarexia. *Psychotherapy: Theory, Research, and Practice*, **18**, 501–507.

White, J., Davison, G. C., & White, K. (1985). Cognitive distortions in the articulated thoughts of depressed patients. Unpublished manuscript, University of Southern California.

Whitehead, A. (1973). Verbal learning and memory in elderly depression. *British Journal of Psychiatry*, **123**, 203–208.

Whitlock, F. A. (1967). The aetiology of hysteria. *Acta Psychiatrica Scandinavica*, **43**, 144–162.

Wickens, D. D., Allen, C. K., & Hill, F. A. (1963). Effects of instruction on extinction of the conditioned GSR. *Journal of Experimental Psychology*, **66**, 235–240.

Wicks-Nelson, R., & Israel, A. C. (1984). *Behavior disorders of childhood.* Englewood Cliffs, N.J.: Prentice-Hall.

Wiens, A. N., & Menustik, C. E. (1983). Treatment outcome and patient characteristics in an aversion therapy program for alcoholism. *American Psychologist*, **38**, 1089–1096.

Wig, N. N., & Varma, V. K. (1977). Patterns of long-term heavy cannabis use in North India and its effects on cognitive functions. A preliminary report. *Drug and Alcohol Dependence*, **2**, 211–219.

Wigdor, B., & Morris, G. (1977). A comparison of twenty-year medical histories of individuals with depressive and paranoid states. *Journal of Gerontology*, **32**, 160–163.

Wiggins, J. (1968). Inconsistent socialization. *Psychological Reports*, **23**, 303–336.

Wilkins, L. T. (1969). *Evaluation of penal measures.* New York: Random House.

Williams, H., & McNicol, K. N. (1969). Prevalence, natural history and relationship of wheezy bronchitis and asthma in children: An epidemiological study. *British Medical Journal*, **4**, 321–325.

Williams, L., Martin, G. L., McDonald, S., Hardy, L., & Lambert, L., Sr. (1975). Effects of a backscratch contingency of reinforcement for table serving on social interaction with severely retarded girls. *Behavior Therapy*, **6**, 220–229.

Williams, R. B., Haney, T. L., Lee, K. L., Kong, Y., Blumenthal, J. A., & Whalen, R. E. (1980). Type A behavior, hostility, and coronary atherosclerosis. *Psychosomatic Medicine*, **42**, 539–549.

Williams, S. L., & Rappoport, A. (1983). Cognitive treatment in the natural environment for agoraphobics. *Behavior Therapy*, **14**, 299–313.

Wilson, G. T., & Abrams, D. (1977). Effects of alcohol on social anxiety and physiological arousal: Cognitive versus pharmacological processes. *Cognitive Therapy and Research*, **1**, 195–210.

Wilson, G. T., & Davison, G. C. (1969). Aversion techniques in behavior therapy: Some theoretical and metatheoretical considerations. *Journal of Consulting and Clinical Psychology*, **33**, 327–329.

Wilson, G. T., & Davison, G. C. (1971). Processes of fear reduction in systematic desensitization. Animal studies. *Psychological Bulletin*, **76**, 1–14.

Wilson, G. T., & Lawson, D. M. (1976). The effects of alcohol on sexual arousal in women. *Journal of Abnormal Psychology*, **85**, 489–497.

Wilson, G. T., & O'Leary, K. D. (1980). *Principles of behavior therapy.* Englewood Cliffs, N.J.: Prentice-Hall.

Wilson, R. C., Christensen, P. R., Merrifield, P. R., & Guilford, J. P. (1975). *Alternate uses test.* Beverly Hills, Calif.: Sheridan Psychological Company.

Wilson, T. D., Goldin, J. C., & Charbonneau-Powis, M. (1983). Comparative efficacy of behavioral and cognitive treatments of depression. *Cognitive Therapy and Research*, **7**, 111–124.

Wilson, W. R. (1975). Unobtrusive induction of positive attitudes. Unpublished doctoral dissertation, University of Michigan.

Winett, R. A., & Winkler, R. C. (1972). Current behavior modification in the classroom: Be still, be quiet, be docile. *Journal of Applied Behavior Analysis*, **5**, 499–504.

Winkler, R. (1977). What types of sex-role behavior should behavior modifiers promote? *Journal of Applied Behavior Analysis*, **10**, 549–552.

Winokur, G. (1963). Sexual behavior: Its relationship to certain effects and psychiatric diseases. In G. Winokur (Ed.), *Determinants of human sexual behavior.* Springfield, Ill.: Charles C. Thomas.

Winokur, G. (1979). Unipolar depression. *Archives of General Psychiatry,* **36,** 47–52.

Winokur, G., & Clayton, P. J. (1967). Family history studies: I. Two types of affective disorders separated according to genetic and clinical factors. In J.Wortis (Ed.), *Recent advances in biological psychiatry.* Vol. 9. New York: Plenum Press.

Winokur, G., Clayton, P. J., & Reich, T. (1969). *Manic-depressive illness.* St. Louis, Mo.: Mosby.

Winokur, A., March, V., & Mendels, J. (1980). Primary affective disorder in relatives of patients with anorexia nervosa. *American Journal of Psychiatry,* **137,** 695–698.

Winters, K. C., & Neale, J. M. (1985). Mania and low self-esteem. *Journal of Abnormal Psychology,* in press

Winters, K. C., Weintraub, S., & Neale, J. M. (1981). Validity of MMPI codetypes in identifying DSM-III schizophrenics, unipolars and bipolars. *Journal of Consulting and Clinical Psychology,* **49,** 486–487.

Wise, T. (1978). Where the public peril begins: A survey of psychotherapists to determine the effects of Tarasoff. *Stanford Law Review,* **31,** 165–190.

Wolberg, L. R. (1954). *The technique of psychotherapy.* New York: Grune and Stratton.

Wold, D. A. (1968). The adjustment of siblings to childhood leukemia. Unpublished medical thesis, University of Washington, Seattle.

Wolf, A. (1949). The psychoanalysis of group. *American Journal of Psychotherapy,* **3,** 16–50.

Wolf, M., Risley, T., & Mees, H. (1964). Application of operant conditioning procedures to the behavior problems of an autistic child. *Behaviour Research and Therapy,* **1,** 305–312.

Wolchik, S. A., Spencer, S. L., & Lisi, I. S. (1983). Volunteer bias in research employing vaginal measures of sexual arousal. *Archives of Sexual Behavior,* **12,** 399–408.

Wolin, S. J. (1980). Introduction: Psychosocial consequences. In *Alcoholism and alcohol abuse among women: Research issues.* Rockville, Md.: National Institute on Alcohol Abuse and Alcoholism.

Wolpe, J. (1958). *Psychotherapy by reciprocal inhibition.* Stanford, Calif.: Stanford University Press.

Wolpe, J. (1980). Cognitive behavior and its roles in psychotherapy: An integrative account. In M. J. Mahoney (Ed.), *Psychotherapy process: Current issues and future directions.* New York: Plenum Press.

Wolpe, J., & Rachman, S. J. (1960). Psychoanalytic "evidence," A critique based on Freud's case of Little Hans. *Journal of Nervous and Mental Disease,* **131,** 135–147.

Woodruff, R. A., Goodwin, D. W., & Guze, S. B. (1974). *Psychiatric diagnosis.* New York: Oxford University Press.

World Health Organiztion (1948). *Manual of the international statistical classification of diseases, injuries and causes of death.* Geneva: WHO.

Wright, J. C. (1976). A comparison of systematic desensitization and social skill acquisition in the modification of social fear. *Behavior Therapy,* **7,** 205–210.

Wright, D. S. (1971). *The psychology of moral behavior.* Harmondsworth, England: Penguin Books.

Yalom, I. D., Green, R., & Fisk, N. (1973). Prenatal exposure to female hormones: Effect on psychosexual development in boys. *Archives of General Psychiatry,* **28,** 554–561.

Yurchenco, H. (1970). *A mighty hard road: The Woody Guthrie Story.* New York: McGraw-Hill.

Zarit, S. H. (1980). *Aging and mental disorders: Psychological approaches to assessment and treatment.* New York: The Free Press.

Zarit, S. H., Eiler, J., & Hassinger, M. (1985). Clinical assessment. In J. E. Birren & K. W. Schaie (Eds.),. *Handbook of psychology of aging.* 2nd ed. New York: Van Nostrand Reinhold.

Zeaman, D., & House, B. J. (1979). A review of attention theory. In N. R. Ellis (Ed.), *Handbook of mental deficiency, psychological theory and research.* 2nd ed. Hillsdale, N.J.: Laurence Erlbaum Associates.

Zeigob, L. E., Arnold, S., & Forehand, R. (1975). An examination of observer effects in parent-child interactions. *Child Development,* **46,** 509–512.

Zerbin-Rüdin, E. (1972). Genetic research and the theory of schizophrenia. *International Journal of Mental Health,* **1,** 42–62.

Ziegler, F. J., Imboden, J. B., & Meyer, E. (1960). Contemporary conversion reactions: A clinical study. *American Journal of Psychiatry,* **116,** 901–910.

Zigler, E. (1969). Development versus difference theories of mental retardation and the problem of motivation. *American Journal of Mental Deficiency,* **73,** 536–556.

Zilbergeld, B., & Evans, M. (1980). The inadequacy of Masters and Johnson. *Psychology Today,* **14,** 28–43.

Zilboorg, G., & Henry, G. W. (1941). *A history of medical psychology.* New York: Norton.

Zimbardo, P. G., Andersen, S. M., & Kabat, L. G. (1981). Paranoia and deafness: An experimental investigation. *Science,* **212,** 1529–1531.

Zimberg, S. (1978). Diagnosis and treatment of elderly alcoholics. *Alcoholism: Clinical and Experimental Research,* **2,** 27–29.

Zitrin, C. M., Klein, D. F., & Woerner, M. G. (1980). Treatment of agoraphobia with group exposure in vivo and imipramine. *Archives of General Psychiatry,* **37,** 63–72.

Zitrin, C. M., Klein, D. F., Woerner, M. G., & Ross, D. C. (1983). Treatment of phobias 1. Comparison of imipramine hydrochloride and placebo. *Archives of General Psychiatry,* **40,** 125–138.

Zucker, K. J., Finegan, J. K., Deering, R. W., & Bradley, S. J. (1984). Two subgroups of gender-problem children. *Archives of Sexual Behavior,* **13,** 27–39.

Zung, W. W. K. (1967). Depression in the normal aged. *Psychosomatics,* **8,** 287–292.

Page viii: Photo of Gerald Davison by Conrad Johnson.
Page ix: Photo of John Neale by Jerry Bushart

Chapter 1
Page 8: The Bettmann Archive. Page 9: The New York Public Library. Page 10: (top) Bildarchiv Pruessicher Kulturbesitz (bottom) H. Roger-Viollet. Page 11: (top left) Radio Times Hulton Picture Library (top right) H. Roger-Viollet (bottom) The Bettmann Archive. Page 12: Courtesy Commonwealth of Massachusetts. Page 13: P. Boyer and S. Nissenbaum, "Ergotism: The Satan Loosed in Salem?" Caporal, L.R., *Science* Volume 192, pp. 21–26. Figure 1, 2 April 1976. Copyright 1976 by the American Association for the Advancement of Science. Page 15: The Trustees of Sir John Soane's Museum. Page 16: Radio Times Hulton Picture Library. Page 17: (top) Bulloz/Art Reference Bureau. (bottom) The Historical Society of Pennsylvania. Page 18: Historical Pictures Service, Inc. Page 19: H. Roger-Viollet. Page 21: News and Publication Service, Stanford University. Page 22: The Bettman Archive.

Chapter 2
Page 28: R. Laird/Leo DeWys. Page 32: (top) The Bettmann Archive (bottom) Edmund Engelman. Page 33: (top) Edmund Engelman (bottom) Courtesy Weidenfeld and Nicolson. Page 36: (top) Alan Carey/The Image Works (bottom) Michael Weisbrot and Family. Page 40: Culver Pictures. Page 42: J.R. Holland/Stock, Boston. Page 50: Michael Rougier/Life Magazine © Time, Inc.

Chapter 3
Page 58: Read D. Brugger/The Picture Cube. Page 59: (top) Leonard Freed/Magnum (bottom) Linda Ferrer, 1981/Woodfin Camp. Page 63: (top) Steven Hansen/Stock, Boston (bottom) Peter Southwick/Stock, Boston.

Chapter 4
Page 69: Copyright 1943 by the President and Fellows of Harvard College; copyright © 1971 by Henry A. Murray. Page 71: Courtesy Dr. Henri F. Ellenberger. Page 75: (top) Richard Wood/Taurus Photos (bottom) Eric Kroll/Taurus Photos. Page 78: Bohdan Hrynewych/Stock, Boston. Page 84: (left) Merrim/Monkmeyer Press Photo (right) Michal Heron/Woodfin Camp. Page 87: Courtesy Daniel O'Leary, Photo by Stella Kupferberg. Page 90: Photography by Charlyce Jones.

Chapter 5
Page 97: Springer/Bettman Film Archive. Page 98: Sidney Harris. Page 102: George Malave/Stock, Boston. Page 103: David S. Strickler/The Picture Cube. Page 106: Harry F. Harlow, Regional Primate Research Center.

Chapter 6
Page 117: Jeff Albertson/Stock, Boston. Page 121: Michal Heron/Woodfin Camp. Page 124: David M. Grossman. Page 126: Enrico Ferorelli/Dot. Page 131: (top) The Bettmann Archive (bottom) Lionel Delevingne/Stock, Boston. Page 133: Tom Ballard/EKM-Nepenthe.

Chapter 7
Page 151: © Menschenfreund. Page 153: © Van Bucher 1970/Photo Researchers. Page 156: (Left) Barbara Alper (right) David McCullin/Magnum. Page 163: Michal Heron.

Chapter 8
Page 166: Courtesy Central Museum der Gemeente, Utrecht. Page 168: (top left and bottom left) Michael Weisbrot and Family. (top right) Rose Skytta/Jeroboam. (bottom right) Randy Matusow. Page 173: Margaret Thompson/The Picture Cube. Page 174: Dr. Jeanne M. Riddle, Dept. of Pathology, Wayne State University-School of Medicine, Detroit, Michigan. Page 175: (top) Sidney Harris (bottom) Fred Ward/Black Star. Page 177: Hazel Hankin. Page 178: Sepp Seitz, 1980/Woodfin Camp. Page 180: American Heart Association. Page 181: Sidney Harris. Page 189: Ken Robert Buck/The Picture Cube.

Chapter 9
Page 195: Bruce Davidson/Magnum. Page 198: Rhoda Sidney/Monkmeyer Press Photo. Page 204: Mark Antman/The Image Works. Page 207: Mark Antman/The Image Works. Page 216: Jean Weyrich, Luxembourg. Page 217: © 1980 Hazel Hankin. Page 218: Paul Fusco/Magnum. Page 220: Sandra Johnson, 1983/The Picture Cube. Page 222: UPI/Bettmann Newsphotos. Page 223: © 1980 Hazel Hankin.

Chapter 10
Page 237: Ellis Herwig/The Picture Cube. Page 239: David Powers/Stock, Boston. Page 241: © 1978 by William L. Apple. Page 243: Michael Douglas/The Image Works. Page 246: Ethan Hoffman/Archive Pictures, Inc.

Chapter 11
Page 251: Lorinda Morris. Page 252: (top) Mark Antman/The Image Works (bottom) Etienne Montes/Gamma/Liaison. Page 225: (top) Tony Korody/Sygma (bottom) Photo Trends. Page 256: Culver Pictures. Page 259: Janice Fullman/The Picture Cube. Page 261: Elinor S. Beckwith/Taurus. Page 264: The Bettmann Archive. Page 266: (top left) Cary Wolinsky/Stock, Boston (bottom) Louise Gubb/Gamma/Liaison (top right) Eric Kroll/Taurus. Page 268: Hazel Hankin. Page 269: Steve Schapiro/Sygma. Page 272: R. Alcorn/Gamma/Liaison. Page 274: Owen Franken/Stock, Boston. Page 277: Culver Pictures.

Chapter 12

Page 292: (left) UPI/Bettmann Newsphotos (right) Robin Laurence/NYT Pictures. Page 295: Sidney Harris. Page 296: Giancarlo Botti/Sygma. Page 299: Mary Stuart Lang. Page 300: Hugh Rogers/Monkmeyer Press Photo. Page 307: Katherine Lambert.

Chapter 13

Page 315: (top) The Bettmann Archive (bottom) Monique Manceau/Photo Researchers Inc. Page 316: Ira Wyman/Sygma. Page 322: Hella Hammid/Rapho-Photo Researchers, Inc. Page 325: Paul Fortin/Stock, Boston. Page 327: Andrew Brilliant/The Picture Cube.

Chapter 14

Page 335: (top) Radio Times Hulton Picture Library (bottom) The Bettmann Archive. Page 339: Courtesy Mrs. Heidi Schneider. Page 341: Professor Harvey Trager, Jane Addams College of Social Work, University of Illinois. Page 342: Grunnitus/Monkmeyr Press Photo. Page 351: Courtesy David Rosenthal. Page 353: Christopher S. Johnson. Page 355: © Yoav/Phototake. Page 357: David R. Weinberger, M.D./Dept. of Health and Human Services/NIMH. Page 359: P. Schön Jensen. Page 360: Michael Weisbrot. Page 363: (top) Burk Uzzle/Magnum (bottom) © Marcia Keegan 1981/Woodfin Camp.

Chapter 15

Page 373: Randy Matusow. Page 380: Michael Weisbrot. Page 383: Courtesy of Albert Bandura, Stanford University. Page 388: United Press International. Page 390: © 1980 Ann Chwatsky/Black Star. Page 391: © 1982 Susan Rosenberg/Photo Researchers, Inc. Page 392: William E. Sauro/NYT Pictures. Page 393: © 1979 Michal Heron/Monkmeyer Press. Photo.

Chapter 16

Page 404: Catherine Ursillo/Photo Researchers, Inc. Page 405: Meri Houtchens-Kitchens/The Picture Cube. Page 409: © 1982 Robert Goldstein/Photo Researchers, Inc. Pages 410 and 411: © Bruce Roberts/Photo Researchers, Inc. Page 412: © 1982 Sepp Seitz/Woodfin Camp. Page 413: F Stop/Taurus Photos. Page 414: © 1982 Robert V. Eckert Jr./The Picture Cube. Page 416: (top) Dean Abramson/Stock, Boston (bottom) Ellis Herwig/Stock Boston. Page 422: Steve Potter/Stock, Boston. Page 427: Alan Carey/The Image Works.

Chapter 17

Page 432: Culver Pictures. Page 433: Bettye Lane/Photo Researchers, Inc. Page 435: Burk Uzzle/Woodfin Camp. Page 436: (top right) Marilyn Sanders/Peter Arnold (top left) Erika Stone/Peter Arnold (bottom left) Sybil Shelton/Peter Arnold (bottom right) Patrick Ward/Stock, Boston. Page 437: Timothy Eagan/Woodfin Camp. Page 439: (top) Sepp Seitz/Woodfin Camp (bottom) Frank Siteman/The Picture Cube. Page 445: Ira Wyman/Sygma. Page 451: Nancy Durrell McKenna/Photo Researchers, Inc. Page 439: Frank Siteman/The Picture Cube. Page 463: (top) Sybil Shelton/Peter Arnold (bottom) © Ulrike Welsch. Page 465: Erika Stone/Photo Researchers, Inc.

Chapter 18

Page 472: (top) Bob Kalman/The Image Works, Inc. (bottom) Alan Carey/The Image Works. Page 473: (top left) Ann McQueen/Stock, Boston (top right) © 1983 Richard Wood/The Picture Cube (bottom) Peter Vandermark/Stock, Boston. Page 474: H.W. Sylvester/Rapho-Photo Researchers. Page 476: Judith D. Sedwick/The Picture Cube. Page 480: AP/Wide World Photos. Page 489: The Bettmann Archive. Page 491: Harriet F. Schenker/Gestalt Institute of Cleveland. Page 492: Paul Fusco/© Magnum Photos. Page 493: © Nancy Bates/The Picture Cube.

Chapter 19

Page 499: Public Relations Dept./Temple University Health Sciences Center. Page 500: Don Hogan Charles/The New York Times. Page 501: Korody/Sygma. Page 510: Courtesy Albert Bandura. Page 511: Institute for Rational-Emotive Therapy. Page 519: Richard Wood/The Picture Cube.

Chapter 20

Page 529: (top) © 1981 Ira Berger (bottom) Michael Weisbrot. Page 531: Richard Kalvar/Magnum Photos. Page 538: Linda Ferrer/Woodfin Camp. Page 542: (top left) Paula Rhodes/The Picture Cube (top right) Harriet Gans/The Image Works (bottom left) P. Price/The Picture Cube (bottom right) Sybil Shelton/Peter Arnold. Page 546: C. Gatewood/The Image Works. Page 547: Mark Antman/The Image Works. Page 551: (top) Timothy Egan/Woodfin Camp (bottom) Leonard Freed/Magnum Photos.

Chapter 21

Page 569: Courtesy Thomas Szasz/Photo by G. Szilasi. Page 570: Fabian/Sygma. Page 571: (left) The New York Times (right) Melloul/Sygma. Page 579: Wide World. Page 583: Richard Hutchings/Photo Researchers, Inc. Page 590: Wide World. Page 592: (top) Bruce Roberts/Photo Researchers, Inc. (bottom) David S. Strickler/The Picture Cube.

DeJonge, G. A., 376
Dekker, E., 186
Delong, M. R., 442
Dement, W. C., 458
Deming, W. E., 336
Demming, B., 256
DeMyer, M., 421, 425, 426
Denhoff, E., 375
Depue, R. A., 197, 206
Descartes, R., 166
Dessonville, C. R., 434, 440, 442, 443, 455, 456, 457
Detterman, D. K., 406
Deutsch, A., 14
DeVries, H. A., 462
Dewys, W. D., 395
Diament, C., 502
Diamond, B., 576
Diamond, M., 407
Diamond, R., 155, 424
Diamond, S., 424
Didion, J., 190
Dietrich, C., 394
DiMascio, A., 535, 558
Dinges, D. F., 160
Djilas, M., 572
Dodson, B., 329
Dogoloff, L. I., 265
Dohrenwend, B., 170
Dole, V., 271
Doleys, D. M., 377
Doll, A., 274
Dollard, J., 258
Domino, E. F., 356
Donaldson, K., 578, 579
Doubros, S. G., 505
Donnellan, A. M., 422, 428
Doris, J., 206
Douglas, J. D., 220
Douglas, V., 375
Dovenmuehle, R. H., 450
Down, L., 408
Drabman, R. S., 395, 507
Dreifuerst, P., 424
Duck, S., 540
Dunaif, S. L., 336
Duncan, G. W., 443, 446
Dunham, H. W., 347
Dunn, M. J., 268, 284
Dunn, V. K., 442
DuPont, R. L., 456
Durkheim, E., 222, 223
Durrell, J., 269
Dworkin, R. B., 173
Dye, C. J., 462
Dyskson, M. W., 162
D'Zurilla, T. J., 516

Eagleston, J. R., 180, 181, 182
Eastman, C., 208
Eccleston, E., 214
Edelbrock, C. S., 372, 390
Edward, I., 564
Edwards, A. L., 75
Edwards, G., 253, 262
Egan, G., 487
Ehrhardt, A., 290
Eiler, J., 434
Eisenberg, L., 382, 425

Eisenstein, R. B., 568
Ellenberger, H. F., 22
Ellingson, R. J., 238
Ellis, A. A., 48, 81, 121, 127, 199, 215, 317, 326, 511, 513, 515, 516, 517, 536
Ellis, H., 314, 315
Ellis, N. R., 406
Elmore, A. M., 189, 190, 191
Elmore, J. L., 535
Ely, 396, 397
Ely, D. L., 179
Emery, R. E., 382
Endicott, J., 69, 70, 231
Engel, B. T., 179
Engle-Friedman, M., 458
Englemann, S., 373
English, H. B., 120
Ennis, B., 580
Enright, J. B., 494
Epictetus, 517
Epstein, L. C., 585
Epstein, L. H., 395, 520
Epstein, S., 91
Erikson, E., 479, 524
Erixon, G., 123
Evans, I. M., 123
Evans, M., 328
Evans, R. I., 277
Eysenck, H. A., 124, 382, 543

Faberow, N. L., 224, 545
Fagan, J., 492
Fagerstrom, K. O., 276
Fain, T., 61
Fairburn, C. G., 398
Fairweather, G. W., 363
Falloon, I. R. H., 539
Fant, E., 575
Farina, A., 14
Farkas, G., 254
Farris, E. J., 179
Feingold, B. F., 378, 379
Feinsilver, D. B., 364
Feldman, P. M., 81
Felner, R. D., 383
Fenichel, O., 257
Fennel, E. B., 167
Fernandez, V., 540
Ferster, C. B., 208, 425
Feuerstein, R., 401
Field, T., 412
Figley, C. R., 139, 141, 142, 143
Filipczak, J., 385
Fillmore, K. M., 259
Finkelhor, D., 297
Finn, S. E., 65
Fischer, M., 352
Fish, F., 455
Fishman, S. T., 532
Fisk, N., 290
Fleming, M., 292
Fletcher, C., 274
Folstein, M. F., 447, 451
Folstein, S., 426
Ford, C., 207
Ford, C. S., 297
Ford, C. V., 462
Ford, D. H., 475, 481, 485, 489

Communication, adequacy in schizophrenics, 343
  deficits in autistic children, 423
  in encounter groups, 530–531
  in families of schizophrenics, 349–350
  and family and marital therapy, 534–536
Community mental health, 544–545, 553
Community psychology, 541–554
  ethics in, 543
  evaluation, 552–553
  and generalized anxiety disorder, 134
  levels of intervention, 541–542
  and older adults, 464–466
  paraprofessionals in, 552
  prevention, 541
  residential programs, 549–550
  seeking versus waiting mode, 541, 543
Competency to stand trial, 568–569
Compulsions, chance reinforcement theory, 136–138
  description, 136
  psychoanalytic theory, 136
Compulsive personality disorder, 232–233
Concordance, definition of, 125
Concrete thought: with idiot savant, 417; Pick's disease, 605;
    senile dementia, 441
Concussions, 604
Conditioned response, definition of, 40
Conditioned stimulus, definition of, 40
Conditioning, see Classical conditioning, Operant conditioning
Conduct disorders and delinquency, 380–386
  etiology, 382–384
  problems of definition, 380–382
Confabulation, 599
Confounds, 104
Confidentiality, limits on, 590–591; in therapy, 587
Congenital syphilis, 409, 411
Consciousness, altering and expansion of with drugs, 250, 254, 264–
    265, 267, 278, 279, 282–285
  derealization, 128, 340; depersonalization, 128, 156, 340
  loss of: see Coma
  see also Dissociative disorders
Control and anxiety, 129–130
  delusions of, 338
  and depression, 199–202
  and ego analysis, 479–485
  and essential hypertension, 177–179
  and nursing homes, 464
  perception of, 130
Control group, 104–105
Controlled drinking, 262–264
Contusion, 604
Conversion disorder, contrasted with malingering, 148
  description, 60, 146–147
  and la belle indifference, 148
  misdiagnosis of, 148
  theories, 148–155
  therapy, 155–156
Convulsions, with Alzheimer's disease, 605; brain tumor, 603; epilepsy,
    602
Convulsive therapy, 560–561
  see also Electroconvulsive therapy
Coprophilia, 305
Coronary heart disease, 179–183
  altering life styles, 547–549
  risk factors, 173, 179–183, 547, 549
  and sexual activity, 460
  type A and type B, 180–183, 189
Corpus callosum, 600, 601
Corpus striatum, in Parkinson's disease, 606

Corrective emotional experience, 126
Correlational method, 99–101
  illusory correlation, 72–73
  positive versus negative, 100
  problems in interpretation, 102
Counseling psychologist, defined, 7
Counterconditioning, 43–44, 498–503
Countertransference, 478
Covert sensitization, 306, 307, 501
Criminal behavior, of the alcoholic, 251, 254; of children of
    schizophrenic mothers, 353; of the drug addict, 265–266, 270
  and marijuana, 277
  see also Antisocial personality disorder
Criminal commitment
  and competency to stand trial, 568–569
  defined, 564
  history of, 564–565, 570
  and the insanity defense, 565–568
  and the mental hospital, 362
  right to treatment, 577–578
  in Soviet Union, 572–573
  Szasz's views on, 569–572
Critical periods, in brain development, 409
Cross-sectional research, 433
Cultural-familial retardation, 407
  family backgrounds, 407
Cushing's syndrome, 603
Cyclazocine, 271–272
Cyclical psychodynamics, 524

Dan, case of, 234
Dangerousness, in civil commitment, 574–575
Davis v. United States, 565n
Deductions, 516
Defense mechanisms, 31, 34, 36–37, 257, 478
Deinstitutionalization, 362–363, 416, 582–583
  of older people, 438
  problems of, 582–583
Delay of reward gradient, 258
Delayed auditory feedback, 23
Delinquency, juvenile, see Conduct disorders and delinquency
Delirium, 446–447, 598–599
  in alcoholism, 257, 602; encephalitis, 598–599; LSD, 282; older
    people, 446, 447
  treatment, 448–450
Delirium tremens (DTs), 251, 257, 602
Delta rhythm, 239
Delusions, of control, 339
  of grandeur; in neurosyphilis, 18, 31, 599; schizophrenia, 338, 342–
    343, 344
  in Huntington's chorea, 602
  organic delusional syndrome, 602
  persecutory, in Alzheimer's disease, 604; with amphetamines, 267;
    and deafness in old age, 454–455; in schizophrenia, 338, 344,
    556; in senile dementia, 440, 444
  and repressed homosexuality (psychoanalytic theory), 344–345
  Schneider's description, 339
Dementia, 440–441, 598–599, 604–606
  in neurosyphilis, 18, 599; older people, 440–441
  treatment, 443–444
Dementia praecox, 334
Demonology, 7, 8–12
  reactions against, 12
Dependency, drug, 250
Dependent personality disorder, 232
Dependent variable, 103
Depersonalization, 128, 156, 340

as an addicting drug, 272–273, 273–275
    effects of, 273
Nicotine gum, 276
NIMH catchment area program, 442
Nomothetic, 99
Nondirective therapy, *see* Client-centered therapy
Norepinephrine, 182n, 213
    in depression, 202, 211, 213, 215, 558; essential hypertension, 182
Nuclei, 600–601
    see also Basal ganglia
Nuremberg Code, 584
Nursing homes, 440, 462–465
Nutritional deficiencies, 599

Obesity in children, 391
Objective anxiety, 35
Obsessive-compulsive disorder, 59–60, 114, 134–138
    theories, 136–137
    therapy, 137–138, 560
Obsessive-compulsive personality, 232
Occipital lobe, 600, 601
O'Connor v. *Donaldson*, 578–580, 582
Occupational drinking, 259
Oedipal conflict, 31, 34, 160, 482
Operant conditioning, 41–42
    in behavior therapy, 127, 372–374, 384–386, 419, 427, 503–508, 524
    in theories of alcoholism, 257–258; asthma, 186–188; depression, 201–202; infantile autism, 426–427; phobias, 120; schizophrenia, 201–202; sociopathy, 240–243
Operationism (operational definition), 95
Opium, 250, 264
Oral stage, 34, 199, 257
Organic affective syndrome, 598, 602, 603
Organic brain syndromes, 598–599, 599–604
    amnestic syndrome, 599
    distinguished from organic mental disorders, 598
    delirium, 598–599; in older people, 440–441, 442, 444
    dementia, 598–599; senile dementia, 437, 440–441, 443–444, 450
    organic affective syndrome, 603; organic delusional syndrome, 602; organic hallucinosis, 602; organic personality syndrome, 603–604
    tests for, 76
Organic delusional syndrome, 602, 603
Organic hallucinosis, 602–603
Organic mental disorders, 57, 58–59, 75, 251, 598
Orgasm: clitoral versus vaginal, 320; simultaneous, 320
Orgasmic dysfunction, 319–320
Orgasmic reorientation, 306
Outcome research, in behavior therapy, 500, 503, 521
    client-centered therapy, 487; family therapy, 539; group therapy, 533–534; in psychoanalytic therapy, 483–485; suicide prevention, 545–547
    definition, 483
    in drug therapy, 556–559; ECT, 560–561; psychosurgery, 559–560
    see also Behavior therapy
Overcontrolled childhood disorders, 372, 386–391
    affective disorders, 386, 390–391
    fears in children, 40–41, 42–43, 116, 119, 127, 387–388
    social withdrawal, 389–390
Overholser v. *O'Beorne*, 567n

Panic attacks, 35, 128
Panic disorder, 59, 115, 128–129
Paradigm, clash, 23; in abnormal psychology, 23; clinical interviews, 68; studies of hypnosis, 24
    consequences of adopting, 50, 52
    definition, 23

as perceptual set, 23
    in psychopathology: humanistic, 48–49; learning, 36–46; physiological, 28–29; psychoanalytic, 29–38
    in therapy: humanistic, 48–49; learning, 48, 50, 522–525; physiological, 29; psychoanalytic, 37–38, 475–485
    see also Behavior therapy, Cognitive theories, Diathesis-stress, Eclecticism, Humanistic therapies, Humanistic views, Learning views, Physiological factors, Psychoanalysis, Psychoanalytic views
Paranoid delusions, and hearing loss in older people; 454–455; repressed homosexuality (psychoanalytic theory), 344–345
    in older people, 452–453; schizophrenia, 343, 344, 388; senile dementia, 444–445
Paranoid disorders, 57, 59, 233, 344
    in older people, 452–456
Paranoid personality disorder, 230, 233
Paranoid schizophrenia, 233, 343, 344
Paraphilias, in DSM-III, 60, 288, 295–308; exhibitionism, 299–301; fetishism, 295–296; incest, 297; masochism, 298; pedophilia (child molesting), 303, 304–305; sadism, 303, 304–305; transvestism, 296; voyeurism (''peeping''), 288, 298–299
    therapies, 305–306
    see also Rape
Paraphrenia, 456
Paraprofessionals, 7, 544, 549, 553
Parataxic distortion, 481
Parental child abuse, and alcoholism, 251
Paresthesia, 146
Parietal lobe, 600, 601
Parkinson's disease, 355, 556, 606
Parsons v. *State*, 565n
Passive-aggressive personality disorder, 233
Pate v. *Robinson*, 568
PCP, 284
Pedophilia, 288, 298
Penis, size and sexual enjoyment, 318
Pepsinogen levels and ulcers, 176
Peptic ulcer, *see* Ulcer
Perception, altered perceptions with psychedelic drugs, 282–285
    in schizophrenia, 338–339, 340–341
Perceptual-deficit theory, of learning disabilities, 373
Persecutory delusions, in Alzheimer's disease, 604; older adults, 453–454; schizophrenia, 339, 344, 556; senile dementia, 440–444
    with amphetamines, 267
Perseveration, in schizophrenics, 338
Personality disorders, description of types, 230–233
    in DSM-III, 57, 60, 230, 236
    and Ellis's set of irrational beliefs, 123
    therapies, 245–247
    see also Antisocial personality disorder
Personality inventories, 73–75
    see also Minnesota Multiphasic Personality Inventory
Personality traits, in studies of asthma, 188; coronary heart disease; 180–183; exhibitionism, 300; incest, 297; LSD use, 285; pedophilia, 298; rape, 302; suicide, 223–224; transvestism, 296–297
    in theories of alcoholism, 258; drug abuse, 270
Petit mal epilepsy, 602n
PET scan, 75–77
Pet therapy, 465
Peyote, 282
Phallic stage, 34
Phenomenological approach, 6
    description of anxiety, 114; depression, 194
    in existential analysis, 49
    in Rogers's client-centered therapy, 49, 485, 517
Phenothiazines, 355, 360, 555–556, 557

Phenotype, definition of, 124
Phenylketonuria (PKU), 29, 62, 409
Phillips Scale of Premorbid Status of Schizophrenia, 336
Phobias, and classical conditioning, 119, 122–123
   description and incidence, 35, 58–59, 115
   physiological factors, 122–126
   subclassification, 115, 117
   theories, 118–119
   therapy, 126–128
Physiological factors, in anorexia nervosa, 393–394; asthma, 185–188; children vulnerable to schizophrenia, 359; conduct disorders, 382, 384; enuresis, 376; essential hypertension, 378–379; hyperactivity, 378–379; infantile autism, 426; mental retardation, 406; phobias, 122–124; sexual dysfunction, 324; sociopathy, 238; somatoform disorder, 154
   in theories of addiction to hard drugs, 270; alcoholism, 259–261; depression, 210, 212–215; schizophrenia, 354–355
Physiological measurement, 294; of anxiety, 86; of sexual arousal, 294
   see also Electrocardiograph, CAT scan
Physiological paradigm, 28–29
   see also Physiological factors
Pick's disease, 605
Pineal gland, 166
Placebo effect, 218, 474–475, 500
Play therapy, 392
Pleasure principle, 30
Plethysmograph, 294
Polydrug abuse, 265–267
Pons, 715
   lesions in Wernicke's disease, 602
Positive spikes, 238
Positive symptoms, 343
Posttraumatic stress disorder, 60, 115
Posttraumatic stress disorder (PTSD)
   treatment of, 142–143
   and Vietnam War, 139–142
Poverty, and mental retardation, 414; older adults, 438, 466; schizophrenia, 345
Predictive validity, *see* Validity
Premature ejaculation, 320–321
Prematurity, and mental retardation, 000; schizophrenia, 359
Premorbid adjustment, in schizophrenia, 336, 358
Premorbid personality, and existential neuroses, 49
Preparedness, in classical conditioning theory of phobias, 122; in fetishisms, 295
Presenile dementias, 604–605
President's Commission on Mental Health, 553, 576, 577
Prevalence, definition, 348
Prevention, in community psychology, 552–553
   of mental retardation, 29, 62, 408, 409, 412, 413–415, 472
Primary process, 30
Privileged communication, in therapy, 587–588
   limits on, 589, 590, 591
Problem-solving, 537
Process research, in behavior therapy, 500–501
   definition, 483
   in insight therapy, 485, 488
Profound mental retardation, 403
Project Headstart, 414
Projection, 37
   in Gestalt therapy, 491, 492–495
Projective hypothesis, 71
Projective tests, 69, 72–73, 199
Pronoun reversal, 423
Propanediols, 554
Pseudocommunity, 453
Psilocybin, 282, 283, 354

Psychedelic drugs, 282, 283–285
   schizophrenia as a psychedelic trip, 347
Psychiatric Epidemiology Research Instrument (PERI), 170
Psychiatric social worker, defined, 7
Psychiatrist, defined, 6
Psychoactive drugs, 6, 555
   for affective disorders, 52, 65, 196, 218–219, 515, 557–559; alcohol withdrawal, 261; amphetamine withdrawal, 270; anxiety, 128, 134; dissociative disorders, 163; generalized anxiety disorder, 134; hyperactivity, 379, 380, 557–558; insomnia, 458; phobias, 127–128; obsessive-compulsive disorder, 137; schizophrenia, 360–365, 556
Psychoanalysis, basic techniques, 475–479
   and behavior therapy, 52, 478, 483, 484, 524–526
   for childhood disorders, 392; depression, 215; dissociative disorders, 162–163, 472; generalized anxiety disorder, 132; obsessive-compulsive disorder, 137; phobias, 126; psycho physiological disorders, 188; psychosexual dysfunctions, 321; schizophrenia, 360, 556
   evaluation, 481–483
Psychoanalyst, defined, 6
Psychoanalystic paradigm, 29–38
   evaluation, 38–39
   structure of the mind, 29–31
   psychosexual stages, 34
Psychoanalytic views, of alcoholism, 257; anorexia nervosa, 396; anxiety, 34–37; conduct disorders, 384; depression, 198–199; dissociative disorders, 160, 162; enuresis, 376; generalized anxiety disorder, 129; homosexuality, 309–311; infantile autism, 425; obsessive-compulsive disorder, 136; paranoid delusions, 344–345; paraphilias, 295–296, 300, 303; psycho physiological disorders, 172; psychosexual dysfunctions, 321, 327; self-control, 508; schizophrenia, 335; somatoform disorders, 150–154; suicide, 222, 223
   and criminal commitment, 570
Psychodrama, 528–529
Psychodynamic, *see* Psychoanalytic
Psychogenesis, 19–22
Psychogenic amnesia, 60, 156, 157
   theories, 157, 162
   therapy, 162
Psychogenic figures, 60, 146
   theories, 157, 162
   therapy, 162
Psychogenic pain disorder, 60, 146
Psychological autopsy, 224
Psychological disorders
   prevalence of, in old age, 442, 450
Psychological tests, 69, 72–77
   intelligence tests, 76–77, 400–401
   organic brain dysfunction tests, 75–76
   personality inventories, 73–75
   projective tests, 72–73
Psychopathologist, defined, 7
Psychopathy, *see* Antisocial personality disorder
Psychophysiological disorders, description, 60, 166, 167
   in DSM-III, 60, 167
   general theories, 171–174
   specific disorders: asthma, 183–188; coronary heart disease, 179–183; essential hypertension, 172, 178–179; migraine headache, 190–191; ulcer, 174–176
   therapies, 188–192; biofeedback treatment, 189–192, 521; drug treatment, 191–192, 554
Psychophysiology, 84
Psychosexual disorders, in DSM-III, 57, 60, 167
   see also Ego-dystonic homosexuality, Gender identity disorders, Paraphilias, Psychosexual dysfunctions

Valium, 128, 554, 554–555
Vineland Social Maturity Scale, 402
Visual disturbances, with alcoholism, 254; LSD, 282, 283; marijuana, 279–282; PCP, 000
   with brain tumor, 603
   tunnel vision, with conversion disorder, 146, 147
Vitamin deficiencies, 602
   in alcoholism, 256
Voodoo death, 130, 166
Voyeurism, 288, 298, 299

Waxy flexibility, 341
Wechsler Adult Intelligence Scale (WAIS), 75
Wechsler Intelligence Scale for Children (WISC), 98
Wernicke's disease, 602
Western Collaborative Group Study, 181
Witch hunts, 9–12, 14
Witchcraft, 9–12, 14

Witches' Hammer, The, 9–12
Withdrawal: in depression, 194; infantile autism, 422; Parkinson's disease, 605–606; schizoid personality disorder, 60, 231; schizophrenia, 52, 342, 343; schizotypal personality disorder, 230–231; school phobia, 389; social withdrawal disorder, 387, 389–390
Withdrawal reactions, effects of expectancy, 270
   in substance dependence, 250, 266, 270–271
"Woolly mammoth," 37, 475, 524
World Health Organization on schizophrenia, 337
Wyatt v. *Anderholt,* 578
Wyatt v. *Stickney,* 577, 582, 593, 595

YAVIS clients, 543
Youngberg v. *Romeo,* 578, 581

Zen and the Art of Motorcycle Maintenance, 22
Zoophilia, 298

**Wiley International Editions
include titles in the fields of:**

Agricultural Engineering
& Agriculture
Anthropology
Biochemistry
Biology
Business Administration
Chemistry
Civil Engineering
Chemical Engineering
Computers & Data Processing
Earth Sciences
Economics
Education
Electrical Engineering
Engineering Mechanics

Geography
Home Economics
Industrial Engineering
Mathematics
Materials Engineering
Mechanical Engineering
Medicine
Physics
Physical Chemistry
Polymer Science
& Technology
Probability & Statistics
Psychology
Sociology
Vocational-Technical

JOHN WILEY & SONS, Inc.
605 THIRD AVENUE
NEW YORK, NEW YORK 10158

ISBN 0-471-83785-7